MUSIC MASTER FILMS AND SHOWS CATALOGUE

Music Master

FILMS & SHOWS

ALMOST 10,000 ENTRIES
FILM SOUNDTRACKS
STAGE SHOWS
RADIO & TV SHOWS
SINGLES ALBUMS
CD's CASSETTES
VIDEOS

CATALOGUE

MUSIC MASTER FILMS AND SHOWS CATALOGUE

First published by John Humphries (Publishing) Ltd. in 1990.

Published by John Humphries (Publishing) Ltd, Music House, 1 De Cham Avenue, Hastings, Sussex, England. TN37 6HE. Telephone: (0424) 715181. Fax: (0424) 422805.

ISBN 0 904520 60 9

General Editor: John Humphries

Book trade enquiries: Harrap Publishing Group Ltd, Chelsea House, 26 Market Square, Bromley, Kent. BR1 1NA. Telephone: 081 313 3484. Fax: 081 313 0702.

Record trade and private enquiries: John Humphries (Publishing) Ltd, Music House, 1 De Cham Avenue, Hastings, Sussex, England. TN37 6HE. Telephone: (0424) 715181. Fax: (0424) 422805.

A full list of our distributors worldwide is published on page 6 of this book.

John Humphries (Publishing) Ltd is a wholly-owned subsidiary of Information Services Ltd.

Associate member of the Directory Publishers Association

Member of the European Association of Directory Publishers

Printed and bound in Great Britain.

MUSIC MASTER FILMS AND SHOWS CATALOGUE

CONTENTS

OTHER MUSIC MASTER TITLES

The Music Master collection now comprises titles to suit musical preferences across the entire range of genres. Already in 1990 we have published our *Jazz, Heavy Metal* and *Music on Video Catalogues,* all new to the Music Master library. Titles planned for publication by the end of 1990 are *Nick Hamlyn's Price Guide for Record Collectors* and the *Music Master Country Music Catalogue.* As well as more new and exciting titles scheduled for 1991, including *Indie Music* and *Caribbean Music,* we have not deserted the revised editions of the information-packed *Labels List (10th edition)* and *Tracks Catalogue (3rd edition).* Of course, don't forget that our giant Music Master Catalogue, 1990 is also now available, containing more details of track listings, recordings, biographies and catalogue numbers than ever before.

To enquire about obtaining any of the titles in the Music Master range or to receive information about our subscription service, contact our Sales Manager, Tracy Dale on Hastings (0424) 715181, or send us a fax on Hastings (0424) 422805.

Meantime, we hope you enjoy this latest in our ever-growing range of reference books! Our introduction on page 7 explains the contents in more detail.

COMPLETE LIST OF DISTRIBUTORS

RECORD TRADE DISTRIBUTION

Record trade orders for Music Master should be sent to the following companies;-

Canada:
RECORD PEDDLER, 12 Brant Street, Toronto, Canada. M5 2MI. Telephone: 416 364 5507.

France:
WOTRE MUSIC DISTRIBUTION, Les Carreaux, Route de Niort, 79410 St. Gelais, France. Telephone: 49 33 45 64. Fax: 49 24 97 47.

Germany:
BELLA MUSICA TONTRAEGER GmbH, Rheinstrasse 26, 7580 Buhl, Germany. Telephone: 7223 27009. Fax: 7223 30109.

Greece:
MUSI COMPACT, Shopping Centre 'Phinikas', 293 Kifissias Avenue, Athens, Greece. Telephone: 01 8015 794. Fax: 01 8016 425,

Holland:
HOME ENTERTAINMENT SERVICES, BV, Klokhoek 1, 3833 GW, Leusden, Netherlands. Telephone: 33 948300. Fax: 33 948709.

Indonesia:
INDY PARAMADELLE, Prince Centre II, 3rd Floor, Room 306, J1 Jenderal Sudirman 3-4, Jakarta, Indonesia. Telephone: 583901. Fax: 5704544.

Italy:
SOUND & VISION, P.O. Box 3196 00121, Ostia, Rome, Italy. Telephone: 06 561 11088

Japan:
UNITED PUBLISHERS SERVICES LTD., Kenkyu-sha Bldg., 9 Kanda Surugadi 2-chrome, Chiyoda-ku, Tokyo, Japan. Telephone: 03 292 7160 and 03 291 4541. Fax: 03 292 8610.

Norway:
AKERS MIC 2A/S, Kongensgi 25, N-0153, Oslo, Norway. Telephone: 472 33 0330.

Singapore:
AUDIO MUSICAL PTE LTD., 162 Rangoon Road, Singapore 0821. Telephone: 292 9896. Fax: 291 6009.

South Africa:
MUSICA CAPE, Techno Square 42, Morningside, Ndabeni, Capetown. Telephone: 21 531 1150
MUSIC TEAM, 33 Scott Street, Waverly, Johannesburg, South Africa. Telephone: 11 887 7317. Fax: 11 887 7357.

Spain and Portugal:
DISCOBI, Luchana 1-4 Dpto 2, 48008, Bilbao, Spain. Telephone: 416 42 31. Fax: 443 00 24. (Also at Rafael Harrera 11, 28036, Madrid. 34-1-314-2114.)

Sweden:
BLITZ RECORDS AB, PO Box 347, S-10124, Stockholm 1, Sweden. Telephone: 8 28 28 90. Fax: 8 29 01 22.

United Kingdom:
ARABESQUE RECORDS LTD, Network House, 29-39 Stirling Road, London. W3 8DJ. Telephone: UK Sales: 081 992 7732. International Sales: 081 992 0098. Fax: 081 992 0340.
CAROLINE EXPORTS, 56 Standard Road, London, England. NW10 6ES. Telephone 081 961 2919.
JOHN HUMPHRIES (PUBLISHING) LTD., 1 De Cham Avenue, Hastings, Sussex, England. TN37 6HE. Telephone: 0424 715181/2. Fax: 0424 422805.
LASGO LTD., Unit 2, Chapmans Park Industrial Estate, 378-388 High Road, Willesden, London, England. NW10 2DY. Telephone: 081 459 8800.
WINDSONG INTERNATIONAL LTD., Election House, Cray Avenue, St. Mary Cray, Orpington, Kent. BR5 3RJ. Telephone: 0689 36969. Fax: 0689 890392.

United States of America
MUSIC/NH, WAYNE GREEN ENTERPRISES, Hancock, New Hampshire 03449, USA. Telephone: 603 525 4201.

BOOK TRADE DISTRIBUTION

Book trade orders for Music Master books should be sent to the following companies:

All Countries (except United States of America):
Harrap Publishing Group Ltd., Chelsea House, 26 Market Square, Bromley, Kent, BR1 1NA. Telephone: 081 313 3484. Fax: 081 313 0702.

United States of America:
Last Gasp of San Francisco, 2180 Bryant street, San Francisco, CA 94110, USA. Telephone (415) 824 6636. Fax: (415) 824 1836.

INTRODUCTION
by George Rankin, Senior Editor of Music Master.

There can be little argument about the fact that many of the greatest songs in the 20th century have been written for musicals and films. Legendary songwriters like George Gershwin, Cole Porter, Lionel Bart, Irving Berlin and Jerome Kern have made a permanent impression on the history of music. When deciding to publish a catalogue detailing as many recordings of a particular type as possible, it is quite often a straightforward affair. For instance, our Heavy Metal and Jazz Catalogues were more clear cut because music generally regarded as belonging to these genres could be identified and their inclusion in the specialist catalogues therefore justified. With the Films and Shows Catalogue, however, the decisions have been many and difficult. Do we include television themes? Do we include radio shows? Do we include videos? What about television commericals which have used pop music tracks as a background? Then there was the matter of all the singles which have been released over the years and have featured on the soundtracks of films. The answer to all these questions was, we felt, best answered by another question. What kind of book did we wish to publish and what kind of person did we envisage would buy it?

The decision was taken that the book ought to be a detailed work of reference listing all film soundtrack recordings, stage musical recordings, television themes and radio recordings held on our computer database at time of going to press. These recordings may come in the form of albums, cassettes or compact discs, but equally may be singles of songs featured in films or shows. The decision was taken not to include television commerical themes as we consider such to be outwith the general heading of films and shows. We have tried wherever possible to include cross references throughout the book to make it easier to find your favourite recordings. To this end, we have also published a reference index at the beginning of the book, (page 11), detailing many recordings which may well appear under more than one heading, or perhaps not the heading you may have expected. For example, *Top Gun* will have a cross reference to see under *Berlin* and the recording *Take My Breath Away*. As much as has been practicable to do, we have tried to cross reference artists and recording titles to make life easier when using this book.

Wherever the information has been available to us, we have indicated whether or not a recording is an Original Film Soundtrack, Original Broadway Cast or Original London Stage Cast. We have taken some liberties by including recordings of radio shows by artists like Tony Hancock. Although not music, we felt as the information was on our database then someone may find it of interest.

The book is further enhanced with the inclusion of several album or CD sleeves as well as stills of scenes from a selection of popular films. Many of the films included in this book were not actually musicals, and it is important that we make this point clear. However, many films have featured popular music soundtracks and this is why we have included them in the book. The same can be said of television themes which are listed here. Many have been released on vinyl and proved to be very popular. The key as ever with a Music Master book is to find the black strip heading you want and, if we have done our job properly, you should be able to find your way round this book to the recordings of your choice! Happy reading and pleasant memories are guaranteed. Finally, sincere thanks to all who helped with the production of this book, especially, Dave Kent, Jason Philpott, Clive Brown, Robin Goodman, Sylvia Davis, Pete Smith, Jimmy Kent, Karen Blackman and Marianne Hyne.

LIST OF ILLUSTRATIONS IN THIS BOOK

Front Cover:
   top row: The Sound of Music *(RCA)*; The Boyfriend *(TER)*; 42nd Street *(RCA)*.

   middle row: Camelot *(TER)*; Lawrence of Arabia *(Silva Screen)*; Thunderbirds are Go *(Silva Screen)*.

   bottom row: Blue Velvet *(TER)*; South Pacific *(RCA)*; Kismet *(TER)*.

Back cover:
   top row: Oklahoma! *(Capitol)*; The Jungle Book *(Hallmark)*; Pretty in Pink *(A & M)*.

   bottom row: G.I. Blues *(RCA)*; The Frog Chorus *(Parlophone)*; Carousel *(Capitol)*.

Inside the book:

**REMEMBER, IF IN DOUBT WHERE TO FIND RECORDING INFORMA-
TION, PLEASE CONSULT OUR REFERENCE INDEX WHICH BEGINS ON
PAGE 11 OF THIS BOOK.**

This reference guide has been published to assist you in finding any recording details not cross-referenced in the main body of the book. The 'subject' column, which is listed alphabetically, is the name of the entry you wish to look up. The 'black strip' column indicates the black strip heading under which you will find the appropriate details and the 'recording' column details the recording under which the details can be found. Some of the recordings may be individual tracks and some may be entire film soundtracks. For instance, details of Absolute Beginners can be found under the black strip Bowie, David. Under this black strip, the details are listed under the recording title Absolute Beginners. All recordings are listed alphabetically under each black strip.

SUBJECT	BLACK STRIP	RECORDING
1969	Hendrix, Jimi	All Along the Watchtower
1984	Wakeman, Rick	1984/The Burning
1984	Eurythmics	1984 - For the Love of Big Brother
2 Outstanding Performances From	Les Miserables	Les Miserables
2 Weeks With Love	Belle Of New York	Belle Of New York/2 Weeks With Love
2 Weeks	In The Good Old ...	In The Good Old Summertime/Good News/....
200 Motels	Zappa, Frank	200 Motels
25 Miles	Starr, Edwin	Twenty Five Miles
36 Hours	Thirty Six Hours	36 Hours
48 Hours	Bus Boys	Boys Are Back in Town
50 Years of Classic Horror	Omen & Others	Omen & Other Themes
60 Years of BBC Theme Music	On The Air	On the Air
633 Squadron	Where Eagles Dare	Where Eagles Dare/633 Squadron
7 Samurai	Rashomon	Rashomon/7 Samurai
9 1/2 Weeks	Taylor, John	I Do What I Do
9 To 5	Parton, Dolly	9 to 5
A Team	Post, Mike	A Team, The
A-Team	Caine, Daniel	A-Team, The
Absolute Beginners	Style Council	Have You Ever Had It Blue
Absolute Beginners	Bowie, David	Absolute Beginners
Academy Award Winners	Baker, Tony	Academy Award Winners
Action Movies	Warner Brothers ...	Great Warner Brothers Action Movies
Addison, John	Tom Jones	Tom Jones/Irma La Douce
Addison, John	Honey Pot	Honey Pot, The
Adventures in Baby Sitting	Starr, Edwin	Twenty Five Miles
Adventures of Huckleberry Finn	Big River	Big River - Adventures of Huckleberry Finn
Adventures of The Heart	Sinatra, Frank	Broadway Kick/Adventures of the Heart
Aid for Armenia	Out Of The Ruins	Out of the Ruins
Aisle Seat	Williams, John (Composer)	Aisle Seat
Albion Market	Fair Deal	Albion Market Theme
Aldredge, Tom	Into The Woods	Into the Woods
Alexander, Jeff	Dirty Dingus Magee	Dirty Dingus Magee
Alfie	Black, Cilla	Alfie
Alfred Hitchcock	Ketcham, Charles	4 Alfred Hitchcock Films
Ali, Dani	Lamb, Annabelle	Damon and Debbie
Alice in Wonderland	Horovitz (Composer)	Alice in Wonderland
All Creatures Great and Small	Pearson, Johnny	All Creatures Great and Small
Allen, Peter	Legs Diamond	Legs Diamond
Allyson, June	Good News	Good News
Alphabet Zoo	McTell, Ralph	Best of Alphabet Zoo
Amerasia	Allen, Terry	Amerasia - The Soundtrack
American Football	Propaganda	Duel
American Gigolo	Blondie	Call Me
American in Paris	Gigi	Gigi/An American in Paris
American in Paris	Gershwin	American in Paris
American in Paris	Gershwin	Rhapsody in Blue/An American in..
American in Paris	London Philharmonic	An American in Paris
American Tail, An	Ronstadt, Linda	Somewhere Out There
American Werewolf in London	Creedence Clearwater...	Bad Moon Rising
Amram, David	Young Savages	Young Savages, The
Andrews, Julie	Sound Of Music	Sound of Music
Andrews, Julie	Thoroughly Modern ...	Thoroughly Modern Millie
Andrews, Julie	Mary Poppins	Mary Poppins
Angst	Schulze, Klaus	Angst
Animal Squad	Dickson, Barbara	Time After Time
Animalympics	Gouldman, Graham	Animalympics
Anna of the Five Towns	London Film Orchestra	Anna of the Five Towns
Annie Get Your Gun	Seven Brides For Seven	Seven Brides For Seven.. /Annie Get Your...
Antarctica	Vangelis	Antarctica

A

The following information was taken from the Music Master database on September 25th, 1990.

Abdication

ABDICATION, THE (Film soundtrack) (Various artists)
Note: Beautiful score by Nino Rota (Romeo and Juliet, The Godfather).
Album: Released Jan '89, on Interior Music by Interior Music Records. Catalogue no: **IM 008**

About Last Night

ABOUT LAST NIGHT (Film soundtrack) (Various artists)
Tracks: / So far so good: Easton, Sheena / Shape of things to come: Hall & Oates / Natural love: Easton, Sheena / Words into action: Jackson, Jermaine / Step by step: Souther, J.D. / Living inside my heart: Seger, Bob / Trials of the heart: Shanks, Nancy / Till you love somebody: Henderson, Michael / If we can get through the night: Davis, Paul / True love: Del Lords / If anybody had a heart: Waite, John.
Album: Released Oct '86, on EMI-America by EMI Records. Deleted Feb '90. Catalogue no: **AML 3109**
Cass: Released Nov '86, on EMI-America by EMI Records. Catalogue no: **TCAML 3109**
CD: Released Oct '86, on EMI-(America) by EMI Records. Deleted Feb '90. Catalogue no: **CDP 746560-2**
CD: Released Feb '90, on EMI-(America) by EMI Records. Catalogue no: **E21 465602**
Cass: Released Feb '90, on EMI-(America) by EMI Records. Catalogue no: **E41E46560**

Absolute Beginners

ABSOLUTE BEGINNERS (COMPLETE SOUNDTRACK) (Various artists)
Tracks: / Absolute beginners: Bowie, David / Killer blow: Sade / Have you ever had it blue?: Style Council / Quiet life: Davies, Ray / Va va voom: Evans, Gil / That's motivation: Bowie, David / Having it all: Eighth Wonder / Rode-rigo Bay: Working Week / Selling out: Gaillard, Slim / Riot city: Dammers, Jerry / Boogie stop shuffle (Rough and the smooth): Evans, Gil / Ted ain't dead: Tenpole Tudor / Volare: Bowie, David / Napoli: Langer, Clive / Little cat (you've never had it so good): Jonas / Absolute beginners (slight refrain): Evans, Gil / Better git it in your soul (the hot and the cool): Evans, Gil / Landlords and tenants: Aitken, Laurel / Santa Lucia: Abban, Ekow / Cool Napoli: Evans, Gil / So what?: Smiley Culture / Absolute beginners: Evans, Gil.
2 LP Set: Released '86, on Virgin by Virgin Records. Catalogue no: **VD 2514**
Cass: Released '86, on Virgin by Virgin Records. Deleted Jun '90. Catalogue no: **TCVD 2514**

ABSOLUTE BEGINNERS (HIGHLIGHTS) (Various artists)
Tracks: / Absolute beginners: Bowie, David / Killer blow: Sade / Have you ever had it blue?: Style Council / Quiet life: Davies, Ray / Va va voom: Evans, Gil / That's motivation: Bowie, David / Having it all: Eighth Wonder / Roderigo Bay: Working Week / Selling out: Gaillard, Slim / Riot city: Dammers, Jerry
Album: Released Jul '87, on Virgin by Virgin Records. Catalogue no: **V 2386**
Album: Released Apr '86, on Virgin by Virgin Records. Deleted May '90. Catalogue no: **OVED 225**
Cass: Released Apr '86, on Virgin by Virgin Records. Deleted Jun '90. Catalogue no: **OVEDC 225**
CD: Released Jul '87, on Virgin by Virgin Records. Catalogue no: **CDV 2386**

ABSOLUTE BEGINNERS (VIDEO) (Various artists)
VHS: Released '88, on Virgin Vi-sion by Virgin Records. Catalogue no: **VVP 160**

Abwarts

DER WESTERN IST EINSAM (Film soundtrack)
Album: Released Jul '72, on Philips (Germany) by PolyGram UK Ltd. Deleted '88. Catalogue no: **6435 155**

Abyss

ABYSS, THE (Film soundtrack) (Various artists)
Album: Released Oct '89, on Varese Sarabande Records(USA) by Varese Sarabande Records (USA). Catalogue no: **VS 5235**
Cass: Released Oct '89, on Varese Sarabande Records(USA) by Varese Sarabande Records (USA). Catalogue no: **VSC 5235**
CD: Released Oct '89, on Varese Sarabande Records(USA) by Varese Sarabande Records (USA). Catalogue no: **VSD 5235**

Accidental Tourist

ACCIDENTAL TOURIST, THE (Film soundtrack) (Various artists)
Note: Directed by Lawrence Kasdan (Body Heat & Silverado) starring William Hurt & Kathleen Turner with music by John Williams (his first score since Empire Of The Sun and Witches of Eastwick).
Album: Released Mar '89, on Warner Bros. by WEA Records. Deleted Jul '90. Catalogue no: **K 925846 1**
Cass: Released Mar '89, on Warner Bros. by WEA Records. Deleted Jul '90. Catalogue no: **K 925846 4**
CD: Released Mar '89, on Warner Bros. by WEA Records. Catalogue no: **K 925846 2**

AC/DC

SHAKE YOUR FOUNDATIONS

Tracks: / Shake your foundations / Stand up / Jailbreak (On 12" only)
Note: From the film Maximum Overdrive

7" Single: Released Jan '86, on Atlantic by WEA Records. Deleted Jun '87. Catalogue no: **A 9474**
12" Single: Released Jan '86, on Atlantic by WEA Records. Deleted Jan '88. Catalogue no: **A 9474 T**
CD Single: on Atlantic by WEA Records. Deleted Jun '87. Catalogue no: **A 9474 CD**

SHAKE YOUR FOUNDA-TIONS (IMPORT)
Tracks: / Shake your foundations
12" Single: Released May '88, on Atlantic (Import) by WEA Records. Catalogue no: **786837 0**

WHO MADE WHO (Soundtrack for the film Maximum Overdrive)
Tracks: / Who made who / You shook me all night long / D.T. / Sink the pink / Ride on / Hell's bells / Shake your foundations / Chase the ace / For those about to rock (we salute you).
Cass: Released May '86, on Atlantic by WEA Records. Catalogue no: **WX 57 C**
CD: Released '88, on Atlantic by WEA Records. Catalogue no: **781 650-2**
Album: Released '88, on Atlantic by WEA Records. Catalogue no: **WX57**

WHO MADE WHO (SINGLE)
Tracks: / Who made who / Guns for hire (live).
Note: From the film Maximum Overdrive.
7" Single: Released May '85, on Atlantic by WEA Records. Deleted Jun '87. Catalogue no: **A 9425**
12" Single: Released May '85, on Atlantic by WEA Records. Deleted Jan '88. Catalogue no: **A 9425 T**
CD Single: Released May '85, on Atlantic by WEA Records. Deleted Jun '87. Catalogue no: **A 9425 CD**

Across 110th Street
ACROSS 110TH STREET (Film Soundtrack) (Various artists)
Tracks: / Across 110th street: *Womack, Bobby & Peace* / If you don't want my love: *Womack, Bobby & Peace* / Quicksand: *Womack, Bobby & Peace* / Do it right: *Womack, Bobby & Peace* / Hang on in there: *Womack, Bobby & Peace* / Across 110th Street (pt 2): *Womack,*

Bobby & Peace / Harlem clavinette: *Johnson, J J & His Orchestra* / Hang on in there: *Johnson, J J & His Orchestra* / Harlem love theme: *Johnson, J J & His Orchestra* / Across 110th Street: *Johnson, J J & His Orchestra* / If you don't want my love: *Johnson, J J & His Orchestra*.
Album: Released '73, on United Artists by EMI Records. Deleted '78. Catalogue no: **UAS 29451**

Act
ACT ,THE (Original Broadway cast with Liza Minnelli) (Various artists)
Tracks: / Shine it on / It's the strangest thing / Bobo's / Turning / Little do they know / Arthur in the afternoon / Money tree / City lights / There when I need him / Hot enough for you?/ Little do they know (reprise) / My own space / Walking papers
Album: Released '79, on DRG (USA) by DRG Records (USA). Deleted '84. Catalogue no: **DRG 6101**
Cass: Released '79, on DRG (USA) by DRG Records (USA). Deleted '84. Catalogue no: **DRGC 6101**
CD: Released '87, on DRG (USA) by DRG Records (USA). Catalogue no: **CDRG 6101**
Album: Released '87, on DRG (USA) by DRG Records (USA). Catalogue no: **MRS 701**
Cass: Released '87, on DRG (USA) by DRG Records (USA). Catalogue no: **MRSC 701**

Action Jackson
ACTION JACKSON (Film soundtrack) (Various artists)
Tracks: / He turned me out: *Pointer Sisters* / Action Jackson: *Madam X* / For the love of money: *Levert* / Undress: *Vanity* / Building up Action Jackson: *Various artists* / Keeping good loving: *Sister Sledge* / Shotgun: *Vanity & David Koz* / Faraway eyes: *Vanity* / Lover's celebration: *SKYY* / To protect and serve: *Jam, M.C. & Pee Wee Jam.*
Cass: Released May '88, on Atlantic by WEA Records. Catalogue no: **790 886 4**
CD: Released 8 Apr '88, on Atlantic by WEA Records. Catalogue no: **K 790 886 2**
Album: Released May '88, on Atlantic by WEA Records. Catalogue no: **790 886 1**

Action Movie Themes
ACTION MOVIE THEMES (Various artists)
CD: Released Apr '87, on Delta (1) by Delta Records. Deleted '88. Catalogue no: **11 081**

Adams, Cliff
SING SOMETHING DISNEY (Adams, Cliff Singers)
Tracks: / Sing something Disney / Magic song, The / Little April showers / With a smile and a song / La la lu / Let's go fly a kite / Casey the pride of them all / Who's afraid of the big bad wolf / When you wish upon a star / Spoonful of sugar, A / Supercalifragilisticexpialidocious / Un-birthday song, The / Love is a song / He's a tramp / Siamese cat song / Ev'rybody wants to be a cat / Never smile at a crocodile / Ballad of Davy Crockett, The / Feed the birds / Some day my prince will come / Lavender blue / When I see an elephant fly / Chim chim cheree / Heigh-ho / Zip-a-dee-doo-dah / Make mine music.
Note: Following the popular release 'Sing Something Silver' (REH/ZCR 546) BBC Records now release 'Sing Something Disney'. The Cliff Adams Singers, heard on Sunday afternoons on Radio 2 in the popular programme 'Sing Something Simple' present their distinctive versions of favourite songs from Walt Disney films. With the strong following for the Cliff Adams Singers and 'Sing Something Simple' this album will be a favourite with adults as well as children.
Album: Released Oct '85, on BBC by BBC Records. Deleted '88. Catalogue no: **REH 574**
Cass: Released Oct '85, on BBC by BBC Records. Deleted 31 Aug '88. Catalogue no: **ZCR 574**

WALTON'S THEME (Adams, Cliff & His singers)
Tracks: / Walton's theme / Chelsea China.
7" Single: Released Mar '77, on Thames by President Records. Deleted '79. Catalogue no: **TH 502**

Adams, Douglas
HITCH HIKERS GUIDE TO THE GALAXY (See under Hitch Hikers Guide...)

Adventurers
ADVENTURERS (Film Soundtrack) (Various artists)

Tracks: / Main title / Children's games / Rome montage / Bolero/ Dax rides / Dax and Amparo (love theme) / Cortequay / Long trek / Search for Amparo / That old black magic / Bitter victory / El Lobo's band / Bed of flowers for Sue Ann
Album: Released '73, on Paramount Deleted '78. Catalogue no: **SPFL 260**

Adventures Of...

ADVENTURES OF BARON MUNCHAUSEN (Film soundtrack) (Various artists) (See panel below)
Album: Released Apr '89, on WEA by WEA Records. Deleted Jul '90. Catalogue no: **K 9258261**
Cass: Released Apr '89, on WEA by WEA Records. Deleted Jul '90. Catalogue no: **K 9258264**
CD: Released Apr '89, on WEA by WEA Records. Deleted Jul '90. Catalogue no: **K 9258262**

ADVENTURES OF ROBIN HOOD (Original soundtrack) (T.E.R label) (Utah Symphony Orchestra
Tracks: / Prologue / Banquet at Nottingham castle / Robin enters the great hall / Escape from the castle / Robin meets Little John / Oath and black arrow / Robin and Friar Tuck / Ambush in Sherwood / Feast in the forest / Robin and Marion / Archery tournament / Escape from the gallows / Love scene / Dagger fight - King Richard in Sherwood / Duel, victory and

epilogue / Coronation procession.
Album: Released Dec '83, on T. E. R. by That's Entertainment Records. Catalogue no: **TER 1066**
Cass: Released Dec '83, on T. E. R. by That's Entertainment Records. Catalogue no: **ZCTER 1066**
CD: Released Jul '84, on T. E. R. by That's Entertainment Records. Catalogue no: **CDTER 1066**

ADVENTURES OF ROBIN HOOD (Silva Screen label) (Various artists)
Cass: Released Jan '89, on Silva Screen by Silva Screen Records. Catalogue no: **C 704.180**
CD: Released Jan '89, on Silva Screen by Silva Screen Records. Catalogue no: **VCD 47202**
CD: Released Jan '89, on Silva Screen by Silva Screen Records. Catalogue no: **FCD 8104**

Advise & Consent

ADVISE AND CONSENT (Original soundtrack) (Various artists)
Note: Score by Jerry Fielding for the Otto Preminger film.
Album: Released Jan '89, on Silva Screen by Silva Screen Records. Catalogue no: **LOC 1068**

After Henry

AFTER HENRY (Various artists)
Note: Starring Prunella Scales.
Cass set: Released Sep '88, on BBC by BBC Records. Catalogue no: **ZBBC 1030**

After The Fox

AFTER THE FOX (Original soundtrack) (Various artists)
Note: Peter Sellers comedy.
Cass: Released Jan '89, on MCA by MCA Records. Catalogue no: **MCAC 25132**
Album: Released Jan '89, on MCA by MCA Records. Catalogue no: **MCA 25132**

Against All Odds

AGAINST ALL ODDS (Film soundtrack) (Various artists)
Tracks: / Against all odds(Take a look at me now): *Collins, Phil* / Violet and blue: *Nicks, Stevie* / Walk through the fire: *Gabriel, Peter* / Balcony: *Big Country (Group)* / Making a big mistake: *Rutherford, Mike* / My male curiosity: *Kid Creole & The Coconuts* / Search, The (main title): *Carlton, Larry & Michel Colombier* / El solitario: *Carlton, Larry & Michel Colombier* / Rock and roll jaguar: *Carlton, Larry & Michel Colombier* / For love alone: *Carlton, Larry* / Race, The: *Carlton, Larry* / Murder of a friend: *Carlton, Larry.*
Cass: Released Aug '88, on Virgin by Virgin Records. Catalogue no: **OVEDC 155**
CD: Released Jun '88, on Virgin by Virgin Records. Catalogue no: **CDV 2313**
Cass: Released Apr '84, on Virgin by Virgin Records. Deleted '88. Catalogue no: **TCV 2313**
Album: Released Aug '88, on Virgin by Virgin Records. Catalogue no: **OVED 155**
Album: Released Apr '84, on Virgin by Virgin Records. Deleted '88. Catalogue no: **V 2313**

AGAINST ALL ODDS (TAKE A LOOK AT ME NOW) (Collins, Phil) (See panel on next page)
Tracks: Against all odds (Take a look at me now): *Collins, Phil* / Making a big mistake: *Rutherford, Mike*
7" Single: Released '84, on Virgin by Virgin Records. Deleted '89. Catalogue no: **VS 674**

Agnes Of God

AGNES OF GOD (Film soundtrack) (Various artists)
Note: Agnes of God, starring Ann Bancroft and Jane Fonda, is a murder mystery set in a convent. The music, by Georges Delerue (Borgias, Silkwood), is performed

Eric Idle in *The Adventures of Baron Munchausen*

Against All Odds - Title song by Phil Collins

by a symphony orchestra and choir.
Cass: Released Jan '89, on T. E. R. by That's Entertainment Records. Catalogue no: **ZCTER 1108**
Album: Released Feb '86, on T. E. R. by That's Entertainment Records. Catalogue no: **TER 1108**
Cass: Released Jan '89, on Silva Screen by Silva Screen Records. Catalogue no: **CTV 81257**

LIVING DAYLIGHTS, THE (See panel opposite)
Tracks: / Living daylights, The / Living daylights, The (instrumental).
Note: Theme from the James Bond film *The living daylights*.
12" Pic: Released Jun '87, on Warner Bros. by WEA Records. Deleted Jul '88. Catalogue no: **W 8305TP**
12" Single: Released 20 Jun '87, on Warner Bros. by WEA Records. Catalogue no: **W 8305 T**
7" Single: Released 20 Jun '87, on Warner Bros. by WEA Records. Catalogue no: **W 8305**

THEMES AND DREAMS (Ainsworth, Alyn Orchestra)
Tracks: / Deer hunter (Cavatina), Theme from / Fantasy / Bright eyes / North star / Xanadu magic / Angel

of the morning / Give us shelter / Chariots of fire / M.A.S.H, Theme from / Chi mai / Waterfalls / Bermuda triangle / Made it through the rain / Imagine / To love the Lord / Riders in the sky / For your eyes only / Sukiyaki / Sailing.
Cass: Released '88, on Pickwick by Pickwick Records. Deleted '89. Catalogue no: **HSC 3102**
Album: Released '88, on Pickwick by Pickwick Records. Deleted '89. Catalogue no: **SHM 3102**

AIN'T MISBEHAVIN' (Original cast) (Various artists)
Tracks: / Lookin' good but feelin' bad / Squeeze me / Handful of keys / How ya baby / Ladies who sing with the band / Yacht club swing / Fat and greasy / Black and blue / I'm gonna sit right down and write myself a letter / Two sleepy people / I can't give you anything but love / It's a sin to tell a lie / Find out what they like / T'ain't nobody's bizness if I do / I've got my fingers crossed / Jitterbug waltz / Lounging at the Waldorf / When the nylons bloom again / Cash for your trash / That ain't right / Mean to me / Your feet's too big / Keepin' out of mischief now / Joint is jumpin' /

Theme from the James Bond film, *The Living Daylights* by A-Ha

Spreadin' rhythm around / Vipers drag / Honeysuckle rose / Ain't misbehavin' / I've got a feeling I'm falling / Off time.
2 LP Set: Released Aug '90, on RCA by BMG Records (UK). Catalogue no: **BL 82965**
CD Set: Released Aug '90, on RCA by BMG Records (UK). Catalogue no: **BD 82965**
2 LP Set: Released Mar '79, on RCA by BMG Records (UK). Deleted '84. Catalogue no: **RL 02965**

Airport

AIRPORT (Original soundtrack) (Various artists)
Note: Composed by Alfred Newman.
Album: Released Jan '89, on Silva Screen by Silva Screen Records. Catalogue no: **255 086.1**

Airwave Orchestra

FOURSCORE (CHANNEL 4 THEME)
Tracks: / Fourscore / Fourscore II.
7" Single: Released Nov '82, on Polydor by Polydor Ltd. Deleted Nov '85. Catalogue no: **CHANN 401**

Alamo

ALAMO, THE (Film soundtrack) (Various artists)
Album: Released Feb '90, on Silva Screen by Silva Screen Records. Catalogue no: **PC 8358**
CD: Released Feb '90, on Silva Screen by Silva Screen Records. Catalogue no: **VSD 5224**

Alamo Bay

ALAMO BAY (Film soundtrack) (Various artists)
Tracks: / Alamo Bay, Theme from: Various artists / Gooks on Main Street: Various artists / Too close: Various artists / Klan meeting: Various artists / Sailfish evening: Various artists / Last stand: Various artists / Quatro vicios: Various artists / Search and destroy: Various artists / Glory: Various artists.
Note: Artists include Ry Cooder, John Hiatt and Caesar Rosas.
Album: Released Feb '86, on Slash by London Records Ltd. Catalogue no: **SLAP 7**
Cass: Released Feb '86, on Slash by London Records Ltd. Catalogue no: **SMAC 7**

Alas Smith & Jones

ALAS SMITH AND JONES (From the TV series) (Smith, Mel & Griff Rhys-Jones)
Cass: Released Nov '85, on BBC by BBC Records. Catalogue no: **ZCF 527**
Album: Released Nov '85, on BBC by BBC Records. Catalogue no: **REB 527**

Alexander The Great

ALEXANDER THE GREAT (Original soundtrack) (Various artists)
Note: Epic score by Mario Nascimbene (The Vikings) for the Richard Burton film.
Album: Released Jan '89, on MGM (Polydor) by Polydor Ltd. Catalogue no: **MG 20148**

Alexanders Ragtime...

ALEXANDERS RAGTIME BAND (Film soundtrack) (Various artists)
Note: Irving Berlin - Alice Faye and Tyrone Power.
Album: Released Jan '89, on Silva Screen by Silva Screen Records. Catalogue no: **HS 406**

Alf

STUCK ON EARTH
Tracks: / Stuck on Earth / Cruisin' on Melmac Interstate.
Note: From the TV series A.L.F. (Alien Life Form)
7" Single: Released 5 Mar '88, on RCA by BMG Records (UK). Deleted May '89. Catalogue no: **PB 41663**
12" Single: Released 5 Mar '88, on RCA by BMG Records (UK). Deleted May '89. Catalogue no: **PT 41804**

Alice In Wonderland

ALICE'S ADVENTURES IN WONDERLAND (Film Soundtrack) (Various artists)
Tracks: / Overture / Curiouser and curiouser and curiouser / You've gotta know when to stop/ Royal procession / Last word is mine / Dum and Dee dance, and nursery rhyme / Pun song / I've never been this far before / Me I never knew / Lobster quadrille/ Will you walk a little faster / They told me you have been to her / Me I never knew / Playout music.
Album: Released '73, on Warner

Bros. by WEA Records. Deleted '78. Catalogue no: **K 56009**

ALICE IN WONDERLAND (TV Special) (Various artists)
Tracks: / All on a golden afternoon: Various artists / Readin', ritin and rithmetic: Dotrice, Karen / Decisions: Connor, Kenneth / Speak roughly to your little boy: Reid, Beryl & Dorothy Squires / Lobster quadrille, The: Howard, Frankie / Beautiful soup: Howard, Frankie & Harry H Corbett / Mad Hatters tea party, The: Forsyth, Bruce/Karen Dotrice/Fenella Fielding & Tommy Cooper / Ceremonial march: Dotrice, Karen/Peggy Mount & Arthur Haynes / Love makes the world goes round: Reid, Beryl / I'll have you executed on the spot: Haynes, Arthur & Peggy Mount / I remember the incident: Connor Kenneth / All on a golden afternoon (reprise): Various artists.
2 LP Set: Released Sep '81, on MFP by Music For Pleasure. Deleted Sep '86. Catalogue no: **MFP 1013**
Cass Set: Released Sep '81, on MFP by Music For Pleasure. Deleted Sep '86. Catalogue no: **TCMFP 1013**

Alice's Restaurant

ALICE'S RESTAURANT (Film soundtrack) (Guthrie, Ario)
Tracks: / Alice's restaurant massacre / Chilling of the evening / Ring around a rosy rag / Now and then I'm going home / Motorcycle song, The / Highway in the wind.
CD: Released Jul '88, on Reprise (USA). Catalogue no: **K 244045**
Album: Released Mar '70, on Reprise by WEA Records. Deleted '75. Catalogue no: **RSLP 6267**
Album: Released Jul '87, on Reprise (USA). Catalogue no: **K 44045**

Alien

ALIEN (Film soundtrack) (National Philharmonic Orchestra)
Tracks: / Alien (main title) / Face hugger, The / Breakaway / Acid test / Landing, The / Droid, The / Recovery, The / Alien planet, The / Shaft, The
Album: Released '79, on 20th Century by Phonogram Ltd. Deleted '84. Catalogue no: **T 593**.
Album: Released '80, on 20th

Century by Phonogram Ltd. Deleted '85. Catalogue no: **CT 593**
Album: Released Jun '87, on Silva Screen by Silva Screen Records. Deleted Mar '90. Catalogue no: **FILM 003**
Cass: Released Jun '87, on Silva Screen by Silva Screen Records. Catalogue no: **FILMC 003**
CD: Released Sep '88, on Silva Screen by Silva Screen Records. Catalogue no: **FILMCD 003**

Aliens

ALIENS (Film soundtrack) (London Symphony Orchestra)
Tracks: / Going after Newt / Sublevel 3 / Ripley's rescue / Atmosphere Station / Futile escape / Dark discovery / Bishop's countdown / Resolution / Hyperspace.
Note: Composed and conducted by James Horner.
Cass: Released Aug '86, on T. E. R. by That's Entertainment Records. Catalogue no: **ZCTER 1115**
CD: Released Oct '89, on T. E. R. by That's Entertainment Records. Catalogue no: **CDTER 1115**
Album: Released Aug '86, on T. E. R. by That's Entertainment Records. Catalogue no: **TER 1115**
CD: Released Jan '89, on Silva Screen by Silva Screen Records. Catalogue no: **VCD 47263**

All Creatures Great...

ALL CREATURES GREAT AND SMALL (See under Pearson, Johnny)

All That Jazz

ALL THAT JAZZ (Film soundtrack) (Various artists)
Tracks: / On Broadway: *Benson, George* / Michelle: *Burns, Ralph* / Take off with us: *Bergman, Sandahl & Chorus Vivaldi* / Ponte vecchio: *Burns, Ralph* / Everything old is new again: *Allen, Peter* / South Mount Sinai parade: *Burns, Ralph* / After you've gone: *Palmer, Leland* / There'll be some changes made: *Reinking, Ann* / Who's sorry now?: *Burns, Ralph* / Some of these days: *Foldi, Erzsebet* / Going home now: *Burns, Ralph* / Bye bye love: *Vereen, Ben & Roy Scheider* / Vivaldi concerti in G: *Burns, Ralph*.
Cass: Released Jan '89, on Casablanca by PolyGram UK Ltd. Catalogue no: **7268 030**

Cass: Released Jan '89, on Silva Screen by Silva Screen Records. Catalogue no: **822869.4**
Album: Released Jan '89, on Silva Screen by Silva Screen Records. Deleted Mar '90. Catalogue no: **822 869.1**
Album: Released Jul '80, on Casablanca by PolyGram UK Ltd. Deleted Jul '85. Catalogue no: **NBLP 7198**
Album: Released Sep '84, on Casablanca (Holland) by PolyGram UK Ltd. Catalogue no: **912 804 5**

ALL THAT JAZZ (VIDEO) (Various artists)
Note: Rating: 15.
VHS: Released '88, on CBS-Fox by CBS-Fox Video. Catalogue no: **109550**

Allen, Terry

AMERASIA - THE SOUNDTRACK
Album: Released Mar '90, on Fete Catalogue no: **FETE4**

'Allo 'Allo

'ALLO 'ALLO (The war diaries of Rene Artois) (Various artists)
Cass set: Released Nov '89, on BBC by BBC Records. Catalogue no: **ZBBC 1094**

Almost Perfect Affair

ALMOST PERFECT AFFAIR, AN (Film soundtrack) (Various artists)
Note: Composed by Georges Delerue.
Album: Released Jan '89, on

Silva Screen by Silva Screen Records. Catalogue no: **STV 81132**

Almost Summer

ALMOST SUMMER (Original soundtrack) (Various artists)
Cass: Released Jun '78, on MCA by MCA Records. Catalogue no: **TC MCF 2840**
Album: Released Jun '78, on MCA by MCA Records. Catalogue no: **MCF 2840**

Alpha Omega

ALPHA OMEGA (West End cast) (Various artists)
Cass set: Released Dec '79, on United Artists by EMI Records. Deleted '84. Catalogue no: **2TCK 101**
2 LP Set: Released Dec '79, on United Artists by EMI Records. Deleted '84. Catalogue no: **UAR 101**

ALPHA OMEGA (Film Soundtrack)
Album: Released '86, on Myrrh by Word Records (UK). Catalogue no: **MYR R 1210**
Cass: Released '86, on Myrrh by Word Records (UK). Catalogue no: **MYR C 1210**

Altered States

ALTERED STATES (Film soundtrack) (Various artists)
Note: Composed by John Corigliano.
Cass: Released Jan '89, on Silva Screen by Silva Screen Records. Catalogue no: **AGK 1 5066**
Album: Released Jan '89, on

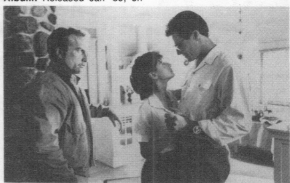

Richard Dreyfuss, Holly Hunter and Brad Johnson in Steven Spielberg's *Always*

Silva Screen by Silva Screen Records. Catalogue no: **AGL 1 5066**

Always

ALWAYS (Film soundtrack) (Various artists) (See panel on previous page)
Tracks: / Smoke gets in your eyes: *Various artists* / Cowboy man: *Various artists* / Fool in love, A: *Various artists* / Follow me: *Various artists* / Saying goodbye: *Various artists* / Return, The: *Various artists* / Seeing Dorinda: *Various artists* / Promise to Hap: *Various artists* / Dorinda solo flight: *Various artists* / Boomerang love: *Various artists* / Give me your heart: *Various artists* / Among the clouds: *Various artists* / Pete in heaven: *Various artists* / Pete and Dorinda: *Various artists* / Rescue operation: *Various artists* / Intimate conversation: *Various artists* / Old timer's shack, The: *Various artists.*
Album: Released Apr '90, on MCA by MCA Records. Catalogue no: **MCG 6085**
Cass: Released Apr '90, on MCA by MCA Records. Catalogue no: **MCGC 6085**
CD: Released Apr '90, on MCA by MCA Records. Catalogue no: **DMCG 6085**

Amadeus

AMADEUS (Film soundtrack) (Various artists)
CD Set: Released Feb '85, on London Records by London Records Ltd. Catalogue no: **825 126-2**
Cass set: Released Feb '85, on London Records by London Records Ltd. Catalogue no: **LONDC 6**
2 LP Set: Released Feb '85, on London Records by London Records Ltd. Catalogue no: **LONDP 6**

AMADEUS (2) (More music from Original Soundtrack) (Various artists)
Album: Released '88, on London Records by London Records Ltd. Catalogue no: **LONLP 7**
Cass: Released '88, on London Records by London Records Ltd. Catalogue no: **LONC 7**
CD: Released '88, on London Records by London Records Ltd. Catalogue no: **827 267 2**

AMADEUS (VIDEO) (Various artists)
VHS: Released Oct '88, on Warner Home Video by WEA Records. Catalogue no: **PES 38548**

Amazing Grace & Chuck

AMAZING GRACE & CHUCK (Film soundtrack) (Various artists)
Note: Recent score by Elmer Bernstein for Gregory Peck film.
Album: Released Jan '89, on Silva Screen by Silva Screen Records. Catalogue no: **STV 81312**
Cass: Released Jan '89, on Silva Screen by Silva Screen Records. Catalogue no: **CTV 81312**
CD: Released Jan '89, on Silva Screen by Silva Screen Records. Catalogue no: **VCD 47285**

Amerasia

AMERASIA (Film soundtrack) (See under Allen, Terry)

American Anthem

AMERICAN ANTHEM (Film soundtrack) (Various artists)
Tracks: / Two hearts: *Parr, John* / Run to her: *Mr. Mister* / Same direction: *INXS* / Battle of the dragon: *Nicks, Stevie* / Wings to fly: *Nash, Graham* / Take it easy: *Taylor, Andy* / Wings of love: *Taylor, Andy* / Love and loneliness: *Thompson, Chris* / Angel eyes: *Taylor, Andy* / Arthur's theme: *Various artists.*
CD: Released Apr '87, on Atlantic by WEA Records. Deleted Aug '87. Catalogue no: **781 661-2**
Album: Released Aug '86, on Atlantic by WEA Records. Deleted Aug '87. Catalogue no: **781 661-1**
Cass: Released Aug '86, on Atlantic by WEA Records. Deleted Aug '87. Catalogue no: **781 661-4**

American Flyers

AMERICAN FLYERS (Film soundtrack) (See also Ritenour, Lee)
Album: Released Sep '76, on United Artists by EMI Records. Catalogue no: **UAG 29991**

American Gigolo

AMERICAN GIGOLO (Film soundtrack) (Various artists)
Note: Composed by Georgio Moroder.
Album: Released '80, on Polydor

by Polydor Ltd. Deleted Feb '90. Catalogue no: **POLS 1018**
Album: Released Jan '89, on Silva Screen by Silva Screen Records. Deleted Feb '90. Catalogue no: **813632.1**
Cass: Released '80, on Polydor by Polydor Ltd. Deleted Feb '90. Catalogue no: **POLSC 1018**
Album: Released '80, on Polydor by Polydor Ltd. Deleted '85. Catalogue no: **2391 447**
Cass: Released Jan '89, on Silva Screen by Silva Screen Records. Catalogue no: **813632.4**

American Graffiti

AMERICAN GRAFFITI VOL.1 (Various artists)
Tracks: / Rock around the clock: *Haley, Bill & The Comets* / Sixteen candles: *Crests* / Runaway: *Shannon, Del* / Why do fools fall in love: *Lymon, Frankie & The Teenagers* / That'll be the day: *Holly, Buddy & The Crickets* / Maybe baby: *Holly, Buddy & The Crickets* / Fanny Mae: *Brown, Buster* / At the hop: *Flash Cadillac & The Continental Kids* / She's so fine: *Flash Cadillac & The Continental Kids* / Goodnight well it's time to go: *Spaniels* / See you in September: *Tempos* / Surfin' safari: *Beach Boys* / All summer long: *Beach Boys* / He's the great imposter: *Fleetwoods* / Almost grown: *Berry, Chuck* / Johnny B. Goode: *Berry, Chuck* / Smoke gets in your eyes: *Platters* / Only you: *Platters* / Great pretender, The: *Platters* / Little darlin': *Diamonds* / Stroll, The: *Diamonds* / Peppermint twist: *Dee, Joey & The Starlighters* / Ya, Ya: *Dorsey, Lee* / Ain't that a shame: *Domino, Fats* / I only have eyes for you: *Flamingos* / Get a job: *Silhouettes* / To the aisle: *Five Satins* / Do you wanna dance: *Freeman, Bobby* / Party doll: *Knox, Buddy* / Come go with me: *Del-Vikings* / You're sixteen: *Burnette, Johnny* / Love potion No.9: *Clovers* / Since I don't have you: *Skyliners* / Chantilly lace: *Big Bopper* / Teen angel: *Dinning, Mark* / Crying in the chapel: *Till, Sonny & The Orioles* / Thousand miles away: *Heartbeats* / Heart and soul: *Cleftones* / Green onions: *Booker T & The MGs* / Barbara Ann: *Regents* / Book of love: *Monotones.*
Cass set: Released Sep '85, on MCA by MCA Records. Cata-

logue no: **MCLDC 617**
2 LP Set: Released '74, on MCA by MCA Records. Deleted '85. Catalogue no: **MCSP 253**
2 LP Set: Released Sep '85, on MCA by MCA Records. Catalogue no: **MCLD 617**
Cass set: Released '74, on MCA by MCA Records. Deleted '85. Catalogue no: **MCSPC 253**

American Heroes

AMERICAN HEROES (Film soundtrack) (Various artists)
Album: Released Sep '80, on WEA by WEA Records. Deleted Sep '85. Catalogue no: **AHLP 1**
Cass: Released Sep '80, on WEA by WEA Records. Deleted Sep '85. Catalogue no: **AHC 1**

American Hot Wax

AMERICAN HOT WAX (Film soundtrack) (Various artists)
Album: Released '78, on A&M by A&M Records. Deleted '88. Catalogue no: **AMLM 66500**

American In Paris

AMERICAN IN PARIS (VIDEO) (Various artists)
VHS: Released '88, on MGM/UA (Video) by MGM/UA Video. Catalogue no: **SMV 100061**

AMERICAN IN PARIS / LES GIRLS (Film soundtrack) (Various artists)
Tracks: / Why am I so gone: *Various artists* / 'S wonderful: *Various artists* / Love is here to stay: *Various artists* / I'll build a stairway to paradise: *Various artists* / I got rhythm: *Various artists* / American in Paris Ballet, An: *Various artists* / Les Girls: *Various artists* / You're just too, too: *Various artists* / Ca c'est l'amour: *Various artists* / Ladies in waiting: *Various artists*.
Album: Released '73, on MGM (Polydor) by Polydor Ltd. Deleted '78. Catalogue no: **2353 068**
Cass: Released '73, on MGM (Polydor) by Polydor Ltd. Deleted '78. Catalogue no: **3110 007**
Album: Released Feb '87, on CBS by CBS Records & Distribution. Deleted Jun '88. Catalogue no: **CBS 70286**
CD: Released Feb '87, on CBS by CBS Records & Distribution. Catalogue no: **CD 70286**
Cass: Released Feb '87, on CBS by CBS Records & Distribution.

Deleted Jun '88. Catalogue no: **40 70286**

American Pop

AMERICAN POP (Original soundtrack) (Various artists)
Tracks: / Hell is for children: *Benatar, Pat* / Summertime: *Big Brother & The Holding Company* / California dreamin': *Mamas & Papas* / Turn me loose: *Fabian* / This train: *Peter, Paul & Mary* / Somebody to love: *Levy, Marcy* / Purple haze: *Hendrix, Jimi* / Take five: *Brubeck, Dave Quartet* / You send me: *Cooke, Sam* / People are strange: *Doors*.
Album: Released Sep '81, on MCA by MCA Records. Deleted Sep '86. Catalogue no: **MCF 3118**

American Tail

AMERICAN TAIL, AN (Film Soundtrack) (Various artists)
Tracks: / American tail (main theme): *Persoff, Nehemiah/John Guarcieri/Warren Hays* / Cossack cats, The: *Persoff, Nehemiah/John Guarcieri/Warren Hays* / There are no cats in America: *Persoff, Nehemiah/John Guarcieri/Warren Hays* / Storm, The: *Plummer, Christopher/Phillip Glasser* / Give me your tired, your poor: *Plummer, Christopher/Phillip Glasser* / Never say never: *Plummer, Christopher/Phillip Glasser* / Market place, The: *Glasser, Phillip/Betsy Cathcart* / Somewhere out there (instrumental): *Glasser, Phillip/Betsy Cathcart* / Somewhere out there: *Ronstadt, Linda & James Ingram* / Releasing the secret weapon: *Deluise, Dom & Phillip Glasser* / Duo, A: *Deluise, Dom & Phillip Glasser* / Great fire: *London Symphony Orchestra* / Reunited: *London Symphony Orchestra* / Flying away: *London Symphony Orchestra* / End credits: *London Symphony Orchestra*
Cass: Released Jun '87, on MCA by MCA Records. Deleted Dec '89. Catalogue no: **MCFC 3367**
CD: Released Jun '87, on MCA by MCA Records. Deleted Dec '89. Catalogue no: **DMCF 3367**
Album: Released Jun '87, on MCA by MCA Records. Deleted Dec '89. Catalogue no: **MCF 3367**

AMERICAN TAIL, AN (Original film score) (Horner, James)
Album: Released Feb '90, on

MCA by MCA Records. Catalogue no: **MCA 39096**
Cass: Released Feb '90, on MCA by MCA Records. Catalogue no: **MCAC 39096**

Americathon

AMERICATHON (Film soundtrack) (Various artists)
Album: Released Dec '79, on CBS by CBS Records & Distribution. Deleted '84. Catalogue no: **CBS 70172**

Anastasia

ANASTASIA (Film soundtrack) (Munich Philharmonic Orchestra)
Tracks: / Main title (part 1) / Ballroom, The / Siberia / Sled, The / Family only, A / The cellar / Berlin bridge / Confronting Sophie / After the interview / Railroad car / Main title (part 2) / Denial / Shopping spree / Romanoffs, The / At the Astor / Russian antiques / Darya says no / Luncheonette, The / Anna and Erich / Ekaterinburg / Back to Europe.
Note: Alfred Newman score to the 1950's Ingrid Bergman film.
Cass: Released 30 May '87, on Silva Screen by Silva Screen Records. Catalogue no: **SLIMC 10**
Album: Released 30 May '87, on Silva Screen by Silva Screen Records. Catalogue no: **SLIM 10**
Album: Released Jan '89, on Silva Screen by Silva Screen Records. Catalogue no: **STV 81125**

ANASTASIA: THE MYSTERY OF ANNA (TV soundtrack) (Various artists)
Tracks: / Main title (part 1): *Various artists* / Ballroom, The: *Various artists* / To Siberia: *Various artists* / Sled, The: *Various artists* / Ekaterinberg: *Various artists* / Family only: The cellar: *Various artists* / Berlin Bridge: *Various artists* / Confronting Sophie: *Various artists* / After the interview: *Various artists* / Railroad car, The: *Various artists*.
Note: TV Mini series with score by Laurence Rosenthal.
Album: Released Jan '89, on Silva Screen by Silva Screen Records. Catalogue no: **FILM 010**
Cass: Released Jan '89, on Silva Screen by Silva Screen Records. Catalogue no: **FILMC 010**
CD: Released Jan '89, on Silva

A 8

Screen by Silva Screen Records. Catalogue no: **FILMCD 010**

Anchors Aweigh

ANCHORS AWEIGH (Film soundtrack) (Various artists)
Album: Released '88, on Curtain Calls (USA) by Music & Arts Programs of America (USA). Catalogue no: **CC 100/17**
Album: Released Jan '89, on Silva Screen by Silva Screen Records. Catalogue no: **SH 2024**
ANCHORS AWEIGH (VIDEO) (Various artists)
VHS: Released Aug '88, on Pickick Video by Pickwick Records. Catalogue no: **SMV 10309**

And The Ship Sails On

AND THE SHIP SAILS ON (Film soundtrack) (Various artists)
Tracks: / Convoi funebre: *Various artists* / Le depart: *Various artists* / De la cuisine au salon: *Various artists* / Le cygne: *Various artists* / Pas de trois: *Various artists* / L'escalier d'honneur: *Various artists* / Valse de l'archiduchesse: *Various artists* / Glass-concertino: *Various artists* / Clare de lune: *Various artists* / Kolo vlah: *Various artists*.
Note: This Fellini film received much critical acclaim. Featured in the cast is Italian soprano Mara Zampieri.
Album: Released Jun '84, on SPI Milan (France) Catalogue no: **A 228**
Cass: Released Jun '84, on SPI Milan (France) Catalogue no: **C 228**

Andersen, Hans

HANS ANDERSEN (London revival cast) (Various artists)
Tracks: / Overture: *Various artists* / Thumbelina: *Various artists* / Truly loved: *Various artists* / Dare to take a chance: *Various artists* / Jenny kissed me: *Various artists* / Inch worm, The: *Various artists* / Ecclesiasticus (I can spell): *Various artists* / Wonderful Copenhagen: *Various artists* / I'm Hans Christian Andersen: *Various artists* / Don't talk to me about those happy days: *Various artists* / Have I stayed away too long: *Various artists* / Ugly duckling, The: *Various artists* / No two people: *Various artists* / Kings new clothes, The: *Various artists*

/ Anywhere I wander: *Various artists*.
Album: Released Oct '85, on Flashback by Mainline Records. Catalogue no: **FBLP 8080**
Cass: Released Oct '85, on Flashback by Mainline Records. Catalogue no: **ZCFBL 8080**

Anderson, Angry

Tracks: / Suddenly.
Note: Used as the theme to Scott and Charlene's wedding in the Australian soap *Neighbours*.
7" Single: Released Nov '88, on Food For Thought by Music For Nations Records. Catalogue no: **YUM 113**

Anderson, Laurie

HOME OF THE BRAVE (Original soundtrack)
Tracks: / Smoke rings / White lily / Late show, The / Talk normal / Language is a virus from outer space / Radar / Sharkey's night / Credit racket.
Album: Released Apr '87, on WEA by WEA Records. Deleted Jul '90. Catalogue no: **925400 1**
Cass: Released Apr '87, on WEA by WEA Records. Deleted Jul '90. Catalogue no: **925400 4**
CD: Released Apr '87, on WEA by WEA Records. Deleted Jul '90. Catalogue no: **925400 2**

Andrews, Julie

BROADWAY'S FAIR
Album: Released '84, on CBS by CBS Records & Distribution. Deleted '87. Catalogue no: **CAMEO 32415**
Cass: Released '84, on CBS by CBS Records & Distribution. Deleted '87. Catalogue no: **CAMEO 40 32415**

JULIE ANDREWS AND CAROL BURNETT AT LINCOLN CENTRE (Andrews, Julie & Carol Burnett)
Cass: Released Jan '89, on Silva Screen by Silva Screen Records. Catalogue no: **BT 31153**
Album: Released Jan '89, on Silva Screen by Silva Screen Records. Catalogue no: **AS 31153**

MARY POPPINS (Film soundtrack) (See under Mary Poppins)

SOUND OF MUSIC (Film soundtrack) (See under Sound Of Music)

THOROUGHLY MODERN MILLIE (Film soundtrack) (See under Thoroughly Modern Millie)

VICTOR VICTORIA (Film soundtrack) (See under Victor Victoria)

Andromeda Strain

ANDROMEDA STRAIN, THE (Original soundtrack) (Various artists)
Note: Composed by Gil Melle.
Album: Released Jan '89, on Silva Screen by Silva Screen Records. Catalogue no: **KRS 5513**

Andy Capp

ANDY CAPP (London stage cast, with Tom Courteney) (Various artists)
Tracks: / On my street: *Various artists* / I ought to be ashamed of myself: *Various artists* / We're waiting: *Various artists* / Good evening: *Various artists* / Good old legs: *Various artists* / I have a dream: *Various artists* / Oh gawd men...beasts: *Various artists* / Point of view: *Various artists* / Spend, spend, spend: *Various artists* / Don't tell me that again: *Various artists* / Frozen moments: *Various artists* / I could not have dreamed him: *Various artists* / Hermione: *Various artists* / Goin' to Barcelona: *Various artists* / When you've lived in love with someone: *Various artists* / Mr. Scrimmett: *Various artists* / Trouble with people: *Various artists* / It's better to be in simple harmony: *Various artists* / Wedding: *Various artists*.
Note: Featuring songs written by Alan Price.
Album: Released Feb '83, on Key by Key Records. Deleted '87. Catalogue no: **KEY 4**
Cass: Released Feb '83, on Key by Key Records. Deleted '87. Catalogue no: **KEYC 4**

Angel Heart

ANGEL HEART (Film soundtrack) (Various artists)
Tracks: / Harry angel: *Jones, Trevor and Courtney Pine* / Honeymoon blues: *Smith, Bessie* / Nightmare: *Jones, Trevor and Courtney Pine* / Girl of...: *Gray, Glen & The Casa Loma Orchestra* / I got this thing about...: *Jones,*

Trevor and Courtney Pine / Right key but the wrong keyhole: *Various artists* / Rainy rainy day: *McGhee, Brownie* / Looking for Johnny: *Jones, Trevor and Courtney Pine* / Soul on fire: *Baker, Laverne* / Bloodmare: *Jones, Trevor and Courtney Pine* / Johnny favourite: *Jones, Trevor and Courtney Pine.*

CD: Released '89, on Island by Island Records. Catalogue no: **IMCD 76**

Cass: Released Sep '87, on Antilles/New Directions by Island Records. Catalogue no: **ANC 8709**

Album: Released Sep '87, on Antilles/New Directions by Island Records. Catalogue no: **AN 8709**

CD: Released Sep '87, on Antilles/New Directions by Island Records. Catalogue no: **ANCD 8709**

Angel & The Soldier Boy

ANGEL AND THE SOLDIER BOY, THE (Film Soundtrack) (Clannad & Tom Conti)
Tracks: / Dream in the night, A / Pirates, The / Soldier boy, The / Angel, The / Flies, The / Spider, The / Cat, The / Jolly Roger, The / Into the picture / Pirates merrymaking / Finding the key / Pirates on the island / Sea and storm / Love theme, The / Chase, The / Toys, The / Rescue, The / Back to the book / Dream in the night (instrumental).
Note: The Angel & The Soldier Boy is an exquisitely animated film featuring an original music score by Clannad. Based on the best selling novel by Peter Collington, the film was produced by Joy Whitby, creator of Playschool and Jackanory, and directed by award winning animator Alison De Vere. It has been over a year in the making and contains more than 50,000 individual drawings. It is a beautiful story full of heroism and emotion and is destined to become a classic for children of all ages. In the quiet of the night, while a little girl sleeps, pirates rob her piggy bank and kidnap her toy soldier boy. Plucking up her courage, the soldier's friend, the angel, sets out to make a daring rescue. It is narrated by Tom Conti.
CD: Released Dec '89, on RCA by BMG Records (UK). Catalogue no: **PD 74328**

Album: Released Dec '89, on RCA by BMG Records (UK). Catalogue no: **PL 74328**

Cass: Released Dec '89, on RCA by BMG Records (UK). Catalogue no: **PK 74328**

ANGEL AND THE SOLDIER BOY, THE (VIDEO) (Clannad & Tom Conti)
Tracks: / Dream in the night, A (instrumental) / Pirates, The / Soldier boy, The / Angel, The / Flies, The / Spider, The / Cat, The / Jolly Roger, The / Into the picture / Pirates merrymaking, The / Finding the key / Pirates on the island / Sea and storm, The / Love theme, The / Chase, The / Toys, The / Rescue, The / Back to the book / Dream in the night, A.
VHS: Released Dec '89, on BMG Video Catalogue no: **790 329**

Animal House

ANIMAL HOUSE (Film soundtrack) (Various artists)
Tracks: / Faber College theme: *Berstein, Elmer* / Louie Louie: *Belushi, John* / Twistin' the night away: *Belushi, John* / Tossin' and turnin': *Lewis, Bobby* / Shama lama ding dong: *Various artists* / Hey Paula: *Paul and Paula* / Animal house: *Bishop, Stephen* / Money (that's what I want): *Belushi, John* / Let's dance: *Montez, Chris* / Dream girl: *Bishop, Stephen* / (What a) wonderful world: *Cooke, Sam* / Shout: *Various artists* / Intro: *Various artists.*
Album: Released Mar '79, on MCA by MCA Records. Catalogue no: **MCF 2868**

Cass: Released 21 Nov '87, on MCA by MCA Records. Catalogue no: **MCLC 1867**

CD: Released Aug '87, on MCA by MCA Records. Catalogue no: **MCAD 31023**

Album: Released 21 Nov '87, on MCA by MCA Records. Catalogue no: **MCL 1867**

Animalympics

ANIMALYMPICS (See under Gouldman, Graham)

Anna

ANNA (Original film soundtrack) (Various artists)
Note: Composed by Greg Hawkes.
Album: Released Jan '89, on Silva Screen by Silva Screen Records. Catalogue no: **STV 81353**

Annie

ANNIE (1982 film soundtrack) (Various artists)
Tracks: / Tomorrow: *Various artists* / It's a hard knock life: *Various artists* / Maybe: *Various artists* / Dumb dog: *Various artists* / Sandy: *Various artists* / I think I'm gonna like it here: *Various artists* / Little girls: *Various artists* / We got Annie: *Various artists* / Let's go on to the movies: *Various artists* / Sign: *Various artists* / You're never fully dressed without a smile: *Various artists* / Easy street: *Various artists* / Finale: *Various artists.*
Album: Released '82, on CBS by CBS Records & Distribution. Catalogue no: **CBS 70219**

Cass: Released '82, on CBS by CBS Records & Distribution. Catalogue no: **40 70219**

CD: Released Feb '90, on CBS (import) by CBS Records & Distribution. Catalogue no: **CK 38000**

ANNIE - BROADWAY (Original Broadway cast) (Various artists)
CD: Released Jan '89, on CBS (import) by CBS Records & Distribution. Catalogue no: **CK 34712**

Cass: on CBS by CBS Records & Distribution. Catalogue no: **40 70157**

ANNIE - LONDON (Original London cast) (Various artists)
Tracks: / Overture / Maybe / Hardknock life, The / Tomorrow / We'd like to thank you / Herbert Hoover / Little girls / I think I'm gonna like it here / NYC / Easy street / You won't be an orphan for long / You're never fully dressed without a smile / Tomorrow, reprise / Something was missing / I don't need anything but you / Annie / New deal for Christmas, A.
Cass: Released Jul '87, on CBS by CBS Records & Distribution. Deleted 17 Apr '89. Catalogue no: **40 70160**

ANNIE - STORY (Original childrens soundtrack and story) (Various artists)
Tracks: / Tomorrow: *Various artists* / Hard knock life, The: *Various artists* / Maybe: *Various artists* / Sandy: *Various artists* / I think I'm gonna like it here: *Various artists* / We got Annie: *Various artists* / You're never fully dressed without

a smile: *Various artists* / Easy street: *Various artists* / Maybe (reprise): *Various artists* / Finale: *Various artists*.

Note: This record tells the entire story of the film with music, dialogue and sound effect highlights complete with additional narration. The album comes in a very special package containing an illustration of the films popular cast, plus a special Annie board game for children to play as they listen.

Album: Released Jul '87, on CBS by CBS Records & Distribution. Catalogue no: **CBS 32239**

ANNIE (VIDEO) (Various artists)
VHS: Released Oct '88, on RCA by BMG Records (UK). Catalogue no: **CVT 20072**

Annie Get Your Gun

ANNIE GET YOUR GUN (London revival cast) (Various artists)
Tracks: / Overture: *Various artists* / Colonel Buffalo Bill: *Various artists* / I'm a bad bad man: *Various artists* / Doin' what comes natur'lly: *Various artists* / Girl that I marry,The: *Various artists* / You can't get a man with a gun: *Various artists* / There's no business like show business: *Various artists* / They say it's wonderful (plus reprise): *Various artists* / Moonshine lullaby: *Various artists* / My defenses are down: *Various artists* / Wild horse ceremonial dance: *Various artists* / I'm an indian too: *Various artists* / I got lost in his arms: *Various artists* / I got the sun in the morning: *Various artists* / Old fashioned wedding: *Various artists* / Anything you can do: *Various artists* / Finale: *Various artists*.
Album: Released '86, on First Night Records. Catalogue no: **CAST 4**
Cass: Released '86, on First Night Records. Catalogue no: **CASTC 4**
CD: Released '86, on First Night Records. Catalogue no: **CASTCD4**

ANNIE GET YOUR GUN (Studio Cast Recording) (Various artists)
Album: Released Jan '89, on Silva Screen by Silva Screen Records. Catalogue no: **PS 2360**

Cass: Releasetd Jan '89, on Silva Screen by Silva Screen records. Catalogue no: **PST 2360**

ANNIE GET YOUR GUN (Original Soundtrack) (MCA label) (Various artists)
Tracks: / Doin' what comes naturally / Moonshine lullaby / You can't get a man with a gun / I'm an Indian too / They say it's wonderful / Anything you can do / I got lost in his arms / I got the sun in the morning / Girl that I marry / My defences are down / Who do you love I hope / There's no business like show business
Album: Released '87, on MCA by MCA Records. Catalogue no: **MCL 1660**
Cass: Released '87, on MCA by MCA Records. Catalogue no: **MCLC 1660**

ANNIE GET YOUR GUN (Original Soundtrack) (Silva Screen label) (Various artists)
Album: Released Jan '89, on Silva Screen by Silva Screen Records. Catalogue no: **SH 2053**
Cass: Released Jan '89, on Silva Screen by Silva Screen Records. Catalogue no: **CSH 2053**
CD: Released Jan '89, on Silva Screen by Silva Screen Records. Catalogue no: **1124.2**

ANNIE GET YOUR GUN / SEVEN BRIDES FOR SEVEN BROTHERS (Film Soundtracks) (See under Seven Brides For..)

Another Time

ANOTHER TIME ANOTHER PLACE (Theme from) (Various artists)
Tracks: / Another time another place (theme from)
12" Single: released '86, on T.E.R. by That's Entertainment Records. Catalogue no: **STER 12007**

Antony & Cleopatra

ANTONY AND CLEOPATRA (Film Soundtrack) (Various artitsts)
Tracks: / Main title (love theme) / Give me to drink Mandragora (Cleopatras theme) / Confrontation with Pompey / Antony and Octavia (Caesar's sister) / Barge she sat in / One will tear the other / Battle of Actium / Prelude to part

2 (love theme) / Whither hast thou led me to Egypt / Death of Enobarbus / He goes forth gallantly / Sometimes we see a cloud that's dragonish / Death of Antony (love theme) / Pretty worm of Nilus / She shall be buried by her Antony (end titles)
Album: Released '73, on MGM (Polydor) by Polydor Ltd. Deleted '78. Catalogue no: **2383 109**
Cass: Released '73, on MGM (Polydor) by Polydor Ltd. Deleted '78. Catalogue no: **3170 056**

Any Which Way You Can

ANY WHICH WAY YOU CAN (Original Soundtrack) (Various artists)
Tracks: / Beers to you: *Various artists* / Any which way you can: *Various artists* / You're the reason God made Oklahoma: *Various artists* / Whiskey heaven: *Various artists* / One too many women in your life: *Various artists* / Cow patti: *Various artists* / Acapulco: *Various artists* / Any way you want me: *Various artists* / Cotton eyed Clint: *Various artists* / Orangutan hall of fame: *Various artists* / Too loose: *Various artists* / Good guys and the bad guys: *Various artists*.
Note: Songs from the Clint Eastwood film.
Album: Released Feb '81, on Warner Bros. by WEA Records. Deleted '85. Catalogue no: **K 56884**
Album: Released Jan '89, on Silva Screen by Silva Screen Records. Catalogue no: **HS 3499**

Anyone Can Whistle

ANYONE CAN WHISTLE (Original cast recording) (Various artists)
Note: The Stephen Sondheim show starring Angela Lansbury and Lee Remick.
Cass: Released Jan '89, on Silva Screen by Silva Screen Records. Catalogue no: **PST 02480**
Cass: Released Jan '89, on Silva Screen by Silva Screen Records. Deleted Mar '90. Catalogue no: **BT 32608**
CD: Released Jan '89, on CBS (import) by CBS Records & Distribution. Catalogue no: **CK 02480**
Album: Released Jan '89, on Silva Screen by Silva Screen Records. Deleted Mar '90. Catalogue

no: **AS 32608**

Anyone For Dennis

ANYONE FOR DENNIS (Original London cast) (Various artists)
Cass: Released Oct '81, on RCA by BMG Records (UK). Catalogue no: **RCAK 6006**
Album: Released Oct '81, on RCA by BMG Records (UK). Catalogue no: **RCALP 6006**

Anything Goes

ANYTHING GOES (Musical show 88) (Various artists)
CD: Released '88, on RCA by BMG Records (UK). Catalogue no: **RD 87769**
Cass: Released '88, on RCA by BMG Records (UK). Catalogue no: **RK 87769**
Album: Released '88, on RCA by BMG Records (UK). Catalogue no: **RL 87769**

ANYTHING GOES (Revival 1969 London Cast) (Various artists)
Tracks: / Overture (Anything Goes): *Various artists* / You're the top: *Various artists* / Bon voyage: *Various artists* / It's delovely: *Various artists* / Heaven hop: *Various artists* / Friendship: *Various artists* / Let's do it: *Various artists* / Anything goes: *Various artists* / Public enemy number one: *Various artists* / Let's step out: *Various artists* / Let's misbehave: *Various artists* / Blow, Gabriel, blow: *Various artists* / All through the night: *Various artists* / Take me back to Manhattan: *Various artists* / I get a kick out of you: *Various artists* / Finale: *Various artists*
Album: Released Sep '84, on T.E.R. by That's Entertainment Records. Catalogue no: **TER 1080**
Cass: Released Sep '84, on T.E.R. by That's Entertainment Records. Catalogue no: **ZCTER 1080**

ANYTHING GOES (Original London cast recording) (Various artists)
Tracks: / Anything goes (prelude): *Various artists* / There's no cure like travel: *Various artists* / You're the top: *Various artists* / I want to row on the crew: *Various artists* / Friendship: *Various ar-*

tists / Anything goes: *Various artists* / Public enemy no: 1: *Various artists* / Goodbye, little dream, goodbye: *Various artists* / All through the night: *Various artists* / Buddie beware: *Various artists* / I get a kick out of you: *Various artists* / Bon voyage: *Various artists* / Easy to love: *Various artists* / Sailor's tey: shanty: *Various artists* / It's delovely: *Various artists* / Entrace: *Various artists* / Blow Gabriel, blow: *Various artists* / Be like the bluebird: *Various artists* / Gypsy in me, The: *Various artists* / I get a kick out of you: *Various artists*
Album: Released Sep '89, on First Night by First Night Records. Catalogue no: **CAST 18**
Cass: Released Sep '89, on First Night by First Night Records. Catalogue no: **CASTC 18**
CD: Released Sep '89, on First Night by First Night Records. Catalogue no: **CASTCD 18**

ANYTHING GOES (1962 Revival Cast) (Various artists)
Album: Released Jan '89, on Silva Screen by Silva Screen Records. Catalogue no: **FLS 15100**
CD: Released Jan '89, on Silva Screen by Silva Screen Records. Catalogue no: **EK 15100**

ANYTHING GOES (New 89 Studio version)
Tracks: / Anything goes overture: *Various artists* / I get a kick out of you: *Various artists* / Bon voyage: *Various artists* / All through the night: *Various artists* / There'll always be a fair lady: *Various artists* / Where are the men: *Various artists* / You're the top: *Various artists* / You're the top (Encore): *Various artists* / There'll always be a lady fair (reprise): *Various artists* / Anything goes (Finale): *Various artists* / Entr'acte: *Various artists* / Public enemy No. 1: *Various artists* / What a joy to be young: *Various artists* / Blow, Gabriel, blow: *Various artists* / Be like the bluebird: *Various artists* / Buddie beware: *Various artists* / Gypsy in me, The: *Various artists* / Finale ultimo: *Various artists* / There's no cure like travel: *Various artists* / Kate the great: *Various artists* / Waltz down the aisle: *Various artists*
Cass: Released Oct '89, on EMI by EMI Records. Catalogue no: **EL**

7498484
Album: Released Oct '89, on EMI by EMI Records. Catalogue no: **EL 7498481**
CD: Released Oct '89, on EMI by EMI Records. Catalogue no: **CDC 749 848 2**

ANYTHING GOES/BANDWAGON (Original cast recordings) (Various artists)
Note: Cole Porter shows with Mary Martin.
Album: Released Jan '89, on Silva Screen by Silva Screen Records. Catalogue no: **AML 4751**

ANYTHING GOES/PANAMA HATTIE (Original soundtracks) (Various artists)
Note: Cole Porter musical starring Ethel Merman.
Album: Released Jan '89, on Silva Screen by Silva Screen Records. Catalogue no: **SH 2043**

Apartment Zero

APARTMENT ZERO (Film soundtrack) (Various artists)
Tracks: / Buenos Aires Capriccio - Main title: *Various artists* / Jack's appearance: *Various artists* / Deal, The: *Various artists* / Crime in the night: *Various artists* / Rescue: *Various artists* / Friendship: *Various artists* / Victim number 13: *Various artists* / Air of love: *Various artists* / Suspicions: *Various artists* / Cambalache: *Various artists* / Training Jack: *Various artists* / Invaded by neighbours: *Various artists* / Capriccio 2: *Various artists* / Touch of death: *Various artists* / Lament: *Various artists* / Farewell to Laura: *Various artists* / Hell: *Various artists* / Fight, The: *Various artists* / Last supper: *Various artists* / Apartment zero - End title: *Various artists*.
Album: Released Oct '89, on Filmtrax by Filmtrax Records. Deleted Feb '90. Catalogue no: **MOMENT 120**
Cass: Released Oct '89, on Filmtrax by Filmtrax Records. Deleted Aug '90. Catalogue no: **MOMENTC 120**
CD: Released Oct '89, on Filmtrax by Filmtrax Records. Catalogue no: **MOMENTD 120**

Apocalypse Now

APOCALYPSE NOW (Film Soundtrack) (Various artists)
Note: A Francis Coppola film.
CD: Released '88, on Elektra by

Elektra Records (UK). Catalogue no: **960 826 2**
CD: Released Jan '89, on Silva Screen by Silva Screen Records. Catalogue no: **90001.2**
Album: Released Dec '79, on Elektra by Elektra Records (UK). Deleted Jan '90. Catalogue no: **K 62025**

Apology

APOLOGY (Film soundtrack) (Various artists)
Note: Composed by Maurice Jarre.
Album: Released Jan '89, on Silva Screen by Silva Screen Records. Catalogue no: **STV 81284**

Applause

APPLAUSE (Original Broadway Cast) (Various artists)
Tracks: / Overture: *Various artists* / Backstage babble/ First nighters: *Various artists* / Think how it's gonna be (when we're gonna...): *Various artists* / But alive: *Various artists* / Best night of my life: *Various artists* / Who's that girl: *Various artists* / Applause: *Various artists* / Hurry back: *Various artists* / Fasten your seat belt: *Various artists* / Welcome to the theatre: *Various artists* / Good friends: *Various artists* / One halloween: *Various artists* / Something greater: *Various artists* / Finale: *Various artists*.
Album: Released '73, on Probe Deleted '78. Catalogue no: **SPB 1055**
Album: Released Nov '82, on MCA by MCA Records. Deleted '87. Catalogue no: **MCL 1724**

Apres La Guerre

APRES LA GUERRE (AFTER THE WAR) (1989 French Film) (Knieper,Jurgen)
CD: Released Feb '90, on SPI Milan (France) Catalogue no: **CDCH 386**

April Fools Day

APRIL FOOLS DAY (Original soundtrack) (Various artists)
Note: Horror score by Charles Bernstein.
Album: Released Jan '89, on Silva Screen by Silva Screen Records. Catalogue no: **STV 81278**

Arabesque

ARABESQUE (Film soundtrack) (Various artists)

Note: Composed by Henry Mancini.
Album: Released Jan '89, on RCA by BMG Records (UK). Catalogue no: **NL 43757**

Archers

VINTAGE ARCHERS (Various artists)
Note: Great moments from radio's longest running serial.
Cass set: Released Sep '88, on BBC by BBC Records. Catalogue no: **ZBBC 1036**

VINTAGE ARCHERS 2 (Various artists)
Cass set: Released Oct '89, on BBC by BBC Records. Catalogue no: **ZBBC 1080**

Archy & Mehitabel

ARCHY & MEHITABEL (Original Broadway cast) (Various artists)
Note: Starring Carol Channing.
Album: Released Jan '89, on Silva Screen by Silva Screen Records. Catalogue no: **AOL 4963**

Are You Lonesome

ARE YOU LONESOME TO-NIGHT (Original London cast) (Various artists)
Tracks: / Peace in the valley: *Various artists* / Heartbreak hotel: *Various artists* / That's alright mama: *Various artists* / I don't care if the sun don't shine: *Various artists* / Loving you: *Various artists* / Blue suede shoes: *Various artists* / Hound dog: *Various artists* / If I can dream: *Various artists* / All my trials: *Various artists* / NBC-TV special (1968): *Various artists* / You gave me a mountain: *Various artists* / I was the one: *Various artists* / If we never meet again: *Various artists* / Are you lonesome tonight: *Various artists*.
Album: Released Dec '85, on First Night by First Night Records. Catalogue no: **CAST 1**
Cass: Released Dec '85, on First Night by First Night Records. Catalogue no: **CASTC 1**

Aria

ARIA (1987 FilmSoundtrack) (Various artists)
Album: Released '87, on RCA by BMG Records (UK). Catalogue no: **BL 86587**
Cass: Released '87, on RCA by BMG Records (UK). Catalogue no: **BK 86587**

CD: Released '87, on RCA by BMG Records (UK). Catalogue no: **BD 86587**

ARIA (VIDEO) (Various artists)

Note: Aria is a collection of images put together by such directors as Jean Luc Goddard, Derek Jarman, Ken Russell, Julian Temple and is set to various classical pieces by such composers as Puccini, Wagner and Verdi.
VHS: Released Jun '89 on Virgin Vision. Catalogue no: **VVD 546**

Aristocats

ARISTOCATS, THE (Film soundtrack)
Album: Released Dec '87, on Walt Disney Catalogue no: **WD 020**
Cass: Released Dec '87, on Walt Disney Catalogue no: **WDC 020**

Arizona Colt

ARIZONA COLT (Film Soundtrack) (Various artists)
Album: Released Jan '89, on Silva Screen by Silva Screen Records. Catalogue no: **SP 8060**

Armstrong, Louis

ARMED FORCES RADIO SERVICE (Armstrong, Louis / His Orchestra)
Album: Released Jun '86, on Duke. Catalogue no: **D 1021**

HELLO DOLLY (SINGLE)
Tracks: / Hello Dolly.
Note: From the film/show 'Hello Dolly'
7" Single: Released Apr '64, on London-American by Decca Records. Deleted Apr '69. Catalogue no: **HLR 9878**

PORGY AND BESS (Armstrong, Louis / Ella Fitzgerald)
Tracks: / Summertime / I got plenty o' nuttin' / My man's gone now / Bess, you is my woman now / It ain't necessarily so / There's a boat that's leaving shortly for New York / Bess, oh where's my Bess? / I'm on my way / I loves you, Porgy / Woman is a sometime thing.
Album: Released Jan '78, on Verve by Polygram Distribution. Catalogue no: **2632 052**
Cass: Released Jan '78, on Verve by Polygram Distribution. Catalogue no: **3507 034**
CD: Released '83, on Verve by

Polygram Distribution. Catalogue no:**810 049-2**
CD: Released on Polydor by Polygram Distribution. Catalogue no:**827 475-2**
Album: Released May '85, on Verve by Polygram Distribution. Catalogue no:**171 110 5**
Cass: Released May '85, on Verve by Polygram Distribution. Catalogue no:**100 7016**
Album: Released Jun '89, on Verve by Polygram Distribution. Catalogue no:**827 475 1**
Cass: Released Jun '89, on Verve by Polygram Distribution. Catalogue no: **350 150**

THEME FROM THREEPENNY OPERA
Tracks: / Theme from Threepenny Opera
7" Single: Released Apr '56, on Philips. Deleted Apr '61. Catalogue no: **PB 574**

WHAT A WONDERFUL WORLD (OLD GOLD)
Tracks: / What a wonderful world / Hello Dolly.
Note: Featured in the film 'Good Morning Vietnam'.
7" Single: Released Mar '90, on Old Gold. Catalogue no: **OG 9419**

WHAT A WONDERFUL WORLD / HELLO DOLLY
Tracks: / What a wonderful world / Hello Dolly.
Note: Featured in the film 'Good Morning Vietnam'.
7" Single: Released Jul '86, on MCA. Catalogue no: **MCA 706**

WHAT A WONDERFUL WORLD (SINGLE)
Tracks: / What a wonderful world / Game of love.
Note: Featured in the film 'Good Morning Vietnam'.
7" Single: Released Mar '88, on A&M by A&M Records. Catalogue no: **AM 435**
12" Single: Released Mar '88, on A&M by A&M Records. Catalogue no: **AMY 435**

Arnold, Malcolm
BRIDGE ON THE RIVER KWAI
(See under Bridge On The River Kwai)

Arnold, P.P.
ELECTRIC DREAMS
Tracks: / Electric dreams.
Note: From the film Electric Dreams.
7" Single: Released Aug '84, on 10 Records by Virgin Records. Deleted '86. Catalogue no: **TEN 29**
12" Single: Released Aug '84, on 10 Records by Virgin Records. Deleted '86. Catalogue no: **TEN 29-12**

SUPERGRASS
Tracks: / Supergrass / Inside man.
Note: From the film of the same name.
7" Single: Released Dec '85, on Island by Island Records. Catalogue no: **IS 257**

Around The World...
AROUND THE WORLD IN 80 DAYS (Film soundtrack) (Various artists)
Album: Released Jan '89, on MCA by MCA Records. Catalogue no: **MCA 37986**
Cass: Released Jan '89, on MCA by MCA Records. Catalogue no: **MCAC 37986**
CD: Released Jan '89, on MCA by MCA Records. Catalogue no: **MCAD 31134**

Art Of Noise
DRAGNET
Tracks: / Dragnet / Dragnet (aon mix).
Note: From the film of the same name.
7" Single: Released Jul '87, on China by Polydor Ltd. Catalogue no: **WOK 14**
12" Single: Released Jul '87, on China by Polydor Ltd. Catalogue no: **WOKX 14**
Cassingle: Released Jul '87, on China by Polydor Ltd. Catalogue no: **WOK 14 MC**

Arthur
ARTHUR (1980 film) (Various artists)
Album: Released '80, on Warner Bros. by WEA Records. Catalogue no: **BS 3582**

ARTHUR 2: ON THE ROCKS (Original film soundtrack) (Various artists)
Tracks: / Love is my decision: *Various artists* / Gravity: *Various artists* / Secret: *Various artists* / Speed of light: *Various artists* / Boys night out: *Various artists* / Best of times, The: *Various artists* / Locomotion, The: *Various artists* / Reflections: *Various artists* /

Devotion: *Various artists* / Arthur love theme: *Various artists*.
Note: Featuring Chris De Burgh, Kylie Minogue, O.M.D., Brenda Russell, Steve Kahn, Donald Fagen & Burt Bacharach.
Album: Released 20 Feb '89, on A&M by A&M Records. Catalogue no: **393 916-1**
Cass: Released 20 Feb '89, on A&M by A&M Records. Catalogue no: **393 916-4**
CD: Released 20 Feb '89, on A&M by A&M Records. Catalogue no: **393 916-2**

ARTHUR 2: ON THE ROCKS (Original film score) (Various artists)
Album: Released Jan '89, on Silva Screen by Silva Screen Records. Catalogue no: **SP 3916**
Cass: Released Jan '89, on Silva Screen by Silva Screen Records. Catalogue no: **CS 3916**

Aspects of Love
ASPECTS OF LOVE (Original London cast) (Various artists)
Tracks: / Love changes everything / Seeing is believing / Chason d'enfante / She's far better off without you / Leading lady / There's more to love / First man you remember, The / Falling / Anything but lonely / Cafe, The / Memory of a happy moment, The / Everybody loves a hero / Stop wait please / Other pleasures / Mermaid song / Journey of a lifetime / Hand me the wine and the dice.
Album: Released Aug '89, on Really Useful Records by Really Useful Group. Catalogue no: **841 126 1**
Cass: Released Aug '89, on Really Useful Records by Really Useful Group. Catalogue no: **841 126 4**
CD: Released Aug '89, on Really Useful Records by Really Useful Group. Catalogue no: **841 126 2**

Assoluto Naturale
ASSOLUTO NATURALE (Film soundtrack) (Various artists)
Note: Score by Ennio Morricone.
Album: Released Jan '89, on Cerebus (USA) Catalogue no: **C'BUS 112**

Astaire, Fred
FRED ASTAIRE AND GINGER ROGERS STORY, THE (Astaire, Fred & Ginger Rogers)
Tracks: / Half of it dearie blues,

The / High hat / My one and only / Not my girl / Crazy feet / Night and day / I've got you on my mind / Fine romance, A / Music makes me / Out for no good / I won't dance / I got a new lease of life / Puttin' on the ritz / Cheek to cheek / You'll be reminded of me / I used to be colour blind / I can't be bothered now / Wedding cake walk, The / If swing goes, I go too / They can't take that away from me / Weekend in the country, A / You'll never know / By myself / Something's gotta give / Before the parade passes by.

Cass: Released May '89, on Deja Vu. Catalogue no: **DVREMC 09**

CD: Released May '89, on Deja Vu. Catalogue no: **DVRECD 09**

GOLDEN AGE OF FRED ASTAIRE

Tracks: / Top hat, white tie and tails / Fine romance, A / Cheek to cheek / I wanna be a dancin' man / They can't take that away from me / One for my baby / Night and day / Something's gotta give / Foggy day, A / Isn't this a lovely day / They all laughed / That's entertainment.

Note: Licensed from Liberty Records, the great Fred Astaire with recordings made in 1976. Each track was featured in one of Astaire's many successful films, including titles written by Irving Berlin, George Gershwin, Cole Porter, Jerome Kern and Johnny Mercer.

Album: Released Sep '83, on Golden Age by EMI Records. Deleted Sep '88. Catalogue no: **GX 2511**

Cass: Released May '88, on MFP by EMI Records. Deleted Apr '90. Catalogue no: **TC MFP 5827**

Album: Released May '88, on MFP by EMI Records. Deleted Apr '90. Catalogue no: **MFP 5827**

GOLDEN AGE OF FRED ASTAIRE VOL.2

Album: Released Jul '85, on Golden Age by EMI Records. Catalogue no: **GX 41 2538 1**

Cass: Released Jul '85, on Golden Age by EMI Records. Catalogue no: **GX 41 2538 4**

SOUNDTRACKS, VOICES AND THEMES (Astaire, Fred & Gene Kelly)

Album: Released '88, on DRG (USA) by DRG Records (USA). Catalogue no: **MRS 509**

STARRING FRED ASTAIRE

Tracks: / No strings / Isn't this a lovely day / Top hat, white tie and tails / Cheek to cheek / Piccolino, The / We saw the sea / Let yourself go / I'd rather lead a band / I'm putting all my eggs in one basket / Let's face the music and dance / I'm building up to an awful let-down / Pick yourself up / Way you look tonight / Waltz in swing time, The / Fine romance, A / Bojangles of Harlem / Never gonna dance / Slap that bass / Beginner's luck / They all laughed / Let's call the whole thing off / They can't take that away from me / Shall we dance / I can't be bothered now / Things are looking up / Foggy day in London town, A / Nice work if you can get it / I used to be colour blind / Change partners / Yam, The.

2 LP Set: Released Aug '86, on Avan-Guard Catalogue no: **VS2LP 32472**

Cass set: Released Aug '86, on Avan-Guard Catalogue no: **VS2C 32472**

STARRING FRED ASTAIRE (Single album)

Album: Released Aug '87, on CBS by CBS Records & Distribution. Deleted Aug '90. Catalogue no: **460127 1**

Cass: Released Aug '87, on CBS by CBS Records & Distribution. Deleted Jan '90. Catalogue no: **460127 4**

CD: Released Jan '90, on CBS by CBS Records & Distribution. Catalogue no: **4655892**

At The Drop Of A Hat

AT THE DROP OF A HAT (London cast) (Various artists)

Album: Released Mar '60, on Philips by Phonogram Ltd. Deleted '65. Catalogue no: **PMC 1033**

A-Team

A-TEAM, THE (Theme from) (See under Caine, Daniel

A-TEAM, THE (Theme from) (See under Post, Mike)

A-TEAM, THE (Original Score) (Various artists)

Tracks: / A-team, Theme from: *Various artists* / Young Hannibal: *Various artists* / B. A. 's ride: *Various artists* / A-team in New York City, The: *Various artists* / Bandits: *Various artists* / Taxi chase: *Various artists* / A-team

escape, The: *Various artists* / A-team prepare for war, The: *Various artists* / Showtime: *Various artists* / Move sucker: *Various artists* / Let's get busted: *Various artists* / Murdock's "face": *Various artists* / Helicopters: *Various artists* / More bandits: *Various artists.*

Album: Released Oct '85, on MFP by EMI Records. Catalogue no: **41 5733 1**

Cass: Released Oct '85, on MFP by EMI Records. Catalogue no: **41 5733 4**

Athena

ATHENA (Original soundtrack) (Various artists)

Note: Starring Jane Powell and Debbie Reynolds.

Album: Released Jan '89, on Silva Screen by Silva Screen Records. Catalogue no: **MPT 2**

Atlantic City

ATLANTIC CITY (Film soundtrack) (Various artists)

Note: Composed by Michel Legrand.

CD: Released Jan '89, on DRG (USA) by DRG Records (USA). Catalogue no: **CDRG 6104**

Album: Released May '82, on DRG (USA) by DRG Records (USA). Deleted '87. Catalogue no: **SL 6104**

Album: Released '88, on DRG (USA) by DRG Records (USA). Catalogue no: **DRG 6104**

Cass: Released Jan '89, on DRG (USA) by DRG Records (USA). Catalogue no: **DRGC 6104**

Atlantic Realm

ATLANTIC REALM (See under Clannad for details)

Atomic Cafe

ATOMIC CAFE (Film Soundtrack) (Various artists)

Album: Released '88, on Rounder (USA) by Rounder Records (USA). Catalogue no: **ROUNDER 1034**

Cass: Released '88, on Rounder (USA) by Rounder Records (USA). Catalogue no: **ROUNDER 1034C**

Au Revoir Les Enfants

AU REVOIR LES ENFANTS (Film soundtrack) (Various artists)

Note: Music from the Louis Malle film.

CD: Released Jan '89, on Silva

Screen by Silva Screen Records. Catalogue no: **VCD 70443**
Cass: Released Jan '89, on Silva Screen by Silva Screen Records. Catalogue no: **C 704.430**
Album: Released Jan '89, on Silva Screen by Silva Screen Records. Catalogue no: **704.430**

Auf Wiedersehn Pet

AUF WIEDERSEHN PET (TV soundtrack) (Various artists)
Cass: Released Jan '84, on Towerbell Catalogue no: **ZCAUF 1**
Album: Released Jan '84, on Towerbell Catalogue no: **AUF 1**

Australian TV's ...

AUSTRALIAN TV'S GREATEST HITS (Original Television Themes) (Various artists)
Tracks: / Neighbours: *Various artists* / Prisoner cell block H (theme from): *Various artists* / Sullivans, The: *Various artists* / Sons and daughters: *Various artists* / Anzacs: *Various artists* / Skippy: *Various artists* / Paul Hogan show, The: *Various artists* / Young doctors, The:

Various artists / Chopper squad: *Various artists* / Country practice, A: *Various artists* / Carsons law: *Various artists*.
Album: Released Nov '88, on Silva Screen by Silva Screen Records. Catalogue no: **FILM 028**
Cass: Released Nov '88, on Silva Screen by Silva Screen Records. Catalogue no: **FILMC 028**
CD: Released Nov '88, on Silva Screen by Silva Screen Records. Catalogue no: **FILMCD 028**

AUSTRALIAN TV'S GREATEST HITS 3 (Various artists)
CD: Released Jan '89, on Silva Screen by Silva Screen Records. Catalogue no: **FILMCD 034**

Auty, Peter

WALKING IN THE AIR (Auty, Peter & The Sinfonia Of London)
Tracks: / Walking in the air.
Note: 'From the film The Snowman'.
7" Single: Released Dec '85, on Stiff by Stiff Records. Deleted '88. Catalogue no: **LAD 1**

Avengers...

AVENGERS / NEW AVENGERS / PROFESSIONALS (Original soundtracks)
Note: TV scores by Laurie Johnson.
CD: Released Jan '89, on Silva Screen by Silva Screen Records. Catalogue no: **VCD 47270**
Album: Released Jan '89, on Silva Screen by Silva Screen Records. Catalogue no: **ASV 95003**

Aviator

AVIATOR, THE (Film soundtrack) (Various artists)
Note: Film starring Christopher Reeve with score by Dominic Frontiere.
Album: Released Jan '89, on Silva Screen by Silva Screen Records. Catalogue no: **STV 81240**

Awakening

AWAKENING, THE (Film soundtrack) (Bolling, Claude)
Album: Released Feb '90, on Silva Screen by Silva Screen Records. Catalogue no: **ERS6520**

B

The following information was taken from the Music Master database on September 25th, 1990.

B Project

WAR THEME FROM ROCKY IV

Tracks: / War theme from Rocky IV / War, the fanfare.

12" Single: Released Mar '86, on Certain by Certain Records. Catalogue no: **12 ACERT 7**

7" Single: Released Mar '86, on Certain by Certain Records. Catalogue no: **ACERT 7**

Baal

Baal (See under Bowie, David)

Babes In Arms

BABES IN ARMS (Original soundtrack) (Various artists)

Note: Starring Judy Garland and Mickey Rooney.

Album: Released Jan '89, on Silva Screen. Catalogue no: **SH 2077**

BABES IN ARMS (Studio cast) (Various artists)

Album: Released Jan '89, on Silva Screen. Catalogue no: **AOS 2570**

Cass: Released Jan '89, on Silva Screen. Catalogue no: **BT 2570**

BABES IN ARMS/BABES ON BROADWAY (Various artists)

2 LP Set: Released '88, on Curtain Calls (USA) by Music & Arts Programs of America (USA). Catalogue no: **CC 100/6-7**

Baby

BABY (Original Broadway cast) (Various artists)

Tracks: / Opening: *Various artists* / We start today: *Various artists* / What could be better?: *Various artists* / Plaza song: *Various artists* / Baby, baby, baby: *Various artists* / I want it all: *Various artists* / At night she comes home to me: *Various artists* / Fatherhood blues: *Various artists* / Romance: *Various artists* / I chose right: *Various artists* / Story goes on: *Various artists* / Ladies singing their song: *Various artists* /

Patterns: *Various artists* / Romance 2: *Various artists* / Easier to love: *Various artists* / Romance 3: *Various artists* / Two people in love: *Various artists* / And what if we had loved like that?: *Various artists* / Birth: *Various artists* / Finale: *Various artists*.

Note: Cast: Liz Callaway, Beth Fowler, James Congdon, Todd Graff. Conductor: Peter Howard. Songs by David Shire, Richard Maltby Jnr.

Album: Released Mar '84, on T. E. R. by That's Entertainment Records. Catalogue no: **TER 1089**

Cass: Released Mar '84, on T. E. R. by That's Entertainment Records. Catalogue no: **ZCTER 1089**

CD: Released Oct '84, on T. E. R. by That's Entertainment Records. Catalogue no: **CDTER 1089**

Baby Love

BABY LOVE (Original soundtrack to Lemon Popsicle 5) (Various artists)

Tracks: / Take good care of my baby: *Vee, Bobby* / Summertime blues: *Cochran, Eddie* / Teen beat: *Nelson, Sandy* / You send me: *Cooke, Sam* / Sweet little sixteen: *Berry, Chuck* / Dream lover: *Darin, Bobby* / Rescue me: *Bass, Fontella* / Locomotion, The: *Little Eva* / Maybellene: *Berry, Chuck* / Sixteen candles: *Crests* / Splish splash: *Darin, Bobby* / He's so fine: *Chiffons* / Keep a knockin': *Little Richard* / Crazy love: *Anka, Paul* / Apache: *Cherokees* / What a wonderful world: *Cooke, Sam* / Multiplication: *Darin, Bobby* / Pretty little angel eyes: *Lee, Curtis* / Speedy Gonzales: *Boone, Pat* / Wanderer: *Dion* / Girl can't help it, The: *Little Richard* / Raunchy: *Justis, Billy* / Twilight time: *Platters* / Who put the bomp: *Mann, Barry* / Rhythm of the rain: *Cascades* / Only sixteen: *Cooke, Sam* / Silence is golden: *Tremeloes* / Ginny come lately: *Hyland, Brian* / Tiger: *Fabian* / End of the world: *Davis, Skeeter* / Bend me shape me: *Amen Corner* / Wipe out: *Surfaris* / Sixteen candles: *Crests*.

Cass set: Released Nov '85, on Red Bus by Red Bus Records. Catalogue no: **ZCRBM 8571**

2 LP Set: Released Nov '85, on Red Bus by Red Bus Records. Catalogue no: **RBMD 8571**

Back to the Future II - the successful sequel starring Michael J Fox and Christopher Lloyd

Babylon

BABYLON (Original soundtrack) (Various artists)
Tracks: / Deliver me from my enemies: *Yabby U* / Turn me loose: *Prophet, Michael* / Free Africa: *Yabby U* / Whap 'n' bap 'n': / *Roy.* / Beefy's tune: *Bovell, Dennis* / Thank you for the many things you've done: *Cassandra* / Hey jay children: *Aswad* / Manhunter: *Bovell, Dennis* / Jazterpiece: *Bovell, Dennis* / Warrior charge: *Aswad.*
Album: Released Oct '80, on Chrysalis by Chrysalis Records. Catalogue no: **CHR 1294**
Cass: Released '83, on Chrysalis by Chrysalis Records. Deleted '86. Catalogue no: **ZCHR 1294**

Bachelor Party

BACHELOR PARTY (Original soundtrack) (Various artists)
Tracks: / American heartbeat '84: *Various artists* / Something isn't right: *Various artists* / Crazy over you: *Various artists* / Little demon: *Various artists* / Wind out: *Various artists* / Bachelor party: *Various artists* / What kind of hell: *Various artists* / Alley oop: *Various artists* / Why do good girls like bad boys: *Various artists* / Dream of the West: *Various artists* / Translation: *Various artists* / Equals: *Various artists* / Appointment with the master, An: *Various artists* / Settlement song, The: *Various artists* / Long time living: *Various artists* / Stranger still: *Various artists* / Come all ye faces: *Various artists.*
Album: Released Dec '84, on I.R.S (Illegal) by I.R.S.Records. Catalogue no: **IRSA 7051**

Back To The Future

BACK TO THE FUTURE (18 Sci-fi film themes) (Various artists)
CD: Released '88, on Laser Catalogue no: **CD 86006**

Back To The Future

BACK TO THE FUTURE (Film soundtrack) (Various artists)
Album: Released Feb '86, on MCA by MCA Records. Catalogue no: **MCF 3285**
CD: Released '88, on MCA by MCA Records. Catalogue no: **DIDX 422**
CD: Released '86, on MCA by MCA Records. Catalogue no: **MCAD 6144**

CD: Released Feb '86, on MCA by MCA Records. Catalogue no: **DMCF 3285**
Cass: Released Feb '86, on MCA by MCA Records. Catalogue no: **MCFC 3285**

BACK TO THE FUTURE II (Film soundtrack) (Various artists) (See picture on previous page)
Tracks: / Back to the future II (main theme): *Various artists* / Hoverboard chase: *Various artists* / My father: *Various artists* / If they ever did: *Various artists* / Book, The: *Various artists* / Burn the book: *Various artists* / Western union: *Various artists* / Future, The: *Various artists* / Flying delorean, A: *Various artists* / Alternate 1985: *Various artists* / Pair of Docs: *Various artists* / Tunnel chase: *Various artists* / Back to the future II (end title): *Various artists.*
Album: Released Jan '90, on MCA by MCA Records. Catalogue no: **MCG 6072**
Cass: Released Jan '90, on MCA by MCA Records. Catalogue no: **MCGC 6072**
CD: Released Jan '90, on MCA by MCA Records. Catalogue no: **DMCG 6072**

Backlash

BACKLASH (Film soundtrack) (Various artists)
Album: Released May '85, on Criminal Damage by Arkdor Records. Catalogue no: **CRILP 126**
Album: Released '88, on Playlist Catalogue no: **PLAY 002**

Backstreet

BACKSTREET (Original soundtrack) (Various artists)
Note: Score by Frank Skinner for the Susan Hayward film.
Album: Released Jan '89, on Silva Screen by Silva Screen Records. Catalogue no: **DL 79097**

Bad & The Beautiful

BAD AND THE BEAUTIFUL (1952 Film Soundtrack) (Various artists)
Cass: on Polydor by Polydor Ltd. Catalogue no: **422 385 4**
CD: on Polydor by Polydor Ltd. Catalogue no: **422 385 2**

Badarou, Wally

KISS OF THE SPIDERWO-

MAN (See under Kiss of The...)

Bad Dreams

BAD DREAMS (Film soundtrack) (Various artists)
Note: Film with music by Jay Ferguson (formerly of Spirit and Jo Jo Gunne).
Album: Released Jan '89, on Silva Screen by Silva Screen Records. Catalogue no: **704.560**

Baghdad Cafe

BAGHDAD CAFE (Film soundtrack) (Various artists)
Tracks: / Calling you: *Steele, Jevette* / Zwifach: *Blasmusik, Deihinger* / C major prelude: *Flagg, Darron* / Calling you: *Telson, Bob* / Blues harp: *Galison, William* / Brenda, Brenda: *Steele, Jevette* / Calliope: *Telson, Bob.*
Cass: Released Oct '88, on Island by Island Records. Deleted '90. Catalogue no: **ICT 18**
Cass: Released '90, on Island by Island Records. Catalogue no: **ICM 2005**
CD: Released Oct '88, on Island by Island Records. Catalogue no: **CIDST 18**
CD: Released Feb '90, on Island by Island Records. Catalogue no: **CID 5718**
Album: Released Oct '88, on Island by Island Records. Catalogue no: **ISTA 18**
Cass: Released '90, on Island by Island Records. Catalogue no: **842 817 4**
CD: Released Feb '90, on Island by Island Records. Catalogue no: **IMCD 102**

Baker, Tony

ACADEMY AWARD WINNERS (Baker, Tony & His Orchestra)
Tracks: / Continental, The / Lullaby of Broadway / Way you look tonight / Sweet Leilani / Thanks for the memory / Over the rainbow / When you wish upon a star / Last time I saw Paris, The / White Christmas / You'll never know / Swingin' on a star / It might as well be Spring / On the Atchison, Topeka and the Santa Fe / Zip a dee doo dah / Buttons and bows / Baby, it's cold outside / Mona Lisa.
CD: Released Jul '89, on Pickwick by Pickwick Records. Catalogue no: **PWKS 655**

Cass: Released Jul '89, on Pickwick by Pickwick Records. Catalogue no: **HSC 655**

Baker's Wife

BAKER'S WIFE, THE (London Cast) (Various artists)
Album: Released Jul '90, on T. E. R. by That's Entertainment Records. Catalogue no: **TER2 1175**
Album: Released '90, on Take Home Tunes(USA) by Film Score Records (USA). Catalogue no: **THT 772**
CD: Released Jul '90, on T. E. R. by That's Entertainment Records. Catalogue no: **CDTER 1175**
Cass: Released Jul '90, on That's Entertainment(see T.E.R.) Catalogue no: **ZCTED 1175**

Ball, Kenny

AT THE MOVIES
Tracks: / Raiders of the Lost Ark / Mrs. Robinson / As time goes by / Arthur's theme / I love you, Samantha / Cavatina / March of the Siamese children / Mona Lisa / When you wish upon a star / Hello, Dolly / Green leaves of summer / Ben / Bare necessities / I wanna be like you.
Cass: Released Sep '87, on MFP by EMI Records. Deleted Apr '90. Catalogue no: **TCMFP 5803**
Album: Released Sep '87, on MFP by EMI Records. Deleted Aug '89. Catalogue no: **MFP 5803**
HELLO DOLLY (SINGLE) (Ball, Kenny & His Jazzmen)
Tracks: / Hello Dolly.
7" Single: Released Jun '64, on Pye Jazz Today Deleted '67. Catalogue no: **7 NJ 2071**

Ball, Michael

FIRST MAN YOU REMEMBER, THE (Ball, Michael & Diana Morrison)
Tracks: / First man you remember, The / Mermaid song / Love changes everything (original cast version) (Only on 12" and CD single.).
Note: 'From the stage show Aspects Of Love'.
CD Single: Released Sep '89, on Really Useful Records by Really Useful Group. Deleted Jul '90. Catalogue no: **RURCD 6**
10" Single: Released Oct '89, on Really Useful Records by Really Useful Group. Catalogue no:

RURT 6
7" Single: Released Sep '89, on Really Useful Records by Really Useful Group. Catalogue no: **RUR 6**
12" Single: Released Sep '89, on Really Useful Records by Really Useful Group. Catalogue no: **RURX 6**

LOVE CHANGES EVERYTHING

Tracks: / Love changes everything.
Note: From the stage show 'Aspects Of Love'.
12" Single: Released Jan '89, on Really Useful Records by Really Useful Group. Catalogue no: **RUR X 3**
CD Single: Released Jan '89, on Really Useful Records by Really Useful Group. Deleted Jul '90. Catalogue no: **RURCD 3**
7" Single: Released Jan '89, on Really Useful Records by Really Useful Group. Catalogue no: **RUR 3**

Band

LAST WALTZ, THE (Film soundtrack)
Tracks: / Last waltz, The / Up on Cripple Creek / Who do you love / Helpless / Stage fright / Coyote / Dry your eyes / It makes no difference / Such a night / Night they drove old Dixie down / Mystery train / Mannish boy / Further on up the road / Shape I'm in, The / Down South in New Orleans / Ophelia / Tura lura larai (That's an Irish lullaby) / Caravan / Life is a carnival / Baby let me follow you down / I don't believe you (she acts like we never have met) / Forever young / I shall be released / Last waltz suite, The / Well, The / Evangeline / Out of the blue / Weight, The.
CD: Released Jul '88, on Warner Bros. by WEA Records. Catalogue no: **K 266076**
LP Set: Released Apr '78, on Warner Bros. by WEA Records. Deleted Jan '90. Catalogue no: **K 66076**
Cass: Released Apr '78, on Warner Bros. by WEA Records. Catalogue no: **K4 66076**

LAST WALTZ, THE (SINGLE)
Tracks: / Last waltz, The / Out of the blue.
7" Single: Released Jun '78, on Warner Bros. by WEA Records.

Deleted '81. Catalogue no: **K 17187**

LAST WALTZ , THE (VIDEO)
Note: Running time: 112 mins. Scorcese directs The Bands farewell concert with a host of guest stars (Clapton, Van Morrison, Emmylou, Dylan, Joni, Diamond, Neil Young et al) and candid interviews.
VHS: Released Jun '88, on Warner Home Video by WEA Records. Catalogue no: **PES 99354**

Band Of Angels (Film)

BAND OF ANGELS (Film soundtrack) (Various artists)
Tracks: / Band of angels: *Various artists* / Death of a scoundrel: *Various artists* / Charge of the light brigade: *Various artists* / Four wives: *Various artists* / Searchers, The: *Various artists* / Stolen life, A: *Various artists*.
Note: Score by Max Steiner for Clark Gable film. Music in the same style as his Gone With The Wind.
CD: Released Sep '87, on Silva Screen by Silva Screen Records. Catalogue no: **LXCD 3**
Album: Released Jan '89, on Silva Screen by Silva Screen Records. Catalogue no: **ERM 6003**

Bandolero (Film)

BANDOLERO (1968 Film soundtrack) (Various artists)
Tracks: / Trap, The: *Various artists* / El jefe: *Various artists* / Bait, The: *Various artists* / Ambushed: *Various artists* / Sabinas: *Various artists* / Dee's proposal: *Various artists* / Across the river: *Various artists* / Bad day for a hanging, A: *Various artists* / Better way, A: *Various artists*.
Album: Released Jan '90, on Edel (West Germany) Catalogue no: **TCS 1001.1**
CD: Released Jan '90, on Edel (West Germany) Catalogue no: **TCS 1001.2**

Bandwagon

BANDWAGON (Original soundtrack) (Various artists)
Tracks: / Overture: *Various artists* / Sweet music: *Various artists* / High and low: *Various artists* / Hoops: *Various artists* / Confessions: *Various artists* / New sun in the sky: *Various artists* / I love Louisa: *Various artists* / Ballet music:

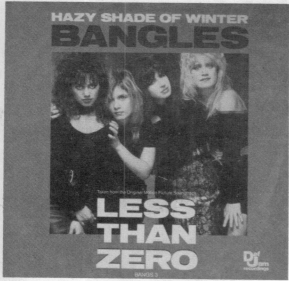

The Bangles - Hazy Shade of Winter from *Less than Zero*

Various artists / Beggars waltz: *Various artists* / White heat: *Various artists* / I've got you on my mind: *Various artists* / Maybe I love you too much: *Various artists* / My temptation: *Various artists* / Heart of stone: *Various artists* / Gold diggers song (we're in the money): *Various artists*.
Note: Starring Fred Astaire and Jack Buchanan.
Album: Released '73, on RCA by BMG Records (UK). Deleted '78. Catalogue no: **LSA 3082**
Cass: Released Jan '89, on MCA by MCA Records. Deleted Mar '90. Catalogue no: **MCAC 25015**
Album: Released Jan '89, on MCA by MCA Records. Catalogue no: **MCA 25015**

BANDWAGON (VIDEO) (Various artists)
Note: Teams Fred Astaire with an all-star cast including Cyd Charisse. Running time: 108 minutes. Cert: U.
VHS: Released Mar '88, on MGM/UA (Video) by MGM/UA Video. Catalogue no: **SMV 10113**

Bang On A Drum
BANG ON A DRUM (Childrens

TV Show) (Various artists)
Tracks: / Early in the morning: *Various artists* / Brush, brush, brush: *Various artists* / Sunbeams play: *Various artists* / I am here: *Various artists* / Caterpillars only crawl: *Various artists* / Wheels keep turning: *Various artists* / I like peace, I like quiet: *Various artists* / Building up my house: *Various artists* / Israeli boat song, The: *Various artists* / One potato, two potato: *Various artists* / Bang on a drum: *Various artists* / Jump: *Various artists* / Paper song, The: *Various artists* / Down on the farm: *Various artists* / Fidget: *Various artists* / Come to the shops: *Various artists* / What do we do with this and that: *Various artists* / Circus is coming: *Various artists* / Build it up: *Various artists* / I think I've got a cold: *Various artists* / You can stamp your feet: *Various artists* / Playaway: *Various artists*.
Cass: Released Oct '76, on BBC by BBC Records. Catalogue no: **MRMC 004**
Album: Released Oct '76, on BBC by BBC Records. Deleted '87. Catalogue no: **REC 242**

BANG ON A DRUM AGAIN (Childrens TV Show) (Various

artists)
Tracks: / Head and shoulders, knees and toes: *Various artists* / How do you feel today: *Various artists* / Paddle your own canoe: *Various artists* / Hey you: *Various artists* / Elephants on a piece of string: *Various artists* / Hokey cokey: *Various artists* / Spells: *Various artists* / Wiggle my ears: *Various artists* / Stand up sit down: *Various artists* / Zoom: *Various artists* / Step aside: *Various artists* / How high does a fly fly: *Various artists* / Well Jemima, let's go shopping: *Various artists* / Share: *Various artists* / Wouldn't it be funny: *Various artists* / Rain makes all things beautiful, The: *Various artists*.
Album: Released Jul '83, on BBC by BBC Records. Deleted 31 Aug '88. Catalogue no: **REC 474**
Cass: Released Jul '83, on BBC by BBC Records. Deleted 31 Aug '88. Catalogue no: **ZCM 474**

Bangles
HAZY SHADE OF WINTER (See picture on left)
Tracks: / Hazy shade of winter (remix) / She's lost you.
Note: 'From the film Less Than Zero'.
7" Pic: Released Feb '88, on Def Jam Deleted Aug '88. Catalogue no: **BANGS P3**
7" Single: Released 1 Feb '88, on CBS by CBS Records & Distribution. Deleted Jun '88. Catalogue no: **BANGS Q3**
CD Single: Released Feb '88, on CBS by CBS Records & Distribution. Deleted Jan '89. Catalogue no: **BANGS C3**
7" Single: Released Feb '88, on Def Jam Deleted Aug '88. Catalogue no: **BANGS 3**
12" Single: Released Feb '88, on Def Jam Deleted Aug '88. Catalogue no: **BANGS T3**

Banjo Man
BANJO MAN (Original soundtrack) (Various artists)
Tracks: / Lonesome Ruben: *Scruggs, Earl* / Battle of New Orleans: *Nitty Gritty Dirt Band* / You ain't goin' nowhere: *Baez, Joan* / Freight train boogie: *Watson, Doc & Merle* / T for Texas: *Scruggs, Earl* / Roll over Beethoven: *Byrds* / Me and Bobby McGee: *Elliot, Ramblin' Jack* / Mr. Tambourine

man: *Byrds* / Black mountain rag: *Watson, Doc & Merle* / Night they drove old dixie down, The: *The: Baez, Joan* / Diggy liggy lo: *Nitty Gritty Dirt Band* / Blowin' in the wind: *Baez, Joan* / Foggy mountain breakdown: *Scruggs, Earl* / Billy Fehr: *Elliot, Ramblin' Jack.*
Album: Released Feb '79, on Sire by Sire Records. Catalogue no: **SRK 6026**

Bar Mitzvah Boy

BAR MITZVAH BOY (Original cast recording) (Various artists)
Tracks: / Overture: *Various artists* / Why?: *Various artists* / If only a little bit sticks: *Various artists* / Bar mitzvah of Elliot Green: *Various artists* / This time tomorrow: *Various artists* / Thou shalt not: *Various artists* / Harolds of this world: *Various artists* / We've done alright: *Various artists* / Simchas: *Various artists* / You wouldn't be you: *Various artists* / Rita's request: *Various artists* / Sun shines out of your eyes: *Various artists* / Where is the music coming from: *Various artists* / I've just begun: *Various artists.*
Cass: Released Jan '79, on CBS by CBS Records & Distribution. Deleted Jan '84. Catalogue no: **CBS 40 70162**
Album: Released Jan '79, on CBS by CBS Records & Distribution. Deleted Jan '84. Catalogue no: **CBS 70162**

Barabbas (Film)

BARABBAS (1962 Film soundtrack) (Various artists)
Album: on Citadel (USA) by Varese Sarabande Records (USA). Catalogue no: **CT 7034**

Barbosa-Lima, Carlos

RHAPSODY IN BLUE/WEST SIDE STORY (Barbosa-Lima, Carlos/Sharon Isbin)
Tracks: / I feel pretty / Scherzo/Somewhere / Cha-cha / Something's coming / Maria / America / Cool / Tonight / I have a love/Finale / Jasbo brown eyes / Liza / Prelude No.3 / Rhapsody in blue.
Note: Carlos Barbosa-Lima & Sharon Isbin have earned their place amongst the top classical guitarists. For this recording, Carlos respectfully arranged the music of two of the greatest composers of this century-George Gershwin &

Leonard Bernstein. Virtuoso interpretations of the finest contemporary compositions.
Cass: Released Oct '88, on Concord by Concord Jazz Records (USA). Catalogue no: **CC 2012C**
CD: Released Oct '88, on Concord by Concord Jazz Records (USA). Catalogue no: **CCD 42012**
Album: Released Oct '88, on Concord by Concord Jazz Records (USA). Catalogue no: **CC 2012**

Barker, Ronnie

GOING STRAIGHT (Theme to the BBC T.V. series)
Tracks: / Going straight / String bean queen.
7" Single: Released Feb '78, on EMI by EMI Records. Deleted '80. Catalogue no: **EMI 2768**

PORRIDGE (With original cast) (Various artists)
Cass: Released Apr '77, on BBC by BBC Records. Deleted '88. Catalogue no: **ZCF 270**
Album: Released Oct '79, on BBC by BBC Records. Deleted '84. Catalogue no: **REB 270**

TWO RONNIES (Barker, Ronnie & Ronnie Corbett)
Cass: Released Oct '76, on BBC by BBC Records. Deleted '88. Catalogue no: **RMC 4054**
Album: Released Oct '76, on BBC by BBC Records. Deleted '88. Catalogue no: **RED 257**

TWO RONNIES VOL 2 (Barker, Ronnie & Ronnie Corbett)
Cass: Released Nov '77, on BBC by BBC Records. Deleted '85. Catalogue no: **ZCF 300**
Album: Released Nov '77, on BBC by BBC Records. Deleted '87. Catalogue no: **REB 300**

Barking Light

LONG GOOD FRIDAY, THE (THEME FROM)
Tracks: / Long good friday, The (theme from).
7" Pic: Released 1 Dec '88, on Woof Deleted Aug '89. Catalogue no: **WOOFP 2**

LONG MARCH (THEME FROM)
Tracks: / Long March, Theme from / March on.
7" Single: Released Jan '89, on Kennel Deleted Aug '89. Catalogue no: **WOOF 1**
7" Pic: Released May '89, on Total

Deleted Aug '89. Catalogue no: **WOOF P1**

Barkleys Of Broadway

BARKLEYS OF BROADWAY, THE (Film soundtrack) (Various artists)
Note: Starring Fred Astaire and Ginger Rogers.
Album: Released Jan '89, on Silva Screen by Silva Screen Records. Catalogue no: **STK 116**

BARKLEYS OF BROADWAY, THE (VIDEO) (Various artists)
VHS: Released Sep '89, on MGM/UA (Video) by MGM/UA Video. Catalogue no: **SMV 10321**

Barnes, Billy

BILLY BARNES IN LA (Original cast recordings) (Various artists)
Album: Released Jan '89, on Silva Screen by Silva Screen Records. Catalogue no: **AEI 1134**

BILLY BARNES SINGS MOVIE STAR (Original cast recordings) (Various artists)
Album: Released Jan '89, on Silva Screen by Silva Screen Records. Catalogue no: **AEI 1142**

Barnum

BARNUM (Original London stage cast) (Various artists)
Tracks: / There is sucker born every minute: *Various artists* / Museum song: *Various artists* / Prince of humbug: *Various artists* / Colours of my life: *Various artists* / Join the circus: *Various artists* / Come follow the band: *Various artists* / One brick at a time: *Various artists* / Black and white: *Various artists* / Love makes such fools of us all: *Various artists* / I like your Style: *Various artists* / Bigger isn't better: *Various artists* / At least I tried: *Various artists* / Thank God I'm old: *Various artists.*
Album: Released Jan '89, on Silva Screen by Silva Screen Records. Deleted Mar '90. Catalogue no: **JS 36576**
Album: Released '81, on Chrysalis by Chrysalis Records. Catalogue no: **CDL 1348**
CD: Released Jan '89, on CBS (import) by CBS Records & Distribution. Catalogue no: **CK 36576**
Cass: Released Jan '89, on Silva Screen by Silva Screen Records. Catalogue no: **PST 36576**

Cass: Released '81, on Chrysalis by Chrysalis Records. Catalogue no: **ZCDL 1348**

BARNUM (VIDEO) (Various artists)

Note: Straight from its sucess on the West-end stage, Michael Crawford stars in this lively circus musical. Running time: 112 mins.
VHS: Released Jan '89, on BBC Video by BBC Video. Catalogue no: **BBCV 4201**

Barrie, J.M. (Author)

PETER PAN (Original play and music) (Various artists)

Cass set: Released Oct '89, on BBC by BBC Records. Catalogue no: **ZBBC 1085**

Barrie, Ken

POSTMAN PAT

Tracks: / Postman Pat / Handy man song.
7" Single: Released Jul '82, on Post Music Deleted '85. Catalogue no: **PP 001**

Barry, John

BEAT GIRL/STRINGBEAT (Film soundtracks) (Barry, John Seven & Orchestra)

Tracks: / Beat girl (main title) / Off beat, The / I did what you told me / Lindon Home Rock / Timeout / Sharks, The / Beat girl song / City 2000 A.D., The / Stripper, The / Cave, The / Made you / Car chase (night chase) / Chicken / Blues for beatniks / It's legal / Immediate pleasure, The / Blondie's strip / End shot / Slaughter in Soho / It doesn't matter anymore / Sweet talk / Moody river / There's life in the old boy yet / Handful of songs, A / Like waltz / Rodeo / Donna's theme / Starfire / Baubles, bangles and beads / Zapata / Rum dee dum dee dah / Spanish harlem / Man from Madrid / Challenge, The.
CD: Released Aug '90, on Play It Again Sam(Belgium) by Play It Again Sam (Belgium). Catalogue no: **PLAY 001**

BEST OF JOHN BARRY

Tracks: / Thunderball / 007 / We have all the time in the world / Curiouser and curiouser / Strip drive / Diamonds are forever / Dolls house / Goldfinger / Love among the ruins / Adventurer / Yesternight suite / Midnight cowboy.
Album: Released Jul '81, on Poly-

dor by Polydor Ltd. Deleted '86. Catalogue no: **2384 120**

COTTON CLUB (See under Cotton Club)

FILM MUSIC OF JOHN BARRY (16 Great themes)

Tracks: / Born free / Lion in Winter, The / Wrong box, The / Ipcress file, The / Thunderball / Whisperers, The / Goldfinger.
Note: 16 great themes by John Barry from his films of the 1960's.
CD: Released Jan '89, on CBS (import) by CBS Records & Distribution. Catalogue no: **CK 44376**
Cass: Released Jan '89, on Silva Screen by Silva Screen Records. Catalogue no: **JST 44376**

FROM RUSSIA WITH LOVE

Tracks: / From Russia with love.
7" Single: Released Nov '63, on Ember. Deleted '66. Catalogue no: **S 181**

HIT AND MISS (Barry, John Seven & Orchestra)

Tracks: / Hit and miss / Big guitar / Rodeo / Big fella / Walk don't run / Bee's knees / Ev'ry which way / Beat girl / Human jungle, The / I'm movin' on / Zapata / Like waltz / Black stockings / James Bond theme / Lost patrol / Magnificent seven, The / Hideaway / Menace / Never let go / Sharks.
Album: Released Mar '82, on See For Miles by See For Miles Records. Catalogue no: **CM 110**
Album: Released Apr '88, on C5 by C5 Records. Catalogue no: **C5-516**
Cass: Released Mar '82, on See For Miles by See For Miles Records. Catalogue no: **CMK 110**
CD: Released Jun '88, on C5 by C5 Records. Catalogue no: **C5CD 516**
Cass: Released Jun '88, on C5 by C5 Records. Catalogue no: **C5K-516**

HIT AND MISS (SINGLE) (Barry, John Seven)

Tracks: / Hit and miss.
Note: From the TV show Juke Box Jury.
7" Single: Released Mar '60, on Columbia by EMI Records. Deleted '63. Catalogue no: **DB 4414**

JAMES BOND THEME

Tracks: / James Bond theme.
7" Single: Released Nov '62, on Columbia by EMI Records.

Deleted '65. Catalogue no: **DB 4898**

KNACK (See under Knack)

MAGNIFICENT SEVEN, THE

Tracks: / Magnificent seven, The.
7" Single: Released Mar '61, on Columbia by EMI Records. Deleted '64. Catalogue no: **DB 4598**

MAN WITH THE GOLDEN GUN (See under Man With The Golden Gun)

MIDNIGHT COWBOY

Tracks: / Midnight cowboy.
7" Single: Released Sep '80, on United Artists by EMI Records. Catalogue no: **UP 634**

MUSIC FROM THE BIG SCREEN

Tracks: / James Bond / Whisperers / Mr. Kiss Kiss Bang / King rat / You only live twice / Thunderball / Ipcress file / Chase Dutchman / From Russia with love / On her Majesty's secret service / Fun city / Knack / We have all the time in the world / Born free / Midnight cowboy / Girl with the sun in her hair / Wrong box / More things change / Goldfinger.
Cass: Released Mar '86, on Ditto by Pickwick Records. Catalogue no: **DTO 10229**

MUSIC OF...

Tracks: / Born free / You only live twice / Goldfinger / Whisperers / From Russia with love / Wednesday's child / Quiller memorandum / Space march (capsule in space) / Girl with the sun in her hair, The / Thunderball / Wrong box, The / James Bond theme / 007 / Mister kiss kiss bang bang / Chase, The / King rat / Seance on a wet afternoon / Ipcress file, The / Midnight cowboy / Romance for guitar & orchestra, Theme from / On Her Majesty's secret service / Appointment, Theme from / Lion in Winter, The.
2 LP Set: Released Jun '76, on CBS by CBS Records & Distribution. Catalogue no: **CBS 22014**

PERSUADERS, THE

Tracks: / Persuaders, The.
7" Single: Released Dec '71, on CBS by CBS Records & Distribution. Deleted '74. Catalogue no: **CBS 7469**

Soundtrack to *Basket Case II* (Silva Screen)

VERY BEST OF JOHN BARRY
Tracks: / 007 / Thunderball / Diamonds are forever.
Album: Released Sep '81, on Polydor by Polydor Ltd. Deleted Sep '86. Catalogue no: **MID 1009**
Cass: Released Jun '81, on Polydor by Polydor Ltd. Catalogue no: **3192 627**

Bashville
BASHVILLE (Original Cast Recording) (Various artists)
Tracks: / Prelude: *Various artists* / Fancy Free: *Various artists* / Lydia: *Various artists* / 8-9-10: *Various artists* / One pair of hands: *Various artists* / Gentleman's true to his code, A: *Various artists* / Because I love her: *Various artists* / Take the road to the ring: *Various artists* / Entr'acte: *Various artists* / Hymn to law and order: *Various artists* / Blackman's burden: *Various artists* / He is my son: *Various artists* / Bashville: *Various artists* / Boats are burned: *Various artists* / Finale: *Various artists*.
Cass: Released Jan '84, on T. E. R. by That's Entertainment Records. Catalogue no: **ZCTER 1072**
Album: Released Jan '84, on T. E. R. by That's Entertainment Rec-

ords. Catalogue no: **TER 1072**

Basket Case
BASKET CASE 2 & FRANKENHOOKER (Original soundtracks) (Renzetti, Joe) (See picture above)
Tracks: / I'm pregnant, I'm dead / Granny at freak tent / Barbecue / Original main titles / Out of hospital / Out of window / Big escape, The / Room of memories / In the attic / Granny meeting / In love / Frankenhooker (main titles) / Lookin' for hookers / Jeffrey and parts / Creation, The / Eyeball, The / Happy day / Jeffrey fixes Elizabeth / Zoro killing.
CD: Released '89, on Silva Screen by Silva Screen Records. Catalogue no: **FILMCD 073**

Bassey, Shirley
DIAMONDS ARE FOREVER
Tracks: / Diamonds are forever.
7" Single: Released Jan '72, on United Artists by EMI Records. Deleted '75. Catalogue no: **UP 35263**

GOLDFINGER
Tracks: / Goldfinger.
7" Single: Released Oct '64, on Columbia by EMI Records.

Deleted '67. Catalogue no: **DB 7360**
MOONRAKER
Tracks: / Moonraker.
7" Single: Released Jul '79, on United Artists by EMI Records. Deleted '82. Catalogue no: **UP 602**

Bat 21
BAT 21 (Film soundtrack) (Various artists)
Note: Music by Christopher Young. Starring Gene Hackman.
Album: Released Dec '88, on Take 7. Catalogue no: **VS 5202**
CD: Released Dec '88, on Take 7. Catalogue no: **VSD 5202**
Cass: Released Dec '88, on Take 7. Catalogue no: **VSC 5202**

Batman....
BATMAN (See under Prince)
BATMAN THEME (Hefti, Neal)
Tracks: / Batman theme.
12" Single: Released May '88, on Bam Caruso by Demon Records. Catalogue no: **PABL 107**
7" Single: Released May '88, on Bam Caruso by Demon Records. Catalogue no: **NRIC 107**

BATMAN THEME, THE (Hefti, Neal)
Tracks: / Batman theme / Batman theme (inst).
12" Single: Released Mar '88, on WEA by WEA Records. Catalogue no: **Y 7180T**

Batt, Mike
SUMMERTIME CITY
Tracks: / Summertime city.
Note: From the TV show *'Seaside Special'*.
7" Single: Released Aug '75, on Epic by CBS Records & Distribution. Deleted '78. Catalogue no: **EPC 3460**

Batteries Not Included
BATTERIES NOT INCLUDED (Film soundtrack) (Various artists) (See picture on next page)
Note: James Horner score for the Steven Spielberg production.
Cass: Released Jan '89, on MCA by MCA Records. Deleted Dec '89. Catalogue no: **MCAC 6225**
Album: Released Jan '89, on MCA by MCA Records. Deleted

Jessica Tandy and Hume Cronyn break into a dance in *Batteries not Included*

Dec '89. Catalogue no: **MCA 6225**
CD: Released Jan '89, on MCA by MCA Records. Catalogue no: **MCAD 6225**

Battle Of Britain

BATTLE OF BRITAIN (Music from film plus others) (Various artists)
Tracks: / Battle of Britain theme: *Various artists* / Aces high march: *Various artists* / Lull before the storm, The: *Various artists* / Work and play: *Various artists* / Death and destruction: *Various artists* / Briefing and the luftwaffe: *Various artists* / Prelude to battle: *Various artists* / Victory assured: *Various artists* / Defeat: *Various artists* / Hitler's headquarters: *Various artists* / Return to base: *Various artists* / Threat: *Various artists* / Civilian tragedy: *Various artists* / Offensive build-up: *Various artists* / Attack: *Various artists* / Personal tragedy: *Various artists* / Battle in the air: *Various artists* / Absent friends: *Various artists* / Battle of Britain theme - end title: *Various artists* / Operation crossbow (theme): *Various artists* / Monte Carlo or bust (theme): *Various artists* / Trap, The (theme): *Various artists* / Those magnificent men in their flying machines: *Various artists*.
Cass: Released Aug '90, on MGM (EMI) Catalogue no: **794 865 4**
Album: Released Aug '90, on MGM (EMI) Catalogue no: **794 865 1**

CD: Released Aug '90, on MGM (EMI) Catalogue no: **CDP 794 865 2**
Cass: Released Aug '90, on MGM (EMI) Catalogue no: **TCMGM 21**
Album: Released Aug '90, on MGM (EMI) Catalogue no: **LPMGM 21**
CD: Released Aug '90, on MGM (EMI) Catalogue no: **CDMGM 21**

BATTLE OF BRITAIN (Film 1969) (Various artists)
Album: Released Dec '77, on Sunset (Liberty). Catalogue no: **SLS 50407**

Battle Of Neretva

BATTLE OF NERETVA (Film soundtrack) (Various artists)
Tracks: / Prelude: *Various artists* / Retreat, The: *Various artists* / Separation: *Various artists* / From Italy: *Various artists* / Chetnik's march: *Various artists* / Farewell: *Various artists* / Partisan march: *Various artists* / Pastorale: *Various artists* / Turning point, The: *Various artists* / Death of Danica, The: *Various artists* / Victory: *Various artists*.
Note: Composed by Bernard Herrmann & performed by the London Philharmonic Orchestra.
CD: Released Jan '89, on Silva Screen by Silva Screen Records. Catalogue no: **SCCD 5005**
Album: Released Jan '89, on Silva Screen by Silva Screen Records. Catalogue no: **SCAR 5005**

Battlestar Galactica

BATTLESTAR GALACTICA

(Film Soundtrack) (Various artists)
Album: Released Apr '79, on MCA by MCA Records. Deleted '83. Catalogue no: **MCF 2860**
Album: Released Jan '89, on MCA by MCA Records. Catalogue no: **252 602 1**
Cass: Released Apr '79, on MCA by MCA Records. Catalogue no: **MCFC 2860**

Bauhaus

BELA LUGOSI'S DEAD
Tracks: / Bela Lugosi's dead / Boys / Dark entries (demo).
Note: From the film 'The Hunger'.
12" Single: Released Sep '86, on Small Wonder by Small Wonder Records. Catalogue no: **TEENY 2**
12" Pic: Released '87, on Small Wonder by Small Wonder Records. Catalogue no: **TEENY 2P**
CD Single: Released May '88, on Small Wonder by Small Wonder Records. Catalogue no: **TEENY 2CD**

BBC...

BBC 1922-1972 (TV and Radio extracts) (Various artists)
Album: Released Nov '72, on BBC by BBC Records. Deleted '77. Catalogue no: **BBC 50**

BBC CHILDREN'S TV THEMES (Various artists)
Tracks: / Doctor Who theme: *Various artists* / Captain Zep: *Various artists* / Magic roundabout: *Various artists* / Paddington bear: *Various artists* / Animal magic: *Various artists* / Dukes of Hazzard: *Various artists* / Watch: *Various artists* / Trumpton: *Various artists* / Monkey: *Various artists* / Heads and tails: *Various artists* / Saturday Superstore: *Various artists* / Blue Peter: *Various artists* / Willo the wisp: *Various artists* / Grange hill: *Various artists* / Pink panther: *Various artists* / Swap shop: *Various artists* / Take Hart: *Various artists* / Monkee's theme, The: *Various artists* / Mr. Men: *Various artists* / Think again: *Various artists* / Playschool: *Various artists*.
Album: Released Oct '83, on BBC by BBC Records. Deleted 31 Aug '88. Catalogue no: **REH 486**
Cass: Released Oct '83, on BBC by BBC Records. Deleted 31 Aug

'88. Catalogue no: **ZCR 486**

BBC'S FOLK ON 2 PRESENTS NORTHUMBRIAN FOLK (Various artists)

Tracks: / Northwalbottle rapper sword dance, The: *Monkseaton Morris Men* / Morpeth rant: *Oselton, Dennis & Archie Bertram* / Border shepherd, A: *Bertram, Archie* / College valley hunt, The: *Davenport, Bob/Marsden Rattlers* / Bobby Shaftoe: *Washington Greys* / Cushie butterfield: *Washington Greys* / Lambton worm, The: *Marsden Rattlers* / Chevy Chase: *Ross, Colin* / Blow the wind southerly: *Norman, Anne* / Sea lore: *Davenport, Bob* / Story of Grace Darling, The: *White, Kate (Mrs.)* / My bonnie lad: *Davenport, Bob* / Keel row, The: *Adamson, Edith carillon* / Hadrian's wall: *Dobson, Scott* / Keep your feet still Geordie Hinny: *Davenport, Bob/Marsden Rattlers* / Durham miners gala, The: *Elliot, John* / In the bar room: *Elliots of Birtley* / Water o' Tyne, The: *Norman, Anne* / Wor nanny's a mazer: *Marsden Rattlers* / Dan Leno's hornpipe: *Ellwood, Johnson* / Blaydon Races, The: *Davenport, Bob/Marsden Rattlers*.
Album: Released '83, on BBC by BBC Records. Deleted '88. Catalogue no: **REC 118**

BBC Comedy...

BBC COMEDY THEMES (Various artists)

Tracks: / Goodies theme: *Various artists* / Fawlty Towers: *Various artists* / Likely lads: *Various artists* / Some mothers do 'av 'em: *Various artists* / Q.8: *Various artists* / Steptoe and son: *Various artists* / Monty Python: *Various artists* / Mash: *Various artists* / Dad's army: *Various artists* / Going straight: *Various artists* / Last of the Summer wine: *Various artists* / Liver birds: *Various artists* / Rise and fall of Reginald Perrin: *Various artists* / It ain't half hot Mum: *Various artists*.
Album: Released Nov '80, on BBC by BBC Records. Deleted Nov '85. Catalogue no: **REH 387**

BBC Concert Orchestra

ASPECTS OF ANDREW LLOYD WEBBER

Tracks: / Music of the night / Memory / Variations / Don't cry for me Argentina / Anything but lonely / Tell me on a Sunday / Jellicle ball, The / Loves changes everything / I only want to say / Pie Jesu / Close every door to me / Buenos Aires / I don't know how to love him / Aspects of Andrew.
Album: Released Oct '89, on BBC by BBC Records. Catalogue no: **REB 750**
CD: Released Oct '89, on BBC by BBC Records. Catalogue no: **BBCCD 750**
Cass: Released Oct '89, on BBC by BBC Records. Catalogue no: **ZCF 750**

FRIDAY NIGHT IS MUSIC NIGHT

Cass: Released Nov '85, on BBC by BBC Records. Deleted 31 Aug '88. Catalogue no: **ZCR 583**
Album: Released Nov '85, on BBC by BBC Records. Deleted 31 Aug '88. Catalogue no: **REH 583**

BBC Space Themes

BBC SPACE THEMES (Various artists)

Tracks: / Apollo: *Various artists* / Also sprach Zarathustra: *Various artists* / Moonbase 3: *Various artists* / A for Andromeda: *Various artists* / Sky at night: *Various artists* / Fanfare for the common man: *Various artists* / Journey into space: *Various artists* / Astronauts: *Various artists* / Blake's 7: *Various artists* / Star trek: *Various artists* / Mars: *Various artists* / Tomorrow's world: *Various artists* / Dr. Who: *Various artists*.
Album: Released Jan '79, on BBC by BBC Records. Deleted Jan '84. Catalogue no: **REH 324**

BBC Sporting Themes

BBC SPORTING THEMES (Various artists)

Tracks: / Grandstand: *Various artists* / Wimbledon: *Various artists* / Match of the day: *Various artists* / Ski Sunday (pop goes Bach): *Various artists* / Test cricket: *Various artists* / Snooker: *Various artists* / Rugby special: *Various artists* / Sportsnight: *Various artists* / Question of sport: *Various artists* / Darts: *Various artists* / Commonwealth games: *Various artists* / world Cup: *Various artists* / Rugby: *Various artists* / Sport on Two: *Various artists* / Athletics: *Various artists* / Bowls: *Various artists* .
Note: Some of the most well known BBC TV sporting themes are gathered here by Pickwick Records.
CD: Released '88, on Pickwick by Pickwick Records. Catalogue no: **PWKS 648**
Cass: Released '88, on Pickwick by Pickwick Records. Catalogue no: **HSC 648**

BBC Symphony Orch.

LAST NIGHT OF THE PROMS

Album: Released '88, on BBC by BBC Records. Catalogue no: **REH 290**

The Bear: director Jean-Jacques Annaud with his young star - La Douce

BBC Records. Catalogue no: **ZCR 290**

LAST NIGHT OF THE PROMS '82

Album: Released Nov '82, on K-Tel by K-Tel Records. Catalogue no: **NE 1198**

Cass: Released Nov '82, on K-Tel by K-Tel Records. Catalogue no: **CE 2198**

Beach Boys

KOKOMO

Tracks: / Kokomo / Tutti frutti.
Note: From the film 'Cocktail'.
12" Single: Released Nov '88, on Elektra by Elektra Records (UK). Catalogue no: **EKR 85T**
7" Single: Released Nov '88, on Elektra by Elektra Records (UK). Deleted Jan '90. Catalogue no: **EKR 85**

Beaches

BEACHES (See under Midler, Bette)

Bear

BEAR, THE (Film soundtrack) (Various artists) (See picture on previous page)
CD: Released '89, on Ariola by BMG Records (UK). Catalogue no: **609446**
Cass: Released '89, on Ariola by BMG Records (UK). Catalogue no: **409446**
Album: Released '89, on Ariola by BMG Records (UK). Catalogue no: **209446**

Beast (Film)

BEAST, THE (Original soundtrack) (Various artists)
Note: A harrowing war film that becomes a moving near Biblical allegory... represents a stellar achievement for all involved. Mark Isham's eerie moody score adds to the suspense.
Cass: Released Jan '89, on A&M (import) Catalogue no: **C 3919**
Album: Released Jan '89, on A&M (import) Catalogue no: **SP 3919**
CD: Released Jan '89, on A&M (import) Catalogue no: **CD 3919**

Beastmaster

BEASTMASTER, THE (Original soundtrack) (Various artists)
Note: Conan style score by Lee Holdridge.
Cass: Released Jan '89, on Silva Screen by Silva Screen Records. Catalogue no: **CTV 81174**
Album: Released Jan '89, on Silva Screen by Silva Screen Records. Catalogue no: **STV 81174**

Beat Girl

BEAT GIRL (See under Barry, John) (See picture below)

Beat Street

BEAT STREET (Film soundtrack) (Various artists)
Tracks: / Beat street breakdown: *Grandmaster Melle Mel & The Furious Five* / Baptize the beat: *System* / Strangers in a strange world: *Burton, Jenny & Patrick Jude* / Frantic situation: *Beatstreet* / Beat street strut: *Juicy* / Us girls: *Green, Sharon, Lisa Counts & Debbie D* / This could be the night: *Mizelle, Cindy* / Breaker's revenge: *Baker, Arthur* / Tu carino - Carmen's theme: *Blades, Ruben*.
CD: Released Jul '84, on Atlantic by WEA Records. Deleted '87. Catalogue no: **780 154-2**
Album: Released Jul '84, on Atlantic by WEA Records. Deleted Aug '87. Catalogue no: **780 154-1**

Cass: Released Jul '84, on Atlantic by WEA Records. Catalogue no: **780 154-4**

BEAT STREET (VIDEO) (Various artists)
Note: Cert: 15.
VHS: Released '88, on Orion Cheapies Catalogue no: **V 7016**

BEAT STREET VOLUME 2 (Original soundtrack) (Various artists)
Tracks: / Son of beat street: *Jazzy Jay* / Give me all: *Jazzy Jay* / No thin's gonna come easy: *B, Tina* / Santa's rap: *Various artists* / It's alright by me: *Various artists* / Battle cry: *Various artists* / Phony four MC's-wappin': *Various artists* / Into the night: *Various artists*.
Cass: Released Oct '84, on Atlantic by WEA Records. Deleted Aug '87. Catalogue no: **780 158-4**
Album: Released Oct '84, on Atlantic by WEA Records. Deleted Aug '87. Catalogue no: **780 158-1**

Beatles

HARD DAY'S NIGHT, A (Original Soundtrack)
Tracks: / I should have known better / If I fell / I'm happy just to dance with you / And I love her / Tell me

Music from the film *Beat Girl* (Play It Again Sam)

why / Can't buy me love / Hard days night, A / Anytime at all / I'll cry instead / Things we said today / When I get home / You can't do that / I'll be back.

Album: Released Nov '88, on Parlophone by EMI Records. Deleted Aug '89. Catalogue no: **PCS 3058**

Album: Released Nov '88, on Parlophone by EMI Records. Catalogue no: **PMC 1230**

Cass: Released Nov '88, on Parlophone by EMI Records. Deleted Aug '89. Catalogue no: **TCPCS 3058**

Cass: Released Aug '64, Parlophone by EMI Records. Catalogue no: **TCPMC 1230**

CD: Released Feb '87, on Parlophone by EMI Records. Catalogue no: **CDP 746 437 2**

HARD DAY'S NIGHT, A (EP) VOL. 1

7" EP: Released Nov '64, on Parlophone by EMI Records. Catalogue no: **GEP 8920**

HARD DAYS NIGHT, A (EP) VOL. 2

7" EP: Released Dec '64, on Parlophone by EMI Records. Catalogue no: **GEP 8924**

HARD DAY'S NIGHT, A (SINGLE)

Tracks: / Hard day's night, A / Things we said today.

7" Single: Released Jul '64, on Parlophone by EMI Records. Catalogue no: **R 5160**

7" Pic: Released Jul '84, on Parlophone by EMI Records. Deleted Aug '90. Catalogue no: **RP 5160**

CD 3": Released on Parlophone by EMI Records. Catalogue no: **CD3R 5160**

HARD DAY'S NIGHT (VIDEO)

VHS: Released '84, on Vestron Video. Catalogue no: **VA 14188**

HELP (Original soundtrack)

Tracks: / Help / Night before, The / You've got to hide your love away / I need you / Another girl / You're going to lose that girl / Ticket to ride / Act naturally / It's only love / You like me too much / Tell me what you see / I've just seen a face / Yesterday / Dizzy Miss Lizzy.

Cass: Released Nov '87, on Parlophone by EMI Records. Catalogue no: **TCPCS 3071**

Album: Released Nov '88, on Parlophone by EMI Records. Catalogue no: **PCS 3071**

CD: Released Apr '87, on Parlophone by EMI Records. Catalogue no: **CDP 746 439 2**

Album: Released Jun '81, on Parlophone by EMI Records. Deleted '87. Catalogue no: **PMC 1255**

HELP (SINGLE)

Tracks: / Help / I'm down.

CD 3": Released Mar '89, on Parlophone by EMI Records. Catalogue no: **CD3R 5305**

7" Pic: Released Jul '85, on Parlophone by EMI Records. Deleted Aug '90. Catalogue no: **RP 5305**

7" Single: Released Jul '85, on Parlophone by EMI Records. Catalogue no: **R 5305**

HELP (VIDEO)

VHS: Released 26 Mar '90, on Video Collection by Video Collection. Catalogue no: **VC 3337**

MAGICAL MYSTERY TOUR

Tracks: / Magical mystery tour / Fool on the hill / Flying / Blue jay way / Your mother should know / I am the walrus / Hello goodbye / Strawberry fields forever / Penny Lane / Baby you're a rich man / All you need is love.

Album: Released Nov '88, on Parlophone by EMI Records. Catalogue no: **PCTC 255**

CD: Released Sep '87, on Parlophone by EMI Records. Catalogue no: **CDP 748 062 2**

CD: Released Sep '87, on Parlophone by EMI Records. Catalogue no: **CDPCTC 255**

Cass: Released Nov '87, on Parlophone by EMI Records. Catalogue no: **TCPCS 3077**

MAGICAL MYSTERY TOUR (EP)

Tracks: / Magical mystery tour / Blue Jay way / Your mother should know / I am the walrus / Fool on the hill, The / Flying.

7" Set: Released '67, on Parlophone by EMI Records. Catalogue no: **SMMT 1**

MAGICAL MYSTERY TOUR (VIDEO)

VHS: Released 26 Mar '90, on Video Collection by Video Collection. Catalogue no: **VC 3338**

MAKING OF HELP, THE

VHS: Released Sep '89, on Vexfilms. Catalogue no: **TIN 1V**

READY STEADY GO SPECIAL (Beatles live)

Tracks: / Love me do / Please please me / I wanna hold your hand / All you need is love / Twist and shout / She loves you.

Note: Duration 23 minutes. Monochrome.

VHS: Released Apr '85, on PMI by EMI Records. Catalogue no: **MVR 99 0041 2**

Beta: Released Jun '86, on PMI by EMI Records. Catalogue no: **MXR 99 0041 4**

REEL MUSIC

Tracks: / Hard day's night, A / I should have known better / Can't buy me love / And I love her / Help / You've got to hide your love away / Ticket to ride / Magical mystery tour / I am the walrus / Yellow submarine / All you need is love / Let it be / Get back / Long and winding road, The.

Note: Fourteen tracks from the soundtrack albums of The Beatles five movies.

Cass: Released Mar '82, on Parlophone by EMI Records. Catalogue no: **TC PCS 7218**

Album: Released Mar '82, on Parlophone by EMI Records. Catalogue no: **PCS 7218**

SOMETHING NEW (IMPORT)

Note: This Canadian-only release was aimed specifically at the collectors when first issued. It contains the best tracks from the 'Hard Day's Night' LP plus other interesting tracks like 'Komm, gib mir deine hand' which is 'I want to hold your hand' in German.

Album: Released Sep '88, on Capitol (import). Catalogue no: **ST 2108**

TWIST AND SHOUT

Tracks: / Twist and shout / Taste of honey, A / Do you want to know a secret / There's a place.

Note: Featured in the film 'Ferris Bueller's Day Off'.

7" EP: Released '63, on Parlophone by EMI Records. Catalogue no: **GEP 8882**

YELLOW SUBMARINE (Film soundtrack)

Tracks: / Yellow submarine / Only a northern song / All you need is love / Hey bulldog / It's all too much / All together now / Pepperland / Sea of time / Sea of holes / Sea of monsters / March of the meanies / Pepperland laid to waste / Yellow submarine in Pepperland.

Cass: Released Nov '87, on Parlophone by EMI Records. Catalogue no: **TCPCS 7070**

Album: Released Nov '88, on Parlophone by EMI Records. Catalogue no: **PCS 7070**

Album: Released Aug '81, on Parlophone by EMI Records. Deleted Aug '86. Catalogue no: **PCM 7070**

CD: Released Aug '87, on Parlophone by EMI Records. Catalogue no: **CDP 746 445 2**

CD: Released Aug '87, on Parlophone by EMI Records. Catalogue no: **CDPCS 7070**

YELLOW SUBMARINE (VIDEO)
VHS: Released Jun '88, on Warner Home Video by WEA Records. Catalogue no: **PEV 99655**

YELLOW SUBMARINE (SINGLE)
Tracks: / Yellow submarine / Eleanor Rigby.
CD 3": Released May '89, on Parlophone by EMI Records. Catalogue no: **CD3R 5493**
7" Single: Released Aug '86, on Parlophone by EMI Records. Catalogue no: **R 5493**
7" Pic: Released Aug '86, on Parlophone by EMI Records. Deleted Aug '90. Catalogue no: **RP 5493**

Beauty & The Beast

OF LOVE AND HOPE (Music & poetry from Beauty & The Beast) (Various artists)
Tracks: / Beauty & the beast (theme): *Various artists* / Acquainted with the night: *Various artists* / Laura's theme: *Various artists* / Margaret's theme-longing: *Various artists* / On her own-she walks in beauty: *Various artists* / Night of beauty: *Various artists* / Single night, A: *Various artists* / Angel's theme: *Various artists* / Devin's theme-I arise from the dreams of thee: *Various artists* / Promise remembered, A: *Various artists* / Journey's end - Sonnet - CXVI: *Various artists* / Dancing light - Sonnet - XXIX: *Various artists* / Quest, The - Letters to a

young poet (excerpt): *Various artists* / Fear: *Various artists* / You darkness: *Various artists* / Father remembers - composed on Westminster Bridge: *Various artists* / Intimations of immortality: *Various artists* / To cast all else aside: *Various artists* / Riches, not gold: *Various artists* / Catherine's lullabye: *Various artists* / Somewhere I have never travelled: *Various artists* / First time I loved forever, The: *Various artists* / Happy life, A: *Various artists* / This is the creature: *Various artists* / Return, The: *Various artists* / Broken dreams-ode: *Various artists*.
CD: Released Nov '89, on Capitol by EMI Records. Catalogue no: **CDEST 2115**
CD: Released Nov '89, on Capitol by EMI Records. Catalogue no: **CDP 791 583 2**
Album: Released Nov '89, on Capitol by EMI Records. Catalogue no: **EST 2115**
Cass: Released Nov '89, on Capitol by EMI Records. Catalogue no: **TCEST 2115**

Becket (Film)

BECKET (Original soundtrack) (Various artists)
Note: Laurence Rosenthal score for the Peter O Toole/Richard Burton film.
Album: Released Jan '89, on Silva Screen by Silva Screen Records. Catalogue no: **DL 79117**
Album: Released Jan '89, on Silva Screen by Silva Screen Records. Catalogue no: **254 883 1**

Bedknobs & ...

BEDKNOBS AND BROOMSTICKS (Studio cast) (Various artists)
Tracks: / Old home guard: *Various artists* / Step in the right direction: *Various artists* / Age of not believing: *Various artists* / With a flair: *Various artists* / Eglantine: *Various artists* / Portobello Road: *Various artists* / Beautiful briny: *Various artists* / Substitutiary locomotion: *Various artists* / Old home guard: *Various artists* / Reprise: *Various artists*.
Note: Featuring:- Camarata orchestra & Mike Sammes singers
Album: Released '73, on Disneyland by Disneyland-Vista Records (USA). Deleted '78. Catalogue no: **DQ 1326**

Bedroom Window

BEDROOM WINDOW (Original soundtrack) (Various artists)
Note: Thriller with an electronic score by Patrick Gleeson.
Album: Released Jan '89, on Silva Screen by Silva Screen Records. Catalogue no: **STV 81307**

Bee Gees

HOW DEEP IS YOUR LOVE
Tracks: / How deep is your love.
Note: From the film 'Saturday Night Fever.'
7" Single: Released Oct '77, on RSO by Polydor Ltd. Deleted Oct '80. Catalogue no: **2090 259**

JIVE TALKIN'
Tracks: / Jive talkin'.
Note: Featured in the film 'Saturday Night Fever.'
7" Single: Released Jun '75, on RSO by Polydor Ltd. Deleted Jun '78. Catalogue no: **2090 160**

JIVE TALKING (OLD GOLD)
Tracks: / Jive talkin' / You should be dancing.
7" Single: Released Mar '86, on Old Gold by Old Gold Records. Catalogue no: **OG 9587**

NIGHT FEVER
Tracks: / Night fever / Down the road.
Note: From the film 'Saturday Night Fever'.
7" Single: Released Apr '78, on RSO by Polydor Ltd. Deleted Apr '81. Catalogue no: **RSO 002**

SOMEONE BELONGING TO SOMEONE
Tracks: / Someone belonging to someone / Saturday night fever medley / Night fever.
Note: Featured in the film 'Staying Alive.'
7" Single: Released Sep '83, on RSO by Polydor Ltd. Deleted Sep '86. Catalogue no: **RSO 96**
12" Single: Released Sep '83, on RSO by Polydor Ltd. Deleted Sep '86. Catalogue no: **RSOX 96**

STAYIN' ALIVE
Tracks: / Stayin' alive / If I can't have you.
Note: Featured in the films 'Saturday Night Fever' and 'Staying Alive.'
7" Single: Released Feb '78, on RSO by Polydor Ltd. Deleted Feb '81. Catalogue no: **2090 267**

WOMAN IN YOU

Tracks: / Woman in you / Staying alive.

Note: Featured in the film 'Stayin' Alive.'

7" Single: Released Jul '83, on RSO by Polydor Ltd. Deleted Jul '86. Catalogue no: **RSO 94**

12" Single: Released Jul '83, on RSO by Polydor Ltd. Deleted Jul '86. Catalogue no: **RSOX 94**

YOU SHOULD BE DANCING

Tracks: / You should be dancing.

Note: Featured in the film 'Saturday Night Fever.'

7" Single: Released Jul '76, on RSO by Polydor Ltd. Deleted Jul '79. Catalogue no: **2090 195**

Beetlejuice

BEETLEJUICE (Film soundtrack) (Various artists)

Tracks: / Day o: *Belafonte, Harry* / Jump in the line: *Belafonte, Harry* / Main titles: *Various artists* / Travel music: *Various artists* / Book, The: *Various artists* / Enter..."The family"/Sand worm planet: *Various artists* / Fly, The: *Various artists* / Lydia discovers?: *Various artists* / In the model: *Various artists* / Juno's theme: *Various artists* / Beetle-snake: *Various artists* / Sold: *Various artists* / Flyer, The: *Various artists* (Track includes: Lydia's pep talk.) / Incantation: *Various artists* / Lydia strikes a bargain: *Various artists* / Showtime: *Various artists* / Laughs: *Various artists* / Wedding, The: *Various artists* / Aftermath: *Various artists* / End credits: *Various artists*.

CD: Released Aug '88, on Geffen by Geffen Records (USA). Catalogue no: **924202 2**

Album: Released Aug '88, on Geffen by Geffen Records (USA). Deleted Jul '90. Catalogue no: **924202 1**

Cass: Released Aug '88, on Geffen by Geffen Records (USA). Catalogue no: **924202 4**

Beiderbecke Collection

BEIDERBECKE COLLECTION (See under Ricotti, Frank)

Believers

BELIEVERS, THE (Film soundtrack) (Various artists)

Note: Supernatural thriller, score by J.P. Robinson.

Album: Released Jan '89, on Silva Screen by Silva Screen Records. Catalogue no: **STV 81328**

Belizaire...

BELIZAIRE - THE CAJUN (See under Doucet, Michael)

Bell, Book & Candle

BELL, BOOK AND CANDLE (Film soundtrack) (Duning, George)

Album: Released Mar '79, on Citadel (USA) by Varese Sarabande Records (USA). Catalogue no: **CT 6006**

Bell, Maggie

HAZELL

Tracks: / Hazell / Night flighting.

Note: Theme from the TV series.

7" Single: Released Mar '78, on Swansong Catalogue no: **SSK 19412**

Belle

BELLE (OR THE BALLAD OF DR CRIPPEN) (Original London cast) (Various artists)

Tracks: / Ain't a shame?: *Various artists* / Ballad of Dr Crippen, The: *Various artists* / Belle: *Various artists* / Bird of paradise: *Various artists* / Bravest of men, The: *Various artists* / Cold water: *Various artists* / Michigan: *Various artists* / Devil's bands man, The: *Various artists* / Colonies: *Various artists* / Dit dit song, The: *Various artists* / Don't ever leave me: *Various artists* / Fairy godmother: *Various artists* / Fifty years ago: *Various artists* / I can't stop singing: *Various artists* / Lovely London: *Various artists* / Meet me at the Strand: *Various artists* / Mr Lasherwood and mighty Mick: *Various artists* / Minstrel song, The: *Various artists* / Pils, pils, pils: *Various artists* / Pint of wallop, A: *Various artists* / Policeman's song: *Various artists* / Song of our future: *Various artists* / Waltzing with you: *Various artists* / You are mine: *Various artists* / You can't beat a British crime: *Various artists*.

Album: Released Apr '83, on T.E.R. by That's Entertainment Records. Catalogue no: **TER 1048**

Cass: Released Apr '83, on T.E.R. by That's Entertainment Records. Catalogue no: **ZCTER 1048**

Belle Of New York

BELLE OF NEW YORK (Film soundtrack) (Various artists)

Tracks: / Baby doll: *Various artists* / Oops: *Various artists* / Seeing is believing: *Various artists* / I wanna be a dancing man: *Various artists* / Bachelor dinner song: *Various artists* / Naughty but nice: *Various artists* / Belle of New York: *Various artists* / Let a little love come in: *Various artists*.

Album: Released '79, on EMI (Import) Deleted '84. Catalogue no: **DS 15004**

Cass: Released '79, on EMI (Import) Deleted '84. Catalogue no: **TCDS 15004**

BELLE OF NEW YORK / 2 WEEKS WITH LOVE (Original soundtracks) (Various artists)

Note: A Harry Warden musical. Starring Fred Astaire and Jane Powell.

Cass: Released Jan '89, on MCA by MCA Records. Catalogue no: **MCAC 39082**

Album: Released Jan '89, on MCA by MCA Records. Catalogue no: **MCA 39082**

BELLE OF NEW YORK / GOOD NEWS (Various artists)

Tracks: / When I'm out with the belle of New York: *Various artists* / Oops!: *Astaire, Fred* / Naughty but nice: *Ellis, Anita* / Bachelor's dinner song: *Astaire, Fred* / Baby doll: *Astaire, Fred* / Bride's wedding day, A: *Ellis, Anita* / Seeing's believing: *Astaire, Fred* / I wanna be a dancin' man: *Astaire, Fred* / Good news: *McCracken, Joan* / He's a ladies man: *Lawford, Peter* / Lucky in love: *Marshall, Pat/Peter Lawford/June Allyson* / French lesson, The: *Allyson, June/Peter Lawford* / Best things in life are free: *Allyson, June/Peter Lawford* / Pass that peace pipe: *McCracken, Joan* / Just imagine: *Allyson, June* / Varsity drag, The: *Allyson, June/Peter Lawford* / Wonder why?: *Powell, Jane* / Dark is the night: *Powell, Jane* / Paris: *Lamas, Fernando* / We never talk much: *Darrieux, Danielle* / There's danger in your eyes, cherie: *Darrieux, Danielle*.

CD: Released Aug '90, on MGM (EMI) Catalogue no: **CDMGM 23**

Cass: Released Aug '90, on MGM (EMI) Catalogue no: **TCMGM 23**

Album: Released Aug '90, on

Soundtrack to the film *Ben Hur* **(Silva Screen)**

MGM (EMI) Catalogue no: **794 869 1**
Album: Released Aug '90, on MGM (EMI) Catalogue no: **LPMGM 23**
Cass: Released Aug '90, on MGM (EMI) Catalogue no: **794 869 4**
CD: Released Aug '90, on MGM (EMI) Catalogue no: **CDP 794 869 2**

Belle Stars

IKO IKO
Tracks: / Iko iko / Reason.
Note: Featured in the film 'Rainman'.
7" Single: Released Jun '82, on Stiff by Stiff Records. Catalogue no: **BUY 150**

IKO IKO (RE-ISSUE)
Tracks: / Iko iko / Las Vegas / Iko iko (12" mix) / Iko iko (bonus beats) (12" only.).
12" Single: Released May '89, on Capitol by EMI Records. Deleted Oct '89. Catalogue no: **203 405 6**
7" Single: Released May '89, on Capitol by EMI Records. Deleted Oct '89. Catalogue no: **203 387 7**
12" Single: Released May '89, on Capitol by EMI Records. Deleted Oct '89. Catalogue no: **12CL 537**

7" Single: Released May '89, on Capitol by EMI Records. Deleted Oct '89. Catalogue no: **CL 537**

Bells Are Ringing

BELLS ARE RINGING (Film soundtrack) (Various artists)
CD: Released Feb '90, on Silva Screen by Silva Screen Records. Catalogue no: **CDP 92060.2**
Cass: Released Jan '89, on Silva Screen by Silva Screen Records. Catalogue no: **92060.4**

BELLS ARE RINGING (Original Broadway Cast) (Various artists)
Tracks: / Overture: *Various artists* / Bells are ringing: *Various artists* / It's a perfect relationship: *Various artists* / On my own: *Various artists* / It's a simple little system: *Various artists* / It is a crime: *Various artists* / Hello, hello there: *Various artists* / I met a girl: *Various artists* / Long before I knew you: *Various artists* / Mu-cha-cha: *Various artists* / Just in time: *Various artists* / Drop that name: *Various artists* / Party's over, The: *Various artists* / Saltzburg: *Various artists* / Midas touch, The: *Various artists* / I'm goin' back.
Album: Released Apr '83, on CBS

Cameo by CBS Records & Distribution. Catalogue no: **CBS 32254**
Cass: Released Apr '83, on CBS Cameo by CBS Records & Distribution. Catalogue no: **40-32254**
Cass: Released Jan '89, on Silva Screen by Silva Screen Records. Catalogue no: **PST 2006**
CD: Released Jan '89, on CBS (Import) by CBS Records & Distribution. Deleted Mar '90. Catalogue no: **CK 02006**
Cass: Released Jan '89, on Silva Screen by Silva Screen Records. Deleted Mar '90. Catalogue no: **JST 02006**
Album: Released Jan '89, on Silva Screen by Silva Screen Records. Deleted Mar '90. Catalogue no: **AOS 2006**

Belly Of An Architect

BELLY OF AN ARCHITECT (1987 film soundtrack) (Various artists)
Album: Released '88, on Factory by Factory Records. Catalogue no: **FACT 195**
CD: Released '88, on Factory by Factory Records. Catalogue no: **FACD 195**

Beloved Screen Music

BELOVED SCREEN MUSIC (Various artists)
Tracks: / Over the rainbow: *Various artists* / Gonna fly now: *Various artists* / Speak softly love: *Various artists* / Ben Hur love theme: *Various artists* / Raindrops keep falling on my head: *Various artists* / Summertime in Venice: *Various artists* / East of Eden: *Various artists* / Tara's theme: *Various artists* / From Russia with love: *Various artists* / Plein soleil: *Various artists* / Love is many splendored thing: *Various artists*.
Album: Released Mar '82, on Denon Deleted '88. Catalogue no: **SX 7008**

Ben Hur

(Also see under Rozso, Miklos)

BEN HUR (Original Soundtrack Musical Highlights) (Various artists) (See picture above)
Tracks: / Prelude: *Various artists* / Adoration of the magi: *Various artists* / Roman march: *Various ar-*

tists / Friendship: *Various artists* / Love theme on Ben Hur: *Various artists* / Burning desert: *Various artists* / Rowing of the gallery slaves: *Various artists* / Naval battle: *Various artists* / Return to Judea: *Various artists* / Victory parade: *Various artists* / Mother's love: *Various artists* / Lepers search for Christ: *Various artists* / Procession to calvary: *Various artists* / Miracle and finale: *Various artists*.
Album: Released '73, on MGM (Polydor) by Polydor Ltd. Deleted '78. Catalogue no: **2353 030**

BEN HUR (Film soundtrack) (Various artists)
Tracks: / Ben Hur prelude: *Various artists* / Adoration of the Magi, The: *Various artists* / Roman march: *Various artists* / Friendship: *Various artists* / Love theme from Ben Hur: *Various artists* / Burning desert, The: *Various artists* / Rowing of the galley slaves, The: *Various artists* / Naval battle: *Various artists* / Return to Judea: *Various artists* / Victory parade: *Various artists* / Mother's love, The: *Various artists* / Leper's search for the Christ, The: *Various artists* / Procession to Calvary, The: *Various artists* / Miracle and finale. The:
CD: Released Jan '90, on MGM (EMI) Catalogue no: **CDMGM 8**
CD: Released Jan '90, on MGM (EMI) Catalogue no: **CDP 793 304 2**
Album: Released Jan '90, on MGM (EMI) Catalogue no: **LPMGM 8**
Cass: Released Jan '90, on MGM (EMI) Catalogue no: **TCMGM 8**
Album: Released Jan '90, on MGM (EMI) Catalogue no: **793 304 1**
Cass: Released Jan '90, on MGM (EMI) Catalogue no: **793 304 4**

BEN HUR (Film soundtrack) (Rome Symphony Orchestra)
Tracks: / Prelude / Miracle and finale, The / Procession to Calvary / Lepers search for the Christ / Mother's love, The / Victory parade / Return to Judea / Naval battle / Rowing of the galley slaves / Burning desert, The / Ben Hur love theme / Roman march / Adoration of the Magi, The.
Album: Released Jul '86, on CBS by CBS Records & Distribution. Catalogue no: **CBS 70276**

Cass: Released Jul '86, on CBS by CBS Records & Distribution. Deleted Aug '87. Catalogue no: **40 70276**
CD: Released '86, on CBS by CBS Records & Distribution. Deleted Jan '89. Catalogue no: **CD 70276**

BEN HUR (1925 Film soundtrack) (Davis, Carl/Liverpool Philharmonic Orchestra)
Tracks: / Ben Hur opening theme / Nativity / Esther and the young prince / Roman march and disaster / Galley slave / Pirates / Iras the Egyptian / Chariot race / Ben Hur's return / Via Lolorosa / Earthquake / New day.
Album: Released Nov '89, on Silva Screen by Silva Screen Records. Catalogue no: **FILM 043**
Cass: Released Nov '89, on Silva Screen by Silva Screen Records. Catalogue no: **FILMC 043**
CD: Released Nov '89, on Silva Screen by Silva Screen Records. Catalogue no: **FILMCD 043**

BEN HUR (ORIGINAL ISSUE) (Film soundtrack) (Various artists)
Album: Released Nov '60, on MGM (EMI) Deleted '65. Catalogue no: **MGM C 802**

Benatar, Pat
INVINCIBLE
Tracks: / Invincible / Invincible (instrumental).
Note: Taken from the film, 'The Legend Of Billie Jean.'
12" Single: Released '86, on Chrysalis by Chrysalis Records. Catalogue no: **PATX 3**
7" Single: Released Oct '85, on Chrysalis by Chrysalis Records. Deleted '88. Catalogue no: **PAT 3**

Bennett, Alan
ALAN BENNETT DOUBLE BILL (Forty Years On And A Woman Of No Importance) (Gielgud, Sir John/Patricia Routledge)
Cass set: Released Sep '88, on BBC by BBC Records. Catalogue no: **ZBBC 1029**

FORTY YEARS ON
Cass: Released May '84, on BBC by BBC Records. Deleted Apr '89. Catalogue no: **ZCF 504**

Bennett, Chris
BILLY'S THEME

Tracks: / Midnight express / Billy's theme.
Note: Taken from 'Midnight Express'.
7" Single: Released Jun '79, on Casablanca by PolyGram UK Ltd. Deleted '82. Catalogue no: **CAN 138**

Berlin
TAKE MY BREATH AWAY
Tracks: / Take my breath away / Radar radio / You've lost that lovin' feeling (Extra track on 12" only).
Note: Featured in the film 'Top Gun.'
7" Single: Released Oct '86, on CBS by CBS Records & Distribution. Deleted Aug '88. Catalogue no: **A 7320**
12" Single: Released Oct '86, on CBS by CBS Records & Distribution. Deleted Aug '88. Catalogue no: **TA 7320**

Berlin Affair
BERLIN AFFAIR, THE (Film soundtrack) (Various artists)
Note: Composed by Pino Donaggio.
Album: Released Jan '89, on Silva Screen by Silva Screen Records. Catalogue no: **A 286**
Cass: Released Jan '89, on Silva Screen by Silva Screen Records. Catalogue no: **C 286**

Berlin Blues
BERLIN BLUES (Film soundtrack) (Various artists)
Note: Film starring Julia Migenes (Carmen). She also performs the songs composed by Lalo Schifrin.
CD: Released Jan '89, on SPI Milan (France) Deleted Feb '90. Catalogue no: **CDCH 357**
Album: Released Jan '89, on Silva Screen by Silva Screen Records. Catalogue no: **A 357**

Bernstein, Elmer
MAGNIFICENT 7/RETURN OF THE MAGNIFICENT SEVEN
Album: Released '70, on Sunset (Liberty) by EMI Records. Deleted '75. Catalogue no: **SLS 50171**

MIDAS RUN, THE (Film soundtrack)
Album: Released '79, on Citadel (USA) by Varese Sarabande Records (USA). Catalogue no: **CT 6016**

MOVIE & TV THEMES
CD: on Mobile Fidelity Sound Lab(USA) by Mobile Fidelity Records (USA). Catalogue no: **MFCD 851**

SCALPHUNTERS (See under Scalphunters)

SONS OF KATIE ELDER (See under Sons of Katie Elder)

STACCATO'S THEME (Also see under Staccato)
Tracks: / Staccato's theme.
7" Single: Released Jan '60, on Capitol by EMI Records. Deleted '63. Catalogue no: **CL 15101**

SUMMER AND SMOKE (See under Summer & Smoke)

Bertha
BERTHA (Children's TV series) (Various artists)
Tracks: / Bertha: *Various artists* / Mrs. Tupp: *Various artists* / Packing and stacking: *Various artists* / Flying bear, The: *Various artists* / Mr. Duncan: *Various artists* / Turning wheels: *Various artists* / Tom the robot: *Various artists* / Isn't it nice: *Various artists* / Mr. Willmake: *Various artists* / Tracy's robot song: *Various artists* / Spottiswood march: *Various artists* / Roy the apprentice: *Various artists*.
Note: Record to accompany the children's series Bertha, with music and lyrics by Brian Daly, responsible for the highly successful Postman Pat.
Cass: Released Oct '85, on BBC by BBC Records. Deleted Apr '89. Catalogue no: **ZCR 585**
Album: Released Oct '85, on BBC by BBC Records. Deleted Apr '89. Catalogue no: **REH 585**

Best Little Whorehouse
BEST LITTLE WHOREHOUSE IN TEXAS (Original Broadway cast) (Various artists)
Album: Released Jan '89, on MCA by MCA Records. Catalogue no: **MCA 37218**
Cass: Released Jan '89, on MCA by MCA Records. Catalogue no: **MCAC 37218**
CD: Released Jun '88, on MCA (USA) by MCA Records (USA). Catalogue no: **31007**
BEST LITTLE WHOREHOUSE IN TEXAS (Show soundtrack)

(Various artists)
Tracks: / 20 fans: *Various artists* / Lil' ole bitty pissant country place, A: *Various artists* / Girl, you're a woman: *Various artists* / Watch dog theme: *Various artists* / Texas has a whorehouse in it: *Various artists* / Twenty hour of lovin': *Various artists* / Doatsy Mae: *Various artists* / Aggie song, The: *Various artists* / Bus from Amarillo, The: *Various artists* / Sidestep, The: *Various artists* / No lies: *Various artists* / Good old girl: *Various artists* / Hard candy Christmas: *Various artists* / Finale: *Various artists*.
Album: Released Mar '81, on MCA by MCA Records. Deleted '89. Catalogue no: **MCF 3093**
Cass: Released Mar '81, on MCA by MCA Records. Deleted '89. Catalogue no: **MCFC 3093**
CD: Released Jan '89, on MCA by MCA Records. Catalogue no: **MCAD 31007**

BEST LITTLE WHOREHOUSE IN TEXAS (VIDEO) (Various artists)
VHS: Released Jan '89, on CIC Video Catalogue no: **VHR 1072**

Best Revenge
BEST REVENGE (See under Emerson, Keith)

Best Shot
BEST SHOT (Film soundtrack) (Various artists)
Tracks: / Best shot: *Various artists* / You did good: *Various artists* / Coach stays, The: *Various artists* / Pivot, The: *Various artists* / Get the ball: *Various artists* / Town meeting: *Various artists* / Finals, The: *Various artists*.
Album: Released Aug '87, on T. E. R. by That's Entertainment Records. Catalogue no: **TER 1141**
Cass: Released Aug '87, on T. E. R. by That's Entertainment Records. Catalogue no: **ZCTER 1141**
CD: Released Aug '87, on T. E. R. by That's Entertainment Records. Catalogue no: **CDTER 1141**

Betjemania
BETJEMANIA (Original London cast) (Various artists)
Album: Released May '89, on T. E. R. by That's Entertainment Records. Catalogue no: **TER 1002**

Betrayed
BETRAYED (Music by Bill

Conti) (Various artists)
Tracks: / Main title: *Various artists* / Way, The: *Various artists* / Shoot the horse: *Various artists* / Bank robbery, The: *Various artists* / Kill me Kathy: *Various artists* / To the bank: *Various artists* / Riding to work: *Various artists* / Guns: *Various artists* / Passing time: *Various artists* / End title: *Various artists*.
Cass: Released Jan '89, on Varese Sarabande Records (USA) by Varese Sarabande Records (USA). Catalogue no: **VSC 70470**
CD: Released Jul '89, on T. E. R. by That's Entertainment Records. Catalogue no: **CDTER 1163**
Album: Released Jan '89, on Varese Sarabande Records (USA) by Varese Sarabande Records (USA). Catalogue no: **VS 70470**
CD: Released Jan '89, on Varese Sarabande Records(USA) by Varese Sarabande Records (USA). Catalogue no: **VSD 70470**
Cass: Released Jul '89, on T. E. R. by That's Entertainment Records. Catalogue no: **ZCTER 1163**

Betty Blue
BETTY BLUE (Film soundtrack) (Yared, Gabriel)
Tracks: / Betty et Zorg / Des orages pour la nuit / Cargo voyage / La poubelle cuisine / Humecter la monture / Le petit Nicolas / Gyneco zebre / Comme les deux doigts de la main / Zorg et Betty / Chili con carne / C'est le vent, Betty / Un coucher de soleil accroche dans les arbres / Lisa rock / Le coeur en skai mauve / Bungalow zen / 37'2 le matin / Maudits maneges.
Note: Composed by Gabriel Yared.
CD: Released Oct '86, on Virgin by Virgin Records. Catalogue no: **CDV 2396**
Cass: Released Sep '86, on Virgin by Virgin Records. Catalogue no: **TCV 2396**
Album: Released Sep '86, on Virgin by Virgin Records. Catalogue no: **V 2396**

Beverly Hills Cop
BEVERLY HILLS COP (Film soundtrack) (Various artists)
Tracks: / New attitude: *Labelle, Patti* / Don't get stopped in Beverly Hills: *Shalamar* / Do you really (want my love)?: *Junior* / Emer-

gency: Robbins, Rockie / Neutron dance: Pointer Sisters / Heat is on: Frey, Glenn / Gratitude: Elfman, Danny / Stir it up: Labelle, Patti / Rock 'n' roll me again: System / Axel F: Faltermeyer, Harold.

CD: Released '85, on MCA by MCA Records. Catalogue no: **DMCF 3253**

Cass: Released '88, on MCA by MCA Records. Catalogue no: **MCLC 1870**

Cass: Released '85, on MCA by MCA Records. Catalogue no: **MCFC 3253**

Album: Released '88, on MCA by MCA Records. Catalogue no: **MCL 1870**

Album: Released '85, on MCA by MCA Records. Catalogue no: **MCF 3253**

CD: Released Jul '88, on MCA by MCA Records. Catalogue no: **DMCL 1870**

BEVERLY HILLS COP II (Film soundtrack) (Various artists)
Tracks: / Shakedown: Seger, Bob / Be there: Pointer Sisters / In deep: Sexton, Charlie / Hold on: Hart, Corey / I want your sex: Michael, George / Better way: Ingram, James / Love/Hate: Pebbles / Cross my broken heart: Jets (American) / 36 lovers: Ready For The World / I can't stand it: Sue Ann / All revved up: Jackson, Jermaine.
Note: The album includes tracks from Bob Seger, James Ingram, Pointer Sisters and the Jets.
Cass: Released Jul '87, on MCA by MCA Records. Catalogue no: **MCFC 3383**
Album: Released Jul '87, on MCA by MCA Records. Catalogue no: **MCF 3383**
CD: Released Jul '87, on MCA by MCA Records. Catalogue no: **DMCF 3383**

Beyond The Fringe

BEYOND THE FRINGE (Broadway 1962) (Various artists)
Note: Featuring Peter Cook, Dudley Moore, Jonathan Miller & Alan Bennett
Cass: Released '90, on EMI by EMI Records. Catalogue no: **92055.4**
CD: Released '90, on EMI by EMI Records. Catalogue no: **CDP 92055.2**

BEYOND THE FRINGE (ORIGINAL ISSUE) (London cast) (Various artists)
Album: Released Jul '61, on Parlophone by EMI Records. Deleted '66. Catalogue no: **PMC 1145**

Beyond The Rainbow

BEYOND THE RAINBOW (Original London cast) (Various artists)
Tracks: / Come join us at the table: Various artists / Pity: Various artists / Ding dong song: Various artists / Throw it away: Various artists / Time for love: Various artists / Tiny ant: Various artists / San Crispino: Various artists / Consolation: Various artists / Love according to me: Various artists / I want you: Various artists / Clementine: Various artists.
Cass: Released '79, on MCA by MCA Records. Deleted '84. Catalogue no: **MCFC 2874**
Album: Released '79, on MCA by MCA Records. Deleted '84. Catalogue no: **MCF 2874**

Beyond The Valley ...

BEYOND THE VALLEY OF THE DOLLS (Film Soundtrack) (Various artists)
Tracks: / Beyond the valley of the dolls: Various artists / Come with the gentle people: Various artists / Look on up at the bottom: Various artists / Girl from the city: Various artists / In the long run: Various artists / Beyond the valley of the dolls: Various artists / Sweet talkin' candy man: Various artists / Find it: Various artists / Ampersand: Various artists / Once I had love: Various artists / I'm coming home: Various artists / Beyond the valley of the dolls: Various artists.
Album: Released '73, on Stateside by EMI Records. Deleted '78. Catalogue no: **SSL 10311**

Beyond Therapy

BEYOND THERAPY (Film soundtrack) (Various artists)
Cass: Released '88, on SPI Milan (France) Catalogue no: **C 301**
Album: Released '88, on SPI Milan (France) Catalogue no: **A 301**

Bicat, Nick

IRISH RM (THEME)

Tracks: / Irish RM (theme) / Major Yates fancy / Haste to the wedding.
7" Single: Released Feb '83, on Ritz by Ritz Records. Catalogue no: **RITZ 035**

WETHERBY (See under Wetherby)

Biddu Orchestra

STUD (THEME FROM)
Tracks: / Stud (Theme from) / Unfinished journey.
7" Single: Released Apr '78, on Epic by CBS Records & Distribution. Deleted '80. Catalogue no: **EPC 6317**

Big Blue

BIG BLUE, THE (Film soundtrack) (Various artists)
Tracks: / Big Blue overture, The: Various artists / Rescue in a wreck: Various artists / Huacracocha: Various artists / Remembering a heart beat: Various artists / Homo delphinus: Various artists / Virgin Islands: Various artists / For Enzo: Various artists / My lady blue: Various artists / Deep blue dream: Various artists / In raya: Various artists / Between the sky scrapers: Various artists / Let them try (instrumental): Various artists / Synchronised instant: Various artists / Monastery of Amorgos, The: Various artists / Leaving the world behind: Various artists.
Note: New film from Luc Besson (director of Subway) with music from the composer of Subway, Eric Serra. Major French box office hit.
Album: Released Jan '89, on Silva Screen by Silva Screen Records. Catalogue no: **70609**
Cass: Released Jan '89, on Silva Screen by Silva Screen Records. Catalogue no: **50609**
Cass: Released Nov '88, on Virgin by Virgin Records. Catalogue no: **TCV 2541**
CD: Released Nov '88, on Virgin by Virgin Records. Catalogue no: **CDV 2541**
Album: Released Nov '88, on Virgin by Virgin Records. Catalogue no: **V 2541**
CD: Released Jan '89, on Silva Screen by Silva Screen Records. Catalogue no: **30145**

BIG BLUE, THE (COMPLETE) (Serra, Eric)

Soundtrack to the film *The Big Country* (Silva Screen)

CD Set: Released Feb '90, on Silva Screen by Silva Screen Records. Catalogue no: **30193**
Album: Released Feb '90, on Silva Screen by Silva Screen Records. Catalogue no: **60065**
Cass: Released Feb '90, on Silva Screen by Silva Screen Records. Catalogue no: **40065**

BIG BLUE, THE VOL. 2 (Serra, Eric)
CD: Released Feb '90, on Silva Screen by Silva Screen Records. Catalogue no: **30667**
Cass: Released Feb '90, on Silva Screen by Silva Screen Records. Catalogue no: **50667**
Album: Released Feb '90, on Silva Screen by Silva Screen Records. Catalogue no: **70667**

Big Broadcast Of 1932

BIG BROADCAST OF 1932, THE (Film Soundtrack) (Various artists)
Note: Starring Bing Crosby and Kate Smith.
Album: Released '89, on Soun'trak (USA) by Silva Screen Records. Catalogue no: **STK 101**
Album: Released Jan '89, on Silva Screen by Silva Screen Records. Catalogue no: **SH 2007**

Big Chill

BIG CHILL, THE (Film Soundtrack) (Various artists)
Tracks: / I heard it through the grapevine: *Gaye, Marvin* / My girl: *Temptations* / Good lovin': *Rascals* / Tracks of my tears: *Robinson, Smokey* / Joy to the world: *Three Dog Night* / Ain't too proud to beg: *Temptations* / (You make me feel like) a natural woman: *Franklin, Aretha* / I second that emotion: *Robinson, Smokey* / Whiter shade of pale, A: *Procul Harum*.
Album: Released Jul '84, on Motown by BMG Records (UK). Catalogue no: **STMR 9021**
Cass: Released Jul '84, on Motown by BMG Records (UK). Catalogue no: **CSTMR 9021**
Album: Released '88, on Motown by BMG Records (UK). Catalogue no: **ZL 72138**
Cass: Released '88, on Motown by BMG Records (UK). Catalogue no: **ZK 72138**
CD: Released Jul '84, on Motown by BMG Records (UK). Catalogue no: **ZD 72347**

Big Country (Film)

BIG COUNTRY (Film soundtrack) (Philharmonia Orchestra)
Tracks: / Big country / Old thunder, The / Waltz, The / War party / Stalking, The / Welcoming / Mackay's triumph / Big Muddy / Death of Buck Hannassey.
Note: Score by Jerome Moss. *The Big Country* was a United Artists release of a William Wyler/Gregory Peck co-production (this was Peck's first venture in that capacity). The cost of the film was in excess of four million dollars, which for the late 1950's was certainly on the extravagant side. The film, as with Wyler's *Friendly Persuasion* (1956), featured a hero who refuses to act in accordance with Western traditions and ethics. Jim McKay is slow to anger and hesitant to fight and does not prove his courage unless it suits him to do so. Westerns of the 1950's had become overblown and self conscious, as with Fred Zinneman's *High Noon* (1952) or George Stevens *Shane* (1953) or they were off beat and psychologically intense - John Ford's *The Searchers* (1956). Wyler continued this trend with *The Big Country*, but it was to be filmed on a far more grandiose scale with an all star cast. Ace cinematographer Franz Planer was hired to photograph the film in wide screen Technirama and glorious Technicolor to accentuate the rugged Californian and Arizonian locations of Stockton Ranch and the Mojave Desert. For such a seemingly simple story *The Big Country* had very elongated screenplay credits which gives some indication of the problems involved to getting a manageable script. At one point Leon Uris (author of *Exodus*) was brought in on the re-writes and he produced two different versions of the story, only to have both rejected. After these and other re-writes, filming finally Began but this ran far from smoothly and was beset by problems and rows. The rows were mostly between the two producers (and close friends) with Peck walking off the set and later threatening a lawsuit. (Wyler and Peck did not speak to each other for nearly two years

after the filming but eventually 'made-up' and remained the best of friends.)

The film premiered in America on October 1st 1958, to mixed reviews - varying from the lukewarm to the sublime. Time Magazine described it as as 'a starkly beautiful, carefully written Western that demands comparison with *Shane*.' The New York Herald said it was 'astutely and enthusiastically made', while the London Times said 'It is not quite an epic but is touched by epic qualities.' The most bizarre review came from Films & Filming who saw it 'as an allegory, with Major Terrill as a Fascist dictator and Hannassey running his less prosperous community like a Communist dictator.' The film was and still is criticised for being overlong at 166 minutes (in fact over 4 hours of usable footage was shot), however, Wyler uses this to his advantage, ironically contrasting the often puny, petty, almost comical characters against the vast landscapes. The film contains many other such contrasts one between the opposed families - the well bred and expensively dressed Terrills and the ragged and illiterate Hannasseys, the differences betwen the cultured McKay and the virile Leech and between the spoiled and bitchy Patricia, and the quiet and dignified Julie. It is these dichotomies which give the film is rich textures and balance against the broad cinemascope canvas. Unifying all of these divergent elements and providing the driving force in the action is the powerful score by Jerome Moss. (Silva Screen)

DAT: Released Jan '89, on Silva Screen by Silva Screen Records. Deleted Feb '90. Catalogue no: **FILMDT 030**

Cass: Released Jan '89, on Silva Screen by Silva Screen Records. Catalogue no: **FILMC 030**

Album: Released Jan '89, on Silva Screen by Silva Screen Records. Catalogue no: **FILM 030**

CD: Released Jan '89, on Silva Screen by Silva Screen Records. Catalogue no: **FILMCD 030**

BIG COUNTRY, THE (Film soundtrack) (Various artists)
Tracks: / Big country, The: *Various artists* / Welcoming, The: *Vari-*

ous artists / Old thunder: *Various artists* / McKay's triumph: *Various artists* / Waltz: *Various artists* / Old waltz, The: *Various artists* / Big muddy: *Various artists* / War party gathers, The: *Various artists* / McKay in Blanco Canyon: *Various artists* / Death of Buck Hannassey: *Various artists* / Stalking, The: *Various artists*.

Cass: Released Jan '79, on Hallmark by Pickwick Records. Deleted '88. Catalogue no: **HSC 343**

Album: Released Jan '79, on Hallmark by Pickwick Records. Deleted '88. Catalogue no: **SHM 968**

BIG COUNTRY/HOW THE WEST WAS WON (Various artists)
Tracks: / Big country, The: *Various artists* (Big Country.) / Welcoming, The: *Various artists* (Big Country.) / Old thunder: *Various artists* (Big Country.) / McKay's triumph: *Various artists* (Big Country.) / Waltz, The: *Various artists* (Big Country.) / Old house, The: *Various artists* (Big Country.) / Big muddy: *Various artists* (Big Country.) / War party gathers, The: *Various artists* (Big Country.) / McKay in Blanco Canyon: *Various artists* (Big Country.) / Death of Buck Hannassey, The: *Various artists* (Big Country.) / Stalking, The: *Various artists* (Big Country.) / Big country, The: *Various artists* (Big Country.) / How the west was won (main title): *Various artists* (How The West Was Won.) / Home in the meadow: *Reynolds, Debbie* (How The West Was Won.) / Cleve and the mule: *Various artists* (How The West Was Won.) / Raise a ruckus: *Reynolds, Debbie/Ken Darby Singers* (How The West Was Won.) / Come share my life: *Various artists* (How The West Was Won.) / Marriage proposal, The: *Various artists* (How The West Was Won.) / Cheyennes: *Various artists* (How The West Was Won.) / He's Linus' boy: *Various artists* (How The West Was Won.) / Climb a higher hill: *Various artists* (How The West Was Won.) / What was your name in the States?: *Reynolds, Debbie* (How The West Was One.) / No goodbye: *Various artists* (How The West Was Won.) / How the west was won (finale): *Darby, Ken Singers* (How The West Was Won.).

Note: Medley: Home in the meadow - Ken Darby Singers; 900 miles - Dave Guard & The Whiskeyhill Singers, Ken Darby Singers; On the banks of the Sacramento - Ken Darby Singers; When Johnny comes marching home & I'm bound for the promised land - Ken Darby Singers; Battle hymn of the republic - Ken Darby Singers. (How The West Was Won).

Cass: Released Apr '90, on MGM (EMI) Catalogue no: **TCMGM 12**

CD: Released Apr '90, on MGM (EMI) Catalogue no: **CDP 791 927 2**

Album: Released Apr '90, on MGM (EMI) Catalogue no: **LPMGM 12**

Album: Released Apr '90, on MGM (EMI) Catalogue no: **791 927 1**

CD: Released Apr '90, on MGM (EMI) Catalogue no: **CDMGM 12**

Cass: Released Apr '90, on MGM (EMI) Catalogue no: **791 927 4**

Big Easy

BIG EASY, THE (Original Soundtrack) (Various artists)
Tracks: / Iko iko: *Dixie Cups* / Tipitina: *Professor Longhair* / Ma 'tit fille: *Buckwheat Zydeco* / Colinda / Tell it like it is: *Neville, Aaron & the Neville Bros* / Zydeco gris gris: *Beausoleil* / Oh yeah: *Simien, T & the mallet playboys* / Hey hey: *Wild Tchoupitoulas* / Closer to you: *Quaid, Dennis* / Savour, pass...: *Swan Silvertones*.

Cass: Released '87, on Island by Island Records. Catalogue no: **ICT 14**

Cass: Released '90, on Island by Island Records. Catalogue no: **ICM 2006**

Cass: Released '90, on Island by Island Records. Catalogue no: **846 000 4**

CD: Released '89, on Island by Island Records. Catalogue no: **IMCD 31**

Album: Released 7 Nov '87, on Island by Island Records. Catalogue no: **ISTA 14**

CD: Released '87, on Island by Island Records. Catalogue no: **CID 14**

Big River

BIG RIVER - ADVENTURES OF HUCKLEBERRY FINN (Original Broadway cast)

(Various artists)

Tracks: / Overture(Big river): *Various artists* / Do you wanna go to heaven?: *Various artists* / Boys, The: *Various artists* / Waitin' for the light to shine: *Various artists* / Guv'ment: *Various artists* / Hand for the hog: *Various artists* / I, Huckleberry, me: *Various artists* / Muddy water: *Various artists* / Crossing, The: *Various artists* / River in the rain: *Various artists* / When the sun goes down in the south: *Various artists* / Entracte: *Various artists* / Royal nonesuch, The: *Various artists* / Worlds apart: *Various artists* / Arkansas: *Various artists* / How blest we are: *Various artists* / You oughta be here with me: *Various artists* / Leavin's not the only way to go: *Various artists* / Waitin' for the light to shine (reprise): *Various artists* / Free at last: *Various artists* / Muddy water (reprise): *Various artists*.

Note: Big River, based on Mark Twain's Adventures of Huckleberry Finn, won seven Tony Awards in 1985, including that of best musical. The score is by Roger Miller.

CD: Released Jan '89, on MCA by MCA Records. Catalogue no: **MCAD 6147**

Album: Released Feb '86, on MCA by MCA Records. Deleted Jan '88. Catalogue no: **MCF 3304**

Big Town (Film)

BIG TOWN (Film soundtrack) (Various artists)

Tracks: / Fever: *John, Little Willie* / Ruby baby: *Drifters* / Drown in my own tears: *Charles, Ray* / Home of the blues: *Cash, Johnny* / Mack the knife: *Darin, Bobby* / Since I met you baby: *Hunter, Ivory Joe* / Shake, rattle and roll: *Turner, Big Joe* / Goodnight my love, pleasant dreams: *Belvin, Jesse* / Jim Dandy: *Baker, Laverne* / Big town: *Self, Ronnie*.

Cass: Released Sep '87, on Atlantic by WEA Records. Catalogue no: **K 781 769 4**

Album: Released Sep '87, on Atlantic by WEA Records. Catalogue no: **K 781 769 1**

Big Trouble In Little...

BIG TROUBLE IN LITTLE CHINA (Film soundtrack) (Coup De Villes)

Tracks: / Big trouble in little China / Pork chop / Coup de villes / Pork chop express / Alley, The / Here comes the storm / Lo Pan's Domain / Escape from wing kong / Into the spirit path / Great Arcade, The / Final escape, The.

Album: Released Nov '86, on Silva Screen by Silva Screen Records. Deleted May '90. Catalogue no: **FILM 008**

CD: Released Jan '89, on Silva Screen by Silva Screen Records. Catalogue no: **ENG 73227.2**

Cass: Released Nov '86, on Silva Screen by Silva Screen Records. Catalogue no: **FILMC 008**

Big Western Film

BIG WESTERN FILM THEMES (Various artists)

Tracks: / High noon: *Various artists* / True grit: *Various artists* / Good, the bad and the ugly, The: *Various artists* / Magnificent seven, The: *Various artists* / Man from Laramie, The: *Various artists* / Hang 'em high: *Various artists*.

Cass: on AIM (Budget Cassettes) Catalogue no: **AIM 118**

Bigfoot & The...

BIGFOOT & THE HENDERSONS (Film soundtrack)

(Various artists)

Cass: Released '88, on MCA by MCA Records. Catalogue no: **MCFC 3416**

Album: Released '88, on MCA by MCA Records. Catalogue no: **MCF 3416**

Bilitis

BILITIS (Film soundtrack) (Lai, Francis)

Tracks: / Bilitis / Promenade / Le deux nudites / Spring time ballet / L'abre / I need a man / Melissa / La campagne / Scene d'amour / Rainbow / Bilitis.

CD: Released Feb '90, on Warner Bros.(Germany) by WEA Records. Catalogue no: **56412.2**

Cass: Released Apr '78, on United Artists by EMI Records. Catalogue no: **TCK 30161**

Album: Released '88, on Warner Bros.(Germany) by WEA Records. Catalogue no: **WB 56412**

CD: Released '88, on WEA by WEA Records. Catalogue no: **256 412**

Album: Released Apr '78, o

Music from the film *Bitter Sweet* (TER)

United Artists by EMI Records. Catalogue no: **UAS 30161**

Bill & Ted's ...

BILL AND TED'S EXCELLENT ADVENTURE (Film soundtrack) (Various artists)
Tracks: / Play with me: *Extreme* / Boys and girls are doing it: *Vital* / Not so far away: *Burtnick, Glenn* / Dancing with a gypsy: *Tora Tora* / Father time: *Shark Island* / I can't break away: *Big Pig* / Dangerous: *Shark Island* / Walk away: *Bricklin* / In time: *Robb, Robbie* / Two heads are better than one: *Power Tools*.
CD: Released Apr '90, on A&M by A&M Records. Catalogue no: **CDA 391**
CD: Released Apr '90, on A&M by A&M Records. Catalogue no: **393 915 2**
Album: Released Apr '90, on A&M by A&M Records. Catalogue no: **AMA 391**
Cass: Released Apr '90, on A&M by A&M Records. Catalogue no: **AMC 391**
Cass: Released Apr '90, on A&M by A&M Records. Catalogue no: **393 915 4**

Billion Dollar Brain

BILLION DOLLAR BRAIN (Film soundtrack) (Various artists)
Note: Ken Russell film starring Michael Caine. Music by Richard Rodney Bennett.
Cass: Released Jan '89, on MCA by MCA Records. Catalogue no: **MCAC 25091**
Album: Released Jan '89, on MCA by MCA Records. Catalogue no: **MCA 25091**

Biograph Girl

BIOGRAPH GIRL (Film soundtrack) (Various artists)
Cass: Released May '89, on T. E. R. by That's Entertainment Records. Catalogue no: **ZCTER 1003**
Album: Released Apr '83, on T. E. R. by That's Entertainment Records. Catalogue no: **TER 1003**

Bird

BIRD (See under Parker, Charlie)

Birdy

BIRDY (See under Gabriel, Peter)

Bird With The ...

BIRD WITH THE CRYSTAL PLUMAGE (Film soundtrack) (Various artists)
Note: Composed by Ennio Morricone.
Album: Released Jan '89, on Cerebus (USA) Catalogue no: **C'BUS 108**

Birth Of A Nation

BIRTH OF A NATION, THE (Original soundtrack) (Various artists)
Tracks: / Bringing the African to America: *Various artists* / Abolitionists, The: *Various artists* / Austin Stoneman: *Various artists* / Elsie Stoneman: *Various artists* / Old Southland: *Various artists* / Boys at play: *Various artists* / Cotton fields: *Various artists* / Love strain: *Various artists* / Stoneman library: *Various artists* / Lydia Brown: *Various artists*.
Note: New digital recording of the Original 1915 score for the D.W. Griffith Silent by Joseph Carl Breil.

2 LP Set: Released Jan '89, on Silva Screen by Silva Screen Records. Catalogue no: **LXDR 701-2**
CD: Released Jan '90, on Silva Screen by Silva Screen Records. Catalogue no: **LSCD 701**

Bitter Sweet

BITTER SWEET (Film soundtrack) (Various artists) (See picture on previous page)
Tracks: / Opening: *Various artists* / That wonderful melody: *Various artists* / Call of life, The: *Various artists* / If you could only come with me: *Various artists* / I'll see you again: *Various artists* / Polka: *Various artists* / What is love?: *Various artists* / Last dance: *Various artists* / Finale: *Various artists* / Opening chorus (Life in the morning): *Various artists* / Ladies of the town: *Various artists* / If love were all: *Various artists* / Dear little cafe: *Various artists* / Bitter sweet waltz: *Various artists* / Officer's chorus (we wish to order wine): *Various artists* / Tokay: *Various artists* / Bonne nuit, merci: *Various artists* / Kiss me: *Various artists* / Ta-ra-ra-boom-de-ay: *Various artists* / Alas,

the time is past: *Various artists* / We all wear a green carnation: *Various artists* / Zigeuner: *Various artists* / Finale: *Various artists*.
Album: Released Mar '89, on T. E. R. by That's Entertainment Records. Catalogue no: **TER2 1160**
Cass: Released Mar '89, on T. E. R. by That's Entertainment Records. Catalogue no: **ZCTED 1160**
CD: Released Mar '89, on T. E. R. by That's Entertainment Records. Catalogue no: **CDTER2 1160**

Black Belly Of The ...

BLACK BELLY OF THE TARANTULA (Original soundtrack) (Various artists)
Note: Composed by Ennio Morricone.
Album: Released Jan '89, on Cerebus (USA) Catalogue no: **C'BUS 116**

Black Cauldron

BLACK CAULDRON (Film soundtrack) (Various artists)
Note: Music by Elmer Bernstein. Dialogue from the film features John Hurt, Freddie Jones, Nigel Hawthorne, Arthur Malet.
CD: Released Jan '89, on Silva Screen by Silva Screen Records. Catalogue no: **VCD 47241**
Cass: Released Oct '85, on BBC by BBC Records. Deleted '88. Catalogue no: **ZCR 578**
Album: Released Oct '85, on BBC by BBC Records. Deleted '88. Catalogue no: **REH 578**
Album: Released Jan '86, on Colosseum (West Germany) Catalogue no: **CST 8009**
Album: Released Jan '89, on Silva Screen by Silva Screen Records. Catalogue no: **STV 81253**
Cass: Released Jan '89, on Silva Screen by Silva Screen Records. Catalogue no: **CTV 81253**

Black, Cilla

ALFIE
Tracks: / Alfie.
Note: Theme from the film.
7" Single: Released Mar '66, on Parlophone by EMI Records. Deleted '69. Catalogue no: **R 5427**
SURPRISE SURPRISE
Tracks: / Surprise surprise / Put

Paul Newman stars in Touchstone Pictures 1989 production
Blaze

your heart where your love is.
Note: Theme from the TV series.
7" Single: Released Dec '85, on Towerbell. Catalogue no: **TOW 81**

Black Dyke Mills Band
THEMES FROM FILMS, TV & STAGE
Tracks: / Last of the summer wine / Galloping home / Hustle, The / Country canter / Pink panther, Theme from / Washington behind closed doors / Star wars (Luke Skywalker) / Ben Kenobi / Princess Leia's theme / Rebel spaceship / Down the throne room / Alla marcia, from Karelia suite, Op. 11 / Adagio, from "Sparticus and Phrygia" / Don't cry for me Argentina / Eagle has landed, The / Clayhanger / Good word / King and I / Getting to know you / I have dreamed / I whistle a happy tune / March of the Siamese children / Finale.
Album: Released Jul '79, on RCA by BMG Records (UK). Catalogue no: **PL 25220**

Black Hole
BLACK HOLE (Film soundtrack) (Various artists)
Cass: Released Jan '80, on Pickwick by Pickwick Records. Deleted '85. Catalogue no: **HSC 3017**
Album: Released Jan '80, on Pickwick by Pickwick Records. Deleted Jan '85. Catalogue no: **SHM 3017**

Cass: Released Dec '82, on Disneyland by Disneyland-Vista Records (USA). Catalogue no: **D 25DC**
Album: Released Dec '82, on Disneyland by Disneyland-Vista Records (USA). Catalogue no: **D 381**

Black Orpheus
BLACK ORPHEUS (ORFEU NEGRO) (Original soundtrack) (Various artists)
Cass: Released Sep '83, on Philips (France) by PolyGram UK Ltd. Catalogue no: **8124 734**
Album: Released Sep '83, on Philips (France) by PolyGram UK Ltd. Catalogue no: **8124 731**

Black Rain
BLACK RAIN (Film soundtrack) (Various artists)
Cass: Released Feb '90, on Virgin by Virgin Records. Catalogue no: **TCV 2607**
Album: Released Feb '90, on Virgin by Virgin Records. Catalogue no: **V 2607**
CD: Released Feb '90, on Virgin by Virgin Records. Catalogue no: **CDV 2607**

Black Stallion
BLACK STALLION (Film soundtrack) (Various artists)
Cass: Released '88, on Liberty by EMI Records. Catalogue no: **L4T**

10279
Album: Released '88, on Liberty by EMI Records. Catalogue no: **LT 10279**
Album: Released Jun '80, on United Artists by EMI Records. Deleted '85. Catalogue no: **UAG 30306**

Black, Stanley
ITV THEMES (Black, Stanley & LSO)
Tracks: / Upstairs downstairs / Black Beauty (galloping home) / Hill Street blues / L.A. law / Minder / Professionals, The.
Cass: Released Oct '88, on Hallmark by Pickwick Records. Catalogue no: **HSC 3247**
CD: Released Oct '88, on Pickwick by Pickwick Records. Catalogue no: **PWKS 516**
Album: Released Oct '88, on Hallmark by Pickwick Records. Catalogue no: **SHM 3247**

Blade Runner (Film)
BLADE RUNNER (Film soundtrack) (Various artists)
Cass: Released Nov '82, on Full Moon (USA) Catalogue no: **K4 99262**
CD: Released Jul '88, on WEA by WEA Records. Catalogue no: **250 002 2**
Album: Released Nov '82, on Full Moon (USA) Catalogue no: **K 99262**

Blake, Howard
GRANPA (Film soundtrack)
Note: Sarah Brightman, Peter Ustinov.
Cass: Released '88, on CBS by CBS Records & Distribution. Catalogue no: **HBC 1**
Album: Released '88, on CBS by CBS Records & Distribution. Catalogue no: **HB 1**
CD: Released '88, on CBS by CBS Records & Distribution. Catalogue no: **CDHB 1**

WALKING IN THE AIR
Tracks: / Walking in the air / Dance of the snowmen.
7" Pic: Released Dec '87, on CBS by CBS Records & Distribution. Deleted Jun '88. Catalogue no: **WA 3950**
7" Single: Released Nov '87, on CBS by CBS Records & Distribution. Deleted Jun '88. Catalogue no: **GA 3950**

Various Artists - *Blondel* (MCA)

7" Single: Released Nov '87, on CBS by CBS Records & Distribution. Deleted Jun '88. Catalogue no: **QTA 3950**

BLAME IT ON RIO (Film soundtrack) (Various artists)
Note: Songs from the Michael Caine film.
Album: Released Jan '89, on Silva Screen by Silva Screen Records. Catalogue no: **STV 81210**

BLAZE (Film soundtrack) (Various artists) (See picture on previous page)
Tracks: / Main title: *Various artists* / One night: *Various artists* / Next time you see me: *Various artists* / Drive to the general store: *Various artists* / Sho bar: *Various artists* / When the Saints go marching in: *Various artists* / Fine day for a walk: *Various artists* / To the couch and beyond: *Various artists* / Precious Lord: *Various artists* / Louisiana 1927: *Various artists*.
CD: Released Feb '90, on A&M by A&M Records. Catalogue no: **CDA 3932**
Cass: Released Feb '90, on A&M by A&M Records. Catalogue no:

AMC 3932
Album: Released Feb '90, on A&M by A&M Records. Catalogue no: **AMA 3932**

BLESS THE BEASTS AND CHILDREN (Film Soundtrack) (Various artists)
Tracks: / Bless the beasts and children: *Various artists* / Botton's dream: *Various artists* / Down the line: *Various artists* / Bless the beasts and children: *Various artists* / Lost: *Various artists* / Bless the beasts and children: *Various artists* / Down the line: *Various artists* / Journey's end: *Various artists* / Stampede: *Various artists* / Free: *Various artists* / Requiem: *Various artists*.
Album: Released '73, on A&M by A&M Records. Deleted '78. Catalogue no: **AMLS 64322**

BLIND DATE (1987 Film soundtrack) (Various artists)
Album: Released Aug '87, on Silva Screen by Silva Screen Records. Catalogue no: **FILM 016**
CD: Released Aug '87, on Silva Screen by Silva Screen Records.

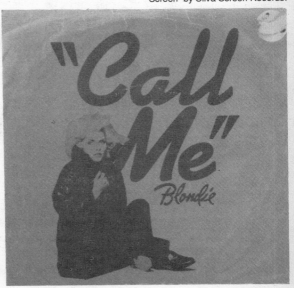

Blondie - "Call Me" (from the film *American Gigolo*)

Catalogue no: **FILMCD 016**
Cass: Released Aug '87, on Silva Screen by Silva Screen Records. Catalogue no: **FILMC 016**

Blitz (Show)

BLITZ (Original London cast) (Various artists)
Tracks: / Our hotel: *Various artists* / Tell him, Tell her: *Various artists* / I want to whisper something: *Various artists* / We're going to the country: *Various artists* / Day after tomorrow, The: *Various artists* / Another morning: *Various artists* / Who's this geezer Hitler?: *Various artists* / Be what you wanna be: *Various artists* / Opposities: *Various artists* / Entr'acte: *Various artists* / Far away: *Various artists* / Down the Lane: *Various artists* / Petticoat Lane(On a Saturday ain't so nice): *Various artists* / So tell me: *Various artists* / Mums and Dads: *Various artists* / Who wants to settle down?: *Various artists* / Is this gonna be a wedding?: *Various artists* / Duty calls: *Various artists* / Blitz(finale): *Various artists*.
Cass: Released Apr '83, on T. E. R. by That's Entertainment Records. Catalogue no: **ZCTER 1056**
Album: Released Jan '89, on Silva Screen by Silva Screen Records. Catalogue no: **AEI 1117**
Album: Released Apr '83, on T. E. R. by That's Entertainment Records. Catalogue no: **TER 1056**

Blondel

BLONDEL (Original Cast) (Rice, Tim) (See panel on previous page)
Tracks: / Monk's introduction / Blondel and Fiona / Ministry of Reudal affairs, The / Last of my troubles, The / Lionheart / No rhyme for Richard / Trio / Assassins song / Running back for more / Blondel in Europe / Saladin days / I can't wait to be King / Inn at Salzburg, The / Blondel's search / Duke of Austria's quarters, The / Cell, The / Westminster Abbey / I'm a monarchist.
Note: Lyrics by Tim Rice. Music by Stephen Oliver.
Cass: Released Nov '83, on MCA by MCA Records. Catalogue no: **DBLC 1**
Album: Released Nov '83, on MCA by MCA Records. Catalogue no: **DBL 1**

Blondie

CALL ME (See picture on previous page)
Tracks: / Call me / Call me (instrumental) / Call me (Spanish version).
Note: Featured in the film 'American Gigolo'.
7" Single: Released Apr '80, on Chrysalis by Chrysalis Records. Deleted '85. Catalogue no: **CHS 2414**
12" Single: Released Apr '80, on Chrysalis by Chrysalis Records. Deleted '85. Catalogue no: **CHS 12 2514**

CALL ME (2)
Tracks: / Call me.
CD Single: Released Jan '89, on Chrysalis by Chrysalis Records. Catalogue no: **CHSCD 3342**
12" Single: Released Jan '89, on Chrysalis by Chrysalis Records. Deleted Jun '90. Catalogue no: **CHS 123 342**
7" Single: Released Jan '89, on Chrysalis by Chrysalis Records. Deleted Jun '90. Catalogue no: **CHS 3342**

CALL ME (OLD GOLD)
Tracks: / Call Me / Union city blue.
7" Single: Released Feb '87, on Old Gold by Old Gold Records. Catalogue no: **OG 9676**

UNION CITY BLUE
Tracks: / Union city blue / Living in the real world.
Note: From the film 'Union City'.
7" Single: Released '82, on Chrysalis by Chrysalis Records. Deleted '87. Catalogue no: **CHS 2400**

Blood & Sand

BLOOD AND SAND (1941 Film soundtrack) (Various artists)
Cass: on Polydor by Polydor Ltd. Catalogue no: **417 850 4**
CD: on Polydor by Polydor Ltd. Catalogue no: **417 850 2**

Blood Brothers

BLOOD BROTHERS (1988 London Cast Recording) (Various artists)
Album: Released Mar '89, on First Night by First Night Records. Catalogue no: **CAST 17**
CD: Released Mar '89, on First Night by First Night Records. Catalogue no: **CASTCD 17**
Cass: Released Mar '89, on First Night by First Night Records. Catalogue no: **CASTC 17**

Blood On The Sun

BLOOD ON THE SUN (Film soundtrack) (Various artists)
Album: Released Mar '79, on Citadel (USA) by Varese Sarabande Records (USA). Catalogue no: **CT 6031**

Bloodline

BLOODLINE (Original soundtrack) (Various artists)
Note: Composed by Ennio Morricone.
Album: Released Jan '89, on Silva Screen by Silva Screen Records. Catalogue no: **STV 81131**

Bloomer Girl

BLOOMER GIRL (Original Broadway cast) (Various artists)
Note: Harold Arlen/Celeste Holm.
Cass: Released Jan '89, on MCA by MCA Records. Catalogue no: **MCAC 1536**
Album: Released Jan '89, on MCA by MCA Records. Catalogue no: **MCA 1536**

Bloomfield

BLOOMFIELD (Film Soundtrack) (Various artists)
Tracks: / Opening theme (Nimrod's theme): *Various artists* / Loner: *Various artists* / Nimrod's exit from Eirad: *Various artists* / Love theme: *Various artists* / Title theme: *Various artists* / Swinging Greek: *Various artists* / Eitan's salty drive: *Various artists* / Homing in on the next trade wind: *Various artists* / Eitan's pays the penalty: *Various artists* / Eight in the arena: *Various artists* / Hail the conquering hero: *Various artists* / Closing love theme: *Various artists* / Eitan does his net: *Various artists* / Hello my life: *Various artists* / On top of the world: *Various artists* / Distraction: *Various artists*.
Album: Released '73, on Pye Deleted '78. Catalogue no: **NSPL 18376**

Blue Beard (Film)

BLUE BEARD (1972 Film soundtrack) (Various artists)
Album: Released Jan '89, on Cerebus (USA) Catalogue no: **C'BUS 105**

Music from the film *Blue Velvet* (TER)

Blue City

BLUE CITY (See under Cooder, Ry)

Blue Hawaii

BLUE HAWAII (See under Presley, Elvis)

Blue Lagoon

BLUE LAGOON, THE (Original soundtrack) (Various artists)
Tracks: / Blue lagoon (love theme): *Various artists* / Fire: *Various artists* / Island, The: *Various artists* / Sands of time, The: *Various artists* / Paddy's death: *Various artists* / Children grow, The: *Various artists* / Lord of the lagoon: *Various artists* / Underwater courtship: *Various artists* / Kiss, The: *Various artists*.
CD: Released Jun '88, on Silva Screen by Silva Screen Records. Catalogue no: **SCCD 1018**
Album: Released Jan '81, on TK Catalogue no: **TKR 70195**

Blue Max

BLUE MAX (Film soundtrack) (Various artists)
Tracks: / Dream machine: *Various artists* / Sing song blues: *Various*

artists / Bad bad amigo: *Various artists* / Hangman: *Various artists* / Need your love: *Various artists* / Flying to Moscow: *Various artists* / Paid assassin: *Various artists* / Camera, camera: *Various artists* / Photographing gold: *Various artists* / Murder at the movies: *Various artists* / I know you're there: *Various artists* / Wait for the new one: *Various artists*.
Album: Released Jan '79, on Charisma by Virgin Records. Deleted '88. Catalogue no: **CAS 1142**
Album: Released Mar '79, on Citadel (USA) by Varese Sarabande Records (USA). Catalogue no: **CT 6008**
CD: Released Jan '89, on Silva Screen by Silva Screen Records. Catalogue no: **VCD 47238**
Album: Released Nov '80, on Citadel (USA) by Varese Sarabande Records (USA). Deleted Nov '85. Catalogue no: **CT 7007**

Blue Peter

BLUE PETER (See under Oldfield, Mike)

Blue Skies

BLUE SKIES (1946 film soundtrack) (Various artists)
Note: Starring Bing Crosby and Fred Astaire.
Album: Released Jan '89, on Silva Screen by Silva Screen Records. Catalogue no: **SH 2095**

Blue Thunder

BLUE THUNDER (1983 film soundtrack) (Various artists)
Note: Composed by Ennio Morricone.
Cass: Released Jan '89, on MCA by MCA Records. Deleted Feb '90. Catalogue no: **MCAC 6122**
Album: Released Nov '83, on MCA by MCA Records. Deleted Nov '88. Catalogue no: **MCF 3183**
Album: Released Jan '89, on MCA by MCA Records. Catalogue no: **MCA 6122**

Blue Velvet

BLUE VELVET (Film soundtrack) (Various artists) (See picture on left)
Tracks: / Night streets/Sandy and Jeffrey: *Various artists* / Frank Jeffrey's dark side: *Various artists* / Mysteries of love(2 versions): *Various artists* / Frank returns: *Various artists* / Blue velvet: *Vinton, Bobby* / Lumberton USA/Going down to Lincoln: *Various artists* / Akron meets the blues: *Various artists* / In dreams: *Orbison, Roy* / Honky tonk: *Doggett, Bill* / Love letters: *Lester, Ketty* / Mysteries of love: *Various artists* / Blue star: *Various artists*.
Cass: Released May '87, on T. E. R. by That's Entertainment Records. Catalogue no: **ZCTER 1127**
CD: Released May '87, on T. E. R. by That's Entertainment Records. Catalogue no: **CDTER 1127**
Album: Released May '87, on T. E. R. by That's Entertainment Records. Catalogue no: **TER 1127**

Blues Brothers (Film)

BLUES BROTHERS (Various artists)
Tracks: / Shake a tall feather: *Charles, Ray* / Think: *Franklin, Aretha* / Minnie the moocher: *Calloway, Cab* / Rawhide: *Blues Brothers* / Jailhouse rock: *Blues Brothers* / She caught the Katy: *Blues Brothers* / Gimme some lovin': *Blues Brothers* / Old land-

mark: Blues Brothers / Sweet home Chicago: Blues Brothers / Peter Gunn: Blues Brothers
CD: Released Feb '87, on Atlantic by WEA Records. Catalogue no: **K250 715**
Album: Released Oct '80, on Atlantic by WEA Records. Catalogue no: **K 50715**
Cass: Released Oct '80, on Atlantic by WEA Records. Catalogue no: **K4 50715**

BLUES BROTHERS (VIDEO)
VHS: Released Feb '90, on CIC Video Catalogue no: **VHR 1382**

EVERYBODY NEEDS SOMEBODY TO LOVE (RE-ISSUE) (Blues Brothers)
Tracks: / Everybody needs somebody to love / Think / Shotgun blues (Available on 12" format only).
Note: From the film "*The blues brothers*"
CD Single: Released Mar '90, on Atlantic by WEA Records. Catalogue no: **A 7951CD**
7" Single: Released Oct '80, on Atlantic by WEA Records. Deleted Oct '83. Catalogue no: **K 11625**
Cassingle: Released Mar '90, on Atlantic by WEA Records. Catalogue no: **A 7951C**
12" Single: Released Mar '90, on Atlantic by WEA Records. Catalogue no: **A 7951T**
7" Single: Released Mar '90, on Atlantic by WEA Records. Catalogue no: **A 7951**

GIMME SOME LOVIN' (Blues Brothers)
Tracks: / Gimme some lovin' / She caught the Katie.
Note: Taken from the film "*The blues brothers*".
7" Single: Released Jul '80, on Atlantic by WEA Records. Deleted '82. Catalogue no: **K 11499**

Blues In The Night

BLUES IN THE NIGHT (Original London Cast) (Various artists)
Cass: Released Sep '87, on First Night by First Night Records. Catalogue no: **SCENE C 9**
Album: Released Sep '87, on First Night by First Night Records. Catalogue no: **SCENE 9**
CD: Released Sep '87, on First Night by First Night Records. Catalogue no: **SCENE CD9**

Blues On 2

BLUES ON 2 (Various artists)
Album: Released Jun '88, on BBC by BBC Records. Catalogue no: **REN 610**
Cass: Released Jun '88, on BBC by BBC Records. Catalogue no: **ZCN 610**

Boat

BOAT, THE (Original Soundtrack) (Various artists)
Album: Released Apr '82, on WEA by WEA Records. Catalogue no: **K 58366**

Bob & Carol, Ted &...

BOB & CAROL, TED & ALICE (1969 film soundtrack) (Various artists)
Album: on Bulldog (USA) by Bulldog Records (USA). Catalogue no: **BD 1013**

Body

BODY, THE (See under Waters, Roger)

Bo-Lero

BO-LERO (1984 Film soundtrack) (Various artists)
Note: Bo Derek film. Composed by Peter Bernstein.
Album: Released Jan '89, on Silva Screen by Silva Screen Records. Catalogue no: **STV 81228**
Cass: Released Jan '89, on Silva Screen by Silva Screen Records. Catalogue no: **C 266**

BO-LERO (Various artists)
Cass: Released Nov '84, on Avon by Avon Records. Catalogue no:

ADK 506
Album: Released Nov '84, on Avon by Avon Records. Catalogue no: **ADL 506**

Bolling, Claude

AWAKENING (See under Awakening)

Bon Jovi, Jon

BLAZE OF GLORY (Inspired by the film Young Guns II)
Album: Released Aug '90, on Vertigo by Phonogram Ltd. Catalogue no: **846 473 1**
Cass: Released Aug '90, on Vertigo by Phonogram Ltd. Catalogue no: **846 473 4**
CD: Released Aug '90, on Vertigo by Phonogram Ltd. Catalogue no: **846 473 2**

BLAZE OF GLORY (SINGLE)
Tracks: / Blaze of glory / You really got me now / Blood money (12" & CD single only).
7" Single: Released Aug '90, on Vertigo by Phonogram Ltd. Catalogue no: **JBJ 1**
12" Single: Released Aug '90, on Vertigo by Phonogram Ltd. Catalogue no: **JBJ 112**
CD Single: Released Aug '90, on Vertigo by Phonogram Ltd. Catalogue no: **JBJCD 1**
Cassingle: Released Aug '90, on Vertigo by Phonogram Ltd. Catalogue no: **JBJMC 1**

Boogie

RUM AND COCA-COLA (Original London cast) (Various artists)

Willem Dafoe and Tom Cruise in *Born on the Fourth of July* based on the novel by Ron Kovic

Tracks: / Rum and coca-cola: *Various artists* / Leader of the pack: *Various artists*.

7" Single: Released May '89, on T.E.R. by That's Entertainment Records. Catalogue no: **STER 001**

Booker, Bob

WHEN YOU'RE IN LOVE THE WHOLE WORLD IS JEWISH (Original Soundtrack) (Booker, Bob & George Foster)
Tracks: / Would you believe it / Hobby, The / My husband, the monster / Ballad of Irving / Shoe repair shop / Divorce, kosher style / Voyage to the bottom of the sea / Things might have been different / Call from Greenwich village, A / Great bank robbery, The / Discussion in the airplane / Miami beach / Schtick / Kidnapping, The / Bar mitzvah / When you're in love the whole world is Jewish.
Album: Released Jul '87, on MCA by MCA Records. Deleted Jul '90. Catalogue no: **MCL 1670**
Cass: Released Jul '87, on MCA by MCA Records. Deleted Sep '90. Catalogue no: **MCLC 1670**

Border

BORDER, THE (Film soundtrack) (Various artists)
Album: Released May '82, on MCA by MCA Records. Catalogue no: **MCF 3133**

Born Free

BORN FREE (Film soundtrack) (Various artists)
Tracks: / Born free: *Various artists* / Hunt: *Various artists* / Elsa at play: *Various artists* / Death of Pati: *Various artists* / Waiting for joy: *Various artists* / Killing at Kiunga: *Various artists* / Born free: *Various artists* / Holiday with Elsa: *Various artists* / Flirtation: *Various artists* / Warthog: *Various artists* / Fight of the lioness: *Various artists* / Reunion: *Various artists* / Born free: *Various artists*.
Album: Released '73, on Polydor by Polydor Ltd. Deleted '78. Catalogue no: **2315 031**

Born On The 4th Of July

BORN ON THE FOURTH OF JULY (Film soundtrack) (Various artists) (See picture on previous page)
Tracks: / Hard rain's gonna fall:

Brickell, Edie / Brown eyed girl: *Morrison, Van* / My girl: *Temptations* / Venus: *Avalon, Frankie* / Prologue: *Various artists* / Shooting of Wilson, The: *Various artists* / Homecoming: *Various artists* / Born on the Bayou: *Broken Homes* / American pie: *McLean, Don* / Soldier boy: *Shirelles* / Moon river: *Mancini, Henry* / Early days, Massapequa, 1957, The: *Various artists* / Cua Viet River, Vietnam 1968: *Various artists* / Born on the fourth of July: *Various artists*.
Cass: Released Feb '90, on MCA by MCA Records. Catalogue no: **MCAC 6340**
CD: Released Feb '90, on MCA by MCA Records. Catalogue no: **DMCG 6079**
CD: Released Feb '90, on MCA by MCA Records. Catalogue no: **MCAD 6340**
Album: Released Feb '90, on MCA by MCA Records. Catalogue no: **MCG 6079**
Cass: Released Feb '90, on MCA by MCA Records. Catalogue no: **MCGC 6079**
Album: Released Feb '90, on MCA by MCA Records. Catalogue no: **MCA 6340**

Born To Dance

BORN TO DANCE (Film soundtrack) (Various artists)
Note: Starring Eleanor Powell and Frances Langford.
Album: Released Jan '89, on Silva Screen by Silva Screen Records. Catalogue no: **SH 2088**
Album: Released '88, on CIF Catalogue no: **CIF 3001**

Borsalino

BORSALINO (Film Soundtrack) (Various artists)
Tracks: / Generique: *Various artists* / La reussite: *Various artists* / Arts deco: *Various artists* / Tango Marseillais: *Various artists* / Les roses: *Various artists* / Escalade: *Various artists* / Theme Borsalino: *Various artists* / Les annees folles: *Various artists* / Prends moi matelot: *Various artists* / Lola tango: *Various artists* / Exoticana: *Various artists* / La plangue: *Various artists* / Borsalino blues: *Various artists*.
Album: Released '73, on Paramount Deleted '78. Catalogue no: **SPFL 263**

Boston Pops Orchestra

POPS IN SPACE
Tracks: / Superman march / Superman love theme / Empire strikes back (excerpts) / Star Wars (Excerpts from.) / Close Encounters of the Third Kind suite.
Album: Released Dec '80, on Philips by Phonogram Ltd. Deleted '86. Catalogue no: **9500921**
CD: Released Jan '86, on Philips by Phonogram Ltd. Catalogue no: **412 884-2**

SATURDAY NIGHT FIEDLER
Tracks: / Saturday night fever medley / Stayin' alive / Night fever / Manhattan skyline / Night on disco mountain / Disco inferno / Bachmania.
Album: Released '85, on Polygram by PolyGram UK Ltd. Catalogue no: **2310688**

Bostonians

BOSTONIANS (1984 Film soundtrack) (Various artists)
Tracks: / River charles, The: *Various artists* / Bostonians, The: *Various artists* / Bostonians:opening titles(variations on America): *Various artists* / At Miss Birdseye's meeting: *Various artists* / Verena's education: *Various artists* / Annabel Lee: *Various artists* / Faith healing: *Various artists* / Getting ready for Basil: *Various artists* / In Henry Burrage's rooms: *Various artists* / Verena's debut: *Various artists* / Wednesday Club, The: *Various artists* / In Central park: *Various artists* / July 4th celebrations: *Various artists* / Summer days at Marmion: *Various artists* / By the sea: *Various artists* / Bostonians: End titles: *Various artists*.
Album: Released Jan '85, on Audiotrax Deleted '87. Catalogue no: **ATX LP 02**
Cass: Released Jan '85, on Audiotrax Deleted '87. Catalogue no: **ZCA TX 02**

Bottle Boys

BOTTLE BOYS
Tracks: / Bottle boys.
Note: Theme from the TV series.
7" Single: Released Sep '84, on Sierra by Sierra Records. Deleted Jun '87. Catalogue no: **FED 2**

Bounty Killer

BOUNTY KILLER, THE (Film Soundtrack) (Various artists)
Note: Score by Stelvio Cipriani.
Album: Released Jan '89, on Silva Screen by Silva Screen Records. Catalogue no: **PHCAM 011**

Bourne Identity

BOURNE IDENTITY, THE (Original Television soundtrack) (Various artists)
Tracks: / Bourne identity, The (Main title): *Various artists* / French children, The: *Various artists* / Fishing village: *Various artists* / Arrival in Zurich: *Various artists* / Incident at the bank: *Various artists* / Jason and Marie: *Various artists* / Red door, The: *Various artists* / Discovery: *Various artists* / Chernak dead: *Various artists* / Valois bank: *Various artists* / Wild goose chase: *Various artists* / Carlos as confessor: *Various artists* / Trocadero, The: *Various artists* .
CD: Released Jan '90, on Silva Screen by Silva Screen Records. Catalogue no: **RVF 6005D**

Bowie, David

ABSOLUTE BEGINNERS
Tracks: / Absolute beginners (7" only) / Absolute beginners (dub mix) (On all versions) / Absolute beginners (full length version) (CD & 12" only).
Note: Theme from the film.
12" Single: Released Mar '86, on Virgin by Virgin Records. Deleted Mar '90. Catalogue no: **VS 838-12**
12" Single: Released Mar '86, on Virgin by Virgin Records. Deleted '89. Catalogue no: **VSG 838-12**
CD 3": Released '88, on Virgin by Virgin Records. Catalogue no: **CDT 20**
7" Single: Released Mar '86, on Virgin by Virgin Records. Deleted May '90. Catalogue no: **VS 838**
7" Pic: Released Mar '86, on Virgin by Virgin Records. Deleted '86. Catalogue no: **VSS 838**

BAAL'S HYMN
Tracks: / Baal's hymn / Drowned girl, The / Remembering Marie / Dirty song, The / Ballad of the adventurers.
Note: From the BBC TV play 'Baal'.
12" Single: Released Jul '83, on RCA (Germany) by BMG Music International. Deleted '85. Catalogue no: **PG 45092**
7" EP: Released Mar '82, on RCA by BMG Records (UK). Deleted '85. Catalogue no: **BOW 11**

CAT PEOPLE
Tracks: / Cat people / Paul's theme (jogging chase).
Note: Featured in the film.
12" Single: Released Dec '83, on MCA by MCA Records. Catalogue no: **MCAT 770**
7" Single: Released Apr '82, on MCA by MCA Records. Deleted '85. Catalogue no: **MCA 770**

CHRISTIANE F.WIR KINDER VOM BAHNOF ZOO
Tracks: / V-2 Schneider / TVC-15 / Heroes / Helden / Boys keep swinging / Sense of double / Station to station / Look back in anger / Stay / Warszawa.
Note: Film soundtrack by David Bowie featuring music from the albums 'Station To Station', 'Low', 'Heroes' and 'Lodger'.
Cass: Released May '81, on RCA by BMG Records (UK). Catalogue no: **RCAK 3074**
Album: Released May '81, on RCA by BMG Records (UK). Catalogue no: **RCALP 3074**

FAME 90
Tracks: / Fame 90 (Gass mix) / Fame 90 (Queen Latifah's rap version) (Not on 12" or picture disc.) / Fame 90 (Bonus beats mix) (7" Picture disc only.) / Fame 90 (House mix) (12" & CD single only.) / Fame 90 (Hip hop mix) (12" only.).
Note: Featured in the film 'Pretty Woman'.
7" Pic: Released Mar '90, on EMI-America by EMI Records. Catalogue no: **FAMEPD 90**
7" Single: Released Mar '90, on EMI-America by EMI Records. Catalogue no: **203 805 7**
7" Pic: Released Mar '90, on EMI-America by EMI Records. Catalogue no: **203 805 0**
7" Single: Released Mar '90, on EMI-America by EMI Records. Catalogue no: **203 805 8**
Cassingle: Released Mar '90, on EMI-America by EMI Records. Catalogue no: **203 805 4**
Cassingle: Released Mar '90, on EMI-America by EMI Records. Catalogue no: **TCFAME 90**
7" Single: Released Mar '90, on EMI-America by EMI Records.

Catalogue no: **FAME 90**
12" Single: Released Mar '90, on EMI-America by EMI Records. Catalogue no: **203 805 6**
12" Single: Released Mar '90, on EMI-America by EMI Records. Catalogue no: **12FAME 90**
CD Single: Released Mar '90, on EMI-America by EMI Records. Catalogue no: **203 805 2**
CD Single: Released Mar '90, on EMI-America by EMI Records. Catalogue no: **CDFAME 90**
12" Single: Released Mar '90, on EMI-America by EMI Records. Catalogue no: **12FAMES 90**
7" Single: Released Mar '90, on EMI-America by EMI Records. Catalogue no: **FAMES 90**
12" Single: Released Mar '90, on EMI-America by EMI Records. Catalogue no: **203 809 8**

LOVE YOU TILL TUESDAY
Tracks: / Love you till Tuesday / London boys / Ching-a-ling / Laughing gnome, The / Liza Jane / When I'm five / Space oddity / Sell me a coat / Rubber band / Let me sleep beside you / When I live my dream.
Note: This is the album soundtrack from the film 'Love You Till Tuesday' (available on Polygram video). Contains several rare or unreleased recordings including 'Ching-A-Ling' and 'Sell Me A Coat' (both performed by Bowie and his friends Hermione Farthingale and John Hutchinson under the collective name of Feathers); the original, embryonic recording of Bowie's classic 'Space Oddity'; alternative versions of 'Let Me Sleep Beside You' and 'When I Live My Dream'; and the superb 'When I'm Five', originally recorded for a BBC radio session. Three non-film songs make up the album: 'Liza Jane', 'London Boys' and 'Laughing Gnome'.
Album: Released May '84, on Deram by Decca International. Catalogue no: **BOWIE 1**
Cass: Released May '84, on Deram by Decca International. Catalogue no: **BOWMC 1**

LOVE YOU TILL TUESDAY (VIDEO)
Tracks: / Love you till Tuesday / Sell me a coat / Let me sleep beside you / When I'm five / Ching-a-ling / Rubber band / When I live my dream / Space oddity.

London Revival Cast recording of *The Boyfriend* (TER)

Note: Running time: 28 mins.
VHS: Released Oct '89, on Spectrum (1) Catalogue no: **SPC 00022**
VHS: Released '88, on Channel 5 by Channel 5 Video. Catalogue no: **CFV 00132**

THIS IS NOT AMERICA (Bowie, David/Pat Metheny Group)
Tracks: / This is not America.
Note: Featured in Falcon & The Snowmen.
7" Single: Released Jan '85, on EMI-America by EMI Records. Deleted Jan '90. Catalogue no: **EA 190**
12" Single: Released Jan '85, on EMI-America by EMI Records. Deleted Aug '89. Catalogue no: **12EA 190**

UNDERGROUND
Tracks: / Underground / Underground (instrumental).
Note: From the film Labyrinth.
7" Single: Released Jun '86, on EMI-America by EMI Records. Deleted Oct '87. Catalogue no: **EA 216**
12" Single: Released Jun '86, on EMI-America by EMI Records. Deleted Oct '87. Catalogue no: **12 EA 216**

WHEN THE WIND BLOWS
Tracks: / When the wind blows (7" only) / When the wind blows (instrumental) / When the wind blows (extended mix) (12" only).
Note: Theme from the film.
12" Single: Released Oct '86, on Virgin by Virgin Records. Catalogue no: **VS 906-12**
7" Single: Released Oct '86, on Virgin by Virgin Records. Catalogue no: **VS 906**

WHITE LIGHT, WHITE HEAT
Tracks: / White light, white heat / Cracked actor.
Note: From Ziggy Stardust - the motion picture.
7" Single: Released Nov '83, on RCA by BMG Records (UK). Deleted '86. Catalogue no: **RCA 372**

ZIGGY STARDUST THE MOTION PICTURE (Original soundtrack)
Tracks: / Watch that man / Moonage daydream / Suffragette city / Changes / Time / All the young dudes / Space oddity / White light, white heat / My death / Wild eyed boy from Freecloud, The / Oh you pretty things / Hang onto yourself / Ziggy Stardust / Cracked actor /

Width of a circle, The / Let's spend the night together / Rock 'n' roll suicide.
CD Set: Released Nov '83, on RCA by BMG Records (UK). Catalogue no: **PD 84862**
2 LP Set: Released Nov '83, on RCA by BMG Records (UK). Deleted Nov '89. Catalogue no: **PL 84862**
Cass set: Released Nov '83, on RCA by BMG Records (UK). Catalogue no: **PK 84862**

ZIGGY STARDUST & THE SPIDERS FROM MARS (VIDEO)
Note: Cert: PG.
VHS: Released Oct '84, on Thorn-Emi (Video) by EMI Records. Catalogue no: **TVE 90 21132**

Boy Who Could Fly

BOY WHO COULD FLY, THE (Film soundtrack) (Various artists)
Note: Composed by Bruce Broughton.
Album: Released Jan '89, on Silva Screen by Silva Screen Records. Deleted Feb '90. Catalogue no: **STV 81299**
CD: Released Jan '89, on Silva Screen by Silva Screen Records. Deleted Feb '90. Catalogue no: **VCD 47279**
Cass: Released Jan '89, on Silva Screen by Silva Screen Records. Catalogue no: **CTV 81299**

Boy Who Grew Too Fast

BOY WHO GREW TOO FAST, THE (Opera soundtrack) (Various artists)
Album: Released Mar '89, on T.E.R. by That's Entertainment Records. Catalogue no: **TER 1125**
Cass: Released Mar '89, on T.E.R. by That's Entertainment Records. Catalogue no: **ZCTER 1125**
CD: Released Mar '89, on T.E.R. by That's Entertainment Records. Catalogue no: **CDTER 1125**

Boyfriend

BOYFRIEND, THE (1954 Musical show) (Various artists)
Tracks: / Boyfriend, The (overture): *Various artists* / Perfect young ladies: *Various artists* / Boyfriend, The: *Various artists* / Won't you

charleston with me: *Various artists* / Fancy forgetting: *Various artists* / I could be happy with you: *Various artists* / Sur la plage: *Various artists* / Room in Bloomsbury, A: *Various artists* / You-don't-want-to-play-with-me blues, The: *Various artists* / Safety in numbers: *Various artists* / Riviera, The: *Various artists* / It's never too late to fall in love: *Various artists* / Carnival tango: *Various artists* / Poor little Pierrette: *Various artists* / Boyfriend, The finale: *Various artists.*

Cass: Released Oct '89, on RCA by BMG Records (UK). Catalogue no: **GK 60056**

CD: Released Oct '89, on RCA by BMG Records (UK). Catalogue no: **GD 60056**

BOYFRIEND, THE (1984 London revival cast) (Various artists) (See picture on previous page)

Tracks: / Overture: *Various artists* / Perfect young ladies: *Various artists* / Boyfriend: *Various artists* / Won't you Charleston with me?: *Various artists* / Fancy forgetting: *Various artists* / I could be happy with you: *Various artists* / Sur la plage: *Various artists* / Room in Bloomsbury, A: *Various artists* / It's nicer in Nice: *Various artists* / You-don't-want-to-play-with-me blues: *Various artists* / Safety in numbers: *Various artists* / Riviera, The: *Various artists* / It's never too late to fall in love: *Various artists* / Poor little Pierrette: *Various artists* / Finale: *Various artists.*

Album: Released Dec '84, on T.E.R. by That's Entertainment Records. Catalogue no: **TER 1095**
Cass: Released Dec '84, on T.E.R. by That's Entertainment Records. Catalogue no: **ZCTER 1095**
CD: Released Dec '84, on T.E.R. by That's Entertainment Records. Catalogue no: **CDTER 1095**

BOYFRIEND, THE (MCA) (Original Broadway cast) (Various artists)

Note: Starring Sandy Wilson and Judy Carne.
Album: Released Jan '89, on MCA by MCA Records. Catalogue no: **MCA 1537**
Cass: Released Jan '89, on MCA by MCA Records. Catalogue no: **MCAC 1537**

BOYFRIEND, THE (SILVA SCREEN) (1971 Film soundtrack) (Various artists)

Note: Songs from the Ken Russell version of the Sandy Wilson show starring Twiggy.
Cass: Released Jan '89, on Silva Screen by Silva Screen Records. Deleted Mar '90. Catalogue no: **MCAC 39069**
Album: Released Jan '89, on Silva Screen by Silva Screen Records. Catalogue no: **MCA 39069**

BOYFRIEND, THE (T.E.R.) (1967 London revival cast) (Various artists)

Tracks: / Overture: *Various artists* / Perfect young ladies: *Various artists* / Boyfriend: *Various artists* / Won't you Charleston with me?: *Various artists* / Fancy forgetting: *Various artists* / I could be happy with you: *Various artists* / Sur le plage: *Various artists* / Room in Bloomsbury, A: *Various artists* / It's nicer in Nice: *Various artists* / You-don't-want-to-play-with-me blues: *Various artists* / Safety in numbers: *Various artists* / Riviera, The: *Various artists* / It's never too late to fall in love: *Various artists* / Poor little Pierette: *Various artists* / Finale: *Various artists.*
Note: Sandy Wilson's musical conducted by Grant Hossack and starring Cheryl Kennedy, Tony Adams, Nicholas Bennett and Ann Beech.
Cass: Released Sep '84, on T.E.R. by That's Entertainment Records. Deleted May '89. Catalogue no: **ZCTER 1054**
Album: Released Sep '84, on T.E.R. by That's Entertainment Records. Deleted May '89. Catalogue no: **TER 1054**

BOYFRIEND, THE (VIDEO) (Various artists)

Note: Encapsulates the stunning elegance and wide-eyed innocence of the roarings '20's. Running time: 105 minutes. Cert: U.
VHS: Released Jun '89, on MGM/UA (Video) by MGM/UA Video. Catalogue no: **SMV 10306**

BOYFRIEND, THE/GOODBYE MR. CHIPS (Various artists)

Tracks: / Boyfriend, The (overture): *Various artists* (The Boyfriend. Hortense with boys & girls.) / Perfect young ladies: *Various artists* (The Boyfriend. Hortense & the girls: Maisie/Fay/Nancy/Dulcie.) / I could be happy with you: *Various artists* (The Boyfriend. Polly & Tony.) / Fancy forgetting:

Various artists (The Boyfriend. Percy & Mme. Dubonnet.) / Sur la plage: *Various artists* (The Boyfriend. Hortense & The Company.) / You are my lucky star: *Various artists* (The Boyfriend. Polly.) / It's never too late to fall in love: *Various artists* (The Boyfriend. Max & Fay.) / Won't you charleston with me?: *Various artists* (The Boyfriend. Tony/Maisie/The Boys & Girls.) / You-don't-want-to-play-with-me-blues, The: *Various artists* (The Boyfriend. Mme Dubonnet/Percy & The Girls.) / Room in Bloomsbury, A: *Various artists* (The Boyfriend. Polly & Tony.) / It's nicer in Nice: *Various artists* (The Boyfriend. Hortense & The Company.) / All I do is dream of you: *Various artists* (The Boyfriend. Polly.) / Safety in numbers: *Various artists* (The Boyfriend. Maisie & The Boys: Tommy/Peter/Michael/Alphonse.) / Poor little pierrette: *Various artists* (The Boyfriend. Polly & Mme. Dubonnet.) / Riviera, The - The Boyfriend chorus (finale): *Various artists* (The Boyfriend. The Company.) / Goodbye Mr. Chips overture: *Various artists* (Goodbye Mr. Chips.) / London is London: *Clark, Petula* (Goodbye Mr. Chips.) / And the sky smiled: *Clark, Petula* (Goodbye Mr. Chips.) / When I am older: *Various artists* (Goodbye Mr. Chips.) / Walk through the world: *Clark, Petula* (Goodbye Mr. Chips.) / Schooldays: *Clark, Petula & Boys* (Goodbye Mr. Chips.) / When I was younger: *O'Toole, Peter* (Goodbye Mr. Chips.) / You and I: *Clark, Petula* (Goodbye Mr. Chips.) / Fill the world with love: *O'Toole, Peter & Boys* (Goodbye Mr. Chips.).

Album: Released Apr '90, on MGM (EMI) Catalogue no: **794 291 1**

CD: Released Apr '90, on MGM (EMI) Catalogue no: **CDMGM 20**
Album: Released Apr '90, on MGM (EMI) Catalogue no: **LPMGM 20**
CD: Released Apr '90, on MGM (EMI) Catalogue no: **CDP 794 291 2**
Cass: Released Apr '90, on MGM (EMI) Catalogue no: **794 291 4**
Cass: Released Apr '90, on MGM (EMI) Catalogue no: **TCMGM 20**

IT'S NEVER TOO LATE TO FALL IN LOVE (Boyfriend Cast)

Tracks: / It's never too late to fall in love / Won't you Charleston with me.

7" Single: Released Dec '84, on T. E. R. by That's Entertainment Records. Catalogue no: **STER 9**

Boys From Brazil

BOYS FROM BRAZIL (Film soundtrack) (Various artists)
Album: Released Mar '79, on A&M by A&M Records. Deleted '88. Catalogue no: **AMLH 64731**

Boys From Syracuse

BOYS FROM SYRACUSE (1963 London Cast) (Various artists)
Tracks: / Boys from Syracuse: Overture: *Various artists* / I had twins: *Various artists* / Dear old Syracuse: *Various artists* / What can you do with a man?: *Various artists* / Falling in love with love: *Various artists* / Shortest day of the year, The: *Various artists* / This can't be love: *Various artists* / Ladies of the evening: *Various artists* / He and she: *Various artists* / You have cast your shadow on the sea: *Various artists* / Come with me: *Various artists* / Sing for your supper: *Various artists* / Oh! Diogenes: *Various artists* / Boys from Syracuse: Finale: *Various artists*.
Album: Released Apr '85, on T. E. R. by That's Entertainment Records. Catalogue no: **TER 1078**
Cass: Released Apr '85, on T. E. R. by That's Entertainment Records. Catalogue no: **ZCTER 1078**

BOYS FROM SYRACUSE, THE (Studio cast with Jack Cassidy) (Various artists)
Album: Released Jan '89, on Silva Screen by Silva Screen Records. Catalogue no: **COS 2580**

Brainstorm (Film)

BRAINSTORM (1983 Film Soundtrack) (Various artists)
Tracks: / Brainstorm: Main Theme: *Various artists* / Lilian's heart attack: *Various artists* / Gaining access to the tapes: *Various artists* / Michael's gift to Karen: *Various artists* / First playback: *Various artists* / Race for time: *Various artists* / Final play-

back/End titles: *Various artists*.
Note: Composed by James Horner.
CD: Released Jan '89, on Silva Screen by Silva Screen Records. Deleted Feb '90. Catalogue no: **VCD 47215**
Cass: Released Jan '89, on Silva Screen by Silva Screen Records. Deleted Feb '90. Catalogue no: **CTV 81197**
Album: Released Nov '83, on T. E. R. by That's Entertainment Records. Catalogue no: **TER 1074**

Brave One

BRAVE ONE, THE (1956 film soundtrack) (Various artists)
Note: Composed by Victor Young.
Album: Released Jan '89, on Silva Screen by Silva Screen Records. Catalogue no: **AEI 3107**

Breakdance

BREAKDANCE (1984 Film soundtrack) (Various artists)
Tracks: / Breakin'...There's no stopping us: *Ollie & Jerry* / When I.C.U: *Ollie & Jerry* / Radiotron: *Firefox* / Stylin',profilin': *Firefox* / Din daa daa: *Kranz, George* / Gotta have the money: *Donn, Steve* / Believe in the beat: *Townes, Carol Lynn* / Set it out: *Midway* / I don't wanna come down: *Scott, Mark* / Oye mamacita: *Rags & Ritches*.
Cass: Released Jun '87, on Polydor by Polydor Ltd. Deleted Oct '88. Catalogue no: **POLDC 5147**
Album: Released Jun '87, on Polydor by Polydor Ltd. Deleted Oct '88. Catalogue no: **POLD 5147**
CD: Released Jun '87, on Polydor by Polydor Ltd. Deleted Oct '88. Catalogue no: **821 919-2**

BREAKDANCE 2 - ELECTRIC BOOGALOO (Film soundtrack) (Various artists)
Tracks: / Electric boogaloo: *Ollie & Jerry* / Radiotron: *Firefox* / Din daa daa: *Kranz, George* / When I.C.U.: *Ollie & Jerry* / Gotta have the money: *Donn, Steve* / Believe in the beat: *Townes, Carol Lynn* / Set it out: *Midway* / I don't wanna come down: *Scott, Mark* / Stylin' profilin': *Firefox* / Oye Mamacita: *Rags & Riches*.
Cass: Released Dec '84, on Polydor by Polydor Ltd. Deleted '89. Catalogue no: **POLDC 5168**
Album: Released Dec '84, on

Polydor by Polydor Ltd. Deleted Oct '88. Catalogue no: **POLD 5168**
CD: Released Dec '84, on Polydor by Polydor Ltd. Deleted '89. Catalogue no: **823 696-2**

BREAKDANCE (VIDEO) (Various artists)
Note: The feature film about a young girl dancer and two hot black break-dancers who climbed to fame on a new music and dance style,with plenty of hip-hop music. Running time: 88 mins.
VHS: Released Oct '88, on Guild Home Video by Guild Home Video. Catalogue no: **V 9325**
VHS: Released Sep '84, on Guild Home Video by Guild Home Video. Catalogue no: **888 83218**

Breakfast At Tiffany's

BREAKFAST AT TIFFANY'S (1961 film soundtrack) (Various artists)
Tracks: / Moon river: *Mancini, Henry* / Something for cat: *Mancini, Henry* / Sally's tomato: *Mancini, Henry* / Mr. Yunioshi: *Mancini, Henry* / Big blow-out, The: *Mancini, Henry* / Hub caps and tail lights: *Mancini, Henry* / Breakfast at Tiffany's: *Mancini, Henry* / Latin Go-lightly: *Mancini, Henry* / Holly: *Mancini, Henry* / Loose caboose: *Mancini, Henry* / Big heist, The: *Mancini, Henry* / Moon river cha cha: *Mancini, Henry*.
Album: Released May '88, on RCA by BMG Records (UK). Catalogue no: **NL 89905**
Cass: Released May '88, on RCA by BMG Records (UK). Deleted Jul '89. Catalogue no: **NK 89905**
CD: Released Feb '90, on Silva Screen by Silva Screen Records. Catalogue no: **2362.2**
CD: Released Apr '88, on RCA by BMG Records (UK). Deleted Jul '89. Catalogue no: **ND 89905**

Breakfast Club (Film)

BREAKFAST CLUB (1985 Film soundtrack) (Various artists) (See picture on next page)
Tracks: / Don't you (forget about me): *Simple Minds* / Fire in the twilight: *Wang Chung* / We are not alone: *De Vito, Karla* / Heart too hot to hold: *Johnson, Jesse* / Waiting: *Daly, Elizabeth* / Didn't I tell you?: *Kennedy, Joyce* / I'm the dude: *Forsey, Keith* / Dream montage: *Forsey, Keith* / Reggae, The: *Forsey, Keith* / Love theme: *Forsey,*

ORIGINAL MOTION PICTURE SOUNDTRACK

THE BREAKFAST CLUB

Music from the film *The Breakfast Club* (A&M)

Keith.
Cass: Released Mar '87, on MCA by MCA Records. Catalogue no: **MCFC 3368**
CD: Released Apr '87, on MCA by MCA Records. Catalogue no: **DMCF 3368**
Album: Released May '85, on A&M by A&M Records. Catalogue no: **AMA 5045**
CD: Released '88, on A&M by A&M Records. Catalogue no: **CDA 5045**
Cass: Released May '85, on A&M by A&M Records. Catalogue no: **AMC 5045**
Album: Released Mar '87, on MCA by MCA Records. Catalogue no: **MCF 3368**

Breaking Glass

BREAKING GLASS (1980 film soundtrack) (O'Connor, Hazel)
Tracks: / Writing on the wall / Monsters in disguise / Come into the air / Big brother / Who needs it / Will you? / Eighth day / Top of the wheel / Calls the tune / Blackman / Give me an inch / If only.
CD: Released '88, on A&M by A&M Records. Catalogue no: **CDA 4820**

Album: Released Aug '80, on A&M by A&M Records. Catalogue no: **AMLH 64820**
Cass: Released Aug '80, on A&M by A&M Records. Catalogue no: **CAM 64820**
BREAKING GLASS (VIDEO)
VHS: Released '88, on Virgin Music Video (see Virgin Vision) Catalogue no: **VVA 154**
VHS: Released Sep '86, on Picture Time Video Catalogue no: **P 094 D**

Bretts

BRETTS (See under Clayderman, Richard)

Bride (Film)

BRIDE, THE (1985 film soundtrack) (Various artists)
Note: Score from the film starring Sting. Music by Maurice Jarre and The Royal Philharmonic Orchestra.
Album: Released Jan '89, on Silva Screen by Silva Screen Records. Catalogue no: **STV 81254**
Album: Released Jan '86, on Colosseum (West Germany) Catalogue no: **CST 8007**
Cass: Released Jan '89, on Silva

Screen by Silva Screen Records. Catalogue no: **CTV 81254**

Brideshead Revisited

BRIDESHEAD REVISITED (Original TV Theme) (Various artists)
Tracks: / Brideshead Revisited, Theme from: *Various artists* / Going to Brideshead: *Various artists* / First visit, The: *Various artists* / Venice nocturne: *Various artists* / Sebastian's summer: *Various artists* / Hunt, The: *Various artists* / Sebastian against the world: *Various artists* / Julia in love: *Various artists* / Julia: *Various artists* / Rain in venice: *Various artists* / General strike: *Various artists* / Fading light: *Various artists* / Julia's theme: *Various artists* / Sebastian alone: *Various artists* / Orphans of the storm: *Various artists* / Finale: *Various artists*.
Cass: Released Nov '81, on Chrysalis by Chrysalis Records. Catalogue no: **ZCDL 1367**
Special: Released Jan '82, on Chrysalis by Chrysalis Records. Deleted Jan '87. Catalogue no: **CBOX 1**
Album: Released Nov '81, on Chrysalis by Chrysalis Records. Catalogue no: **CDL 1367**
CD: Released May '87, on Chrysalis by Chrysalis Records. Catalogue no: **CPCD 1367**

Bridge On The River...

BRIDGE ON THE RIVER KWAI (Film soundtrack) (Arnold, Malcolm)
CD: Released Feb '90, on Silva Screen by Silva Screen Records. Catalogue no: **VSD 5213**

Brigadoon

BRIGADOON (Film soundtrack) (Various artists)
Album: Released Jan '89, on MCA by MCA Records. Catalogue no: **MCA 39062**
Cass: Released Jan '89, on MCA by MCA Records. Catalogue no: **MCAC 39062**
Album: Released Jan '89, on Silva Screen by Silva Screen Records. Catalogue no: **COS 2540**
Cass: Released Jan '89, on Silva Screen by Silva Screen Records. Catalogue no: **BT 2540**

BRIGADOON (Original Broadway Cast) (Various artists)

CD: Released Jan '89, on Silva Screen by Silva Screen Records. Catalogue no: **1001.2**

Cass: Released Jan '89, on Silva Screen by Silva Screen Records. Catalogue no: **1001.4**

CD: Released Aug '90, on Silva Screen by Silva Screen Records. Catalogue no: **GD 81001**

Cass: Released Aug '90, on Silva Screen by Silva Screen Records. Catalogue no: **GK 81001**

BRIGADOON (1988 London cast recording) (Various artists)

Album: Released Oct '88, on First Night by First Night Records. Catalogue no: **CAST 16**

Album: Released Oct '88, on First Night by First Night Records. Catalogue no: **CASTC 16**

CD: Released Oct '88, on First Night by First Night Records. Catalogue no: **CASTCD 16**

BRIGADOON (Various artists)

Tracks: / Almost like being in love: *Various artists* / There but for you go I: *Various artists* / Brigadoon: *Various artists* / Prologue: *Various artists* / Down on MacConnachy Square: *Various artists* / Weather on the hill: *Various artists* / Waitin' for my dearie: *Various artists* / I'll go home with Bonnie Jean: *Various artists* / Come to me, bend me: *Various artists*.

Cass: Released Feb '87, on CBS by CBS Records & Distribution. Deleted Aug '88. Catalogue no: **450233 4**

Album: Released Feb '87, on CBS by CBS Records & Distribution. Deleted Jun '88. Catalogue no: **450233 1**

Bright Lights...

BRIGHT LIGHTS, BIG CITY (1988 Film Soundtrack) (Various artists)

Tracks: / Good Love: *Prince* / True faith: *New Order* / Divine emotions: *Narada* / Kiss and tell: *Ferry, Bryan* / Pleasure little treasure: *Depeche Mode* / Century's end: *Fagen, Donald* / Obsessed: *Noise Club* / Love Attack: *Konk* / Ice cream days: *Hall, Jennifer* / Pump up the volume: *M/A/R/R/S*.

CD: Released Jun '88, on Warner Bros. by WEA Records. Catalogue no: **925 688 2**

Cass: Released '88, on Warner Bros. by WEA Records. Cata-

logue no: **925 688 4**

Album: Released '88, on Warner Bros. by WEA Records. Catalogue no: **925 688 1**

Brightman, Sarah

PHANTOM OF THE OPERA (See under Harley, Steve)

Brighton Beach Memoirs

BRIGHTON BEACH MEMOIRS (1987 Film Soundtrack) (Various artists)

Tracks: / Good morning glory: *Various artists* / Drop me off in Harlem: *Various artists* / You and the night: *Various artists* / Nora on Broadway: *Various artists* / My inspiration: *Various artists* / Whistling in the dark: *Various artists* / As grand as you are: *Various artists* / Stickball: *Various artists* / Funeral procession, The: *Various artists* / I hate my name: *Various artists* / Mrs. Murphy: *Various artists* / Blanche's theme: *Various artists* / Cemetery sequence (main title): *Various artists* / Finale: *Various artists*.

Cass: Released Feb '87, on MCA by MCA Records. Deleted Jan '88. Catalogue no: **IMCAC 6193**

Album: Released Feb '87, on MCA by MCA Records. Deleted Jan '88. Catalogue no: **IMCA 6193**

Brimstone & Treacle

BRIMSTONE & TREACLE (1982 Film Soundtrack) (Various artists)

Tracks: / When the roll is called up yonder: *Various artists* / Brimstone and treacle: *Sting* / Narration: *Sting* / How stupid Mr. Bates: *Police* / Only you: *Sting* / I burn for you: *Police* / Spread a little happiness: *Sting* / We got the beat: *Go-Go's* / You know I had the strangest dreams: *Sting* / Up the junction: *Squeeze* / Bless this house: *Brimstone chorale The* / Kind of loving, A: *Police*.

Note: Soundtrack album that features the music of Sting, The Police and even cuts from the Go Go's and Squeeze. Included on the album is the massive hit single *Spread a little happiness* and four other solo Sting tracks, with six brand new Police tracks, a rare collection indeed.

Album: Released Sep '82, on A&M by A&M Records. Catalogue no: **AMLH 64915**

Cass: Released Sep '82, on A&M by A&M Records. Catalogue no: **CAM 64915**

Broadway Blockbusters

BROADWAY BLOCKBUSTERS (Various artists)

Tracks: / There's no business like show business: *Various artists* / There is nothin' like a dame: *Various artists* / Carousel waltz: *Various artists* / 76 trombones: *Various artists* / Everything's coming up roses: *Various artists* / Bali ha'i: *Various artists* / Hello Dolly: *Various artists* / Baubles, bangles and beads: *Various artists* / People: *Various artists* / I love Paris: *Various artists* / Give my regards to Broadway: *Various artists* / Ol' man river: *Various artists* / 'Till there was you: *Various artists* / Wunderbar: *Various artists* / Some enchanted evening: *Various artists* / I talk to the trees: *Various artists* / Stranger in Paradise: *Various artists* / C'est magnifique: *Various artists* / What kind of fool am I?: *Various artists* / If I were a rich man: *Various artists* / I could have danced all night: *Various artists* / Gigi: *Various artists* / I feel pretty: *Various artists* / I've grown accustomed to her face: *Various artists*.

Cass set: Released May '86, on Ditto by Pickwick Records. Catalogue no: **DTO 10239**

Broadway Danny Rose

BROADWAY DANNY ROSE (1984 Film Soundtrack) (Various artists)

Note: Songs from the Woody Allen film.

Cass: Released Jan '89, on Silva Screen by Silva Screen Records. Deleted Feb '90. Catalogue no: **C 236**

Album: Released Jan '89, on Silva Screen by Silva Screen Records. Catalogue no: **A 236**

Broadway Hits

BROADWAY HITS (Various artists)

Cass: Released Feb '80, on Bravo by Pickwick Records. Deleted '88. Catalogue no: **BRC 2506**

Broadway Magic

BROADWAY MAGIC (VOL 1) 1950'S (Various artists)

CD: Released Feb '90, on CBS (import) by CBS Records & Distribution. Catalogue no: **CK 40660**

BROADWAY MAGIC VOL 2 1960'S (Various artists)
CD: Released Feb '90, on CBS (import) by CBS Records & Distribution. Catalogue no: **CK 40698**

BROADWAY MAGIC VOL 3 1970'S (Various artists)
CD: Released Feb '90, on CBS (import) by CBS Records & Distribution. Catalogue no: **CK 40699**

Broadway Melody

BROADWAY MELODY OF 1938 (Film Soundtrack) (Various artists)
Note: Starring Robert Taylor and Judy Garland.
Album: Released Jan '89, on Silva Screen by Silva Screen Records. Catalogue no: **MPT 3**

BROADWAY MELODY OF 1940 (Film soundtrack) (Various artists)
Album: Released Jan '89, on CIF Catalogue no: **CIF 3002**

Bronco Billy

BRONCO BILLY (Film Soundtrack) (Various artists)
Cass: Released Aug '80, on Elektra by Elektra Records (UK). Deleted '85. Catalogue no: **K4 52231**
Album: Released Aug '80, on Elektra by Elektra Records (UK). Deleted '85. Catalogue no: **K 52231**

Brond

BROND (THEME FROM) (See under Nelson, Bill)

BROND (THEME FROM) (See under Scala)

Brown, Charlie

BOY NAMED CHARLIE BROWN (Film Soundtrack) (Various artists)
Tracks: / Boy named Charlie Brown: *Various artists* / Cloud dreams: *Various artists* / Charlie Brown and his allstars: *Various artists* / We lost again: *Various artists* / Blue Charlie Brown: *Various artists* / Time to go to school: *Various artists* / I only dread one day at a time: *Various artists* / Failure face: *Various artists* / By golly I'll show 'em: *Various artists* / Class champion: *Various artists* / I before E:

Various artists / School spelling bee: *Various artists* / Champion Charlie Brown: *Various artists* / Start boning up on your spelling: *Various artists* / Charlie Brown: *Various artists* / You'll either be a hero or a goat: *Various artists* / Bus station: *Various artists* / Bus wheel blues: *Various artists* / Do piano players make a lot of money: *Various artists* / I've got to get my blanket back: *Various artists* / Big city: *Various artists* / Snoopy on ice: *Various artists* / Found blanket: *Various artists* / National spelling bee: *Various artists* / B E A G E L: *Various artists* / Bus wheel blues: *Various artists* / Home coming: *Various artists* / I'm never going to school again: *Various artists* / Welcome home Charlie Brown: *Various artists* / Boy named Charlie Brown: *Various artists*.
Album: Released '73, on CBS by CBS Records & Distribution. Deleted '78. Catalogue no: **70078**

Brown, Joe

WHAT A CRAZY WORLD (See under What A Crazy World)

Buck Rogers

BUCK ROGERS (TV soundtrack) (Various artists)
Album: Released Apr '81, on MCA by MCA Records. Catalogue no: **MCF 3013**

Budgie (Show)

BUDGIE (1988 show recording) (Various artists)
Album: Released Dec '88, on MCA by MCA Records. Deleted Dec '89. Catalogue no: **MCG 6035**
CD: Released Dec '88, on MCA by MCA Records. Deleted Dec '89. Catalogue no: **DMCG 6035**
Cass: Released Dec '88, on MCA by MCA Records. Deleted Dec '89. Catalogue no: **MCGC 6035**

Bugsy Malone

BUGSY MALONE (1976 film soundtrack) (Various artists)
Tracks: / Bad guys: *Various artists* / Bugsy Malone: *Various artists* / Down and out: *Various artists* / Fat Sam's grand slam: *Various artists* / I'm feeling fine: *Various artists* / My name is Tallalah: *Various artists* / Ordinary fool: *Various artists* / So you wanna be a boxer: *Various artists* / Tomorrow: *Various ar-*

tists / You give a little love: *Various artists*.
Note: Film directed by Alan Parker. Words and music by Paul Williams. Originally released August 1976.
Album: Released Jun '83, on Polydor by Polydor Ltd. Catalogue no: **2442 142**
Cass: Released Jun '83, on Polydor by Polydor Ltd. Catalogue no: **3170 285**

BUGSY MALONE (VIDEO) (Various artists)
VHS: Released Jun '89, on Cinema Club Catalogue no: **CC 1031**
VHS: Released '88, on Video Collection by Video Collection. Catalogue no: **VC 3217**

Bull Durham

BULL DURHAM (1988 film soundtrack) (Various artists)
Note: Film starring Kevin Costner (No Way Out, The Untouchables) with songs by Joe Cocker, The Fabulous Thunderbirds, Los Lobos, John Fogerty and George Thorogood.
CD: Released Jan '89, on Silva Screen by Silva Screen Records. Catalogue no: **C2 90586**
Cass: Released Jan '89, on Silva Screen by Silva Screen Records. Catalogue no: **C4 90586**
Album: Released Jan '89, on Silva Screen by Silva Screen Records. Catalogue no: **C1 90586**

Burglar

BURGLAR (1988 film soundtrack) (Various artists)
CD: Released Jan '89, on Silva Screen by Silva Screen Records. Catalogue no: **MCAD 6201**
Cass: Released Jan '89, on Silva Screen by Silva Screen Records. Catalogue no: **MCFC 3340**
Album: Released Jan '89, on Silva Screen by Silva Screen Records. Catalogue no: **MCF 3340**

Burnett, Carol

JULIE ANDREWS AND CAROL BURNETT (See under Andrews, Julie)

Burning Secret (Film)

BURNING SECRET/FRUIT MACHINE/DIAMOND SKULLS (Film Soundtracks) (Zimmer, Hans)
CD: Released Feb '90, on SPI Milan

(France) Catalogue no: **CDCH 530**

Bus Boys

BOYS ARE BACK IN TOWN
Tracks: / Boys are back in town / I get lost.
Note: Used as the title song for *48 Hours*
7" Single: Released Apr '83, on Arista by BMG Records (UK). Catalogue no: **ARIST 528**

Busby, Colin

TEN GREAT TV THEMES (Busby, Colin Swinging Brass)
Tracks: / Rocky / Charlie's angels / Hotel / Cagney and Lacey / Rockford files / Hill Street blues / Quincy / Dynasty / Soap / Dallas.
Note: Includes Dynasty, Dallas, Soap
Cass: Released Jul '86, on Horatio Nelson by Horatio Nelson Records & Tapes Ltd.. Catalogue no: **CYU 107**
Album: Released Jul '86, on Horatio Nelson by Horatio Nelson Records & Tapes Ltd.. Catalogue no: **YU 107**

Buster (Film)

BUSTER (1988 Film Soundtrack) (Various artists)
Tracks: / Two hearts: *Collins, Phil* / Just one look: *Hollies* / Big noise: *Collins, Phil* / Robbery: *Dudley, Anne* / I got you babe: *Sonny & Cher* / Keep on running: *Spencer Davis Group* (On LP & cassette only) / Loco in Acapulco: *Four Tops* / How do you do it: *Gerry & The Pacema-*

kers / I just don't know what to do with myself: *Springfield, Dusty* / Sweets for my sweet: *Searchers* / Will you still be waiting?: *Dudley, Anne* / Groovy kind of love: *Collins, Phil.*
Note: "Buster starring Phil Collins and Julie Walters as Buster and June Edwards. The film tells the story of their involvement in the Great Train Robbery and its effects on their relationship." (Virgin 1988)
Album: Released 12 Sep '88, on Virgin by Virgin Records. Catalogue no: **V 2544**
Cass: Released 12 Sep '88, on Virgin by Virgin Records. Catalogue no: **TCV 2544**
CD: Released Nov '88, on Virgin by Virgin Records. Catalogue no: **CDV 2544**

Butch Cassidy

BUTCH CASSIDY AND THE SUNDANCE KID (Original Soundtrack) (Various artists)
Note: Composed by Burt Bacharach.
Cass: Released Jan '89, on MCA (Import) by MCA Records. Catalogue no: **CS 3159**
CD: Released Feb '90, on MCA (Import) by MCA Records. Catalogue no: **CD 3159**
Album: Released Jan '89, on MCA (Import) by MCA Records. Catalogue no: **SP 3159**

Bye Bye Birdie

BYE BYE BIRDIE (1960 Orig-

inal Broadway Cast) (Various artists)
Note: Featuring Dick Van Dyke.
CD: Released Feb '90, on CBS (import) by CBS Records & Distribution. Catalogue no: **CK 2025**
Album: Released Jan '89, on Silva Screen by Silva Screen Records. Catalogue no: **COS 2025**
Cass: Released Jan '89, on Silva Screen by Silva Screen Records. Catalogue no: **BT 2025**
Cass: Released Mar '90, on CBS (import) by CBS Records & Distribution. Catalogue no: **JST 2025**

BYE BYE BIRDIE (FILM) (Film Soundtrack) (Various artists)
Note: Starring Dick Van Dyke.
Cass: Released Jan '89, on Silva Screen by Silva Screen Records. Catalogue no: **AYK 1 3947**
CD: Released Jan '89, on Silva Screen by Silva Screen Records. Catalogue no: **1081.2**
Album: Released Jan '89, on Silva Screen by Silva Screen Records. Deleted Mar '90. Catalogue no: **AYL 1 3947**

BYE BYE BIRDIE (ORIGINAL ISSUE) (London cast) (Various artists)
Album: Released Jun '61, on Philips by Phonogram Ltd. Deleted '66. Catalogue no: **ABL 3385**

Byrne, David

TRUE STORIES (See under True Stories)

The following information was taken from the Music Master database on September 25th, 1990.

Cabaret

CABARET (Original Broadway cast - 1966) (Various artists)
Album: Released Jan '89, on CBS (import) by CBS Records & Distribution. Deleted Mar '90. Catalogue no: **CK 3040**
Cass: Released Mar '90, on Silva Screen by Silva Screen Records. Catalogue no: **PST 3040**

CABARET (Original London cast) (Various artists)
Cass: Released Jul '77, on Embassy by CBS Records & Distribution. Catalogue no: **40 31490**

CABARET (1986 London revival cast) (Various artists)
Tracks: / Wilkommen: *Various artists* / So what: *Various artists* / Don't tell mama: *Various artists* / Perfectly marvellous: *Various artists* / Two ladies: *Various artists* / It couldn't please me more: *Various artists* / Why should I wake up: *Various artists* / Money, money, money: *Various artists* / Married: *Various artists* / Meeskite: *Various artists* / Tomorrow belongs to me: *Various artists* / If you could see her: *Various artists* / Maybe this time: *Various artists* / What would you do: *Various artists*.
Album: Released Aug '86, on First Night by First Night Records. Catalogue no: **CAST 5**
Cass: Released Aug '86, on First Night by First Night Records. Catalogue no: **CASTC 5**

CABARET (1972 Film Soundtrack) (Various artists)
Tracks: / Wilkommen: *Various artists* / Mein herr: *Various artists* / Two ladies: *Various artists* / Maybe this time: *Various artists* / Sitting pretty: *Various artists* / Tiller girls: *Various artists* / Money, money,: *Various artists* / Heiraten (married): *Various artists* / If you could see her: *Various artists* / Tomorrow belongs to me: *Various artists* / Cabaret: *Various artists* / Finale: *Various artists*.

Album: Released '88, on CBS by CBS Records & Distribution. Catalogue no: **CBS 70273**
Cass: Released '88, on CBS by CBS Records & Distribution. Catalogue no: **40 70273**
CD: Released May '87, on CBS by CBS Records & Distribution. Catalogue no: **CD 70273**
Album: Released Apr '82, on ABC Records by MCA Records. Catalogue no: **MCL 1664**
Cass: Released Apr '82, on ABC Records by MCA Records. Catalogue no: **MCLC 1664**
CD: Released Aug '90, on MCA by MCA Records. Catalogue no: **DMCL 1664**

CABARET (Film Soundtrack) (Original issue) (Various artists)
Album: Released Mar '73, on Probe Deleted '76. Catalogue no: **SPB 1052**

CABARET (VIDEO) (Various artists)
Note: Cert: 15.
VHS: Released '88, on Video Gems Catalogue no: **R 1037**

Cabin In The Sky

CABIN IN THE SKY (1943 film musical) (Various artists)
Album: Released '88, on Hollywood Soundstage (USA) Catalogue no: **HS 5003**

CABIN IN THE SKY/PORGY & BESS (Original Broadway cast) (Various artists)
Album: Released Jan '89, on Silva Screen by Silva Screen Records. Catalogue no: **AEI 1107**

Caddyshack

CADDYSHACK (Various artists)
Album: Released Oct '80, on CBS by CBS Records & Distribution. Deleted Oct '85. Catalogue no: **CBS 70192**

CADDYSHACK 2 (1983 film soundtrack) (Various artists)
Album: Released Feb '90, on Col-

umbia (USA) by CBS Records (USA). Catalogue no: **SC 44317**
CD: Released Jan '89, on CBS (import) by CBS Records & Distribution. Catalogue no: **CK 44317**
Cass: Released Feb '90, on Columbia (USA) by CBS Records (USA). Catalogue no: **SCT44317**

Cagney, James

SUSPENSE (Cagney, James and Herbert Marshall)
Tracks: / No escape / Thirty nine steps.
Album: Released Feb '88, on Radio Archives (USA) by Kiner Ents.(USA). Catalogue no: **LP 103**

YANKEE DOODLE BOY
Tracks: / Yankee doodle boy / Over there.
7" Single: Released Oct '78, on United Artists by EMI Records. Deleted '81. Catalogue no: **UP 36353**

Cagney & Lacey

CAGNEY & LACEY (See under Caine, Daniel)

Caine, Daniel

A-TEAM, THE
Album: Released Aug '84, on Indiana by Indiana Records. Catalogue no: **A-TP 4444**
Cass: Released Aug '84, on Indiana by Indiana Records. Catalogue no: **A-TC 4444**

A-TEAM, THEME FROM
Tracks: / A team, Theme from / Young Hannibal.
7" Single: Released Sep '84, on Indiana by Indiana Records. Catalogue no: **B-TS 1111**

CAGNEY AND LACEY
Tracks: / Cagney and Lacey / Mike Hammer / Lou Grant / St. Elsewhere / Magnum / Taxi / Simon & Simon / Hill Street blues.
Album: Released Nov '85, on Indiana by Indiana Records. Catalogue no: **CALT 3333**
Cass: Released Nov '85, on Indiana by Indiana Records. Catalogue

no: **CALP 3333**

Cal

CAL (1984 film soundtrack) (Knopfler, Mark)
Tracks: / Irish Boy / Road, The / Waiting for her / Irish love / Secret place, A/ Where will you go / Father and son / Meeting at the trees / Potato picking / In a secret place / Fear and hatred / Love and guilt / Long road, The.
Album: Released Oct '84, on Vertigo by Phonogram Ltd. Catalogue no: **VERH 17**
Cass: Released Oct '84, on Vertigo by Phonogram Ltd. Catalogue no: **VERHC 17**
CD: Released Nov '84, on Vertigo by Phonogram Ltd. Catalogue no: **822 769-2**

Calamity Jane

CALAMITY JANE (VIDEO) (Various artists)
Note: Running time: 99 mins.
VHS: Released Jun '89, on Warner Home Video by WEA Records. Catalogue no: **PES 11209**

CALAMITY JANE/I'LL SEE YOU IN MY DREAMS (Original soundtrack) (Various artists)

Cass: Released Jan '89, on Silva Screen by Silva Screen Records. Catalogue no: **BT 19661**
Album: Released Jan '89, on Silva Screen by Silva Screen Records. Catalogue no: **P 19661**

CALAMITY JANE/PYJAMA GAME (Film soundtrack) (Various artists)
Tracks: / Deadwood stage: *Various artists* / I can do without you: *Various artists* / Black hills of Dakota, The: *Various artists* / Just blew in from the Windy City: *Various artists* / Woman's touch, A: *Various artists* / Higher than a hawk (deeper than a well): *Various artists* / 'Tis Harry I'm plannin' to marry: *Various artists* / Secret love: *Various artists* / Pajama game, The: *Various artists* / And racing with the clock: *Various artists* / I'm not at all in love: *Various artists* / I'll never be jealous again: *Various artists* / Once a year day: *Various artists* / Small talk: *Various artists* / There once was a man: *Various artists* / Hernando's hideaway: *Various artists* / Finale: *Various artists*.
Album: Released Sep '82, on CBS by CBS Records & Distribution. Deleted Jan '89. Catalogue

no: **CBS 32196**
Cass: Released Sep '82, on CBS by CBS Records & Distribution. Deleted Jan '89. Catalogue no: **40 32196**

CALAMITY JANE (Orginal Soundtrack) (Various Artists) (See panel below)
Tracks: / Deadwood Stage: *Day, Doris* / I can do without you: *Day, Doris and Howard Keel* / Black hills of Dakota: *Day, Doris* / Just blew in from the windy city: *Day, Doris* / Woman's touch, A: *Day, Doris* / Higher than a hawk: *Keel, Howard* / 'Tis Harry I'm plannin' to marry: *Day, Doris* / Secret love: *Day, Doris*
Album: Released on Philips, Catalogue no: **BBR 8104**

California Holiday

CALIFORNIA HOLIDAY (Film soundtrack) (See under Presley, Elvis)

California Raisins

CALIFORNIA RAISINS SING THE HIT SONGS
Cass: Released May '89, on Dino Entertainment by Dino Entertainments. Catalogue no: **GRAMC 1**
Album: Released May '89, on Dino Entertainment by Dino Entertainments. Catalogue no: **GRALP 1**
CD: Released May '89, on Dino Entertainment by Dino Entertainments. Catalogue no: **GRACD 1**

I HEARD IT THROUGH THE GRAPEVINE (Lead vocals Buddy Miles)
Tracks: / I heard it through the grapevine / Lean on me.
7" Single: Released Apr '89, on Dino Entertainment by Dino Entertainments. Catalogue no: **GRAPE 1**

MEET THE RAISINS
Album: Released Jun '89, on Atlantic by WEA Records. Deleted Jul '90. Catalogue no: **K 781917 1**
Cass: Released Jun '89, on Atlantic by WEA Records. Catalogue no: **K 781917 4**
CD: Released Jun '89, on Atlantic by WEA Records. Catalogue no: **K 781917 2**

California Suite

CALIFORNIA SUITE (1978 film soundtrack) (Various ar-

Calamity Jane - soundtrack on the Philips label, featuring Doris Day and Howard Keel

Camelot - soundtrack on the TER label, featuring Richard Harris.

tists)
Tracks: / California main title: *Various artists* / California suite love theme: *Various artists* / Black battle: *Various artists* / Hannah's daughter: *Various artists* / Black folks: *Various artists* / Academy awards: *Various artists* / Beverly Hills: *Various artists* / California end credits: *Various artists*.
Album: Released Jan '89, on CBS by CBS Records & Distribution. Catalogue no: **CBS 73991**
Cass: Released Mar '79, on CBS by CBS Records & Distribution. Catalogue no: **40 70168**
Album: Released Mar '79, on CBS by CBS Records & Distribution. Catalogue no: **CBS 70168**

<h3>Call It Love</h3>

CALL IT LOVE (Original London cast) (Various artists)
Album: Released Mar '85, on T. E. R. by That's Entertainment Records. Catalogue no: **TER 1083**

<h3>Call Me Madam</h3>

CALL ME MADAM (1950 Original Broadway cast) (Various artists)
Tracks: / Hostess with the mostes' on the ball, The: *Various artists* /
Can you use any money today?: *Various artists* / Washington square dance: *Various artists* / Lichtenburg: *Various artists* / Marrying for love: *Various artists* / Ocarina, The: *Various artists* / It's a lovely day: *Various artists* / Best thing for you, The: *Various artists* / Something to dance about: *Various artists* / Once upon a time today: *Various artists* / They like Ike: *Various artists*.
Album: Released '83, on MCA by MCA Records. Catalogue no: **MCL 1726**
Cass: Released '83, on MCA by MCA Records. Catalogue no: **MCLC 1726**

CALL ME MADAM (1952 Original London cast) (Various artists)
Cass: Released May '89, on T. E. R. by That's Entertainment Records. Catalogue no: **ZCTER 1062**
Album: Released May '89, on T. E. R. by That's Entertainment Records. Catalogue no: **TER 1062**

<h3>Camelot</h3>

CAMELOT (1964 Original London cast) (Various artists)
Cass: Released Jun '88, on First Night by First Night Records.
Catalogue no: **OCRC 4**
Album: Released Jun '88, on First Night by First Night Records. Catalogue no: **OCR 4**

CAMELOT (1961 Original Broadway Cast) (Various artists)
Tracks: / Camelot overture: *Various artists* / I wonder what the king is doing tonight: *Various artists* / Simple joys of maidenhood, The: *Various artists* / Camelot: *Various artists* / Follow me: *Various artists* / Lusty month of May, The: *Various artists* / C'est moi: *Various artists* / Then you may take me to the fair: *Various artists* / How to handle a woman: *Various artists* / If ever I would leave you: *Various artists* / Parade: *Various artists* / Before I gaze at you again: *Various artists* / Seven deadly virtues, The: *Various artists*.
Cass: Released '83, on CBS by CBS Records & Distribution. Catalogue no: **40 7009**
CD: Released Jan '89, on CBS (import) by CBS Records & Distribution. Catalogue no: **CK 32602**
Album: Released '83, on CBS by CBS Records & Distribution. Catalogue no: **CBS 7009**
Cass: Released Mar '90, on CBS (import) by CBS Records & Distribution. Catalogue no: **PST 32602**

CAMELOT (1967 Film Soundtrack) (Various artists)
Tracks: / Overture: *Various artists* / I wonder what the king is doing tonight: *Various artists* / Simple joys of maidenhood: *Various artists* / Camelot and the wedding ceremony: *Various artists* / c'est moi: *Various artists* / Lusty month of May, The: *Various artists* / Follow me: *Various artists* / How to handle a woman: *Various artists* / Take me to the fair: *Various artists* / If ever I would leave you: *Various artists* / What do the simple folk do: *Various artists* / I loved you once in silence: *Various artists* / Guenevere: *Various artists*.
CD: Released Jan '89, on Silva Screen by Silva Screen Records. Catalogue no: **3102.2**
Album: Released Nov '68, on Warner Bros. by WEA Records. Deleted '73. Catalogue no: **WS 1712**
Cass: Released '74, on Warner Bros. by WEA Records. Cata-

logue no: **K4 56001**
Album: Released '74, on Warner-Bros. by WEA Records. Catalogue no: **K 56001**

CAMELOT (1982 London revival cast) (Various artists) (See panel on previous page)
Tracks: / Camelot overture - prologue: *Various artists* / Camelot: *Various artists* / Simple joys of maidenhood: *Various artists* / I wonder what the king is doing tonight: *Various artists* / C'est moi: *Various artists* / Follow me: *Various artists* / Joust: *Various artists* / Lusty month of may, The: *Various artists* / Resolution: *Various artists* / Then you may take me to the fair: *Various artists* / How to handle a woman: *Various artists* / Entracle madrigal: *Various artists* / Before I gaze at you again: *Various artists* / Die on goodness: *Various artists*
CD: Released May '87, on T. E. R. by That's Entertainment Records. Catalogue no: **CDTER 1030**
Cass: Released Mar '89, on T. E. R. by That's Entertainment Records. Catalogue no: **ZCTER 1030**
Album: Released Mar '89, on T. E. R. by That's Entertainment Records. Catalogue no: **TER 1030**

CAMELOT (ORIGINAL ISSUE) (Original London cast) (Various artists)
Album: Released Jan '65, on H.M.V. by EMI Records. Deleted '70. Catalogue no: **CLP 1756**
Album: Released Sep '64, on CBS by CBS Records & Distribution. Deleted '69. Catalogue no: **APG 60001**

CAMELOT (VIDEO) (Various artists)
VHS: Released Mar '88, on Warner Home Video by WEA Records. Catalogue no: **PES 61084**

Camille Claudel

CAMILLE CLAUDEL (1989 film soundtrack) (Yared, Gabriel)
CD: Released Feb '90, on Virgin (France) by Virgin Records. Catalogue no: **30673**
Album: Released Feb '90, on Virgin (France) by Virgin Records. Catalogue no: **70673**
Cass: Released Feb '90, on Virgin (France) by Virgin Records. Catalogue no: **50673**

Camorra

CAMORRA (THE NAPLES

CONNECTION) (Film Soundtrack) (Various artists)
Note: Film by Lina Wertmuller with music by Tony Esposito.
Album: Released Jan '89, on Silva Screen by Silva Screen Records. Catalogue no: **A 291**

Canal

CANAL/ASHES AND DIAMONDS/GENERATION, A (Various artists)
Tracks: / Generation, The: *Various artists* / Canal: *Various artists* / Ashes & diamonds: *Various artists*.
Album: Released Apr '83, on T. E. R. by That's Entertainment Records. Catalogue no: **TER 1053**

Can-Can

CAN CAN (1960 film soundtrack) (Various artists)
Tracks: / Entr'acte: *Orchestra* / It's all right with me: *Sinatra, Frank* / Come along with me: *MacLaine, Shirley* / Live and let live: *Chevalier, Maurice & Louis Jordan* / You do something to me: *Jordan, Louis* / Let's do it: *Sinatra, Frank & Shirley MacLaine* / Can can: *Orchestra* / I love Paris: *Chorus* / Montmartre: *Sinatra, Frank & Maurice Chevalier* / C'est magnifique: *Sinatra, Frank* / Maidens typical of France: *Chorus & Orchestra* / Just one of those things: *Chevalier, Maurice* / I love Paris: *Sinatra, Frank & Maurice Chevalier*.
Album: Released May '85, on Capitol by EMI Records. Deleted Jun '89. Catalogue no: **ED 2605701**
Album: Released Nov '88, on Virgin by Virgin Records. Catalogue no: **V 2570**
Cass: Released May '85, on Capitol by EMI Records. Deleted '88. Catalogue no: **ED 2605704**
Cass: Released Nov '88, on Virgin by Virgin Records. Deleted Jun '90. Catalogue no: **TCV 2570**
CD: Released Nov '88, on Virgin by Virgin Records. Catalogue no: **CDV 2570**

CAN CAN (Film Soundtrack) (Import) (Various artists)
Album: Released '83, on EMI (Germany) by EMI Records. Catalogue no: **IC 038 80566**
Cass: Released Mar '90, on Capitol (import) Catalogue no: **CDP 91248.4**

CD: Released Feb '90, on Capitol (import) Catalogue no: **CDP 91248 2**

Candide

CANDIDE (Original Broadway cast) (Various artists)
Tracks: / Candide: Overture: *Various artists* / Best of all possible worlds, The: *Various artists* / What's the use?: *Various artists* / It must be so: *Various artists* / Glitter and be gay: *Various artists* / Oh, happy me: *Various artists* / Mazurka: *Various artists* / You were dead you know: *Various artists* / My love: *Various artists* / I am easily assimilated: *Various artists* / Eldorado: *Various artists* / Quiet: *Various artists* / Bon Voyage: *Various artists* / Gavotte: *Various artists* / Make our garden grow: *Various artists*.
Album: Released '84, on CBS by CBS Records & Distribution. Catalogue no: **CBS 60337**
Cass: Released '84, on CBS by CBS Records & Distribution. Catalogue no: **CBS 40 60337**

CANDIDE (New York City Opera version) (Various artists)
Tracks: / Fanfare - life is happiness indeed: *Various artists* / Best of all possible worlds: *Various artists* / Happy instrumental - Oh happy we: *Various artists* / Candide begins his travels: *Various artists* / It must be so (Candide's meditation): *Various artists* / Westphalian fanfare - Chorale - Battle music: *Various artists* / Entrance of the jew: *Various artists* / Glitter and be gay: *Various artists* / Earthquake music - Dear boy: *Various artists* / Autoda-fe (What a day): *Various artists* / Candide's lament: *Various artists* / You were dead you know: *Various artists* / Travel (to the stables): *Various artists* / I am easily assimilated: *Various artists* / Quartet finale: *Various artists* / Entr'acte: *Various artists* / Ballad of the new world: *Various artists* / My love: *Various artists* / Barcarolle: *Various artists* / Alleluia: *Various artists* / Eldorado: *Various artists* / Sheep song: *Various artists* / Governor's waltz: *Various artists* / Bon voyage: *Various artists* / Quiet: *Various artists* / Constantinople: *Various artists* / What's the use: *Various artists* / Finale - Make our garden grow

Album: Released '84, on New World by President Records. Catalogue no: **NW 340/1**
Cass: Released '84, on New World by President Records. Catalogue no: **NWMC 340/1**
CD: Released '84, on New World by President Records. Catalogue no: **NWCD 340/1**

CANDIDE (1988 musical opera) (Various artists)
Album: Released Jan '89, on Silva Screen by Silva Screen Records. Deleted Mar '90. Catalogue no: **PS 2350**
Cass: Released Jan '89, on Silva Screen by Silva Screen Records. Catalogue no: **PST 2350**
Album: Released Jul '88, on T. E. R. by That's Entertainment Records. Catalogue no: **TER 1156**
Cass: Released Jul '88, on T. E. R. by That's Entertainment Records. Catalogue no: **ZCTER 1156**
CD: Released Jul '88, on T. E. R. by That's Entertainment Records. Deleted Mar '90. Catalogue no: **CDTER 1156**

Cannon & Ball

BOYS IN BLUE
Tracks: / Boys in blue / Big star.
Note: Theme from the film.
7" Single: Released '83, on MFP by EMI Records. Catalogue no: **FP 908**

Cannonball Fever

CANNONBALL FEVER (1989 film soundtrack) (Various artists)
Album: Released Feb '90, on Silva Screen by Silva Screen Records. Catalogue no: **CST 8042**
CD: Released Feb '90, on Silva Screen by Silva Screen Records. Catalogue no: **CST 348042**

Can't Stop The Music

CAN'T STOP THE MUSIC (Original Soundtrack) (Various artists)
Album: Released Aug '80, on Mercury by Phonogram Ltd. Deleted '83. Catalogue no: **6399 051**
Cass: Released '80, on Mercury by Phonogram Ltd. Deleted '83. Catalogue no: **7199 051**

Cantabile

MUSIC OF THE NIGHT
Tracks: / Starlight Express (From

Starlight Express) / Song on the sand (From La Cage aux Folles.) / Love makes the world go round (From Me & My Girl.) / Music of the night (From The Phantom of the Opera.) / Little shop of horrors (From the Film) / Oh what a circus (From Evita) / Losing my mind (From Follies) / Rum tum tugger, The (From Cats.) / Bring him home (From Les Miserables.) / Tell me it's not true (From Blood Brothers) / Anthem (From Chess.) / She's so beautiful (From Time).
Cass: Released Oct '87, on Columbia by EMI Records. Catalogue no: **TC SCX 6712**
Album: Released Oct '87, on Columbia by EMI Records. Deleted May '90. Catalogue no: **SCX 6712**
CD: Released Nov '87, on Columbia by EMI Records. Deleted Aug '90. Catalogue no: **CDP 748 639 2**
CD: Released Nov '87, on Columbia by EMI Records. Deleted Aug '90. Catalogue no: **CDSCX 6712**

Canterbury Tales

CANTERBURY TALES (1968 Original London cast) (Various artists)
Tracks: / Canterbury tales: Overture: *Various artists* / Chaucer's Prologue: *Various artists* / Song of welcome: *Various artists* / Goodnight hymn: *Various artists* / Canterbury day: *Various artists* / I have a noble cock: *Various artists* / Darling, let me teach you how to kiss: *Various artists* / Nicholas' and Alisons' love duet: *Various artists* / Some call it love: *Various artists* / Chanticleer and Pertelote duet: *Various artists* / Chanticleer, Pertelote, Fox trio: *Various artists* / Fill your glass: *Various artists* / Pilgrims' riding music: *Various artists* / Come on and marry me, honey: *Various artists* / When I was a boy: *Various artists* / Where are the girls of yesterday?: *Various artists* / If she has never loved before: *Various artists* / I'll give my love a ring: *Various artists* / Chaucer speech: *Various artists* / I am forever dated: *Various artists* / Opening of the Wife of Bath's tale: *Various artists* / What do women most desire?: *Various artists* / April song: *Various artists* / Arrival at Canterbury, The: *Various artists* / Love will conquer all: *Various artists* / Chaucer's epilogue: *Various artists* / Canterbury tales: Finale: *Various artists*.

Album: Released Sep '84, on T. E. R. by That's Entertainment Records. Catalogue no: **TER 1076**
Cass: Released Sep '84, on T. E. R. by That's Entertainment Records. Catalogue no: **ZCTER 1076**

Captive

CAPTIVE (Original Soundtrack) (See under Edge (U2 guitarist))

Car Trouble

CAR TROUBLE (1986 Film Soundtrack) (Various artists)
Tracks: / Car trouble...Hearts on fire!: *Meatloaf* / Unchained melody: *Sayer, Leo* / Mated: *Grant, David & Jaki Graham* / Second choice: *Flesh* / Send my heart: *Adventures* / Mony mony: *Idol, Billy* / Break these chains: *Icehouse* / Only ones, The: *UFO* / Stay away: *Woyehyeh* / True love ways: *Adventures.*
Note: Produced by Meatloaf, Alan Tarney, Derek Bramble, Flesh and Bob Sargeant.
Cass: Released Feb '86, on Chrysalis by Chrysalis Records. Catalogue no: **ZCHR 1523**
Album: Released Feb '86, on Chrysalis by Chrysalis Records. Catalogue no: **CHR 1523**

Car Wash

CAR WASH (Film Soundtrack) (See under Rose Royce)

Cara, Irene

FAME
Tracks: / Fame.
Note: Theme from the film.
7" Single: Released Jul '82, on RSO by Polydor Ltd. Deleted Jul '85. Catalogue no: **RSO 90**

FLASHDANCE WHAT A FEELING
Tracks: / Flashdance... what a feeling / Love theme from flashdance / Found it.
Note: Theme from the film.
12" Single: Released '84, on Casablanca by PolyGram UK Ltd. Deleted 31 May '89. Catalogue no: **CANX 1016**
7" Single: Released '84, on Casablanca by PolyGram UK Ltd. Deleted 31 May '89. Catalogue no: **CAN 1016**

Caravans (Film)

CARAVANS (Various artists)

Album: Released Feb '79, on CBS by CBS Records & Distribution. Deleted Feb '84. Catalogue no: **CBS 70164**

Card

CARD, THE (Original London cast) (Various artists)
Album: Released Jan '89, on Silva Screen by Silva Screen Records. Catalogue no: **AEI 1124**

Cardinal

CARDINAL, THE (1963 film soundtrack) (Various artists)
Tracks: / Stonebury: *Various artists* / Dixieland: *Various artists* / Tango: *Various artists* / Cardinal's faith, The: *Various artists* / They haven't got the girls in the USA: *Various artists* / Cardinal in Vienna, The: *Various artists* / Anne-Marie: *Various artists* / Cardinal's decision, The: *Various artists* / Way down South: *Various artists* / Cardinal themes, The: *Various artists.*
Note: Score by Jerome Moross (The Big Country) for the Otto Preminger film.
Album: Released Jan '89, on Silva Screen by Silva Screen Records. Catalogue no: **ERS 6518**
Cass: Released Sep '87, on RCA (Spain) Catalogue no: **NK 43754**
Album: on RCA (Spain) Catalogue no: **NL 43754**
CD: Released Sep '87, on RCA (Spain) Catalogue no: **PRCD 1778**

Care Bears

CARE BEARS MOVIE (1985 film soundtrack) (Various artists)
Tracks: / Care-a-lot: *King, Carole* / Home is in your heart: *King, Carole* / Nobody cares like a bear: *Sebastian, John* / When you care you are not afraid to try: *Sebastian, John* / In a Care Bear family: *Sebastian, John* / Look out! He's after you: *Woodward, Walt & David Bird.*
Cass: Released '85, on Cherry Lane by Cherry Lane Productions. Catalogue no: **ZCPIP 717**
Album: Released '85, on Cherry Lane by Cherry Lane Productions. Deleted '90. Catalogue no: **PIPLP 717**

CARE BEARS TO THE RESCUE
Album: Released Nov '85, on Cherry Lane by Cherry Lane Productions. Catalogue no: **ELF 23802**
Cass: Released Nov '85, on Cherry Lane by Cherry Lane Productions. Catalogue no: **ZCELF 23802**
Cass: Released Apr '88, on Tempo by Warwick Records. Catalogue no: **00 104 127-4**

Carefree

CAREFREE (Various artists)
Note: Fred Astaire and Ginger Rogers at the peak of their careers.
VHS: Released May '87, on Video Collection by Video Collection. Catalogue no: **VC 3048**

Careful He Might ...

CAREFUL HE MIGHT HEAR YOU (1983 film soundtrack) (Various artists)
Note: Australian film score by Ray Cook.
Album: Released Jan '89, on Varese Sarabande Records(USA) by Varese Sarabande Records (USA). Catalogue no: **STV 81221**

Carmen

CARMEN (Film soundtrack 1984) (Various artists)
Cass: Released '85, on Erato by BMG Records (UK). Catalogue no: **MCE 75113**
CD: Released '85, on Erato by BMG Records (UK). Catalogue no: **ECD 88037**
LP Set: Released '85, on Erato by BMG Records (UK). Catalogue no: **NUM 75113**

CARMEN (Film soundtrack 1983) (Various artists)
Cass: Released '84, on Polydor by Polydor Ltd. Catalogue no: **POLDC 5134**
CD: Released '84, on Polydor by Polydor Ltd. Catalogue no: **817 247-2**
Album: Released '84, on Polydor by Polydor Ltd. Catalogue no: **POLD 5134**

CARMEN(FILM) (Film soundtrack 1984:Highlights) (Various artists)
CD: Released '85, on Erato by BMG Records (UK). Catalogue no: **ECD 88041**
Album: Released '85, on Erato by BMG Records (UK). Catalogue no: **NUM 75120**
Cass: Released '85, on Erato by BMG Records (UK). Catalogue no: **MCE 75120**

Carmen, Eric

HUNGRY EYES
Tracks: / Hungry eyes / Where are you tonight? (on 12" only) / I've had the time of my life (12" only.).
Note: From the film 'Dirty Dancing'.
7" Single: Released Jan '88, on RCA by BMG Records (UK). Deleted Sep '90. Catalogue no: **PB 49593**
12" Single: Released May '88, on RCA by BMG Records (UK). Deleted May '89. Catalogue no: **PT 49594**
CD Single: Released Jun '89, on RCA by BMG Records (UK). Deleted Jul '89. Catalogue no: **PD 49594**

Carmen Jones

CARMEN JONES (Film Soundtrack) (Various artists)
Tracks: / Overture: *Various artists* / Dere's a cafe on de corner: *Various artists* / You talk jus' like my man: *Various artists* / Dat's love (habanera): *Various artists* / Dis flower: *Various artists* / Beat out dat rhythm on a drum: *Various artists* / Stan' up an' fight: *Various artists* / Whizzin' away along de track: *Various artists* / Card song: *Various artists* / My Joe: *Various artists* / Finale: *Various artists.*
Album: Released '73, on One-Up by EMI Records. Deleted '78. Catalogue no: **OU 2005**

CARMEN JONES (Original Broadway cast) (Various artists)
Album: Released Jan '89, on MCA by MCA Records. Catalogue no: **MCA 1531**
Cass: Released Jan '89, on MCA by MCA Records. Catalogue no: **MCAC 1531**

CARMEN JONES (Film Soundtrack (re-issue)) (Various artists)
Album: on RCA by BMG Records (UK). Deleted Jul '89. Catalogue no: **BL 80046**
Cass: on RCA by BMG Records (UK). Catalogue no: **BK 80046**
Cass: Released Mar '90, on Silva Screen by Silva Screen Records. Catalogue no: **1881.4**
CD: Released Jan '89, on Silva Screen by Silva Screen Records. Catalogue no: **1881.2**

Carnival

CARNIVAL (Original Broad-

way cast 1961) (Various artists)
CD: Released Feb '90, on Silva Screen by Silva Screen Records. Catalogue no: **937195.2**

Carny
CARNY (1980 film soundtrack) (Various artists)
Album: Released '82, on Warner Bros. by WEA Records. Catalogue no: **HS 3455**

Carousel
CAROUSEL (1945 Broadway cast) (Various artists)
Tracks: / Carousel waltz: *Various artists* / You're a queer one, Julie Jordan: *Various artists* / Mister snow: *Various artists* / If I loved you: *Various artists* / Soliloquy: *Various artists* / June is bustin' out all over: *Various artists* / When the children are asleep: *Various artists* / Blow high, blow low: *Various artists* / Real nice clambake: *Various artists* / There's nothin' so bad for a woman: *Various artists* / What's the use of wondering?: *Various artists* / Highest judge of all: *Various artists* / You'll never walk alone: *Various artists*.
Note: First production - 1945 - with Jan Clayton, John Raitt, Jean Darling, Christine Johnson, Eric Mattson, Mervyn Vie, Connie Baxter.
CD: Released Jan '89, on MCA by MCA Records. Catalogue no: **6395.2**
Album: Released Mar '82, on MCA by MCA Records. Catalogue no: **MCL 1661**
Cass: Released Mar '82, on MCA by MCA Records. Catalogue no: **MCLC 1661**

CAROUSEL (1956 Film Soundtrack) (See panel opposite)
CD: Released May '87, on Capitol by EMI Records. Catalogue no: **CDP 746 635 2**
Cass: Released Nov '70, on Capitol by EMI Records. Catalogue no: **TCSW 694**
Album: Released Nov '58, on Capitol by EMI Records. Deleted Aug '90. Catalogue no: **LCT 6105**

Carpenter, John
THEY LIVE (Film Soundtrack) (See under They Live)

Carreras, Jose
JOSE CARRERAS SINGS ANDREW LLOYD WEBBER
Tracks: / Memory / Phantom of the opera / Music of the night, The / You / Pie Jesu / Tell me on a Sunday / Half a moment / There's me / Starlight express / Unexpected song / Love changes everything.
Cass: Released 16 Oct '89, on WEA by WEA Records. Catalogue no: **WX 325C**
CD: Released Nov '89, on WEA by WEA Records. Catalogue no: **2569242**
Album: Released 16 Oct '89, on WEA by WEA Records. Catalogue no: **WX 325**

Carthage In Flames
CARTHAGE IN FLAMES (Film soundtrack) (Various artists)
Note: Epic score by Mario Nascimbene
Album: Released Jan '89, on Silva Screen by Silva Screen Records. Catalogue no: **IM 010**

Cartouche
CARTOUCHE (Original soundtrack) (Various artists)
CD: Released Feb '90, on Silva Screen by Silva Screen Records. Catalogue no: **PCD 104**

Casablanca
CASABLANCA (Radio performance) (Various artists)
Note: Starring Humphrey Bogart and Ingrid Bergman.
Album: Released Jan '89, on Silva Screen by Silva Screen Records. Catalogue no: **MR 1099**

CASABLANCA & OTHER CLASSIC THEMES FROM HUMPHREY BOGART FILMS (Film Soundtracks) (National Philharmonic Orchestra)
Note: Conducted by Charles Gerhardt.
Album: Released Jan '89, on Silva Screen by Silva Screen Records. Catalogue no: **AGL 13782**
Cass: Released Jan '89, on Silva Screen by Silva Screen Records. Catalogue no: **CGK 13782**

Casino Royale
CASINO ROYALE (Film soundtrack) (Various artists)

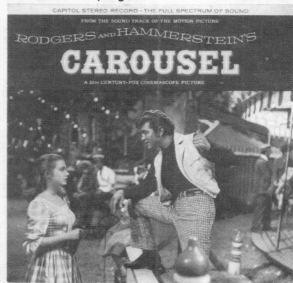

Carousel - soundtrack on the Capitol label, with Gordon MacRae and Shirley Jones.

Album: Released Jul '67, on RCA by BMG Records (UK). Deleted '69. Catalogue no: **SF 7874**

Cassandra Crossing

CASSANDRA CROSSING (Film soundtrack) (Various artists)
Album: Released Mar '79, on Citadel (USA) by Varese Sarabande Records (USA). Catalogue no: **CT 6020**

Cast A Giant Shadow

CAST A GIANT SHADOW (1966 film soundtrack) (Various artists)
Note: Elmer Bernstein score for the Kirk Douglas film set in Israel.
Album: Released Jan '89, on MCA by MCA Records. Deleted Feb '90. Catalogue no: **MCA 25093**
Cass: Released Jan '89, on MCA by MCA Records. Catalogue no: **MCAC 25093**

Castaway

CASTAWAY (Film soundtrack) (Various artists)
Tracks: / Be kind to my mistakes: Various artists / Catamaran: Various artists / Chemistry: Various artists / Clair De Lune: Various artists / Fata Morgana: Various artists / End title: Various artists / Island, The: Various artists / Memories of tango: Various artists / Healing: Various artists / Castaway: Various artists.
Cass: Released Mar '87, on EMI by EMI Records. Deleted Nov '88. Catalogue no: **TC-EMC 3529**
Album: Released Mar '87, on EMI by EMI Records. Deleted Nov '88. Catalogue no: **EMC 3529**

Castle, Roy

RECORD BREAKERS
Note: Music from the TV series.
Album: Released Nov '81, on Glenmore Catalogue no: **GLR 626**

Casualites Of War

CASUALITES OF WAR (1989 film soundtrack) (Various artists)
Tracks: / Casualties of war: Various artists / Trapped in a tunnel: Various artists / No escape: Various artists / Abduction: Various artists / No hope: Various artists / Rape, The: Various artists / Death of Oahn, The: Various artists /

Healing, The: Various artists / Fragging, The: Various artists / Waste her: Various artists / Elegy for a dead cherry: Various artists / Elegy for Brown: Various artists.
Cass: Released Jan '90, on CBS by CBS Records & Distribution. Catalogue no: **466 016 4**
Album: Released Feb '90, on CBS (import) by CBS Records & Distribution. Catalogue no: **CB 45359**
CD: Released Feb '90, on CBS (import) by CBS Records & Distribution. Catalogue no: **CK 45359**
Album: Released Jan '90, on CBS by CBS Records & Distribution. Catalogue no: **466 016 1**
CD: Released Jan '90, on CBS by CBS Records & Distribution. Catalogue no: **466 016 2**
Cass: Released Feb '90, on CBS (import) by CBS Records & Distribution. Catalogue no: **CBT45359**

Cat People

CAT PEOPLE (1982 film soundtrack) (Various artists)
Tracks: / Cat people (putting out fire): Bowie, David & Giorgio Moroder / Autopsy: Moroder, Giorgio / Irena's theme: Moroder, Giorgio / Night rabbit: Moroder, Giorgio / Leopard tree dream: Moroder, Giorgio / Paul's theme: Various artists / Myth, The: Moroder, Giorgio / To the bridge: Moroder, Giorgio / Transformation seduction: Moroder, Giorgio / Bring the prod: Moroder, Giorgio.
Album: Released Apr '82, on Backstreet by MCA Records. Deleted Jan '88. Catalogue no: **MCF 3138**
Cass: Released Apr '82, on Backstreet by MCA Records. Deleted Jan '88. Catalogue no: **MCFC 3138**

Cats

CATS (Original Broadway cast) (Various artists)
2 LP Set: Released Apr '83, on Geffen by Geffen Records (USA). Deleted Jan '88. Catalogue no: **GEF 88615**
2 LP Set: Released Jun '81, on Polydor by Polydor Ltd. Catalogue no: **CATX 001**
Cass set: Released Jun '81, on Polydor by Polydor Ltd. Catalogue no: **CATXC 001**

CD Set: Released Jun '84, on Polydor by Polydor Ltd. Catalogue no: **817 810-2**

CATS (GERMAN VERSION) (Original soundtrack) (Various artists)
CD: Released '88, on Polydor by Polydor Ltd. Catalogue no: **817 365 2**

HIGHLIGHTS FROM CATS (Various artists)
Album: Released Aug '88, on Polydor by Polydor Ltd. Catalogue no: **839 415-1**
CD: Released Aug '88, on Polydor by Polydor Ltd. Catalogue no: **839 415-2**
Cass: Released Aug '88, on Polydor by Polydor Ltd. Catalogue no: **839 415-4**

Cats Eye

CATS EYE (1985 Original soundtrack) (Various artists)
Note: Horror film based on Stephen King short stories. Music by Alan Silvestri.
Album: Released Jan '89, on Silva Screen by Silva Screen Records. Catalogue no: STV 81241
Cass: Released Jan '89, on Silva Screen by Silva Screen Records. Deleted Feb '90. Catalogue no: CTV 81241

Cats Eyes

CATS EYES (THEME FROM) (See under Kongos, John)

Cavalcade

CAVALCADE (Original London cast) (Various artists)
Album: Released Jan '89, on Silva Screen by Silva Screen Records. Catalogue no: AEI 1149

Cavalcade Of London

CAVALCADE OF LONDON THEATRE (Various artists)
Tracks: / Oh what a lovely war (overture): Various artists / I'll make a man of you: Various artists / Heilige nacht: Various artists / Christmas day in the cookhouse: Various artists / Goodbyee: Various artists / Pieces of eight: Various artists / Last to go: Various artists / Buy British: Various artists / Perchance to dream: Various artists / Love is my reason: Various artists / Pacific 1860: Various artists / Uncle Harry: Various artists / Strike a light: Various artists /

Another love: *Various artists* / Stop the world, I want to get off: *Various artists* / What kind of fool am I: *Various artists* / Oliver: *Various artists* / As long as he needs me: *Various artists* / Reviewing the situation: *Various artists* / On the brighter side: *Various artists* / Lord Oxshott's dilemma: *Various artists* / One dam' thing after another: *Various artists* / My heart stood still: *Various artists* / Wait a minim: *Various artists* / Ag pleez Daddy: *Various artists* / This'll make you whistle: *Various artists* / World of Suzie Wong: *Various artists* / Ding dong song: *Various artists* / Nicol: *Various artists* / Mia Carlotta: *Various artists* / May I feel said he: *Various artists* / Canterbury tales: *Various artists* / I have a noble cock: *Various artists* / If she has never loved before: *Various artists* / Little dog laughed: *Various artists* / Run rabbit run: *Various artists* / Flanagan and Allen: *Various artists* / Late joys: *Various artists* / Bird on Nellie's hat: *Various artists* / Ghost train: *Various artists* / Conclusion: *Various artists* / Anything goes: *Various artists* / I get a kick out of you: *Various artists* / Wunder bar: *Various artists* / Hand in hand: *Various artists* / Two fools: *Various artists* / Life: *Various artists* / Someday I'll find you: *Various artists* / Lock up your daughters: *Various artists* / Kiss me again: *Various artists* / Ballad of the liver bird: *Various artists* / Half a sixpence: *Various artists* / Flash bang wallop: *Various artists* / File on Dr Fink: *Various artists* / Look at me now: *Various artists* / Hush a bye: *Various artists* / Sir Walter Raleigh: *Various artists* / This can't be love: *Various artists* / Berinthia's recitation: *Various artists* / Fortune thou art a bitch: *Various artists* / Gumboot dance: *Various artists* / King Kong: *Various artists* / Other people's babies: *Various artists* / Dit dit song: *Various artists* / End of the news: *Various artists* / Jacob and sons: *Various artists* / Coat of many colours: *Various artists* / Any dream will do: *Various artists* / First weekend in June: *Various artists* / Ordinary people: *Various artists* / No other love: *Various artists* / Have a try: *Various artists* / Vacancy: *Various artists* / Yonder blessed moon: *Various artists* / Fings: *Various artists* / Desert song: *Various artists* / Romance:

Various artists / Alice blue gown: *Various artists* / Why do I love you: *Various artists* / Boadicea: *Various artists* / Let the people sing: *Various artists* / Dogs they had a party: *Various artists* / Late late show: *Various artists* / No strings: *Various artists*.

LP Set: Released '79, on Decca by Decca International. Deleted '84. Catalogue no: **D 140 D 4**

CCS

WHOLE LOTTA LOVE
Tracks: / Whole lotta love.
Note: Used as the theme to BBC's *Top Of The Pops* during the 1970's.
7" Single: Released Oct '70, on RAK by EMI Records. Deleted Oct '73. Catalogue no: **RAK 104**
7" Single: Released '84, on EMI Golden 45's by EMI Records. Catalogue no: **G45 20**

Census Taker

CENSUS TAKER, THE (Residents) (See panel below)
Tracks: / Creeping dread / Census taker, The / Talk / End of home / Emotional music / Secret seed / Easter woman/Simple song / Hellno / Where is she / Innocence de-

cayed / Romanian/Nice old man / Margaret Freeman / Lights out/Where is she / Passing the bottle / Census taker returns, The.
Album: Released '85, on Episode by Zomart Records. Catalogue no: **ED 21**

Centennial Summer

CENTENNIAL SUMMER/STATE FAIR (Film soundtrack) (Various artists)
Album: Released Jan '89, on CIF Catalogue no: **CIF 3009**

Certain Fury

CERTAIN FURY (1985 Original soundtrack) (Various artists)
Note: Music from the Irene Cara/Tatum O'Neil thriller.
Album: Released Jan '89, on Silva Screen by Silva Screen Records. Catalogue no: **STV 81239**

Certain Smile

CERTAIN SMILE, A (Original soundtrack) (Various artists)
Note: Score by Alfred Newman.
Album: Released Jan '89, on Silva Screen by Silva Screen Records. Catalogue no: **LAALP 004**

The Census Taker - soundtrack by The Residents (Episode)

Cetera, Peter
GLORY OF LOVE
Tracks: / Glory of love / On the line.
Note: Featured in the film 'Karate Kid'.
7" Single: Released Jul '86, on Warner Bros. by WEA Records. Catalogue no: **W 8662**
12" Single: Released Jul '86, on Warner Bros. by WEA Records. Deleted Jan '88. Catalogue no: **W 8662T**

Cha Cha
CHA CHA (Film soundtrack) (Various artists)
Tracks: / Love you like I love myself: *Brood, Herman* / Doin' it: *Brood, Herman* / You can't beat me: *Brood, Herman* / Jilted: *Brood, Herman* / Elvis: *Brood, Herman* / Never be clever: *Brood, Herman* / Home: *Lovich, Lene* / Pick up: *Phoney & The Hardcore* / Foolin': *Phoney & The Hardcore* / Sweet memories: *Floor Van Zutphen* / Take it all in: *Meteors* / It's you, only you: *Meteors* / Herman's door: *Hagen, Nina* / Herman's first high: *Hagen, Nina* / You don't fit: *Inside Nipples* / 2-2-get-her: *Monika Tuen A Kkwoei* / Sonny blues: *Sonny & The Dulfer Gang* / No more conversations: *Street Beats* / Bop: *Dulfer Gang* / I don't wanna lose you: *White Honey*.
Album: Released Feb '80, on Ariola by BMG Records (UK). Deleted '85. Catalogue no: **ARL 5039**

Chamberlain, Richard
THEME FROM DR KILDARE-3 STARS WILL SHINE TONIGHT
Tracks: / Dr Kildare, Theme from.
7" Single: Released Jun '62, on MGM (EMI) Deleted Jun '65. Catalogue no: **MGM 1160**

Chameleon
CHAMELEON
Note: "Carmina Valles" theme tune from BBC TV's Summer Lease
CD: Released Nov '89, on Total Catalogue no: **FLYCD 100**
Cass: Released Nov '89, on Total Catalogue no: **FLYMC 100**
Album: Released Nov '89, on Total Catalogue no: **FLYLP 100**

Champ
CHAMP, THE (Film soundtrack) (Various artists)

Tracks: / If you remember me: *Various artists* / Main title: *Various artists* / Cha cha do Brazil, A: *Various artists* / Serenade in G, K 525 eine kleine nachtmusik: *Various artists* / Nothing but a groove: *Various artists* / Find out way: *Various artists* / Gym montage: *Various artists* / T.J.'s theme: *Various artists* / Champ (theme from): *Various artists* / Salon du Miami: *Various artists* / Visiting hours: *Various artists* / Gone: *Various artists*.
Album: Released '77, on Planet by BMG Records (UK). Deleted '82. Catalogue no: **K 52152**

Champions
CHAMPIONS (Theme from) (See under Davis, Carl)

Chancer
CHANCER (Music from the ITV programme) (See under Hammer, Jan)

Charade (Film)
CHARADE (Original soundtrack) (Various artists)
CD: Released Jan '89, on Silva Screen by Silva Screen Records. Catalogue no: **2755.2**

Charles, Ray
SHAKE YOUR TAIL FEATHER
Tracks: / Shake your tail feather / Minnie the moocher.
Note: Featured in the film 'The Blues Brothers'.
7" Single: Released Oct '80, on Atlantic by WEA Records. Deleted Oct '83. Catalogue no: **K 11615**

Charlie Chalk
CHARLIE CHALK (Various artists)
Note: Songs and music from the TV series.
Cass: Released Aug '89, on Redrock by Redrock Records. Catalogue no: **ZCHARL 1**
CD: Released Aug '89, on Redrock by Redrock Records. Catalogue no: **CDHARL 1**
Album: Released Aug '89, on Redrock by Redrock Records. Catalogue no: **CHARLP 1**

CHARLIE CHALK (SINGLE) (Original Television Theme) (Various artists)
Tracks: / Charlie Chalk: *Various artists*.
7" Single: Released Aug '89, on

Redrock by Redrock Records. Catalogue no: **CHARLIE 1**

Charlie Girl
CHARLIE GIRL (1986 London revival cast) (Various artists)
Tracks: / Charlie girl overture: *Various artists* / Most ancestral home of all, The: *Various artists* / Bells will ring: *Various artists* / I love him, I love him: *Various artists* / What would I get from being married?: *Various artists* / Let's do a deal: *Various artists* / My favourite occupation: *Various artists* / What's the magic?: *Various artists* / When I hear music I dance: *Various artists* / I 'ates money: *Various artists* / Charlie Girl waltz: *Various artists* / Party of a lifetime: *Various artists* / Like love: *Various artists* / That's it: *Various artists* / Washington: *Various artists* / Fish and chips: *Various artists* / Society twist: *Various artists* / You never know what you can do: *Various artists* / Finale: *Various artists*.
Note: The cast includes Cyd Charisse, Dora Bryan, Paul Nicholas, Mark Wynter, Nicholas Parsons and Linda Hull. David Heneker and John Taylor wrote the music and Ian McMillan conducts.
Album: Released Jul '87, on First Night by First Night Records. Catalogue no: **CAST 3**
Cass: Released Jul '87, on First Night by First Night Records. Catalogue no: **CASTC 3**

Charlotte's Web
CHARLOTTE'S WEB (Film Soundtrack) (Various artists)
Tracks: / Charlotte's web - main theme: *Various artists* / There must be something more: *Various artists* / I can talk: *Various artists* / Chin up: *Various artists* / Mother Earth and Father Time: *Various artists* / We've got lots in common: *Various artists* / Vertiable smorgasbord: *Various artists* / Deep in the dark: *Various artists* / Chin up march: *Various artists* / Zuckerman's famous pig: *Various artists* / Charlotte's farewell: *Various artists* / End title: *Various artists*.
Album: Released '73, on Paramount Deleted '78. Catalogue no: **SPFL 285**

Chart Show
CHART SHOW: DANCE ALBUM VOL 2 (Various ar-

tists)

Cass: Released 24 Apr '89, on Chrysalis by Chrysalis Records. Catalogue no: **ZDD 7**

Album: Released 24 Apr '89, on Chrysalis by Chrysalis Records. Catalogue no: **ADD 7**

CD: Released 24 Apr '89, on Chrysalis by Chrysalis Records. Catalogue no: **CCD 7**

CHART SHOW: ROCK THE NATION VOL.2 (Various artists)

Cass: Released Apr '89, on Dover by Chrysalis Records. Catalogue no: **ZDD 4**

CD: Released Apr '89, on Dover by Chrysalis Records. Catalogue no: **CCD 4**

Album: Released Apr '89, on Dover by Chrysalis Records. Catalogue no: **ADD 4**

CHART SHOW, THE (Rock The Nation) (Various artists)

CD: Released 19 Mar '88, on Chrysalis by Chrysalis Records. Catalogue no: **CCD 1629**

Album: Released 19 Mar '88, on Chrysalis by Chrysalis Records. Catalogue no: **CHR 1629**

Cass: Released 19 Mar '88, on Chrysalis by Chrysalis Records. Catalogue no: **ZCHR 1629**

CHART SHOW, THE - DANCE HITS (Various artists)

Tracks: / I found lovin': *Fatback Band* / Real thing, The: *Jellybean featuring Steven Dante* / Lies: *Butler, Jonathan* / C'est la vie: *Nevil, Robbie* / Rock steady: *Whispers* / Living in a box: *Living In A Box* / Looking for a new love: *Watley, Jody* / Boops (here to go): *Sly & Robbie* / You sexy thing: *Hot Chocolate* / Once bitten twice shy: *Williams, Vesta* / Pump up the volume: *M/A/R/R/S* / House nation: *Housemaster Boyz & The Rude Boy Of House* / Don't stop (jammin'): *L.A. Mix* / This brutal house: *Nitro Deluxe* / Put the needle to the record: *Criminal Element Orchestra* / F.L.M.: *Mel & Kim* / Crush on you: *Jets (American)* / Another step (closer to you): *Wilde, Kim & Junior* / Step right up: *Graham, Jaki* / I found lovin': *Walsh, Steve*.

Note: Double album and cassette contain twenty 12" mixes. Compact disc track listing: M/A/R/R/S-Pump up the volume / House Master Boyz & The Rude Boy Of

House-House nation / Mel & Kim-FLM / Living In A Box-Living in a box(dance mix) / Jody Watley-Looking for a new love / Sly & Robbie-Boops(Here to go) / Vesta Williams-Once bitten twice shy / Fatback Band-I found lovin' / Jellybean featuring Steven Dante-The real thing / Jonathan Butler-Lies(extended version) / Robb Nevil-C'est la vie.

Cass set: Released Nov '87, on Dover by Chrysalis Records. Catalogue no: **ZDD 1**

2 LP Set: Released Nov '87, on Dover by Chrysalis Records. Catalogue no: **ADD 1**

CD: Released Nov '87, on Dover by Chrysalis Records. Catalogue no: **CCD 1**

Chas & Dave

IN SICKNESS AND IN HEALTH

Tracks: / In sickness and in health.

Note: Theme from the TV series.

7" Single: Released Sep '85, on BBC by BBC Records. Deleted Sep '87. Catalogue no: **RESL 176**

Chateau Vallon

CHATEAU VALLON (TV Soundtrack) (Various artists)

Tracks: / La commanderie: *Various artists* / Puissance et loire: *Various artists* / Les kovalic: *Various artists* / Le commissaire nicolo: *Various artists* / La mort d'antonin: *Various artists* / La depeche: *Various artists* / Suspence aux sablions: *Various artists* / Les rues de' chateavallon: *Various artists* / Berg, Theme des: *Various artists* / When fortune reigns: *Sanderson, Richard* / Chateau Vallon: *Various artists* / Paul et Catherine: *Various artists* / Florence, Theme de: *Various artists* / Magouille: *Various artists* / Bernard et albertas: *Various artists* / La chantage: *Various artists*.

Cass: Released Feb '87, on Carrere Catalogue no: **CAC 225**

Album: Released Feb '87, on Carrere Catalogue no: **CAL 225**

Chess

CHESS (1984 London cast) (Various artists) (See panel below)

Tracks: / Merano: *Various artists* / Russian and Molokov: *Various artists* / Where I want to be: *Various artists* / Opening ceremony: *Various artists* / Quartet: *Various artists* / American and Florence:

Chess **- lyrics by Time Rice, music by Bjorn Ulvaeus and Benny Anderson of Abba.**

Various artists / Nobody's side: Various artists / Chess: Various artists / Mountain duet: Various artists / Florence sings: Various artists / Embassy lament: Various artists / One night in Bangkok: Various artists / Heaven help my heart: Various artists / Argument: Various artists / I know him so well: Various artists / Deal (no deal): Various artists / Pity the child: Various artists / Endgame: Various artists / You and I: Various artists.
Note: Starring Elaine Paige, Denis Quilley, Barbara Dickson, Murray Head. Music by Tim Rice, Benny Anderson, Bjorn Ulvaeus. Anders Eljas conducts the London Symphony Orchestra.
CD: Released Nov '84, on RCA by BMG Records (UK). Catalogue no: PD 70500
Cass: Released Nov '84, on RCA by BMG Records (UK). Catalogue no: PK 70500
2 LP Set: Released Nov '84, on RCA by BMG Records (UK). Catalogue no: PL 70500

CHESS PIECES (Studio cast recordings) (Various artists)
Tracks: / Merano: London Symphony Orchestra / Ambrosian Singers / Arbiter, The: Skifs, Bjorn / Nobody's side: Paige, Elaine / Chess: London Symphony Orchestra / Mountain duet: Paige, Elaine and Tommy Korberg / Embassy lament: Bamber, Peter, Alan Byers, Leslie Fyson & Vernon Midgley / Anthem: Korberg, Tommy / One night in Bangkok: Head, Murray / I know him so well: Paige, Elaine & Barbara Dickson / You and I - the story of Chess: Paige, Elaine, Tommy Korberg & The Ambrosian Singers.
Cass: Released Oct '85, on Telstar by Telstar Records (UK). Catalogue no: STAC 2274
Album: Released Oct '85, on Telstar by Telstar Records (UK). Catalogue no: STAR 2274

Cheyenne Autumn

CHEYENNE AUTUMN (1964 film soundtrack) (Various artists)
Tracks: / Indians arrive: Various artists / Friend Deborah: Various artists / School house, The: Various artists / Archer: Various artists / Rejection: Various artists / truth: Various artists / Entr'acte: Various

artists / River crossing: Various artists / Sick girl: Various artists / Battle, The: Various artists / Dodge city: Various artists / Old chief: Various artists / Lead our people home: Various artists / Death: Various artists.
CD: Released Jun '88, on Silva Screen by Silva Screen Records. Catalogue no: LXCD 4

Chieftains

BALLAD OF THE IRISH HORSE (Film Soundtrack Recording)
Cass: Released '87, on Claddagh (Ireland) by Claddagh Records (Ireland). Catalogue no: 4 CCF 15
Album: Released Jun '85, on Shanachie by Shanachie Records (USA). Catalogue no: SHAN 79051
Album: Released '87, on Claddagh (Ireland) by Claddagh Records (Ireland). Catalogue no: CCF 15

YEAR OF THE FRENCH, THE (Original Soundtrack)
Cass: Released Aug '88, on Claddagh (Ireland) by Claddagh Records (Ireland). Catalogue no: 4CC 36
Album: Released Aug '88, on Claddagh (Ireland) by Claddagh Records (Ireland). Catalogue no: CC 36
Album: Released '88, on Topic by Topic Records. Catalogue no: CCLP 36

Children Of A Lesser God

CHILDREN OF A LESSER GOD (1986 film soundtrack) (Various artists)
Tracks: / Silence and sound: Various artists / Sarah sleeping: Various artists / Rain pool: Various artists / Underwater love: Various artists / On the ferry: Various artists / James and Sarah: Various artists / Goodnight: Various artists / Boomerang: Various artists.
Album: Released Jan '89, on GNP Crescendo (USA) by GNP Crescendo Records (USA). Catalogue no: GNPS 8007
Cass: Released Jan '89, on GNP Crescendo (USA) by GNP Crescendo Records (USA). Catalogue no: GNPC 8007
CD: Released '88, on GNP Crescendo (USA) by GNP Crescendo

Records (USA). Catalogue no: GNPD 8007

Children's BBC

THEMES FROM CHILDREN'S BBC (Various artists)
Tracks: / Postman Pat: Various artists / Fireman Sam: Various artists / Doctor Who: Various artists / Muppet babies, The: Various artists / Jim'll fix it: Various artists / Grange Hill: Various artists / Mop 'n' Smiff: Various artists / Trumpton: Various artists / Heads and tails: Various artists / Familyness, The: Various artists / Paddington Bear: Various artists / Willy Fog: Various artists / Camberwick Green: Various artists / Hokey cokey: Various artists / Magic roundabout, The: Various artists / Bertha: Various artists / Henry's cat: Various artists / Willo the wisp: Various artists / Playschool: Various artists / Dogtanian and The Three Muskethounds: Various artists.
CD: Released May '89, on Pickwick by Pickwick Records. Catalogue no: PWKS 650
Cass: Released Jul '88, on Pickwick by Pickwick Records. Catalogue no: HSC 650

Child's Play

CHILD'S PLAY (Various artists)
Tracks: / Getting dressed: Various artists / Heigh ho: Various artists / House at Pooh Corner: Various artists / Orville's song: Various artists / Willo the wisp: Various artists / Doctor Who: Various artists / Clapping song, The: Various artists / Henry's cat: Various artists / Mr. Greedy's song: Various artists / If your happy and you know it: Various artists / Mr. Happy: Lowe, Arthur / Train song: Various artists / Winkle the zoo cat is lost and found: Morris, Johnny / Polly put the kettle on: Various artists.
Cass: Released Mar '84, on BBC by BBC Records. Deleted '88. Catalogue no: ZCA 498
Album: Released Mar '84, on BBC by BBC Records. Deleted '88. Catalogue no: REA 498

Childs Play (Film)

CHILDS PLAY (Film Soundtrack)
Note: Score by Joe Renzetti

CD: Released February 1990, on SPI Milan Catalogue no: **CDCH 382**

Chinatown

CHINATOWN (Original soundtrack) (Various artists)
Note: Score by Jerry Goldsmith.
Album: Released Jan '89, on Silva Screen by Silva Screen Records. Catalogue no: **255 092.1**

Chish & Fips

CHISH AND FIPS SONGBOOK (Television Soundtrack) (Various artists)
Cass: Released 7 Nov '87, on First Night by First Night Records. Catalogue no: **SCENEC 11**
Album: Released 7 Nov '87, on First Night by First Night Records. Catalogue no: **SCENE 11**

Chitty Chitty ...

CHITTY CHITTY BANG BANG (Film soundtrack) (Various artists)
Album: Released Feb '69, on United Artists by EMI Records. Deleted '73. Catalogue no: **SULP 1200**

CHITTY CHITTY BANG BANG (VIDEO) (Various artists)
Note: Running time: 137 mins.
VHS: Released '88, on Warner Home Video by WEA Records. Catalogue no: **PES 99253**

Chocolate Soldier

CHOCOLATE SOLDIER/NAUGHTY MARIETTA (Original Stage Cast) (Various artists)
Cass: Released Jan '89, on Silva Screen by Silva Screen Records. Catalogue no: **BT 13707**
Album: Released Jan '89, on Silva Screen by Silva Screen Records. Catalogue no: **P 13707**

Choice Of Arms

CHOICE OF ARMS (Original Soundtrack Recording) (Various artists)
Album: Released '88, on DRG (USA) by DRG Records (USA). Catalogue no: **SL 9510**

Choirboys

CHOIRBOYS (Film soundtrack) (Various artists)
Album: Released Mar '78, on

MCA (USA) by MCA Records (USA). Catalogue no: **MCA 2326**

Chorus Line

CHORUS LINE (Original Broadway cast) (Various artists)
Tracks: / I hope I get it: *Various artists* / I can do that: *Various artists* / At the ballet: *Various artists* / Sing: *Various artists* / Hello twelve, hello thirteen, hello love: *Various artists* / Nothing: *Various artists* / Music and the mirror, The: *Various artists* / Dance:Ten looks three: *Various artists* / One: *Various artists* / What I did for love: *Various artists* / One, reprise: *Various artists* / Chorus line:Finale: *Various artists*.
CD: Released Jan '89, on CBS (import) by CBS Records & Distribution. Catalogue no: **CK 33581**
Album: Released '88, on CBS by CBS Records & Distribution. Catalogue no: **70149**
Cass: Released Dec '76, on CBS by CBS Records & Distribution. Catalogue no: **40 70149**

CHORUS LINE, A (VIDEO) (Various artists)
Note: Cert: PG.
VHS: Released Oct '88, on Channel 5 by Channel 5 Video. Catalogue no: **CFV 07612**

CHORUS LINE - FILM (Film soundtrack) (Various artists)
Tracks: / I hope I get it: *Various artists* / Who am I anyway?: *Various artists* / I can do that: *Various artists* / Surprise, Surprise: *Various artists* / Nothing: *Various artists* / Let me dance for you: *Various artists* / Dance:ten looks three: *Various artists* / One(rehearsal and finale versions): *Various artists* / What I did for love: *Various artists* / Looks:three: *Various artists*.
CD: on Casablanca by PolyGram UK Ltd. Deleted Feb '88. Catalogue no: **826 306-2**
Cass: Released Jan '86, on Casablanca by PolyGram UK Ltd. Deleted 18 Jul '88. Catalogue no: **CANHC 11**
Album: Released Jan '86, on Casablanca by PolyGram UK Ltd. Deleted 18 Jul '88. Catalogue no: **CANH 11**

Chosen

CHOSEN (HOLOCAUST 2000), THE (Film soundtrack)

(Various artists)
Note: Composed by Ennio Morricone.
Album: Released Jan '89, on Cerebus (USA) Catalogue no: **C'BUS 103**

Chouans

CHOUANS (1988 film soundtrack) (Various artists)
Note: New score by Georges Delerue for a Philippe De Broca film set in the Napoleonic period.
Cass: Released Jan '89, on Silva Screen by Silva Screen Records. Deleted Feb '90. Catalogue no: **76.538**
CD: Released Jan '89, on Silva Screen by Silva Screen Records. Catalogue no: **96.538**
Album: Released Jan '89, on Silva Screen by Silva Screen Records. Catalogue no: **66.538**

Christabel

CHRISTABEL (TV soundtrack) (Various artists)
Tracks: / Christabel: *Various artists.*
12" Single: Released Dec '88, on BBC by BBC Records. Catalogue no: **12 RXL 229**

Christiane F

CHRISTIANE F, WIR KINDER VON BAHNOF ZOO (Film soundtrack) (See under Bowie, David)

Christians

FORGOTTEN TOWN
Tracks: / Forgotten town / Why waltz / One in a million / Man oh man / Look around.
Note: From the TV series *It's my city.*
CD Single: Released Feb '87, on Art & Soul by Island Records. Deleted Jun '88. Catalogue no: **CID 291**
7" Single: Released Jan '87, on Island by Island Records. Deleted Jun '88. Catalogue no: **IS 291**
12" Single: Released '88, on Island by Island Records. Deleted Dec '88. Catalogue no: **12 IS 291**

Christine

CHRISTINE (1) (1984 Film soundtrack) (Various artists)
Tracks: / Bad to the bone: *Thorogood, George & The Destroyers* / Not fade away: *Holly, Buddy & The Crickets* / Pledging my love: *Ace,*

Johnny / We belong together: *Robert & Johnny* / Keep a knockin': *Little Richard* / I wonder why: *Dion/Belmonts* / Harlem nocturne: *Viscounts* / Little bitty pretty one: *Harris, Thurston* / Rock 'n' roll is here to stay: *Danny & The Juniors* / Christine attacks: *Carpenter, John & Alan Howarth* / Bony Moronie: *Williams, Larry.*
CD: Released '86, on Motown by BMG Records (UK). Catalogue no: **ZD 72139**
Album: Released Jul '84, on Motown by BMG Records (UK). Catalogue no: **STMR 9022**
Cass: Released Jul '84, on Motown by BMG Records (UK). Catalogue no: **CSTMA 9022**
Album: Released '86, on Motown by BMG Records (UK). Catalogue no: **ZL 72139**
Cass: Released '86, on Motown by BMG Records (UK). Catalogue no: **ZK 72139**

CHRISTINE (2) (1984 film soundtrack) (Carpenter, John)
CD: Released Jan '90, on Colosseum (West Germany) Catalogue no: **VSCD 5240**
Album: Released Jan '90, on Colosseum (West Germany) Catalogue no: **VS 5240**
Cass: Released Jan '90, on Colosseum (West Germany) Catalogue no: **VSC 5240**

Chronicle Of A Death...

CHRONICLE OF A DEATH FORETOLD (1987 film soundtrack) (Piccioni, Piero)
Tracks: / Bolero lento / Seis cuerdas de amor / El manicero / Pavana para una muerte anunciada / Una cancion / Flora / Canoa / Presagio nocturno / Amar y vivir / Suite final.
Cass: Released '89, on Virgin by Virgin Records. Catalogue no: **OVEDC 266**
CD: Released '88, on Virgin by Virgin Records. Catalogue no: **CDV 2441**
Album: Released '89, on Virgin by Virgin Records. Catalogue no: **OVED 266**
Cass: Released Jul '87, on Virgin by Virgin Records. Deleted 13 Feb '89. Catalogue no: **TCV 2441**
Album: Released Jul '87, on Virgin by Virgin Records. Deleted 13 Feb '89. Catalogue no: **V 2441**

Chronos
CHRONOS (Original Soundtrack) (Stern, Michael)
CD: Released '86, on Sonic Atmospheres (USA) by Silva Screen Records. Catalogue no: **CD 312**

Chrysanthemum
CHRYSANTHEMUM (Original London cast) (Various artists)
Album: Released Jan '89, on Silva Screen by Silva Screen Records. Catalogue no: **AEI 1108**

Chulas Fronteras
CHULAS FRONTERAS (Film soundtrack) (Various artists)
Album: Released May '81, on Arhoolie (USA) by Arhoolie Records (USA). Catalogue no: **ARHOOLIE 3005**
Cass: Released '88, on Arhoolie (USA) by Arhoolie Records (USA). Catalogue no: **C 3005**

CHULUS FRONTERAS (Video) (Various artists)
Note: The classic film about Tex-Mex music with Los Alegres de Teran, Flaco Jimenez, Lydia Mendoza, Los Pinguinos del Norte, Narciso Martinez etc. Running time: 60 mins.
VHS: Released '88, on Brazos Videos Catalogue no: **BF 101**

Cincinnati Kid
CINCINNATI KID, THE (1965 film soundtrack) (Various artists)
Note: Lalo Schifrin score for the Steve McQueen film, with Ray Charles performing the theme song.
Album: Released Jan '89, on MCA by MCA Records. Catalogue no: **MCA 25012**
Cass: Released Jan '89, on MCA by MCA Records. Deleted Feb '90. Catalogue no: **MCAC 25012**

Cincinnati Pops Orch.
STAR TRACKS (Cincinnati Pops Orchestra)
Tracks: / Star wars / Empire strikes back / Return of the Jedi / Close encounters of the third kind / Superman / E.T. / Raiders of the lost ark.
CD: Released Jul '84, on Telarc Catalogue no: **CD 80094**
Album: Released Jul '84, on Telarc Deleted Jul '89. Catalogue no:

DG 10094

Cinderella
CINDERELLA (Film Soundtrack) (Various artists)
Tracks: / Cinderella: *Various artists* / Dream is a wish your heart makes: *Various artists* / Oh sing sweet nightingale: *Various artists* / Work song: *Various artists* / Dream a wish your heart makes, A: *Various artists* / Bibbidi boddidi boo: *Various artists* / Cinderella arrives at the ball: *Various artists* / So this is love: *Various artists* / Finale: *Various artists.*
Album: Released '73, on Disneyland by Disneyland-Vista Records (USA). Deleted '78. Catalogue no: **DQ 1207**

CINDERELLA (TV Soundtrack) (Various artists)
Album: Released Jan '89, on Silva Screen by Silva Screen Records. Catalogue no: **AOS 2005**
CD: Released Jan '89, on CBS (import) by CBS Records & Distribution. Catalogue no: **CK 02005**
Cass: Released Jan '89, on Silva Screen by Silva Screen Records. Catalogue no: **BT 2005**
Cass: Released Jan '89, on Silva Screen by Silva Screen Records. Catalogue no: **JST 02005**

CINDERELLA (Film Soundtrack) (Various artists)
Album: Released Dec '87, on Walt Disney Catalogue no: **WD 012**
Cass: Released Dec '87, on Walt Disney Catalogue no: **WDC 012**

CINDERELLA (1959 Original London Cast) (Various artists)
Tracks: / Cinderella (Overture): *Various artists* / In my own little corner: *Various artists* / Very special day, A: *Various artists* / Do I love you because you are beautiful?: *Various artists* / Prince is giving a ball: *Various artists* / Marriage type love: *Various artists* / Stepsisters' lament: *Various artists* / Your majesties, a list of bare necessities: *Various artists* / When you're driving through the moonlight: *Various artists* / lovely night, A: *Various artists* / Impossible: *Various artists* / No other love: *Various artists* / Ten minutes ago: *Various artists* / You and me: *Various artists* / Cinderella (Finale): *Various artists.*
Album: Released Apr '83, on T. E.

R. by That's Entertainment Records. Catalogue no: **TER 1045**
Cass: Released Apr '83, on T. E. R. by That's Entertainment Records. Catalogue no: **ZCTER 1045**

CINDERELLA (1957 TV MUSICAL) (Rodgers & Hammerstein's Show Time)
CD: Released Feb '90, on CBS (import) by CBS Records & Distribution. Catalogue no: **CK 2005**
Cass: Released Mar '90, on Silva Screen by Silva Screen Records. Catalogue no: **PST 2005**

Cindy-ella

CINDY-ELLA (Original London cast) (Various artists)
Tracks: / High summer day: *Various artists* / Like a peach: *Various artists* / Let me hold your hand: *Various artists* / Hush-a-bye: *Various artists* / Cindy-Ella: *Various artists* / Motherless child: *Various artists* / Li'l Ella, play on yo'harp: *Various artists* / You gotta look distainful: *Various artists* / Go 'way f'om mah window: *Various artists* / Look on me with a loving eye: *Various artists* / Oh the first time: *Various artists* / Plenty good room: *Various artists* / Shoe shine shoe: *Various artists* / You're worried now: *Various artists* / Stranger: *Various artists* / Bring a little bit pumpkin: *Various artists* / Cindy: *Various artists* / Nobody's business: *Various artists* / Raise a ruckus: *Various artists* / You ain't a-gonna sit and take yo' ease: *Various artists* / There's a man goin' roun' givin' cards: *Various artists* / De midnight special: *Various artists* / Git along home: *Various artists* / Cindy, cindy: *Various artists* / I gotta shoe: *Various artists* / Man no good for nothin': *Various artists* / Nobody knows the trouble I've seen: *Various artists* / Swing low sweet chariot: *Various artists* / Troubles of the world: *Various artists*.
Album: Released '85, on DRG (USA) by DRG Records (USA). Catalogue no: **DS 15023**

Cine Movie

CINE MOVIE (Various artists)
Tracks: / Psycho prelude: *Various artists* / De lift (ending): *Various artists* / Elephant man theme, The: *Various artists* / Enchantment At Tugu: *Various artists* / Russian Christmas Theme: *Various artists*

/ Vivement dimanche: *Various artists* / La notte: *Various artists* / Days of heaven: *Various artists* / North by North West theme: *Various artists* / Von Kern's Attack: *Various artists* / Suite Pour Choeur Et Orchestre: *Various artists* / Le Reve I: *Various artists* / Train ride to Brooklyn: *Various artists* / Garcon: *Various artists* / Folie douce: *Various artists* / My name is nobody (theme): *Various artists*.
Note: Superb compilation of main themes from well-known movies such as 'Psycho', 'Elephant Man', 'Sophie's choice' and 'The year of living dangerously'.
Album: Released Nov '86, on SPI Milan (France) Catalogue no: **A 289**
Cass: Released Nov '86, on SPI Milan (France) Catalogue no: **C 289**

Cinema Favourites

CINEMA FAVOURITES (Various artists)
Album: Released Jan '89, on Burlington Records by Plant Life Records. Catalogue no: **BUR 023**
Cass: Released Jan '89, on Burlington Records by Plant Life Records. Catalogue no: **4BUR 023**

Cinema Hits Album

CINEMA HITS ALBUM, THE (Various artists)
Note: Artists include: Duran Duran/Irene Cara/Eurythmics
Album: Released Mar '86, on Towerbell Catalogue no: **TVLP 9**
Cass: Released Mar '86, on Towerbell Catalogue no: **ZCTV 9**

Cinema Weekend

CINEMA WEEKEND (Various artists)
Tracks: / 2001 - a space oddyssey: *Various artists* / Platoon: *Various artists* / Elephant man: *Various artists* / Diva: *Various artists* / Children of a lesser god: *Various artists* / Untouchables, The: *Various artists* / Dangerous moonlight: *Various artists* / Excalibur: *Various artists* / Death in Venice: *Various artists* / Room with a view: *Various artists* / Barry Lyndon: *Various artists* / Amadeus: *Various artists*.
CD: on Decca by Decca International. Catalogue no: **421 397 2**
Cass: on Decca by Decca International. Catalogue no: **421 397 4**

Citizen Kane

CITIZEN KANE (London Philharmonic Orchestra) (Various artists)
Tracks: / Citizen Kane:Overture / Jane Eyre / Devil and Daniel Webster, The: Sleigh-ride / Snows of Kilimanjaro, The: Interlude / Jason and the argonauts / Citizen Kane Variations / Citizen Kane: Ragtime / Citizen Kane:Finale / Swing your partners / Memory waltz, The.
Note: Including music from London Philharmonic Orchestra, National Philharmonic Orchestra and Bernard Herrmann.
CD: Released Aug '88, on Decca by Decca International. Catalogue no: **417 852-2**
Cass: Released Aug '88, on Decca by Decca International. Catalogue no: **417 852-4**

City Heat (Film)

CITY HEAT (Film soundtrack) (Various artists)
Album: Released May '85, on WEA by WEA Records. Catalogue no: **WEA 9252191**

Clambake

CLAMBAKE (Film Soundtrack) (See under Presley, Elvis)

Clan Of The Cave Bear

CLAN OF THE CAVE BEAR (1986 film soundtrack) (Various artists)
Note: Composed by Alan Silvestri.
Album: Released Sep '86, on Colosseum (West Germany) Catalogue no: **CST 8013**
Album: Released Jan '89, on Silva Screen by Silva Screen Records. Catalogue no: **STV 81274**
CD: Released Jan '89, on Silva Screen by Silva Screen Records. Deleted Feb '90. Catalogue no: **VCD 47252**
Cass: Released Jan '89, on Silva Screen by Silva Screen Records Deleted Feb '90. Catalogue no: **CTV 81274**

Clannad

ANGEL AND THE SOLDIER (See Under Angel & The Soldier)

ATLANTIC REALM
Tracks: / Atlantic realm / Predator / Moving thru / Berbers, The / Signs of life / In flight / Ocean of light /

Drifting / Under Neptune's cape / Voyager / Primeval sun / Child of the sea / Kirk pride, The.
Note: Music from the BBC programme *Atlantic Realm*
CD: Released 16 Jan '89, on BBC by BBC Records. Catalogue no: **BBC CD 727**
Cass: Released 16 Jan '89, on BBC by BBC Records. Catalogue no: **ZCF 727**
Album: Released 16 Jan '89, on BBC by BBC Records. Catalogue no: **REB 727**

HARRY'S GAME THEME
Tracks: / Harry's game (theme from) / Strayed away.
7" Single: Released Oct '82, on RCA by BMG Records (UK). Deleted Aug '89. Catalogue no: **RCA 292**

LEGEND
Tracks: / Robin (the hooded man) / Now is here / Herne / Together we / Darkmere / Strange land / Scarlet inside / Lady Marian / Battles / Ancient forest.
CD: Released Aug '88, on RCA by BMG Records (UK). Catalogue no: **ND 71703**
Cass: Released Aug '88, on RCA by BMG Records (UK). Catalogue no: **NK 71703**
Cass: Released Mar '84, on RCA by BMG Records (UK). Deleted Apr '88. Catalogue no: **PK 70188**
Album: Released Aug '88, on RCA by BMG Records (UK). Catalogue no: **NL 71703**
CD: Released Mar '84, on RCA by BMG Records (UK). Deleted Apr '88. Catalogue no: **PD 70188**
Album: Released '89, on Tara (Ireland) by Tara Records (Ireland). Catalogue no: **TA 3012**
Album: Released Mar '84, on RCA by BMG Records (UK). Deleted Apr '88. Catalogue no: **PL 70188**

ROBIN OF SHERWOOD
Note: Music from the TV series.
CD: Released Jul '86, on Duck by Duck Records. Deleted '88. Catalogue no: **925166 2**
Album: Released Jul '86, on Starblend by Starblend Records. Catalogue no: **ERLC 1**
Cass: Released Jul '86, on Starblend by Starblend Records. Catalogue no: **ERLK 1**

ROBIN OF SHERWOOD (SINGLE)

Tracks: / Robin of Sherwood.
Note: Theme from the TV series.
7" Single: Released May '84, on RCA by BMG Records (UK). Deleted May '87. Catalogue no: **HOOD 1**
7" Single: Released May '86, on RCA by BMG Records (UK). Catalogue no: **PB 40681**

Clapton, Eric
EDGE OF DARKNESS (T.V. theme) (Clapton, Eric & Michael Kamen)
Tracks: / Shoot out / Edge of darkness.
Cassingle: Released Nov '85, on BBC by BBC Records. Catalogue no: **ZRSL 178**
12" Single: Released Nov '85, on BBC by BBC Records. Catalogue no: **12 RSL 178**
CD 3": Released Feb '89, on BBC by BBC Records. Catalogue no: **CDRSL 178**
7" Single: Released Jan '86, on BBC by BBC Records. Catalogue no: **RESL 178**

ERIC CLAPTON ON WHISTLE TEST
VHS: Released Oct '84, on BBC Video by BBC Video. Catalogue no: **BBCV 3025**
VHS: Released '88, on BBC Video by BBC Video. Catalogue no: **BBCV 4020**

Clark, Petula
GENTLEMEN AND PLAYERS (T.V. Theme)
Tracks: / Gentlemen and players.
7" Single: Released Apr '88, on Eagle (West Germany) by Bear Family Records (Germany). Catalogue no: **EAGLE 2**

Clash Of The Titans
CLASH OF THE TITANS (Film Soundtrack) (Various artists)
Album: Released Aug '81, on CBS by CBS Records & Distribution. Deleted Aug '86. Catalogue no: **CBS 73588**

Classic...
CLASSIC BRITISH FILM THEMES OF THE '40'S & '50'S (Various artists)
Tracks: / Way to the stars, The: *Various artists* / Cornish rhapsody: *Various artists* / Voice in the night, A: *Various artists* / Warsaw concerto: *Various artists* / Dream of Olwen: *Various artists* / Saga of Odette, The: *Various artists* / Carriage and pair: *Various artists* / Long forgotten melody: *Various artists* / Portrait of Clare: *Various artists* / Beggar's theme, The: *Various artists.*
Album: Released Apr '87, on Golden Age by EMI Records. Catalogue no: **GX 2551**
Cass: Released Apr '87, on Golden Age by EMI Records. Catalogue no: **TC-GX 2551**
Cass: Released Feb '84, on Retrospect by EMI Records. Catalogue no: **TC SH 384**
Album: Released Feb '84, on Retrospect by EMI Records. Catalogue no: **SH 384**

CLASSIC TV THEMES (Various artists)
Album: Released Oct '80, on Decca by Decca International. Deleted '88. Catalogue no: **SPA 580**

Classic Film Scores...
CLASSIC FILM SCORES BY ALFRED NEWMAN (Newman, Alfred)
Tracks: / Captain from Castile / How to marry a millionaire / Wuthering heights / Down to the sea in ships / Bravados / Anastasia / Best of everything / Airport / Song of Bernadette / Robe.
Album: on RCA by BMG Records (UK). Catalogue no: **GL 43437**
Cass: on RCA by BMG Records (UK). Catalogue no: **GK 43437**

CLASSIC FILM SCORES BY BERNARD HERRMANN (Herrmann, Bernard)
Tracks: / Citizen Kane / On dangerous ground / Beneath the 12 mile reef / Hangover square / White witch doctor.
Cass: on RCA by BMG Records (UK). Catalogue no: **GK 43448**
Album: on RCA by BMG Records (UK). Catalogue no: **GL 43448**

CLASSIC FILM SCORES BY DIMITRI TIOMKIN (Tiomkin, Dimitri)
Tracks: / Lost horizon / Guns of Navarone / Big sky / Fourposter / Friendly persuasion / Search for paradise.
Album: on RCA by BMG Records (UK). Catalogue no: **GL 43445**
Cass: on RCA by BMG Records (UK). Catalogue no: **GK 43445**

CLASSIC FILM SCORES BY FRANZ WAXMAN (Waxman, Franz)

Tracks: / Sunset Boulevard / Prince Valient / Place in the sun / Bride of Frankenstein / Old acquaintance Rebecca / Philadelphia story / Taras Bulba.

Album: on RCA by BMG Records (UK). Catalogue no: **GL 43442**
Cass: on RCA by BMG Records (UK). Catalogue no: **GK 43442**

CLASSIC FILM SCORES BY MAX STEINER (Steiner, Max)

Tracks: / Gone with the wind / Now voyager / Saratoga trunk / Charge of the Light Brigade / Four wives / Big sleep / Johnny Belinda / Since you went away / Informer / Fountainhead.

Album: on RCA by BMG Records (UK). Catalogue no: **GL 43447**
Cass: on RCA by BMG Records (UK). Catalogue no: **GK 43447**

CLASSIC FILM SCORES BY MIKLOS ROZSA (Rozsa, Miklos)

Tracks: / Spellbound / Red house / Thief of Baghdad / Lost weekend / Four feathers / Double indemnity / Knights of the round table / Jungle book / Ivanhoe.

Cass: on RCA by BMG Records (UK). Catalogue no: **GK 43443**
Album: on RCA by BMG Records (UK). Catalogue no: **GL 43443**

CLASSIC FILM SCORES FOR BETTE DAVIS (Various artists)

Tracks: / Now voyager: *Various artists* / Dark victory: *Various artists* / Stolen life: *Various artists* / Private lives of Elizabeth and Essex: *Various artists* / Mr Skeffington: *Various artists* / In this, our life: *Various artists* / All about Eve: *Various artists* / Jezebel: *Various artists* / Beyond the forest: *Various artists* / Juarez: *Various artists* / Letter: *Various artists* / All this and heaven too: *Various artists.*

Cass: on RCA by BMG Records (UK). Catalogue no: **GK 43436**
Album: on RCA by BMG Records (UK). Catalogue no: **GL 43436**

CLASSIC FILM SCORES FOR ERROL FLYNN (Various artists)

Tracks: / Captain Blood: *Various artists* / Adventures of Don Juan: *Various artists* / Sea hawk: *Various artists* / They died with their boots

on: *Various artists* / Dodge city: *Various artists* / Objective Burma: *Various artists* / Sun also rises: *Various artists* / Robin Hood: *Various artists.*

Cass: on RCA by BMG Records (UK). Catalogue no: **GK 43444**
Album: on RCA by BMG Records (UK). Catalogue no: **GL 43444**

CLASSIC FILM SCORES FOR HUMPHREY BOGART (Various artists)

Tracks: / Casablanca: *Various artists* / Passage to Marseille: *Various artists* / Treasure of the Sierra Madre: *Various artists* / Big sleep: *Various artists* / Two Mrs Carrolls: *Various artists* / Caine Mutiny: *Various artists* / To have and have not: *Various artists* / Sabrina: *Various artists* / Virginia city: *Various artists* / Key Largo: *Various artists.*

Album: on RCA by BMG Records (UK). Catalogue no: **GL 43439**
Cass: on RCA by BMG Records (UK). Catalogue no: **GK 43439**

CLASSIC FILM SCORES OF ERICH WOLFGANG KORNGOLD (Korngold (composer))

Tracks: / Elizabeth and Essex / Prince and the pauper / Anthony Adverse / Sea wolf / Deception / Another dawn / Of human bondage / Sea hawk / Adventures of Robin Hood / Juarez / King's row / Constant nymph / Captain Blood / Between two worlds / Deception / Devotion / Escape me never.

Cass: on RCA by BMG Records (UK). Catalogue no: **GK 43446**
Album: on RCA by BMG Records (UK). Catalogue no: **GL 43446**

Classic Movie Music

CLASSIC MOVIE MUSIC VOL 1 (Various artists)

Tracks: / Platoon: *Various artists* / Apocalypse now: *Various artists* / Bostonians, The: *Various artists* / Testimony: *Various artists* / Amadeus: *Various artists* / Out of Africa: *Various artists* Brief encounter: *Various artists.*

Album: Released Sep '88, on AVM by AVM Records. Deleted Jan '90. Catalogue no: **AVMC 1006**
Cass: Released Sep '88, on AVM by AVM Records. Deleted May '90. Catalogue no: **AVMC 1006**
CD: Released Sep '88, on AVM by AVM Records. Deleted May '90. Catalogue no: **AVMCD 1006**

CLASSIC MOVIE MUSIC VOL

2 (Various artists)

Tracks: / Trading places: *Various artists* / 49th parallel: *Various artists* / Eddie Duchin story: *Various artists* / Story of three lovers: *Various artists* / Slaughterhouse 5: *Various artists.*

CD: Released Jan '89, on AVM by AVM Records. Deleted May '90. Catalogue no: **AVMCD 1015**
Cass: Released Jan '89, on AVM by AVM Records. Deleted May '90. Catalogue no: **AVMC 1015**
Album: Released Jan '89, on AVM by AVM Records. Deleted Jan '90. Catalogue no: **AVM 1015**

CLASSIC MOVIE MUSIC VOL 3 (Various artists)

Tracks: / Raging bull, Theme from: *Various artists* (Intermezzo from Cavalleria Rusticana) / Room with a view: *Various artists* / Manhattan: *Various artists* / Lonely passion of Judith Hearne, The: *Various artists* / 2001: *Various artists* / Fantasia: *Various artists.*

Cass: Released Feb '89, on AVM by AVM Records. Deleted May '90. Catalogue no: **AVMC 1026**
Album: Released Feb '89, on AVM by AVM Records. Deleted Jan '90. Catalogue no: **AVM 1026**
CD: Released Feb '89, on AVM by AVM Records. Deleted May '90. Catalogue no: **AVMCD 1026**

Classic Themes For...

CLASSIC THEMES FOR CLASSIC FILMS (Various artists)

Tracks: / Apocalypse now: *Various artists* / Barry Lyndon: *Various artists* / Clockwork orange, A: *Various artists* / Gallipoli: *Various artists* / Elephant man: *Various artists* / Deer hunter: *Various artists* / Diva: *Various artists* / Kramer vs Kramer: *Various artists* / Ordinary people: *Various artists* / 10: *Various artists* / Raging bull: *Various artists* / 2001 - a space odyssey: *Various artists.*

Cass set: on CBS by CBS Records & Distribution. Catalogue no: **MGT 39495**

Classmates

CLASSMATES (See under Paige, Elaine)

Clayderman, Richard

BRETTS, THEME FROM
Tracks: / Bretts, Theme from / Eastenders, Theme from.

7" Single: Released Nov '87, on Decca by Decca International. Deleted '88. Catalogue no: **RC 110**

PLAYS THE LOVE SONGS OF ANDREW LLOYD WEBBER

Tracks: / Phantom of the opera / Music of the night / Love changes everything / High flying adored / Seeing is believing / All I ask of you / Don't cry for me Argentina / Another suitcase in another hall / Tell me on a Sunday / I don't know how to love him / Memory / Take that look off your face.

Album: Released Nov '89, on Polygram by PolyGram UK Ltd. Catalogue no: **828 175 1**

CD: Released Nov '89, on Polygram by PolyGram UK Ltd. Catalogue no: **828 175 2**

Cass: Released Nov '89, on Polygram by PolyGram UK Ltd. Catalogue no: **828 175 4**

Cliff, Jimmy

MANY RIVERS TO CROSS

Tracks: / Many rivers to cross.
Note: Featured in the film 'The Harder They Come'.

12" Single: Released '83, on Trojan by Trojan Records. Catalogue no: **TROT 9075**

YOU CAN GET IT IF YOU REALLY WANT

Tracks: / You can get it if you really want / Many rivers to cross
Note: Featured in the film 'The Harder They Come'.

7" Single: Released May '77, on Island by Island Records. Deleted '79. Catalogue no: **WIP 6397**

Clockwork Orange

CLOCKWORK ORANGE, A (Film Soundtrack) (Various artists)

Tracks: / Clockwork orange, A: *Carlos, Walter* / Thieving magpie, The: *Various artists* / Ninth Symphony (Second Movement-Abridged): *Various artists* / March From A Clockwork Orange: *Carlos, Walter* / William Tell: *Carlos, Walter* / Pomp and circumstance march no.1: *Various artists* / Pomp and circumstance march no.4: *Various artists* / Timesteps (excerpt): *Carlos, Walter* / Overture to the sun: *Carlos, Walter* / I want to marry a lighthouse keeper: *Various artists* / Suicide Scherzo: *Carlos, Walter* / Singin' In The Rain:

Astaire, Fred.

CD: Released Apr '84, on Warner Bros. by WEA Records. Deleted '87. Catalogue no: **K2 46127**

CD: Released '88, on Warner Bros. by WEA Records. Catalogue no: **K 257 32**

Cass: Released Jul '84, on Warner Bros. by WEA Records. Catalogue no: **K4 46127**

CD: Released Feb '90, on Silva Screen by Silva Screen Records. Catalogue no: **2573.2**

Album: Released Jul '84, on Warner Bros. by WEA Records. Deleted Jan '90. Catalogue no: **K 46127**

Close Encounters...

CLOSE ENCOUNTERS OF THE THIRD KIND THEME (Various artists)

Tracks: / Close encounters of the third kind: *Various artists.*

7" Single: Released Feb '78, on Arista by BMG Records (UK). Deleted '81. Catalogue no: **ARISTA 177**

CLOSE ENCOUNTERS OF THE THIRD KIND (Film soundtrack) (Various artists)

Tracks: / Close encounters of the third kind - mountain vision / Nocturnal pursuit / Abduction of Barry, The / I can't believe it's real / Climbing Devil's Tower / Arrival of Sky Harbor

Album: Released Mar '78, on Arista by BMG Records (UK). Catalogue no: **DLART 2001**

Cass: Released Mar '78, on Arista by BMG Records (UK). Catalogue no: **TLART 2001**

CLOSE ENCOUNTERS OF THE THIRD KIND / STAR WARS (Film soundtracks) (Various artists)

Album: Released Mar '78, on RCA Red Seal by BMG Records (UK). Catalogue no: **RL 12698**

CLOSE ENCOUNTERS/STAR WARS (National Philharmonic Orchestra)

Tracks: / Star wars / Little people work, The / Here they come! / Princess Leia Final battle, The / Close encounters of the third kind.

CD: Released '86, on RCA by BMG Records (UK). Catalogue no: **RCD 13650**

CLOSE ENCOUNTERS OF THE THIRD KIND / STAR

WARS (Film Soundtracks) (Los Angeles Philharmonic Orchestra)

Tracks: / Star Wars (main title) / Princess Leia's theme / Little people, The / Cantina band / Battle, The / Throne room and end title / Close encounters of the third kind
Cass: Released Feb '78, on Decca by Decca International. Deleted '88. Catalogue no: **KSXC 6885**

Cass: Released Feb '78, on Decca by Decca International. Catalogue no: **417 846-4**

CLOSE ENCOUNTERS OF THE THIRD KIND (Own version) (Tew, Alan Orchestra)

Tracks: / Close encounters of the third kind / You make me wanna boogie.

7" Single: Released March '88 on CBS by CBS Records & Distribution. Deleted '80. Catalogue no: **CBS 6138**

CLOSE ENCOUNTERS OF THE THIRD KIND (Own version) (Pourcel, Franck & His Orchestra)

Tracks: / Close encounters of the third kind / Space

7" Single: Released '78, on EMI, by EMI Records. Deleted '80. Catalogue no: **EMI 2772**

Club Paradise

CLUB PARADISE (1986 film soundtrack) (Various artists)

Album: Released '87, on CBS by CBS Records & Distribution. Catalogue no: **CBS 70298**

Cass: Released '87, on CBS by CBS Records & Distribution. Catalogue no: **40 70298**

Coal Miner's Daughter

COAL MINER'S DAUGHTER (film soundtrack) (Various artists)

Tracks: / Titanic, The / Blue moon of Kentucky / There he goes / I'm a honky tonk girl / Amazing grace / Walking after midnight / Crazy / I fall to pieces / Sweet dreams / Back in my baby's arms / One's on the way / You ain't woman enough / You're lookin' at country / Coal miner's daughter

Cass: Released Mar '87, on MCA by MCA Records. Catalogue no: **MCLC 1847**

Album: Released Apr '81, on MCA by MCA Records. Catalogue no: **MCF 3068**

Cass: Released Apr '81, on MCA by MCA Records. Catalogue no: **MCFC 3068**

Album: Released Mar '87, on MCA by MCA Records. Catalogue no: **MCL 1847**

Cobra

COBRA (1986 film soundtrack) (Various artists)
Tracks: / Voice of America's son: *Cafferty, John & The Beaver Brown Band* / Feel the heat: *Beauvoir, Jean* / Loving on borrowed time: *Knight, Gladys & Bill Medley* / Skyline: *Levay, Sylvester* / Hold on to your vision: *Wright, Gary* / Suave: *Miami Sound Machine* / Cobra: *Levay, Sylvester* / Angel of the city: *Tepper, Robert* / Chase: *Levay, Sylvester* / Two into one: *Medley, Bill and Carmen Twillie*.
CD: Released Oct '86, on CBS by CBS Records & Distribution. Deleted Jan '89. Catalogue no: **CD 70297**
Cass: Released Aug '86, on Scotti Bros (USA) by WEA Records. Deleted '90. Catalogue no: **40 70297**
Album: Released Aug '86, on Scotti Bros (USA) by WEA Records. Deleted '90. Catalogue no: **SCT 70297**

Cobert, Robert

WINDS OF WAR (See under Winds Of War)

Cochran, Eddie

TWENTY FLIGHT ROCK
Tracks: / Twenty flight rock / Teenage cutie.
Note: Featured in the film 'The Girl Can't Help It.'
7" Single: Released Mar '80, on United Artists by EMI Records. Catalogue no: **UP 618**

Cocker, Joe

UP WHERE WE BELONG (Cocker, Joe and Jennifer Warnes)
Tracks: / Up where we belong.
Note: (Title song from the film *An Officer And A Gentleman*)
7" Single: Released Jun '86, on Capitol by EMI Records. Deleted '88. Catalogue no: **CL 413**
12" Single: Released Jun '86, on Capitol by EMI Records. Deleted '88. Catalogue no: **12CL 413**

WITH A LITTLE HELP FROM

MY FRIENDS (Original issue)
Tracks: / With a little help from my friends
Note: Theme to the award winning Channel 4 series 'The Wonder Years'
7" Single: Released Oct '68, on Regal Zonophone. Deleted Oct '71. Catalogue no: **RZ 3013**

WITH A LITTLE HELP FROM MY FRIENDS (Re-issue)
Tracks: / With a little help from my friends
7" Single: Released Aug '82, on Cube Records. Deleted '84. Catalogue no: **BAK 9**
12" Single: Released Sept '86, on Archive 4 Records. Catalogue no: **TOF 109**

WITH A LITTLE HELP FROM MY FRIENDS (Old Gold)
Tracks: / With a little help from my friends
7" Single: Released Mar '90, on Old Gold Records. Catalogue no: **OG 9232**

Cocktail

COCKTAIL (1988 film soundtrack) (Various artists)
Tracks: / Wild again: *Starship* / Powerful stuff: *Fabulous Thunderbirds* / Since when: *Nevil, Robbie* / Don't worry, be happy: *McFerrin, Bobby* / Hippy hippy shake: *Georgia Satellites* / Kokomo: *Beach Boys* / Rave on: *Mellencamp, John Cougar* / All shook up: *Cooder, Ry* / Oh, I love you so: *Smith, Preston* / Tutti frutti: *Little Richard*.
Cass: Released Oct '88, on Elektra by Elektra Records (UK). Catalogue no: **EKT 54C**
CD: Released Oct '88, on Elektra by Elektra Records (UK). Catalogue no: **960 806 2**
Album: Released Oct '88, on Elektra by Elektra Records (UK). Catalogue no: **EKT 54**

Cocoanuts

COCOANUTS (Film soundtrack) (Various artists)
Cass: Released Jan '89, on Silva Screen by Silva Screen Records. Catalogue no: **CSH 2059**
Album: Released Jan '89, on Silva Screen by Silva Screen Records. Catalogue no: **SH 2059**

Cocoon

COCOON (1985 film sound-

track) (Various artists)
Tracks: / Ascension, The: *Various artists* / Cocoon, Theme from: *Various artists* / Thru' the window: *Various artists* / Lovemaking, The: *Various artists* / Chase, The: *Various artists* / Rose's death: *Various artists* / Boys are out, The: *Various artists* / Returning to the sea: *Various artists* / Gravity: *Various artists* / Discovered in the poolhouse: *Various artists* / First tears: *Various artists* / Sad goodbyes: *Various artists*.
CD: Released Dec '85, on Polydor (Germany) by Polydor Ltd. Catalogue no: **827 041-2**
Album: Released Sep '85, on Polydor by Polydor Ltd. Catalogue no: **827 041-1**
Cass: Released Sep '85, on Polydor by Polydor Ltd. Catalogue no: **827 041-4**

COCOON 2: THE RETURN (1989 film soundtrack) (Various artists)
CD: Released Feb '90, on Silva Screen by Silva Screen Records. Catalogue no: **VSD 5211**
Cass: Released Feb '90, on Silva Screen by Silva Screen Records. Catalogue no: **VSC 5211**
Album: Released Feb '90, on Silva Screen by Silva Screen Records. Catalogue no: **VS 5211**

Cold Cut

WHAT'S THAT NOISE
Note: Theme for BBC TV's Reportage DEF II
Cass: Released Jan '89, on Ahead Of Our Time by Big Life Records. Catalogue no: **CCUTMC 1**
Album: Released Jan '89, on Ahead Of Our Time by Big Life Records. Catalogue no: **CCUTLP 1**
CD: Released Jan '89, on Ahead Of Our Time by Big Life Records. Catalogue no: **CCUTCD 1**

Cold Feet

COLD FEET (Film soundtrack) (Various artists)
Tracks: / Afternoon roundup: Various artists / Shoot the doc: Various artists Just remember: Various artists / Watch my lips: Various artists / Cowboy reggae: Various artists / Monty shows off infidel: Various artists / Maureen and

Kenny on the road: *Various artists* / Survival camp: *Various artists* / Infidel's and inspiration: *Various artists* / Isometrics: *Various artists* / Monty stole the horse: *Various artists* / It's a sham/workin' man: *Various artists* / Sheriff's a preacher, The: *Various artists* / Lizard boots, size 100: *Various artists* / Good morning: *Various artists* / Maureen's monologue: *Various artists* / Sceered fitless: *Various artists* / Monty hides infidel: *Various artists* / Have a Turkish fig: *Various artists* / Chasin' Monty: *Various artists* / Kenny's in the vat: *Various artists* / Happy now and forever: *Various artists*.
Album: Released Sep '89, on Varese Sarabande Records(USA) by Varese Sarabande Records (USA). Catalogue no: **VS 5231**
Cass: Released Dec '90, on Varese Sarabande Records(USA) by Varese Sarabande Records (USA). Catalogue no: **VSC5231**
CD: Released Feb '90, on Varese Sarabande Records(USA) by Varese Sarabande Records (USA). Catalogue no: **VSD 5231**

Cole, Nat "King"

MONA LISA
Tracks: / Mona Lisa / Kings Cross-follow Anderson.
Note: From the film 'Mona Lisa'.
7" Single: Released Aug '86, on Capitol by EMI Records. Deleted Oct '87. Catalogue no: **CL 414**

Colette

COLETTE (Original Stage Cast) (Various artists)
Tracks: / You can be sure of spring / He's a captain / I'm special / Ambitious / I never make the same mistake / Paree / Our relationship / Attention will wander / Alone with myself / You've got to do what you will do / We'll stick together / Little girl / Nothing special / Little touch of powder / Love with someone younger / Will he ever be back / Little red room.
Cass: Released Sep '80, on Evolution by Evolution Records. Catalogue no: **RSC 1006**
Album: Released Sep '80, on Evolution by Evolution Records. Catalogue no: **RSR 1006**

Collins, Phil

AGAINST ALL ODDS (See under Against All Odds)
GROOVY KIND OF LOVE

Tracks: / Groovy kind of love / Big noise (inst) / Will you still be waiting (performed by Anne Dudley).
Note: From the film *Buster*.
7" Single: Released Aug '88 on Virgin by Virgin Records. Catalogue no: **VS 1117**
12" Single: Released 'Aug '88 on Virgin by Virgin Records. Deleted '89. Catalogue no: **VST 1117**
12" Single: Released Aug '88 on Virgin by Virgin Records. Catalogue no: **VSTG 1117**
CD Single: Released '88 on Virgin by Virgin Records. Catalogue no: **VSCD 1117**

SEPARATE LIVES Collins, Phil & Marylin Martin)
Tracks: / Separate lives / Only you and I know / Only you and I know (extended mix).
Note: from the film *White Nights*.
7" Single: Released Nov '85 on Virgin by Virgin Records. Catalogue no: **VS 818**
12" Single: Released Nov '85 on Virgin by Virgin Records. Catalogue no: **VS 818-12**

TWO HEARTS
Tracks: / Two hearts / Robbery, The (excerpt) / Robbery, The (full length version).
Note: from the film *Buster*.
7" Single: Released Nov '88 on Virgin by Virgin Records. Catalogue no: **VS 1141**
12" Single: Released Nov '88 on Virgin by Virgin Records. Catalogue no: **VST 1141**
CD Single: Released '88 on Virgin by Virgin Records. Catalogue no: **VSCD 1141**

Collister, Christine

WARM LOVE GONE COLD
Tracks: / Warm love gone cold / Cavatina (From Act 2 of the Marriage of Figaro.) / Warm love gone cold - extended version (On 12" version only.) / For Lucille (12" only.).
Note: Theme from the TV series "The Life And Loves Of A She Devil".
7" Single: Released Sep '86, on BBC by BBC Records. Deleted 31 Aug '88. Catalogue no: **RESL 199**
12" Single: Released Sep '86, on BBC by BBC Records. Deleted 31 Aug '88. Catalogue no: **12 RSL 199**

Colonel Redl

COLONEL REDL-ZDENKO TAMASSI (1985 Film Soundtrack) (Colonel Kilgore's Vietnamese Formation Surf Team)
Cass: Released Dec '85, on SPI Milan (France) Catalogue no: **CCH 018**
Album: Released Dec '85, on SPI Milan (Fr) Catalogue no: **ACH 018**

Color Of Money

COLOR OF MONEY, THE (1986 Film Soundtrack) (Various artists)
Tracks: / Who owns this place?/ It's in the way you use it / Let yourself in for it / Don't tell me nothin' / Two brothers and a stranger / Standing on the edge of love / Modern blues / Werewolves of London/ My baby's in love with another guy / Color of money (main title).
Cass: Released Feb '87, on MCA by MCA Records. Deleted Apr '88. Catalogue no: **MCGC 6023**
CD: Released May '87, on MCA by MCA Records. Deleted Apr '88. Catalogue no: **DMCG 6023**
Album: Released Feb '87, on MCA by MCA Records. Deleted Apr '88. Catalogue no: **MCG 6023**

Color Purple

COLOR PURPLE, THE (Film soundtrack) (Various artists)
Tracks: / Overture/ Main title / Celie leaves with Mr Corrine and Olivia / Nettie teaches Celie / Separation / Celie and Harpo grow up / Mr. dresses to see Shug / Sophia leaves Harpo / Celie cooks Shug breakfast / Three on the road / Bus pulls out / First letter / Letter search / Nellie's letters / High life / Heaven belongs to you / Katutoka Corrine / Celie shaves Mr / Scarification ceremony / I'm here / Champagne train/ Reunion / Finale / Careless love / Dirty dozens / Miss Celie's blues / Junk bucket blues / Don't make me, no never mind / My heart will always lead me back to you / Body and soul/ Maybe God is tryin' to tell you somethin'.
CD Set: Released Jan '89, on Silva Screen by Silva Screen Records. Catalogue no: **925389 2**
2 LP Set: Released Aug '86, on Qwest (USA) by Qwest Records (USA). Catalogue no: **925389 1**
Cass set: Released Aug '86, on Qwest (USA) by Qwest Records (USA). Catalogue no: **925389 4**

Colors

COLORS (1988 film soundtrack) (Various artists)
Tracks: / Colors: *Ice-T* / Six gun:

Decadent Dub Team / Let the rhythm run: *Salt 'N' Pepa* / Butcher shop: *Kool G Rap* / Paid in full: *Eric B & Rakim* / Raw: *Big Daddy Kane* / Mad mad world: *Seven A 3* / Go on girl: *Shante, Roxanne* / Mind is a terrible thing to waste, A: *M.C. Shan* / Everywhere I go: *James, Rick.*
Note: "The best-ever rap compilation. Make your day. Buy this record." (Malu Halasa, Record Mirror, 14 May 1988.)
CD: Released Apr '88, on Warner Bros. by WEA Records. Catalogue no: **K 925713 2**
Album: Released Apr '88, on Warner Bros. by WEA Records. Catalogue no: **K 925713 1**
Cass: Released Apr '88, on Warner Bros. by WEA Records. Catalogue no: **K 925713 4**

Columbia Orchestra
BEST OF SCREEN MUSIC
Tracks: / Love story / Godfather love theme / Some enchanted evening / Melodie en sous sol / Lara's theme / Treize jours en France / Around the world / Pein soleil / La lacon particuliere, Theme de / Ticuliere / Il ferroviere / From Russia with love.
Album: Released Mar '82, on Denon Deleted '88. Catalogue no: **SX 7001**

DANCING THROUGH SILVER SCREEN (Columbia Ballroom Orchestra)
Tracks: / New York, New York / Mrs. Robinson / I just called to say I love you / As time goes by / Sentimental journey / Stranger in the night / Way we were, The / Gonna fly now / Mona Lisa / When you wish upon a star / Tammy / Fascination / Around the world / Scarborough fair / Sound of silence, The / Chariots of fire / To love again / Over the rainbow.
CD: Released '88, on Denon Catalogue no: **DC-8504**

Comedians..
COMEDIANS SING, THE (Various artists)
Album: Released Oct '76, on BBC by BBC Records. Deleted '87. Catalogue no: **REB 251**

Comedians (Film)
COMEDIANS, THE (film '67 soundtrack) (Various artists)
Note: Laurence Rosenthal score for the Richard Burton/Elizabeth Taylor film.
Album: Released Jan '89, on MCA by MCA Records. Catalogue no: **MCA 25002**
Cass: Released Jan '89, on MCA by MCA Records. Deleted Feb '90. Catalogue no: **MCAC 25002**

Comic Relief
UTTERLY UTTERLY LIVE
Cass: Released May '86, on WEA by WEA Records. Catalogue no: **WX 51C**
Album: Released May '86, on WEA by WEA Records. Catalogue no: **WX 51**

Comic Strip
COMIC STRIP (Various artists)
Album: Released Nov '81, on Springtime by Springtime Records. Catalogue no: **HAHA 6001**
Cass: Released Nov '81, on Springtime by Springtime Records. Catalogue no: **CHACHA 6001**

Coming To America
COMING TO AMERICA (1988 film soundtrack) (Various artists) (See panel below)
Tracks: / Coming to America: *System* / Better late than never: *Cover Girls* / All dressed up: *DeBarge, Chico* / I like it like that: *Rodgers, Michael* / That's the way it is (acid house remix): *Mel & Kim* / Addicted to you: *Levert* / Comin' correct: *Fad, J.J.* / Living the good life: *Sister Sledge* / Transparent: *Hendryx, Nona* / Come into my life: *Branigan, Laura/Joe Esposito.*
Album: Released Jul '88, on Atlantic by WEA Records. Catalogue no: **790 958-1**
Cass: Released Jul '88, on Atlantic by WEA Records. Deleted Jul '90. Catalogue no: **790 958-4**
CD: Released Jul '88, on Atlantic by WEA Records. Catalogue no: **790 958-2**

Commancheros
COMMANCHEROS/TRUE GRIT (Film soundtracks) (Various artists)
Note: New digital recordings of two Elmer Bernstein scores for John Wayne westerns.
CD: Released Jan '89, on Silva Screen by Silva Screen Records. Catalogue no: **VCD 47236**
Cass: Released Jan '89, on Silva Screen by Silva Screen Records. Catalogue no: **C 704.280**
Album: Released Jan '89, on Silva Screen by Silva Screen Records. Catalogue no: **704.280**

Commanding Sea
Commanding Sea (See under Davis, Carl)

Company Of Wolves
COMPANY OF WOLVES (film '81 soundtrack) (Various artists)
Album: Released Dec '84, on T. E. R. by That's Entertainment Records. Catalogue no: **TER 1094**

Scene from the film *Coming to America* - starring Eddie Murphy and Arsenio Hall

Company (Show)

COMPANY (Broadway cast) (Various artists)
CD: Released Jan '89, on CBS (import) by CBS Records & Distribution. Catalogue no: **CK 03550**
Album: Released Jan '89, on Silva Screen by Silva Screen Record Deleted Mar '90. Catalogue no: **PS 3550**
Cass: Released Jan '89, on Silva Screen by Silva Screen Records. Catalogue no: **PST 3550**

Competition (Film)

COMPETITION, THE (Original soundtrack) (Various artists)
Note: Composed by Lalo Schifrin.
Album: Released Jan '89, on MCA by MCA Records. Catalogue no: **MCA 1520**
Cass: Released Jan '89, on MCA by MCA Records. Deleted Feb '90. Catalogue no: **MCAC 1520**

Conan The Barbarian

CONAN THE BARBARIAN (film soundtrack) (Various artists)
Tracks: / Anvil of crom: *Various artists* / Riddle of steel - riders of doom: *Various artists* / Gift of fury: *Various artists* / Wheel of pain: *Various artists* / Atlantean sword: *Various artists* / Theology civilization wifeing: *Various artists* / Search, The: *Various artists* / Orgy: *Various artists* / Funeral pyre: *Various artists* / Battle of the mounds: *Various artists* / Orphans of doom: *Various artists* / Awakening, The: *Various artists*.
Note: Score by Basil Poledouris.
Album: Released '82, on MCA by MCA Records. Catalogue no: **MCF 3146**
Album: Released '89, on RCA by BMG Records (UK). Catalogue no: **PL 37666**
Album: Released Jan '89, on MCA by MCA Records. Catalogue no: **MCA 1566**
Cass: Released '89, on RCA by BMG Records (UK). Catalogue no: **PK 37666**
Cass: Released Jan '89, on MCA by MCA Records. Catalogue no: **MCAC 1566**

Conan The Destroyer

CONAN: THE DESTROYER (1983 film soundtrack) (Various artists)

Note: Score by Basil Poledouris.
Album: Released Jan '89, on MCA by MCA Records. Catalogue no: **MCA 6135**
Cass: Released Jan '89, on MCA by MCA Records. Catalogue no: **MCAC 6135**

Connection (film)

CONNECTION (1961 film soundtrack) (Various artists)
Album: Released '90, on Boplicity by Ace Records. Catalogue no: **BOP 4**

Connick, Harry Jr

WHEN HARRY MET SALLY (Original soundtrack)
Cass: Released Nov '89, on CBS by CBS Records & Distribution. Catalogue no: **465 753 4**
Album: Released Nov '89, on CBS by CBS Records & Distribution. Catalogue no: **465 753 1**
CD: Released Nov '89, on CBS by CBS Records & Distribution. Catalogue no: **465 753 2**

Connolly, Billy

SUPER GRAN (TV theme)
Tracks: / Super gran / Yootha's song.
7" Single: Released Feb '85, on Stiff by Stiff Records. Catalogue no: **BUY 218**

Conseill De Famille

CONSEILL DE FAMILLE (Original soundtrack) (Various artists)
Note: Composed by Georges Delerue.
Cass: Released Jan '89, on Silva Screen by Silva Screen Records. Deleted Feb '90. Catalogue no: **C 264**
Album: Released Jan '89, on Silva Screen by Silva Screen Records. Catalogue no: **A 264**

Consort

BY THE SWORD DIVIDED (Original Television Theme)
Tracks: / By the sword divided / Arnescote.
7" Single: Released Nov '83, on BBC by BBC Records. Deleted Sep '87. Catalogue no: **RESL 137**

MISS MARPLE THEME
Tracks: / Miss Marple theme / St Mary Mead.
7" Single: Released Dec '84, on

BBC by BBC Records. Deleted Apr '89. Catalogue no: **RESL 153**

Conti, Bill

Betrayed (See under 'Betrayed')

DYNASTY
Tracks: / Dynasty / Falcon Crest.
7" Single: Released Feb '83, on Arista by BMG Records (UK). Catalogue no: **ARIST 520**

GONNA FLY NOW
Tracks: / Gonna fly now / Reflections.
7" Single: Released Mar '77, on United Artists by EMI Records. Deleted '79. Catalogue no: **UP 36230**

Contours

DO YOU LOVE ME?
Tracks: / Do you love me / Money.
Note: "Currently a hot favourite with Dirty Dancing Fans, "Do You Love Me?" was a massive American hit back in 1962 when it reached number 2. On this side of the Atlantic it spawned cover versions by the Dave Clark Five and Brian Poole and The Tremeloes, both versions becoming top ten hits in the UK simultaneously". (RCA Records, May 1988). Featured in the films Dirty Dancing and The Wanderers.
7" Single: Released 31 May '88, on Motown by BMG Records (UK). Catalogue no: **ZB 41903**
12" Single: Released 31 May '88, on Motown by BMG Records (UK). Catalogue no: **ZT 41904**

Convoy

CONVOY (film soundtrack) (Various artists)
Tracks: / Convoy: *McCall, C.W.* / Lucille: *Rogers, Kenny* / Don't it make my brown eyes blue?: *Gayle, Crystal* / Cowboys don't get lucky all the time: *Watson, Gene* / I cheated on a good woman's love: *Craddock, Billy Crash* / Okie from Muskogee: *Haggard, M.* / Southern nights: *Campbell, Glen* / Keep on the sunnny side: *Watson, Doc* / Blanket on the ground: *Spears, Billie Jo* / Walk right back: *Murray, Anne*.
Album: Released '83, on Conifer Catalogue no: **IC 064 85597**
Album: Released Oct '78, on Capitol by EMI Records. Deleted '81. Catalogue no: **EST 24590**

Conway, Russ

SONGS FROM STAGE AND SCREEN

Tracks: / Cabaret / Man and a woman, A / Love story / I want to be happy / Born free / Everything's coming up roses / Days of wine and roses / Hello Dolly / Good old bad old days / I will wait for you / Charly girl / Charade / Raindrops keep falling on my head / Moon river / Put on a happy face / Thoroughly modern Millie.

Cass: Released Jul '86, on PRT Flashback Catalogue no: **ZCFBL 8097**

Album: Released Jul '86, on PRT Flashback Catalogue no: **FBLP 8097**

TERRY FOX THEME

Tracks: / Terry Fox theme / Floriana.

7" Single: Released Jun '84, on Music & Media Catalogue no: **RUSS 1**

Cooder, Ry

BLUE CITY (Film soundtrack)

Tracks: / Blue city down / Elevation 13 foot / True believers/Marianne / Nice bike / Greenhouse / Billy and Annie / Pops and timer /Tell me something slick / Blue city / Don't take your guns to town / Leader of men, A / Not even key west.

Album: Released Jul '86, on Warner Bros. by WEA Records. Catalogue no: **925386 1**

Cass: Released Jul '86, on Warner Bros. by WEA Records. Deleted Aug '87. Catalogue no: **925386 4**

CROSSROADS (1986 film soundtrack)

Tracks: / See you in hell, blind boy / Nitty gritty Mississippi / He made a woman out of me / Feelin' bad blues / Somebody's calling my name / Willie Brown blues / Walkin' away blues / Crossroads / Down in Mississippi / Cotton needs pickin' / Viola lee blues.

Album: Released Jul '86, on Warner Bros. by WEA Records. Catalogue no: **925399 1**

Cass: Released Jul '86, on Warner Bros. by WEA Records. Catalogue no: **925399 4**

JOHNNY HANDSOME (Film soundtrack)

Album: Released Sep '89, on WEA by WEA Records. Catalogue no: **WX 307**

Cass: Released Sep '89, on WEA by WEA Records. Catalogue no: **WX 307C**

Album: on WEA by WEA Records. Catalogue no: **925 996 1**

Cass: on WEA by WEA Records. Catalogue no: **925 996 4**

CD: on WEA by WEA Records. Catalogue no: **925 996 2**

LONG RIDERS, THE (Film soundtrack)

Tracks: / Long riders, The / I'm a good old rebel / Seneca square dance / Archie's funeral (hold to God's unchanging hand) / I always knew that you were the one / Rally round the flag / Wildwood boys / Better things to think about / My grandfather / Cole Younger polka / Escape from Northfield / Leaving Missouri / Jesse James.

Cass: on Warner Bros. by WEA Records. Catalogue no: **K4 56826**

Album: on Warner Bros. by WEA Records. Catalogue no: **K 56826**

PARIS TEXAS

(Film soundtrack) (See under Paris Texas)

Cook, Barbara

BARBARA COOK SINGS THE WALT DISNEY SONG BOOK

Tracks: / When you wish upon a star / Give a little whistle / Pink elephants on parade / When I see an elephant fly / With a smile and a song / Lavender blue / Zip-a-dee-doo-dah / Dream is a wish your heart makes, A / Second star to the right / Baby mine / Someone's waiting for you / Sooner or later / I'm late / Some day my prince will come.

CD: Released Feb '89, on Pickwick by Pickwick Records. Catalogue no: **PWK 090**

Cass: Released Oct '88, on Hallmark by Pickwick Records. Catalogue no: **HSC 3248**

Album: Released Oct '88, on Hallmark by Pickwick Records. Catalogue no: **SHM 3248**

Cook, The Thief ...

COOK, THE THIEF, HIS WIFE AND HER LOVER, THE (1989 film soundtrack) (Various artists)

Tracks: / Memorial: Nyman, Mi-chael Band / Miserre paraphase Nyman, Michael Band / Miserere London Voices / Coupling: Nyman Michael Band / Book depository Nyman, Michael Band.

Cass: Released '90, on Virgin by Virgin Records. Catalogue no TCVE 53

CD: Released '90, on Virgin by Virgin Records. Catalogue no CDVE 53

Album: Released '90, on Virgin by Virgin Records. Catalogue no VE 53

Cooke, Sam

WONDERFUL WORLD (SINGLE)

Tracks: / Chain gang / Cupi (available on 12" version only) Change is gonna come, A (available on 12" version only) / Wonderful world.

Note: Featured in the film 'Witness'.

12" Single: Released Mar '86, on RCA by BMG Records (UK) Catalogue no: **PT 49872**

7" Single: Released Jul '60, on H.M.V. by EMI Records. Deleted Jul '63. Catalogue no: **POP 754**

7" Single: Released Mar '86, on RCA by BMG Records (UK) Deleted Sep '90. Catalogue no **PB 49871**

Cooper, Alice

HE'S BACK (THE MAN BE HIND THE MASK)

Tracks: / Billion Dollar babies He's back (the man behind the mask).

Note: Featured in the film Friday 13th IV.

12" Single: Released Oct '86, on MCA by MCA Records. Catalogue no: **MCAT 1090**

7" Single: Released Oct '86, on MCA by MCA Records. Catalogue no: **MCA 1090**

SCHOOL'S OUT (OLD GOLD

Tracks: / School's out / Elected.

Note: Featured in film 'Rock'n'roll high school'.

7" Single: Released Sep '85, on Old Gold by Old Gold Records Catalogue no: **OG 9519**

SCHOOL'S OUT (SINGLE)

Tracks: / School's out.

Note: Featured in film 'Rock'n'roll high school'.

7" Single: Released Nov '76, on

Warner Bros. by WEA Records. Catalogue no: **K 16287**

7" Single: Released Jul '72, on Warner Bros. by WEA Records. Deleted '75. Catalogue no: **K 16188**

Cooper, Tom

TOM COOPER SINGS GREAT SONGS FROM MOVIE MUSICALS

Tracks: / Lullaby of Broadway / I'm old fashioned / I got out of bed on the right side / This is the moment / Spring will be a little late this year / Strictly USA / I've got my love to keep me warm / Long ago and far away / Pick yourself up / My heart tells me / Change partners / Maybe this time.

Note: This new LP is one of the nicest surprises we at Hindsight have had in a long time. Tom Cooper's brand of singing is reminiscent of Astaire, Kelly and even Van Johnson in his heyday. This is a kind of lost art in an age when most recording artists are bellowing at the top of their respective lungs and paying very little attention to the melody and lyrics. This brand new recording, with a 30 piece orchestra, includes a duet with the sterling Betty Garrett, This album is very special. We are certain you will enjoy it. It has had excellent reviews including this one - 'It gives me great joy to recommend .... a very special album for people who relish movie music and love to hear it sung with panache, feeling and sensitivity. The songs are remarkable, unhackneyed things you don't hear everyday'. Rex Reed, New York Daily News.

Album: Released '89, on Hindsight Catalogue no: **IN 218**

Copeland, Stewart

DON'T BOX ME IN (Copeland, Stewart/Stan Ridgeway)

Tracks: / Don't box me in / Drama at home.

Note: Featured in the film 'Rumblefish.'

7" Single: Released Jan '84, on A&M by A&M Records. Deleted '86. Catalogue no: **AM 177**

EQUALIZER AND OTHER CLIFFHANGERS

Tracks: / Lurking solo / Music box / Screaming Lord Cole and the comanches / Equalizer busy equalizing, The / Green fingers (ten thumbs) / Archie David in overtime / Tancred ballet / Dark ships / Flowershop quintet / Rag pole dance.

CD: Released '89, on I.R.S (Illegal) by I.R.S.Records. Catalogue no: **ILPCD 36**

EQUALIZER, THE (SINGLE)

Tracks: / Equalizer, The / Equalizer (edit), The.

7" Single: Released 21 Nov '87, on I.R.S (Illegal) by I.R.S.Records. Catalogue no: **IRM 147**

12" Single: Released 21 Nov '87, on I.R.S (Illegal) by I.R.S.Records. Catalogue no: **IRMT 147**

EQUALIZER (TV Soundtrack)

CD: Released 26 Feb '88, on MCA by MCA Records. Deleted Dec '89. Catalogue no: **DMIRF 1029**

Album: Released 26 Feb '88, on I.R.S (Illegal) by I.R.S.Records. Deleted Dec '89. Catalogue no: **MIRF 1029**

Cass: Released 26 Feb '88, on I.R.S (Illegal) by I.R.S.Records. Deleted Dec '89. Catalogue no: **MIRFC 1029**

RUMBLE FISH (Film Soundtrack)

Tracks: / Don't box me in / Tulsa tango / Our mother is alive / Party at someone else's place / Biff gets stomped by Rust James / Brothers on wheels / West Tulsa rags / Father on the stairs.

Cass: Released Jan '84, on A&M by A&M Records. Catalogue no: **CXM 64983**

Album: Released Jan '84, on A&M by A&M Records. Catalogue no: **AMLX 64983**

Copkiller

COPKILLER (1983 Film Soundtrack) (Various artists)

Album: Released Mar '86, on General Music (France) Catalogue no: **803 074**

Cass: Released Mar '86, on General Music (France) Catalogue no: **804 074**

Corbett, Harry H.

MORE JUNK (Corbett, Harry H./Wilfred Brambell)

Album: Released Mar '64, on Pye Deleted '69. Catalogue no: **NPL 18090**

STEPTOE & SON (Corbett, Harry H./Wilfred Brambell)

Album: Released '69, on Marble Arch Catalogue no: **MAL 1160**

Album: Released Mar '63, on Pye Deleted '68. Catalogue no: **NPL 18081**

Album: Released '72, on Hallmark by Pickwick Records. Deleted '88. Catalogue no: **HMA 238**

STEPTOE & SON VOL.2 (Corbett, Harry H./Wilfred Brambell)

Album: Released Mar '64, on Pye Deleted '69. Catalogue no: **GGL 0217**

Corbett, Ronnie

TWO RONNIES (See under Barker, Ronnie)

Corbucci, Sergio

MUSIC FROM 3 SERGIO CORBUCCI WESTERNS (Various artists)

Note: Ennio Morricone scores for: The Hellbenders, Companeros and Che C'Entriamo noi con la revolutione.

Album: Released Jan '89, on Silva Screen by Silva Screen Records. Catalogue no: **IMGM 009**

Cordell, Frank

BRITISH FILM MUSIC (Cordell, Frank & The Phoenix Orchestra)

Tracks: / Ring of bright water / Demon (God told me to).

Album: Released Jan '83, on Phoenix Digital Deleted '85. Catalogue no: **DGS 1004**

Coronation Street

CORONATION STREET (Original cast) (Various artists)

Cass: Released Oct '87, on K-Tel by K-Tel Records. Catalogue no: **OCE 2378**

Album: Released Oct '87, on K-Tel by K-Tel Records. Catalogue no: **ONE 1378**

Cosmos

COSMOS (TV Soundtrack) (Various artists)

Tracks: / Heaven and hell: Vangelis / Symphony No. 11 (Shostakovich): *Shostakovich (composer)* / Alpha: *Vangelis* / Depicting the cranes in their nest: *Japanese Trad* / Canon A 3 in D on

ground: *Various artists* / Four seasons (spring), The: *Vivaldi (composer)* / Sea named Solaris: *Bach(composer)* / Partita no. 3: *Bach(composer)* / Symphony No. 19 (Hovhaness): *Hovhaness* / Legacy: *Synergy* / Russian easter festival overture: *Rimsky-Korsakov (composer)* / Inside the heart of the universe: *Takemitsu* / Fly night bird: *Buchanan* / Beauborg part 2: *Vangelis* / Rite of spring, The / Entends tu les chiens aboyer / Sky: *Vangelis* / Bulgarian shepherdess song: *Trad* / Heaven and hell (part 1): *Vangelis*.
Album: Released Aug '81, on RCA by BMG Records (UK). Deleted Aug '86. Catalogue no: **RCALP 5032**
Cass: Released '84, on RCA by BMG Records (UK). Deleted '87. Catalogue no: **BK 89334**
Album: Released '84, on RCA by BMG Records (UK). Deleted '87. Catalogue no: **BL 89334**

Cotton Club

COTTON CLUB (Film soundtrack) (Barry, John)
Album: Released Feb '90, on Silva Screen by Silva Screen Records. Catalogue no: **GHS 24062**
Cass: Released Feb '90, on Silva Screen by Silva Screen Records. Catalogue no: **M5G 24062**

COTTON CLUB (Film soundtrack) (Various artists)
Tracks: / Mooche, The: *Various artists* / Cotton Club stomp No.2: *Various artists* / Drop me off in Harlem: *Various artists* / Creole love call: *Various artists* / ring dem bells: *Various artists* / East St. Louis toodle-oo: *Various artists* / Truckin': *Various artists* / Ill wind: *Various artists* / Cotton Club stomp No.1: *Various artists* / Mood indigo: *Various artists* / Minnie the moocher: *Various artists* / Copper coloured gal: *Various artists* .
CD: Released '88, on CBS by CBS Records & Distribution. Catalogue no: **CD CBS 702 96**
CD: Released Aug '88, on Giants of Jazz by Hasmick Promotions. Catalogue no: **CD 53022**
Album: Released Sep '87, on Lotus Catalogue no: **LOP 14 105**
Album: Released May '85, on Geffen by Geffen Records (USA). Deleted '87. Catalogue no: **GEF 70260**
Cass: Released May '85, on Gef-

fen by Geffen Records (USA). Deleted '87. Catalogue no: **40 70260**

COTTON CLUB, THE (1985 Film Soundtrack) (Various artists)
Tracks: / Cotton Club stomp: *Ellington, Duke and his Cotton Club Orchestra* / Just a crazy song: *Robinson, Bill 'Bojangles'* / Am I blue?: *Waters, Ethel* / Heebie jeebies: *Webb, Chick/his orchestra* / I must have that man: *Hall, Adelaide* / Stormy weather: *Arlen, Harold* / When you're smiling: *Armstrong, Louis/his orchestra* / Lazybones: *Williams, Midge* / Old yazoo: *Calloway, Cab & His Orchestra* / Honey just for you: *Kirk, Andy/his Twelve Clouds of Joy* / Between the Devil and the deep blue sea: *Armstrong, Louis/his orchestra* / Sweet rhythm: *Lunceford, Jimmie/his Chickasaw Syncopators* / Blues I love to sing, The: *Hall, Adelaide* / Kicking the gong around: *Calloway, Cab & His Orchestra* / Serenade to a wealthy widow: *Foresythe, Reginald* / Jubilee stomp: *Ellington, Duke and his Cotton Club Orchestra* / I can't give you anything but love: *Waters, Ethel* / Doin' the new low down: *Mills, Irving*.
Album: Released 1 Oct '84, on Living Era by Academy Sound & Vision Records. Catalogue no: **AJA 5031**
CD: Released Oct '88, on Living Era by Academy Sound & Vision Records. Catalogue no: **CD AJA 5031**
Cass: Released 1 Oct '84, on Living Era by Academy Sound & Vision Records. Catalogue no: **ZC AJA 5031**

Cotton Comes To ...

COTTON COMES TO HARLEM (Film soundtrack) (Various artists)
Tracks: / Cotton comes to Harlem: *Various artists* / Coffin Ed and Grave Digger: *Various artists* / Going home: *Various artists* / Sunlight shining: *Various artists* / Man in distress: *Various artists* / Harlem meldey: *Various artists* / Black enough: *Various artists* / Stockyard: *Various artists* / Loving ballad: *Various artists* / Deke: *Various artists* / Down in my soul: *Various artists* / Harlem by day: *Various artists* / My salvation: *Various ar-

tists* / Ed and Digger: *Various artists*.
Note: Music and songs by Galt MacDermott (composer of Hair).
Cass: Released Jan '89, on MCA by MCA Records. Deleted Feb '90. Catalogue no: **MCAC 25133**
Album: Released '73, on United Artists by EMI Records. Deleted '78. Catalogue no: **UAS 29119**
Album: Released Jan '89, on MCA by MCA Records. Catalogue no: **MCA 25133**

Count Of Luxembourg

COUNT OF LUXEMBOURG (Sadler's Wells Cast) (Various artists)
Cass: Released Apr '83, on T. E. R. by That's Entertainment Records. Catalogue no: **ZCTER 1050**
Album: Released Apr '83, on T. E. R. by That's Entertainment Records. Catalogue no: **TER 1050**
CD: Released Apr '83, on T. E. R. by That's Entertainment Records. Catalogue no: **CDTER 1050**

Countess Maritza

COUNTESS MARITZA (Sadler's Wells cast) (Various artists)
Cass: Released Apr '83, on T. E. R. by That's Entertainment Records. Catalogue no: **ZCTER 1051**
Album: Released Apr '83, on T. E. R. by That's Entertainment Records. Catalogue no: **TER 1051**
CD: Released Apr '83, on T. E. R. by That's Entertainment Records. Catalogue no: **CDTER 1051**

Country (film)

COUNTRY (1985 Film Soundtrack) (Various artists)
Album: Released '87, on Windham Hill by Windham Hill Records (USA). Catalogue no: **WH 1039**
Cass: Released '87, on Windham Hill by Windham Hill Records (USA). Catalogue no: **WHC 1039**

Country Diary Of...

COUNTRY DIARY OF AN EDWARDIAN LADY (See under Lord, Jon)

Countryman

COUNTRYMAN (1980 Film soundtrack) (Various artists)
Cass set: Released May '82, on Island by Island Records. Deleted Jul '87. Catalogue no:

ZISTDA 1
2 LP Set: Released May '82, on Island by Island Records. Catalogue no: **ISTDA 1**

COUNTRYMAN (VIDEO) (Various artists)
VHS: Released '88, on Channel 5 by Channel 5 Video. Catalogue no: **CFV 05882**

Coup De Villes

BIG TROUBLE IN LITTLE CHINA (THEME)
Tracks: / Big trouble in little China / Pork chop express.
7" Single: Released Nov '86, on Silva Screen by Silva Screen Records. Catalogue no: **SILVA 101**

Courier

COURIER (1988 film soundtrack) (Various artists)
Tracks: / Burn clear: *Something Happens* / Wild white house: *Hothouse Flowers* / Kill the one I love: *Lord John White* / Courier - it's a dangerous game, The: *Aslan* / Silly dreams: *Cry Before Dawn* / Walk to the water: *U2* / Painted villain: *McManus, Declan* / Stalkin': *McManus, Declan* / Funeral music: *McManus, Declan* / Rat poison: *McManus, Declan* / Unpainted villain: *McManus, Declan* / Last boat leaving: *McManus, Declan*.
Note: Music by U2, Aslan, Elvis Costello etc.
Cass: Released Feb '88, on Virgin by Virgin Records. Deleted Jun '90. Catalogue no: **TCV 2517**
CD: Released '88, on Virgin by Virgin Records. Catalogue no: **CDV 2517**
Album: Released 12 Feb '88, on Virgin by Virgin Records. Deleted May '90. Catalogue no: **V 2517**

Cousteau's Amazon

COUSTEAU'S AMAZON (Film soundtrack)
Note: TV Documentary with a John Scott score.
Album: Released Jan '89, on Silva Screen by Silva Screen Records. Catalogue no: **STV 81220**

Cover Girl (Film)

COVER GIRL/YOU WERE NEVER LOVELIER (1944 film soundtracks) (Various artists)
Note: Starring Rita Hayworth and Gene Kelly.

Album: Released Jan '89, on Silva Screen by Silva Screen Records. Catalogue no: **CC 100.24**

Covington, Julie

DON'T CRY FOR ME ARGENTINA
Tracks: / Don't cry for me Argentina.
7" Single: Released Oct '88, on MCA by MCA Records. Catalogue no: **MCA 260**

Coward, Noel

BITTER SWEET (See under Bitter Sweet)

GREAT SHOWS
Tracks: / **From** *Bitter sweet:* / I'll see you again / If love were all / Dear little cafe' / Zigeuner / **From** *Cavalcade:* / Lover of my dreams / Twentieth century blues / Toast to England / **From** *Conversation piece:* / I'll follow my secret heart / Regency rakes / Charming, charming / Dear little soldiers / There's always something fishy about the French / English lessons / Melanie's aria / Nevermore / **From** *Operette:* / Countess Mitzi / Dearest love / Gypsy melody / Stately homes of England The / Where are the songs we sung? / **From** *Ace of clubs:* / Nothing can last forever / I'd never know / Something about a sailor / My kind of man / This could be true / Josephine / Sail away / Why does love get in the way / In a boat on a lake with my darling / Chase me Charlie / Evening in summer / I like America / Three juvenile delinquents.
Note: A third re-issue from the series of Noel Coward double album packages originally released on World Records. Features a selection from some of the favourite shows written by Coward - the songwriter, director, actor, novelist, playwrite and singer. Sleeve notes give a brief history of each of the five shows paid tribute in this collection: *Bitter sweet, Cavalcade,* Conversation piece, *Operette,* and *Ace of clubs;* along with scenes from the shows pictured on the gatefold inner spread.
2 LP Set: Released Nov '86, on Retrospect by EMI Records. Deleted 31 Jul '88. Catalogue no: **SHB 179**

Cass Set: Released Nov '86, on Retrospect by EMI Records. Deleted 31 Jul '88. Catalogue no: **TC SHB 179**

NOEL COWARD SINGS HIS SCORE (The girl who came to supper)
Album: Released Jul '79, on DRG (USA) by DRG Records (USA). Deleted Jan '89. Catalogue no: **SL 5178**

Cowboy (Film)

COWBOY (Film soundtrack) (Various artists)
Note: George Duning score.
Album: Released Jan '89, on Silva Screen by Silva Screen Records. Catalogue no: **DL 8684**

Cradle Will Rock

CRADLE WILL ROCK, THE (1985 Original London cast) (Various artists)
Tracks: / Moll's song: *Various artists* / I'll show you guys: *Various artists* / Solicitin': *Various artists* / Hard times/the sermon: *Various artists* / Croon spoon: *Various artists* / Freedom of the press, The: *Various artists* / Let's do something: *Various artists* / Honolulu: *Various artists* / Summer weather: *Various artists* / Love duet(Gus and Sadie): *Various artists* / Don't let me keep you: *Various artists* / Ask us again: *Various artists* / Art for arts sake: *Various artists* / Nickel under your foot, The: *Various artists* / Cradle will rock, The: *Various artists* / Joe worker: *Various artists* / Cradle will rock, The(Final scene): *Various artists*.
Album: Released Oct '85, on T. E. R. by That's Entertainment Records. Catalogue no: **TER 1105**
CD: Released '86, on T. E. R. by That's Entertainment Records. Deleted Mar '90. Catalogue no: **CDTER 1105**
Cass: Released Oct '85, on T. E. R. by That's Entertainment Records. Deleted Mar '90. Catalogue no: **ZCTER 1105**

Crawford, Joan

SELECTIONS FROM HER FILMS
Album: Released Jan '89, on Silva Screen by Silva Screen Rec-

ords. Catalogue no: **CC 100-23**

Crawford, Michael

MICHAEL CRAWFORD - STAGE AND SCREEN
Tracks: / West Side story / What'll I do / Unexpected song / If I loved you / Before the parade passes by / When you wish upon a star / In the still of the night / Memory / Not a day goes by / Bring him home / You'll never walk alone.
Cass: Released Nov '87, on Telstar by Telstar Records (UK). Catalogue no: **STAC 2308**
Album: Released Nov '87, on Telstar by Telstar Records (UK). Catalogue no: **STAR 2308**
CD: Released Nov '87, on Telstar by Telstar Records (UK). Catalogue no: **TCD 2308**

MUSIC OF THE NIGHT (Crawford, Michael & Sarah Brightman)
Note: Taken from the musical 'Phantom Of The Opera'
Tracks: Music of the night / Wishing you were somehow here again.
7" Single: Released Jan '87, on Polydor by Polydor Ltd. Catalogue no: **POSP 803**
12" Single: on Polydor by Polydor Ltd. Deleted Aug '87. Catalogue no: **POSPX 803**

Crawlspace

CRAWLSPACE (1985 film soundtrack) (Various artists)
Note: Sci/Fi horror film with score by Pino Donaggio (Dressed To Kill, Piranha, Don't look now)
Album: Released Jan '89, on Silva Screen by Silva Screen Records. Catalogue no: **STV 81279**

Creatures The World

CREATURES THE WORLD FORGOT/WHEN DINOSAURS RULED (Film soundtracks) (Various artists)
Note: 2 Scores by Mario Nascimbene (The Vikings, 1 Million Years BC)..
Album: Released Jan '89, on Silva Screen by Silva Screen Records. Catalogue no: **LD 3**

Creedence Clearwater

BAD MOON RISING
Tracks: / Bad moon rising / Have you ever seen the rain? / Keep on chooglin' (Track on 12in single only.).
Note: Featured in the film 'An

American Werewolf In London'.
7" Single: Released Aug '69, on Liberty by EMI Records. Deleted Aug '72. Catalogue no: **LBF 15230**
7" Single: Released Jun '88, on Fantasy by Ace Records. Deleted Jan '90. Catalogue no: **NS 124**
12" Single: Released Jun '88, on Fantasy by Ace Records. Deleted Jan '90. Catalogue no: **NST 124**
7" Single: Released Oct '81, on Fantasy by Ace Records. Catalogue no: **GOLD 530**

BAD MOON RISING (OLD GOLD)
Tracks: / Long as I can see the light / Bad moon rising.
7" Single: Released Sep '85, on Old Gold by Old Gold Records. Catalogue no: **OG 9569**

Creepshow (Film)

CREEPSHOW (1982 film soundtrack) (Various artists)
Note: Film of Stephen King short stories. Horror score by John Harrison.
Album: Released Jan '89, on Silva Screen by Silva Screen Records. Catalogue no: **STV 81160**

Crimes Of The Heart

CRIMES OF THE HEART (1987 film soundtrack) (Various artists)
Tracks: / Crimes of the heart:Introduction: *Various artists* / Crimes of the heart: *Various artists* / Meg: *Various artists* / Ice cream: *Various artists* / Doc Porter: *Various artists* / Babe: *Various artists* / Night to day: *Various artists* / Broom chase: *Various artists* / Lonely hearts club: *Various artists* / Meg and Babe: *Various artists* / Study: *Various artists* / Flirtation: *Various artists* / Wily Jay: *Various artists* / Toes: *Various artists* / Bus ride: *Various artists* / Old Grandaddy: *Various artists* / Sunset: *Various artists* / Crimes of the heart:main theme: *Various artists* / Wily Jay away: *Various artists* / Dusk for night: *Various artists* / Crimes: *Various artists* / Crimes of the heart:End title: *Various artists*.
Note: Composed by Georges Delerue.
Album: Released May '89, on T. E. R. by That's Entertainment Records. Catalogue no: **TER 1130**

CD: Released Jan '89, on T. E. R. by That's Entertainment Records. Deleted Feb '90. Catalogue no: **VCD 47278**
Cass: Released Jan '89, on T. E. R. by That's Entertainment Records. Deleted Feb '90. Catalogue no: **CTV 81298**

Criminal Law

CRIMINAL LAW (1988 film soundtrack) (Various artists)
Note: Music by Jerry Goldsmith.
CD: Released Dec '88, on Take 7 Catalogue no: **VSD 5210**
Cass: Released Feb '90, on Varese Sarabande Records(USA) by Varese Sarabande Records (USA). Catalogue no: **VSC 5210**
Album: Released Dec '88, on Take 7 Catalogue no: **VS 5210**

Crisp, Quentin

AN EVENING WITH QUENTIN CRISP
Cass: Released '88, on DRG (USA) by DRG Records (USA). Catalogue no: **S2LC 5188**
2 LP Set: Released '88, on DRG (USA) by DRG Records (USA). Catalogue no: **S2L 5188**
2 LP Set: Released '81, on Cherry Red by Cherry Red Records. Catalogue no: **DRED 2**

Croad, Terry Orchestra

JOHN WILLIAMS WORKS (Croad, Terry Grand Orchestra)
Tracks: / Superman / Close encounters of the third kind, Theme from / Jaws 2, Theme from / Star wars / Black Sunday, Theme from / Midway march / Fury, The (main title) / I want to spend my life with you / Earthquake - Main title / Eiger Sanction, Theme from / Cinderella Liberty, love theme.
Album: Released Mar '82, on Denon Deleted '88. Catalogue no: **SX 7006**

SCREEN REPORT (Croad, Terry Grand Orchestra)
Tracks: / Death on the Nile love theme / Don't ask to stay until tomorrow / Heaven can wait / Convoy / Love song / Superman / Nobody does it better / Goodbye girl / Olivers story love theme / How deep is your love / You light up my life.
Album: Released Mar '82, on Denon Deleted '88. Catalogue no:

SX 7011

Crocodile Dundee

CROCODILE DUNDEE (1986 film soundtrack) (Various artists)
Tracks: / Mick and his mate: *Various artists* / Cyril: *Various artists* / Walkabout bounce, The: *Various artists*/ Goodnight Walter: *Various artists* / In the truck: *Various artists* / Buffalo, The: *Various artists* / In the boat: *Various artists* / Never never land: *Various artists* / Death roll, The: *Various artists* / Sunset: *Various artists* / Nice one Skippy: *Various artists* / Walk in the bush: *Various artists* / Would you mind?: *Various artists* / Mick meets New York: *Various artists* / G'day: *Various artists* / Yessir: *Various artists* / Mad, bad and dangerous: *Various artists* / Pimp, The: *Various artists* / Stone the crows: *Various artists*/ That's not a knife: *Various artists*/ Oh Richard: *Various artists* / Pimp returns, The: *Various artists* / Crocodile Dundee, Theme from: *Various artists.*
Album: Released Dec '86, on Silva Screen by Silva Screen Records. Catalogue no: **FILM 009**
CD: Released Dec '86, on Silva Screen by Silva Screen Records. Catalogue no: **FILMCD 009**
Cass: Released Dec '86, on Silva Screen by Silva Screen Records. Catalogue no: **FILMC 009**

Cromwell

CROMWELL (Dialogue And Music From Soundtrack) (Various artists)
Tracks: / Main title - Why are you leaving England ?: *Various artists* / This is the common land: *Various artists* / Declare war on my own people: *Various artists* / Parliament...is not a gathering of lackeys...: *Various artists* / My Lord Strafford, you will rid us of ...: *Various artists*/ Warrant upon a charge of high treason: *Various artists* / Institution known as democracy, An: *Various artists* / This nation is now in a state of civil war: *Various artists* / Battle at Edgehill: *Various artists* / New army: *Various artists* / Of God, we have him: *Various artists* / Battle at Naseby: *Various artists* / King Charles is arrested: *Various artists*/ Army will not stand down: *Various artists*/ England without a king is unthinkable, An:

Various artists / I will have this king's head, aye...: *Various artists* / I am no ordinary prisoner, sir: *Various artists* / Warrant for the death of a king: *Various artists* / From a corruptible to an incorruptible crown: *Various artists* / I will see this nation properly governed: *Various artists* / Epilogue: *Various artists.*
Album: Released '73, on Capitol by EMI Records. Deleted '78. Catalogue no: **EST 640**

Cronaca Familiare

CRONACA FAMILIARE/BANDITI A ORGOSOLO (Film soundtracks) (Various artists)
Note: 2 Scores by Goffredo Petrassi & V Bucchi.
Album: Released Jan '89, on Interior Music by Interior Music Records. Catalogue no: **IM 014**

Crooked Mile

CROOKED MILE, THE (Original London cast) (Various artists)
Album: Released Jan '89, on Silva Screen by Silva Screen Records. Catalogue no: **AEI 1115**

Crosby, Bing

AROUND THE WORLD
Tracks: / Around the world.
7" Single: Released May '57, on Brunswick by Decca Records. Deleted May '60. Catalogue no: **05674**

BING CROSBY ON THE AIR - 1934
Album: Released Jan '79, on Sandy Hook (USA) Catalogue no: **SH 2002**

BING CROSBY ON THE AIR VOL 1
Tracks: / I'm hummin', I'm singin' / Heebie jeebies / I kiss your hand madame / Just a-wearyin' for you / Why don't you practise what you preach? / Love in bloom / On the sentimental side / I simply adore you / Smiles / Remember me / Guilty / Kissable baby / I cried for you / As time goes by.
Album: Released Feb '88, on Spokane (USA) by Kiner Ents.(USA). Catalogue no: **SPO-KANE 1**

BING IN THE THIRTIES VOL.1
Tracks: / Someone else may be there while I'm gone / At long last love / I'm just wild about Harry /

Have you forgotten? / I'm building a sailboat of dreams / That sly old gentleman / Ciribiribin / After all / Blame it on my youth / Japanese sandman / Things might have been different / Easy to remember / Alexander's ragtime band / Old faithful / Lullaby of Broadway.
Album: Released Feb '88, on Spokane (USA) by Kiner Ents.(USA). Catalogue no: **SPO-KANE 12**
Album: Released May '79, on Spokane (USA) by Kiner Ents.(USA). Catalogue no: **SPO-KANE 14**

BING IN THE THIRTIES VOL.1 (JSP Label)
Album: Released Aug '84, on JSP by JSP Records. Catalogue no: **JSP 1076**

BING IN THE THIRTIES VOL.2 (JSP Label)
Album: Released Jan '85, on JSP by JSP Records. Catalogue no: **JSP 1084**

BING IN THE THIRTIES VOL.3 (On the air from Kraft Music Hall)
Tracks: / Where or when / Can I forget you / Smarty / Remember me / Smile / On the beach at Waikiki / Let's call a heart a heart / So do I / 1,2, button your shoe / With all my heart / Here lies love / Please.
Album: Released Jun '84, on Spokane (USA) by Kiner Ents.(USA). Catalogue no: **SPOKANE 24**

BING IN THE THIRTIES VOL.3 (JSP label)
Album: Released Sep '86, on JSP by JSP Records. Catalogue no: **JSP 1104**

BING IN THE THIRTIES VOL.4 (On the air from Kraft Music Hall)
Tracks: / Dipsy doodle, The / On the sentimental side / On moonlight bay / I see your face before me / Moon of Manakoora / Gypsy love song / Thanks for the memory / Gypsy in my soul / You're a sweetheart / My heart stood still / Side by side / Old flame never dies, An / Sympathy / My heart is taking lessons / Down where the trade wind blows / Whistle while you work / Let's waltz for old times sake / I'd love to live in loveland / I simply adore you.
Album: Released Jun '84, on Spo-

kane (USA) by Kiner Ents.(USA). Catalogue no: **SPOKANE 25**

BING IN THE THIRTIES VOL.5 (On the air from Kraft Music Hall)

Tracks: / Ti-pi-ti-pi-tin / On the sentimental side / Mexicali rose/Sweet as a song / Where the blue of the night / My heart is taking lessons / I can dream, can't I / Don't be that way / Home town / Call me up some rainy afternoon / Love walked right in / One song / Cuddle up a little closer / Little lady make believe / You're an education / Hello Hawaii, how are you? / Flat foot floogie / Lovelight in the starlight / Silver on the Sage / Someone else may be there while I'm gone / Naturally.
Album: Released Jun '84, on Spokane (USA) by Kiner Ents.(USA). Catalogue no: **SPOKANE 26**

BING IN THE THIRTIES VOL.6

Tracks: / Small fry / Now it can be told / Ride, Tenderfoot, ride / Sleep Kentucky baby / Garden of the moon / You must have been a beautiful baby / Ya got me / Red wing / My reverie / Dipsy doodle / Who blew out the flame / Don't be that way / Lullaby in rhythm / Hurry home / When you're a long, long way from home / Funny old hills, The / I cried for you / I have eyes / Old folks / Lonesome road.
Album: Released Feb '88, on Spokane (USA) by Kiner Ents.(USA). Catalogue no: **SPOKANE 27**

BING IN THE THIRTIES VOL.7

Tracks: / Between a kiss and a sigh / Thanks for everything / Deep in a dream / Together / Missouri waltz / Could be / Teacher teacher / Umbrella man / Penny serenade / Yaaka hula hickey dula / I dream of Jeannie with the light brown hair / S'posin' / Little Sir Echo / Sing a song of sunbeams / East side of heaven / Honolulu / I get along without you very well / Sweet Genevieve / You're the only star in my blue heaven.
Album: Released Feb '88, on Spokane (USA) by Kiner Ents.(USA). Catalogue no: **SPOKANE 28**

BING IN THE THIRTIES VOL.8

Tracks: / Hang your heart on a hickory limb / I want a girl / Little Sir Echo / I'm building a sailboat of dreams / Class will tell / We've come a long way together / Mickey / Our love / Tuck me to sleep in my old Kentucky home / Delightful delirium / Wishing will make it so / Snug as a bug in a rug / Oh by jingo, oh by gee / Go fly a kite / Apple for teacher, An / Are you having any fun / If I knew then / Scatterbrain / I can't believe that you're in love with me.
Album: Released Feb '88, on Spokane (USA) by Kiner Ents.(USA). Catalogue no: **SPOKANE 29**

BING IS BACK (Philco radio time programme)

Tracks: / I got the sun in the morning / Moonlight bay / Put it there, pal / Love on a greyhound bus / Cynthia / Connecticut / A-huggin' and a-chalkin' / I've got you under my skin / Tearbucket Jim / And so to sleep.
Album: Released Jun '79, on Totem Catalogue no: **TOTEM 1002**

BING SINGS BROADWAY

Cass: Released '82, on MCA by MCA Records. Deleted '87. Catalogue no: **MCLC 1730**
Album: Released '82, on MCA by MCA Records. Deleted '87. Catalogue no: **MCL 1730**

BING'S MUSIC HALL HIGHLIGHTS

Tracks: / It's only a paper moon / You brought a new kind of love to me / Candle light and wine / Easter parade / Nevada / Put your arms around me honey / As time goes by / My ideal / After you've gone / After a while / I'm making believe / Cuddle up a little closer / Moonlight bay / Side by side.
Album: Released Oct '86, on Spokane (USA) by Kiner Ents.(USA). Catalogue no: **SPOKANE 16**

BIRTH OF THE BLUES JANUARY 23, 1951

Tracks: / Birth of the blues / Cake walk, The / Basin Street blues / Thats what I like about the south / Ida, sweet as apple cider / That's a plenty / Cuddle up a little closer / Memphis blues / Wait till the sun shines Nellie / Dixieland band / My melancholy baby / Way down yonder in New Orleans / Waiter, the porter & the upstairs maid, The / St Louis blues / Ballin' the Jack.
Album: Released Feb '88, on Spokane (USA) by Kiner Ents.(USA). Catalogue no: **SPO-**

KANE 9

EASY TO REMEMBER 1931-36

Tracks: / Out of nowhere / Now that you're gone / Love you funny thing / You're still in my heart / Let's try again / I'm playing with fire / What do I care it's home / I've got to pass your house to get to my house / I would if I could but I can't / Let's spend an evening at home / I'm hummin'-I'm whistlin'-I'm singin' / Someday, sweetheart / Two cigarettes in the dark / It's easy to remember / My heart and I / Moonburn / Lovely lady / Let's call a heart a heart / South sea island magic / I never realised.
Note: Songs from films, shows, showbiz.
Cass: Released Jan '88, on Saville by Conifer Records. Catalogue no: **CSVL 190**
Album: Released Jan '88, on Saville by Conifer Records. Catalogue no: **SVL 190**

GOING HOLLYWOOD

Tracks: / Stein song, The / Out of nowhere / Ya got love / You're getting to be a habit with me / Ghost of a chance / Please / Here lies love / Down the old ox road / One, two, button your shoe / House that Jack built for Jill / Where the turf meets the surf / After all / Incurably romantic / It came upon a midnight clear / You tell me your dream / Second time around / Mister booze / Style / Don't be a do-badder.
Album: Released Feb '88, on Crosbyana Catalogue no: **UNKNOWN**

GOLDEN AGE OF AMERICAN RADIO

Tracks: / Where the blue of the night / Lady of Spain / Hello, hello / For me and my gal / Young at heart / Lazy river / Paper doll / Where is your heart / It might as well be Spring / It's only a paper moon / That's a plenty / You go to my head / Zip-a-dee-doo-dah / Tell me why / I can dream, can't I / Takes two to Tango / Mona Lisa / I'd have baked a cake (If I knew you were comin') / On a slow boat to China / You brought a new kind of love to me / My love parade / Louise / Mimi / You gotta start off each day / You belong to me / Wish you were here / May the Good Lord bless and keep you / Lullaby of

Broadway.

Note: Includes duets with Judy Garland, Maurice Chevalier, The Mills Brothers and Bob Hope.

Album: Released '78, on United Artists by EMI Records. Catalogue no: **UAK 30115**

HAVIN' FUN (Live broadcasts 1949-50) (Crosby, Bing & Louis Armstrong)

Album: Released 11 Apr '87, on Jasmine by Hasmick Promotions. Catalogue no: **JASM 2508**

Album: Released Jan '88, on Sounds Rare Catalogue no: **SR 5009**

Cass: Released 11 Apr '87, on Jasmine by Hasmick Promotions. Catalogue no: **JASMC 2508**

HOLIDAY INN AND THE BELLS OF ST. MARY'S (Radio adaptations)

Tracks: / White Christmas / Happy holiday / Abraham / Be careful, it's my heart / Easter parade / Aren't you glad you're you / Bells of St. Mary's.

Album: Released May '79, on Spokane (USA) by Kiner Ents.(USA). Catalogue no: **SPOKANE 15**

KRAFT MUSIC HALL APRIL 16, 1942

Tracks: / K-K-K-Katy / Arthur Murray taught me dancing in a hurry / Miss you / He comes from timbuck-three / Make believe / I'll be with you in apple blossom time / Little Bo Peep has lost her Jeep / Pass the bisquits Mirandy / It's Mary / Way you look tonight / Song of the islands.

Album: Released Feb '88, on Spokane (USA) by Kiner Ents.(USA). Catalogue no: **SPOKANE 4**

KRAFT MUSIC HALL APRIL 30, 1942

Tracks: / Hey Mable, Wait for me / He's wonderful / Friendship / It's Mary / It's somebody else's moon not mine / I'll be with you in apple blossom time / Malaguena / Blues in the night / Oh how I miss you tonight / Embraceable you / I remember you.

Album: Released Feb '88, on Spokane (USA) by Kiner Ents.(USA). Catalogue no: **SPOKANE 3**

KRAFT MUSIC HALL DECEMBER 24, 1942

Tracks: / Adeste fideles / Steam is on the beam, The / Why don't you fall in love with me? / Red river valley / God rest ye merry gentlemen / You'd be so nice to come home to / Silent night.

Album: Released May '79, on Spokane (USA) by Kiner Ents.(USA). Catalogue no: **SPOKANE 13**

KRAFT MUSIC HALL JANUARY 29, 1942

Tracks: / Caisson's go rolling along, The / Chattanooga choo choo / You made me love you / Deep in the heart of Texas / Blue Danube, The / Blues in the night / Rose O'Day / Gypsy airs / Home on the range / Who calls?.

Album: Released Feb '88, on Spokane (USA) by Kiner Ents.(USA). Catalogue no: **SPOKANE 11**

KRAFT MUSIC HALL MARCH 12, 1942

Tracks: / I like it, how about you? / MacNamara's band / I don't want to walk without you / Story of Jenny, The / My darling Nellie Gray / That's a plenty / Three young fillies / We're the gang that feeds the army / Anvil chorus / Miss you.

Album: Released Feb '88, on Spokane (USA) by Kiner Ents.(USA). Catalogue no: **SPOKANE 2**

KRAFT MUSIC HALL MAY 27, 1937

Tracks: / How could you? / My melancholy baby / You're here, you're there / Land of the sky blue water / Time on my hands / My little buckaroo / Forgotten waltz / Lullaby for a bazooka / Flight of the bumble bee / Where are you?.

Album: Released Feb '88, on Spokane (USA) by Kiner Ents.(USA). Catalogue no: **SPOKANE 7**

KRAFT MUSIC HALL MAY 29, 1941

Tracks: / Can't you tell? / Kerry dance, The / You're a double lovely / It was wonderful then / Stomp Caprice / Frankie and Johnny / All through the night / Hut sut song, The / Maria Elena / Things I love, The / Because of you.

Album: Released Feb '88, on Spokane (USA) by Kiner Ents.(USA). Catalogue no: **SPOKANE 17**

MUSIC HALL HIGHLIGHTS (Crosby, Bing & John Scott Trotter Orchestra)

Tracks: / My minds on you / Moonlight on the Ganges / Moon won't talk, The / Maria Ellena / Last night's gardenias / Yours / Play fiddle, play / Goodbye now / It was wonderful then / You walked by / Say si si / Fool's rush in / May I never love again / Loch Lomond / My heart tells me / It makes no difference now.

Album: Released Oct '86, on Spokane (USA) by Kiner Ents.(USA). Catalogue no: **SPOKANE 19**

PEACE ON EARTH (Crosby, Bing & David Bowie)

Tracks: / Peace on Earth / Little drummer boy / Fantastic voyage.

7" Single: Released Nov '82, on RCA by BMG Records (UK). Catalogue no: **BOW 12**

12" Single: Released Dec '82, on RCA by BMG Records (UK). Catalogue no: **BOWT 12**

RADIO MEMORIES

Tracks: / When the blue of the night / Little lady make believe / My heart is taking lessons / Gypsy in my soul, The / Whistle when you work.

Cass: Released Sep '89, on Radio Memories Catalogue no: **TRM 20029**

RADIO YEARS, THE

CD: Released '88, on GNP Crescendo (USA) by GNP Crescendo Records (USA). Catalogue no: **GNPD 9051**

RADIO YEARS, VOL 1

Cass: Released '88, on GNP Crescendo (USA) by GNP Crescendo Records (USA). Catalogue no: **GNP5 9044**

Album: Released '87, on PRT by Castle Communications Records. Catalogue no: **PYL 6036**

Cass: Released '87, on PRT by Castle Communications Records. Catalogue no: **PYM 6036**

Album: Released '88, on GNP Crescendo (USA) by GNP Crescendo Records (USA). Catalogue no: **GNPS 9044**

Album: Released Nov '85, on PRT by Castle Communications Records. Catalogue no: **NCP 704**

Cass: Released Nov '85, on PRT by Castle Communications Records. Catalogue no: **ZCN 704**

RADIO YEARS, VOL 2

Album: Released Jun '86, on PRT by Castle Communications Records. Catalogue no: **NCP 707**
Album: Released '87, on PRT by Castle Communications Records. Catalogue no: **PYL 6037**
Cass: Released '88, on GNP Crescendo (USA) by GNP Crescendo Records (USA). Catalogue no: **GNP5 9046**
Album: Released '88, on GNP Crescendo (USA) by GNP Crescendo Records (USA). Catalogue no: **GNPS 9046**
CD: Released '88, on GNP Crescendo (USA) by GNP Crescendo Records (USA). Catalogue no: **GNPD 9052**
Cass: Released '87, on PRT by Castle Communications Records. Catalogue no: **PYM 6037**
Cass: Released Jun '86, on PRT by Castle Communications Records. Catalogue no: **ZCNCP 707**

RADIO YEARS, VOL 3

Tracks: / Zip a dee doo dah / Takes two to tango / Valencia / How are things in Glocca Morra / On top of Old Smokey / Great day / If this is love / Luck old sun / Louise / Mimi / Don't let the stars get in your eyes.
Cass: Released '88, on GNP Crescendo (USA) by GNP Crescendo Records (USA). Catalogue no: **GNP5 9047**
Cass: Released '87, on PRT by Castle Communications Records. Catalogue no: **PYM 6038**
Album: Released '87, on PRT by Castle Communications Records. Catalogue no: **PYL 6038**
Album: Released '88, on GNP Crescendo (USA) by GNP Crescendo Records (USA). Catalogue no: **GNPS 9047**
Cass: Released Jan '87, on PRT by Castle Communications Records. Catalogue no: **ZCNCP 710**
Album: Released Jan '87, on PRT by Castle Communications Records. Catalogue no: **NCP 710**

RADIO YEARS, VOL 4

Tracks: / Hello Hello / Moonlight Bay / Cuanto Lagusta / Lullaby of Broadway / I can dream, can't I / Hand holdin' music / Surrey with the fringe on top / May the good Lord bless and keep you / If I knew you were coming I'd've baked a cake / You've gotta start each day

with a song / I don't know why, I just do.
Album: Released '88, on GNP Crescendo (USA) by GNP Crescendo Records (USA). Catalogue no: **GNPS 9048**
Album: Released '87, on PRT by Castle Communications Records. Catalogue no: **PYL 6039**
Album: Released Jan '87, on PRT by Castle Communications Records. Catalogue no: **NCP 711**
Cass: Released '87, on PRT by Castle Communications Records. Catalogue no: **PYM 6039**
Cass: Released Jan '87, on PRT by Castle Communications Records. Catalogue no: **ZCNCP 711**
Cass: Released '88, on GNP Crescendo (USA) by GNP Crescendo Records (USA). Catalogue no: **GNP5 9048**

SING YOU SINNERS (January 15, 1940)

Tracks: / I've got a pocketful of dreams / Don't let that moon get away.
Album: Released Feb '88, on Spokane (USA) by Kiner Ents.(USA). Catalogue no: **SPOKANE 8**

TRUE LOVE (SINGLE) (Crosby, Bing & Grace Kelly)

Tracks: / True love.
Note: From the film *High Society*.
7" Single: Released Nov '67, on Capitol by EMI Records. Deleted Nov '59. Catalogue no: **CL 14645**
7" Single: Released Nov '83, on Capitol by EMI Records. Deleted Nov '88. Catalogue no: **CL 315**

TWO COMPLETE PROGRAMS (Crosby, Bing/Bob Hope & Judy Garland)

Album: Released Jun '79, on Totem. Catalogue no: **TOTEM 1009**

WHITE CHRISTMAS (RADIO SHOW)

Album: on Black Lion. Catalogue no: **BLM 52099**

WHITE CHRISTMAS (SINGLE)

Tracks: / White Christmas / God rest ye merry gentlemen.
Note: From the film *Holiday Inn*.
7" Single: Released Dec '85, on MCA by MCA Records. Deleted Dec '88. Catalogue no: **BING 1**
7" Single: Released Dec '88, on MCA by MCA Records. Catalogue no: **MCA 111**

ZING A LITTLE ZONG (Crosby, Bing & Jane Wyman)

Tracks: / Zing a little zong.
7" Single: Released Dec '52, on Brunswick by Decca Records. Deleted Dec '55. Catalogue no: **04981**

Cross, Christopher

ARTHUR'S THEME

Tracks: / Arthur's theme / Minstrel gigolo.
Note: Featured in the film.
7" Single: Released Sep '81, on Warner Bros. by WEA Records. Deleted Jun '87. Catalogue no: **K 17847**

ARTHUR'S THEME (OLD GOLD)

Tracks: / Arthur's theme / Sailing.
7" Single: Released Jul '90, on Old Gold by Old Gold Records. Catalogue no: **OG 9935**

Cross Of Iron

CROSS OF IRON (Film soundtrack) (Various artists)

Tracks: / Steiner's theme: *Various artists* / Main title: *Various artists* / Mikael: *Various artists* / Steiner's report: *Various artists* / Captain Stransky: *Various artists* / Mikael's death: *Various artists* / Terrace, The: *Various artists* / Memories and hallucinations: *Various artists* / Eva: *Various artists* / Return to the front: *Various artists* / I hate all officers: *Various artists* / Bridge house, The: *Various artists* / Massacre, The: *Various artists* / Last confrontation: *Various artists* / Finale: *Various artists*.
Album: Released Jan '77, on EMI by EMI Records. Catalogue no: **EMA 782**

Crossing Delancey

CROSSING DELANCEY (1988 film soundtrack) (Various artists)

Note: Music by Paul Chihara.Starring Amy Irving (Anastasia, The mystery of Anna).
CD: Released Dec '88, on Take 7 Catalogue no: **VSD 5201**
Album: Released Dec '88, on Take 7 Catalogue no: **VS 5201**
Cass: Released Jan '89, on Take 7 Catalogue no: **VSC 5201**

Crossover Dreams

CROSSOVER DREAMS (1986 film soundtrack) (Various ar-

tists)
Tracks: / Elegua soyu: *Various artists* / Good for baby: *Various artists* / Rudy's theme: *Various artists* / Todos vuelven: *Various artists* / Liz's theme: *Various artists* / Goodbye el barrio: *Various artists* / Llora timbero: *Various artists* / Sin te: *Various artists* / Ecue-yambo-o: *Various artists* / Otra dia, otra amore: *Various artists* / El down: *Various artists* / Todos vuelven reprise: *Various artists* / Rudy's theme (reprise): *Various artists*.
Cass: Released Apr '86, on Elektra by Elektra Records (UK). Catalogue no: **EKT 36 C**
Album: Released Apr '86, on Elektra by Elektra Records (UK). Deleted Aug '87. Catalogue no: **EKT 36**

Crown House
CROWN HOUSE (Various artists)
Note: 1988's major Radio 4 serial - a gripping family saga set in the twenties.
Cass set: Released Sep '88, on BBC by BBC Records. Catalogue no: **ZBBC 1045**

Crowther, Leslie
WORLD I'D LIKE TO SEE

(Crowther, Leslie & Bernie Winters)
Tracks: / World I'd like to see / Strollin'.
7" Single: Released May '83, on Monarch by Monarch Records. Catalogue no: **MON 041**

Cruising (Film)
CRUISING (Film Soundtrack) (Various artists)
Tracks: / Heat of the moment: *Various artists* / Loneliness: *Various artists* / Spy boy: *Various artists* / When I close my eyes I see blood: *Various artists* / Lump: *Various artists* / Shakedown: *Various artists* / Pullin' my string: *Various artists* / Lion's share: *Various artists* / It's so easy: *Various artists* / Hypnotize: *Various artists*.
Album: Released '80, on CBS by CBS Records & Distribution. Deleted '85. Catalogue no: **70182**

Cry Freedom
CRY FREEDOM (1987 film soundtrack) (Various artists)
Tracks: / Crossroads-a dawn raid: *Various artists* / Gumboots: *Various artists* / Black township: *Various artists* / Shebeen Queen: *Various artists* / Asking for trouble: *Various artists* / Dangerous country: *Various artists* / Mor-

tuary, The: *Various artists* / Funeral, The: *Various artists* / Detention: *Various artists*.
CD: Released 20 Feb '88, on MCA by MCA Records. Catalogue no: **DMCG 6029**
Cass: Released Feb '88, on MCA by MCA Records. Catalogue no: **MCGC 6029**
Album: Released Feb '88, on MCA by MCA Records. Catalogue no: **MCG 6029**

Cut
CUT - VOL. 1 (Out-takes from Hollywood Musicals) (Various artists)
Album: Released '88, on DRG (USA) by DRG Records (USA). Catalogue no: **SBL 12586**

CUT - VOL. 2 (Out-takes from Hollywood Musicals) (Various artists)
Album: Released '88, on DRG (USA) by DRG Records (USA). Catalogue no: **SBL 12587**

Cyborg
CYBORG (1989 film soundtrack) (Various artists)
CD: Released Dec '89, on Silva Screen by Silva Screen Records. Deleted Apr '90. Catalogue no: **FILMCD 050**

D

The following information was taken from the Music Master database on September 25th, 1990.

Dad (Film)

DAD (1989 film soundtrack) (Various artists) (See panel below)
Tracks: / Dad prologue and main title: *Various artists* / Saying goodnight/Mopping the floor: *Various artists* / Playing catch / The Farm: *Various artists* / Vigil, The/Taking dad home: *Various artists* / Dad / Recovery: *Various artists* / Greenhouse, The: *Various artists* / Goodbyes: *Various artists*.
CD: Released Mar '90, on MCA (Import) by MCA Records. Catalogue no: **MCAD 6359**
Album: Released Mar '90, on MCA (Import) by MCA Records. Catalogue no: **MCA 6359**
Cass: Released Mar '90, on MCA (Import) by MCA Records. Catalogue no: **MCAC 6359**

Dad's Army

DAD'S ARMY
Tracks: / Dad's Army overture / Put that light out / Carry on on the home front / Command post / When can I have a banana again / King is still in London, The / Lords of the air / Siefgried line - We'll meet again / Floral dance, The / Nightingale sang in Berkeley Square, A / Radio personalities of 1940.
Album: on Warner Bros. by WEA Records. Catalogue no: **K 56186**

Dallas

DALLAS-THE MUSIC STORY (T.V. soundtrack) (Various artists) (See also under Lee, Johnny)
Tracks: / I wanna reach out and touch: *Brooks, Karen* / Makin' up for lost time (the Dallas lovers' song): *Gayle, Crystal & Gary Morris* / Few good men, A: *Forester Sisters* / J.R., who do you think you are?: *Keel, Howard* / Working man's song (the Ewing/Barnes legacy): *Cook, Bob* / Loneliness in Lucy's eyes (the life Sue Ellen is living): *Lee, Johnny* / I'm a survivor: *Harrison, Jenilee as Jamie Ewing* / If I knew then what I know now: *Morris, Gary* / Dallas (Dallas dreams): *Various artists* / Theme from: *Ripp, Artie & Black Gold* / Who killed Jock Ewing?: *Various artists*.
Album: Released Jul '86, on Warner Bros. by WEA Records. Catalogue no: **925325 1**
Cass: Released Jul '86, on Warner Bros. by WEA Records. Catalogue no: **925325 4**

Daltrey, Roger

FREE ME
Tracks: / Free me / McVicar.
Note: Featured in the film 'McVicar.'
7" Single: Released Aug '80, on Polydor by Polydor Ltd. Deleted Aug '83. Catalogue no: **2001 980**

MCVICAR (Film soundtrack)
Tracks: / Bitter and twisted / Escape / Free me / Just a dream away / McVicar / My time is gonna come / Waiting for a friend / White City lights / Without your love.
Album: Released '80, on Polydor by Polydor Ltd. Catalogue no: **POLD 5034**
Cass: Released '80, on Polydor by Polydor Ltd. Deleted Mar '87 Catalogue no: **POLDC 5034**

WITHOUT YOUR LOVE
Tracks: / Without your love / Say it ain't so, Joe.
Note: Featured in the film McVicar.
7" Single: Released Oct '80, on Polydor by Polydor Ltd. Deleted Oct '83. Catalogue no: **POSP 181**

Dames At Sea

DAMES AT SEA (1989 touring cast) (Various artists)
Tracks: / Wall Street: *Various artists* / It's you: *Various artists* / Broadway baby: *Various artists* / That mister man of mine: *Various artists* / Choo choo honeymoon: *Various artists* / Sailor of my dreams, The: *Various artists* / Singapore Sue: *Various artists* / Broadway baby (reprise): *Various artists* / Good times are here to stay: *Various artists* / Entracte: *Various artists* / Dames at sea: *Various artists* / Beguine, The: *Various artists* / Raining in my heart: *Various artists* / There's something about you: *Various artists* / Echo waltz, The: *Various*

Veteran actor Jack Lemmon plays bingo with
Ted Danson in *Dad*

artists / Star tar: *Various artists* / Let's have a simple wedding: *Various artists* / Dames at sea (overture): *Various artists*.
CD: Released Jul '89, on T. E. R. by That's Entertainment Records. Deleted Mar '90. Catalogue no: **CDTER 1169**
Album: Released Jan '89, on Silva Screen by Silva Screen Records. Catalogue no: **AOS 3330**
Album: Released Jul '89, on T. E. R. by That's Entertainment Records. Catalogue no: **TER 1169**
Cass: Released Jan '89, on Silva Screen by Silva Screen Records. Catalogue no: **BT 3330**
Cass: Released Jul '89, on T. E. R. by That's Entertainment Records. Deleted Mar '90. Catalogue no: **ZCTER 1169**

Damien: Omen 2

DAMIEN: OMEN 2 (See under Omen (Film)

Damn Yankees

DAMN YANKEES (1958 film musical) (Various artists)
Album: Released '90, on RCA (Australia) Catalogue no: **LOC 1047**
Cass: Released Aug '90, on Silva Screen by Silva Screen Records. Catalogue no: **GK 83948**
Album: Released Jan '89, on RCA (USA) Catalogue no: **AYL 1 3848**
Cass: Released Jan '89, on RCA (USA) Catalogue no: **AYK 1 3848**
CD: Released Aug '90, on Silva Screen by Silva Screen Records. Catalogue no: **GD 83948**

DAMN YANKEES (VIDEO) (Various artists)
VHS: Released '88, on Warner Home Video by WEA Records. Catalogue no: **PES 11196**

Damsel In Distress

DAMSEL IN DISTRESS / THE SKY'S THE LIMIT (Film soundtracks) (Various artists)
Note: Starring Fred Astaire and George Burns.
Album: Released Jan '89, on Silva Screen by Silva Screen Records. Catalogue no: **CC 100.19**

Da/My Left Foot

DA/MY LEFT FOOT (Bernstein, Elmer)
Tracks: / Mother / Therapy / Study for Christy / For mother / Love

spoken / Temptress / Secrets / Goodbye / Unspoken fear / Church and witches / Happy moment / Struggle and frustration / Da and memories / Drown the dog / Old matters / Resolution.
Album: Released Feb '90, on Varese Sarabande Records(USA) by Varese Sarabande Records (USA). Catalogue no: **VS 5244**
Cass: Released Feb '90, on Varese Sarabande Records(USA) by Varese Sarabande Records (USA). Catalogue no: **VSC 5244**
CD: Released Feb '90, on Varese Sarabande Records(USA) by Varese Sarabande Records (USA). Catalogue no: **VSD 5244**

Dan Dare

DAN DARE (Various artists)
Cass set: Released Mar '90, on BBC by BBC Records. Catalogue no: **ZBBC 1129**

Dance Craze

DANCE CRAZE (1981 Film Soundtrack) (Various artists)
Tracks: / Concrete jungle: *Specials* / Mirror in the bathroom: *Beat* / Lip up Fatty: *Bad Manners* / Three minute hero: *Selector* / Easy life: *Bodysnatchers* / Big shot: *Beat* / One step beyond: *Madness* / Ranking full stop: *Beat* / Man at C & A: *Specials* / Missing words: *Selector* / Inner London violence: *Bad Manners* / Night boat to Cairo: *Madness* / Too much pressure: *Selector* / Nite klub: *Specials*.
Cass: Released Feb '81, on Two-Tone by Chrysalis Records. Catalogue no: **ZCHRT 5004**
Album: Released Feb '81, on Two-Tone by Chrysalis Records. Catalogue no: **CHRTT 5004**

DANCE CRAZE: LIVE (VIDEO)
VHS: Released Dec '88, on Chrysalis Video by Chrysalis Records. Catalogue no: **UNKNOWN**

Dance With A Stranger

DANCE WITH A STRANGER (1985 Film Soundtrack) (Various artists)
Note: Featuring Mari Wilson. Composed by Richard Hartley.
Album: Released Jan '89, on Varese Sarabande Records(USA) by Varese Sarabande Records (USA). Catalogue no: **STV 81251**
Album: Released Feb '85, on Compact Organisation Deleted

'87. Catalogue no: **PACT 7**
Cass: Released Jul '85, on Compact Organisation Deleted '87. Catalogue no: **CPACT 7**

Dancers (film)

DANCERS (1987 Film Soundtrack) (Various artists)
CD: Released '89, on CBS by CBS Records & Distribution. Catalogue no: **CD 42565**
Cass: Released '89, on CBS by CBS Records & Distribution. Catalogue no: **40 42565**
Album: Released '89, on CBS by CBS Records & Distribution. Catalogue no: **CBS 42565**

Dancing Thru The Dark

DANCING THRU THE DARK (Various artists)
Tracks: / Paradise: *Various artists* / Power and the glory, The: *Various artists* / Jam it jam: *Various artists* / Dancin' thru the dark: *Various artists* / Shoe shine: *Various artists* / I'm livin' a life of love: *Various artists* / Caribbean queen (no more love): *Various artists* / Get busy: *Various artists* / People all around the world: *Various artists* / So many people: *Various artists* / Once in a lifetime: *Various artists*.
CD: Released Mar '90, on Jive by Zomba Records. Catalogue no: **CHIP 92**
Cass: Released Mar '90, on Jive by Zomba Records. Catalogue no: **HIPC 92**
Album: Released Mar '90, on Jive by Zomba Records. Catalogue no: **HIP 92**

Danger UXB

DANGER UXB (Performed by the Simon Park Orchestra)
Tracks: / Danger UXB (main title) / Waltz theme / We'll meet again / Honeysuckle and the bee / Nightingale sang in Berkeley Square / Till the lights of London shine again / Where or when / You are my sunshine / Moonlight becomes you / Who's taking you home tonight / Into each life some rain must fall.
Cass: Released Feb '79, on Decca by Decca International. Deleted Feb '84. Catalogue no: **KSKL 5304**
Album: Released Feb '79, on Decca by Decca International. Deleted Feb '84. Catalogue no: **SKL 5304**

Dangerous Liaisons

DANGEROUS LIAISONS (1988 Film Soundtrack) (Various artists)
Tracks: / Dangerous Liaisons (main title): *Various artists* / O Malheureuse iphigenie: *Various artists* / Beneath the surface: *Various artists* / Her eyes are closing: *Various artists* / Tourvel's flight: *Various artists* / Concerto in A minor for 4 harpsichords: *Various artists* / Success: *Various artists* / Madame de Tourvel: *Various artists* / Valmont's first move: *Various artists* / Staircase, The: *Various artists* / Key, The: *Various artists* / Ombra mau fu: *Various artists* / Ombra mai fu reprise / Mirror, The: *Various artists* / Beyond my control: *Various artists*.
Album: Released 6 Mar '89, on Virgin by Virgin Records. Catalogue no: **V 2583**
CD: Released 6 Mar '89, on Virgin by Virgin Records. Catalogue no: **CDV 2583**
Cass: Released 6 Mar '89, on Virgin by Virgin Records. Catalogue no: **TCV 2583**

Dark Crystal

DARK CRYSTAL, THE (Film Soundtrack) (Various artists)
Album: Released Apr '83, on CBS by CBS Records & Distribution. Catalogue no: **CBS 702 33**

Dark Eyes

DARK EYES (Film Soundtrack) (Various artists)
Note: Music by Francis Lai from the award winning film directed by Nikita Mikhalov and starring Marcello Mastroianni.
Cass: Released Jan '89, on DRG (USA) by DRG Records (USA). Catalogue no: **SBLC 12592**
Album: Released Jan '89, on DRG (USA) by DRG Records (USA). Catalogue no: **SBL 12592**
CD: Released Jan '89, on DRG (USA) by DRG Records (USA). Catalogue no: **CDSBL 12592**

Dark Shadows

DARK SHADOWS II (TV Soundtrack) (Various artists)
Note: TV score by Robert Cobert.
Album: Released Jan '89, on Silva Screen by Silva Screen Records. Catalogue no: **DS**

00001

Dark Star (Film)

DARK STAR (Film Soundtrack) (Various artists)
Album: Released Jan '90, on Colosseum (West Germany) Catalogue no: **CT 7022**

Davidson, Howard

DISCOVERIES UNDERWATER
Tracks: / B'Breath / Panarea / No one shall enter the ship / Aqua sub aqua / Isle Royal / Atocha / Truk lagoon.
Cass: Released Mar '88, on BBC by BBC Records. Catalogue no: **ZCF 677**
CD: Released Mar '88, on BBC by BBC Records. Catalogue no: **BBC CD 677**
Album: Released Mar '88, on BBC by BBC Records. Catalogue no: **REB 677**

VOYAGE OF THE HEROES
Tracks: / Voyage of the heroes.
7" Single: Released Oct '85, on BBC by BBC Records. Deleted 31 Aug '88. Catalogue no: **RESL 169**

Davis, Bette

MISS BETTE DAVIS
Tracks: / They're either too young or too old / Life is a lonely thing / Until it's time for you to go / Growing older, feeling younger / It can't be wrong / I've written a letter to Daddy / Loneliness / Mother of the bride / Hush hush sweet Charlotte / Speech from 'All About Eve' / I wish you love.
Album: Released Feb '83, on T. E. R. by That's Entertainment Records. Catalogue no: **PRS 1001**

Davis, Carl

CHAMPIONS THEME (Davis, Carl & Philharmonia Orch.)
Tracks: / Champions theme / Grand National.
7" Single: Released Apr '84, on Island by Island Records. Catalogue no: **IS 161**

COMMANDING SEA, THE (TV Soundtrack)
Tracks: / Golden Hind / Pipeline and underwater / Sailing from Plymouth and storm / Fair stood the wind for France / Prayer / Freedom ride / Finale ride / Oppenheimer / Investigations / Here comes the army / Glorious New Mexico / Old curiosity shop, The / Punch and Judy / Waxworks and the races / Respect the law / Malignant dwarf.
Cass: Released Apr '81, on EMI by EMI Records. Deleted '88. Catalogue no: **TC-EMC 3361**
Album: Released Apr '81, on EMI by EMI Records. Deleted '88. Catalogue no: **EMC 3361**

NAPOLEON (Film Soundtrack) (Davis, Carl/Michael Colombier)
Tracks: / Eagle of destiny / Teaching the Marseillaise / Reunion in Corsica / Pursued / Double storm / Drums of the 6th Regiment / Victor of Toulon / Bal des victimes / Tambourin / Acting lesson / Ghosts / Peroration / Strange conductor in the sky.
Cass: Released May '83, on Chrysalis by Chrysalis Records. Deleted '87. Catalogue no: **ZCDL 1423**
Album: Released May '83, on Chrysalis by Chrysalis Records. Catalogue no: **CDL 1423**

RAINBOW (See under Rainbow (Film) for information)

SILENTS, THE (Music to 10 silent movies) (Davis, Carl/London Philharmonic Orchestra)
Tracks: / Napoleon / Crowd, The / Flesh and the devil / Show people / Broken blossoms / Wind, The / Thief of Baghdad, The / Big parade, The / Greed / Old Heidelberg.
Note: Music to ten classic silent movies composed and conducted by Carl Davis. Cover includes black and white stills from the movies which were all made between 1919 and 1929.
Album: Released Nov '88, on Virgin Classics by Virgin Records. Catalogue no: **VC 790 785 1**
Cass: Released Nov '88, on Virgin Classics by Virgin Records. Catalogue no: **VC 790 785 4**
CD: Released Nov '88, on Virgin Classics by Virgin Records. Catalogue no: **VC 790 785 2**

Davis, Miles

SIESTA (Film Soundtrack) (Davis, Miles/Marcus Miller)
Tracks: / Lost in Madrid part 1 / Kitt's kiss / Theme for Augustine / Seduction, The / Submission / Conchita / Lost in Madrid part 4 / Clair / Afterglow / Siesta / Lost in

Madrid part 2 / Wind / Kiss / Lost in Madrid Part 3 / Lament / Rat dance - the call / Lost in Madrid part 5 / Ls Felez.

Album: Released Feb '88, on Warner Bros. by WEA Records. Catalogue no: **K 925655 1**

Cass: Released Feb '88, on Warner Bros. by WEA Records. Deleted Jul '90. Catalogue no: **K 925655 4**

CD: Released Feb '88, on Warner Bros. by WEA Records. Catalogue no: **K 925655 2**

Dawn Of The Dead

DAWN OF THE DEAD (Original soundtrack) (Various artists)

Note: Horror score by Italian group 'Goblin'.

CD: Released Jan '89, on Silva Screen by Silva Screen Records. Catalogue no: **VCD 47106**

Cass: Released Feb '90, on Cinevox by Cinevox Italy. Catalogue no: **CIAK 75035**

Album: Released Jan '89, on Silva Screen by Silva Screen Records. Catalogue no: **VC 81106**

Album: Released Feb '90, on Cinevox by Cinevox Italy. Catalogue no: **CIA 5035**

Day, Doris

BLACK HILLS OF DAKOTA

Tracks: / Black hills of Dakota, The.

Note: Featured in the film 'Calamity Jane.'

7" Single: Released Aug '54, on Philips by Phonogram Ltd. Deleted '57. Catalogue no: **PB 287**

DAY AT THE MOVIES, A

CD: Released Jan '89, on CBS (import) by CBS Records & Distribution. Catalogue no: **CK 44371**

Cass: Released Jan '89, on Silva Screen by Silva Screen Records. Catalogue no: **JST 44371**

DAY IN HOLLYWOOD

Cass: Released Mar '90, on Silva Screen by Silva Screen Records. Catalogue no: **PST 44371**

GREAT MOVIE HITS

Tracks: / Do not disturb / What every girl should know / Move over, darling / Canadian capers / Twinkle lullaby / Pillow talk / Please don't eat the daisies / Tunnel of love / Julie / Send me no flowers / More I see you, The / At last / Come to baby do / I had the cra-

ziest dream... / I'll never smile again / I remember you / Serenade in blue / I'm beginning to see the light / It could happen to you / It's been a long long time / Sentiental journey.

Album: Released Jun '85, on CBS (Blue Diamond) by CBS Records & Distribution. Catlogue no: **CBS 22181**

Cass: Released Jun '85, on CBS (Blue Diamond) by CBS Records & Distribution. Catlogue no: **40 22181**

GREAT MOVIE STARS

Tracks: / Que sera sera / It's magic / Secret love / Somebody loves me (From the movie 'Lullaby of Broadway'.) / Please don't talk about me when I'm gone / Lullaby of Broadway / Just one of those things / Everybody loves my baby / Love me or leave me / Never look back / I'll never stop loving you / At sundown / I want to be happy / Tea for two / Oh me, oh my / You my love / Hold me in your arms / Moonlight bay / By the light of the silvery moon / Julie.

Album: Released Sep '87, on Lotus Catalogue no: **LOP 14 132**

Cass: Released Sep '87, on Lotus Catalogue no: **LCS 14132**

HOORAY FOR HOLLYWOOD

2 LP Set: Released Jan '89, on Silva Screen by Silva Screen Records. Catalogue no: **AC2 5**

Cass: Released Jan '89, on Silva Screen by Silva Screen Records. Catalogue no: **XPT 5**

LULLABY OF BROADWAY (See under Lullaby of Broadway)

MOVE OVER, DARLING

Tracks: / Deadwood stage (Extra track on 12" only.) / Move over, darling / Teachers pet.

Note: Theme to the film.

12" Single: Released Apr '87, on CBS by CBS Records & Distribution. Deleted Nov '87. Catalogue no: **LEGST 1**

7" Single: Released Apr '87, on CBS by CBS Records & Distribution. Deleted Nov '87. Catalogue no: **LEGS 1**

7" Single: Released Mar '64, on CBS by CBS Records & Distribution. Deleted '67. Catalogue no: **AAG 183**

ON THE AIR - WITH LES BROWN

Album: Released Jan '89, on Silva Screen by Silva Screen Records. Catalogue no: **SH 2011**

Cass: Released Jan '89, on Silva Screen by Silva Screen Records. Catalogue no: **CSH 2011**

ON THE AIR - WITH LES BROWN, VOL 2

Cass: Released Jan '89, on Silva Screen by Silva Screen Records. Catalogue no: **CSH 2078**

Album: Released Jan '89, on Silva Screen by Silva Screen Records. Catalogue no: **SH 2078**

SECRET LOVE

Tracks: / Secret love / Que sera sera (Whatever will be will be).

7" Single: Released Mar '90, on Old Gold by Old Gold Records. Catalogue no: **OG 9091**

Day, Edith

EDITH DAY IN RIO RITA, ROSE MARIE & SHOWBOAT

Album: Released Mar '79, on Monmouth Evergreen Catalogue no: **MES 7058**

Day In Hollywood...

DAY IN HOLLYWOOD A NIGHT IN UKRAINE, A (Original Broadway cast) (Various artists)

Album: Released '88, on DRG (USA) by DRG Records (USA). Catalogue no: **SBL 12580**

Cass: Released '88, on DRG (USA) by DRG Records (USA). Deleted Mar '90. Catalogue no: **SBLC 12580**

CD: Released '88, on DRG (USA) by DRG Records (USA). Catalogue no: **CDSBL 12580**

De Paul, Lynsey

NO HONESTLY (SINGLE)

Tracks: / No honestly.

Note: Theme from the TV series.

7" Single: Released Nov '74, on Jet by Jet Records. Deleted '77. Catalogue no: **JET 747**

Dead

DEAD, THE (1988 film soundtrack) (Various artists)

Note: Music by Alex North from John Huston's last film as a director.

CD: Released Jan '89, on Varese Sarabande Records(USA) by Varese Sarabande Records (USA). Catalogue no: **VCD 47341**

Cass: Released Jan '89, on Varese Sarabande Records(USA) by Varese Sarabande Records (USA). Catalogue no: **CTV 81341**
Album: Released Jan '89, on Varese Sarabande Records(USA) by Varese Sarabande Records (USA). Catalogue no: **STV 81341**

Dead Heat

DEAD HEAT ('88 film soundtrack) (Various artists)
Note: Horror/comedy/thriller starring Treat Williams and Vincent Price. Music by Ernest Troost.
Album: Released Jan '89, on Silva Screen by Silva Screen Records. Catalogue no: **704.570**

Dead Poets Society

DEAD POETS SOCIETY (Film soundtrack) (Various artists) (see panel below)
CD: Released Apr '90, on SPI Milan (France) Catalogue no: **CDCH 558**
Cass: Released Apr '90, on SPI Milan (France) Catalogue no: **C 558**
Album: Released Apr '90, on SPI Milan (France) Catalogue no: **A 558**

Deadly Friend

DEADLY FRIEND (1986 film soundtrack) (Various artists)
Note: Horror score by Charles Bernstein.
Album: Released Jan '89, on Varese Sarabande Records(USA) by Varese Sarabande Records (USA). Catalogue no: **STV 81291**

Dean, Letitia

SOMETHING OUTA NOTHING (Dean, Letitia & Paul Medford)
Tracks: / Something outa nothing / Time square (instrumental).
Note: Featured in the soap opera 'Eastenders.'
7" Single: Released Oct '86, on BBC by BBC Records. Deleted 31 Aug '88. Catalogue no: **RESL 203**
12" Single: Released Oct '86, on BBC by BBC Records. Deleted 31 Aug '88. Catalogue no: **12 RSL 203**

Dear World

DEAR WORLD (Original Broadway cast) (Various artists)
Album: Released Jan '89, on Silva Screen by Silva Screen Records. Catalogue no: **ABOS 3260**
Cass: Released Jan '89, on Silva Screen by Silva Screen Records. Catalogue no: **BT 3260**

Death Before Dishonour

DEATH BEFORE DISHONOUR (Original soundtrack) (Various artists)
Note: Composed by Brian May (Mad Max).
Album: Released Jan '89, on Silva Screen by Silva Screen Records. Catalogue no: **STV 81310**

Death In Venice

DEATH IN VENICE (1971 film soundtrack) (Various artists)
Note: The original soundtrack from the classic Luchino Visconti film

starring Dirk Bogarde. Including the music of Gustav Mahler.
Album: Released '83, on RCA (Germany) by BMG Music International. Catalogue no: **26.21149**
Album: Released Jan '89, on CBS by CBS Records & Distribution. Catalogue no: **CBS 70097**

Death Of A Scoundrel

DEATH OF A SCOUNDREL (Film soundtrack) (Various artists)
Note: Music by Max Steiner plus suites from his other scores: The Searchers, 4 Wives, The Charge Of The Light Brigade.
Album: Released Jan '89, on Silva Screen by Silva Screen Records. Catalogue no: **ERM 6004**

Death Of A Soldier

DEATH OF A SOLDIER (1987 film soundtrack) (Various artists)
Tracks: / Boys from the USA: Various artists / Annie's jive: Various artists / In the mood: Various artists / Dinah might: Various artists / Sentimental dreams: Various artists / Boogie woogie bugle boy: Various artists / Jersey Trott: Various artists / Sweetie pie: Various artists / When Johnny comes marching home: Various artists / Swanston Street parade: Various artists / Overture: Various artists / Mud murder: Various artists / Shoot-out: Various artists / Pauline's murder: Various artists.
Note: Music from the film Death of a Soldier, composed by Allen Zavod and capturing the musical spirit of the 40s and the golden era of the big bands. Sleeve notes by Woody Herman and Cab Calloway.
Album: Released Jul '87, on DRG (USA) by DRG Records (USA). Deleted Jan '89. Catalogue no: **SBL 12001**

Death Of The American...

DEATH OF THE AMERICAN EMPIRE (Original soundtrack) (Various artists)
Note: Award winning Canadian film, music by Francois Dompierre.
Album: Released Jan '89, on Silva Screen by Silva Screen Records. Catalogue no: **A 298**

Deathwish

DEATHWISH II (See under Page, Jimmy)

An uplifting experience for Robin Williams in the much acclaimed *Dead Poets Society*

DeBarge

WHO'S JOHNNY?
Tracks: / Who's Johnny? / Love me in a special way / Rhythm.
Note: Featured in the film 'Short Circuit.'
7" Single: Released May '86, on Motown by BMG Records (UK). Deleted '88. Catalogue no: **ELD 1**
12" Single: Released May '86, on Motown by BMG Records (UK). Deleted '88. Catalogue no: **ELDT 1**

Deceivers (Film)

DECEIVERS, THE (1988 film soundtrack) (Various artists)
Note: A new film from Merchant / Ivory Productions, directed by Nicholas Meyer and starring Pierce Brosnan. Music composed and conducted by John Scott with the Graunke Symphony Orchestra.
Cass: Released Jan '89, on RCA by BMG Records (UK). Deleted Jul '89. Catalogue no: **BK 87722**
Album: Released Jan '89, on RCA by BMG Records (UK). Deleted Jul '89. Catalogue no: **BL 87722**
CD: Released Jan '89, on RCA by BMG Records (UK). Deleted Jul '89. Catalogue no: **BD 87722**

Decline Of The ...

DECLINE OF THE AMERICAN EMPIRE (1986 film soundtrack) (Various artists)
Album: Released '88, on Carrere (France) Catalogue no: **CAR 66390 1**

Decline Of Western...

DECLINE OF WESTERN CIVILISATION (Part II - The metal years) (Various artists)
Tracks: / Under my wheels: *Cooper, Alice* / Bathroom wall: *Faster Pussycat* / Cradle to the grave: *Motorhead* / You can run but you can't hide: *Armoured Saint* / In my darkest hour: *Megadeth* / Prophecy: *Queensryche* / Brave, The: *Metal Church* / Foaming at the mouth: *Rigor Mortis* / Colleen: *Seduce*.
CD: Released Jul '88, on Capitol by EMI Records. Deleted Jan '90. Catalogue no: **CDP 790 205 2**
CD: Released Jul '88, on Capitol by EMI Records. Deleted Jan '90. Catalogue no: **CDEST 2065**
Cass: Released Jul '88, on Capitol by EMI Records. Catalogue no:

TCEST 2065
Album: Released Jul '88, on Capitol by EMI Records. Deleted May '90. Catalogue no: **EST 2065**

DECLINE OF WESTERN CIVILISATION PART II (VIDEO) (The metal years) (Various artists)
Note: For Penelope Spheeris (director of Suburbia, Boys next door and Dudes), Metal Years is a radical development from her 1979 nihilistic Los Angeles punk rock documentary, The Decline Of Western Civilisation. This time around, she delves into the thunderous world of heavy metal music. This is quite possibly the fastest, funniest, heaviest, loudest and most sexist collection of live concert performances and interviews ever commited to video. Metal Years introduces its audience to a winning combination of metal vigilantes, raised from the ashes of a myriad of heavy rock offshoots and tribes including speed metal, thrash metal, hardcore, glam, blues and heavy rock. Spheeris interviews 80's glam band Poison, experiences the vodka pouring deathwish antics of WASP guitarist Chris Holmes, drops in on Ozzy Osbourne as he attempts to make breakfast and reminisce about his clean up campaign at the Betty Ford clinic and his self-confessed naivety when he fronted his first band Black Sabbath, converses with the Godfather of rock theatre Alice Cooper and listens to Megadeth's lead singer denying that the group's lyrics have any connection with sex or death. Penelope also hangs out with the more established and successful bands like Aerosmith, Motorhead and Kiss, with the latter eager to boast about their privileged and extravagant rock lifestyle, not to mention their sheer animal magnetism towards the opposite sex. Kiss frontman Paul Stanley pontificates about his hedonistic, Peter Pan philosophy, declaring that 'anybody can make it if they really want to'. In a more ludicrous vein, he discusses the insignificane of money while sprawled across a huge bed surrounded by a luscious assortment of long legged groupies. Rating: 18. Running time: 90 mins.
VHS: Released '88, on Palace

Video by Virgin Records. Catalogue no: **PVC 3020 M**

Dee, Kiki

STAR
Tracks: / Star / Give it up.
Note: TV theme for 'Opportunity Knocks.'
7" Single: Released '82, on Ariola by BMG Records (UK). Deleted '87. Catalogue no: **ARO 251**

Deep In My Heart

DEEP IN MY HEART (VIDEO) (Various artists)
VHS: Released Sep '89, on MGM/UA (Video) by MGM/UA Video. Catalogue no: **SMV 10626**

DEEP IN MY HEART/WORDS & MUSIC (Original soundtracks) (Various artists)
CD: Released Jan '89, on MCA by MCA Records. Catalogue no: **MCAD 5949**

Deep Star Six

DEEP STAR SIX (1989 film soundtrack) (Various artists)
Tracks: / Shock wave: *Various artists* / On eht edge: *Various artists* / Our baby's heartbeat: *Various artists* / Seatrack attack: *Various artists* / That morning: *Various artists* / Rescue, The: *Various artists* / Alone: *Various artists* / Plan, The: *Various artists* / Shark darts: *Various artists* / Snyder snaps: *Various artists* / Swim to the mini-sub: *Various artists*.
CD: Released Jan '90, on Silva Screen by Silva Screen Records. Catalogue no: **MAF 7004D**

Deep Throat

DEEP THROAT (1974 film soundtrack) (Various artists)
Album: Released Jul '81, on Sandy Hook (USA) Catalogue no: **SH 2036**

Deerhunter

DEERHUNTER, THE (1978 film soundtrack) (Various artists)
CD: Released Feb '90, on Silva Screen by Silva Screen Records. Catalogue no: **CDP 920582**
Cass: Released Jan '89, on Silva Screen by Silva Screen Records. Catalogue no: **4 XOO 11940**
Cass: Released Feb '90, on Silva Screen by Silva Screen Records. Catalogue no: **92058.4**

Album: Released Jan '89, on Silva Screen by Silva Screen Records. Catalogue no: **SOO 11940**

Def Con

DEF CON 4: DEFENCE CONDITION NO. 4 (1985 film soundtrack) (Various artists)
Note: Music by Christopher Young (Hellraiser, Elm St 2).
Album: Released Apr '90, on Geffen by Geffen Records (USA). Catalogue no: **7599260491**
CD: Released Apr '90, on Geffen by Geffen Records (USA). Catalogue no: **7599260492**
Album: Released Jan '89, on Cerebus (USA) Catalogue no: **C'BUS 212**
Cass: Released Apr '90, on Geffen by Geffen Records (USA). Catalogue no: **7599260494**

Del Mero Corazon

DEL MERO CORAZON (Film soundtrack)
Album: Released May '81, on Arhoolie (USA) by Arhoolie Records (USA). Catalogue no: **ARHOOLIE 3015**

Delerue, Georges

TRUE CONFESSIONS (See under True Confession)

Delinquents

DELINQUENTS (Film soundtrack) (Various artists) (See panel below)
Cass: Released Mar '90, on PWL by PWL Records. Catalogue no:

HFC 11
CD: Released Mar '90, on PWL by PWL Records. Catalogue no: **HFCD 11**
Album: Released Mar '90, on PWL by PWL Records. Catalogue no: **HF 11**

Delta Force

DELTA FORCE / KING SOLOMON'S MINES (Original Sound Track) (Various artists)
CD: Released Jan '89, on SPI Milan (France) Deleted Feb '90. Catalogue no: **CD 290**
Album: Released Jun '86, on SPI Milan (France) Catalogue no: **A 290**
Cass: Released Jun '86, on SPI Milan (France) Catalogue no: **C 290**

Denton, Richard

GREAT EGG RACE (Denton, Richard & Martin Cook)
Tracks: / Great egg race / Scramble.
7" Single: Released Jan '79, on BBC by BBC Records. Deleted '82. Catalogue no: **RESL 65**

HONG KONG BEAT & OTHER BBC FAVOURITES (Denton, Richard & Martin Cook)
Tracks: / Hong Kong beat / Tomorrows world / Jet lag / Spangler / Quiller / Inside story / Great egg race / Diamonds in the sky / General direction / Circuit eleven Miami / Chasing the dragon / Scramble.
Album: Released Sep '81, on

BBC by BBC Records. Deleted Sep '86. Catalogue no: **REH 385**

THEME FROM THE HONG KONG BEAT (Denton, Richard & Martin Cook)
Tracks: / Theme from the Hong Kong beat.
7" Single: Released Apr '78, on BBC by BBC Records. Deleted Apr '81. Catalogue no: **RESL 52**

Derrick Melodien

DERRICK MELODIEN (Original Soundtrack) (Various artists)
CD: Released '88, on Teldec (1) by ASV (Academy Sound & Vision). Catalogue no: **8.2414 2**

Desert Song

DESERT SONG (Various artists)
Cass: Released Feb '89, on Silva Screen by Silva Screen Records. Catalogue no: **BT 831**
Album: Released '71, on Starline (EMI) by EMI Records. Deleted '76. Catalogue no: **SRS 5053**
Album: Released Feb '89, on Silva Screen by Silva Screen Records. Catalogue no: **ACL 831**
Album: Released Oct '77, on Retrospect by EMI Records. Catalogue no: **SH 254**
Album: Released '73, on Monmouth Evergreen Catalogue no: **MES 7054**

DESERT SONG, THE (VIDEO) (Various artists)
Note: Unforgettable songs by Sigmund Romberg and Oscar Hammerstein. Running time: 106 mins.
VHS: Released Jun '89, on Warner Home Video by WEA Records. Catalogue no: **PES 11864**

Desperately Seeking...

DESPERATELY SEEKING SUSAN (Original Soundtrack) (Various artists)
CD: Released Feb '90, on Varese Sarabande Records(USA) by Varese Sarabande Records (USA). Catalogue no: **VSD 47291**

DESPERATELY SEEKING SUSAN / MAKING MR RIGHT (1987 film soundtracks) (Various artists)
Note: Starring Madonna and Rosanna Arquette. Music by Thomas Newman.
CD: Released Jan '89, on Varese

The Delinquents - Australian soap star Kylie Minogue in her feature film debut.

Sarabande Records(USA) by Varese Sarabande Records (USA). Catalogue no: **VCD 47291**
Album: Released Jan '89, on Varese Sarabande Records(USA) by Varese Sarabande Records (USA). Catalogue no: **STV 81320**
Cass: Released Jan '89, on Varese Sarabande Records(USA) by Varese Sarabande Records (USA). Catalogue no: **CTV 81320**

Destination Moon

DESTINATION MOON (Original soundtrack) (Various artists)
Note: 1950's sci/fi score by Leith Stevens.
Album: Released Jan '89, on Silva Screen by Silva Screen Records. Catalogue no: **STV 81130**

Destry Rides Again

DESTRY RIDES AGAIN (Original 1979 London cast) (Various artists)
Tracks: / Bottle neck: *Various artists* / Ladies: *Various artists* / Hoop-de-dingle: *Various artists* / Tomorrow morning: *Various artists* / Ballad of gun: *Various artists* / I know your kind: *Various artists* / I hate him: *Various artists* / Anyone would love you: *Various artists* / Ev'ry once in a while: *Various artists* / Destry rides again:Finale act I: *Various artists* / Are you ready Gyp Watson?: *Various artists* / Not guilty: *Various artists* / Only time will tell: *Various artists* / That ring on the finger: *Various artists* / I say hello: *Various artists* / Destry rides again: Finale act II: *Various artists* / Curtain call: *Various artists*.
Album: Released Apr '83, on T. E. R. by That's Entertainment Records. Catalogue no: **TER 1034**
Cass: Released Apr '83, on T. E. R. by That's Entertainment Records. Catalogue no: **ZCTER 1034**

Deux Hommes Dans ...

DEUX HOMMES DANS LA VILLE/LES SEINS DE GLACE (Original soundtrack) (Various artists)
Note: 2 Very rare Phillippe Sarde scores.
Album: Released Jan '89, on Silva Screen by Silva Screen Records. Catalogue no: **PHCAM 05**

Devil At 4 O Clock

DEVIL AT 4 O CLOCK, THE

(Original soundtrack) (Various artists)**
Note: Composed by George Dunning.
Album: Released Jan '89, on Silva Screen by Silva Screen Records. Catalogue no: **STV 81136**

Devil's Paradise

DEVIL'S PARADISE, THE (1987 film soundtrack) (Various artists)
Note: Film starring Jurgen Prochno (Das Boot) and Sam Waterson (The Killing Fields). Music by Jurgen Knieper (Wings of Desire).
Album: Released Jan '89, on Silva Screen by Silva Screen Records. Catalogue no: **ACH 034**

Devo

DOCTOR DETROIT, THEME FROM
Tracks: / Doctor Detroit, Theme from / King of soul.
7" Single: Released Jun '83, on MCA by MCA Records. Catalogue no: **MCA 822**
12" Single: Released Jun '83, on MCA by MCA Records. Catalogue no: **MCAT 822**

Dexy's Midnight Runners

BECAUSE OF YOU
Tracks: / Because of you / Kathleen / Mavoureen / Sometimes theme (12" only).
Note: TV theme for Brush Strokes.
7" Single: Released Oct '86, on Mercury by Phonogram Ltd. Deleted '87. Catalogue no: **BRUSH 1**
12" Single: Released Oct '86, on Mercury by Phonogram Ltd. Deleted '87. Catalogue no: **BRUSH 112**

Diamond, Jim

HI HO SILVER
Tracks: / Hi ho silver / Hi ho silver (instrumental).
Note: TV theme tune for Boon.
7" Single: Released Jan '86, on A&M by A&M Records. Deleted Mar '88. Catalogue no: **AM 296**
12" Single: Released Jan '86, on A&M by A&M Records. Deleted Mar '88. Catalogue no: **AMY 296**

Diamond, Neil

AMERICA
Tracks: / America / Songs of life.
Note: Taken from the film 'The Jazz Singer'

7" Single: Released Apr '81, on Capitol by EMI Records. Deleted Apr '84. Catalogue no: **CL 16197**
HELLO AGAIN
Tracks: / Hello again / Amazed and confused.
Note: Taken from the film 'The Jazz Singer'
7" Single: Released Feb '81, on Capitol by EMI Records. Deleted '84. Catalogue no: **CL 16176**
JAZZ SINGER, THE (Film soundtrack)
Tracks: / America / Adorn o lume / You baby / Love on the rocks / Amazed and confused / Robert E. Lee, The / Summer love / Hello again / Acapulco / Hey Louise / Songs of life / Jerusalem / Kol nidre / My name is Yussel / America (reprise).
CD: Released Jul '84, on Capitol by EMI Records. Catalogue no: **CDEAST 12120**
Album: Released Nov '80, on Capitol by EMI Records. Catalogue no: **EAST 12120**
Cass: Released Nov '80, on Capitol by EMI Records. Catalogue no: **TCEAST 12120**
CD: Released Jul '84, on Capitol by EMI Records. Catalogue no: **CDP 746 026 2**
JONATHAN LIVINGSTONE SEAGULL (Original Soundtrack)
Tracks: / Prologue / Be (parts 1 - 3) / Flight of the gull / Dear father (parts 1 - 3) / Skybird (parts 1 & 2) / Lonely looking sky / Odyssey, The (anthem).
CD: Released '86, on CBS by CBS Records & Distribution. Catalogue no: **CD 69047**
Album: Released '86, on CBS by CBS Records & Distribution. Catalogue no: **CBS 69047**
Cass: Released '82, on Caedmon (USA) by Caedmon Records (USA). Catalogue no: **CDL 51639**
LOVE ON THE ROCKS
Tracks: / Love on the rocks / Acapulco.
Note: Taken from the film 'The Jazz Singer'
7" Single: Released Nov '80, on Capitol by EMI Records. Catalogue no: **CL 16173**

Diamonds Are Forever

DIAMONDS ARE FOREVER (See under Bassey, Shirley)

Dick Barton

DICK BARTON (Various artists)

Cass set: Released Sep '89, on BBC by BBC Records. Catalogue no: **ZBBC 1063**

Dick Tracy

DICK TRACY (Film soundtrack) (Various artists)
Tracks: / Dick Tracy (theme): *Various artists* / After the 'kid': *Various artists* / Crime spree: *Various artists* / Breathless theme: *Various artists* / Big boy, bad boy: *Various artists* / Tess' theme: *Various artists* / Slimy D.A.: *Various artists* / Breathless comes on: *Various artists* / Meet the blank: *Various artists* / Story unfolds, The: *Various artists* / Tess' theme (reprise): *Various artists* / Chase, The: *Various artists* / Showdown (reunited): *Various artists* / Dick Tracy (finale): *Various artists*.
CD: Released Jun '90, on Warner Bros. by WEA Records. Catalogue no: **7599262362**
Album: Released Jun '90, on Warner Bros. by WEA Records. Catalogue no: **7599262361**
Cass: Released Jun '90, on Warner Bros. by WEA Records. Catalogue no: **7599262364**

Dick Turpin

DICK TURPIN (See under King, Denis)

Dickson, Barbara

ANOTHER SUITCASE ANOTHER HALL
Tracks: / Another suitcase in another hall.
Note: Featured in the stage show 'Evita'.
7" Single: Released Feb '77, on MCA by MCA Records. Deleted '80. Catalogue no: **MCA 266**

BLOOD BROTHERS (Original London Cast)
Tracks: / Narration / Marilyn Monroe / My child / Devil's got your number, The / Easy terms / Just a game / Sunday afternoon / My friend / Bright new day / One summer narration / Saying a word / Miss Jones (sign of the times) / Prison song / Light romance / There's a madman / Tell me it's not true.
CD: Released Nov '89, on Legacy by Legacy Records. Deleted Jul

'90. Catalogue no: **LLMCD 3007**
Album: Released Jul '83, on Legacy by Legacy Records. Catalogue no: **LIM 101**
Cass: Released Nov '89, on Legacy by Legacy Records. Deleted Jul '90. Catalogue no: **LLMK 3007**
Album: Released Nov '89, on Legacy by Legacy Records. Deleted Jul '90. Catalogue no: **LLM 3007**

I KNOW HIM SO WELL (Dickson, Barbara & Elaine Paige)
Tracks: / I know him so well.
Note: Taken from the stage show 'Chess'
12" Single: Released Dec '84, on RCA by BMG Records (UK). Catalogue no: **CHEST 3**
7" Single: Released Dec '84, on RCA by BMG Records (UK). Deleted Jun '90. Catalogue no: **CHESS 3**

TIME AFTER TIME
Tracks: / Time after time (Theme music from BBC series Animal Squad) / She moved through the fair.
7" Single: Released Sep '86, on K-Tel by K-Tel Records. Catalogue no: **BABS 1**

Die Hard

DIE HARD 2 (See under Kamen, Michael)

Die Unendiche...

DIE UNENDICHE GESCHICHTE (AND OTHER DIGITAL THEMES) (Original Soundtrack) (Various artists)
CD: Released '88, on WEA by WEA Records. Catalogue no: **250 396 2**

Digital Space

DIGITAL SPACE (London Symphony Orchestra)
Tracks: / Star wars / Tribute to a bad man / Lady Hamilton / Airport / Things to come / Windjammer / Big country / Red pony / 49th parallel / Spitfire prelude and fugue.
2 LP Set: Released Dec '79, Catalogue no: **VCDMM 1000 20**
CD: Released Jan '89, on Silva Screen by Silva Screen Records. Catalogue no: **VCD 47229**

Digital Themes

DIGITAL THEMES SPECTACULAR (Various artists)

Tracks: / Dallas: *Various artists* / My name is Bond: *Various artists* / Rocky medley: *Various artists* / Chariots of fire: *Various artists* / Knot's Landing: *Various artists* / Raiders of the lost ark: *Various artists* / Falcon Crest: *Various artists* / Only love: *Various artists* / Where no man has gone before: *Various artists* / Chi Mai: *Various artists* / Dynasty: *Various artists* / Those magificent men in their flying machine: *Various artists* / Rockford files: *Various artists* / Eastenders: *Various artists* / Warship: *Various artists* / Barwick green: *Various artists* / Dambusters, The: *Various artists* / Longest day, The: *Various artists* / Cockleshell heroes: *Various artists*.
CD: Released Feb '88, on Bandleader by Bandleader Records. Catalogue no: **BNA 5011**

DIGITAL THEMES SPECTACULAR VOL. 2 (Various bands)
Tracks: / 2001 / Superman / Hill Street blues / Kojak / Cagney and Lacey / Dempsey and Makepiece / Dad's army / TV Sports themes / Cavatina / 633 squadron / Swing march / Trap, The / Howards way / Last starfighter, The / Masterpiece, The / Nobilmente / Things to come / Bridge too far, A / Squadron / In party mood / Liberty bell / Black hole, The / Lawrence of Arabia / Elizabeth Tudor / Battle of Britain, The.
Note: Featuring some outstanding film blockbusters and a host of television music from both sides of the Atlantic. The very best military bands coupled with outstanding digital recordings.
CD: Released Aug '89, on Bandleader by Bandleader Records. Catalogue no: **BNA 5031**

Dikker, Loek

PASCALIS ISLAND (See under Pascalis Island)

Diner

DINER (1982 film soundtrack) (Various artists)
CD Set: Released Feb '90, on Silva Screen by Silva Screen Records. Catalogue no: **60107.2**
Cass set: Released Jan '89, on Silva Screen by Silva Screen Records. Catalogue no: **90107.4**
2 LP Set: Released Jan '89, on Silva Screen by Silva Screen Rec-

ords. Deleted Feb '90. Catalogue no: **60107.1**

Dingo Girl

DINGO GIRL (Stage show) (Various artists)
Album: Released Mar '89, on Larrikin (Australia) by Topic Records. Catalogue no: **LRF 119**

Dinosaurs (film)

DINOSAURS (Film soundtrack) (Various artists)
Note: Composed by David Spear.
Album: Released Jan '89, on Cerebus (USA) Catalogue no: **C'BUS 213**

Dion

RUNAROUND SUE (OLD GOLD)
Tracks: / Runaround Sue / Lonely teenager.
Note: Featured in the film 'That'll Be The Day'.
7" Single: Released Jun '88, on Old Gold by Old Gold Records. Catalogue no: **OG 9404**

RUNAROUND SUE (SINGLE)
Tracks: / Runaround Sue / Runaway girl.
7" Single: Released Nov '61, on Top Rank (1) Deleted '64. Catalogue no: **JAR 586**
7" Single: Released '81, on RCA Golden Grooves by BMG Records (UK). Catalogue no: **GOLD 526**

Dirty Dancing

DIRTY DANCING (1987 film soundtrack) (Various artists)
Tracks: / I've had the time of my life: *I've had the time of my life / Be my baby: Ronettes /* She's like the wind: *Swayze, Patrick & Wendy Fraser /* Hungry eyes: *Carmen, Eric /* Stay: *Williams, Maurice & The Zodiacs /* Yes: *Clayton, Merry /* You don't own me: *Blow Monkeys /* Hey baby: *Channel, Bruce /* Overload: *Zappacosta /* Love is strange: *Mickey & Sylvia /* Where are you tonight: *Johnston, Tom /* In the still of the night: *Five Satins.*
Cass: Released Oct '87, on RCA by BMG Records (UK). Catalogue no: **BK 86408**
Album: Released Oct '87, on RCA by BMG Records (UK). Catalogue no: **BL 86408**
CD: Released Oct '87, on RCA by BMG Records (UK). Catalogue no: **BD 86408**

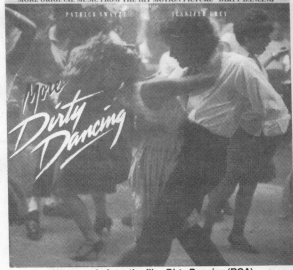

More music from the film *Dirty Dancing* (RCA)

MORE DIRTY DANCING (1987 Film Soundtrack) (Various artists) (See panel above)
Tracks / I've had the time of my life: *Morris, John Orchestra /* Big girls don't cry: *Four Seasons /* Merengue: *Lloyd, Michael & Le Disc /* Some kind of wonderful: *Drifters /* Johnny's mambo: *Lloyd, Michael & Le Disc /* Do you love me: *Contours /* Love man: *Redding, Otis /* Wipe out: *Surfaris, The /* These arms of mine: *Redding, Otis /* De todo un poco: *Lloyd, Michael & Le Disc /* Cry to me: *Burke, Solomon /* Trot the fox: *Lloyd, Michael & Le Disc /* Will you love me tomorrow: *Shirelles /* Kellerman's anthem: *Emile Bergstein Chorale*
Cass: Released Apr '88, on RCA by BMG Records (UK). Catalogue no: **BK 86965**
Album: Released Apr '88, on RCA by BMG Records (UK). Catalogue no: **BL 86965**
CD: Released Apr '88, on RCA by BMG Records (UK). Catalogue no: **BD 86965**

Dirty Dancing (TV Series)

DIRTY DANCING (VOL 1 VIDEO) (Various artists)
Note: From the American TV Series of the same name.
VHS: Released Mar '90, on Vestron Video Catalogue no: **VA 17419**

DIRTY DANCING (VOL 2 VIDEO) (Various artists)
VHS: Released Mar '90, on Vestron Video Catalogue no: **VA 17420**

DIRTY DANCING (VOL 3 VIDEO) (Various artists)
VHS: Released Mar '90, on Vestron Video Catalogue no: **VA17421**

DIRTY DANCING (VOL 4 VIDEO) (Various artists)
VHS: Released Mar '90, on Vestron Video Catalogue no: **VA 17422**

DIRTY DANCING (VOL 5 VIDEO) (Various artists)
VHS: Released Mar '90, on Vestron Video Catalogue no: **VA 17423**

DIRTY DANCING (VOL 6 VIDEO) (Various artists)
VHS: Released Mar '90, on Vestron Video Catalogue no: **VA 17424**

Dirty Dingus Magee

DIRTY DINGUS MAGEE (1970 film soundtrack) (Various artists)
Note: Music by Jeff Alexander for the Frank Sinatra comedy western.,
Album: Released Jan '89, on MCA by MCA Records. Catalogue no: **MCA 25095**
Cass: Released Jan '89, on MCA by MCA Records. Deleted Feb '90. Catalogue no: **MCAC 25095**

Dirty Dozen

DIRTY DOZEN (Film Soundtrack) (Various artists)
Tracks: / Dirty dozen theme: *Various artists* / Building the barracks: *Various artists* / Battle begins: *Various artists* / Girls of the evening: *Various artists* / Dirty dozen: *Various artists* / Einsam: *Various artists* / Mission accomplished: *Various artists* / Bramble bush: *Various artists* / Col. Breedy's folly: *Various artists* / Sham battle/ Don't sit under the apple tree: *Various artists* / Chateau: *Various artists* / Switchhitters: *Various artists* / Finale and end title: *Various artists*.
Album: Released '73, on Polydor by Polydor Ltd. Deleted '78. Catalogue no: **2315 049**
Cass: Released Feb '87, on CBS by CBS Records & Distribution. Deleted Jun '88. Catalogue no: **450229 4**
Album: Released Feb '87, on CBS by CBS Records & Distribution. Deleted Jun '88. Catalogue no: **450229 1**

DIRTY DOZEN/HANNIBAL BROOKS (Various artists)
Tracks: / Dirty dozen, The (main title): *Various artists* / Building the barracks: *Various artists* / Battle begins: *Various artists* / Girls of the evening: *Various artists* / Dirty dozen, The: *Various artists* / Erinsam: *Siegfried, Sibylle* / Mission accomplished (Destruction of the chateau): *Various artists* / Bramble bush: *Lopez, Trini* / Col. Breed's folly: *Various artists* / Sham battle, The (Interpolating: Don't sit under the...): *Various artists* / Chateau, The: *Various artists* / Switch-hitters: *Various artists* / Dirty dozen, The (finale and end title): *Various artists* / Hannibal Brooks march (main theme): *Various artists* / Journey to Innsbruck: *Various ar-*

tists / Peace and understanding: *Various artists* / Hanniball Brooks love theme: *Various artists* (Hannibal Brooks.) / Elephant shake (Lucy's theme): *Various artists* (Hannibal Brooks.) / Respite: *Various artists* / Walk in the woods: *Various artists* / Hannibal's rest: *Various artists* / Tyrolean folk dance: *Various artists* / Across the river: *Various artists* / Sickness in the family: *Various artists* / Lucy's theme: *Various artists* / Peace and understanding (reprise): *Various artists* / Approaching the frontier: *Various artists* / Hannibal Brooks love theme (reprise): *Various artists*.
CD: Released Apr '90, on MGM (EMI) Catalogue no: **CDMGM 17**
CD: Released Apr '90, on MGM (EMI) Catalogue no: **CDP 794 252 2**
Cass: Released Apr '90, on MGM (EMI) Catalogue no: **TCMGM 17**
Album: Released Apr '90, on MGM (EMI) Catalogue no: **794 252 1**
Cass: Released Apr '90, on MGM (EMI) Catalogue no: **794 252 4**
Album: Released Apr '90, on MGM (EMI) Catalogue no: **LPMGM 17**

Disappearing World

DISAPPEARING WORLD, THE (Various artists)
CD: Released Sep '89, on Saydisc by Amon Ra Records. Catalogue no: **CD-SDL 376**
Cass: Released Sep '89, on Saydisc by Amon Ra Records. Catalogue no: **CSDL 376**

Disney

40 WALT DISNEY ORIGINALS (Various artists)
Tracks: / Mary Poppins: *Various artists* / Bambi: *Various artists* / Snow White: *Various artists* / So dear to my heart: *Various artists* / Summer magic: *Various artists* / Bedknobs and broomsticks: *Various artists* / Winnie the pooh: *Various artists* / Pinocchio: *Various artists* / Step in time: *Various artists* / Journey: *Various artists* / Jolly holiday: *Various artists* / My own home: *Various artists* / Feed the birds: *Various artists* / Love is a song: *Various artists* / County fair: *Various artists* / Maggie's theme: *Various artists* / Beautiful briny: *Various artists* / Dwarfish yodelling

song: *Various artists* / Higitus figitus: *Various artists* / Follow the leader: *Various artists* / Stick to it ivity: *Various artists* / Lavender blue: *Various artists* / You can fly: *Various artists* / Second star to the right: *Various artists* / When you wish upon a star: *Various artists* / Wonderful thing about tiggers: *Various artists* / Ugly bug ball: *Various artists* / Old home guard: *Various artists* / Portobello Road: *Various artists* / Most befudding thing: *Various artists* / Gallant Captain Hook: *Various artists* / Rain, rain, rain came down down down: *Various artists* / Magic song: *Various artists* / Madam Mim: *Various artists*.
Cass set: Released Oct '79, on Pickwick by Pickwick Records. Deleted '84. Catalogue no: **PLDC 8010**
2 LP Set: Released Oct '79, on Pickwick by Pickwick Records. Deleted '84. Catalogue no: **PLD 8010**

BEST OF DISNEY (Various artists)
Tracks: / Dream is a wish your heart makes, A: *Various artists* (From Cinderella) / When you wish upon a star: *Various artists* (From Pinocchio) / Supercalifragilisticexpialidocious: *Various artists* (From Mary Poppins) / When I see an elephant fly: *Various artists* (From: Dumbo) / I've got no strings: *Various artists* (From: Pinocchio.) / Bella Notte: *Various artists* (From Lady and the Tramp) / Creulla de ville: *Various artists* (From 101 Dalmations) / Some day my prince will come: *Various artists* (From Snow White.) / Bare necessities: *Various artists* (From Jungle Book.) / Give a little whistle: *Various artists* (From Pinocchio) / Jolly 'Oliday: *Various artists* (From Mary Poppins) / Bibbidi bobbidi boo: *Various artists* (From Cinderella) / Trust in me: *Various artists* (From Jungle Book.) / Second star to the right: *Various artists* (From Peter Pan.) / Little April showers: *Various artists* (From Bambi.) / Spoonful of sugar: *Various artists* (From Mary Poppins.) / He's a tramp: *Various artists* (From Lady and the Tramp.) / Appreciate the lady: *Various artists* (From The Fox and the Hound.) / Chim chim cheree: *Various artists* (From Mary Poppins) / Following the leader: *Various ar-*

tists (From Peter Pan.) / I wanna be like you: *Various artists* (From Jungle Book.) / Feeds the birds: *Various artists* (From Mary Poppins.) / Whistle while you work: *Various artists* (From Snow White.) / Look out for Mr. Stork: *Various artists* (From Dumbo.) / Heigh ho: *Various artists* (From Snow White.) / Hi-diddle-dee-dee: *Various artists* (From Pinocchio.) / When you wish upon a star (recap.): *Various artists* (From Pinocchio.).

Cass: Released Feb '87, on MFP by EMI Records. Deleted Aug '89. Catalogue no: **TCMFP 5783**

Album: Released Oct '85, on BBC by BBC Records. Deleted '88. Catalogue no: **REH 573**

Album: Released Feb '87, on MFP by EMI Records. Deleted Aug '89. Catalogue no: **MFP 5783**

Cass: Released Oct '85, on BBC by BBC Records. Deleted '88. Catalogue no: **ZCR 573**

CHRISTMAS FAVOURITES (Various artists)
Album: Released Oct '79, on Hallmark by Pickwick Records. Catalogue no: **SHM 93980**

DISNEY CLASSICS FOR CHILDREN (Various artists)
Tracks: / Peer Gynt suite: *Various artists* / In the hall of the mountain king: *Various artists* / Nutcracker suite: *Various artists* / Young persons guide to the orchestra: *Various artists* / Petit suite d'orchestre: *Various artists* / Childrens games: *Various artists* / Marche (trumpet tambour): *Various artists* / Berceuse (la poupee): *Various artists* / Impromptu: *Various artists* / Duo (petit Mari, petit femme): *Various artists* / Galop (le bal): *Various artists* / Mendelssohn violin concerto in E minor: *Various artists* / Grofe Grand Canyon suite: *Various artists* / Swan lake: *Various artists*.

Album: Released Dec '76, on Golden Hour Catalogue no: **GH 857**

DISNEY HITS (Various artists)
Tracks: / When you wish upon a star: *Various artists* / Thomas O'Malley cat: *Various artists* / Give a little whistle: *Various artists* / When I see an elephant fly: *Various artists* / Who's afraid of the big bad wolf: *Various artists* / Ugly bug ball, The: *Various artists* / Whistle while you work: *Various artists* / Winnie the pooh: *Various artists* / Heigh ho: *Various artists* / Siamese cat song:

Various artists / Bare necessities: *Various artists* / Supercalifragilisticexpialidocious: *Various artists* / Colonel Hathi's march: *Various artists* / Trust in me: *Various artists* / That's what friends are for: *Various artists* / I wanna be like you: *Various artists* / Never smile at a crocodile: *Various artists* / Feed the birds: *Various artists* / Aristocats, The: *Various artists* / Hi-diddle-dee-dee: *Various artists* / Ev'rybody wants to be a cat: *Various artists* / My own home: *Various artists* / I've got no strings: *Various artists*.

Cass: Released May '86, on Hour Of Pleasure by EMI Records. Catalogue no: **HR 8102**

Cass: Released May '86, on Hour Of Pleasure by EMI Records. Catalogue no: **HR 4181024**

DISNEY (See also under Cook, Barbara)

DISNEY'S ORIGINAL SOUNDTRACK COLLECTION VOL 1 (Various artists)
Album: Released Nov '76, on Hallmark by Pickwick Records. Deleted '88. Catalogue no: **SHM 906**

DISNEY'S ORIGINAL SOUNDTRACK COLLECTION VOL 2 (Various artists)
Album: Released Nov '76, on Hallmark by Pickwick Records. Deleted '88. Catalogue no: **SHM 907**

DISNEY'S ORIGINAL SOUNDTRACK COLLECTION VOL 3 (Various artists)
Album: Released '76, on Hallmark by Pickwick Records. Deleted '88. Catalogue no: **SHM 908**

DISNEY'S ORIGINAL SOUNDTRACK COLLECTION VOL 4 (Various artists)
Album: Released Nov '76, on Hallmark by Pickwick Records. Deleted '88. Catalogue no: **SHM 909**

GOLDEN HOUR: DISNEY (Various artists)
Tracks: / Whistle while you work: *Various artists* / Heigh ho: *Various artists* / Bare necessities: *Various artists* / Little April showers: *Various artists* / Zip-a-dee-doo-dah: *Various artists* / Spoonful of sugar, A: *Various artists* / Winnie the Pooh: *Various artists* / Ballad of Davy Crockett, The: *Various artists* / Everybody wants to be a cat: *Various artists*

/ Bibbidi bobbidi boo: *Various artists* / Mickey's big show: *Various artists* / Donald Duck recites Mary had a little lamb: *Various artists* / Little Boy Blue: *Various artists* / Clara Cluck song: *Various artists* / Mickey Mouse march: *Various artists* / Who's afraid of the big bad wolf?: *Various artists* / Donald Duck song: *Various artists* / Hi-diddle-dee-dee: *Various artists* / Three caballeros: *Various artists* / He's a tramp: *Various artists* / Feed the birds: *Various artists* / Never smile at a crocodile: *Various artists* / Portobello Road: *Various artists* / Sorcerer's apprentice, The: *Various artists* / When you wish upon a star: *Various artists*.

Album: Released Oct '76, on Golden Hour Catalogue no: **GH 856**

GOLDEN HOUR PRESENTS DISNEY TODAY (Various artists)
Tracks: / Zip-a-dee-doo-dah: *Various artists* / Chim chim cheree: *Various artists* / Bare necessities: *Various artists* / He's a tramp: *Various artists* / Winnie the pooh: *Various artists* / Second star to the right: *Various artists* / It's a small world: *Various artists* / Bibbidi bobbidi boo: *Various artists* / Whistle while you work: *Various artists* / I'm wishing: *Various artists* / Heigh ho: *Various artists* / With a smile and a song: *Various artists* / Some day my prince will come: *Various artists* / Mickey Mouse march: *Various artists* / Give a little whistle: *Various artists* / When you wish upon a star: *Various artists* / Little April showers: *Various artists* / Mule train: *Various artists* / Dream is a wish your heart makes, A: *Various artists* / I've got no strings: *Various artists* / Lavender blue: *Various artists* / Siamese cat song: *Various artists* / Once upon a dream: *Various artists* / When I see an elephant fly: *Various artists* / These are the best times: *Various artists* / Feed the birds: *Various artists* / Spoonful of sugar: *Various artists* / Supercalifragilisticexpialidocious: *Various artists*.

Album: on Golden Hour Catalogue no: **GH 860**

GREATEST HITS: WALT DISNEY (Various artists)
Tracks: / When you wish upon a star: *Various artists* / I've got no strings: *Various artists* / I wanna be like you: *Various artists* / Bare

necessities: *Various artists* / Who's afraid of the big bad wolf?: *Various artists* / When I see an elephant fly: *Various artists* / Ballad of Davy Crockett, The: *Various artists* / Zip a dee doo dah: *Various artists* / Wonderful thing about tiggers: *Various artists* / Spoonful of sugar, A: *Various artists* / Supercalifragilisticexpialidocious: *Various artists* / Ugly bug ball, The: *Various artists* / Whistle while you work: *Various artists* / Heigh ho!: *Various artists*.

Cass: Released Dec '83, on Disneyland by Disneyland-Vista Records (USA). Catalogue no: **WD 43**

Album: Released Dec '83, on Disneyland by Disneyland-Vista Records (USA). Catalogue no: **WD 3**

MORE DISNEY FAVOURITES (Various artists)

Tracks: / Happy mouse: *Various artists* / Ugly bug ball, The: *Various artists* / I wanna be like you: *Various artists* / Give a little whistle: *Various artists* / Siamese cat song: *Various artists* / Wonderful thing about tiggers: *Various artists* / Love is a song: *Various artists* / Supercalifragilisticexpialidocious: *Various artists* / Pink elephants: *Various artists* / You can fly, you can fly: *Various artists* / Oo-de-lally: *Various artists* / Whale of a tale, A: *Various artists* / Thomas O'Malley cat: *Various artists* / Dream is a wish your heart makes, A: *Various artists* / Unbirthday song, The: *Various artists* / Beautiful briny, The: *Various artists* / Minnie's yoo-hoo: *Various artists* / Goofy commercials: *Various artists* / End title: *Various artists*.

Album: Released Dec '76, on Golden Hour Catalogue no: **GH 850**

ORIGINAL SOUNDTRACK PARADE, VOL. 1 (Various artists)

Note: Songs from Mary Poppins, Bambi, Sleeping Beauty, Lady and the Tramp, Pinocchio, Jungle Book, Peter Pan, Robin Hood.

2 LP Set: on Pickwick by Pickwick Records. Catalogue no: **PDA 029**

PARADE VOL 2 (Various artists)

Tracks: / Songs from the song of the south: *Various artists* / Aristocats, The: *Various artists* / Dumbo: *Various artists* / Winnie the Pooh: *Various artists* / Snow White and

the seven dwarfs: *Various artists* / Alice in Wonderland: *Various artists* / 101 dalmations: *Various artists* / Cinderella: *Various artists*.

2 LP Set: on Pickwick by Pickwick Records. Catalogue no: **PDA 030**

WALT DISNEY STORIES FOR CHILDREN (Various artists)

Tracks: / Peter and the wolf: *Various artists* / Mickey and the beanstalk: *Various artists* / Fee fi fo fum: *Various artists* / My favourite dream: *Various artists* / My what a happy day: *Various artists* / Three little pigs: *Various artists* / Who's afraid of the big bad wolf: *Various artists* / Little engine that could: *Various artists*.

Album: Released Jan '77, on Golden Hour Deleted '80. Catalogue no: **GH 858**

WALT DISNEY SUPER SOUNDTRACK ORIGINALS

Tracks: / Supercalifragilisticexpialidocious / Little April shower / Thomas O Malley cat / Once upon a dream / He's a tramp / Chim chim cheree / Bibbidi bobbidi boo / I've got no strings / Whistle while you work / I wanna be like you / Bare necessities / Bella notte / Trust in me / Everybody wants to be a cat / Give a little whistle / Someone is waiting for you / Siamese cat song / Zip a dee doo dah / When I see an elephant fly / Spoonful of sugar.

Cass: Released '79, on Pickwick by Pickwick Records. Deleted '82. Catalogue no: **PLC 7008**

Album: Released '79, on Pickwick by Pickwick Records. Deleted '82. Catalogue no: **PLE 7008**

Disorderlies

DISORDERLIES (1987 film soundtrack) (Various artists)

Tracks: / Don't treat me like this: *Anita* / Edge of a broken heart: *Bon Jovi* / Trying to dance: *Kimmel, Tom* / Roller one: *Art Of Noise* / Fat off my back: *Guthrie, Gwen* / Work me down: *Hunter, Laura* / Baby you're a rich man: *Fat Boys* / I heard a rumour: *Bananarama* / Disorderly conduct: *Latin Rascals* / Big money: *Cashflow*.

Cass: Released Jul '87, on London Records by London Records Ltd. Deleted Feb '89. Catalogue no: **LONC 46**

CD: Released Jul '87, on London Records by London Records Ltd. Deleted Feb '88. Catalogue no:

833 274 2

Album: Released Aug '87, on London Records by London Records Ltd. Deleted Feb '89. Catalogue no: **LONLP 46**

DISORDERLIES (VIDEO) (Various artists)

Note: PG rated. Running time is 83 minutes. The Fat Boys movie in which the blubbery trio are hired to look after a gamblers ailing millionaire uncle but singularly fail to tip him to eternal rest. Indeed when they take him into the nightlife the old codger is suddenly revitalised while his nephew gets more desparate for the inheritance. Slapstick and farce with plenty of rap and loadsacalories. Features their hit with the Beach Boys 'Wipe Out'.

VHS: Released Jun '88, on Warner Home Video by WEA Records. Catalogue no: **PES 11752**

Diva

DIVA (1982 film soundtrack) (Various artists)

Note: Original score by Vladimir Cosma plus the aria from 'La Wally' performed by Wilhelmenia Fernandez.

Album: Released '88, on Pacific by Pacific Records. Catalogue no: **PR 2001**

Cass: Released '88, on DRG (USA) by DRG Records (USA). Catalogue no: **SLC 9503**

Album: Released '88, on DRG (USA) by DRG Records (USA). Catalogue no: **SL 9503**

CD: Released '88, on Pacific (USA) Catalogue no: **CH 061**

Cass: Released '88, on Pacific by Pacific Records. Catalogue no: **PRC 2001**

Divine Madness

DIVINE MADNESS (See under Midler, Bette)

Divorce Me, Darling

DIVORCE ME, DARLING (Original 1965 London cast) (Various artists)

Tracks: / Divorce me darling: Overture: *Various artists* / Here we are in nice again: *Various artists* / Someone to dance with: *Various artists* / Whatever happened to love?: *Various artists* / Lights! Music!: *Various artists* / On the loose: *Various artists* / Maisie: *Various artists* / Paradise hotel, The: *Various artists* / No harm done: *Various artists* / Together again: *Various artists* / Divorce me darling: *Various artists* / Here am I(but where's the guy): *Various artists* / Out of step: *Various artists* / You're absolutely me: *Various artists* / Back where we started: *Various artists* / Blondes for danger: *Various artists* / Swing time is here stay: *Various artists* / Divorce me, darling: Finale: *Various artists*.

Cass: Released Jan '85, on T. E. R. by That's Entertainment Records. Catalogue no: **ZCTER 1077**

Album: Released '79, on EMI (Import) Deleted '84. Catalogue no: **DS 15009**

Album: Released Jan '85, on T. E. R. by That's Entertainment Records. Catalogue no: **TER 1077**

Django

DJANGO (Original soundtrack) (Various artists)
Note: Spaghetti Western score by Luis Bacalov.
Album: Released Jan '89, on Silva Screen by Silva Screen Records. Catalogue no: **IMGM 002**

DJANGO SPARA PER PRIMO (HE SHOOTS FIRST) (Original soundtrack) (Various artists)
Note: Composed by Bruno Nicolai.
Album: Released Jan '89, on Silva Screen by Silva Screen Records. Catalogue no: **IM 012**

DJANGO'S REVENGE (Original soundtrack) (Various artists)
Note: Composed by Gianfranco Plenizio.
Album: Released Jan '89, on Silva Screen by Silva Screen Records. Catalogue no: **CST 8030**

Do I Hear A Waltz

DO I HEAR A WALTZ (Original Broadway cast) (Various artists)
Note: Richard Rodgers/Stephen Sondheim show with Elizabeth Seal.
Cass: Released Feb '89, on Silva Screen by Silva Screen Records. Catalogue no: **BT 2770**
Album: Released Feb '89, on Silva Screen by Silva Screen Records. Catalogue no: **AKOS 2770**

Do Patent Black Shoes

DO PATENT BLACK SHOES (Original Broadway cast) (Various artists)

Album: Released Feb '89, on Silva Screen by Silva Screen Records. Catalogue no: **DP 18852**

Do The Right Thing

DO THE RIGHT THING (1989 film soundtrack) (Various artists)
Tracks: / Fight the power: *Public Enemy* / My fantasy: *Riley, Teddy Featuring Guy* / Party hearty: *E.U.* / Can't stand it: *Steel Pulse* / Prove to me: *Perri* / We love (jingle): *Take 6* / Feel so good: *Perri* / Don't shoot me: *Take 6* / Hard to say: *Perry, Lori & Gerald Alston* / Why don't we try: *John, Keith* / Never explain love: *Jarreau, Al* / Tu y yo: *Blades, Ruben*.
CD: Released Jun '89, on Motown by BMG Records (UK). Catalogue no: **ZB 72665**
Cass: Released Jun '89, on Motown by BMG Records (UK). Catalogue no: **ZK 72665**
Album: Released Jun '89, on Motown by BMG Records (UK). Catalogue no: **ZL 72665**
Album: Released Jul '89, on Motown by BMG Records (UK). Catalogue no: **MOT 6272**

D.O.A. (film)

D.O.A. (DEAD ON ARRIVAL) (Film soundtrack) (Various artists)
Note: Touchstone Production starring Dennis Quaid, Meg Ryan and Charlotte Rampling. Music by Chaz Jankel.
CD: Released Jan '89, on Varese Sarabande Records(USA) by Varese Sarabande Records (USA). Catalogue no: **VCD 70461**
Album: Released Jan '89, on Varese Sarabande Records(USA) by Varese Sarabande Records (USA). Catalogue no: **704.610**

Doctor Detroit

DOCTOR DETROIT (Film soundtrack) (Various artists) (See also under Devo)
Album: Released Nov '83, on MCA by MCA Records. Deleted Nov '88. Catalogue no: **MCF 3175**

Doctor Exx Band

SUPERMAN (THEME FROM)
Tracks: / Superman (theme from) / Panic on Planet K.
7" Single: Released Jan '79, on Pye Deleted '83. Catalogue no: **7N 46151**

Doctor No

DOCTOR NO (Film soundtrack) (Various artists)
Tracks: / James Bond theme: *Various artists* / Kingston calypso: *Various artists* / Island speaks, The: *Various artists* / Under the mango tree: *Various artists* / Jump up: *Various artists* / Doctor No's fantasy: *Various artists* / Boy chase: *Various artists* / Love at last: *Various artists* / Jamaican rock: *Various artists* / Audio bongo: *Various artists* / Twisting with James: *Various artists* / Jamaica jazz: *Various artists*.
Note: Composed and conducted by Monty Norman.
Album: Released Jul '87, on Liberty by EMI Records. Deleted Aug '89. Catalogue no: **EMS 1265**
Cass: Released Jul '87, on Liberty by EMI Records. Deleted Jun '89. Catalogue no: **TCEMS 1265**
Album: Released Mar '83, on EMI by EMI Records. Deleted Mar '88. Catalogue no: **1C 054 82922**

Doctor Who

DOCTOR WHO - THE MUSIC (BBC Radiophonic Workshop)
Tracks: / Tardis / Sea devils, The / Meglos / Kassia's wedding music / Threat of Melkur, The / Exploring the lab / Nyassa is hypnotized / Leisure hive, The / Omega field force / Ergon threat / Termination of the doctor / Banqueting music / TSS machine attacked / Janissary band / Subterranean caves / Requiem / March of the Cybermen / Doctor Who theme.
Cass: Released Mar '83, on BBC by BBC Records. Catalogue no: **ZCR 462**
Album: Released Mar '83, on BBC by BBC Records. Catalogue no: **REH 462**

DOCTOR WHO- THE MUSIC VOL 2 (BBC Radiophonic Workshop)
Tracks: / Five doctors, The / King's demon, The / Enlightenment / Warriors of the deep / Awakening, The / Resurrection of the daleks / Planet of fire / Caves of Androzani.
Album: Released Feb '85, on BBC by BBC Records. Catalogue no: **REH 552**
Cass: Released Feb '85, on BBC by BBC Records. Catalogue no:

ZCR 552

DOCTOR WHO (VARIATIONS ON A THEME) (Various artists)

CD Single: Released Dec '89, on Metro by Hit Records. Catalogue no: **CDMMI 4**

DOCTOR WHO'S 25TH AN-NIVERSARY ALBUM (Various artists)

Tracks: / Tardis: *Various artists* / Doctor Who theme: *Various artists* / Gavrok's search: *Various artists* / Child's return, A: *Various artists* / Towers el paradiso: *Various artists* / Burton's escape: *Various artists* / Drinksmat dawning: *Various artists* / Future pleasure: *Various artists* / Newreel past: *Various artists* / Sting, The: *Various artists* / 8891 Royale: *Various artists* / White flag: *Various artists* / Guards of silence: *Various artists* / Making of Pex, The: *Various artists* / Cemetery chase: *Various artists* / Brain, The: *Various artists* / Here's to the future: *Various artists* / Goodbye Doctor: *Various artists* / Doctor Who: *Various artists.*
Note: The only album to include all the versions of the Doctor Who theme, including the previously unreleased music from the last series. (Nov 88)
Cass: Released Dec '88, on BBC by BBC Records. Catalogue no: **ZCF 707**
Album: Released Dec '88, on BBC by BBC Records. Catalogue no: **REB 707**
CD: Released Dec '88, on BBC by BBC Records. Catalogue no: **BBC CD 707**

Doctor Zhivago

DOCTOR ZHIVAGO (Film soundtrack) (Jarre, Maurice)

Tracks: / Overture from Dr Zhivago / Lara leaves Yuri / At the student cafe / Komarovsky and Lara's rendezvous / Revolution / Tonya arrives at Varykino / Yuri writes a poem for Lara / Lara's theme.
Note: Composed and conducted by Maurice Jarre.
Album: Released Jul '86, on CBS by CBS Records & Distribution. Deleted Jun '88. Catalogue no: **CBS 70274**
Cass: Released Dec '79, on Listen For Pleasure by EMI Records. Catalogue no: **TC LFP 7054**
Cass: Released Jul '86, on CBS

by CBS Records & Distribution. Deleted Jan '89. Catalogue no: **40 70274**
CD: Released Mar '87, on CBS by CBS Records & Distribution. Deleted Jan '89. Catalogue no: **CD 70274**
CD: Released Jun '88, on MCA (USA) by MCA Records (USA). Catalogue no: **31184**

DOCTOR ZHIVAGO (ORIGINAL ISSUE) (Film soundtrack) (Various artists)

Album: Released Jul '67, on MGM (EMI) Deleted '71. Catalogue no: **MGM C 8007**

DOCTOR ZHIVAGO/RYAN'S DAUGHTER (Various artists)

Tracks: / Dr Zhivago overture: *Various artists* (Doctor Zhivago) / Doctor Zhivago (main title): *Various artists* (Doctor Zhivago) / Lara leaves Yuri: *Various artists* (Doctor Zhivago) / At the student cafe: *Various artists* (Doctor Zhivago) / Komarovsky and Lara's rendezvous: *Various artists* (Doctor Zhivago) / Revolution: *Various artists* (Doctor Zhivago) / Lara's theme: *Various artists* (Doctor Zhivago) / Funeral, The: *Various artists* (Doctor Zhivago) / Sventytski's waltz: *Various artists* (Doctor Zhivago) / Yuri escapes: *Various artists* (Doctor Zhivago) / Tonya arrives at Varykino: *Various artists* (Doctor Zhivago) / Yuri writes a poem for Lara: *Various artists* (Doctor Zhivago) / Ryan's daughter (main title): *Various artists* (Ryan's daughter) / Major, The: *Various artists* (Ryan's daughter) / You don't want me then: *Various artists* (Ryan's daughter) / Michael's theme: *Various artists* (Ryan's daughter) / Ride through the woods: *Various artists* (Ryan's daughter) / Obsession: *Various artists* (Ryan's daughter) / Shakes, The: *Various artists* (Ryan's daughter) / Rosy on the beach: *Various artists* (Ryan's daughter) / Song of the Irish rebels: *Various artists* (Ryan's daughter) / Rosy and the schoolmaster: *Various artists* (Ryan's daughter) / Michael shows Randolph his strange treasure: *Various artists* (Ryan's daughter) / Rosy's theme: *Various artists* (Ryan's daughter).
CD: Released Jan '90, on MGM (EMI) Catalogue no: **CDP 793 298 2**

Cass: Released Jan '90, on MGM (EMI) Catalogue no: **793 298 4**
Album: Released Jan '90, on MGM (EMI) Catalogue no: **LPMGM 3**
CD: Released Jan '90, on MGM (EMI) Catalogue no: **CDP 793 298 2**
CD: Released Jan '90, on MGM (EMI) Catalogue no: **CDMGM 3**
Cass: Released Jan '90, on MGM (EMI) Catalogue no: **TCMGM 3**
Album: Released Jan '90, on MGM (EMI) Catalogue no: **793 298 1**

Dogs In Space

DOGS IN SPACE (1987 film soundtrack) (Various artists)

Tracks: / Dog food: *Pop, Iggy* / Dogs in space: *Various artists* / Win, lose: *Olsen, Ollie* / Anthrax: *Gang Of Four* / Skysaw: *Eno, Brian* / True love: *Marching Girls* / Shivers: *Boys Next Door* / Diseases: *Thrush and the Cunts* / Pumping ugly: *Primitive Calculators* / Golf course: *Hutchence, Michael* / Shivers: *Hoy, Marie and friends* / Endless sea: *Pop, Iggy* / Rooms for the memory: *Hutchence, Michael.*
Note: Cult Australian movie about the post-punk Melbourne underground of the late 70's. Features: Ollie Olsen, The Birthday Party (also as 'The Boys Next Door'), as well as imported classics by Iggy Pop, Brian Eno and the Gang of Four.
Album: Released 28 Sep '87, on Chase (Australia) Catalogue no: **CLPX 14**
CD: Released 16 May '88, on Mercury by Phonogram Ltd. Deleted 31 Jul '89. Catalogue no: **832 748-2**
Cass: Released 16 May '88, on Mercury by Phonogram Ltd. Deleted 31 Jul '89. Catalogue no: **MERHC 122**
Album: Released 16 May '88, on Mercury by Phonogram Ltd. Deleted 31 Jul '89. Catalogue no: **MERH 122**

Dolby's Cube

HOWARD THE DUCK (See under Howard The Duck)

Dolby, Thomas

GOTHIC (Film soundtrack)

Tracks: / Fantasmagoria / Byronic love / Shelleymania / Mary's theme / Party games / Gipsy girl / Crucifix

/ Fundamental source, The / Sin and buggery / Impalement / Leech juice / Restless sleep 1,2 & 3 / It's his! / Coitus per stigmata / Once we vowed eternal love / Riddled with guilt / Metamorphosis / Hangman / Beast in the crypt, The / Final seance, The / Funeral by the lake / No ghosts in daylight / To the grave / Devil is an Englishman, The (Featuring Screamin' Lord Byron) / Skull pulse / Trickle of blood, A.

Cass: Released Feb '87, on Virgin by Virgin Records. Deleted Jun '90. Catalogue no: **OVEDC 229**
CD: Released '88, on Virgin by Virgin Records. Catalogue no: **CDV 2417**
Cass: Released Feb '87, on Virgin by Virgin Records. Deleted '88. Catalogue no: **TCV 2417**
Album: Released Feb '87, on Virgin by Virgin Records. Catalogue no: **OVED 229**
Album: Released Feb '87, on Virgin by Virgin Records. Deleted '88. Catalogue no: **V 2417**

Dolls Life

DOLLS LIFE, A (Original Broadway cast) (Various artists)
Note: Comden/Green & Grossman with George Hearn.
Album: Released Feb '89, on Silva Screen by Silva Screen Records. Catalogue no: **P 18846**

Dolly Sisters

DOLLY SISTERS, THE (1945 film musical soundtrack) (Various artists)
Note: Staring Betty Grable and June Haver.
Album: Released Jan '89, on CIF Catalogue no: **CIF 3010**

Domani Accadra

DOMANI ACCADRA/STRANA LA VITA (Original soundtrack) (Various artists)
Note: 2 Scores by probably the most inventive of today's Italian composers: Nicola Piovani (Kaos, Good Morning Babylon).
Album: Released Jan '89, on Interior Music by Interior Music Records. Catalogue no: **IM 016**

Dominick & Eugene

DOMINICK & EUGENE (1988 film soundtrack) (Various artists)
Note: Film starring Tom Hulce (Amadeus), Ray Liotta and Jamie Lee Curtis. Score by Trevor Jones (Excalibur, Runaway Train)
Cass: Released Jan '89, on Varese Sarabande Records(USA) by Varese Sarabande Records (USA). Catalogue no: **704.540C**
Album: Released Jan '89, on Silva Screen by Silva Screen Records. Catalogue no: **704.540**
CD: Released Jan '89, on Varese Sarabande Records(USA) by Varese Sarabande Records (USA). Catalogue no: **VCD 70454**

Don Giovanni

DON GIOVANNI (1979 film soundtrack) (Various artists)
Cass: Released '81, on CBS by CBS Records & Distribution. Catalogue no: **40 73888**
Album: Released '81, on CBS by CBS Records & Distribution. Catalogue no: **CBS 73888**

Don Pasquale

DON PASQUALE (VIDEO) (Various artists)
VHS: Released '88, on Screen Legends (video) by Pickwick Video. Catalogue no: **SL 2007**

Don't Look Now

DON'T LOOK NOW (1973 film soundtrack) (Various artists)
Tracks: / John's theme: *Various artists* / Candles for Christine: *Various artists* / John's vision: *Various artists* / Through the street: *Various artists* / Dead end: *Various artists* / Christine is dead: *Various artists* / Strange happenings: *Various artists* / Searching for Laura: *Various artists* / Laura comes back: *Various artists* / Laura's theme: *Various artists*.
CD: Released Oct '89, on T. E. R. by That's Entertainment Records. Catalogue no: **CDTER 1007**
Album: Released Apr '83, on T. E. R. by That's Entertainment Records. Catalogue no: **TER 1007**

Don't Make Waves

DON'T MAKE WAVES (Original soundtrack) (Various artists)
Note: Score by Vic Mizzy.
Album: Released Jan '89, on MCA by MCA Records. Catalogue no: **MCA 25134**
Cass: Released Jan '89, on MCA by MCA Records. Catalogue no: **MCAC 25134**

Doors

END, THE
Tracks: / End, The / Delta.
Note: Featured in the film *Apocalypse Now*
12" Single: Released Dec '88, on Elektra (Import) by Elektra/Asylum/Nonesuch Records (USA). Catalogue no: **ELK 22032**
7" Single: Released Jan '80, on Elektra by Elektra Records (UK). Deleted '83. Catalogue no: **K 12400**

Double Deckers (TV)

DOUBLE DECKERS (Music From TV Soundtrack) (Various artists)
Tracks: / It's a day and a half: *Various artists* / To the countryside: *Various artists* / Good day at Yellowrock: *Various artists* / With a little bit of love: *Various artists* / I gotta get through: *Various artists* / Get on board: *Various artists* / Life is an wonderful thing: *Various artists* / Grannie's rocking chair: *Various artists* / One man band: *Various artists* / Welcome to the party: *Various artists* / Fat ladies: *Various artists*.
Album: Released '73, on Capitol by EMI Records. Deleted '78. Catalogue no: **EST 672**

Double Trouble

DOUBLE TROUBLE (See under Presley, Elvis)

Doucet, Michael

BELIZAIRE - THE CAJUN (Film soundtrack) (Doucet, Michael & Beausoleil)
Cass: Released Aug '87, on Arhoolie (USA) by Arhoolie Records (USA). Catalogue no: **C 5038**
Album: Released Aug '87, on Ar-

hoolie (USA) by Arhoolie Records (USA). Catalogue no: **ARHOOLIE 5038**

Down Argentine Way

DOWN ARGENTINE WAY (1945 film musical soundtrack) (Various artists)
Album: Released Jan '89, on Silva Screen by Silva Screen Records. Catalogue no: **HS 5013**

Down By Law

DOWN BY LAW (See under Lurie, John)

Down & Out In Beverley

DOWN AND OUT IN BEVERLEY HILLS (1986 film soundtrack) (Various artists)
Tracks: / Great gosh a' mighty: *Little Richard* / Tutti frutti: *Little Richard* / California girls: *Roth, David Lee* / El Tecalitleco: *Mariachi Vargas de Tecalitian* / I love L.A.: *Newman, Randy* / Down and out in Beverly Hills: *Summers, Andy* / Search for Kerouac: *Summers, Andy* / Nouvelle cuisine: *Summers, Andy* / Wave hands like clouds: *Summers, Andy* / Mission blues, The: *Summers, Andy* / Jerry's suicide attempt: *Summers, Andy.*
Cass: Released May '86, on MCA by MCA Records. Deleted Jan '88. Catalogue no: **MCFC 3320**
Album: Released May '86, on MCA by MCA Records. Deleted Jan '88. Catalogue no: **MCF 3320**
CD: Released Jun '88, on MCA (USA) by MCA Records (USA). Catalogue no: **31062**

Down Twisted

DOWN TWISTED (1987 film soundtrack) (Various artists)
Note: Score by Berlin Game.,
Album: Released Jan '89, on Silva Screen by Silva Screen Records. Catalogue no: **STV 81305**

D'Oyly Carte

LAST NIGHT COLLECTION,

THE
Tracks: / Yeoman of the guard / Trial by jury / Pirates of Penzance / HMS Pinafore / Iolanthe / Grand duke, The / Princess Ida / Ruddigore / Mikado, The / Gondoliers, The.
CD: Released 21 Aug '89, on Castle Collector Series by Castle Communications Records. Catalogue no: **CCSCD 228**
Album: Released 21 Aug '89, on Castle Collector Series by Castle Communications Records. Catalogue no: **CCSLP 228**
Cass: Released 21 Aug '89, on Castle Collector Series by Castle Communications Records. Catalogue no: **CCSMC 228**

Dragnet

DRAGNET (1988 film soundtrack) (Various artists)
Album: Released May '87, on MCA by MCA Records. Deleted Dec '89. Catalogue no: **MCF 3414**
CD: Released May '87, on MCA by MCA Records. Deleted Dec '89. Catalogue no: **DMCF 3414**
Cass: Released May '87, on MCA by MCA Records. Deleted Dec '89. Catalogue no: **MCFC 3414**

Drake's Dream

DRAKE'S DREAM (Original cast) (Various artists)
Tracks: / At the court of Queen Elizabeth: *Various artists* / I've always had a dream: *Various artists* / Let's get goin': *Various artists* / Take a little time: *Various artists* / When the winds command us away: *Various artists* / She plays a dangerous game: *Various artists* / Between today and tomorrow: *Various artists* / Sedition: *Various artists* / Waiting isn't easy: *Various artists* / Gold: *Various artists* / Nova Albion: *Various artists* / God of the waters: *Various artists* / Spice of life: *Various artists* / Oh Lord protect us: *Various artists* / Fa la la: *Vari-*

ous artists / Sailing around: *Various artists* / Finale: *Various artists.*
Album: Released '77, on President by President Records. Catalogue no: **PTLS 1068**

Drama...

20 BBC DRAMA THEMES (Various artists)
Tracks: / Cleopatras: *Various artists* / Squadron: *Various artists* / Shoestring: *Various artists* / Chinese detective, The: *Various artists* / Telford's change: *Various artists* / Blake 7: *Various artists* / Aphrodite inheritance: *Various artists* / We the accused: *Various artists* / Scorpion: *Various artists* / Who pays the ferryman: *Various artists* / Chi Mai: *Various artists* / Smiley's people: *Various artists* / Poldark: *Various artists* / Penmarric: *Various artists* / Mackenzie: *Various artists* / Horseman riding by: *Various artists* / Nancy Astor: *Various artists* / Nanny: *Various artists* / To serve them all my day's: *Various artists* / Palisers: *Various artists.*
Cass: Released Apr '83, on BBC by BBC Records. Catalogue no: **ZCR 464**
Album: Released Apr '83, on BBC by BBC Records. Deleted Apr '89. Catalogue no: **REH 464**

Draughtsman's Contract

DRAUGHTSMAN'S CONTRACT, THE (1983 film soundtrack) (Various artists)
Tracks: / Queen of the night: *Nyman, Michael* / Disposition of the linen, The: *Nyman, Michael* / Watery death, A: *Nyman, Michael* / Garden is becoming a robe room, The: *Nyman, Michael* / Chasing sheep is best left to shepherds: *Nyman, Michael* / Eye for optical theory, An: *Nyman, Michael* / Bravura in the face of grief: *Nyman, Michael.*
Album: Released Feb '83, on Charisma by Virgin Records.

Catalogue no: **CAS 1158**
Album: Released '88, on DRG (USA) by DRG Records (USA).
Catalogue no: **SL 9513**
CD: Released Feb '90, on Silva Screen by Silva Screen Records.
Catalogue no: **CDSL 9513**
Cass: Released '88, on DRG (USA) by DRG Records (USA).
Catalogue no: **SLC 9513**
CD: Released Apr '89, on Charisma by Virgin Records. Catalogue no: **CASCD 1158**

Dream Academy

PLEASE PLEASE LET ME GET WHAT I WANT
Tracks: / Please please let me get what I want.
Note: Featured in 'Ferris Bueller's Day Off'.
7" Single: Released Nov '85, on Blanco Y Negro by Blanco Y Negro Records. Catalogue no: **NEG 20**
12" Single: Released Nov '85, on Blanco Y Negro by Blanco Y Negro Records. Catalogue no: **NEG 20T**

Dream Girls

DREAM GIRLS (Original 1981 Broadway cast) (Various artists)
Tracks: / Move (you're stepping on my heart): *Various artists* / Fake your way to the top: *Various artists* / Cadillac car: *Various artists* / Ain't no party: *Various artists* / When I first saw you: *Various artists* / I am changing: *Various artists* / Steppin' to the bad side: *Various artists* / Family: *Various artists* / I meant you no harm: *Various artists* / Rap, The: *Various artists* / Firing of Jimmy: *Various artists* / I miss you, old friend: *Various artists* / Dream girls: *Various artists* / Press conference: *Various artists* / And I'm telling you, I'm not going: *Various artists* / One night only: *Various artists* / Hard to say goodbye: *Various artists* / My love: *Various artists*.
Note: This is the original Broadway cast album of the show which made a star of Jennifer Holliday.
Album: Released Jul '82, on Geffen by Geffen Records (USA). Catalogue no: **GEF 85578**
Cass: Released Jul '82, on Geffen by Geffen Records (USA). Catalogue no: **40 85578**

Morgan Freeman and Jessica Tandy in the film of the Pullitzer prize winning comedy *Driving Miss Daisy*

CD: Released '88, on Geffen by Geffen Records (USA). Catalogue no: **2007 2**

Dream On (Film)

DREAM ON - WRECK ON THE HIGHWAY (Various artists)
CD: Released Jul '90, on BBC by BBC Records. Catalogue no: **BBCCD 769**
Album: Released Jul '90, on BBC by BBC Records. Catalogue no: **REB 769**

Dreamscape

DREAMSCAPE (Film soundtrack) (Jarre, Maurice)
Note: Electronic score by Maurice Jarre.
Album: Released Dec '84, on Sonic Atmospheres (USA) by Silva Screen Records. Catalogue no: **SONIC 102**
CD: Released Jan '89, on Sonic Atmospheres (USA) by Silva Screen Records. Catalogue no: **CD 302**

Dressed To Kill

DRESSED TO KILL (1981 film soundtrack) (Various artists)
Album: Released Jan '89, on Varese Sarabande Records(USA) by Varese Sarabande Records (USA). Catalogue no: **STV 81148**
CD: Released Jan '89, on Varese Sarabande Records(USA) by Varese Sarabande Records (USA). Catalogue no: **VCD 47148**

Driving Miss Daisy

DRIVING MISS DAISY (Film soundtrack) (Zimmer, Hans) (see panel above)
CD: Released Feb '90, on Silva Screen by Silva Screen Records. Catalogue no: **VSD 5246**
Cass: Released Feb '90, on Silva Screen by Silva Screen Records. Catalogue no: **VSC5246**
Album: Released Feb '90, on Silva Screen by Silva Screen Records. Catalogue no: **VS5246**

Drowing By Numbers

DROWNING BY NUMBERS (See under Nyman, Michael)

Drugstore Cowboy

DRUGSTORE COWBOY (Film soundtrack) (Various artists)
Tracks: / For all we know: *Lincoln, Abbey & Geri Allan* / Little things: *Goldsboro, Bobby* / Put a love in your heart: *DeShannon, Jackie* / Psychotic reaction: *Count Five* / Judy in disguise: *Fred, John & His Playboy Band* / Israelites, The: *Dekker, Desmond & The Aces* / Yesterday's Jones: *Various artists* / Morpheus ascending: *Various artists* / Monkey frenzy: *Various artists* / Wonder waltz: *Various artists* / White gardenia: *Various artists* / Floating hex, The: *Various artists* / Mr F Wadd: *Various artists* / Eligy mirror: *Various artists* / Panda the dog: *Various artists* / Heist and hat: *Various artists* / Strategy song: *Various artists* / Bob's new life: *Various artists* / Clockworks: *Various artists* / Cage iron: *Various artists* /

Goodnight Nadine: *Various artists.*
Album: Released Mar '90, on
Novus by BMG Records (UK).
Catalogue no: **PL 83077**
CD: Released Mar '90, on Novus
by BMG Records (UK). Catalogue
no: **PD 83077**
Cass: Released Mar '90, on
Novus by BMG Records (UK).
Catalogue no: **PK 83077**

Duck You Sucker

**DUCK YOU SUCKER (Film
Soundtrack) (Various artists)**
Tracks: / Duck you sucker - main
title: *Various artists* / Love: *Various
artists* / Green table: *Various artists* / March of the beggars: *Various artists* / Dead sons: *Various
artists* / Addio: *Various artists* /
Jokes on the side: *Various artists* /
Mexico and Ireland: *Various artists*
/ Inventions for John: *Various artists* / Counter revolution: *Various
artists* / After the explosion: *Various artists.*
Album: Released '73, on United
Artists by EMI Records. Deleted
'78. Catalogue no: **UAS 29345**

Dudes

**DUDES (1988 film sound-
track) (Various artists)**
Tracks: / Rock 'n' roll outlaw: *Keel*
/ Show no mercy: *W.A.S.P.* /
These boots were made for walk-
ing: *Megadeth* / Jesus came driv-
ing: *Leather Nun* / Lost highway:
Little Kings / Amazing grace: *Vai,
Steve* / Urban struggle: *Vandals* /
Vengeance...: *Steel, Simon and
The Claw* / Time forgot you: *Lethal
Weapon* / Mountain son: *Jane's
Addiction* / Dudes showdown:
Bernstein & Co.
Album: Released Jun '88, on
MCA by MCA Records. Deleted
Dec '89. Catalogue no: **MCF 3419**
CD: Released Jun '88, on MCA by
MCA Records. Deleted Dec '89.
Catalogue no: **MCAD 6212**
Cass: Released Jun '88, on MCA
by MCA Records. Deleted Dec
'89. Catalogue no: **MCFC 3419**

Duel At Diablo

**DUEL AT DIABLO (1965 film
soundtrack) (Various artists)**
Note: Western score by Neil Hefti.
Cass: Released Jan '89, on MCA
by MCA Records. Deleted Feb
'90. Catalogue no: **MCAC 1436**
Album: Released Jan '89, on
MCA by MCA Records. Cata-

logue no: **MCA 1436**

Duel Of The Titans

**DUEL OF THE TITANS (Orig-
inal soundtrack) (Various artists)**
Note: Epic score by Piero Piccioni.
Album: Released Jan '89, on
Silva Screen by Silva Screen Records. Catalogue no: **PHCAM 06**

Dukes Of Hazzard

**DUKES OF HAZZARD (TV
Soundtrack) (Various artists)**
Tracks: / Good ol' boys: *Booke,
Sorrell* / Laughing all the way to the
bank: *Booke, Sorrell* / Duellin'
Dukes: *Booke, Sorrell* / General
Lee: *Cash, Johnny* / Flash: *Best,
James* / Up on cripple creek:
Wopat, Tom / Cover girl eyes: *Ker-
shaw, Doug* / Keep between them
ditches: *Kershaw, Doug* / Ballad of
the General Lee: *Kershaw, Doug* /
In the driver's seat: *Schneider,
John* / Down home, American girl:
Bach, Catherine.
Album: Released '82, on Scotti
Bros (USA) by WEA Records.
Catalogue no: **SCT 85593**
Cass: Released '82, on Scotti
Bros (USA) by WEA Records.
Catalogue no: **40 85593**

**STORIES FROM THE DUKES
OF HAZZARD (Various ar-
tists)**
Cass: Released May '84, on Spot
by Pickwick Records. Catalogue
no: **SPC 8550**
Album: Released May '84, on
Spot by Pickwick Records. Catalogue no: **SPR 8550**

Dulfer, Candy

**LILY WAS HERE (See under
Lily Was Here)**

Dumbo

**DUMBO (Film Soundtrack)
(Various artists)**
Tracks: / Look out for Mr. Stork:
Various artists / Casey Junior:
Various artists / It's a circus dayb
again: *Various artists* / Dumbo:
Various artists / Pink elephants on
parade: *Various artists* / Dumbo
and Timothy: *Various artists* / Py-
ramid of elephants: *Various artists*
/ Dumbo disgraced: *Various artists*
/ When I see an elephant fly: *Vari-
ous artists* / Dumbo's triumph:
Various artists / Finale: *Various ar-
tists* / Song of the roustabouts:

Various artists.
Album: Released Oct '84, on Walt
Disney Deleted '88. Catalogue
no: **REC 542**
Cass: Released Oct '84, on Walt
Disney Catalogue no: **ZCM 542**
Album: Released '73, on Disney-
land by Disneyland-Vista Records
(USA). Deleted '78. Catalogue no:
DQ 1204
Album: Released Dec '82, on Dis-
neyland by Disneyland-Vista Rec-
ords (USA). Catalogue no: **D 324**
Cass: Released Dec '82, on Dis-
neyland by Disneyland-Vista Rec-
ords (USA). Catalogue no: **D 3DC**

Dune (Film)

**DUNE (1985 film soundtrack)
(Various artists)**
Tracks: / Dune: *Various artists* /
Dune prologue: *Various artists* /
Dune main title: *Various artists* /
Robot fight: *Various artists* / Leto's
theme: *Various artists* / Box, The:
Various artists / Floating fat man,
The: *Various artists* / Trip to Ar-
rakis: *Various artists* / First attack:
Various artists / Phrophecy theme:
Various artists / Dune (desert
home): *Various artists* / Paul meets
Chani: *Various artists* / Prelude
(take my hand): *Various artists* /
Paul takes the water of life: *Various
artists* / Big battle, The: *Various ar-
tists* / Paul kills Feyd: *Various artists*
/ Final dream: *Various artists* / Take
my hand: *Various artists.*
CD: Released Dec '84, on Polydor
by Polydor Ltd. Deleted Mar '88.
Catalogue no: **823 770-2**
Album: Released Dec '84, on
Polydor by Polydor Ltd. Catalogue
no: **823 770-1**
Cass: Released Dec '84, on Polydor by Polydor Ltd. Deleted Mar
'88. Catalogue no: **823 770-4**

Dunwich Horror

**DUNWICH HORROR, THE
(1970 film soundtrack) (Various artists)**
Note: Composed by Les Baxter.
Album: Released Jan '89, on
Silva Screen by Silva Screen Records. Catalogue no: **VC 81103**

Dunwich Story

**DUNWICH STORY, THE (Film
soundtrack) (Various artists)**
Album: Released Jul '90, on Voxx
(USA) by Bomp/Voxx Records
(USA). Catalogue no: **VOXX
200063**

Duran Duran

VIEW TO A KILL, A

Tracks: / View to a kill, A / View to a kill, A (version).

Note: Used as the title theme to the James Bond film View to a kill

Special: Released May '85, on Parlophone by EMI Records. Deleted '86. Catalogue no: **DU-RANG 007**

7" Single: Released May '85, on Parlophone by EMI Records. Catalogue no: **DURAN 7**

7" Single: Released May '85, on Parlophone by EMI Records. Deleted Aug '89. Catalogue no: **DURAN 007**

Durbin, Deanna

MOVIE SONGS

Tracks: / Lover / Danny boy / In the spirit of the moment / When you're away / Russian medley / Night and day / Spring in my heart / Prince, The / Old refrain, The / Moonlight bay / I'll take you home again Kathleen.

Note: Side one tracks 1 & 2 featured in the film Because Of Him. Tracks 3,4,5 & side two track 3 featured in His Butler's Sister. Side two track 1 featured in Lady On The Train. Track 2 feature in First Love. Track 4 featured in The Amazing Mrs. Holliday. Tracks 5 & 6 featured in For The Love Of Mary.

Album: Released Apr '82, on Coral by MCA Records. Deleted Apr '88. Catalogue no: **MCL 1668**

Cass: Released Apr '82, on Coral by MCA Records. Deleted Apr '88. Catalogue no: **MCLC 1668**

SONGS OF THE SILVER SCREEN

Tracks: / One night of love / My heart is singing / You're as pretty as a picture / Mighty like a rose / Give me a little kiss / Granada / Carousel in the park / Waltz song from Romeo and Juliet / La capinera (the wren) / Goodbye / I love to whistle / Going home / With a heart that's free / Largo al factotum / Seguidilla / Serenade to the stars, A / Chapel bells / When I sing / Viennese waltz.

Note: The continual demand for Deanna Durbin records prompts this brand new compilation of 20 much-sought-after tracks. Beautifully packaged, this album will delight her many admirers. Mono.

Cass: Released May '86, on MCA by MCA Records. Catalogue no: **MCGC 6007**

Album: Released May '86, on MCA by MCA Records. Catalogue no: **MCG 6007**

Dury, Ian

PROFOUNDLY IN LOVE WITH PANDORA (TV theme)

Note: From the TV Series Diary of Adrian Mole aged 13 ¾

Tracks: / Profoundly in love with Pandora / Eugenius (you're a genuis).

7" Pic: Released Nov '85, on EMI by EMI Records. Deleted Jul '87.

Catalogue no: **EMIP 5534**

7" Single: Released Nov '85, on EMI by EMI Records. Deleted Oct '87. Catalogue no: **EMI 5534**

Dylan, Bob

DON'T LOOK BACK

Note: Running time: 96 mins. A 1965 semi-documentary by D A Pennebaker follows the Pasha of Protest around Britain, and includes several highly atmospheric performances by Dylan, Joan Baez and Donavan. An intriguing black and white portrait of a hero in his youth.

VHS: Released Sep '88, on Virgin Vision by Virgin Records. Catalogue no: **VVD 251**

PAT GARRET AND BILLY THE KID (Film soundtrack)

Tracks: / Main title / Cantina theme (Workin' for the law) / Billy 1 / Bunkhouse theme / River theme / Turkey chase / Knocking on Heaven's door / Final theme / Billy 4 / Billy 7.

Album: Released Sep '73, on CBS by CBS Records & Distribution. Deleted '78. Catalogue no: **CBS 69042**

Album: Released Apr '82, on CBS by CBS Records & Distribution. Deleted Jan '89. Catalogue no: **CBS 32098**

Cass: Released Apr '82, on CBS by CBS Records & Distribution. Deleted Jan '89. Catalogue no: **40 32098**

The following information was taken from the Music Master database on September 25th, 1990.

Earth Girls Are Easy

EARTH GIRLS ARE EASY (1989 film soundtrack) (Various artists)
Album: Released Nov '89, on WEA by WEA Records. Catalogue no: **925 835 1**
Cass: Released Nov '89, on WEA by WEA Records. Catalogue no: **925 835 4**

Eastenders

EASTENDERS SING-A-LONG (Various artists)
Tracks: / Hello, hello, who's your lady friend: *Various artists* / Man who broke the bank at Monte Carlo, The: *Various artists* / Ship ahoy: *Various artists* / It's a long way to Tipperary: *Various artists* / I do like to be beside the seaside: *Various artists* / Pack up your troubles in your old kit bag: *Various artists* / Goodbye Dolly Gray: *Various artists* / Don't dilly dally on the way: *Various artists* / Run rabbit run: *Various artists* / Wot'cher (knocked 'em in the Old Kent Road): *Various artists* / Waiting at the church: *Various artists* / Strollin': *Various artists* / Underneath the arches: *Various artists* / Home town: *Various artists* / Lily of Laguna: *Various artists* / On mother Kelly's doorstep: *Various artists* / I'm forever blowing bubbles: *Various artists* / Barrow boy song, The: *Various artists* / Lambeth walk: *Various artists* / Nice cup of tea, A: *Various artists* / Daddy wouldn't buy me a bow-wow: *Various artists* / I'm Henery the eighth I am: *Various artists* / Boiled beef and carrots: *Various artists* / Any old iron: *Various artists* / My old man's a dustman: *Various artists* / I've got a lovely bunch of coconuts: *Various artists* / Knees up Mother Brown: *Various artists* / Give my regards to Broadway: *Various artists* / Are you from Dixie: *Various artists* / If you knew Susie: *Various artists* / Maybe it's because I'm a Londoner: *Various artists* / Hold your hand out you naughty boy: *Various artists* / Who were you with last night: *Various artists* / How ya gonna keep 'em down on the farm: *Various artists* / Baby face: *Various artists* / Four leaf cloveer: *Various artists* / Toot, toot, tootsie goodbye: *Various artists* / Somebody stole my gal: *Various artists* / Put your arms around me honey: *Various artists* / Oh Johnny, oh Johnny oh: *Various artists* / Yes sir, that's my baby: *Various artists* / For me and my gal: *Various artists* / Shine on Harvest moon: *Various artists* / Who's sorry now: *Various artists* / You made me love you: *Various artists* / It had to be you: *Various artists* / Some of these days: *Various artists* / Alabamy bound: *Various artists* / Waiting for the Robert E. Lee: *Various artists* / When you're smiling: *Various artists* / California here I come: *Various artists* / Swanee: *Various artists* / Roll out the barrel: *Various artists* / Row row row: *Various artists* / She'll be coming round the mountain: *Various artists*.
Note: The cast of the popular soap opera singing their all time cockney favourites
Album: Released Nov '85, on BBC by BBC Records. Deleted Sep '87. Catalogue no: **REB 586**
Album: Released Oct '86, on MFP by EMI Records. Deleted '89. Catalogue no: **MFP 5779**
Cass: Released Nov '85, on BBC by BBC Records. Deleted Sep '87. Catalogue no: **ZCF 586**
Cass: Released Oct '86, on MFP by EMI Records. Deleted '89. Catalogue no: **TCMFP 5779**

Easter Parade

EASTER PARADE (Film soundtrack) (Various artists)
Tracks: / Steppin' out with my baby: *Various artists* / Fella with an umbrella, A: *Various artists* / Shaking the blues away: *Various artists* / Medle y: *Various artists* / Couple of swells, A: *Various artists* / It only happens when I dance with you: *Various artists* / Better luck next time: *Various artists* / Easter parade: *Various artists*.
Note: Medley contains: I love a piano/ Snooky ookums/ When the midnight train leaves for Alabam' *Various artists*.
CD: Released Jun '87, on CBS by CBS Records & Distribution. Deleted Jan '89. Catalogue no: **CD 70288**
Cass: Released Jul '86, on CBS by CBS Records & Distribution. Deleted Jun '88. Catalogue no: **40 70288**
Album: Released Jul '86, on CBS by CBS Records & Distribution. Deleted Jun '88. Catalogue no: **CBS 70288**

EASTER PARADE (VIDEO) (Various artists)
VHS: Released '88, on MGM/UA (Video) by MGM/UA Video. Catalogue no: **SMV 10256**

EASTER PARADE/SINGIN' IN THE RAIN (Film soundtracks) (Various artists)
CD: Released Jan '89, on MCA by MCA Records. Catalogue no: **MCAD 6179**

Easton, Sheena

FOR YOUR EYES ONLY (SINGLE)
Tracks: / For your eyes only / Runaway.
Note: Used as the title song for the James Bond film *For your eyes only*
7" Single: Released Jun '81, on EMI by EMI Records. Deleted Jun '89. Catalogue no: **EMI 5195**

Easy Rider

EASY RIDER (Film soundtrack) (Various artists) (See panel on next page)
Tracks: / Pusher, The: *Steppenwolf* / Born to be wild: *Steppenwolf* / Weight, The: *Band* / I wasn't born to follow: *Byrds* / If you want to be a bird: *Holy Modal Rounders* / Don't Bogart me: *Fraternity of Man* / If six was nine: *Hendrix, Jimi Experience* / Kyrie Eleison Mardi Gras: *Electric Prunes* / It's alright, ma (I'm only bleeding): *McGuinn, Roger* / Ballad of Easy Rider:

McGuinn, Roger.
Album: Released Dec '69, on Stateside by EMI Records. Deleted '73. Catalogue no: **SSL 5018**
Cass: Released Apr '89, on Castle Classics by Castle Communications Records. Catalogue no: **CLAMC 139**
Album: Released '87, on Castle Classics by Castle Communications Records. Catalogue no: **CLALP 139**
Album: Released Feb '82, on ABC Records by MCA Records. Catalogue no: **MCL 1647**
Cass: Released Feb '82, on ABC Records by MCA Records. Catalogue no: **MCLC 1647**

Eat The Rich

EAT THE RICH (1987 film soundtrack) (Various artists) (See also under Motorhead)
Tracks: / Eat the rich: *Motorhead* / Terrorists: *Brint, Simon* / Nosher in the bar: *Eccleston, Danny* / Arriba salsa: *Brint, Simon* / Doctor Rock: *Motorhead* / On the road: *Motorhead* / Car approach: *Brint, Simon* / Pistol in my pockets: *Various artists* / Orgasmatron: *Motorhead* / Bess: *Wurzel* / End title: *Eccleston, Danny.*

SONGS AS PERFORMED IN THE MOTION PICTURE

The soundtrack to *Easy Rider* (Stateside)

Cass: Released 7 Nov '87, on Filmtrax by Filmtrax Records. Deleted Aug '89. Catalogue no: **MOMENTC 108**
CD: Released 7 Nov '87, on Filmtrax by Filmtrax Records. Deleted Apr '90. Catalogue no: **MOMENTCD 108**
Album: Released 7 Nov '87, on Filmtrax by Filmtrax Records. Deleted Nov '89. Catalogue no: **MOMENT 108**

Eating Raoul

EATING RAOUL (1983 Original soundtrack) (Various artists)
Note: Composed by Arlon Ober
Album: Released Jan '89, on Silva Screen by Silva Screen Records. Catalogue no: **STV 81164**

Echo & The Bunnymen

PEOPLE ARE STRANGE
Tracks: / People are strange.
Note: Featured in the film 'The Lost Boys'.
12" Single: Released Feb '88, on WEA by WEA Records. Deleted Jan '90. Catalogue no: **YZ 175T**
7" Single: Released Feb '88, on WEA by WEA Records. Deleted Jan '90. Catalogue no: **YZ 175**

Eddie & The Cruisers

EDDIE AND THE CRUISERS (1983 film soundtrack) (Various artists)
Tracks: / On the dark side: *Various artists* / Tender years: *Various artists* / Runaround Sue: *Various artists* / Down on my knees: *Various artists* / Hang up my rock and roll shoes: *Various artists* / Wild summer nights: *Various artists* / Boardwalk angel: *Various artists* / Betty Lou's got a new pair of shoes: *Various artists* / Those oldies but goodies(remind me of you): *Various artists* / Season in hell: *Various artists.*
Album: Released '85, on Scotti Bros (USA) by WEA Records. Catalogue no: **SCT 25702**
Cass: Released '85, on Scotti Bros (USA) by WEA Records. Catalogue no: **40 25702**

EDDIE AND THE CRUISERS II (Eddie lives) (Various artists)
Tracks: / Runnin' thru the fire: *Various artists* / Open road: *Various artists* / Emotional storm: *Various artists* / Garden of Eden: *Various artists* / Some like it hot: *Various artists* / Just a matter of time: *Various artists* / Maryia: *Various artists* / Pride and passion: *Various artists* / NYC song: *Various artists* / (Keep my love) alive: *Various artists.*
CD: Released Jul '90, on Polydor by Polydor Ltd. Catalogue no: **8420462**
Album: Released Jul '90, on Polydor by Polydor Ltd. Catalogue no: **8420461**
Cass: Released Jul '90, on Polydor by Polydor Ltd. Catalogue no: **8420464**

EDDIE & THE CRUISERS (VIDEO) (Various artists)
Note: Cert: PG.
VHS: Released '88, on Entertainment In Video Catalogue no: **MRV 1004**

Eddy, Duane

BALLAD OF PALADIN
Tracks: / Ballad of Paladin.
Note: Theme tune to the 1950's TV western *Paladin*
7" Single: Released Aug '62, on RCA by BMG Records (UK). Deleted '67. Catalogue no: **RCA 1300**

PETER GUNN THEME

Tracks: / Peter Gunn.
7" Single: Released Jun '59, on London-American by Decca Records. Deleted '64. Catalogue no: **HLW 8879**
7" Single: Released May '68, on London-American by Decca Records. Deleted '71. Catalogue no: **HLW 10191**

ROCKESTRA THEME
Tracks: / Rockestra theme / Blue city.
12" Single: Released Sep '87, on Capitol by EMI Records. Deleted Nov '88. Catalogue no: **12CL 463**
7" Single: Released Sep '87, on Capitol by EMI Records. Deleted 31 Jul '88. Catalogue no: **CL 463**

Eddy Duchin Story
EDDY DUCHIN STORY (Film soundtrack) (Various artists)
Tracks: / To love again: *Various artists* (Based on Chopin's E Flat Nocturne.) / Manhattan: *Various artists* / Shine on harvest moon: *Various artists* / It must be true: *Various artists* / Whispering: *Various artists* / Dizzy fingers: *Various artists* / You're my everything: *Various artists* / Chopsticks: *Various artists* / On the sunny side of the street: *Various artists* / Brazil: *Various artists* / La vie en rose: *Various artists*.
Album: Released Apr '82, on Coral by MCA Records. Deleted '87. Catalogue no: **MCL 1666**
Cass: Released Apr '82, on Coral by MCA Records. Deleted '87. Catalogue no: **MCLC 1666**

Edge Of Darkness
EDGE OF DARKNESS (See under Clapton, Eric)

Edge (U2 Guitarist)
CAPTIVE (1986 film Soundtrack) (Edge & Sinead O'Connor)
Tracks: / Rowena's theme / Heroine (theme from 'Captive') / One foot in heaven / Strange party, The / Hiro's theme 1 / Drift / Dream theme, The / Djinn / Island / Hiro's theme 2.
Cass: Released Sep '86, on Virgin by Virgin Records. Deleted 13 Feb '89. Catalogue no: **TCV 2401**
Cass: Released '89, on Virgin by Virgin Records. Catalogue no: **OVEDC 257**
CD: Released '87, on Virgin by Virgin Records. Catalogue no: **CDV 2401**
Album: Released Sep '86, on Virgin by Virgin Records. Deleted 13 Feb '89. Catalogue no: **V 2401**
Album: Released '89, on Virgin by Virgin Records. Catalogue no: **OVED 257**

HEROINE (Theme from 'Captive') (Edge & Sinead O'Connor)
Tracks: / Heroine / Heroine (mix II).
7" Single: Released Sep '86, on Virgin by Virgin Records. Catalogue no: **VS 897**
12" Single: Released Sep '86, on Virgin by Virgin Records. Catalogue no: **VS 897-12**

Edith Et Marcel
EDITH ET MARCEL (1983 Film soundtrack) (Various artists)
Tracks: / La vie en rose: *Various artists* / Un homme comme les autres: *Various artists* / L'effet qu'tum'fais: *Various artists* / C'est peutetre ca: *Various artists* / Je t'ai dans la peau: *Various artists* / Medley d'Edith et Marcel: *Various artists* / Avant toi (Versailles): *Various artists* / Le fanion de la legion: *Various artists* / La Marseillaise: *Various artists* / Qu'est ce qu'on attend: *Various artists* / Pour etre heureux: *Various artists* / Insensiblement: *Various artists* / C'est un gars: *Various artists* / La priere: *Various artists* / Viens au creux de mon epaule: *Various artists* / Avant toi (Versailles): *Various artists* / Le chant d'amour: *Various artists* / Bal dans ma rue: *Various artists* / Le diable de la bastille: *Various artists* / Margot coeur gros: *Various artists* / Comme moi: *Various artists* / C'est marveilleux (du film): *Various artists* / La fould: *Various artists* / L'homme que J'aimerai: *Various artists* / Je n'attendais que toi: *Various artists* / La mer: *Various artists* / Le club des sanc: *Various artists* / La mort de Cerdan: *Various artists* / Combat de boxe: *Various artists* / Avec toi: *Various artists*.
Note: *Edith et Marcel*, A major new film about the life of Edith Piaf. Edith Piaf recordings and new music specially written by Francis Lai and performed by Charles Aznavour who also stars in the film. *Edith et Marcel* has been made by the world famous French director Claude Lelouch.

Cass: Released May '83, on EMI by EMI Records. Catalogue no: **TCDUO 131**
Album: Released May '83, on EMI by EMI Records. Catalogue no: **DUO 131**

Edith Strategy
EDITH STRATEGY (Original soundtrack) (Various artists)
CD: Released Jul '90, on Big Cat by Big Cat Records. Catalogue no: **ABB 19 CD**
Album: Released Jul '90, on Big Cat by Big Cat Records. Catalogue no: **ABB 19**

Educating Rita
EDUCATING RITA (See under Hentschel, David)

Egyptian
EGYPTIAN, THE (1954 film soundtrack) (Various artists)
Note: Epic score by Alfred Newman & Bernard Herrmann.
Cass: Released Jan '89, on MCA by MCA Records. Deleted Mar '90. Catalogue no: **MCAC 1523**
Album: Released Jan '89, on MCA by MCA Records. Catalogue no: **MCA 1523**
Cass: Released Aug '90, on Varese Sarabande Records(USA) by Varese Sarabande Records (USA). Catalogue no: **VSC 5258**

Eight & A Half
EIGHT AND A HALF (1963 Film Soundtrack) (Various artists)
Album: Released '90, on RCA by BMG Records (UK). Catalogue no: **NL 33210**
Cass: Released '90, on RCA by BMG Records (UK). Catalogue no: **NK 33210**

Eighteen TV/Film Themes
EIGHTEEN TV/FILM THEMES (Various artists)
Tracks: / To have and to hold: *Stock, Catherine* / Me and my girl: *Skellern, Peter* / Cats eyes: *Kongos, John* / Two of us, The: *Silsoe* / Aztec gold: *Silsoe* / Walk on: *New Horizon* / Tales of the unexpected: *Grainer, Ron Orchestra* / Cavatina: *Williams, John* / Prospects: *Made in England* / Dempsey and Makepeace: *Various artists* / Woman of substance: *Various artists* / Reilly: *Various artists* / Anna of the five towns: *Various artists* /

All passion spent: *Various artists* / Onedin line, The: *Various artists* / Lovè for Lydia: *Various artists* / Lillie: *Various artists* / Monsignor Quixote: *Various artists*.

Cass: Released Dec '86, on Sierra by Sierra Records. Catalogue no: **CFEDM 1**

Album: Released Dec '86, on Sierra by Sierra Records. Catalogue no: **FEDM 1**

Eighty Four Charing...

84 CHARING CROSS ROAD (1987 film soundtrack) (Various artists)

Tracks: / Fanfare maintitle (the journey): *Various artists* / Book of love poems: *Various artists* / Marks and co: *Various artists* / Dear speed: *Various artists* / Christmas gift, 1949: *Various artists* / Nora writes: *Various artists* / Church sonata in A: *Corelli (Composer)* / Pilgrimage - Helene and Frank: *Various artists* / Wedding, The: *Various artists* / Subway, The: *Various artists* / Love between friends: *Various artists* / Tred softly: *Various artists* / Helen's first letter: *Various artists* / Business as usual: *Various artists* / Festival of Britain conga: *Various artists* / Daydream: *Various artists* / Meeting Ginny and Ed: *Various artists* / Move, The, 1958/9: *Various artists* / New year, 1960 (Auld lang syne): *Various artists* / Hopes fade: *Various artists* / Love between friends (reprise): *Various artists* / Closing credits: *Various artists*.

Note: Starring Anne Bancroft & Anthony Hopkins. The story of an American authoress's postal relationship with an antiquarian bookshop at 84.

Cass: Released Apr '87, on T. E. R. by That's Entertainment Records. Catalogue no: **ZCTER 1129**

Album: Released Apr '87, on T. E. R. by That's Entertainment Records. Catalogue no: **TER 1129**

El Amor Brujo

EL AMOR BRUJO (1986 film soundtrack) (Various artists)

Tracks: / El amor brujo: *Various artists* / Alborea: *Various artists* / Tangos de boda: *Various artists* / La Mosca: *Various artists* / Azucar Moreno: *Various artists* / Adagio: *Various artists* / Los peces en el rio: *Various artists* / Como el agua:

Various artists / Tu mira: *Various artists* / Se pone como ina fiera: *Various artists* / Alegrias: *Various artists* / Cancion del tendedero: *Various artists*.

CD: Released Nov '86, on EMI by EMI Records. Deleted Dec '89. Catalogue no: **CDC 747586-2**

El Cid

EL CID (1961 film soundtrack) (Various artists)

Tracks: / El Cid overture: *Various artists* / Prelude: *Various artists* / Palace music: *Various artists* / Fight for Calahorra: *Various artists* / 13 knights: *Various artists* / Farewell: *Various artists* / Intermezzo: *Various artists* / El Cid march, The: *Various artists* / Twins, The: *Various artists* / Battle of Valencia: *Various artists* / Cid's death, The: *Various artists* / Legend and epilogue, The: *Various artists*.

Cass: Released Jan '90, on MGM (EMI) Catalogue no: **TCMGM 5**

Cass: Released Jan '90, on MGM (EMI) Catalogue no: **793 301 4**

CD: Released Jan '90, on MGM (EMI) Catalogue no: **CDMGM 5**

Album: Released Jan '90, on MGM (EMI) Catalogue no: **793 301 1**

Album: Released Jan '90, on MGM (EMI) Catalogue no: **LPMGM 5**

CD: Released Jan '90, on MGM (EMI) Catalogue no: **CDP 793 301 2**

EL CID (Film Soundtrack) (Various artists)

Cass: Released Jan '89, on MCA by MCA Records. Deleted Mar '90. Catalogue no: **MCAC 25005**

Album: Released Jan '89, on MCA by MCA Records. Catalogue no: **MCA 25005**

Album: Released '73, on MGM (Polydor) by Polydor Ltd. Deleted '78. Catalogue no: **2353 046**

El Dorado (Film)

EL DORADO (1988 film soundtrack) (Various artists)

Note: Spanish film from Carlos Saura (director of A Love Bewitched, Carmen). Music by Alejandro Masso.

Cass: Released Jan '89, on SPI Milan (France) Catalogue no: **C 342**

CD: Released Jan '89, on SPI Milan (France) Catalogue no: **CD 342**

Album: Released Jan '89, on

Silva Screen by Silva Screen Records. Catalogue no: **LAALP 1007**

Album: Released Jan '89, on SPI Milan (France) Catalogue no: **A 342**

Electric Dreams

ELECTRIC DREAMS (1984 film soundtrack) (Various artists) (See also under Arnold, P.P.)

Tracks: / Electric dreams: *Arnold, P.P.* / Video: *Lynne, Jeff* / Dream, The: *Culture Club* / Duel, The: *Moroder, Giorgio* / Now you are mine: *Terry, Helen* / Love is love: *Culture Club* / Chase runner: *Heaven 17* / Let it run: *Lynne, Jeff* / Madeline's theme: *Moroder, Giorgio* / Together in electric dreams: *Moroder, Giorgio & Philip Oakey*.

CD: Released Oct '84, on Virgin by Virgin Records. Deleted 13 Feb '89. Catalogue no: **CDV 2318**

Album: Released Sep '84, on Virgin by Virgin Records. Deleted 13 Feb '89. Catalogue no: **V 2318**

Cass: Released Sep '84, on Virgin by Virgin Records. Deleted 13 Feb '89. Catalogue no: **TCV 2318**

ELECTRIC DREAMS (VIDEO) (Various artists)

Note: Cert: PG.

VHS: on Virgin Vision by Virgin Records. Catalogue no: **VVC 061**

Beta: on Virgin Vision by Virgin Records. Catalogue no: **VVC 061 B**

Electric Horseman

ELECTRIC HORSEMAN, THE (Film soundtrack) (Various artists)

Tracks: / Midnight rider: *Nelson, Willie* / My heroes have always been cowboys: *Nelson, Willie* / Mamas don't let your babies grow up to be..: *Nelson, Willie* / Hands on the wheel: *Nelson, Willie* / Electro-phantasma: *Various artists* / Rising star: *Various artists* / Electric horseman: *Various artists* / Tumbleweed morning: *Various artists* / Disco magic: *Various artists* / Freedom: *Various artists* / Epilogue: *Various artists*.

Note: Music from the Robert Redford/Jane Fonda film.

Cass: Released Jan '89, on Silva Screen by Silva Screen Records. Catalogue no: **JST 36327**

CD: Released Jan '89, on CBS (import) by CBS Records & Distribution. Catalogue no: **CK 36327**

Cass: Released Apr '80, on CBS

E.L.O. - 'I'm Alive' from the film *Xanadu*

by CBS Records & Distribution. Catalogue no: **40 70177**

Album: Released Apr '80, on CBS by CBS Records & Distribution. Catalogue no: **70177**

Album: Released Jan '89, on Silva Screen by Silva Screen Records. Catalogue no: **JS 36327**

Ellis, Vivian

THREE BY VIVIAN ELLIS (Original cast recordings) (Various artists)
Tracks: / I want to see the people happy: *Various artists* / London Town: *Various artists* / Who's the lady: *Various artists* / Let us go down the river: *Various artists* / Other men: *Various artists* / Love me not: *Various artists* / Tough at the top: *Various artists* / I'm on fire: *Various artists* / Blood and iron: *Various artists* / Interlude: *Various artists* / I don't want to marry: *Various artists* / I feel a new fellow: *Various artists* / I wish I could sing: *Various artists* / Really a rather nice man: *Various artists* / Muffin man: *Various artists* / All the ladies are lovely: *Various artists* / England is a lovely

place: *Various artists* / This is not the end: *Various artists* / And so to bed: *Various artists* / Bartholomew Fair: *Various artists* / Amoamas: *Various artists* / Gaze not on swans: *Various artists* / Love me little, love me long: *Various artists* / Sarabande: *Various artists* / Beauty retire: *Various artists* / Oaths: *Various artists*.
Album: on Retrospect by EMI Records. Catalogue no: **SH 339**

Elmer Gantry

ELMER GANTRY (Original soundtrack) (Various artists)
Note: Score by Andre Previn for the Burt Lancaster film.
Album: Released Jan '89, on Silva Screen by Silva Screen Records. Catalogue no: **MCA 39070**
Cass: Released Jan '89, on Silva Screen by Silva Screen Records. Catalogue no: **MCAC 39070**

E.L.O.

I'M ALIVE (See panel above)
Tracks: / I'm alive / Drum dreams.
Note: From the film Xanadu.
7" Single: Released May '80, on Jet by Jet Records. Deleted '85.

Catalogue no: **JET 195**

XANADU (See under Newton John, Olivia)

Elvira Madigan

ELVIRA MADIGAN (1987 film soundtrack) (Various artists)
Album: Released '89, on H.M.V. by EMI Records. Catalogue no: **ASD 2465**
Cass: Released '89, on H.M.V. by EMI Records. Catalogue no: **TCASD 2465**

Emerson, Keith

BEST REVENGE (Film soundtrack)
CD: Released Oct '86, on Chord by Chord Records. Catalogue no: **CHORDCD 001**
Album: Released Oct '86, on Chord by Chord Records. Catalogue no: **CHORD 001**

HARMAGEDDON / CHINA FREE FALL (Film soundtracks) (Emerson, Keith / Derek Austin)
Tracks: / Theme of Floi / Joe and Michiko / Children of the light / Funny's skate state / Zamedy stomp / Challenge of the psionic fighters / China free fall / Main title / Eight man visions / Magic garden / Summer palace / Space reality / Canton stadium / Chinese star 3.
Album: Released Feb '87, on Chord by Chord Records. Catalogue no: **CHORD 003**

HONKY (Original soundtrack)
CD: Released Apr '85, on Chord by Chord Records. Catalogue no: **CHORDCD 002**
Album: Released May '86, on Chord by Chord Records. Catalogue no: **CHORD 002**

INFERNO (Original soundtrack)
Tracks: / Inferno / Rose's descent into the cellar / Taxi ride, The / Library, The / Sarah in the library vaults / Bookbinder's delight / Rose leaves the apartment / Rose gets it / Elisa's story / Cat attic attack, A / Kazanians tarantella / Mark's discovery / Mater tenebrarum / Inferno (finals) / Cigarettes, ices, etc..
Album: on Atlantic by WEA Rec-

ords. Catalogue no: **K 50753**

Cass: Released Mar '90, on Cinevox by Cinevox Italy. Catalogue no: **CIAK 75022**

Album: Released Mar '90, on Cinevox by Cinevox Italy. Catalogue no: **CIA 5022**

MURDEROCK (Film soundtrack)

CD: Released May '86, on Chord by Chord Records. Catalogue no: **CHORDCD 004**

Album: Released May '86, on Chord by Chord Records. Catalogue no: **CHORD 004**

UP THE ELEPHANT AND ROUND THE CASTLE (TV theme)

Tracks: / Up the elephant & round the castle.

7" Single: Released Dec '83, on Red Bus by Red Bus Records. Catalogue no: **RBUS 85**

EMI Comedy Classics

GOONS (See under Goons)

Emmanuelle (Film)

EMMANUELLE (1974 film soundtrack) (Various artists)

Tracks: / Emmanuelle in the mirror: *Various artists* / Emmanuelle song (french vocal version): *Various artists* / Emmanuelle in Thailand: *Various artists* / Emanuelle steps out: *Various artists* / Emmanuelle theme: *Various artists* / Night club: *Various artists* / Emmanuelle swims: *Various artists* / Emmanuelle in Thailand (variation): *Various artists* / Emmanuelle theme (instrumental): *Various artists* / Emmanuelle song (English vocal version): *Various artists* / Emmanuelle theme (instrumental variation): *Various artists* / Mood: *Various artists* / Emmanuelle theme (uptemp): *Various artists* / Opium den: *Various artists* / Rape sequence: *Various artists* / Cigarette act: *Various artists.*

Album: Released '77, on Warner Bros. by WEA Records. Deleted '82. Catalogue no: **K 56084**

EMMANUELLE 2 (1976 film soundtrack) (Various artists)

Tracks: / Love of loving: *Various artists* / Fantasies of Emmanuelle: *Various artists* / Jade garden, The: *Various artists* / Emmanuelle 2: *Various artists* / Emmanuelles lesson of love: *Various artists* / Arrival of Emmanuelle, The: *Various ar-*

tists / Meeting in Bali: *Various artists* / a: *Various artists.*

Album: on Warner Bros. by WEA Records. Catalogue no: **K 56231**

EMMANUELLE 4 (Original Soundtrack) (Magne, Michael)

Cass: Released May '84, on Carrere (France) Catalogue no: **76084**

Album: Released May '84, on Carrere (France) Catalogue no: **66084**

Emma's War

EMMA'S WAR (1987 film soundtrack) (Various artists)

Tracks: / Emma's theme: *Williams, John (Guitarist)* / My devotion: *Geraldo and his orchestra* / Emma's theme (part 2): *Williams, John (Guitarist)* / I'll never smile: *Geraldo and his orchestra* / Revelation: *Williams, John (Guitarist)* / Our love affair: *Roy, Harry & His Orchestra* / Understanding: *Williams, John (Guitarist)* / So easy to love: *Baker, Josephine* / Readjusting: *Williams, John (Guitarist)* / You're the top: *Merman, Ethel* / Garden music: *Williams, John (Guitarist)* / Emma's war: *Williams, John (Guitarist)* / Quintet in A: *Various artists.*

Cass: Released Jul '87, on Filmtrax by Filmtrax Records. Catalogue no: **MOMENTC 106**

Album: Released Jul '87, on Filmtrax by Filmtrax Records. Catalogue no: **MOMENT 106**

Emmerdale Farm

EMERDALE FARM CHURCH ALBUM (Emmerdale Farm Church Choir)

Tracks: / Guide me oh thou great Jehovah / Lord of tomorrow / Praise my soul / Dear Lord and Father / Following on / When I survey / Lord's my shepherd, The / Don't close the door / All things bright and beautiful / Love / Day thou gavest, The / Emmerdale prayer.

Note: Proceeds to Save the Children.

Album: Released Nov '85, on Spartan Catalogue no: **EEC 053**

Cass: Released Nov '85, on Spartan Catalogue no: **EEC 053**

Empire Of The Sun

EMPIRE OF THE SUN (1987 film soundtrack) (Various artists)

Tracks: / Suo Gan: *Various artists* / Cadillac of the skies: *Various artists* / Jim's new life: *Various artists* / Lost in the crowd: *Various artists* / Imaginary air battle: *Various artists* / Liberation: exsultate justi: *Various artists* / Return of the city, The: *Various artists* / British Grenadiers, The: *Various artists* / Toy planes, home and hearth: *Various artists* / Streets of Shangai, The: *Various artists* / Pheasant hunt, The: *Various artists* / No road home/seeing the bomb: *Various artists* / Exsultate justi: *Various artists.*

CD: Released 19 Mar '88, on WEA by WEA Records. Catalogue no: **K 925688 2**

Cass: Released 19 Mar '88, on WEA by WEA Records. Catalogue no: **K 925668 4**

Album: Released 19 Mar '88, on WEA by WEA Records. Deleted Jul '90. Catalogue no: **K 925668 1**

Empire State

EMPIRE STATE (1987 film soundtrack) (Various artists)

Tracks: / Vicious games: *Yello* / Summerland: *State Project* / Heavens above: *Communards* / Empire state: *State Project* / Argument: *State Project* / Dance floor: *State Project* / Lobby, The: *State Project* / Hollywood bar: *State Project* / Ship of fools: *Chaos 808* / Murder: *New Order* / Money: *Money.*

CD: Released '87, on Priority by Priority Records. Deleted May '90. Catalogue no: **STATECD 1**

Album: Released Jun '87, on Priority by Priority Records. Deleted Apr '90. Catalogue no: **STATELP 1**

Cass: Released Jun '87, on Priority by Priority Records. Deleted Apr '90. Catalogue no: **STATETC 1**

Empire Strikes Back

EMPIRE STRIKES BACK (Film soundtrack) (See also under (Composer) Williams, John)

Tracks: / Imperial march(Darth Vaders march) / Yoda's theme / Asteriod field / Han Solo and the princess(Love theme) / Empire strikes back: Finale / Training of a Jedi knight, The / Yoda and the force / Duel, The / Battle in the snow, The.

CD: Released May '80, on RSO by Polydor Ltd. Deleted Mar '88. Catalogue no: **825 298-2**
Album: Released Aug '80, on RSO by Polydor Ltd. Deleted '85. Catalogue no: **2394 276**
CD: Released Jan '89, on T. E. R. by That's Entertainment Records. Catalogue no: **CDVCD 47204**
Album: Released '80, on RSO by Polydor Ltd. Catalogue no: **2394 257**
Album: Released Jan '89, on Silva Screen by Silva Screen Records. Catalogue no: **827580.1**
CD: Released Apr '84, on T. E. R. by That's Entertainment Records. Deleted Apr '89. Catalogue no: **CD TER 9002**
Album: Released May '80, on RSO by Polydor Ltd. Catalogue no: **RSS 023**
Cass: Released '80, on RSO by Polydor Ltd. Catalogue no: **3216 257**
Cass: Released Jan '89, on Silva Screen by Silva Screen Records. Catalogue no: **827580.4**
Cass: Released May '80, on RSO by Polydor Ltd. Deleted '83. Catalogue no: **TRSS 023**

EMPIRE STRIKES BACK, THE (Various artists)

Tracks: / Asteroid field, The: *Various artists* / Battle in the snow, The: *Various artists* / Duel, The: *Various artists* / Han Solo and the princess: *Various artists* / Imperial march: *Various artists* / Star wars: *Various artists* / Training of a Jedi Knight: *Various artists* / Yoda and the force: *Various artists* / Yoda's theme: *Various artists* / Finale: *Various artists*.
Cass: Released Dec '82, on Disneyland by Disneyland-Vista Records (USA). Catalogue no: **D 151DC**
Album: Released Dec '82, on Disneyland by Disneyland-Vista Records (USA). Catalogue no: **D 451**

Encircled Sea

ENCIRCLED SEA (Various artists) (See panel above)
Tracks: / Water's edge, The: *Various artists* / Earth, fire and water: *Various artists* / Heart of the Mediterranean, The: *Various artists* / Fishermen, The: *Various artists* / Shipbuilders: *Various artists* / Navigators, The: *Various artists* / Great exchange, The: *Various ar-*

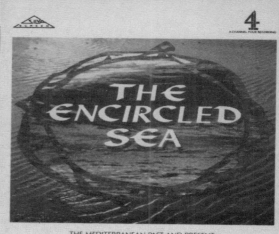

THE MEDITERRANEAN PAST AND PRESENT
MUSIC COMPOSED AND CONDUCTED BY
ROBERT BOYLE

Music From The Channel 4 Series *Encircled Sea*

tists / Gateways and haven: *Various artists* / Theatre of war: *Various artists* / Sea of belief: *Various artists*.
CD: Released Sep '90, on Silva Screen by Silva Screen Records. Catalogue no: **FILMCD 076**
Cass: Released Sep '90, on Silva Screen by Silva Screen Records. Catalogue no: **FILMC 076**

Encore, Encore

ENCORE, ENCORE (Songs from West End stage shows) (London Theatre Orchestra & Singers)
Tracks: / Only He / Memory / Maria / Another suitcase in another hall / I know him so well / Aquarius / Edelweiss / One night in Bangkok / She's so beautiful / Tomorrow / Grease / Hey there / Prepare the way of the Lord / People / Don't cry for me Argentina / I don't know how to love him / Impossible dream, The / Day by day / Sound of music, The / Till there was you.
CD: Released Apr '87, on The Collection by Object Enterprises. Catalogue no: **OP 0002**

Endless Games

ENDLESS GAMES (See under Morricone, Ennio)

Endless Love

ENDLESS LOVE (Original soundtrack) (Various artists)
Tracks: / Endless love: *Various artists* / Dreaming of you: *Various artists* / I was made for lovin' you: *Various artists* / Dreamin': *Various artists*.
Album: on Phonogram by Phonogram Ltd. Catalogue no: **6337 182**
Cass: on Phonogram by Phonogram Ltd. Catalogue no: **7141 182**

Enemies- A Love Story

ENEMIES- A LOVE STORY (Film soundtrack) (Various artists)
Tracks: / Herman: *Various artists* / Tamara: *Various artists* / In the wood: *Various artists* / Masha: *Various artists* / Third wife, A: *Various artists* / Kertchmar Country Club: *Various artists* / Rumba, The: *Various artists* / Baby masha: *Various artists*.
Cass: Released May '90, on Varese Sarabande Records(USA) by Varese Sarabande Records (USA). Catalogue no: **VSC 5253**
CD: Released May '90, on Varese

Sarabande Records (USA) by Varese Sarabande Records (USA). Catalogue no: **VSD 5253**
Album: Released May '90, on Varese Sarabande Records(USA) by Varese Sarabande Records (USA). Catalogue no: **VS 5253**

Enemy Mine

ENEMY MINE (1986 film soundtrack) (Jarre, Maurice)
Tracks: / Fryine IV / Relatioship / Small drac, The / Crater, The / Birth of Zammia / Spring / Scavengers / Davidges lineage / Football game / Before the enemy empire.
Note: Composed by Maurice Jarre.
Album: Released Feb '86, on Colosseum (West Germany) Catalogue no: **CST 8011**
Cass: Released Jan '89, on Varese Sarabande Records(USA) by Varese Sarabande Records (USA). Catalogue no: **CTV 81271**
Album: Released May '89, on T. E. R. by That's Entertainment Records. Catalogue no: **TER 1112**
Cass: Released Feb '86, on Colosseum (West Germany) Catalogue no: **CSTC 8011**
CD: Released Jan '89, on Varese Sarabande Records(USA) by Varese Sarabande Records (USA). Catalogue no: **VCD 47249**

Enigma (Film)

ENIGMA (1982 film soundtrack) (Various artists)
Tracks: / Enigma: main titles: *Various artists* / Alex goes home: *Various artists* / Love theme: *Various artists* / Crossing the frontier: *Various artists* / Escape from Schiller's resturant: *Various artists* / Gasthaus theme, The: *Various artists* / Russian christmas time: *Various artists* / Christmas carol: *Various artists* / Centra builing fire, The: *Various artists* / Karen's arrest: *Various artists* / Dimitri's discovery and farewell: *Various artists* / Enigma: End titles: *Various artists*.
Album: Released '83, on T. E. R. by That's Entertainment Records. Catalogue no: **TER 1027**

Ennemis Intimes

ENNEMIS INTIMES (INTIMATE ENEMIES) (Original soundtrack) (Various artists)
Note: New score from Philippe Sarde (Tess, Pirates, Manhattan Project).

Album: Released Jan '89, on Silva Screen by Silva Screen Records. Catalogue no: **A 350**
CD: Released Jan '89, on Silva Screen by Silva Screen Records. Catalogue no: **CD 350**

Enola Gay

ENOLA GAY (1980 film soundtrack) (Various artists)
Album: Released '88, on Varese Sarabande Records(USA) by Varese Sarabande Records (USA). Catalogue no: **STV 81149**

Enter The Dragon

ENTER THE DRAGON (Film soundtrack) (Various artists)
Tracks: / Sampans: *Various artists* / Monk, The: *Various artists* / Gentle softness, The: *Various artists* / Big battle, The: *Various artists* / Han's island: *Various artists* / Human fly: *Various artists* / Bamboo bird cage: *Various artists* / Broken mirrors: *Various artists* / Enter the dragon, Theme from: *Various artists*.
Album: Released '77, on Warner Bros. by WEA Records. Deleted '82. Catalogue no: **K 46275**

Entertainment USA

ENTERTAINMENT USA (VIDEO) (Various artists)
Note: Cert: PG.
VHS: Released '88, on BBC Video by BBC Video. Catalogue no: **BBCV 4027**

I'LL SLAP YOUR FACE (See under King, Jonathan)

VERY BEST OF ENTERTAINMENT USA (Various artists)
Album: Released Oct '86, on Priority by Priority Records. Catalogue no: **UPTVR 1**

Enya

FROG PRINCE, THE (See under Frog Prince)

Equalizer

EQUALIZER (See under Copeland, Stewart)

Eraserhead

ERASERHEAD (1978 film soundtrack) (Various artists)
Cass: Released Jan '89, on A&M by A&M Records. Catalogue no: **CS 70027**

Album: Released Jan '89, on A&M by A&M Records. Catalogue

no: **SP 70027**
CD: Released Feb '90, on A&M by A&M Records. Catalogue no: **CD 70027**
Album: Released Jan '84, on Alternative Tentacles by Alternative Tentacles Records. Catalogue no: **VIRUS 30**

Eric The Viking

ERIC THE VIKING (Film soundtrack) (Various artists)
Album: Released Nov '89, on Sonet by Sonet Records. Catalogue no: **SNTF 1023**
CD: Released Nov '89, on Sonet by Sonet Records. Catalogue no: **SNCD 1023**

Escalation

ESCALATION/GALILEO (Film soundtracks) (Morricone, Ennio)
Album: Released Feb '90, on Silva Screen by Silva Screen Records. Catalogue no: **RP 017**

Escape From New York

ESCAPE FROM NEW YORK (1981 film soundtrack) (Carpenter, John & Alan Howarth)
Note: Composed by John Carpenter.
Album: Released Dec '81, on T. E. R. by That's Entertainment Records. Catalogue no: **TER 1011**
Cass: Released '89, on Colosseum (West Germany) Catalogue no: **CST 438038**
CD: Released '81, on Varese Sarabande Records(USA) by Varese Sarabande Records (USA). Catalogue no: **VCD47224**
Album: Released '89, on Colosseum (West Germany) Catalogue no: **CL 0004**
Cass: Released Jan '89, on Varese Sarabande Records(USA) by Varese Sarabande Records (USA). Deleted Feb '90. Catalogue no: **CTV 81134**
CD: Released Jan '89, on Silva Screen by Silva Screen Records. Catalogue no: **CDFMC 8**

Essex, David

MUTINY
Note: From the stage show *Mutiny*
Album: Released Oct '83, on Mercury by Phonogram Ltd. Deleted '87. Catalogue no: **MERH 30**
Cass: Released Oct '83, on Mercury by Phonogram Ltd. Deleted

'87. Catalogue no: **MERHC 30**

MYFANWY
Tracks: / Myfanwy / Love theme / Myfanwy (love theme) / Myfanwy (long version)
12" Single: Released Oct, 87, on Arista by BMG Records (UK). Deleted May '89. Catalogue no: **RIST 11**
7" Single: Released Oct, 87, on Arista by BMG Records (UK). Deleted Jun '89. Catalogue no: **RIS 11**
CD Single: Released May, 87, on Arista by BMG Records (UK). Deleted Jul '89. Catalogue no: **RISCD 11**

RIVER, THE
Tracks: / River, The.
Note: Theme to the BBC series *The river*, (starring David Essex)
7" Single: Released Oct '88, on Lamplight by Priority Records. Deleted Sep '89. Catalogue no: **LAMP 4**

TAHITI
Tracks: / Tahiti / Hell.
Note: From the stage show *Tahiti*
7" Single: Released Aug '83, on Mercury by Phonogram Ltd. Deleted'86.Catalogue no: **BOUNT1**

E.T.

E.T. (Disney storyteller version) (Various artists)
Album: Released Mar '83, on WEA by WEA Records. Deleted Mar '88. Catalogue no: **D 456**

E.T. (1982 Film Soundtrack) (various artists)
CD: Released Jan '89, on MCA by MCA Records. Catalogue no: **MCAD 31073**
Cass: Released Jan '89, on MCA by MCA Records. Catalogue no: **MCAC 37264**
Album: Released Jan '89, on MCA by MCA Records. Catalogue no: **MCA 37264**

E.T. -- THE EXTRATERRESTRIAL (Film soundtrack) (Various artists) (See also under Williams, John)
Tracks: / Three million light years from home: *Various artists* / Abandoned and pursued: *Various artists* / E.T.'s halloween: *Various artists* / Flying: *Various artists* / E.T. (phone number): *Various artists* / Over the moon: *Various artists* / Adventure on Earth: *Various artists*.
Cass: Released Oct '88, on MCA

by MCA Records. Catalogue no: **MCLC 1878**
Album: Released Jan '83, on MCA by MCA Records. Catalogue no: **CA 70000**
Album: Released Oct '88, on MCA by MCA Records. Catalogue no: **MCL 1878**
Cass: Released Jan '83, on MCA by MCA Records. Catalogue no: **CAC 70000**
CD: Released Oct '88, on MCA by MCA Records. Catalogue no: **DMCL 1878**

Eurythmics

1984 - FOR THE LOVE OF BIG BROTHER (Film soundtrack)
Tracks: / I did it just the same / Sexcrime (nineteen eighty-four) / For the love of big brother / Winston's diary / Greetings from a dead man / Julia / Doubleplusgood / Ministry of love / Room 101.
Cass: Released Nov '84, on Virgin by Virgin Records. Catalogue no: **OVEDC 207**
Album: Released '84, on Virgin by Virgin Records. Catalogue no: **V 1984**
Album: Released Nov '84, on Virgin by Virgin Records. Catalogue no: **OVED 207**
CD: Released Nov '84, on Virgin by Virgin Records. Catalogue no: **CDV 1984**

SEXCRIME (NINETEEN EIGHTY-FOUR)
Tracks: / Sexcrime (1984) (7" & 12" only) / Sexcrime (1984) (extended remix) (Available on 12" and CD only) / Julia (extended mix) (CD only) / I did it just the same.
CD 3": Released '88, on Virgin by Virgin Records. Catalogue no: **CDT 22**
7" Single: Released Oct '84, on Virgin by Virgin Records. Catalogue no: **VS 728**
12" Single: Released Oct '84, on Virgin by Virgin Records. Deleted Mar '90. Catalogue no: **VS 728-12**

Everett, Kenny

KREMMEN THE MOVIE (Various artists)
Tracks: / Call for Kremmen: *Various artists* / Q's theme: *Various artists* / Pretty Pauline: *Various artists* / Announcer: *Various artists* / Kremmen and Q: *Various artists*.
Cass: Released Aug '80, on EMI by EMI Records. Deleted '85.

Catalogue no: **TCEMC 3342**
Album: Released Aug '80, on EMI by EMI Records. Deleted '85. Catalogue no: **EMC 3342**

SNOT RAP (TV theme)
Tracks: / Snot rap / Snot rap (part 2).
7" Single: Released Mar '83, on RCA by BMG Records (UK). Catalogue no: **KEN 1**
12" Single: Released Mar '83, on RCA by BMG Records (UK). Catalogue no: **KENT 1**

Everett, Rupert

GENERATION OF LONELINESS
Tracks: / Generation of loneliness / Blood under the bridge.
Note: Featured in the film 'Hearts On Fire'.
7" Single: Released May '87, on Chrysalis by Chrysalis Records. Catalogue no: **CHS 3138**
12" Single: Released May '87, on Chrysalis by Chrysalis Records. Catalogue no: **CHS 123138**

Every Which Way But...

EVERY WHICH WAY BUT LOOSE (Film soundtrack) (Various artists)
Tracks: / Every which way but loose: *Rabbitt, Eddie* / Send me down to Tucson: *Tillis, Mel* / I seek the night: *Locke, Sandra* / Coca cola cowboy: *Tillis, Mel* / Monkey see, monkey do: *Crofford, Cliff* / Salty dog blues (instrumental): *Various artists* / I'll wake you up when I get home: *Rich, Charlie* / Red eye special: *Collins, Larry* / Eastwood's alley walk: *Various artists* / Behind closed doors: *Rich, Charlie* / I can't say no to a truck drivin' man: *Chase, Carol* / Under the double eagle (instrumental): *Various artists* / Bikers theme (instrumental): *Various artists* / Don't say you don't love me no more: *Locke, Sandra* / Six pack to go, A: *Thompson, Hank* / Overture (instrumental): *Various artists*.
Album: Released Feb '79, on Elektra by Elektra Records (UK). Catalogue no: **K 52119**

Everybody's All...

EVERYBODY'S ALL AMERICAN (1988 film soundtrack) (Various artists)
Note: Film starring Dennis Quaid (The Right Stuff, The Big Easy, Innerspace) and Jessica Lange (Tootsie, Francis).

Cass: Released Jan '89, on Silva Screen by Silva Screen Records. Catalogue no: **C 41 G 91184**
Album: Released Jan '89, on Silva Screen by Silva Screen Records. Catalogue no: **C 11 G 91184**
CD: Released Jan '89, on Silva Screen by Silva Screen Records. Catalogue no: **C 21 Z 91184**

Everything I Have ...

EVERYTHING I HAVE IS YOURS/SUMMER STOCK/I LOVE (Original TV soundtracks) (Various artists)
CD: Released Jan '89, on MCA by MCA Records. Catalogue no: **MCAD 5948**

Evil Under The Sun

EVIL UNDER THE SUN (Featuring the music of Cole Porter) (Various artists)
Cass: Released May '82, on RCA International by BMG Records (UK). Catalogue no: **INTK 5225**
Album: Released May '82, on RCA International by BMG Records (UK). Catalogue no: **INTS 5225**

Evita

EVITA (1976 Studio recording) (Covington, Julie)
2 LP Set: Released Nov '76, on MCA by MCA Records. Catalogue no: **MCX 503**
2 LP Set: Released May '80, on MCA by MCA Records. Deleted Jan '88. Catalogue no: **MCDW 453**
Cass: Released Nov '76, on MCA by MCA Records. Catalogue no: **MCXC 503**

EVITA (1978 Original London Cast) (Various artists)
Tracks: / Requiem for Evita: *Various artists* / Oh what a circus: *Various artists* / On this night of a thousand stars: *Various artists* / Eva and Magaldi: *Various artists* / Eva, beware of the city: *Various artists* / Buenos Aires: *Various artists* / Goodnight and thank you: *Various artists* / Lady's got potential, The: *Various artists* / Charity concert: *Various artists* / I'd be surprisingly good for you: *Various artists* / Another suitcase in another hall: *Various artists* / Dangerous Jade: *Various artists* / New Argentina, A: *Various artists* / On the balcony of the Casa Rosada: *Various artists* / Don't cry for me Argen-

tina: *Various artists* / High flying, adored: *Various artists* / Rainbow high: *Various artists* / Rainbow tour: *Various artists* / Actress hasn't learned the lines: *Various artists* / And the money kept rolling in: *Various artists* / Santa Evita: *Various artists* / Waltz for Eva and Che: *Various artists* / She is a diamond: *Various artists* / Dice are rolling: *Various artists* / Eva's sonnet: *Various artists* / Eva's final broadcast: *Various artists* / Montage: *Various artists* / Lament: *Various artists* / Cinema in Buenos Aires 26 July 1952, A: *Various artists* / Art of the possible: *Various artists* / Peron's latest flame: *Various artists*
CD: on MCA by MCA Records. Catalogue no: **DMCG 3527**
Cass: Released Jul '85, on MCA by MCA Records. Catalogue no: **MCGC 3527**
Album: Released Jul '85, on MCA by MCA Records. Catalogue no: **MCG 3527**

EVITA : SELECTION FROM THE MUSICAL (Various artists)
Album: Released Jul '77, on Polydor by Polydor Ltd. Catalogue no: **2384 096**

EVITA / JESUS CHRIST SUPERSTAR (Various artists)
Tracks: / Cinema in Buenos Aires July 26.1952, A: *Various artists* / Requiem for Evita: *Various artists* / Oh, what a circus: *Various artists* / On this night of a thousand stars: *Various artists* / Eva and Magaldi: *Various artists* / Eva beware of the city: *Various artists* / Buenos Aires: *Various artists* / Goodnight and thank you: *Various artists* / Lady's got potential, The: *Various artists* / Charity concert: *Various artists* / I'd be surprisingly good for you: *Various artists* / Another suitcase in another hall: *Various artists* / Dangerous Jade: *Various artists* / New Argentina, A: *Various artists* / On the balcony of the Casa Rosada: *Various artists* / Don't cry for me Argentina: *Various artists* / High flying, adored: *Various artists* / Rainbow high: *Various artists* / Rainbow tour: *Various artists* / Actress hasn't learned the lines (you'd like to hear), The: *Various artists* / And the money kept rolling in (and out): *Various artists* / Santa Evita: *Various artists* / Waltz for

Eva and Che: *Various artists* / She is a diamond: *Various artists* / Dice are rolling: *Various artists* / Eva's sonnet: *Various artists* / Eva's final broadcast: *Various artists* / Montage: *Various artists* / Lament: *Various artists* / Heaven on their minds: *Various artists* / Everything's alright: *Various artists* / This Jesus must die: *Various artists* / Hosanna: *Various artists* / Simon Sealnotes: *Various artists* / I don't know how to love him: *Various artists* / Gethsemene: *Various artists* / Pilate's dream: *Various artists* / King Herod's song: *Various artists* / Could we start again please: *Various artists* / Trial before Pilate: *Various artists* / John 19:41: *Various artists* / Forty one: *Various artists*.
Cass: Released Sep '84, on MCA (Twinpax Cassettes) by MCA Records. Deleted Jan '88. Catalogue no: **MCA 2 114**

Ewok Adventures

EWOK ADVENTURES, THE (Original soundtrack) (Various artists)
Note: Composed by Peter Bernstein.
Album: Released Jan '89, on Silva Screen by Silva Screen Records. Catalogue no: **STV 81281**

Excalibur (Film)

EXCALIBUR (Original soundtrack) (New Philharmonic Orchestra/Sir Adrian Boult)
Tracks: / Ride of the Valkyries / Funeral march / Prelude to Tristan and Isolde / O fortuna.
Album: Released Jul '81, on Island by Island Records. Catalogue no: **ILPS 9682**
Cass: Released Jul '81, on Island by Island Records. Catalogue no: **ICT 9682**

Exodus (Film)

EXODUS (1961 motion picture soundtrack) (Various artists)
Tracks: / Exodus: *Various artists* / Summer in Cyprus/Escape: *Various artists* / Ari: *Various artists* / Karen: *Various artists* / Valley of Jezreel: *Various artists* / Fight for survival: *Various artists* / In Jerusalem: *Various artists* / Brothers, The: *Various artists* / Conspiracy: *Various artists* / Prison break: *Various artists* / Dawn: *Various artists* / Fight for

peace: *Various artists* / Hatikvah: *Various artists*.

CD: Released Jan '89, on Silva Screen by Silva Screen Records. Catalogue no: **1058.2**

CD: Released Feb '87, on CBS by CBS Records & Distribution. Deleted Jun '88. Catalogue no: **450234 2**

Cass: Released Feb '87, on CBS by CBS Records & Distribution. Deleted Jun '88. Catalogue no: **450234 4**

Album: Released Feb '87, on CBS by CBS Records & Distribution. Deleted Jun '88. Catalogue no: **450234 1**

EXODUS (ORIGINAL ISSUE) (Film soundtrack) (Various artists)
Album: Released Jun '61, on RCA by BMG Records (UK). Deleted '66. Catalogue no: **RD 27210**

EXODUS/CAST A GIANT SHADOW (Various artists)
Tracks: / Cast a giant shadow (prologue): *Various artists* (Cast A Giant Shadow.) / Land of hope: *Various artists* (Cast A Giant Shadow.) / War in the desert: *Various artists* (Cast A Giant Shadow.) / Magda: *Various artists* (Cast A Giant Shadow.) / Cast a giant shadow: *Various artists* (Cast A Giant Shadow.) / Love me true: *Various artists* (Cast A Giant Shadow. Vocal by Vince Hill.) / Road to Jerusalem, The: *Various artists* (Cast A Giant Shadow.) / Gathering of the forces, The: *Various artists* (Cast A Giant Shadow.) / Victory on the beach: *Various artists* (Cast A Giant Shadow.) / Garden of Abu Gosh: *Various artists* (Cast A Giant Shadow.) / Cast a giant shadow (finale): *Various artists* (Cast A Giant Shadow. The Zemel choir.) / Exodus theme: *Various artists* (Exodus.) / Summer in Cyprus: *Various artists* (Exodus.) / Escape: *Various artists* (Exodus.) / Ari: *Various artists* (Exodus.) / Karen: *Various artists* (Exodus.) / Valley of Jezreel: *Various artists* (Exodus.) / Fight for survival: *Various artists* (Exodus.) / Brothers, The: *Various artists* (Exodus.) / Conspiracy: *Various artists* (Exo-

dus.) / Prison break: *Various artists* (Exodus.) / Dawn: *Various artists* (Exodus.) / Fight for peace: *Various artists* (Exodus.) / Hatikvah: *Various artists* (Exodus.).

Cass: Released Apr '90, on MGM (EMI) Catalogue no: **TCMGM 11**

CD: Released Apr '90, on MGM (EMI) Catalogue no: **CDP 794 486 2**

Cass: Released Apr '90, on MGM (EMI) Catalogue no: **794 286 4**

Album: Released Apr '90, on MGM (EMI) Catalogue no: **LPMGM 11**

Album: Released Apr '90, on MGM (EMI) Catalogue no: **794 286 1**

CD: Released Apr '90, on MGM (EMI) Catalogue no: **CDMGM 11**

Experiment In Terror
EXPERIMENT IN TERROR (Original soundtrack) (Various artists)
Note: Rare Henry Mancini score.
Album: Released Jan '89, on Silva Screen by Silva Screen Records. Catalogue no: **NL 45964**

Explorers (film)
EXPLORERS (1986 film soundtrack) (Various artists)
Note: Music by Jerry Goldsmith.
Album: Released Jan '89, on Silva Screen by Silva Screen Records. Catalogue no: **MCA 6148**
Cass: Released Jan '89, on Silva Screen by Silva Screen Records. Deleted Feb '90. Catalogue no: **MCAC 6148**

Expesso Bongo
EXPRESSO BONGO (See under Richard, Cliff)

Extreme Prejudice
EXTREME PREJUDICE (1987 film soundtrack) (Various artists)
Tracks: / Arrivals: *Various artists* / Cash: *Various artists* / Set-up, The: *Various artists* / Dust: *Various artists* / Identities: *Various artists* / Extreme prejudice: *Various artists* / Plan, The: *Various artists* / To Mexico: *Various artists* / No friendlies: *Various artists* / They didn't

care: *Various artists* / Funeral, The: *Various artists* / Deal, A: *Various artists*.
Note: Jerry Goldsmith score for this action film directed by Walter Hill and starring Nick Holte.
Cass: Released Sep '87, on Silva Screen by Silva Screen Records. Catalogue no: **FILMC 011**
Album: Released Sep '87, on Silva Screen by Silva Screen Records. Deleted Apr '90. Catalogue no: **FILM 011**
CD: Released Sep '87, on Silva Screen by Silva Screen Records. Catalogue no: **FILMCD 011**

Extremes (Film)
EXTREMES (Film Soundtrack Excerpts) (Various artists)
Tracks: / Ear ago, An: *Various artists* / Great Lager Street: *Various artists* / Box man: *Various artists* / Black rose: *Various artists* / Refrigerated warmth: *Various artists* / Let your love run through: *Various artists* / Hit it: *Various artists* / Surely: *Various artists* / Am I not like other birds of prey: *Various artists* / I'm a perfectly happy man: *Various artists* / Words unspoken: *Various artists* / Elvish queen: *Various artists* / We gotta watch out: *Various artists*.
Album: Released '73, on Deram by Decca International. Deleted '78. Catalogue no: **SML 1095**

Eye Of The Needle
EYE OF THE NEEDLE (1982 film soundtrack) (Various artists)
Album: Released Dec '81, on T. E. R. by That's Entertainment Records. Catalogue no: **TER 1010**

Eyes Of Laura Mars
EYES OF LAURA MARS (1978 film soundtrack) (Various artists)
Album: Released Jan '79, on CBS by CBS Records & Distribution. Deleted Jan '84. Catalogue no: **CBS 70163**
Cass: Released Jan '79, on CBS by CBS Records & Distribution. Deleted Jan '84. Catalogue no: **CBS 40 70163**

The following information was taken from the Music Master database on September 25th, 1990.

Fabulous Baker Boys

FABULOUS BAKER BOYS
(See under Grusin, Dave)

Fabulous Singlettes

STOP, IN THE NAME OF LOVE
(Live from The Piccadilly)
Album: Released Oct '88, on First Night by First Night Records. Catalogue no: **SCENE 13**
Cass: Released Oct '88, on First Night by First Night Records. Catalogue no: **SCENEC 13**
CD: Released Oct '88, on First Night by First Night Records. Catalogue no: **SCENECD 13**

Face To Face (film)

FACE TO FACE (FACCIA A FACCIA) (Original Soundtrack) (Various artists)
Note: Composed by Ennio Morricone.
Album: Released Jan '89, on Silva Screen by Silva Screen Records. Catalogue no: **IM 004**

Fagin, Joe

BREAKIN' AWAY
Tracks: / Breakin' away / That's livin' alright.
Note: From the TV series *Auf Wiedersehen Pet*
7" Single: Released Jan '84, on Towerbell Deleted '88. Catalogue no: **UNKNOWN**

THAT'S LIVIN' ALRIGHT
Tracks: / That's livin' alright.
Note: Taken from the TV series *Auf Wiedersehen Pet*
7" Pic: Released Apr '88, on PRT by Castle Communications Records. Catalogue no: **PYS 9**

Fair Deal

ALBION MARKET THEME
Tracks: / Albion Market theme / Connections theme.
7" Single: Released '85, on Columbia by EMI Records. Deleted '88. Catalogue no: **DB 9114**

Falcon & The Snowman

FALCON AND THE SNOWMAN
(1985 Film Soundtrack) (Various artists)
Tracks: / Psalm 121 - flight of the falcon: *Metheny, Pat* / Daulton Lee: *Metheny, Pat* / Chris: *Metheny, Pat* / This is not America: *Metheny, Pat & David Bowie* / Extent of the life: *Metheny, Pat* / Level of description, The: *Metheny, Pat* / Capture: *Metheny, Pat* / Epilogue (psalm 121): *Metheny, Pat*.
Album: Released '85, on EMI by EMI Records. Catalogue no: **EJ 2403051**
Album: Released Apr '85, on EMI-America by EMI Records. Catalogue no: **FAL 1**
Cass: Released '85, on EMI by EMI Records. Catalogue no: **EJ 2403054**

Fall Of The Roman

FALL OF THE ROMAN EMPIRE (Film soundtrack) (Tiomkin, Dimitri)
CD: Released Feb '90, on Silva Screen by Silva Screen Records. Catalogue no: **VSD 5228**

Falling In Love

FALLING IN LOVE (1985 film soundtrack) (Grusin, Dave)
DAT: Released Jul '88, on GRP by GRP Records (USA). Catalogue no: **GRT 9522**
Album: Released Jul '85, on GRP by GRP Records (USA). Catalogue no: **GRPA 9522**
CD: Released Jul '85, on GRP by GRP Records (USA). Catalogue no: **GRPD 9522**

Faltermeyer, Harold

AXEL F
Tracks: / Axel F / Shoot out.
Note: From *Beverly Hills Cop.*
Cassingle: Released Mar '85, on MCA by MCA Records. Deleted '88. Catalogue no: **MCAC 949**
7" Single: Released Oct '87, on MCA by MCA Records. Deleted Dec '89. Catalogue no: **MCA 949**
12" Single: Released Mar '85, on MCA by MCA Records. Deleted Dec '89. Catalogue no: **MCAT 949**
12" Single: Released Oct '87, on MCA by MCA Records. Catalogue no: **MCAX 949**

FLETCH THEME
Tracks: / Fletch theme / Running for love.
7" Single: Released Aug '85, on MCA by MCA Records. Deleted '88. Catalogue no: **MCA 991**
12" Single: Released Aug '85, on MCA by MCA Records. Deleted '88. Catalogue no: **MCAT 991**

'TOP GUN' ANTHEM
Tracks: / Memories / 'Top Gun' anthem.
7" Single: on CBS by CBS Records & Distribution. Deleted 10 Jul '89. Catalogue no: **650 270-0**
7" Single: Released Nov '86, on CBS by CBS Records & Distribution. Catalogue no: **650 270-7**

Fame

FAME (Film soundtrack) (Various artists)
Tracks: / Out here on my own: *Cara, Irene* / Hot lunch jam: *Cara, Irene* / Dogs in the yard: *McCrane, Paul* / Red light: *Clifford, Linda* / Is it okay if I call you mine?: *McCrane, Paul* / Never alone: *Contemporary Gospel Chorus* / Ralph and Monty (dressing room piano): *Gore, Michael* / I sing the body electric: *Various artists* / Fame: *Cara, Irene*.
Note: Digital stereo
Cass: Released Nov '84, on RSO by Polydor Ltd. Catalogue no: **SPEMC 82**
CD: Released Nov '84, on RSO by Polydor Ltd. Deleted Jan '89. Catalogue no: **800034-2**
Album: Released Nov '84, on RSO by Polydor Ltd. Deleted Oct '88. Catalogue no: **SPELP 82**
Album: Released Aug '80, on RSO by Polydor Ltd. Deleted '85. Catalogue no: **2479 253**
Cass: Released '80, on RSO by Polydor Ltd. Deleted '84. Catalogue no: **3216 265**

FAME (VIDEO) (Various artists)
Note: Cert: 15 mins.
VHS: Released Sep '88, on MGM/UA (Video) by MGM/UA Video. Catalogue no: **SMV 10027**

Fame-Music & Songs
FAME-MUSIC & SONGS FROM (Famous dance school choir & orchestra) (Various artists)
Tracks: / I can do anything better than you can: *Various artists* / We got the power: *Various artists* / Out here on my own: *Various artists* / Mannequin: *Various artists* / Starmaker: *Various artists* / Step up to the mike: *Various artists* / Hi fidelity: *Various artists* / It's sonata Mozart: *Various artists* / Show must go on: *Various artists*.
Cass: Released Nov '83, on MFP by EMI Records. Deleted Nov '87. Catalogue no: **TCMFP 4156344**
Album: Released Nov '83, on MFP by EMI Records. Deleted Nov '87. Catalogue no: **MFP 4156341**

Family Ness
FAMILY NESS, (THE) (Various artists)
Tracks: / Angus and Elspeth meet the Loch Ness monster: *Various artists* / Angus and Elspeth buy a puppy: *Various artists* / Speedyness saves the day: *Various artists* / Ferocious-ness loses his roar: *Various artists* / Clever-ness helps with the homework: *Various artists* / Professor Dumkopf gets stuck in a bubble: *Various artists* / Ferocious-ness and the look-alike contest: *Various artists* / Professor Dumkopf and his amazing cannonball: *Various artists* / Babyness and the Mayor's statue: *Various artists* / Clever-ness and the curling championship: *Various artists*.
Note: New BBC kids animated film programme.
Album: Released Oct '84, on BBC by BBC Records. Deleted Apr '89. Catalogue no: **REC 530**
Cass: Released Oct '84, on BBC by BBC Records. Deleted Apr '89. Catalogue no: **ZCM 530**

YOU'LL NEVER FIND A NESSIE IN THE ZOO
Tracks: / You'll never find a Nessie in the zoo / Family Ness.

7" Single: Released Oct '84, on BBC by BBC Records. Deleted 31 Aug '88. Catalogue no: **RESL 155**

Famous Themes
MORE FAMOUS THEMES (Various artists)
Tracks: / Voice of London: *Queen's Hall Light Orchestra* (Queen's Hall Light Orchestra signature tune.) / Calling all workers: *Various artists* (Music while you work.) / Champagne march: *Various artists* (Current Release / Movietime.) / Out of tune march: *Various artists* (Hello Mum.) / Miss world: *Various artists* / Skippy: *Various artists* (Seeing sport.) / Westminster waltz: *Various artists* (In town tonight.) / Star is born, A: *Various artists* (In town tonight.) / Holiday spirit: *Various artists* (In town tonight.) / High adventure: *Various artists* (Friday night is music night.) / Quiet stroll, A: *Various artists* (Farming.) / Looking around: *Various artists* (The Appleyards.) / Country canter: *Various artists* (Horseman riding by, A.) / Moomin: *Various artists* / Shooting star: *Various artists* (Kaleidoscope.) / Muse in Mayfair: *Various artists* (Music goes round.) / Old clockmaker, The: *Various artists* (Jennings at school.) / Melody fair: *Various artists* / Sporting occasion: *Various artists* (Wimbledon closing theme.).
Album: Released Jun '87, on Grasmere by Grasmere Records. Catalogue no: **GRALP 20**
Cass: Released Jun '87, on Grasmere by Grasmere Records. Catalogue no: **GRTC 20**

Fantasia (Film)
FANTASIA (Original soundtrack) (Various artists)
Tracks: / Pastoral symphony (no.6 in F): *Various artists* / Rite of spring, The: *Various artists* / Dance of the hours: *Various artists* / Night on bald mountain: *Various artists* / Ave Maria: *Various artists* / Toccata and fugue in D minor: *Various artists* / Sorcerer's apprentice: *Various artists*.
Note: Film soundtrack: 1982 digital recording cond. Irwin Kostal based on the original scoring by Leopold Stowski.
2 LP Set: Released Oct '84, on Walt Disney Deleted '88. Cata-

logue no: **REQ 537**
Cass set: Released Oct '84, on Walt Disney Deleted '88. Catalogue no: **ZCQ 537**
2 LP Set: Released Aug '82, on Disneyland by Disneyland-Vista Records (USA). Catalogue no: **D 104**
Cass set: Released Aug '82, on Disneyland by Disneyland-Vista Records (USA). Catalogue no: **D 104 VC**

Fantasist
FANTASIST, THE (1987 film soundtrack) (Various artists)
Tracks: / More passionate than we are: *Various artists* / Up on the roof: *Quinn, Paul* / Another day comes another day goes: *Dee, Kiki* / Living in a world turned upside down: *Private Lives* / I'll do it all again: *Heffernen, Honor* / Fantasist, The: *Various artists* / Temple of Venus: *Various artists* / Childhood story: *Various artists* / Clocks: *Various artists* / Rooftops: *Various artists* / Discovery: *Various artists*.
Album: Released Apr '87, on President by President Records. Catalogue no: **PTLS 1085**

Fantasticks
FANTASTICKS (1960 Original Broadway cast) (Various artists)
Tracks: / Try to remember: *Various artists* / Much much more: *Various artists* / Metaphor: *Various artists* / Never say no: *Various artists* / It depends on what you pay: *Various artists* / You wonder how these things begin: *Various artists* / Soon It's gonna rain: *Various artists* / Rape ballet, The: *Various artists* / Happy ending: *Various artists* / This plum is too ripe: *Various artists* / I can see it: *Various artists* / Plant a radish: *Various artists* / Round and round: *Various artists* / There is a curious paradox: *Various artists* / They were you: *Various artists* / Try to remember (Reprise): *Various artists*.
Cass: Released Aug '90, on T. E. R. by That's Entertainment Records. Catalogue no: **ZCTER 1099**
Album: Released Aug '90, on T. E. R. by That's Entertainment Records. Catalogue no: **TER 1099**
CD: Released Jan '89, on Polydor by Polydor Ltd. Catalogue no: **8219432**
CD: Released Aug '90, on T. E. R.

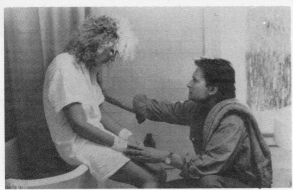

Dan Gallagher (Michael Douglas) tries to comfort a distraught Alex Forrest (Glenn Close) in *Fatal Attraction*

by That's Entertainment Records. Catalogue no: **CDTER 1099**

Farewell To Arms

FAREWELL TO ARMS (Original soundtrack) (Various artists)
Note: Mario Nascimbene score for the Epic starring Rock Hudson and Jennifer Jones.
Album: Released Jan '89, on Silva Screen by Silva Screen Records. Catalogue no: **AUSLP 1014**

Farewell To The King

FAREWELL TO THE KING (1989 film soundtrack) (Poledouris, Basil)
CD: Released Feb '90, on SPI Milan (France) Catalogue no: **CDCH 375**
Album: Released Feb '90, on SPI Milan (France) Catalogue no: **A375**
Cass: Released Feb '90, on SPI Milan (France) Catalogue no: **C375**

Fast Forward

FAST FORWARD (1984 film soundtrack) (Various artists)
Album: Released Jun '85, on Warner Bros. by WEA Records. Catalogue no: **925263 1**
Cass: Released Jun '85, on Warner Bros. by WEA Records. Catalogue no: **925263 4**

FAST FORWARD (VIDEO) (Various artists)
Note: Cert: PG.
VHS: Released '88, on RCA/Columbia (video) by BMG Records (UK). Catalogue no: **CVT 20643**

Fastest Guitar Alive

FASTEST GUITAR ALIVE, THE (1966 film soundtrack) (Various artists)
Note: Music and songs from the Roy Orbison western.
Cass: Released Jan '89, on MCA by MCA Records. Deleted Feb '90. Catalogue no: **MCAC 1437**
Album: Released Jan '89, on MCA by MCA Records. Catalogue no: **MCA 1437**

FASTEST GUITAR ALIVE / YOUR CHEATIN' HEART (Film soundtracks) (Various artists)
Tracks: / Whirlwind: *Various artists* (Fastest Guitar Alive.) / Medicine man: *Various artists* (Fastest Guitar Alive.) / River: *Various artists* (Fastest Guitar Alive.) / Fastest guitar alive, The: *Various artists* (Fastest Guitar Alive.) / Follin' on: *Various artists* (Fastest Guitar Alive.) / Pistolero: *Various artists* (Fastest Guitar Alive.) / Good time party: *Various artists* (Fastest Guitar Alive.) / Heading south: *Various artists* (Fastest Guitar Alive.) / Best friend: *Various artists* (Fastest Guitar Alive.) / There won't be many coming home: *Various artists* (Fastest Guitar Alive.) / Your cheatin' heart: *Various artists* (Your Cheatin' Heart.) / Hey good looking: *Various artists* (Your Cheatin' Heart.) / I saw light: *Various artists* (Your Cheatin' Heart.) / Jambalaya: *Various artists* (Your Cheatin' Heart.) /

Ramblin' man: *Various artists* (Your Cheatin' Heart.) / I'm so lonesome I could cry: *Various artists* (Your Cheatin' Heart.) / Jambalaya: *Various artists* (Your Cheatin' Heart.) / Cold cold heart: *Various artists* (Your Cheatin' Heart.) / Kaw-ligo: *Various artists* (Your Cheatin' Heart.) / I couldn't help it: *Various artists* (Your Cheatin' Heart.) / Hey good looking: *Various artists* (Your Cheatin' Heart.) / Long gone lonesome blue: *Various artists* (Your Cheatin' Heart.) / You win again: *Various artists* (Your Cheatin' Heart.).

Album: Released Apr '90, on MGM (EMI) Catalogue no: **LPMGM 18**
Cass: Released Apr '90, on MGM (EMI) Catalogue no: **TCMGM 18**
Album: Released Apr '90, on MGM (EMI) Catalogue no: **794 274 1**
Cass: Released Apr '90, on MGM (EMI) Catalogue no: **794 274 4**
CD: Released Apr '90, on MGM (EMI) Catalogue no: **CDMGM 18**
CD: Released Apr '90, on MGM (EMI) Catalogue no: **CDP 794 274 2**

Fastway

TRICK OR TREAT (See under Trick Or Treat)

Fatal Attraction

FATAL ATTRACTION (Film soundtrack) (Jarre, Maurice) (See picture above left)
Tracks: / Fatal attraction / Following day / Madness / Where is Ellen / Beth / Confrontation.
Album: Released Dec '87, on PRT by Castle Communications Records. Deleted Jul '90. Catalogue no: **PYL 6035**
Cass: Released Dec '87, on PRT by Castle Communications Records. Deleted Jul '90. Catalogue no: **PYM 6035**

FATAL ATTRACTION (2) (Original soundtrack) (Various artists)
Tracks: / Fatal attraction: *Various artists* / Following Dan: *Various artists* / Madness: *Various artists* / Where is Ellen?: *Various artists* / Beth: *Various artists* / Confrontation: *Various artists*.
Cass: Released '88, on GNP Crescendo (USA) by GNP Crescendo

Records (USA). Deleted May '90. Catalogue no: **GNP5 8011**

CD: Released '88, on GNP Crescendo (USA) by GNP Crescendo Records (USA). Deleted May '90. Catalogue no: **GNPD 8011**

Album: Released '88, on GNP Crescendo (USA) by GNP Crescendo Records (USA). Deleted May '90. Catalogue no: **GNPS 8011**

Fatal Beauty

FATAL BEAUTY (1988 film soundtrack) (Various artists)
Tracks: / Make it my heart: *Allen, Donna* / Just that type of girl: *Madam X* / Casanova: *Levert* / Edge of love: *Howard, Miki* / Criminal: *Shannon* / Red hot: *Gibson, Debbie* / Didn't I blow your mind: *System* / Sin city: *War.*
Cass: Released Apr '89, on Atlantic by WEA Records. Deleted Jul '90. Catalogue no: **K 781 809 4**
CD: Released Apr '89, on Atlantic by WEA Records. Catalogue no: **K 781 809 2**
Album: Released Apr '89, on Atlantic by WEA Records. Deleted Jul '90. Catalogue no: **K 781 809 1**

Father Is Away ...

FATHER IS AWAY ON A BUSINESS TRIP (1987 film soundtrack) (Various artists)
Note: Music from the award winning Yugoslavian film.
Album: Released Jan '89, on Silva Screen by Silva Screen Records. Catalogue no: **A 279**

Father & Son

FATHER AND SON (VATER UND SOHNE) (Original soundtrack) (Various artists)
Note: The German TV series starring Burt Lancaster and Julie Christie. Music by Peer Raaben.
Album: Released Jan '89, on Silva Screen by Silva Screen Records. Catalogue no: **ACH 013**

Fathers & Sons

FATHERS AND SONS (Original soundtrack) (Various artists)
Tracks: / All aboard: *Various artists* / Mean disposition: *Various artists* / Blow wind blow: *Various artists* / You can't lose what you ain't never had: *Various artists* / Walkin' thru the park: *Various artists* / Forty days and forty nights:

Various artists / Standin' round cryin': *Various artists* / I'm ready: *Various artists* / Twenty four hours: *Various artists* / Sugar sweet: *Various artists* / Long distance call: *Various artists* / Baby please don't go: *Various artists* / Honey bee: *Various artists* / Same thing, The: *Various artists* / Got my mojo working (pt 1): *Various artists* / Got my mojo working (pt 2): *Various artists.*
Note: Artists include R.H. Harris & The Soul Stirrers, Original Blind Boys of Mississippi, Sensational Nightingales.
CD: Released Feb '90, on Chess (MCA) by MCA Records. Catalogue no: **CHD 92522**
Album: Released Aug '87, on Spirit Feel by Shanachie Records (USA). Catalogue no: **ACH 013**

FATHERS AND SONS

Tracks: / Twelve's it / Joy forever / Nostalgic / Impressions / Futuristic / Lush life / Jug ain't gone / Time marches on / I can't get started / Tribute to our fathers.
Album: Released Jul '82, on CBS by CBS Records & Distribution. Deleted Jul '87. Catalogue no: **CBS 85786**

Fawlty Towers

FAWLTY TOWERS (TV Soundtrack) (Various artists)
Tracks: / Mrs. Richards: *Various artists* / Health inspectors: *Various artists.*
Cass: Released '80, on BBC by BBC Records. Deleted '85. Catalogue no: **ZCF 377**

FAWLTY TOWERS 1 (Various artists)
Cass set: Released Sep '88, on BBC by BBC Records. Catalogue no: **ZBBC 1006**

FAWLTY TOWERS 2 (Various artists)
Cass set: Released Sep '88, on BBC by BBC Records. Catalogue no: **ZBBC 1015**

FAWLTY TOWERS: A LA CARTE (Various artists)
Album: Released Oct '83, on BBC by BBC Records. Deleted 31 Aug '88. Catalogue no: **REB 484**
Cass: Released Oct '83, on BBC by BBC Records. Deleted 31 Aug '88. Catalogue no: **ZCF 484**

FAWLTY TOWERS: AT YOUR SERVICE (Various artists)

Cass: Released Oct '82, on BBC by BBC Records. Deleted 31 Aug '88. Catalogue no: **ZCF 449**
Album: Released Oct '82, on BBC by BBC Records. Deleted 31 Aug '88. Catalogue no: **REB 449**

FAWLTY TOWERS: EXTRACTS, VOL 1 (Various artists)
Album: Released Nov '79, on BBC by BBC Records. Deleted 31 Aug '88. Catalogue no: **REB 377**
Cass: Released Nov '79, on BBC by BBC Records. Deleted 31 Aug '88. Catalogue no: **ZCF 377**

FAWLTY TOWERS: SECOND SITTING (Original cast) (Various artists)
Cass: Released Jan '81, on BBC by BBC Records. Deleted 31 Aug '88. Catalogue no: **ZCF 405**
Album: Released Jan '81, on BBC by BBC Records. Deleted 31 Aug '88. Catalogue no: **REB 405**

Fear Is The Key

FEAR IS THE KEY (Film Soundtrack) (Budd, Roy & His Orchestra)
Tracks: / Main theme / Car chase / Lousiana ferry / Bayou blues / Swamp / In search of the key / Breakout / Oil rig / From sea bed to surface.
Album: Released '73, on Pye Deleted '78. Catalogue no: **NSPL 18398**

Fedora

FEDORA (1978 film soundtrack) (Various artists)
Album: Released Nov '80, on Varese Sarabande Records (USA) by Varese Sarabande Records (USA). Deleted Nov '85. Catalogue no: **STV 81108**

Feds

FEDS (1988 film soundtrack) (Various artists)
Note: Comedy thriller about 2 U.S. Police women starring Rebecca De Mornay and Mary Gross. Music and songs by Randy Edelman.
Cass: Released Jan '89, on GNP Crescendo (USA) by GNP Crescendo Records (USA). Catalogue no: **GNPC 8014**
Album: Released Jan '89, on GNP Crescendo (USA) by GNP Crescendo Records (USA). Catalogue no: **GNPS 8014**

CD: Released Jan '89, on GNP Crescendo (USA) by GNP Crescendo Records (USA). Catalogue no: **GNPD 8014**

Fellini

FELLINI FILM THEMES (Various artists)
Tracks: / Amarcord: *Various artists* / Juliet of the spirits: *Various artists* / 8-1/2: *Various artists* / La dolce vita: *Various artists* / Satyricon Roma: *Various artists* / White sheik: *Various artists* / I vitteloni: *Various artists* / Il bidone: *Various artists* / Nights of Cabiria: *Various artists* / La strada: *Various artists*.
Cass: Released '88, on Hannibal by Hannibal Records. Catalogue no: **HNBC 9301**
CD: Released '88, on Hannibal by Hannibal Records. Catalogue no: **HNCD 9301**
Album: Released Jan '87, on Hannibal by Hannibal Records. Catalogue no: **HNBL 9301**

FELLINI / ROTA (Film Soundtracks: Music from the films of Fellini) (Various artists)
Tracks: / White Sheikh, The: *Various artists* / I vitelloni: *Various artists* / La strada: *Various artists* / Swindle (il bidone), The: *Various artists* / La notti di cabiria: *Various artists* / La dolce vita: *Various artists* / 8/1/2: *Various artists* / Juliet of the spirits: *Various artists* / Toby Dammit - The clowns: *Various artists* / Satyricon-roma: *Various artists* / Amarcord: *Various artists* / Il casanova (o venezia, venaga): *Various artists* / Il casanova (pin penin): *Various artists* / Orchestra rehearsal: *Various artists*.
Note: Including Amarcord, Casanova, 8 1/2, La Dolce Vita, Satyricon etc. Music composed by Nino Roto.l
CD: Released Nov '89, on Silva Screen by Silva Screen Records. Catalogue no: **FILMCD 004**
Cass: Released Nov '89, on Silva Screen by Silva Screen Records. Catalogue no: **FILMC 004**
Album: Released Nov '89, on Silva Screen by Silva Screen Records. Catalogue no: **FILM 004**

SONGS FROM FELLINI FILMS

(Ranierei, Katyna)
Cass set: Released Jan '89, on Silva Screen by Silva Screen Records. Catalogue no: **C 329/330**
2 LP Set: Released Jan '89, on Silva Screen by Silva Screen Records. Catalogue no: **A 329.330**

Ferrante & Teicher

APARTMENT, THE (THEME FROM)
Tracks: / Apartment, The (Theme from).
7" Single: Released Aug '60, on London-American by Decca Records. Deleted '63. Catalogue no: **HLT 9164**

EXODUS (THEME FROM)
Tracks: / Exodus.
7" Single: Released Jun '61, on H.M.V. by EMI Records. Deleted '64. Catalogue no: **POP 881**
7" Single: Released Mar '61, on London-American by Decca Records. Deleted '64. Catalogue no: **HLT 9298**

Ferry Across The...

FERRY ACROSS THE MERSEY (See under Gerry & The Pacemakers)

Fiddler On The Roof

FIDDLER ON THE ROOF (Original Broadway cast - 1964) (Various artists)
Tracks: / Tradition: *Various artists* / Matchmaker, matchmaker: *Various artists* / If I were a rich man: *Various artists* / Sabbath prayer: *Various artists* / Sunrise, Sunset: *Various artists* / To life: *Various artists* / Miracle of miracles: *Various artists* / Tevye's dream: *Various artists* / Now I have everything: *Various artists* / Do you love me?: *Various artists* / Far from the home I love: *Various artists* / Anatevka: *Various artists*.
CD: Released Aug '90, on RCA by BMG Records (UK). Catalogue no: **RD 87060**
Album: Released '82, on RCA by BMG Records (UK). Catalogue no: **BL 1093**
CD: Released Jan '89, on RCA by BMG Records (UK). Catalogue no: **RCD 1 7060**

FIDDLER ON THE ROOF (1971 Film soundtrack) (Various artists)
Tracks: / Prologue and 'Tradition' and main title: *Various artists* / If I were a rich man: *Various artists* / Sabbath prayer: *Various artists* / To life: *Various artists* / Miracle of miracles: *Various artists* / Tevye's dream: *Various artists* / Sunrise sunset: *Various artists* / Wedding celebration and the bottle dance: *Various artists* / Do you love me?: *Various artists* / Far from the home I love: *Various artists* / Chava ballet sequence: *Various artists* / Anatevka: *Various artists* / Finale: *Various artists* / Matchmaker, matchmaker: *Various artists* / Bottle dance: *Various artists* / Now I have everything: *Various artists* .
CD: Released Jun '87, on EMI. Catalogue no: **CDP 746 091 2**
Cass: Released Jun '87, on EMI. Catalogue no: **2TCK 60011**
Album: Released Jun '87, on EMI. Catalogue no: **UAD 60011**
Album: Released '83, on RCA (Germany). Catalogue no: **2621147**
2 LP Set: Released Apr '72, on United Artists. Catalogue no: **UAD 60011/2**

FIDDLER ON THE ROOF (1967 Original London cast) (Various artists)
Tracks: / Tradition: *Various artists* / Matchmaker, matchmaker: *Various artists* / If I were a rich man: *Various artists* / Sabbath prayer: *Various artists* / To life: *Various artists* / Miracle of miracles: *Various artists* / Tevye's dream: *Various artists* / Sunrise, sunset: *Various artists* / Bottle dance: *Various artists* / Now I have everything: *Various artists* / Do you love me: *Various artists* / Far from the home I love: *Various artists* / Anatevka: *Various artists*.
Album: Released Jul '77, on Embassy. Catalogue no: **CBS 31519**
CD: Released Jan '89, on CBS (Import). Catalogue no: **CK 30742**
Cass: Released Mar '90, on Silva Screen. Catalogue no: **PST 30742**

FIDDLER ON THE ROOF

(ORIGINAL ISSUE) (London cast) (Various artists)
Album: Released Mar '67, on CBS by CBS Records & Distribution. Deleted '72. Catalogue no: **SBPG 70030**

FIDDLER ON THE ROOF (VIDEO) (Various artists)
VHS: Released '88, on Warner Home Video by WEA Records. Catalogue no: **PES 99254**

Field Of Dreams

FIELD OF DREAMS (1989 Film Soundtrack) (Various artists)
Tracks: / Cornfield, The: *Various artists* / Deciding to build the field: *Various artists* / Shoeless Joe: *Various artists* / Timeless street, The: *Various artists* / Old ball players: *Various artists* / Drive home, The: *Various artists* / Field of dreams: *Various artists* / Library, The: *Various artists* / Moonlight Graham: *Various artists* / Night mists: *Various artists* / Doc's memories: *Various artists* / Place where dreams come true: *Various artists* / End credits: *Various artists*.
CD: Released Feb '90, on Silva Screen by Silva Screen Records. Catalogue no: **3060.2**
Album: Released Nov '89, on Brain (Brain (Germany)) Catalogue no: **BL 90386**
CD: Released Nov '89, on Novus by BMG Records (UK). Catalogue no: **PD 83060**
Cass: Released Feb '90, on Silva Screen by Silva Screen Records. Catalogue no: **3060.4**
Cass: Released Nov '89, on Novus by BMG Records (UK). Catalogue no: **PK 83060**
Album: Released Feb '90, on Silva Screen by Silva Screen Records. Catalogue no: **3060.1**
Cass: Released Nov '89, on Brain (Brain (Germany)) Catalogue no: **BK 90386**
CD: Released Nov '89, on Brain (Brain (Germany)) Catalogue no: **BD 90386**
Album: Released Nov '89, on Novus by BMG Records (UK). Catalogue no: **PL 83060**

Fifty...

50 FAVOURITE SHOWSTOPPERS (Various artists)
Cass set: Released Oct '85, on Trio by EMI Records. Deleted

'88. Catalogue no: **TR 4115455**
Cass set: Released Oct '85, on Trio by EMI Records. Deleted '88. Catalogue no: **TR 1545**
Cass: Released Sep '86, on MFP by EMI Records. Catalogue no: **T 1569**

50 YEARS OF ROYAL BROADCASTS Various artists (Various artists)

2 LP Set: Released '74, on BBC by BBC Records. Deleted '88. Catalogue no: **REJ 187**
Cass: Released '74, on BBC by BBC Records. Catalogue no: **HRMC 187**

Fifty Two Pick Up

52 PICK UP (1987 film soundtrack) (Various artists)
Note: Music by Gary Chang for the Roy Schneider/Ann Margaret thriller.
Album: Released Jan '89, on Varese Sarabande Records(USA) by Varese Sarabande Records (USA). Catalogue no: **STV 81300**

Fifty-Five Days At...

FIFTY-FIVE DAYS AT PEKING (Film Soundtrack) (Tiomkin, Dimitri)
CD: Released Feb '90, on Varese Sarabande Records(USA) by Varese Sarabande Records (USA). Catalogue no: **VSD 5233**

Film 81

FILM 81 (Various artists)
Cass: Released Oct '81, on CBS by CBS Records & Distribution. Catalogue no: **40 73634**
Album: Released Oct '81, on CBS by CBS Records & Distribution. Catalogue no: **73634**

Film Classics

FILM CLASSICS (Various artists)
Tracks: / Apocalypse now: *Various artists* / Deer hunter: *Various artists* / 2001 - a space odyssey: *Various artists* / Hannah and her sisters: *Various artists* / 10: *Various artists* / Prizzi's honour: *Various artists* / Out of Africa: *Various artists* / Elephant man: *Various artists* / Platoon: *Various artists*.
CD: Released '87, on DG Catalogue no: **419 630 2**

Film Fantasy

FILM FANTASY (National

Philharmonic Orchestra)
Tracks: / Journey to the centre of the Earth / Seventh voyage of Sinbad / Day the Earth stood still, The / Fahrenheit.
CD: Released '88, on Decca by Decca International. Catalogue no: **421 266 2**

Film Music

CLASSICS OF THE SILVER SCREEN (Kunzel, Erich & the Cincinnati Pops orchestra)
CD: Released Aug '90, on Telarc Catalogue no: **CD 80221**

FILM MUSIC (Various artists)
Tracks: / Les uns et les autres: *Various artists* / Music lovers: *Various artists* / Ludwig: *Various artists* / Senso: *Various artists* / Death in Venice: *Various artists* / Apocalypse now: *Various artists* / Les amants: *Various artists* / Excalibur: *Various artists* / Elvira Madigan: *Various artists* / Aimez-vous Brahms?: *Various artists* / 2001: *Various artists* / Barry Lyndon: *Various artists* / Clockwork orange, A: *Various artists* / Diva: *Various artists* / Carmen Jones: *Various artists*.
CD Set: Released '88, on Angel (1) by EMI Records. Catalogue no: **CDM 762 572 2**

Film Scores

GREAT AMERICAN FILM SCORES (Various artists)
Note: Newly recorded suites from The Kentuckian, Down To The Sea In Ships, Sunrise At Campobello & Love & War.
Album: Released Jan '89, on Silva Screen by Silva Screen Records. Catalogue no: **ERS 6506**

MUSIC FROM THE FILMS OF RAINER WERNER FASSBINDER (Original film scores) (Various artists)
Tracks: / Berlin Alexanderplatz: *Various artists* / Marriage of Maria Braun, The: *Various artists* / Mother Kuster's trip to heaven: *Various artists* / Bolweiser: *Various artists* / Fox and his friends: *Various artists* / Despair: *Various artists* / I only want you to love me: *Various artists* / Satan's brew: *Various artists* / Whity: *Various artists* / Gods of the plague: *Various artists* / Querelle: *Various artists* / Lola: *Various artists* / Third generation, The: *Various artists* / Veroni-

ка voss: *Various artists* / Lili Mareen: *Various artists*.
Album: Released May '89, on T. E. R. by That's Entertainment Records. Catalogue no: **TER 1085**

Film Star Parade

FILM STAR PARADE (Various artists)
Tracks: / I wanna be loved by you: *Kane, Helen* / Please: *Crosby, Bing* / Ich bin von kopf bis fuss auf liebe eingestellt: *Dietrich, Marlene* (Falling in love again (original German version)) / My wife is on a diet: *Cantor, Eddie* / You're always in my arms: *Daniels, Bebe* / Living in clover: *Buchanan, Jack* / Let me sing and I'm happy: *Jolson, Al* / What'll I do?: *Pidgeon, Walter* / Dance of the cuckoos: *Laurel & Hardy* / Eadie was a lady: *Merman, Ethel* / All I need is just one girl: *MacMurray, Fred* / Love, your magic spell is everywhere: *Swanson, Gloria* / Sweet music: *Astaire, Fred & Adele* / I could make a good living at that: *Formby, George* / Don't tell him what's happened to me: *Bankhead, Tallulah* / My rock-a-bye baby: *Moore, Grace* / (I'd like to be) A bee in your boudoir: *Rogers, Charles 'Buddy'* / Love me tonight: *MacDonald, Jeanette/Maurice Chevalier*.
Album: Released 1 Feb '83, on Living Era by Academy Sound & Vision Records. Catalogue no: **AJA 5020**
Cass: Released 1 Feb '83, on Living Era by Academy Sound & Vision Records. Catalogue no: **ZC AJA 5020**

Film & TV Themes

38 FAMOUS FILM & TV THEMES (As Time Goes By) (Various artists)
Tracks: / Rambo: *Various artists* / Only love: *Various artists* / Miami Vice: *Various artists* / Deer hunter: *Various artists* / Mike Hammer: *Various artists* / Merry Christmas Mr. Lawrence: *Various artists* / Beverly Hills cop: *Various artists* / Passage to India, A: *Various artists* / Godfather, The: *Various artists* / St. Elmos fire: *Various artists* / Chariots of fire: *Various artists* / A Team: *Various artists* / Hill Street blues: *Various artists* / Local hero: *Various artists* / Killing fields: *Various artists* / Magnum PI: *Various artists* / Taxi:

Various artists / Amadeus: *Various artists* / Breakfast at Tiffanys: *Various artists* / West side story: *Various artists* / Bilitis: *Various artists* / Barry Lyndon: *Various artists* / Gone with the wind: *Various artists* / Orfeo negro: *Various artists* / Sandpiper: *Various artists* / Ryan's daughter: *Various artists* / La Strada: *Various artists* / Umbrellas of Cherbourg: *Various artists* / Emmanuelle: *Various artists* / Rocky the great: *Various artists* / Gatsby: *Various artists* / Way we were, The: *Various artists* / Romeo and Juliet: *Various artists* / Casablanca: *Various artists* / Summer of 42: *Various artists* / Moulin rouge: *Various artists* / Love's theme: *Various artists* / Man and a woman: *Various artists*.
CD Set: Released Oct '88, on Mainline (2) by Mainline Records. Catalogue no: **266 822 2**

Filmpalast Superhits

FILMPALAST SUPERHITS Soundtrack (Various artists)
CD: Released '88, on Polystar Catalogue no: **819 045 2**

Films Concert

FILMS CONCERT (Compilation of film soundtracks) (Various artists)
Tracks: / Diva: *Various artists* / Kramer versus Kramer: *Various artists* / Apocalypse now: *Various artists* / Clockwork orange, A: *Various artists* / Runaway train: *Various artists* / 2001: *Various artists* / Death in Venice: *Various artists* / E la nave va: *Various artists*.
Note: Compilation of popular film themes.
CD: Released May '87, on SPI Milan (France) Catalogue no: **CD 283**
CD: Released May '87, on SPI Milan (France) Catalogue no: **CDCH 249**

Filmtracks

FILMTRACKS-BEST OF BRITISH FILM MUSIC (Various artists)
Tracks: / Chariots of fire: *Vangelis* / Wall, The: *Pink Floyd* / Going home (theme from Local Hero): *Knopfler, Mark* / Passage to India: *Jarre, Maurice* / Killing fields, The: *Oldfield, Mike* / Dance with a stranger: *Wilson, Mari* / Merry Christmas, Mr Lawrence: *Saka-*

moto, Ryuichi / Honorary consul,The: *Williams, John* / Long road, The(theme from Cal): *Knopfler, Mark* / Joy (theme from comfort and joy): *Knopfler, Mark* / Chain, The: *Dickson, Barbara* / Freedom (theme from Water): *Connolly, Billy* / Always look on the bright side of life: *Idle, Eric* / Company of wolves, The: *Various artists* / Another country: *Various artists* / Bostonians, The: *Various artists* / Champions: *Various artists* / Passage to India, A: *Various artists* / Heat and dust: *Various artists* / Gandhi: *Various artists* / Another time, another place: *Various artists* / Return of the soldier: *Various artists* / Gregory's girl: *Various artists* / Death on the Nile: *Various artists* / Murder on the Orient Express: *Various artists*.
CD: Released May '85, on London Records by London Records Ltd. Catalogue no: **820 252-2**
Album: Released May '85, on London Records by London Records Ltd. Catalogue no: **YEAR 1**
Cass: Released May '85, on London Records by London Records Ltd. Catalogue no: **YEARMC 1**

Filmtrax II

FILMTRAX II (Various artists)
Tracks: / O mio Babbino caro: *Various artists* / Prick up your ears: *Various artists* / My beautiful laundrette: *Various artists* / Mona Lisa: *Various artists* / Emma's war: *Various artists* / High season: *Various artists* / Defence of the realm: *Various artists* / Fourth protocol: *Various artists* / Personal sevices: *Various artists* / Half moon street: *Various artists* / Legend: *Various artists* / Letter to Brezhnev: *Various artists* / Indian summer: *Various artists* / Withnail & I: *Various artists* / Mission, The: *Various artists* / Zina: *Various artists* / Chain, The: *Various artists* / Empire state: *Various artists*.
CD: Released 7 Nov '87, on Filmtrax by Filmtrax Records. Deleted Feb '90. Catalogue no: **MOMCD 107**
Album: Released 7 Nov '87, on Filmtrax by Filmtrax Records. Deleted Feb '90. Catalogue no: **MOMENT 107**
Cass: Released 7 Nov '87, on Filmtrax by Filmtrax Records. Deleted Aug '89. Catalogue no: **MOMENTC 107**

Final Conflict

FINAL CONFLICT: OMEN 3
(See under Omen (Film))

Final Exam

FINAL EXAM, THE (Original soundtrack) (Various artists)
Note: Horror score by Gary Scott.
Album: Released Jan '89, on Silva Screen by Silva Screen Records. Catalogue no: **AEI 3105**

Final Frontier

FINAL FRONTIER (London Symphony Orchestra)
Tracks: / Star Trek / Mars(the Planets suite) / Galaxy 239 / Star Wars / E.T. / Sinbad and the eye of the tiger / When you wish upon a star / Alien / Planet of dreams, The / Final conflict, The / Doctor Who / Indiana Jones / Supergirl / Wild geese, The / Mark of Zorro, The / Superman.
CD Set: Released Jan '86, on Mobile Fidelity Sound Lab (USA) by Mobile Fidelity Records (USA). Catalogue no: **MFCD 2-831**

Finally Sunday

FINALLY SUNDAY (VIVE-MENT DIMANCHE) (Film soundtrack) (Various artists)
Note: Georges Delerue for the Froncois Truffaut film.
Album: Released Jan '89, on Silva Screen by Silva Screen Records. Catalogue no: **A 213**

Fine Mess

FINE MESS, A (Film soundtrack) (Various artists)
Tracks: / Fine mess, A: *Temptations* / Walk like a man: *Mary Jane Girls* / Easier said than done: *DeBarge, Chico* / Can't help falling in love: *McVie, Christine* / Slow down: *Vera, Billy & the Beaters* / Love's closing in: *Jameson, Nick* / Wishful thinking: *Robinson, Smokey* / Moving so close: *Second Generation* / I'm gonna be a wheel someday: *Los Lobos* / Stan & Ollie: *Mancini, Henry.*
Cass: Released Sep '86, on Motown by BMG Records (UK). Deleted '87. Catalogue no: **ZK 72440**
2 LP Set: Released Sep '86, on Motown by BMG Records (UK). Deleted "87. Catalogue no: **ZL 72440**

Fings Ain't What...

FINGS AINT WOT THEY USED T'BE (1959 Original London cast) (Various artists)
Tracks: / Fings ain't what...: Overture: *Various artists* / G'night dearie: *Various artists* / Fings ain't wot they used t'be: *Various artists* / Layin' abaht: *Various artists* / Where it's hot: *Various artists* / Ceiln's comin' dahn, The: *Various artists* / Contempery: *Various artists* / Entr'acte: *Various artists* / Cochran will return: *Various artists* / Polka dots: *Various artists* / Meatface: *Various artists* / Where do little girls go?: *Various artists* / Big time: *Various artists* / Carve up: *Various artists* / Cop a bit of pride: *Various artists* / Student ponce, The: *Various artists.*
Cass: Released Apr '83, on T. E. R. by That's Entertainment Records. Catalogue no: **ZCTER 1047**
Album: Released Apr '83, on T. E. R. by That's Entertainment Records. Catalogue no: **TER 1047**

FINGS AINT WOT THEY USED T'BE (ORIGINAL ISSUE) (London cast) (Various artists)
Album: Released Mar '60, on Decca by Decca International. Deleted '65. Catalogue no: **LK 4346**

Finians Rainbow

FINIANS RAINBOW (Original Broadway cast) (Various artists)
Note: 1947 Broadway Cast with Ella Logan.
Album: Released Feb '89, on Silva Screen by Silva Screen Records. Catalogue no: **PS 2080**
Cass: Released Feb '89, on Silva Screen by Silva Screen Records. Catalogue no: **PST 2080**

FINIANS RAINBOW (1948 Original Broadway Cast) (Various artists)
CD: Released Jan '89, on CBS (import) by CBS Records & Distribution. Catalogue no: **CK 04062**
Cass: Released Jan '89, on CBS (import) by CBS Records & Distribution. Catalogue no: **PST 04062**
Cass: Released Aug '90, on RCA by BMG Records (UK). Catalogue no: **GK 81057**
CD: Released Aug '90, on RCA by BMG Records (UK). Catalogue no:

GD 81057
CD: Released Jan '89, on CBS (import) by CBS Records & Distribution. Catalogue no: **JST 04062**

FINIANS RAINBOW (Reprise Repertory Theatre) (Various artists)
Tracks: / Overture: *Various artists* / This time of the year: *Hi-Lo's* / How are things in Glocca Morra: *Clooney, Rosemary* / If this isn't love: *Martin, Dean* / Look to the rainbow: *Clooney, Rosemary* / Something sort of grandish: *Crosby, Bing/Debbie Reynolds* / Old devil moon: *Various artists* / Necessity: *Davis, Sammy Jnr.* / When I'm not near the girl I love: *Various artists* / When the idle poor become the idle rich: *Monte, Lou* / Begat, The: *McGuire Sisters* / How are things in Glocca Morra (reprise): *Dennis, Clark* / That great come and get it day: *Davis, Sammy Jnr.*
Album: Released Aug '81, on Reprise (USA) Catalogue no: **K 54112**

FINIANS RAINBOW (RE-RE-LEASE) (Various artists)
Note: Original Broadway revival cast of 1960 starring Jeannie Carson, Howard Morris & Bobby Howes.
Cass: Released Jan '89, on Silva Screen by Silva Screen Records. Catalogue no: **1057.4**
CD: Released Jan '89, on Silva Screen by Silva Screen Records. Catalogue no: **1057.2**

Fiorello

FIORELLO (Original Broadway Cast) (Various artists)
CD: Released Feb '90, on EMI (Import) Catalogue no: **CDP 92052.2**

Firewalker

FIREWALKER (1987 film soundtrack) (Various artists)
Note: Music by Gary Chang for the Chuck Norris film.
Album: Released Jan '89, on Silva Screen by Silva Screen Records. Catalogue no: **STV 81303**

First Blood

FIRST BLOOD (1982 Film soundtrack) (Various artists)
Note: Score by Jerry Goldsmith for the first Rambo film. CD contains

extra track not available on the vinyl.
CD: Released Jan '89, on Intrada (USA) Catalogue no: **FMT 800 1 D**
Album: Released Apr '83, on T. E. R. by That's Entertainment Records. Catalogue no: **TER 1038**

First Impressions

FIRST IMPRESSIONS (Original Broadway cast) (Various artists)
Note: Starring Polly Bergman and Hermione Gingold.
Album: Released Jan '89, on Silva Screen by Silva Screen Records. Catalogue no: **AOS 2014**

First Nudie

FIRST NUDIE MUSICAL, THE (Original soundtrack) (Kimmel,Bruce)
CD: Released Feb '90, on Silva Screen by Silva Screen Records. Catalogue no: **XCD 1002**

First Of The Few

FIRST OF THE FEW (1942 film soundtrack) (London Philharmonic Orchestra)
Album: Released '89, on H.M.V. by EMI Records. Catalogue no: **ED 291129 1**
Cass: Released '89, on H.M.V. by EMI Records. Catalogue no: **ED 291129 4**

Fish Called Wanda

FISH CALLED WANDA, A (Original soundtrack) (Various artists)
Note: The soundtrack music from one of 1988's most successful films: co-directed by Charles Crichton and John Cleese and starring Cleese with Jamie Lee Curtis, Kevin Kline and Michael Palin. Music by John Du Prez (Private Function and Monty Python's The Meaning Of Life).
Cass: Released Jan '89, on SPI Milan (France) Catalogue no: **C 376**
Album: Released Jan '89, on SPI Milan (France) Catalogue no: **A 376**
CD: Released Jan '89, on SPI Milan (France) Catalogue no: **CDCH 376**

Fistful Of Dollars

FISTFUL OF DOLLARS, A (Lure of the west, The) (Various artists)

Tracks: / Fistful of dollars: *Various artists* / Magnificent seven, The: *Various artists* / Rawhide: *Various artists* / Ghost riders in the sky: *Various artists* / High chaparrel, The: *Various artists* / Good, the bad and the ugly, The: *Various artists* / Bonanza: *Various artists* / Streets of Laredo: *Various artists* / Man who shot Liberty Valance, The: *Various artists* / Big country, The: *Various artists*.
CD: Released Apr '89, on Ocean (2) Catalogue no: **OCN 2020WD**
Cass: Released Apr '89, on Ocean (2) Catalogue no: **OCN 2020WK**
Album: Released Apr '89, on Ocean (2) Catalogue no: **OCN 2020WL**

FISTFUL OF DOLLARS/FOR A FEW DOLLARS MORE (Original soundtracks) (Various artists)
Cass: Released '89, on RCA (Germany) by BMG Music International. Catalogue no: **NK 70391**
Album: Released '89, on RCA (Germany) by BMG Music International. Catalogue no: **NL 70391**
Album: Released May '70, on RCA/Camden by BMG Records (UK). Deleted '88. Catalogue no: **CDS 1052**
Cass: Released May '74, on RCA/Camden by BMG Records (UK). Catalogue no: **CAM 411**

Fistful Of Dynamite

FISTFUL OF DYNAMITE, A (Original soundtrack) (Various artists)
Note: Sergio Leone western starring James Coburn and Rod Steiger. Music by Ennio Morricone.
Album: Released Jan '89, on Silva Screen by Silva Screen Records. Catalogue no: **NL 70223**
CD: Released Jan '89, on Silva Screen by Silva Screen Records. Catalogue no: **CDCIA5003**

Fitzgerald, Ella

PETE KELLY'S BLUES (See under Lee, Peggy)

Fitzwilly

FITZWILLY (Original soundtrack) (Various artists)
Note: Score by John Williams.a
Cass: Released Jan '89, on MCA by MCA Records. Deleted Feb

'90. Catalogue no: **MCAC 25098**
Album: Released Jan '89, on MCA by MCA Records. Catalogue no: **MCA 25098**

Five Corners

FIVE CORNERS (1988 film soundtrack) (Various artists)
Note: Music by James Newton Howard for the Jodie Foster film.r
Cass: Released Jan '89, on Varese Sarabande Records(USA) by Varese Sarabande Records (USA). Catalogue no: **CTV 81256**
CD: Released Jan '89, on Varese Sarabande Records(USA) by Varese Sarabande Records (USA). Catalogue no: **VCD 47354**
Album: Released Jan '89, on Varese Sarabande Records(USA) by Varese Sarabande Records (USA). Catalogue no: **STV 81354**

Five Easy Pieces

FIVE EASY PIECES (Film Soundtrack) (Various artists)
Tracks: / Stand by your man: *Various artists* / Raffle of a dog: *Various artists* / Freeway dialogue: *Various artists* / Chopin's Fantasy in F minor op.49: *Various artists* / Oil field dialogue: *Various artists* / Bach's Chromatic fantasy and fugue: *Various artists* / Recording studio dialogue: *Various artists* / D I V O R C E: *Various artists* / Dialogue in Rayette's house: *Various artists* / Where there's a fire in your heart: *Various artists* / On the road: *Various artists* / Motel dialogue: *Various artists* / Mozart's E flat major concerto K 271: *Various artists* / Chopin's prelude in E minor op.28 no.4: *Various artists* / Mozart's fantasy in D minor K.397: *Various artists* / Bobby's monologue with his father: *Various artists* / Bobby and Rayette in the car: *Various artists* / Don't touch me: *Various artists*.
Album: Released '73, on CBS by CBS Records & Distribution. Deleted '78. Catalogue no: **70091**

Five Pennies

FIVE PENNIES, THE (Film soundtrack) (Various artists)
Album: Released Jan '60, on London-American by Decca Records. Deleted '64. Catalogue no: **HAU 2189**

Five Star

STAY OUT OF MY LIFE (TV theme)

Tracks: / Stay out of my life / How dare you stay out of my life / If I say yes (Lew Hahn US dub mix*) (* Availble on 12" version only).

Note: Theme for Tyne Tees 'How dare you'.

12" Single: Released Jan '87, on Tent by BMG Records (UK). Catalogue no: **PT 41132**

7" Single: Released Jan '87, on RCA by BMG Records (UK). Catalogue no: **PB 41131**

Flack, Roberta

FIRST TIME I EVER SAW YOUR FACE

Tracks: / First time I ever saw your face / Will you still love me tomorrow.

Note: Taken from the film *Play Misty for me*

7" Single: Released '79, on Atlantic by WEA Records. Deleted '82. Catalogue no: **K 10161**

7" Single: Released '84, on Atlantic by WEA Records. Catalogue no: **K 10845**

Flagrant Desir

FLAGRANT DESIR (1987 film soundtrack) (Various artists)

Note: French film with Sam Waterson and Marisa Berenson. Music by Gabriel Yared (Betty Blue, Moon in the Gutter).

Album: Released Jan '89, on SPI Milan (France) Catalogue no: **A 255**

Flambards

FLAMBARDS (TV Soundtrack) (Various artists)

Cass: Released Jul '81, on Philips by Phonogram Ltd. Deleted '86. Catalogue no: **7231452**

Album: Released Jul '81, on Philips by Phonogram Ltd. Deleted '86. Catalogue no: **9109226**

Flame Trees Of Thika

FLAME TREES OF THIKA, THE (TV soundtrack) (Various artists)

Album: on EMI by EMI Records. Catalogue no: **EMC 3385**

Cass: on EMI by EMI Records. Catalogue no: **TCEMC 3385**

Flaming Star

FLAMING STAR (See under Presley, Elvis)

FLAMING STAR (VIDEO) (Various artists)

Note: Elvis stars in this splendid western. Running time: 92 minutes. Cert. PG.

VHS: Released Jun '89, on CBS-Fox by CBS-Fox Video. Catalogue no: **117350**

Flamingo Kid

FLAMINGO KID (1985 film soundtrack) (Various artists)

Tracks: / Breakaway: *Various artists* / (Love is like a) heatwave: *Various artists* / He's so fine: *Various artists* / One fine day: *Various artists* / Stranger on the shore: *Various artists* / Runaround Sue: *Various artists* / Good golly Miss Molly: *Various artists* / Money (Thats what I want): *Various artists* / It's alright: *Various artists* / Finger poppin' time: *Various artists* / Get a job: *Various artists* / Boys will be boys: *Various artists*.

Album: Released Oct '85, on Motown by BMG Records (UK). Deleted Jun '89. Catalogue no: **ZL 72370**

Cass: Released Oct '85, on Motown by BMG Records (UK). Deleted Jun '89. Catalogue no: **ZK 72370**

Flanders & Swann

AT THE DROP OF A HAT

Tracks: / Transport of delight / Song of reproduction / Gnu song, The / Design for living / Je suis le tenebreux / Songs of our time / Philogical waltz / Satellite moon / Happy song / Song of the weather / Reluctant cannibal, The / Greensleeves / Misalliance / Madeira, m'dear? / Hippopotamus.

Album: Released Dec '78, on Encore by EMI Records. Catalogue no: **ONCR 511**

Cass: Released Dec '78, on Encore by EMI Records. Catalogue no: **TCONCR 511**

AT THE DROP OF ANOTHER HAT

Tracks: / Gas-man cometh, The / Sounding brass / Los Olividados / In the desert / Ill wind / First and second law / All Gali / Horoscope / Friendly duet / Bedstead men / By air / Slow train / Song of patriotic prejudice / Hippo encore.

Cass: Released Jan '79, on Encore by EMI Records. Catalogue no: **TRONCR 512**

Album: Released Dec '78, on Encore by EMI Records. Catalogue no: **ONCR 512**

AT THE DROP OF ANOTHER HAT (ORIGINAL ISSUE) (London cast)

Album: Released Feb '64, on Parlophone by EMI Records. Deleted '69. Catalogue no: **PMC 1216**

BESTIARY OF FLANDERS AND SWANN

Tracks: / Warthog, The (The hog beneath the skin) / Sea horse, The / Chameleon, The / Whale, The (Moby Dick) / Sloth, The / Rhinoceros, The / Twosome-Kang and Jag / Dead ducks / Elephant / Armadillo, The / Spider, The / Threesome (the duck billed platypus) / Hummingbird (The portuguese man of war) / Wild bear, The / Ostrich, The / Wompom, The.

Flash Gordon - 1980 feature film starring Sam J. Jones

Original soundtrack to *Flashdance* (Casablanca)

Album: Released Jan '80, on Encore by EMI Records. Deleted Jun '89. Catalogue no: **ONCR 527**

TRIED BY THE CENTRE COURT
Tracks: / Twice shy / Commonwealth fair / P***P*B****B**D****** / Too many cookers / Vanessa / Tried by the centre court / Paris / Eine kleine nachtmusik cha cha cha / Hundred song / Built-up area / In the bath / Sea fever / Youth of the heart / Food for thought / Bed.
Album: Released Jan '77, on Note by EMI Records. Deleted '81. Catalogue no: **NTS 116**

Flash Gordon
FLASH GORDON (See under Queen) (See picture on previous page)

Flashdance
FLASHDANCE (1983 film soundtrack) (Various artists) (See picture above)
Tracks: / Flashdance... what a feeling: *Cara, Irene* / He's a dream: *Shandi* / Flashdance love theme: *St.John, Helen* / Manhunt: *Kamon, Karen* / Lady, lady, lady: *Esposito, Joe* / Imagination: *Branigan, Laura* / Romeo: *Summer, Donna* / Se-

duce me tonight: *Cycle V* / I'll be here where the heart is: *Carnes, Kim* / Maniac: *Sembello, Michael*.
Cass: Released Aug '83, on Casablanca by PolyGram UK Ltd. Catalogue no: **CANHC 5**
CD: Released Dec '83, on Casablanca by PolyGram UK Ltd. Catalogue no: **811 492 2**
Album: Released Aug '83, on Casablanca by PolyGram UK Ltd. Deleted '88. Catalogue no: **CANH 5**
Album: Released Jun '87, on Casablanca by PolyGram UK Ltd. Catalogue no: **PRICE 111**
Cass: Released Jun '87, on Casablanca by PolyGram UK Ltd. Catalogue no: **PRIMC 111**
CD: Released Dec '88, on CBS by CBS Records & Distribution. Catalogue no: **CDEPC 25730**

FLASHDANCE (VIDEO) (Various artists)
Note: Cert: 15. Running time: 91 mins.
VHS: Released Sep '84, on CIC Video Catalogue no: **VHR 2078**

Flashpoint
FLASHPOINT (See under Tangerine Dream)

Flatt, Lester
FOGGY MOUNTAIN BREAKDOWN (Flatt, Lester & Earl Scruggs)
Tracks: / Foggy mountain breakdown.
Note: Featured in the film 'Bonnie & Clyde'.
7" Single: Released Nov '65, on CBS by CBS Records & Distribution. Deleted Nov '68. Catalogue no: **CBS 3038**

Fleets In
FLEETS IN, THE (1942 film musical soundtrack) (Various artists)
Note: Starring Dorothy Lamour and Betty Hutton.
Album: Released Jan '89, on Silva Screen by Silva Screen Records. Catalogue no: **HS 405**

Flesh & Blood (Film)
FLESH AND BLOOD (1985 film soundtrack) (London Symphony Orchestra)
Note: Music by Basil Poledouris.
Album: Released May '86, on Varese Sarabande Records (USA) by Varese Sarabande Records (USA). Catalogue no: **VS 1012**
Album: Released Jan '89, on Varese Sarabande Records (USA) by Varese Sarabande Records (USA). Catalogue no: **STV 81256**
Cass: Released Jan '89, on Varese Sarabande Records (USA) by Varese Sarabande Records (USA). Catalogue no: **CTV 81256**

Fletch
FLETCH (1985 film soundtrack) (Various artists)
Tracks: / Fletch theme: *Faltermeyer, Harold* / Diggin' in: *Faltermeyer, Harold* / Exotic skates: *Faltermeyer, Harold* / Running for love: *Faltermeyer, Harold* / Bit by bit: *Mills, Stephanie* / Fletch, get outta town: *Hartman, Dan* / Name of the game: *Hartman, Dan* / Running for love: *Farnham, John* / Letter to both sides, A: *Fixx* / Is it over?: *Wilde, Kim*.
Cass: Released Sep '85, on MCA by MCA Records. Deleted Jan '88. Catalogue no: **MCFC 3284**
Album: Released Sep '85, on MCA by MCA Records. Deleted Jan '88. Catalogue no: **MCF 3284**
CD: on MCA by MCA Records.

Flora the Red Menace - Original Off-Broadway Cast (TER)

Catalogue no: **DMCF 3284**

Flight Of The Condor

FLIGHT OF THE CONDOR (T.V. soundtrack) (Guamary)
Tracks: / Floreo de Llamas / Mi raza / Inti illimani / Alturas / De terciopelo negro / Dolencias / A vos te h'ai pesar / Sicuriadas / Danza de Los Quechuas / Papel de plata / Volando / La mariposa / Tema de la Quebrada de Humahuaca / Vasija de barro / Huajra / Lonquita / Llanto de mi madre / Calambito temucano.
CD: Released Jun '86, on BBC by BBC Records. Catalogue no: **BBC CD 440**
Album: Released Dec '83, on BBC by BBC Records. Catalogue no: **REB 440**
Cass: Released Dec '83, on BBC by BBC Records. Catalogue no: **ZCF 440**

Flight Of The Doves

FLIGHT OF THE DOVES (Film Soundtrack) (Various artists)
Tracks: / Theme from Flight of the doves: *Various artists* / Walkin' down O'Connell Street: *Various artists* / Here comes the hawk: *Vari-*ous artists / Runaways: *Various artists* / Fiddler at the fair: *Various artists* / You don't have to be Irish to be Irish: *Various artists* / In search of a dream: *Various artists* / Drop o' the Irish (smuggler's in the cemetary): *Various artists* / Far off place: *Various artists* / Doves in flight: *Various artists* / Hawk on the hunt: *Various artists* / Little boy, little girl: *Various artists*.
Album: Released '73, on Decca by Decca International. Deleted '78. Catalogue no: **SKL 5093**

Flora The Red Menace

FLORA THE RED MENACE (Original Off-Broadway Cast (1987 revival)) (Various artists) (See picture above)
Tracks: / Prologue / unafraid: *Flora The Red Menace* / Street song I: *Flora The Red Menace* / Kid herself, The: *Flora The Red Menace* / All I need is one good break: *Flora The Red Menace* / Not every day of the week: *Flora The Red Menace* / Street song II: *Flora The Red Menace* / Sign here: *Flora The Red Menace* / Street song III: *Flora The Red Menace* / Quiet thing, A: *Flora The Red Menace* / Flame: *Flora The Red Me-*nace / Not every day of the week (reprise): *Flora The Red Menace* (end s1) / Street song IV: *Flora The Red Menace* / Dear love: *Flora The Red Menace* (end act 1) / Keepin' it hot: *Flora The Red Menace* / Street song V: *Flora The Red Menace* / Express yourself: *Flora The Red Menace* / Where did everybody go?: *Flora The Red Menace* / Street song VI: *Flora The Red Menace* / You are you: *Flora The Red Menace* / Joke, The: *Flora The Red Menace* / Quiet thing, A (reprise): *Flora The Red Menace* / Sing happy: *Flora The Red Menace* / Closing scene: *Flora The Red Menace*.
Note: Music: John Kander (also on piano), Lyrics: Fred Ebb, Cast: Veanne Cox, Ray Demattis, Peter Frechette, Maggy Gorrill, Lyn Greene, B.J. Jefferson, Eddie Korbich, Dirk Lumbard, David Ossian. Produced by John Yap. Sleeve note includes brief history by Fred Ebb and plot outline by David Thompson.
Cass: Released 26 May '89, on T. E. R. by That's Entertainment Records. Catalogue no: **ZCTER 1159**
CD: Released 26 May '89, on T. E. R. by That's Entertainment Records. Catalogue no: **CDTER 1159**
Album: Released 26 May '89, on T. E. R. by That's Entertainment Records. Catalogue no: **TER 1159**

Flower Drum Song

FLOWER DRUM SONG (Original Broadway cast) (Various artists) (See picture on next page)
Note: Rodgers & Hammerstein.
Album: Released Jan '89, on Silva Screen by Silva Screen Records. Deleted Mar '90. Catalogue no: **PS 2009**
CD: Released Jan '89, on CBS (import) by CBS Records & Distribution. Catalogue no: **CK 02009**
Cass: Released Feb '90, on Silva Screen by Silva Screen Records. Catalogue no: **PST 2009**

FLOWER DRUM SONG (1960 Original London cast) (Various artists)
Tracks: / Overture: *Various artists* / You are beautiful: *Various artists* / Hundred million miracles, A: *Various artists* / I enjoy being a girl: *Various artists* / I am going to like it here: *Various artists* / Like a god: *Various artists* / Chop suey: *Vari-*

STEREO

DECCA

The Motion Picture Sound Track

RODGERS & HAMMERSTEIN'S

FLOWER DRUM SONG

A ROSS HUNTER Production
in association with
JOSEPH FIELDS
Music Supervised and Conducted by ALFRED NEWMAN
Associate: KEN DARBY
Music by Richard Rodgers
Lyrics by Oscar Hammerstein 2nd
A UNIVERSAL INTERNATIONAL PICTURE

STARRING
NANCY KWAN
JAMES SHIGETA
JUANITA HALL JACK SOO
BENSON FONG AND
MIYOSHI UMEKI

Flower Drum Song - Original Broadway Cast (TER)

ous artists / Don't marry me: *Various artists* / Grant Avenue: *Various artists* / Love look away: *Various artists* / Fan tan fannie: *Various artists* / Gliding through my memoree: *Various artists* / Other generation, The: *Various artists* / Sunday: *Various artists* / Finale: *Various artists*.
Album: Released Apr '83, on T. E. R. by That's Entertainment Records. Catalogue no: **TER 1060**
Cass: Released Apr '83, on T. E. R. by That's Entertainment Records. Catalogue no: **ZCTER 1060**

FLOWER DRUM SONG (ORIGINAL ISSUE) (London cast) (Various artists)
Album: Released May '60, on H.M.V. by EMI Records. Deleted '65. Catalogue no: **CLP 1359**

FLOWER DRUM SONG (ORIGINAL ISSUE) (Broadway cast) (Various artists)
Album: Released Apr '60, on Philips by Phonogram Ltd. Deleted '65. Catalogue no: **ABL 3302**

Flowers In The Attic

FLOWERS IN THE ATTIC (1988 film soundtrack) (Various artists)

Note: Horror film score by Christopher Young (Hellraiser).
Album: Released Jan '89, on T. E. R. by That's Entertainment Records. Catalogue no: **STV 81358**

Fly

FLY, THE (1986 film soundtrack) (Various artists)
Tracks: / Main title: *Various artists* / Last visit, The: *Various artists* / Phone call: *Various artists* / Ronnie calls back: *Various artists* / Particle magazine: *Various artists* / Ronnie's visit: *Various artists* / Fingernails, The: *Various artists* / Creature, The: *Various artists* / Maggot, The/ fly graphic: *Various artists* / Ultimate family, The: *Various artists* / Plasma pool: *Various artists* / Stathis entera: *Various artists* / Seth goes through: *Various artists* / Jump, The: *Various artists* / Armwrestle, The: *Various artists* / Stairs, The: *Various artists* / Baboon teleportation: *Various artists* / Steak montage: *Various artists* / Success with baboon: *Various artists* / Finale: *Various artists*.
Note: Composed by Howard Shore and played by The London Philharmonic Orch.
Cass: Released Mar '87, on T. E.

R. by That's Entertainment Records. Catalogue no: **ZCTER 1120**
CD: Released Jan '89, on T. E. R. by That's Entertainment Records. Catalogue no: **VCD 47272**
Album: Released Mar '87, on T. E. R. by That's Entertainment Records. Catalogue no: **TER 1120**

FLY II, THE (1988 Film Soundtrack) (Various artists)
Tracks: / Fly II, The: *Various artists* / Fly variations: *Various artists* / Spider and the fly, The: *Various artists* / Fly march, The: *Various artists* / Bay 17 mysteries: *Various artists* / What's the magic word: *Various artists* / Come fly with me: *Various artists* / Musica domestica metastasis: *Various artists* / More is coming: *Various artists* / Accelerated Brundle disease: *Various artists* / Bartok barbaro: *Various artists* / Dad: *Various artists*.
Album: Released May '89, on Varese Sarabande Records(USA) by Varese Sarabande Records (USA). Catalogue no: **VS 5220**
CD: Released Feb '90, on Varese Sarabande Records(USA) by Varese Sarabande Records (USA). Catalogue no: **VSD 5220**

FLY,THE / OMEN III (FINAL CONFLICT) (Shore,Howard)
CD: Released Feb '90, on Varese Sarabande Records(USA) by Varese Sarabande Records (USA). Catalogue no: **VSD 47272**

Flying Down To Rio

FLYING DOWN TO RIO (1933 Film Soundtrack) (Various artists)
Album: Released '90, on CIF Catalogue no: **CIF 3004**
VHS: Released May '87, on Video Collection by Video Collection. Catalogue no: **VC 3057**
VHS: Released Jun '89, on Cinema Club Catalogue no: **CC 1017**

FLYING DOWN TO RIO / CAREFREE (Original soundtrack) (Various artists)
Note: Starring Fred Astaire and Ginger Rogers.
Album: Released Jan '89, on Silva Screen by Silva Screen Records. Catalogue no: **SH 2010**
Cass: Released Jan '89, on Silva Screen by Silva Screen Records. Catalogue no: **CSH 2010**

FLYING DOWN TO RIO/GAY DIVORCEE, THE (Various ar-

tists)
VHS: Released '88, on Video Collection by Video Collection. Catalogue no: **DB 0003**

Flynn, Errol

ERROL FLYNN ALBUM, THE
Tracks: / They died with their boots on / Gentleman Jim (Radio versions).
Note: Interview with Errol Flynn by Tony Thomas.
Album: Released Mar '79, on Citadel (USA) by Varese Sarabande Records (USA). Catalogue no: **CT 7003**

SOUND ALBUM, A
Tracks: / Adventures of Robin Hood excerpts.
CD: Released Jan '89, on Silva Screen by Silva Screen Records. Catalogue no: **FCD 8104**

FM (Film)

FM (1978 film soundtrack) (Various artists)
Tracks: / Life in the fast lane, The: *Eagles* / Do it again: *Steely Dan* / Lido shuffle: *Scaggs, Boz* / It keeps you runnin': *Doobie Brothers* / Your smiling face: *Taylor, James* / Life's been good: *Walsh, Joe* / We will rock you: *Queen* / FM (reprise): *Steely Dan* / Night moves: *Seger, Bob* / Fly like an eagle: *Miller, Steve* / Cold as ice: *Foreigner* / Breakdown: *Petty, Tom* / Bad man: *Meisner, Randy* / Tumbling dice: *Ronstadt, Linda* / Poor poor pitiful me: *Ronstadt, Linda* / Livingston Saturday: *Buffett, Jimmy* / There's a place: *Fogelberg, Dan* / Way you are, The: *Joel, Billy*.
2 LP Set: Released Mar '87, on MCA by MCA Records. Deleted Sep '90. Catalogue no: **MCLD 621**
Cass set: Released Mar '87, on MCA by MCA Records. Deleted Sep '90. Catalogue no: **MCLDC 621**
2 LP Set: Released May '78, on MCA by MCA Records. Deleted '83. Catalogue no: **MCSP 284**

Fog

FOG, THE (1979 film soundtrack) (Various artists)
Note: Composed by John Carpenter.
CD: Released Jan '89, on Colosseum (West Germany) Catalogue no: **VCD 47267**
Album: Released Jan '86, on Colosseum (West Germany) Cata-logue no: **CST 8002**
Cass: Released Jan '89, on Varese Sarabande Records (USA) by Varese Sarabande Records (USA). Catalogue no: **CTV 81191**
Album: Released Jan '89, on Varese Sarabande Records (USA) by Varese Sarabande Records (USA). Catalogue no: **STV 81191**

Follies

FOLLIES (1985 Lincoln Center revival cast) (Various artists)
Tracks: / Follies: Overture: *Various artists* / Beautiful girls: *Various artists* / Don't look at me: *Various artists* / Waiting for the girls upstairs: *Various artists* / Rain on the roof: *Various artists* / Ah, Paree: *Various artists* / Broadway baby: *Various artists* / Road you didn't take, The: *Various artists* / In Buddy's eyes: *Various artists* / Who's that woman?: *Various artists* / I'm still here: *Various artists* / Too many mornings: *Various artists* / Right girl, The: *Various artists* / One more kiss: *Various artists* / Could I leave you?: *Various artists* / Loveland: *Various artists* / You're gonna love tomorrow / Love will see us through: *Various artists* / Buddy's blues: *Various artists* / Losing my mind: *Various artists* / Story of Lucy and Jessie, The: *Various artists* / Live, Laugh, Love: *Various artists* / Follies: Finale: *Various artists*.
Album: Released '86, on RCA by BMG Records (UK). Deleted '89. Catalogue no: **BL 87 128**
Cass: Released '86, on RCA by BMG Records (UK). Catalogue no: **BK 87 128**
CD: Released '86, on RCA by BMG Records (UK). Catalogue no: **BD 87 128**

FOLLIES (1971 Original Broadway cast) (Various artists)
Tracks: / Prologue - beautiful girls: *Various artists* / Don't look at me: *Various artists* / Waiting for the girls upstairs: *Various artists* / Ah Paris, Broadway baby: *Various artists* / Road you didn't take, The: *Various artists* / In Buddy's eyes: *Various artists* / Who's that woman: *Various artists* / I'm still here: *Various artists* / Too many mornings: *Various artists* / Right girl, The: *Various artists* / Could I leave you?: *Various artists* / You're
gonna love tomorrow (love will see us through): *Various artists*.
Album: Released Jul '87, on Capitol by EMI Records. Deleted Aug '89. Catalogue no: **EMS 1250**
Cass: Released Jul '87, on Capitol by EMI Records. Catalogue no: **TC EMS 1250**
CD: Released Feb '90, on Silva Screen by Silva Screen Records. Catalogue no: **CDP92094.2**
Cass: Released Mar '90, on Silva Screen by Silva Screen Records. Catalogue no: **92094.4**
CD: Released Aug '90, on Silva Screen by Silva Screen Records. Catalogue no: **RD 87128**

FOLLIES (1987 Original West End cast) (Various artists)
CD: Released Oct '87, on First Night by First Night Records. Catalogue no: **ENCORE CD 3**
Cass: Released Oct '87, on First Night by First Night Records. Catalogue no: **ENCORE C 3**
Album: Released Oct '87, on First Night by First Night Records. Catalogue no: **ENCORE 3**

Follow That Dream

FOLLOW THAT DREAM (VIDEO) (Various artists)
Note: "Wanderer Pops Kwimper and his ex-army son support and care for four orphans. On their travels they spend a night on a Florida beach where they decide to homestead. But for their succesful fishing business soon attracts unwanted competition. And there's trouble in store for Elvis - elected sheriff of the ramshackle community."
VHS: Released Aug '88, on Warner Home Video by WEA Records. Catalogue no: **PES 99460**

Follow That Girl

FOLLOW THAT GIRL (Original London cast) (Various artists)
Album: Released Jan '89, on Silva Screen by Silva Screen Records. Catalogue no: **AEI 1121**

FOLLOW THAT GIRL (ORIGINAL ISSUE) (London cast) (Various artists)
Album: Released May '60, on H.M.V. by EMI Records. Deleted '65. Catalogue no: **CLP 1366**

Follow The Boys

FOLLOW THE BOYS (Original

soundtrack) (Various artists)
Note: Starring Jeanette MacDonald and Andrews Sisters.
Album: Released Jan '89, on Silva Screen by Silva Screen Records. Catalogue no: **HS 5012**

Follow The Fleet

FOLLOW THE FLEET (1936 film musical soundtrack) (Various artists)
Note: With Fred Astaire. Inc. 'Let's face the music and dance'
Album: Released Jan '89, on Silva Screen by Silva Screen Records. Catalogue no: **SH 2099**

FOLLOW THE FLEET (VIDEO) (Various artists)
VHS: Released May '87, on Video Collection by Video Collection. Catalogue no: **VC 3064**

Fool For Love

FOOL FOR LOVE (1986 film soundtrack) (Various artists)
Note: Robert Altman film with songs by Sandy Rogers.
Cass: Released Jan '89, on MCA by MCA Records. Catalogue no: **MCAC 6156**
Album: Released Jan '89, on MCA by MCA Records. Catalogue no: **MCA 6156**

Footloose

FOOTLOOSE (1986 film soundtrack) (Various artists)
Tracks: / Footloose: Loggins, Kenny / Let's hear it for the boy: Williams, Deniece / Almost paradise: Wilson, Ann & Mike Reno / Holding out for a hero: Tyler, Bonnie / Dancing in the street: Shalamar / I'm free (heaven helps the man): Loggins, Kenny / Somebody's eyes: Bonoff, Karla / Girl gets around, The: Hagar, Sammy / Never: Moving Pictures.
Note: Low-price musical feature film recently big in the cinemas, and including items like the title track by Kenny Loggins, and Deniece Willliams "Let's hear it for the boy".
Cass: Released Nov '88, on CBS by CBS Records & Distribution. Catalogue no: **463000 4**
Album: Released Nov '88, on CBS by CBS Records & Distribution. Catalogue no: **463000 1**
CD: Released Nov '88, on CBS by CBS Records & Distribution. Catalogue no: **463000 2**

Cass: Released Mar '84, on CBS by CBS Records & Distribution. Catalogue no: **40 70246**
CD: Released Aug '84, on CBS by CBS Records & Distribution. Catalogue no: **CD 70246**
Album: Released Mar '84, on CBS by CBS Records & Distribution. Catalogue no: **CBS 70246**

FOOTLOOSE (VIDEO) (Various artists)
Note: Cert: 15. Running time: 103 mins.
VHS: Released Sep '84, on CIC Video Catalogue no: **VHR 2098**

For A Few Dollars More

FOR A FEW DOLLARS MORE (Film soundtrack) (Morricone, Ennio)
Album: Released '83, on RCA (Germany) by BMG Music International. Catalogue no: **26 21208**

For Me & My Gal

FOR ME AND MY GAL (Film soundtrack) (Various artists)
Note: 1947 film starring Judy Garland and Ginger Rogers.
Album: Released Jan '89, on Silva Screen by Silva Screen Records. Catalogue no: **STK 107**

For The Term Of His...

FOR THE TERM OF HIS NATURAL LIFE (TV soundtrack) (Walker,Simon)
CD: Released Feb '90, on Silva Screen by Silva Screen Records. Catalogue no: **IMICD 1001**

For Those I Loved

FOR THOSE I LOVED (Original soundtrack) (Various artists)
Tracks: / For those I love: Various artists / First love: Various artists / Insurrection march: Various artists / Past, The: Various artists / Melody mansion: Various artists / Treblinka: Various artists / Escape: Various artists / Zofia: Various artists / Deportation: Various artists / Cafe Sztuka: Various artists / Ghetto uprising, The: Various artists / Fire: Various artists / Hope and the future: Various artists.
Note: Music composed by Maurice Jarre, who also wrote 'Lawrence Of Arabia' and 'Dr Zhivago' themes.
Album: Released Aug '84, on BBC by BBC Records. Deleted '88. Catalogue no: **REH 518**

Cass: Released Aug '84, on BBC by BBC Records. Deleted '88. Catalogue no: **ZCR 518**

FOR THOSE I LOVED - VOL.2 (Various artists)
Album: Released May '85, on General Music (France) Catalogue no: **803 073**
Cass: Released May '85, on General Music (France) Catalogue no: **804 073**

For Whom The Bell

FOR WHOM THE BELL TOLLS (1943 film soundtrack) (Various artists)
Note: Victor Young's classic score (in Stereo) for the Gary Cooper/Ingrid Bergman film.u
CD: Released Jan '89, on Silva Screen by Silva Screen Records. Catalogue no: **DUNCD 112**
Album: Released Jan '89, on Silva Screen by Silva Screen Records. Catalogue no: **DUN 112**

For Your Eyes Only

FOR YOUR EYES ONLY (Film soundtrack) (Various artists) (See also under Easton, Sheena)
Album: Released Jul '81, on United Artists by EMI Records. Deleted '86. Catalogue no: **LBG 30337**
Cass: Released Jul '81, on United Artists by EMI Records. Deleted '86. Catalogue no: **TCLBG 30337**

Forbidden Broadway

FORBIDDEN BROADWAY (Original Broadway cast) (Various artists)
CD: Released Feb '90, on Silva Screen by Silva Screen Records. Catalogue no: **CDSBL12585**
Album: Released '88, on DRG (USA) by DRG Records (USA). Catalogue no: **SBL 12585**
Cass: Released '88, on DRG (USA) by DRG Records (USA). Catalogue no: **SBLC 12585**

Forbidden Planet

FORBIDDEN PLANET (Original soundtrack) (Various artists)
Note: 1954 MGM Sci/fi film with one of the earliest examples of an electronic film score, composed by Louis & Bebe Barron.
Album: Released Jan '89, on GNP Crescendo (USA) by GNP

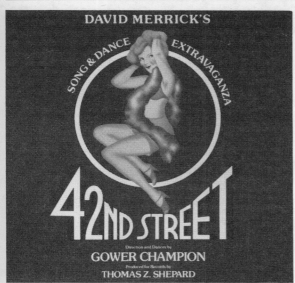

DAVID MERRICK'S

SONG & DANCE EXTRAVAGANZA

42ND STREET

Direction and Dances by
GOWER CHAMPION
Produced for Records by
THOMAS Z. SHEPARD

Forty Second Street - Original Broadway Cast (RCA)

Crescendo Records (USA). Catalogue no: **GNPSPR 001**
Cass: Released Jan '89, on GNP Crescendo (USA) by GNP Crescendo Records (USA). Catalogue no: **GNP5PR 001**

Forbidden Zone

FORBIDDEN ZONE (Original soundtrack) (Various artists)
Note: Composed by Danny Elman.
Album: Released Jan '89, on Silva Screen by Silva Screen Records. Catalogue no: **STV 81170**

Ford, Tennessee Ernie

BALLAD OF DAVY CROCKET
Tracks: / Ballad of Davy Crockett, The.
7" Single: Released Jan '56, on Capitol by EMI Records. Deleted '59. Catalogue no: **CL 14506**

Formula

FORMULA (1982 film soundtrack) (Various artists)
Album: Released '88, on Varese Sarabande Records(USA) by Varese Sarabande Records (USA). Catalogue no: **STV 81153**

Fort Saganne

FORT SAGANNE (Original soundtrack) (London Symphony Orchestra)
Note: Beautiful score for this desert epic by Philippe Sarde (Composer of Tess, Pirates).
Album: Released Jan '89, on Silva Screen by Silva Screen Records. Catalogue no: **A 238**
CD: Released Jan '89, on Silva Screen by Silva Screen Records. Catalogue no: **CDFMC 9**
CD: Released '88, on SPI Milan (France) Catalogue no: **CD 238**
Cass: Released Jan '89, on Silva Screen by Silva Screen Records. Catalogue no: **C 238**

Forty Second Street

42ND STREET (1980 Original Broadway cast) (Various artists) (See picture above)
Tracks: / Overture: *Various artists* / Audition: *Various artists* / Shadow waltz: *Various artists* / Young and healthy: *Various artists* / Go into your dance: *Various artists* / You're getting to be a habit with me: *Various artists* / Getting out of town: *Various artists* / We're in the money: *Various artists* / Dames: *Various artists* / Sunny side to every situation: *Various artists* / Lullaby of Broadway: *Various ar-*

tists / About a quarter to nine: *Various artists* / Shuffle off to Buffalo: *Various artists* / 42nd Street: *Various artists* / Finale: *Various artists* / 42nd Street (reprise - bows): *Various artists*.
Cass: Released '85, on RCA by BMG Records (UK). Catalogue no: **BK 83891**
CD: Released '85, on RCA by BMG Records (UK). Catalogue no: **BD 83891**
Album: Released '85, on RCA by BMG Records (UK). Catalogue no: **BL 83891**

42ND STREET (VIDEO) (Various artists)
VHS: Released Mar '88, on Warner Home Video by WEA Records. Catalogue no: **PES 99202**

Foster, David

ST.ELMO'S FIRE LOVE THEME
Tracks: / St. Elmo's fire love theme / Georgetown.
7" Single: Released Oct '85, on Atlantic by WEA Records. Catalogue no: **A 9528**

SYMPHONY SESSIONS
Tracks: / Piano concerto in G / Time passing / Firedance / Water fountain / Morning to morning / Ballet, The / Conscience / Just out of reach / Winter games / We were close.
CD: Released 6 Feb '88, on Atlantic by WEA Records. Catalogue no: **K 781 799 2**
Cass: Released Feb '88, on Atlantic by WEA Records. Catalogue no: **781 799-4**
Album: Released Feb '88, on Atlantic by WEA Records. Catalogue no: **781 799-1**

Foul Play

FOUL PLAY (Film soundtrack) (Various artists)
Cass: Released Mar '79, on Arista by BMG Records (UK). Deleted '84. Catalogue no: **TCARTY 160**
Album: Released Mar '79, on Arista by BMG Records (UK). Deleted '84. Catalogue no: **ARTY 160**

Four Jills In A Jeep

FOUR JILLS IN A JEEP (Original soundtrack) (Various artists)
Note: Starring Alice Faye and Dick

Haymes.
Album: Released Jan '89, on Silva Screen by Silva Screen Records. Catalogue no: **HS 407**

Four Musketeers

FOUR MUSKETEERS & OTHER SCORES (Film soundtracks)(Various artists)
Tracks: / Four musketeers, The: *Various artists* / Eagle has landed, The: *Various artists* / Voyage of the damned: *Various artists.*
CD: Released '88, on Silva Screen by Silva Screen Records. Catalogue no: **LXCD 5**

Four Tops

BACK TO SCHOOL AGAIN
Tracks: / Back to school again / Rock-a-hula-lula.
Note: Taken from the film *Grease 2*
7" Single: Released Jun '82, on RSO by Polydor Ltd. Deleted '85. Catalogue no: **RSO 89**

LOCO IN ACAPULCO
Tracks: / Loco in Acapulco / Four of us, The / Loco in Acapulco (body mix) (Only on 12" version (611 850)).
Note: Featured in the film *Buster*
Special: Released Jan '89, on Arista by BMG Records (UK). Deleted Oct '89. Catalogue no: **11197**
7" Single: Released Nov '88, on Arista by BMG Records (UK). Deleted Oct '89. Catalogue no: **111850**
12" Single: Released Nov '88, on Arista by BMG Records (UK). Catalogue no: **611730**
CD Single: Released Dec '88, on Arista by BMG Records (UK). Deleted Mar '90. Catalogue no: **661850**
12" Single: Released Jan '89, on Arista by BMG Records (UK). Deleted Oct '89. Catalogue no: **611916**
12" Single: Released Dec '88, on Arista by BMG Records (UK). Deleted Oct '89. Catalogue no: **611850**
Special: Released Jan '89, on Arista by BMG Records (UK). Deleted May '89. Catalogue no: **111850X**

Fourth Man

FOURTH MAN, THE (Original soundtrack) (Various artists)

Note: Composed by Loek Dipper.
Album: Released Jan '89, on Silva Screen by Silva Screen Records. Catalogue no: **STV 81222**

Fourth Protocol

FOURTH PROTOCOL (Film soundtrack)
Tracks: / Fourth protocol / Gorvoshin, Karpov, Borisov / Petrovsky, Preston / Berenson / Mr. Ross, Telecommunications / Disc, The, Gregorio, Glasgow docks / Uranium uranium, how about a drink... / Windows / Vasilievna / Detonator / Zero time / Before I go, kill her, I feel lucky / Traffic jam / Attic, The / Explosions, The / Going home, end titles.
Note: Lalo Schifrin score to the Frederick Forsyth thriller starring Michael Caine and Pierce Brosnan.
Cass: Released Apr '87, on Filmtrax by Filmtrax Records. Deleted Apr '90. Catalogue no: **MOMENTC 109**
CD: Released Jan '89, on Filmtrax by Filmtrax Records. Catalogue no: **MOMENTCD 109**
Album: Released Apr '87, on Filmtrax by Filmtrax Records. Deleted Jan '89. Catalogue no: **MOMENT 109**

Fox & The Hound

FOX AND THE HOUND (Film soundtrack) (Various artists)
Tracks: / Best of friends: *Various artists* / Lack of education: *Various artists* / Huntin' man: *Various artists* / Goodbye may seem forever: *Various artists* / Appreciate the lady: *Various artists.*
Album: Released Oct '85, on BBC by BBC Records. Deleted '88. Catalogue no: **REC 576**
Album: Released Dec '82, on Disneyland by Disneyland-Vista Records (USA). Catalogue no: **D 383**
Cass: Released Dec '82, on Disneyland by Disneyland-Vista Records (USA). Catalogue no: **D 27DC**
Cass: Released Oct '85, on BBC by BBC Records. Deleted '88. Catalogue no: **ZCM 576**

FOX AND THE HOUND (SINGLE)
Tracks: / Fox and the hound: Various artists.
Note: From the film *The fox and the hound.*

12" Pic: Released Dec '82, on Disneyland by Disneyland-Vista Records (USA). Catalogue no: **D 3106**
12" Single: Released Dec '82, on Disneyland by Disneyland-Vista Records (USA). Catalogue no: **D 3823**

Foxes

FOXES (Original motion picture soundtrack) (Various artists)
Cass: Released May '81, on IMS by Polydor Ltd. Catalogue no: **7599 051**
Album: Released May '81, on IMS by Polydor Ltd. Catalogue no: **6685 051**

Fraggle Rock

ALL AROUND THE WORLD
Tracks: / All around the world.
7" Single: Released May '85, on RCA by BMG Records (UK). Catalogue no: **FRAGG 1**

FRAGGLE ROCK (T.V. soundtrack)
Tracks: / Fraggle rock / Follow me / Convincing John / Doozer knitting song / Do it on my own / Wemblin fool / Why? / Lost and found / Working / Travelling Matt / Catch the tail by the tiger / Dum of a son of a gun / Brave boy jump up / Muck and goo / Friendship song / Fraggle rock rock / Beetle song / Easy is the only way to go / Our melody.
Album: Released Mar '84, on RCA by BMG Records (UK). Catalogue no: **PL 70221**
Cass: Released Mar '84, on RCA by BMG Records (UK). Catalogue no: **PK 70221**

FRAGGLE ROCK (SINGLE)
Tracks: / Fraggle rock / Working.
7" Pic: Released Jan '84, on RCA by BMG Records (UK). Catalogue no: **RCAP 389**
7" Single: Released Jan '84, on RCA by BMG Records (UK). Catalogue no: **RCA 389**

Frankie Goes To...

RELAX
Tracks: / Relax / One September Monday.
Note: Featured in the film 'Body Double'.
12" Single: Released Feb '89, on ZTT by ZTT Records. Catalogue no: **601096**

7" Single: Released Jul '84, on ZTT by ZTT Records. Deleted Jul '87. Catalogue no: **ZTAS 1**
7" Pic: Released Aug '84, on ZTT by ZTT Records. Catalogue no: **12 PZTAS 1**
Cass: Released Aug '84, on ZTT by ZTT Records. Catalogue no: **CTIS 102**

TWO TRIBES (Frankie Goes To Hollywood)
Tracks: / Two tribes / Two tribes (carnage mix) (Available on 12" only.).
Note: Used in the film *Supergrass*
7" Pic: Released Jun '84, on ZTT by ZTT Records. Catalogue no: **PZTAS 3**
12" Single: Released Feb '89, on ZTT by ZTT Records. Catalogue no: **601325**
12" Single: Released Jul '84, on ZTT by ZTT Records. Catalogue no: **XZTAS 3**
Cass: Released Aug '84, on ZTT by ZTT Records. Catalogue no: **CS 784**
7" Single: Released Jun '84, on ZTT by ZTT Records. Deleted Jun '88. Catalogue no: **ZTAS 3**
12" Single: Released Jun '84, on ZTT by ZTT Records. Catalogue no: **12 TAS 3**
12" Single: Released Aug '84, on ZTT by ZTT Records. Catalogue no: **XZIP 1**
12" Single: Released '88, on ZTT by ZTT Records. Deleted Dec '88. Catalogue no: **12 ZTS 3**

Frankie & Johnny
FRANKIE AND JOHNNY (See under Presley, Elvis)

Franklin, Aretha
THINK
Tracks: / Think / Respect.
Note: Featured in the film *The Blues Brothers*
7" Single: Released Oct '82, on Atlantic by WEA Records. Deleted Oct '85. Catalogue no: **K 11614**
7" Single: Released May '68, on Atlantic by WEA Records. Deleted '71. Catalogue no: **584 186**

Frantic (Film)
FRANTIC (Film soundtrack) (Various artists)
Tracks: / I'm gonna lose you: *Sim-*

ply Red / Frantic: *Various artists* / On the roofs of Paris: *Various artists* / One flugel horn: *Various artists* / Six short interludes: *Various artists* / Nocturne for Michel: *Various artists* / In the garage: *Various artists* / Paris project, The: *Various artists* / Sadly nostalgic: *Various artists* / Frantic: *Various artists*.
CD: Released Jun '88, on Elektra by Elektra Records (UK). Catalogue no: **K 960782 2**
Cass: Released May '88, on Elektra by Elektra Records (UK). Deleted Jul '90. Catalogue no: **960782 4**
Album: Released May '88, on Elektra by Elektra Records (UK). Deleted Jul '90. Catalogue no: **960782 1**

French Lieutenant's
FRENCH LIEUTENANT'S WOMAN (Film soundtrack) (Various artists)
Note: Composed by Carl Davies.
CD: Released '88, on DRG (USA) by DRG Records (USA). Catalogue no: **CDRG 6106**
Cass: Released '88, on DRG (USA) by DRG Records (USA). Catalogue no: **DRGC 6106**
Album: Released '88, on DRG (USA) by DRG Records (USA). Catalogue no: **DRG 6106**
CD: Released Feb '90, on DRG (USA) by DRG Records (USA). Catalogue no: **CDRG 6108**
Album: Released '83, on DRG (USA) by DRG Records (USA). Deleted Jan '89. Catalogue no: **SL 6106**
Cass: Released '83, on DRG (USA) by DRG Records (USA). Catalogue no: **TC-SL 6106**

Freud
FREUD (Film soundtrack) (Various artists)
Note: Composed by Jerry Goldsmith.
Album: Released Mar '79, on Citadel (USA) by Varese Sarabande Records (USA). Catalogue no: **CT 6019**

Friday Rock Show
FRIDAY ROCK SHOW (Various artists)
Tracks: / What you're doing to me: *Spider* / Don't you ever leave me: *Diamond Head* / Eye of the storm:

Sweet Savage / Dance of the music: *Last Flight* / One helluva night: *Demon* / Edge of the world: *Black Axe* / Belfast: *Witchfynde* / Cuttin' loose: *Xero*.
Note: Bands from the BBC Radio 1 rock show.
Album: Released Nov '81, on BBC by BBC Records. Deleted '88. Catalogue no: **REH 426**
Cass: Released Nov '81, on BBC by BBC Records. Deleted '88. Catalogue no: **ZCR 426**

Friday The 13th
FRIDAY THE 13TH, PART 1,2,& 3 (Original film soundtrack) (Various artists)
Note: Horror film scores by Harry Manfredini.
CD: Released Feb '90, on Silva Screen by Silva Screen Records. Catalogue no: **CDFMC10**
Album: Released Jan '89, on Silva Screen by Silva Screen Records. Catalogue no: **FMC 10**
Album: Released May '83, on Gramavision Catalogue no: **GR 1030**

FRIDAY THE 13TH: THE TV SERIES (Various artists)
Album: Released Jan '90, on Silva Screen by Silva Screen Records. Catalogue no: **GNPS 8018**
Cass: Released Jan '90, on Silva Screen by Silva Screen Records. Catalogue no: **GNP5 8018**
CD: Released Jan '90, on GNP Crescendo (USA) by GNP Crescendo Records (USA). Catalogue no: **GNPD 8018**

Friendly Persuasion
FRIENDLY PERSUASION (Original soundtrack) (Various artists)
Note: Score by Dimitri Tiomkin for the Gary Cooper film.
Album: Released Jan '89, on Silva Screen by Silva Screen Records. Catalogue no: **STV 81165**

Friends (Film)
FRIENDS (Film soundtrack) (Various artists)
Tracks: / Friends: *Various artists* / Honey roll: *Various artists* / Variations on Michelle's song: *Various artists* / Day in the country, A: *Various artists* / Four moods: *Various artists* / Seasons reprise: *Various artists* / Variations on friends

theme (The first kiss): *Various artists* / Can I put you on: *Various artists* / Michelle's song: *Various artists* / I mean't to do my work today (a day in the country): *Various artists*.
Album: Released '73, on Paramount Deleted '78. Catalogue no: **SPFL 269**
Album: Released '83, on ABC Records by MCA Records. Deleted Jan '88. Catalogue no: **MCL 1749**
Cass: Released '83, on ABC Records by MCA Records. Deleted Jan '88. Catalogue no: **MCLC 1749**

Fright Night

FRIGHT NIGHT (Film Soundtrack) (Various artists)
Tracks: / Fright Night: *J.Geils Band* / You can't hide from the beast inside: *Autograph* / Good man in a bad time: *Hunter, Ian* / Rock myself to sleep: *April Wine* / Let's talk: *Devo* / Armies of the night: *Sparks* / Give it up: *King, Evelyn "Champagne"* / Save me tonight: *White Sister* / Boppin' tonight: *Fabulous Fontaines* / Come to me: *Fledel, Brad*.
Cass: Released May '86, on Epic by CBS Records & Distribution. Catalogue no: **40 70270**
Album: Released May '86, on Epic by CBS Records & Distribution. Deleted Oct '89. Catalogue no: **EPC 70270**

Frog Dreaming

FROG DREAMING / WILD DUCK, THE (Original soundtracks) (Various artists)
CD: Released Jan '89, on Silva Screen by Silva Screen Records. Catalogue no: **SCCD 1019**

Frog Prince

FROG PRINCE, THE (Film soundtrack) (Enya)
Cass: Released Oct '85, on Island by Island Records. Catalogue no: **ICT 10**
Album: Released Oct '85, on Island by Island Records. Catalogue no: **ISTA 10**

From Beyond

FROM BEYOND (Original soundtrack) (Various artists)
Note: Horror score by Richard Band.
Album: Released Jan '89, on Enigma by Enigma Records (USA). Catalogue no: **ENIGMA 3240.1**

From Russia With Love

FROM RUSSIA WITH LOVE (Film soundtrack) (See also under Barry, John)
Album: on EMI (Germany) by EMI Records. Catalogue no: **IC 054 82931**
Album: Released Jul '87, on Liberty by EMI Records. Deleted May '90. Catalogue no: **EMS 1267**
Cass: Released Jul '87, on Liberty by EMI Records. Deleted Jun '89. Catalogue no: **TCEMS 1267**

From The Hip

FROM THE HIP (Original soundtrack) (Various artists)
Note: Composed by Paul Zaza.
Album: Released Jan '89, on Silva Screen by Silva Screen Records. Catalogue no: **STV 81309**

Full Metal Jacket

FULL METAL JACKET (Original Soundtrack) (Various artists)
Tracks: / Full metal jacket: *Various artists* / Hello Vietnam: *Various artists* / Chapel of love: *Various artists* / Wooly bully: *Various artists* / I like it like that: *Various artists* / These boots are made for walking: *Various artists* / Surfin' bird: *Various artists* / Marines' hymn, The: *Various artists* / Transition: *Various artists* / Parris Island: *Various artists* / Ruins: *Various artists* / Leonard: *Various artists* / Attack: *Various artists* / Time suspended: *Various artists* / Sniper: *Various artists*.
Album: Released Sep '87, on Warner Bros. by WEA Records. Catalogue no: **925613 1**
CD: Released Sep '87, on Warner Bros. by WEA Records. Catalogue no: **925613 2**
Cass: Released Sep '87, on Warner Bros. by WEA Records. Catalogue no: **925613 4**

I WANNA BE YOUR DRILL INSTRUCTOR
Tracks: / I wanna be your drill instructor / Sniper.
Note: From the film '*Full Metal Jacket*'
12" Single: Released Sep '87, on Warner Bros. by WEA Records. Catalogue no: **W 8187T**

7" Pic: Released Sep '87, on Warner Bros. by WEA Records. Catalogue no: **W 8186TP**
7" Single: Released Sep '87, on Warner Bros. by WEA Records. Catalogue no: **W 8187**

Fun At One

FUN AT ONE (Comedy from Radio 1) (Various artists)
Cass: Released Nov '79, on BBC by BBC Records. Deleted '88. Catalogue no: **ZCF 371**
Album: Released '79, on BBC by BBC Records. Deleted '88. Catalogue no: **REB 371**

MORE FUN AT ONE (Various artists)
Album: Released Nov '80, on BBC by BBC Records. Deleted '88. Catalogue no: **REB 399**

Fun In Acapulco

FUN IN ACAPULCO (VIDEO) (Various artists) (See also under Presley, Elvis)
VHS: Released '88, on Channel 5 by Channel 5 Video. Catalogue no: **CFV 01192**

Funny Commercials...

FUNNY COMMERCIALS AND OTHER RADIO FLUFFS (Various artists)
Album: Released '78, on Tandem Catalogue no: **LP 1901**

Funny Face

FUNNY FACE (Original Soundtrack Recording) (Various artists)
Album: Released '88, on DRG (USA) by DRG Records (USA). Catalogue no: **DS 15001**

Funny Girl

FUNNY GIRL (Film soundtrack) (Various artists)
Tracks: / Overture: *Various artists* / I'm the greatest star: *Various artists* / If a girl isn't pretty: *Various artists* / Roller skate rag: *Various artists* / I'd rather be blue over you (than happy with somebody else): *Various artists* / His love makes me beautiful: *Various artists* / People: *Various artists* / You are woman: *Various artists* / Don't rain on my parade: *Various artists* / Sadie Sadie: *Various artists* / Swan, The: *Various artists* / Funny girl: *Various artists* / My man: *Various artists* / Finale: *Various artists*.

CD: Released May '87, on CBS by CBS Records & Distribution. Deleted Jan '89. Catalogue no: **CD 70044**

Album: Released '87, on CBS by CBS Records & Distribution. Catalogue no: **70 044**

FUNNY GIRL (Original Broadway cast) (Various artists)

Tracks: / Overture: *Various artists* / If a girl isn't pretty: *Various artists* / Cornet man: *Various artists* / Who taught her everything: *Various artists* / His love makes me beautiful: *Various artists* / I want to be seen with you tonight: *Various artists* / Henry Street: *Various artists* / People: *Various artists* / You are woman: *Various artists* / Don't rain on my parade: *Various artists* / Sadie Sadie: *Various artists* / Find yourself a man: *Various artists* / Rat-tat-tat-tat: *Various artists* / Who are you now: *Various artists* / Music that makes me dance, The: *Various artists* / Finale: *Various artists*.

Note: Inc. Barbra Streisand, Sydney Chaplin, Kay Medford, Danny Meehan, Jean Stapleton. Conducted by Milton Rosenstock. Songs by Jule Styne & Bob Merrill.

CD: Released May '87, on EMI by EMI Records. Deleted Jan '90. Catalogue no: **CDP 746 634 2**

Album: Released May '85, on Capitol by EMI Records. Deleted Nov '88. Catalogue no: **EG 2605681**

Cass: Released May '85, on Capitol by EMI Records. Deleted Oct '89. Catalogue no: **EG 2605684**

FUNNY GIRL (ORIGINAL ISSUE) (Film soundtrack) (Various artists)

Album: Released Apr '66, on Capitol by EMI Records. Deleted '70. Catalogue no: **W 2059**

FUNNY GIRL (VIDEO) (Various artists)

VHS: Released Jun '89, on Hollywood Collection Catalogue no: **CVT 10145**

Funny Lady

FUNNY LADY (Original soundtrack) (Various artists)

Album: Released '75, on RCA (USA) Catalogue no: **ALB6 8347**

Cass: Released '75, on RCA (USA) Catalogue no: **ACB6 8347**

Funny Thing

FUNNY THING HAPPENED... (..on the way to the Forum) (Various artists)

Tracks: / Funny thing happened... overture: *Various artists* / Comedy tonight: *Various artists* / Love, I hear: *Various artists* / Lovely: *Various artists* / Pretty little picture: *Various artists* / Everybody ought to have a maid: *Various artists* / I'm calm: *Various artists* / Impossible: *Various artists* / Bring me my bride: *Various artists* / That dirty old man: *Various artists* / That'll show him: *Various artists* / Lovely (2): *Various artists* / Funeral sequence and dance: *Various artists* / Comedy tonight (2): *Various artists*.

Note: Book by B.Shevelove & L.Gelbart: Music and Lyrics by S.Sondheim.

Album: Released Jun '88, on First Night by First Night Records. Catalogue no: **OCR 3**

Cass: Released Jun '88, on First Night by First Night Records. Catalogue no: **OCRC 3**

Album: Released Feb '87, on EMI by EMI Records. Catalogue no: **EMS 1240**

Cass: Released Feb '87, on EMI by EMI Records. Catalogue no: **TC EMS 1240**

Album: Released '88, on DRG (USA) by DRG Records (USA). Catalogue no: **DS 15028**

F.X. (film)

F/X: MURDER BY ILLUSION (Original soundtrack) (Various artists)

Note: Composed by Bill Conti.

Album: Released Jan '89, on Silva Screen by Silva Screen Records. Catalogue no: **STV 81276**

Cass: Released Jan '89, on Silva Screen by Silva Screen Records. Catalogue no: **CTV 81276**

G

The following information was taken from the Music Master database on September 25th, 1990.

G, Bobby

BIG DEAL (Theme from)
Tracks: / Big deal / I want to say.
7" Single: Released Oct '84, on BBC by BBC Records. Deleted '87. Catalogue no: **RESL 151**
12" Single: Released Nov '84, on BBC by BBC Records. Deleted '87. Catalogue no: **12RSL 151**
7" Single: Released Sep '86, on Polydor by Polydor Ltd. Deleted Aug '87. Catalogue no: **POSP 810**
12" Single: Released Sep '86, on Polydor by Polydor Ltd. Deleted Mar '87. Catalogue no: **POSPX 810**

Gabriel, Peter

BIRDY (Film soundtrack)
Tracks: / At night / Floating dogs / Quiet and alone / Close up (from 'Family snapshot') / Birdy's flight (from 'Not one of us') / Slow marimbas / Heat, The (from 'Rhythm of the heat') / Sketchpad with trumpet and voice / Under lock and key (from 'Wallflower') / Powerhouse at the foot of the mountain (from 'San Jacinto').
Cass: Released Mar '85, on Charisma by Virgin Records. Catalogue no: **CASMC 1167**
CD: Released Mar '85, on Charisma by Virgin Records. Catalogue no: **CASCD 1167**
Cass: Released Apr '90, on Virgin by Virgin Records. Catalogue no: **OVEDC 283**
Album: Released Mar '85, on Charisma by Virgin Records. Catalogue no: **CAS 1167**
Album: Released Apr '90, on Virgin by Virgin Records. Catalogue no: **OVED 283**

PASSION (Music for the Last Temptation Of Christ)
Tracks: / Feeling begins, The / Gethsemane / Of these, hope / Lazarus raised / Of these hope (reprise) / In doubt / Different drum, A / Zaar / Troubled / Open / Before night falls / With this love / Sandstorm / Stigmata / Passion / Disturbed / With this love / It is accomplished / Wall of breath / Promise of shadows / Bread and wine.
CD: Released Jun '89, on Virgin by Virgin Records. Catalogue no: **RWCD 1**
2 LP Set: Released Jun '89, on Virgin by Virgin Records. Catalogue no: **RWLP 1**
Cass: Released Jun '89, on Virgin by Virgin Records. Catalogue no: **RWMC 1**

Gadfly

GADFLY, THE (Film soundtrack) (Various artists)
Tracks: / Gadfly, The: Overture: *Various artists* / Contradance: *Various artists* / National holiday: *Various artists* / Gadfly, The: Prelude and waltz: *Various artists* / Galop: *Various artists* / Gadfly, The: Introduction into the dance: *Various artists* / Romance: *Various artists* / Gadfly, The: Interlude: *Various artists* / Nocturne: *Various artists* / Scene: *Various artists* / Gadfly, The: Finale: *Various artists*.
Album: Released '82, on Classics For Pleasure by EMI Records. Catalogue no: **CFP 4144631**
Cass: Released '82, on Classics For Pleasure by EMI Records. Catalogue no: **CFP 4144634**
CD: Released '82, on Classics For Pleasure by EMI Records. Catalogue no: **CDCFP 4463**

Galileo

GALILEO/ESCALATION (Film soundtrack) (Morricone, Ennio)
Album: Released Feb '90, on Silva Screen by Silva Screen Records. Catalogue no: **RP 017**

Gambler

GAMBLER, THE (Original London cast) (Various artists)
Tracks: / Get yer life: *Various artists* / Loach's song: *Various artists* / Horse race: *Various artists* / Barmaid's song: *Various artists* / Ten thousand quid: *Various artists* /

Lullaby: *Various artists* / Danny's song: *Various artists* / Greyhound race: *Various artists* / I've sailed through hell: *Various artists* / Craps: *Various artists* / Easy: *Various artists* / Shaking in the shadows: *Various artists*.
Cass: Released Sep '86, on First Night by First Night Records. Catalogue no: **SCENEC 3**
Album: Released Sep '86, on First Night by First Night Records. Catalogue no: **SCENE 3**

Game Set & Match

GAME SET AND MATCH (T.V. soundtrack) (Various artists)
Album: Released Oct '88, on Chrysalis by Chrysalis Records. Deleted Jun '90. Catalogue no: **CHR 1692**
CD: Released Oct '88, on Chrysalis by Chrysalis Records. Catalogue no: **CCD 1692**
Cass: Released Oct '88, on Chrysalis by Chrysalis Records. Deleted Jun '90. Catalogue no: **ZCHR 1692**

Gandhi

GANDHI (Original soundtrack) (Various artists)
Album: Released Jan '83, on RCA by BMG Records (UK). Catalogue no: **RCALP 6062**
Cass: Released Jan '83, on RCA by BMG Records (UK). Catalogue no: **RCAK 6062**

Gangs All Here

GANGS ALL HERE, THE (Original soundtrack) (Various artists)
Note: Starring Alice Faye and Carmen Miranda.
Album: Released Jan '89, on Silva Screen by Silva Screen Records. Catalogue no: **SH 2009**

Gangsters & Good Guys

GANGSTERS AND GOOD GUYS (Original soundtrack) (Various artists)
Tracks: / Public enemy, The: *Vari-*

ous artists / Petrified forest, The: Various artists / Each dawn I die: Various artists / High sierra: Various artists / Angels with dirty faces: Various artists / Key Largo: Various artists / White heat: Various artists / Roaring 20's, The: Various artists / Big sleep, The: Various artists / Maltese falcon, The: Various artists / To have and have not: Various artists / Across the Pacific: Various artists / Treasure of the Sierra Madre: Various artists / Casablanca: Various artists.

Cass: Released Dec '84, on RCA by BMG Records (UK). Catalogue no: **PK 70566**

Album: Released Dec '84, on RCA by BMG Records (UK). Deleted Jul '89. Catalogue no: **PL 70566**

Garbo, Greta

GARBO (Soundtracks Of Various MGM Films) (Various artists)
Tracks: / Foreward: Pidgeon, Walter / Grand Hotel: Garbo, Greta & John Barrymore / Queen Christina: Garbo, Greta & John Gilbert / Camille: Garbo, Greta & Robert Taylor / Conquest: Garbo, Greta & Charles Boyer / Ninotchka: Various artists / Susan Lennox, her rise and fall: Garbo, Greta & Clark Gable / Anna Christie: Garbo, Greta & Marie Dressler / Anna Karenina: Garbo, Greta & Frederick March / Mata Hari: Various artists.
Album: Released '73, on MGM (Polydor) by Polydor Ltd. Deleted '78. Catalogue no: **2353 059**

Garden Of The...

GARDEN OF THE FINZI-CONTINIS (Film Soundtrack) (Various artists)
Tracks: / Micol's theme: Various artists / Tennis match: Various artists / Giorgio and Micol (love theme): Various artists / Persecution: Various artists / Garden of the Finzi-Continis: Various artists / Meeting at Easter: Various artists / Declaration of war: Various artists / Leaving for Genoble: Various artists / Giorgio's delusion: Various artists / Garden of the Finzi-Continis: Various artists / Villa: Various artists / Childhood memories: Various artists / Garden of the Finzi-Continis (finale): Various artists / Micol's theme (reprise): Various artists.

Album: Released '73, on RCA by BMG Records (UK). Deleted '78. Catalogue no: **SF 8289**

Garfunkel, Art

BRIGHT EYES
Tracks: / Bright eyes / Kehaar's theme.
Note: From the animated film Watership Down
7" Single: Released Mar '79, on CBS by CBS Records & Distribution. Deleted '82. Catalogue no: **CBS 6947**
7" Single: Released Jul '84, on CBS by CBS Records & Distribution. Deleted '86. Catalogue no: **CBS A4598**

Garland, Judy

BEST OF JUDY GARLAND — FROM MGM FILMS
CD: Released Jun '88, on MCA (USA) by MCA Records (USA). Catalogue no: **31176**

BROADWAY MELODY OF 1938 (Film Soundtrack) (See under Broadway Melody)

BROADWAY MELODY OF 1940 (Film Soundtrack) (See under Broadway Melody)

EASTER PARADE (Film Soundtrack) (See under Easter Parade)

FOR ME AND MY GAL (Film Soundtrack) (See under For Me And My Gal)

I COULD GO ON SINGING (Original soundtrack)
Tracks: / I could go on singing / Overture / Hello bluebird / I am the Monarch of the sea (From H.M.S. Pinafore.) / It never was you / By myself / Helicopter ride / Interlude / Matt's dilemma.
Cass: Released Mar '88, on EMI by EMI Records. Deleted 31 Jul '88. Catalogue no: **TCEMS 1288**

MAN THAT GOT AWAY, THE
Tracks: / Man that got away, The.
Note: Used in the 1950's version of the film A star is born
7" Single: Released Jun '55, on Philips by Phonogram Ltd. Deleted '58. Catalogue no: **PB 366**

MEET ME IN ST.LOUIS (Film Soundtrack) (See under Meet Me In St.Louis)

STAR IS BORN, A (Film soundtrack)
Tracks: / Gotta have me go with

you / Man that got away, The / Born in a trunk / I'll get by / You took advantage of me / Black bottom / Peanut vendor / My melancholy baby / Swanee / Here's what I'm here for / It's a new world / Someone at last / Lose that long face.
Cass: Released Jul '84, on CBS Cameo by CBS Records & Distribution. Deleted '87. Catalogue no: **40 32499**
Album: Released Jul '84, on CBS Cameo by CBS Records & Distribution. Deleted Aug '87. Catalogue no: **CBS 32499**
Album: Released '79, on CBS Cameo by CBS Records & Distribution. Deleted '84. Catalogue no: **31695**

THOUSANDS CHEER (Film Soundtrack) (See under Thousands Cheer)

WIZARD OF OZ (Film Soundtrack) (See under Wizard Of Oz)

Gary Byrd's...

GARY BYRD'S SWEET INSPIRATIONS (Various artists)
Album: Released Nov '84, on BBC by BBC Records. Deleted 31 Aug '88. Catalogue no: **REH 548**
Cass: Released Nov '84, on BBC by BBC Records. Deleted 31 Aug '88. Catalogue no: **ZCR 548**

Gator

GATOR (Original soundtrack) (Various artists)
Note: Charles Bernstein score for the Burt Reynolds film.
Album: Released Jan '89, on MCA by MCA Records. Catalogue no: **MCA 25014**
Cass: Released Jan '89, on MCA by MCA Records. Deleted Feb '90. Catalogue no: **MCAC 25014**

Gay Divorcee

GAY DIVORCEE, THE (VIDEO) (Various artists)
Note: Fred and Gingers best film, featuring the spectacular dance routine for 'The Continental'.
VHS: Released Jun '89, on Cinema Club Catalogue no: **CC 1022**
VHS: Released May '87, on Video Collection by Video Collection. Catalogue no: **VC 3046**

GAY DIVORCEE/TOP HAT (Film soundtracks) (Various artists)

Note: Starring Fred Astaire and Ginger Rogers.
Album: Released Jan '89, on Silva Screen by Silva Screen Records. Catalogue no: **STK 105**

Gaye, Marvin

TROUBLE MAN (Film soundtrack)
Tracks: / Trouble man main theme (2) / 'T' plays it cool / Poor Abbey Walsh / Break in (police shoot big) / Cleo's apartment / Trouble man / Trouble man, Theme from / 'T' stands for trouble / Trouble man main theme (1) / Life is a gamble / Deep in it / Don't mess with Mr. T / There goes Mr.T
Album: Released Jul '82, on Motown by BMG Records (UK). Catalogue no: **STMS 5065**
Cass: Released Jul '82, on Motown by BMG Records (UK). Catalogue no: **CSTMS 5065**
Album: Released '86, on Motown by BMG Records (UK). Catalogue no: **WL 72215**
Cass: Released '86, on Motown by BMG Records (UK). Catalogue no: **WK 72215**
CD: Released '86, on Motown by BMG Records (UK). Catalogue no: **ZD 72500**

General Mickey

GENERAL MICKEY (Original Soundtrack) (Various artists)
Tracks: / We're the future: *Various artists* / Now this is a character: *Various artists* / General Mickey: *Various artists* / Can't call you my baby: *Various artists* / When you're bad: *Various artists* / Strangest stranger: *Various artists* / Why don't you look at me?: *Various artists* / We will move the world: *Various artists* / I believe in him: *Various artists* / We wanna see more of you: *Various artists* / Hard times blues: *Various artists* / Edge of darkness: *Various artists* / Nothing's that simple: *Various artists* / Cell with no key: *Various artists* / Why did I go?: *Various artists* / We don't want him here: *Various artists* / We will move the world (reprise): *Various artists* / Why is life?: *Various artists* / Now this is a character (reprise): *Various artists* / General Mickey (reprise): *Various artists*.
Cass: Released Jul '88, on Joncor Music by Joncor Music. Catalogue no: **JM 1**

Genesis (Film)

GENESIS (Original Soundtrack) (Various artists)
Note: Award winning Indian film with music by Ravi Shankar.
CD: Released '88, on SPI Milan (France) Catalogue no: **A 287**
Album: Released Jun '86, on SPI Milan (France) Catalogue no: **A 287**
Cass: Released Jun '86, on SPI Milan (France) Catalogue no: **C 287**

Gentlemen & Players

GENTLEMEN AND PLAYERS (See under Clark, Petula)

Gentlemen Prefer

'GENTLEMEN PREFER BLONDES (Original Broadway cast) (Various artists)
Album: Released Jan '89, on Silva Screen by Silva Screen Records. Catalogue no: **AOS 2310**
Cass: Released Jan '89, on Silva Screen by Silva Screen Records. Catalogue no: **BT 2310**

GENTLEMEN PREFER BLONDES (Original London cast) (Various artists)
Tracks: / Overture: *Ainsworth, Alyn & Orchestra* / It's high time: *Hart, Griffin & Co* / Bye bye baby: *Bryan, Dora and Stewart* / Little girl from little rock: *Bryan, Dora and Stewart* / I love what I'm doing: *Hart, Anne & boys* / Just a kiss apart: *Palmer, Robin* / Sunshine: *Bryan, Middleton & Co* / Mamie is Mimi: *Walsh, Cole & Ty* / You kill me: *Stern, Gerald & Showgirls* / You say you care: *Hart, Anne & Robin Palmer* / Diamonds are a girls best friend: *Bryan, Dora* / Homestick blues: *Bryan, Dora & Anne Hart* / Au revoir babies: *Various artists* / Keeping cool: *Hart, Anne* / Button up: *Bryan, Dora & Stewart*.
Album: Released Apr '83, on T. E. R. by That's Entertainment Records. Catalogue no: **TER 1059**
Cass: Released Apr '83, on T. E. R. by That's Entertainment Records. Catalogue no: **ZCTER 1059**

GENTLEMEN PREFER BLONDES (VIDEO) (Various artists)
VHS: Released '88, on CBS-Fox by CBS-Fox Video. Catalogue no: **101950**

George M

GEORGE M (Original Broadway Cast) (Various artists)
Note: Written by Jerry Herman and starring Joel Grey.
Album: Released Jan '89, on Silva Screen by Silva Screen Records. Deleted Mar '90. Catalogue no: **PS 3200**
Cass: Released Jan '89, on Silva Screen by Silva Screen Records. Catalogue no: **PST 3200**
CD: Released Jan '89, on CBS (import) by CBS Records & Distribution. Catalogue no: **CK 03200**

Georgia Satellites

HIPPY HIPPY SHAKE
Tracks: / Hippy hippy shake / Hand to mouth / Powerful stuff (On 12" version only.).
Note: Featured in the film *Cocktail*.
7" Single: Released Jan '89, on Elektra by Elektra Records (UK). Deleted Jan '90. Catalogue no: **EKR 86**
12" Single: Released Jan '89, on Elektra by Elektra Records (UK). Deleted Jan '90. Catalogue no: **EKR 86 T**

Gerry & The Pacemakers

FERRY ACROSS THE MERSEY (1964 film soundtrack)
Tracks: / It's still rock and roll to me / I'm the one / Unchained melody / Roll over Beethoven / Imagine / Running man / Just the way you are / How do you do it / Ferry 'cross the Mersey.
Album: Released Apr '86, on Castle Showcase by Castle Communications Records. Catalogue no: **SHLP 102**
Album: Released Mar '88, on Beat Goes On by Andy's Records. Catalogue No: **BGOLP 10**
Cass: Released Apr '86, on Castle Showcase by Castle Communications Records. Catalogue no: **SHTC 102**
Album: Released Feb '65, on Columbia by EMI Records. Deleted '70. Catalogue no: **33SX 1676**

Gershwin

AMERICAN IN PARIS (Utah Symphony Orchestra)
Note: Conducted by Maurice Abravanel.
CD: Released Aug '89, on Start by Start Records Ltd.. Catalogue no: **VECD 7518**

Cass: Released Aug '89, on Start by Start Records Ltd.. Catalogue no: **VETC 6518**

AMERICAN IN PARIS: PIANO CONCERTO (Bogas/ Ljubljana Symphony Orchestra/ Nice)
CD: Released Sep '89, on Stradivarii by Michele International Records. Catalogue no: **SCD 6048**

AMERICAN IN PARIS/CUBAN OVERTURE/PORGY AND BESS
CD: Released '83, on RCA by BMG Records (UK). Deleted May '89. Catalogue no: **RCD 14551**

GERSHWIN BROADWAY OVERTURES (Buffalo Philharmonic Orchestra)
Tracks: / Funny face / Girl crazy / Strike up the band / Of thee I sing / Let 'em eat cake / Oh Kay!.
Album: Released '82, on CBS by CBS Records & Distribution. Catalogue no: **CBS 76632**

PORGY AND BESS (Various artists) (See also under Porgy & Bess)
Note: Porgy - Williard White; Bess - Cynthia Haymon; Clara - Carolyn Blackwell; Sportin' Life - Damon Evans; Jake - Bruce Hubbard. Glyndbourne Chorus, the London Philharmonic conducted by Simon Rattle.
CD Set: Released May '89, on H.M.V. by EMI Records. Deleted Aug '89. Catalogue no: **CDPORGY 1**
Cass set: Released May '89, on H.M.V. by EMI Records. Catalogue no: **EX 749 568 4**
Cass set: Released May '89, on H.M.V. by EMI Records. Catalogue no: **TCPORGY 1**
LP Set: Released May '89, on H.M.V. by EMI Records. Catalogue no: **EX 749 568 1**
CD Set: Released May '89, on H.M.V. by EMI Records. Catalogue no: **CDS 749 568 2**
LP Set: Released May '89, on H.M.V. by EMI Records. Catalogue no: **PORGY 1**

RHAPSODY IN BLUE (Various artists)
Note: Performed by the Newton Wayland Denver Symphony Pops
CD: Released '88, on K-Tel by K-Tel Records. Catalogue no: **NCD 3414**
CD: Released Aug '89, on Deutsche Grammophon by PolyGram

Classics. Catalogue no: **427 806 2**
Cass: Released Aug '89, on Deutsche Grammophon by PolyGram Classics. Catalogue no: **427 806 4**

RHAPSODY IN BLUE (2) (Various artists)
Tracks: / Rhapsody in blue: *Various artists* / Piano concerto in F: *Various artists* / Rhapsody on a theme of Paganini (Rachmaninov): *Various artists*.
Note: Artists: Daniel Wayenberg and Orchestre de la Societe des Concerts du Conservatoire and Georges Pretre and Philharmonia Orchestra and Christoph von Dohnanyi.
Cass: Released '89, on EMI Studio by EMI Records. Catalogue no: **769 113 4**
CD: Released '89, on EMI Studio by EMI Records. Catalogue no: **CDM 769 113 2**

RHAPSODY IN BLUE, AN AMERICAN IN PARIS, PORGY AND BESS (Jando/ Budapest Philharmonic Orchestra/ Sandor)
CD: Released Sep '89, on Laserlight Catalogue no: **15 606**

Ghost & Mrs.Muir
GHOST & MRS.MUIR, THE (Film soundtrack) (Various artists)
Note: Classic score by Bernard Herrmann. Newly recorded and conducted by Elmer Bernstein.
Album: Released Jan '89, on Silva Screen by Silva Screen Records. Catalogue no: **704.340**
Cass: Released Jan '89, on Silva Screen by Silva Screen Records. Catalogue no: **C 704.304**
CD: Released Jan '89, on Silva Screen by Silva Screen Records. Catalogue no: **VCD 47254**

Ghostbusters
GHOSTBUSTERS (Theme from) (See under Parker, Ray Jnr)

GHOSTBUSTERS (Original soundtrack) (Various artists)
Tracks: / Ghostbusters: *Parker, Ray Jnr.* / Cleanin' up the town: *Bus Boys* / Savin' the day: *Alessi* / In the name of love: *Thompson Twins* / I can wait forever: *Air Supply* / Hot night: *Branigan, Laura* / Magic: *Smiley, Mick* / Ghostbusters (main title theme): *Bernstein, Elmer* / Dana's theme: *Bernstein,*

Elmer.
Album: Released Oct '87, on RCA by BMG Records (UK). Catalogue no: **208 720**
Cass: Released Oct '87, on RCA by BMG Records (UK). Catalogue no: **408 720**
CD: Released Oct '87, on RCA by BMG Records (UK). Catalogue no: **258 720**

GHOSTBUSTERS 2 (Various artists) (See panel on next page)
Album: Released Jul '89, on MCA by MCA Records. Catalogue no: **MCG 6056**
Cass: Released Jul '89, on MCA by MCA Records. Catalogue no: **MCGC 6056**
CD: Released Jul '89, on MCA by MCA Records. Catalogue no: **DMCG 6056**

GHOSTBUSTERS (From The film Ghostbusters 2) (See under Run DMC)

Ghosts In The Machine
GHOSTS IN THE MACHINE (Music from the Channel 4 programme) (See under Karn, Mick 'Titles')

GI Blues
GI BLUES (Film Soundtrack) (See under Presley, Elvis)
GI BLUES (VIDEO) (Various artists)
VHS: Released '88, on Channel 5 by Channel 5 Video. Catalogue no: **CFV 01202**

Giant
GIANT (Film soundtrack) (Tiomkin, Dimitri)
Cass: Released Feb '90, on Silva Screen by Silva Screen Records. Catalogue no: **92056.4**
CD: Released Feb '90, on Silva Screen by Silva Screen Records. Catalogue no: **CDP 92056.2**

Gibb, Barry
NOW VOYAGER (Film soundtrack)
Tracks: / I am your driver / Fine line / Face to face / Shatterproof / Shine shine / Lesson in love / One night for lovers / Stay alone / Temptation / She says / Hunter.
CD: on Polydor by Polydor Ltd. Catalogue no: **823 429-2**
CD: Released Jun '88, on MCA (USA) by MCA Records (USA).

Harold Ramis and Dan Aykroyd in *Ghostbusters 2*.

Catalogue no: **31096**
Album: Released Oct '84, on Polydor by Polydor Ltd. Catalogue no: **POLH 14**

NOW VOYAGER (VIDEO)
Note: Cert. 15. Running time: 80 mins.
VHS: Released Sep '89, on Castle Hendring Video by Castle Communications Records. Catalogue no: **HEN 2 175 G**

Gibbons, Carroll

ON THE AIR (Gibbons, Carroll & The Savoy Hotel Orpheans)
Tracks: / On the air / Have you met Miss Jones / Comes love / Stairway to the stars / What's new / My heart belongs to Daddy / I don't want to set the world on fire / F.D.R. Jones / Shake down the stars / Accentuate the positive / Tomorrow's sunrise / Cynthia's in love / Over Wyoming / Silver wedding waltz / Francesca / Wandering along / I can dream, can't I / So ends my search for a dream.
Album: Released Jul '84, on President by President Records. Catalogue no: **PLE 513**
Cass: Released Jun '85, on President by President Records. Catalogue no: **TC-PLE 513**

ON THE AIR (The Hartley's Jam broadcasts 1943-1945) (Gibbons, Carroll & The Boyfriends featuring Anne Lenner)
Tracks: Who? / Smoke gets in your eyes / Don't let it bother you / I saw stars / Messengers / Walking the chalk line / I'll see you again / Love is in the air / Coffee in the morning / Tea for two / Continental, The / Lost in a fog / Take a number from one to ten / If the moon turns green / Straight from the shoulder / You turned your head / Other peoples babies / Dinah / What a difference a day makes / Pardon my southern accent / Heatwave.
Album: Released Oct '86, on World Records by EMI Records. Deleted 31 Jul '88. Catalogue no: **SH 360**
Cass: Released Oct '86, on Retrospect by EMI Records. Deleted 31 Jul '88. Catalogue no: **TC SH 360**

ON THE WIRELESS AT 7 PM EACH THURSDAY (Hartley's Jam broadcasts)
Tracks: / My lips and your lips / You've got to admit / I'm so misunderstood / Swing on the gait / Life of the party, The / While there's a 'you' about / Love is just around the corner / Say when / Needle in a haystack / Wrapped around your finger / Body and soul / You fit into the picture / College rhythm / Blue moon / I got rhythm / In my country that means love.
Note: Includes medley 1: I wish I were twins/Sweetheart, I'm dreaming of you/I can't give you anything but love/Your mother's son in law. Medley 2: Who do you think you are/Let's be sensible/Auf wiedersehn, my dear/Pop goes your heart.
Cass: Released Jul '90, on Cedar (EMI) by EMI Records. Catalogue no: **794 321 4**
Cass: Released Jul '90, on Cedar (EMI) by EMI Records. Catalogue no: **TCSH 519**
CD: Released Jul '90, on Cedar (EMI) by EMI Records. Catalogue no: **CDP 794 321 2**
Album: Released Jul '90, on Cedar (EMI) by EMI Records. Catalogue no: **SH 519**
CD: Released Jul '90, on Cedar (EMI) by EMI Records. Catalogue no: **CZ 307**
Album: Released Jul '90, on Cedar (EMI) by EMI Records. Catalogue no: **794 321 1**

Gigi

GIGI (Film Soundtrack) (Various artists)
Tracks: / Overture: *Various artists* / Thank heaven for little girls: *Various artists* / It's a bore: *Various artists* / Parisians: *Various artists* / Waltz at Maxim's (she is not thinking of me): *Various artists* / Night they invented champagne: *Various artists* / I remember it well: *Various artists* / Say a prayer for me tonight: *Various artists* / I'm glad I'm not young anymore: *Various artists* / Gigi: *Various artists* / Finale - thank heaven for little girls: *Various artists*.
Album: Released '73, on MGM (Polydor) by Polydor Ltd. Deleted '78. Catalogue no: **2353 037**
Cass: Released '73, on MGM (Polydor) by Polydor Ltd. Deleted '78. Catalogue no: **3110 041**
Album: Released Jan '59, on MGM (EMI) Catalogue no: **MGM C 770**
Album: Released Jul '86, on CBS by CBS Records & Distribution. Deleted Aug '88. Catalogue no: **CBS 70277**
Cass: Released Jul '86, on CBS by CBS Records & Distribution. Deleted Jan '89. Catalogue no: **40 70277**
CD: Released Mar '87, on CBS by CBS Records & Distribution. Deleted Jan '89. Catalogue no: **CD 70277**

GIGI (Original London cast) (Various artists)
Tracks: / Paris is Paris again: *Various artists* / It's a bore: *Various artists* / Earth and other minor

things: *Various artists* / Thank heaven for little girls: *Various artists* / She's not thinking of me: *Various artists* / Night they invented champagne: *Various artists* / I remember it well: *Various artists* / Gigi: *Various artists* / Gigi (Entr'acte): *Various artists* / Contract, The: *Various artists* / I'm glad I'm not young anymore: *Various artists* / Wide wide world: *Various artists* / Gigi (Finale): *Various artists*.

Album: Released Nov '85, on First Night by First Night Records. Catalogue no: **GIGI 1**
Cass: Released Nov '85, on First Night by First Night Records. Catalogue no: **GIGI C 1**

GIGI (Original Broadway cast) (Various artists)

Tracks: / Overture: *Orchestra* / Thank heaven for little girls: *Drake, Alfred* / It's a bore: *Drake, Alfred & Daniel Massey* / Earth and other minor things: *Wolfe, Karin* / Paris is Paris again: *Drake, Alfred* / She is not thinking of me: *Various artists* / I remember it well: *Drake, Alfred & Maria Karnilova* / Night they invented champagne: *Karnilova, Maria & Daniel Massey* / Gigi: *Massey, Daniel* / Contract, The: *Morehead, Agnes* / In this wide wide world: *Wolfe, Karin* / I'm glad I'm not young anymore: *Drake, Alfred* / Finale: Orchestra / Thank heaven for little girls (Reprise): *Drake, Alfred* /

Album: Released Jan '87, on RCA by BMG Records (UK). Deleted May '89. Catalogue no: **NL 80404**
Cass: Released Jan '87, on RCA by BMG Records (UK). Deleted May '89. Catalogue no: **NK 80404**

GIGI (VIDEO) (Various artists)

VHS: Released '88, on MGM/UA (Video) by MGM/UA Video. Catalogue no: **MGM 10054**
VHS: Released '88, on MGM/UA (Video) by MGM/UA Video. Catalogue no: **SMV 10050**

GIGI/AN AMERICAN IN PARIS (Various artists)

Tracks: / Gigi overture: *Various artists* / Thank heaven for little girls: *Various artists* / It's a bore: *Various artists* / Parisians, The: *Various artists* / Waltz at Maxim's (She is not thinking of me): *Various artists* / Night they invented champagne, The: *Various artists* / I remember it well: *Various artists* /

Say a prayer for me tonight!: *Various artists* / I'm glad I'm not young anymore: *Various artists* / Gigi finale: *Various artists* / 'S wonderful: *Various artists* / Love is here to stay: *Various artists* / I'll build a stairway to paradise: *Various artists* / I got rhythm: *Various artists* / An American in Paris ballet: *Various artists* .

CD: Released Jan '90, on MGM (EMI) Catalogue no: **CDMGM 1**
CD: Released Jan '90, on MGM (EMI) Catalogue no: **CDP 793 296 2**
Cass: Released Jan '90, on MGM (EMI) Catalogue no: **TCMGM 1**
Album: Released Jan '90, on MGM (EMI) Catalogue no: **793 296 1**
Cass: Released Jan '90, on MGM (EMI) Catalogue no: **793 296 4**
Album: Released Jan '90, on MGM (EMI) Catalogue no: **LPMGM 1**

Ginger & Fred

GINGER AND FRED (Film soundtrack) (Various artists)

Note: Music from the Fellini film.
Cass: Released Jan '89, on Silva Screen by Silva Screen Records. Catalogue no: **C 284**
Album: Released Jan '89, on Silva Screen by Silva Screen Records. Catalogue no: **A 284**
CD: Released Feb '90, on Silva Screen by Silva Screen Records. Catalogue no: **CDFMC 4**

Girl Can't Help It

GIRL CAN'T HELP IT, THE (Film soundtrack) (Various artists)

Note: With Little Richard, Jayne Mansfield etc.
LP Pic: Released Jul '88, on Picture Disc Catalogue no: **PD 1050**

GIRL CAN'T HELP IT (SINGLE) (See under Little Richard)

Girl Crazy

GIRL CRAZY (Studio cast) (Various artists)

Note: Starring Mary Martin.
Album: Released Jan '89, on Silva Screen by Silva Screen Records. Catalogue no: **COS 2560**

GIRL CRAZY (Film Soundtrack) (Various artists)

Album: Released Jan '89, on Silva Screen by Silva Screen Rec-

ords. Catalogue no: **HS 5008**

Girl From Ipanema

GIRL FROM IPANEMA (See under Jobim, Antonio Carlos)

Girl In Pink Tights

GIRL IN PINK TIGHTS, THE (Original Broadway cast) (Various artists)

Note: 1954 cast with Zizi Jeanmaire.
Album: Released Jan '89, on Silva Screen by Silva Screen Records. Catalogue no: **AOL 4890**

Girl Most Likely

GIRL MOST LIKELY (The Musical) (Various artists)

Note: Jane Powell in a delightful musical, as a girl who can't decide which of her 3 fiancees to marry!
VHS: Released May '87, on Video Collection by Video Collection. Catalogue no: **VC 3098**

Girlfriend

GIRLFRIEND, THE (Original Mercury Theatre cast) (Various artists)

Cass: Released Dec '87, on T. E. R. by That's Entertainment Records. Deleted Mar '90. Catalogue no: **ZCTER 1148**
Album: Released Mar '90, on T. E. R. by That's Entertainment Records. Catalogue no: **TER 1148**

Girls Girls Girls

GIRLS GIRLS GIRLS (VIDEO) (Various artists)

VHS: Released '88, on Channel 5 by Channel 5 Video. Catalogue no: **CFV 01212**

GIRLS GIRLS GIRLS (Film Soundtrack) (See under Presley, Elvis)

Girls Just Wanna ...

GIRLS JUST WANNA HAVE FUN (Film soundtrack) (Various artists)

Cass: Released '85, on Mercury by Phonogram Ltd. Deleted '90. Catalogue no: **MERHC 72**
CD: Released '87, on Mercury by Phonogram Ltd. Deleted '90. Catalogue no: **824 510-2**
Album: Released '85, on Mercury by Phonogram Ltd. Deleted '90. Catalogue no: **MERH 72**

GIRLS JUST WANNA HAVE FUN (SINGLE) (See under Lauper, Cyndi)

Give My Regards To..

GIVE MY REGARDS TO BROADSTREET (See under McCartney, Paul)

Glass Menagerie

GLASS MENAGERIE, THE (Film soundtrack) (Various artists)
Note: Music by Henry Mancini from the Paul Newman directed film.
Album: Released Jan '89, on MCA by MCA Records. Catalogue no: **MCA 6222**
Cass: Released Jan '89, on MCA by MCA Records. Catalogue no: **MCAC 6222**
CD: Released Jan '89, on MCA by MCA Records. Catalogue no: **MCAD 6222**

Glass, Philip

KOYAANISQATSI (Film soundtrack)
Tracks: / Opening / Vessels / Cloud / Pruitt egoe 5.15 / Closing.
Note: One of the world's finest modern composers with his celebrated soundtrack to the controversial film.
Album: Released Jul '83, on Island by Island Records. Catalogue no: **ISTA 4**
Cass: Released '90, on Island by Island Records. Catalogue no: **ICM 2036**
CD: Released Apr '90, on Antilles/New Directions by Island Records. Catalogue no: **IMCD 98**

POWAQQATSI (Film soundtrack)
CD: Released Aug '88, on Nonesuch Catalogue no: **K 979192 2**
Album: Released Aug '88, on Nonesuch Catalogue no: **K 979192 1**
Cass: Released Aug '88, on Nonesuch Catalogue no: **K 979192 4**

THIN BLUE LINE (Film Soundtrack) (See under Thin Blue Line)

Glenn Miller Story

GLENN MILLER STORY (Film soundtrack) (Various artists)
Tracks: / Moonlight serenade: Various artists / Tuxedo Junction: Various artists / Little brown jug: Various artists / St. Louis blues: Various artists / In the mood: Various artists / String of pearls: Vari-

ous artists / Pennsylvania 6 5000: Various artists / American patrol: Various artists / Basin Street blues: Various artists / Otchi-tchor-hi-ya: Various artists.
Note: Louis Armstrong and The All Stars. Conducted by Joseph Gershenson. Pre-1957.
Album: Released Apr '82, on MCA by MCA Records. Catalogue no: **MCL 1665**
CD: Released Jul '88, on MCA by MCA Records. Catalogue no: **DMCL 1665**
Album: Released Aug '85, Catalogue no: **MCF 3273**
Cass: Released Apr '82, on MCA by MCA Records. Catalogue no: **MCLC 1665**
CD: Released Oct '85, on MCA by MCA Records. Catalogue no: **DMCF 3273**

GLENN MILLER STORY (ACE OF HEARTS) (Film soundtrack) (Various artists)
Album: Released Nov '61, on Ace Of Hearts by Decca Records. Deleted '65. Catalogue no: **AH 12**

Gloriana

GLORIANA (VIDEO) (English National Opera) (Various artists)
VHS: Released 25 Jul '88, on Virgin Vision by Virgin Records. Catalogue no: **VVD 344**

Glynn, Dominic

DOCTOR WHO
Tracks: / Doctor Who / Doctor Who (Cosmic remix).
7" Single: Released Nov '86, on BBC by BBC Records. Catalogue no: **RESL 193**
12" Single: Released Nov '86, on BBC by BBC Records. Catalogue no: **12RXL 193**
Cassingle: Released Nov '86, on BBC by BBC Records. Catalogue no: **ZRXL 193**

Go Between

GO BETWEEN / UMBRELLAS OF CHERBOURG (Film Soundtracks) (See under Legrand, Michel)

Go Into Your Dance

GO INTO YOUR DANCE / WUNDERBAR (Film soundtracks) (Various artists)
Note: Starring Al Jolson.
Album: Released Jan '89, on

Silva Screen by Silva Screen Records. Catalogue no: **SH 2030**

Go Johnny Go

GO JOHNNY GO (Film soundtrack) (Various artists)
Album: Released '85, on Swift by 77 Records. Catalogue no: **JN 5705**

Go West

KING OF WISHFUL THINKING
Tracks: / King of wishful thinking / Tears too late.
Note: Used in the film *Pretty Woman*
7" Single: Released Jul '90, on Chrysalis by Chrysalis Records. Catalogue no: **GOW 8**
12" Single: Released Jul '90, on Chrysalis by Chrysalis Records. Catalogue no: **GOWX 8**
CD Single: Released Jul '90, on Chrysalis by Chrysalis Records. Catalogue no: **GOWCD 8**
Cassingle: Released Jul '90, on Chrysalis by Chrysalis Records. Catalogue no: **GOWMC 8**

Goblin

DAWN OF THE DEAD (Film Soundtrack) (See under Dawn Of The Dead)

GREATEST HITS: GOBLIN
Note: The film music of one of Italy's top rock bands.
Album: Released Jan '89, on Silva Screen by Silva Screen Records. Catalogue no: **ORL 8305**
Cass: Released Jan '89, on Silva Screen by Silva Screen Records. Catalogue no: **ORK 78305**

Goblin Market

GOBLIN MARKET (Original Broadway cast) (Various artists)
Album: Released Mar '90, on T. E. R. by That's Entertainment Records. Catalogue no: **TER 1144**
Cass: Released Mar '90, on That's Entertainment (see T.E.R.) Catalogue no: **ZCTER 1144**
CD: Released Mar '90, on T. E. R. by That's Entertainment Records. Catalogue no: **CDTER 1144**

God Forgives

GOD FORGIVES / KILL OR BE KILLED (Film soundtracks) (See under Kill Or Be Killed) (Various artists)

Godfather

GODFATHER, THE (Film soundtrack) (Various artists)
Tracks: / Godfather waltz (Main title): *Various artists* / I have but one heart: *Various artists* / Pickup, The: *Various artists* / Connie's wedding: *Various artists* / Halls of fear, The: *Various artists* / Sicillian pastorale: *Various artists* / Godfather, Love theme: *Various artists* / Godfather waltz, The: *Various artists* / Appollonia: *Various artists* / New godfather, The: *Various artists* / Baptism: *Various artists* / Godfather finale, The: *Various artists*.
Note: Nino Rota score for the Francis Ford Coppola 'Mafia' film starring Marlon Brando.,
Album: Released '73, on Paramount Deleted '78. Catalogue no: **SPFA 7003**
Cass: Released Aug '88, on Silva Screen by Silva Screen Records. Catalogue no: **FILMC 032**
Album: Released Aug '88, on Silva Screen by Silva Screen Records. Catalogue no: **FILM 032**
CD: Released Aug '88, on Silva Screen by Silva Screen Records. Catalogue no: **FILMCD 032**

Godiego

MONKEY (Music from the TV series)
Tracks: / Birth of the Odyssey / Monkey magic / Fool / Asiatic fever / Dragons and demons / Celebration / Gandhara / Steppin' into your world / Flying / Havoc in heaven / We're heading out West to India / Thank you baby.
Album: Released May '80, on BBC by BBC Records. Deleted '85. Catalogue no: **REB 384**

MONKEY MAGIC
Tracks: / Monkey magic / Gandhara / Thank you baby.
7" Single: Released Sep '80, on BBC by BBC Records. Deleted '83. Catalogue no: **RESL 81**

WATER MARGIN
Tracks: / Water margin, The / Water margin, The (version).
7" Single: Released Oct '77, on BBC by BBC Records. Deleted '80. Catalogue no: **RESL 50**

Gods Must Be Crazy

GODS MUST BE CRAZY (Film soundtrack) (Various artists)
Note: Composed by Johnny Boshnoff.
Album: Released Jan '89, on Silva Screen by Silva Screen Records. Catalogue no: **STV 81243**

Godspell

GODSPELL (London Cast) (Various artists)
Tracks: / Prepare ye the way of the Lord: *Various artists* / Save the people: *Various artists* / Day by day: *Various artists* / Learn your lessons well: *Various artists* / Bless the Lord: *Various artists* / All for the best: *Various artists* / All good gifts: *Various artists* / Light of the world: *Various artists* / Turn back o' man: *Various artists* / Alas for you: *Various artists* / By my side: *Various artists* / We beseech thee: *Various artists* / On the willows: *Various artists* / Finale: *Various artists* / Day by day/ Prepare ye (reprise): *Various artists*
Album: Released '72, on Bell Catalogue no: **BELLS 203**

GODSPELL (American cast recording) (Various artists
Tracks: / Prepare ye the way of the Lord: *Various artists* / Save the people: *Various artists* / Day by day: *Various artists* / Learn your lessons well: *Various artists* / Bless the Lord: *Various artists* / All for the best: *Various artists* / All good gifts: *Various artists* / Light of the world: *Various artists* / Turn back o' man: *Various artists* / Alas for you: *Various artists* / By my side: *Various artists* / We beseech thee: *Various artists* / On the willows: *Various artists* / Finale: *Various artists* / Day by day/ Prepare ye (reprise): *Various artists*)
Album: Released '73, on Bell Deleted '78. Catalogue no: **SBLL 146**

GODSPELL (BROADWAY CAST) (Various artists)
Tracks: / Prepare ye the way of the Lord: *Various artists* / Save the people: *Various artists* / Day by day: *Various artists* / Learn your lessons well: *Various artists* / All for the best: *Various artists* / All good gifts:

Various artists / Light of the world: *Various artists* / Turn back o' man: *Various artists* / By my side: *Various artists* / We beseech thee: *Various artists* / On the willows: *Various artists* / Finale: *Various artists* / Day by day/ Prepare ye (reprise): *Various artists*.
Album: Released Jan '89, on Silva Screen by Silva Screen Records. Catalogue no: **ALB 6**
Cass: Released Jan '89, on Silva Screen by Silva Screen Records. Catalogue no: **ACB6 8304**

Going Steady

GOING STEADY (Film soundtrack) (Various artists)
Album: Released Feb '80, on Warwick by Warwick Records. Deleted '83. Catalogue no: **WW 5078**

Goldberg, Barry

THREE FOR THE ROAD (Film Soundtrack) (See Three For The Road)

Gold Diggers

GOLD DIGGERS (Film soundtrack) (Cooper, Lindsay)
Album: Released '82, on Sync Pulse Catalogue no: **SP 0617**

Golden Age Of...

GOLDEN AGE OF CLASSIC BRITISH FILM THEMES OF 40'S & 50'S (Various artists)
Tracks: / Way to the stars, The: *Two Cities Symphony Orchestra* / Cornish rhapsody: *London Symphony Orchestra* / Voice in the night, A: *Queen's Hall Light Orchestra* / Warsaw concerto: *London Symphony Orchestra* / Dream of Olwen and incidental music, The: *Williams, Charles and His Orchestra* / Mansell concerto, The: *Williams, Charles and His Orchestra* / Saga of Odette, The: *Williams, Charles and His Orchestra* / Carriage and Pair: *Williams, Charles and His Orchestra* / Long forgotten melody: *Williams, Charles and His Orchestra* / Portrait of Clare: *Williams, Charles and His Orchestra* / Beggar's theme, The: *Williams, Charles and His Orchestra* / Voice in the night, A: *Queen's Hall Light Orchestra*.

Cass: Released Mar '87, on Golden Age by EMI Records. Catalogue no: **TC GX 2551**

Album: Released Mar '87, on Golden Age by EMI Records. Catalogue no: **GX 41 2551**

GOLDEN AGE OF HOLLYWOOD STARS (Various artists)

Tracks: / Don Juan: *Various artists* / Jazz singer, The: *Various artists* / Little Caesar: *Various artists* / Public Enemy, The: *Various artists* / Gold diggers of 1933: *Various artists* / I'm a fugitive from a chain gang: *Various artists* / Captain Blood: *Various artists* / Midsummer night's dream, A: *Various artists* / Adventures of Robin Hood: *Various artists* / Jezebel: *Various artists* / Dark victory: *Various artists* / Angels with dirty faces: *Various artists* / Maltese Falcon: *Various artists* / Sea hawk, The: *Various artists* / King's row: *Various artists* / High sierra: *Various artists* / Now, Voyager: *Various artists* / Arsenic and old lace: *Various artists* / Mildred Pierce: *Various artists* / Big sleep, The: *Various artists* / White heat: *Various artists*.

2 LP Set: Released Mar '78, on United Artists by EMI Records. Deleted Oct '89. Catalogue no: **USD 311**

Golden Child

GOLDEN CHILD (Film Soundtrack) (Various artists)

Tracks: / Best man in the world: *Wilson, Ann* / Deeper love: *Morgan, Meli'sa* / Love goes on (theme from the Golden child): *Ashford & Simpson* / Shame on you: *Davis, Martha* / Body talk: *Ratt* / Chosen one, The: *Jackson, Marlon* / Sardo and the child: *Colombier, Michael* / Golden love: *Colombier, Michael* / Confrontation: *Colombier, Michael*.

CD: Released Feb '87, on Capitol by EMI Records. Catalogue no: **CDP 7466582**

CD: Released Apr '87, on Capitol by EMI Records. Deleted '88. Catalogue no: **CDEST 2030**

Cass: Released Feb '87, on Capitol by EMI Records. Deleted Jun '89. Catalogue no: **TCEST 2030**

Album: Released Jan '87, on Capitol by EMI Records. Deleted Nov '88. Catalogue no: **EST 2030**

Golden Lady

GOLDEN LADY (Film soundtrack) (Various artists)

Tracks: / We had it all: *Blonde On Blonde* / Dahlia: *Blonde On Blonde* / Sophisticated like you: *Blonde On Blonde* / Woman is free: *Blonde On Blonde* / Golden lady: *Three Degrees* / Golden lady's theme: *Aznavour, Charles* / Fly me till I die: *Aznavour, Charles* / Praxis: *Aznavour, Charles* / Just making love: *Aznavour, Charles* / We had it all: *Aznavour, Charles*.

Album: Released '79, on Ariola by BMG Records (UK). Deleted '84. Catalogue no: **ARL 5019**

GOLDEN LADY (Single) (See under Three Degrees)

Golden Seal

GOLDEN SEAL, THE (Film soundtrack) (Various artists)

Tracks: / Letting go: *various artists* / Story begins, The: *Various artists* / Voyage to Dutch: *various artists* / Legend, The: *Various artists* / Williwa: *Various artitsts* / Bridge, The: *Various artists* / Face to face: *Various artists* / Frolic, The: *Various artists* / Swimming lessons: *Various artists* / Close call: *Various artists* / Choice, The: *Various artists* / You're safe now: *Various artists* / Goodbye: *various artists*.

Note: The main themes have been composed by John Barry - who also produced the album.

Cass: Released Apr '84, on Compleat (USA) by Compleat Entertainment Corp.(USA). Deleted '85. Catalogue no: **ZCCLT 351**

Album: Released Apr '84, on Compleat (USA) by Compleat Entertainment Corp.(USA). Deleted '85. Catalogue no: **CLTLP 351**

LETTING GO (From the film Golden Seal) (Campbell, Glenn) (See under Campbell, Glenn)

Golden Songs...

GOLDEN SONGS FROM THE SILVER SCREEN (Various artists)

Cass: Released Jan '80, on MFP by EMI Records. Deleted Dec '81. Catalogue no: **TCMFP 50453**

Album: Released Jan '80, on MFP by EMI Records. Deleted Jan '85. Catalogue no: **MFP 50453**

GOLDEN SONGS OF STAGE

AND SCREEN (Various artists)

Tracks: / Around the world: *Monro, Matt* (From Around The World In Eighty Days.) / Somewhere my love: *Dodd, Ken* (Lara's theme from Dr. Zhivago.) / Evergreen: *Love, Geoff & His Orchestra & Singers* (From A Star Is Born.) / Day by day: *Laine, Cleo* (From Godspell.) / Summer knows, The: *Gillies, Stuart* (From the summer of '42.) / Send in the clowns: *Love, Geoff & His Orchestra & Singers* (From A Little Night Music.) / Edelweiss: *Hill, Vince* (From The Sound Of Music.) / Somewhere: *Bassey, Shirley* (From West Side Story.) / Long ago: *Love, Geoff & His Orchestra & Singers* (From No No Nannette) / People: *Bassey, Shirley* (Funny girl.) / Don't cry for me Argentina: *Love, Geoff & His Orchestra & Singers* (From Evita.) / Soliloquy: *Hill, Vince* / Where do I begin: *Love, Geoff & His Orchestra & Singers* (From Love Story.) / Gonna build a mountain: *Monro, Matt* / Alfie: *Black, Cilla* (From Alfie.) / How to handle a woman: *Young, Robert* (From Camelot.) / Sunrise, sunset: *Dodd, Ken* (From Fiddler On The Roof.).

Cass: Released Aug '86, on Hour Of Pleasure by EMI Records. Catalogue no: **HR 8139**

Golden Themes...

GOLDEN THEMES FROM MGM CLASSIC FILMS (Various artists)

CD: Released Jun '88, on MCA (USA) by MCA Records (USA). Catalogue no: **31057**

Golden Voices From ...

GOLDEN VOICES FROM THE SILVER SCREEN VOL. 1 (Various artists)

Album: Released Mar '90, on Globestyle by Ace Records. Catalogue no: **ORBAD 054**

CD: Released Mar '90, on Globestyle by Ace Records. Catalogue no: **CDORBD 054**

GOLDEN VOICES FROM THE SILVER SCREEN VOL. 2 (Various artists)

Album: Released Apr '90, on Globestyle by Ace Records. Catalogue no: **ORBAD 056**

CD: Released Apr '90, on Globestyle by Ace Records. Catalogue

no: **CDORBD 056**

GOLDEN VOICES FROM THE SILVER SCREEN VOL. 3 (Various artists
Tracks: / Dhoondo dhoondo re: *Mangeshkar, Lata* / Sagiya aaj mujhe: *Bhosle & Chorus, Asha* / satyam shivam (part 1): *Mangeshkar, Lata* / Ab reat guzarne vali: *Mangeshkar, Lata* / Leke pahla ahla pyar: *Bhosle/Begum/Rafi* / Hondton pe aisi: *Mangeshkar, Lata* / Salam e ishq: *Mangeshkar, Lata* / Aaj ki raat: *Bhosle & Chorus, Asha* / Satyam shivam (part 2): *Mangeshkar, Lata* / Jean Pehchaan no: *Rafi, Mohammed* / Toote na dil toote na: *Mukesh*
Album: Released 29 May '90, on Globestyle by Ace Records. Catalogue no: **ORBAD 059**
CD: Released 29 May '90, on Globestyle by Ace Records. Catalogue no: **CDORBD 059**

Goldfinger

GOLDFINGER (Theme from) (See under Bassey, Shirley)

GOLDFINGER (Orginal 1964 Soundtrack) (Various artists)
Tracks: / Goldfinger: *Bassey, Shirley* / Into Miami: *Barry, John* / Golden girl: *Barry, John* / Alpine drive (Auric's factory): *Barry, John* / Death of Tilley: *Barry, John* / Oddjob's pressing engagement: *Barry, John* / Laser beam, The: *Barry, John* / Bond back in action again: *Barry, John* / Pussy Galore's flying circus: *Barry, John* / Teasing the Korean: *Barry, John* / Gassing the gangsters: Dawn raid on Fort Knox: *Barry, John*
Album: Released Oct '64, on United Artists by EMI Records. Deleted '68. Catalogue no: **ULP 1076**
Album: Released '73, on Sunset (Liberty) by EMI Records. Deleted '78. Catalogue no: **SLS 50172**

GOLDFINGER (FIlm Soundtrack) (Barry, John)
Tracks: / Goldfinger: *Bassey, Shirley* / Into Miami: *Barry, John* / Golden girl: *Barry, John* / Alpine drive (Auric's factory): *Barry, John* / Death of Tilley: *Barry, John* / Oddjob's pressing engagement: *Barry, John* / Laser beam, The: *Barry, John* / Bond back in action again: *Barry, John* / Pussy Galore's flying circus: *Barry, John* / Teasing the

Gone With The Wind - starring Clarke Gable and Vivien Leigh.

Korean: *Barry, John* / Gassing the gangsters: Dawn raid on Fort Knox: *Barry, John*
Album: Released Jul '87, on Liberty by EMI Records. Deleted May '90. Catalogue no: **EMS 1266**
Cass: Released 17 Jul '87, on Liberty by EMI Records. Deleted Jun '89. Catalogue no: **TCEMS 1266**

GOLDFINGER (Film Soundtrack) (Re-issue) (Various artists)
Album: Released '88, on DRG (USA) by DRG Records (USA). Catalogue no: **2610771**
Cass: Released May '87, on DRG (USA), by DRG Records (USA). Catalogue no: **261077 4**

Goldsmith, Jerry

ISLAND IN THE STREAM
CD: Released Jul '87, on Silva Screen by Silva Screen Records. Catalogue no: **RVF 6003**

OUTLAND (Film Soundtrack) (See under Outland)

PLANET OF THE APES (Film Soundtrack) (See under Planet Of The Apes)

RIO CONCHOS (Film Soundtrack) (See under Rio Con-

chos)

SECRET OF NYMPH (Film Soundtrack) (See under Secret Of Nymph)

SOUNDTRACKS OF JERRY GOLDSMITH WITH THE PHILHARMONIA
Tracks: / Blue Max, The / Man from UNCLE, The / Doctor Kildare / Room 222 / Waltons, The / Barnaby Jones / Masada / Gremlins suite / Sand pebbles / Chinatown / Patch of blue poltergeist, A / Papillon / Wind and the lion / Generals, The / Lionheart.
Album: Released Nov '88, on Decca by Decca International. Catalogue no: **820 757-1**
CD: Released Nov '88, on Decca by Decca International. Catalogue no: **820 757-2**
Cass: Released Nov '88, on Decca by Decca International. Catalogue no: **820 757-4**

WIND AND THE LION (Film Soundtrack) (See under Wind & The Lion)

Goldstein, William

SHOCKER (Film Soundtrack) (See under Shocker)

Gone With The Wind

GONE WITH THE WIND (Film Soundtrack) (Various artists) (See panel on previous page)
Tracks: / Gone with the wind (Main title): *Various artists* / Scarlett and Rhetts first meeting: *Various artists* / Mammy: *Various artists* / Christmas during the war in Atlanta: *Various artists* / Atlanta in flames: *Various artists* / Reconstruction: *Various artists* / Ashley returns to Tara from the war: *Various artists* / Scarlett and Rhett rebuild Tara: *Various artists* / Scarlett makes her demands of Rhett: *Various artists* / Scarletts fall down the staircase: *Various artists* / Bonnies fatal pony ride: *Various artists* / Gone with the wind (Finale): *Various artists*
Album: Released '73, on MGM (Polydor) by Polydor Ltd. Deleted '78. Catalogue no: **2353 031**
Cass: Released Jul '85, on MGM (Polydor) by Polydor Ltd. Catalogue no: **817 116 4**
Album: Released '73, on Columbia by EMI Records. Deleted '78. Catalogue no: **MGM CS 8056**
Album: Released Jul '85, on MGM (Polydor) by Polydor Ltd. Catalogue no: **817 116 1**
CD: Released Jun '87, on MGM (Polydor) by Polydor Ltd. Deleted Jul '88. Catalogue no: **817 116-2**

GONE WITH THE WIND (Original Drury Lane Cast) (Various artists)
Tracks: / Overture - Today's the day: *Various artists* / We belong to you: *Various artists* / Tara: *Various artists* / Two of a kind: *Various artists* / Blissful Christmas/ Home again: *Various artists* / Lonely stranger: *Various artists* / Time for love: *Various artists* / Which way is home: *Various artists* / How often, how often: *Various artists* / If only: *Various artists* / Southern lady: *Various artists* / Marrying for fun: *Various artists* / Blueberry blue: *Various artists* / Strange and wonderful: *Various artists* / Little wonders: *Various artists* / Bonnie gone: *Various artists* / It doesn't matter now/ Finale: *Various artists*.
Album: Released '73, on Columbia by EMI Records. Deleted '78. Catalogue no: **SCXA 9252**

GONE WITH THE WIND (Film soundtrack) (Various artists)

Album: Released Jan '89, on Silva Screen by Silva Screen Records. Catalogue no: **DUN 108**
CD: Released Jan '89, on Silva Screen by Silva Screen Records. Catalogue no: **DUNCD 108**
Cass: Released Feb '90, on Silva Screen by Silva Screen Records. Catalogue no: **9676.4**
CD: Released Feb '90, on Silva Screen by Silva Screen Records. Catalogue no: **9676.2**

GONE WITH THE WIND (Film soundtrack) (Various artists)
Tracks: / Main title: *Various artists* / Scarlett and Rhett's first meeting: *Various artists* / Ashley and Scarlett: *Various artists* / Mammy: *Various artists* / Christmas during the war in Atlanta: *Various artists* / Atlanta in flames: *Various artists* / reconstruction: *Various artists* / Ashley returns to Tara from the war prison: *Various artists* / Scarlett makes her demands of Rhett: *Various artists* / Scarlett's fall down the staircase: *Various artists* / Bonnie's fatal pony ride: *Various artists* / Finale: *Various artists*.
Album: Released Jul '86, on CBS by CBS Records & Distribution. Catalogue no: **CBS 70283**
Cass: Released Jul '86, on CBS by CBS Records & Distribution. Catalogue no: **40 70283**

GONE WITH THE WIND (Various artists)
Cass: Released Mar '90, on RCA by BMG Records (UK). Catalogue no: **GK 80452**
CD: Released Mar '90, on RCA by BMG Records (UK). Catalogue no: **GD 80452**

Good Companions

GOOD COMPANIONS, THE (Original London cast) (Various artists)
Album: Released '88, on DRG (USA) by DRG Records (USA). Catalogue no: **DS 15020**

Good Looks

JIM'LL FIX IT
Note: Used as the theme to BBC's 'Jim'll Fix It'.
Tracks: / Jim'll fix it / Jim has fixed it for you.
7" Single: Released Mar '82, on Radioactive Catalogue no: **RAD 501**

Good Morning Babylon

GOOD MORNING BABYLON (Film Soundtrack) (Various artists)
Note: Music from the Taviani Brothers film by Nicola Piovani.
Cass: Released Sep '87, on Silva Screen by Silva Screen Records. Deleted Feb '90. Catalogue no: **C 300**
CD: Released 25 Sep '87, on SPI Milan (France) Catalogue no: **CDH 300**
Album: Released Sep '87, on Silva Screen by Silva Screen Records. Catalogue no: **A 300**

Good Morning Vietnam

GOOD MORNING VIETNAM (film soundtrack) (Various artists) (See panel on next page)
Tracks: / Nowhere to run: *Reeves, Martha* / I get around: *Beach Boys* / Game of love: *Fontana, Wayne & the Mindbenders* / Sugar and spice: *Searchers* / Liar liar: *Castaways* / Warmth of the sun: *Beach Boys* / I got you: *Brown, James* / Baby please don't go: *Them* / Danger heartbreak dead ahead: *Marvelettes* / Five o'clock world: *Vogues* / California sun: *Rivieras* / What a wonderful world: *Armstrong, Louis*.
Note: "Good Morning Vietnam" is a new comedy-drama about an irreverent DJ on the local Armed Forces radio in Vietnam. It stars Robin Williams of "Mork and Mindy" and "Popeye" fame as the DJ who throws out the old playlist and plays the hits of the day which are now modern classics of popular music. The soundtrack is consequently a superb collection of songs that recreate the atmosphere and emotions of that early Vietnam period in the sixties. It also includes excerpts from Robin Williams' (the film's star) hilarious D.J. monologues.
Album: Released Feb '88, on A&M by A&M Records. Catalogue no: **AMA 3913**
CD: Released Feb '88, on A&M by A&M Records. Catalogue no: **CDA 3913**
Cass: Released Feb '88, on A&M by A&M Records. Catalogue no: **AMC 3913**

NOWHERE TO RUN (See under Reeves, Martha)

GOOD MORNING, VIETNAM

THE ORIGINAL MOTION PICTURE SOUNDTRACK

Robin Williams stars as US Forces DJ Adrian Cronauer in *Good Morning Vietnam*

Good News

GOOD NEWS (Film soundtrack) (Various artists)
Note: Starring June Allyson and Mel Torme.
Album: Released Jan '89, on Silva Screen by Silva Screen Records. Catalogue no: **STK 111**

Good Old Bad Old ...

GOOD OLD BAD OLD DAYS (Original London cast) (Various artists)
Tracks: / Good old bad old days: *Various artists* / Fool who dared to dream: *Various artists* / Wisdom of the world: *Various artists* / Thanksgiving day: *Various artists* / Today/tomorrow/ yesterday: *Various artists* / It's a musical world: *Various artists* / I do not love you: *Various artists* / Cotton pickin' moon: *Various artists* / Good things in life: *Various artists* / People tree: *Various artists* / We've got a cure for everything on Broadway: *Various artists* / Good old bad old days - finale: *Various artists*.
Album: Released '73, on EMI by EMI Records. Deleted '78. Catalogue no: **EMA 751**

GOOD OLD BAD OLD DAYS,

THE (Original London cast) (Various artists)
Album: Released Jan '89, on Silva Screen by Silva Screen Records. Catalogue no: **AEI 1116**

Good, The Bad & The

GOOD, THE BAD AND THE UGLY, THE (Film soundtrack) (Various artists)
Album: Released Oct '68, on United Artists by EMI Records. Deleted '73. Catalogue no: **SULP 1197**

GOOD, THE BAD & THE UGLY, THE (Film Soundtrack) (Various artists)
Tracks: / Good, the bad and the ugly, The: *Various artists* / Sundown, The: *Various artists* / Strong, The: *Various artists* / Desert, The: *Various artists* / Carriage of the spirits, The: *Various artists* / Marcia: *Various artists* / Story of a soldier: *Various artists* / Marcia without hope: *Various artists* / Death of a soldier, The: *Various artists* / Ecstasy of gold: *Various artists* / Trio, The: *Various artists* (Main title theme).
Album: Released '83, on EMI (Holland) by EMI Records. Cata-

logue no: **5C 062 90960**
CD: Released Sep '88, on EMI-Manhattan by EMI Records. Catalogue no: **CZ 63**
Album: Released May '85, on Retrospect by EMI Records. Catalogue no: **EG 2605821**
Cass: Released May '85, on Retrospect by EMI Records. Catalogue no: **EG 2605824**
CD: Released Sep '88, on EMI-Manhattan by EMI Records. Catalogue no: **CDP 748 408 2**

Goodbye Mr Chips

GOODBYE MR CHIPS (Original soundtrack) (Various artists)
Note: Starring Peter O Toole and Petula Clark.
Album: Released Jan '89, on MCA by MCA Records. Catalogue no: **MCA 39066**
Cass: Released Jan '89, on MCA by MCA Records. Deleted Mar '90. Catalogue no: **MCAC 39066**

GOODBYE MR CHIPS (Original cast recording) (Various artists
Tracks: / Roll call: *Various artists* / Fill the world with love: *Various artists* / Would I had lived my life then: *Various artists* / Schooldays: *Various artists* / That's a boy: *Various artists* / Where did my childhood go?: *Various artists* / Boring: *Various artists* / Take a chance: *Various artists* / Walk through the world: *Various artists* / When I'm older: *Various artists* / Miracle: *Various artists* / Day has a hundred pockets, The: *Various artists* / You and I: *Various artists* / What a lot of flowers: *Various artists* / When I was younger: *Various artists* / Goodbye Mr. Chips: *Various artists*.
Album: Released Oct '82, on T. E. R. by That's Entertainment Records. Catalogue no: **TER 1025**
Cass: Released Oct '82, on T. E. R. by That's Entertainment Records. Catalogue no: **ZCTER 1025**

Goodwin, Ron

BLUE STAR (THE MEDIC THEME)
Tracks: / Blue star (The Medic theme).
7" Single: Released Oct '55, on Parlophone by EMI Records. Deleted '58. Catalogue no: **R 4074**

LEGEND OF THE GLASS

MOUNTAIN

Tracks: / Legend of the glass mountain (theme from) / Dream of Olwen - (theme from While I live) / Intermezzo from escape to happiness / Way to the stars, Theme from / Warsaw concerto / Spitfire prelude and Fugue (from first of the few) / Limelight / Rhapsody on a theme by Paganini / Moulin Rouge / Cornish rhapsody.
Album: Released Nov '80, on EMI by EMI Records. Deleted 31 Jul '88. Catalogue no: **THIS 25**
Album: Released May '70, on Studio 2 Deleted '75. Catalogue no: **TWO 220**
Cass: Released Nov '80, on EMI by EMI Records. Catalogue no: **TCTHIS 25**

Goonies

GOONIES (Film soundtrack) (Various artists)

Tracks: / Goonies 'r' good enough: *Lauper, Cyndi* / Eight arms to hold you: *Good Squad* / Love is always: *Bailey, Philip* / I got nothing: *Bangles* / 14K: *Marie, Teena* / Wherever you're goin' (it's alright): *REO Speedwagon* / She's so good to me: *Vandross, Luther* / What a thrill: *Lauper, Cyndi* / Save the night: *Williams, Joseph* / Goonies theme: *Grusin, Dave.*
Cass: Released Nov '85, on Epic by CBS Records & Distribution. Catalogue no: **40 70264**
CD: Released '88, on Epic by CBS Records & Distribution. Deleted Jan '89. Catalogue no: **CD 70264**
Album: Released Nov '85, on Epic by CBS Records & Distribution. Deleted Aug '87. Catalogue no: **EPC 70264**

Goons

BEST OF THE GOON SHOWS VOL.2

Album: Released Dec '60, on Parlophone by EMI Records. Deleted '65. Catalogue no: **PMC 1129**

BEST OF THE GOON SHOWS VOL. 1

Tracks: / Missing No 10 Downing Street, The / Red fort, The.
Album: Released Dec '74, on EMI by EMI Records. Deleted Nov '88. Catalogue no: **EMC 3062**
Cass: Released Dec '74, on EMI by EMI Records. Catalogue no:

TCEMC 3062
Album: Released Nov '59, on Parlophone by EMI Records. Deleted '64. Catalogue no: **PMC 1108**

BLOODNOCK'S ROCK 'N' ROLL

Tracks: / Bloodnock's rock 'n' roll / I love you.
7" Single: Released Oct '75, on Decca by Decca International. Deleted '88. Catalogue no: **F 13609**

DARK SIDE OF THE GOONS

Tracks: / Boiled bananas and carrots / Any old iron / You gotta go now / Will I find my lover today? / Heart of a clown / Fuller's earth / Faith can move mountains / Wormwood Scrubs tango / One love, one lifetime / My September love / Wish I knew / My old dutch / Putting on the smile / I'll make you mine / Postman's knock / Drop of the hard stuff / I'm so ashamed / Here is my heart.
Cass: Released Nov '80, on One-Up by EMI Records. Catalogue no: **TC OU 2232**
Album: Released Nov '80, on One-Up by EMI Records. Catalogue no: **OU 2232**

FIRST MEN ON THE GOON

Tracks: / Foiled by president Fred / Robin Hood and his merry men.
Cass: Released May '79, on Note by EMI Records. Deleted Jun '89. Catalogue no: **TCNTS 170**
Album: Released May '79, on Note by EMI Records. Deleted Nov '88. Catalogue no: **NTS 170**

GOON SHOW CLASSICS, VOL 1

Tracks: / Dreaded batter pudding hurler of Bexhill-on-Sea, The / History of Pliny the Elder, The.
Note: Featuring Peter Sellers, Harry Secombe, Spike Milligan, Ray Ellington, Max Geldray, Wallace Greenslade. Orchestra conducted by Angela Morley. Script by Spike Milligan.
Cass: Released Sep '81, on BBC by BBC Records. Deleted Aug '88. Catalogue no: **RMC 4010**
Album: Released Sep '81, on BBC by BBC Records. Deleted Aug '88. Catalogue no: **REB 177**

GOON SHOW CLASSICS, VOL 2

Tracks: / Jet-propelled guided NAAFI, The / Evils of Bushey

Spon, The.
Note: Featuring Peter Sellers, Spike Milligan, Harry Secombe, Ray Ellington, Max Geldray, Walter Greenslade, with guest A.E. Matthews.
Album: Released Sep '81, on BBC by BBC Records. Deleted Aug '88. Catalogue no: **REB 213**
Cass: Released Sep '81, on BBC by BBC Records. Deleted Aug '88. Catalogue no: **RMC 4026**

GOON SHOW CLASSICS, VOL 3

Tracks: / Lurgi strikes Britain / International Christmas pudding, The.
Note: Featuring Peter Sellers, Spike Milligan, Harry Secombe, Ray Ellington, Max Geldray, Wallace Greenslade; orchestra conducted by Angela Morley; script by Spike Milligan.
Cass: Released Sep '81, on BBC by BBC Records. Deleted Aug '88. Catalogue no: **RMC 4046**
Album: Released Sep '81, on BBC by BBC Records. Deleted Aug '88. Catalogue no: **REB 246**

GOON SHOW CLASSICS, VOL 4

Tracks: / Napoleon's piano / Flea, The.
Note: Featuring Peter Sellers, Spike Milligan, Harry Secombe, Ray Ellington, Max Geldray, Wallace Greenslade.
Album: Released Sep '81, on BBC by BBC Records. Deleted Aug '88. Catalogue no: **REB 291**
Cass: Released Sep '81, on BBC by BBC Records. Deleted Aug '88. Catalogue no: **ZCF 291**

GOON SHOW CLASSICS, VOL 5

Tracks: / Treasure in the lake, The / Greenslade story, The.
Note: Featuring Peter Sellers, Spike Milligan, Harry Secombe.
Cass: Released Sep '81, on BBC by BBC Records. Deleted Apr '89. Catalogue no: **ZCF 339**
Album: Released Sep '81, on BBC by BBC Records. Deleted Apr '89. Catalogue no: **REB 339**

GOON SHOW CLASSICS, VOL 6

Tracks: / Wings over Dagenham / Rent collectors, The.
Note: Featuring Peter Sellers, Spike Milligan, Harry Secombe.
Cass: Released '79, on BBC by

BBC Records. Deleted Apr '89. Catalogue no: **ZCF 366**

Album: Released '79, on BBC by BBC Records. Deleted Apr '89. Catalogue no: **REB 366**

GOON SHOW CLASSICS, VOL 7

Tracks: / Man who never was, The / Case of the missing CD plates, The.

Note: Featuring Peter Sellers, Spike Milligan, Harry Secombe.

Cass: Released Sep '80, on BBC by BBC Records. Deleted Apr '89. Catalogue no: **ZCF 392**

Album: Released Sep '80, on BBC by BBC Records. Deleted Apr '89. Catalogue no: **REB 392**

GOON SHOW CLASSICS, VOL 8

Tracks: / World War 1 / Nasty affair at the Burami oasis.

Note: Featuring Peter Sellers, Spike Milligan, Harry Secombe.

Cass: Released Sep '81, on BBC by BBC Records. Deleted Apr '89. Catalogue no: **ZCF 422**

Album: Released Sep '81, on BBC by BBC Records. Deleted Apr '89. Catalogue no: **REB 422**

GOON SHOW CLASSICS, VOL 9

Tracks: / Call of the West, The / Last smoking Seagoon, The.

Note: Featuring Peter Sellers, Spike Milligan, Harry Secombe.

Cass: Released Sep '82, on BBC by BBC Records. Deleted '88. Catalogue no: **ZCF 444**

Album: Released Sep '82, on BBC by BBC Records. Deleted '88. Catalogue no: **REB 444**

GOON SHOW CLASSICS, VOL 10

Tracks: / Whistling spy enigma, The / I was Monty's treble.

Note: Featuring Peter Sellers, Spike Milligan, Harry Secombe.

Album: Released Oct '83, on BBC by BBC Records. Deleted '88. Catalogue no: **REB 481**

Cass: Released Oct '83, on BBC by BBC Records. Deleted '88. Catalogue no: **ZCF 481**

GOON SHOW CLASSICS, VOL 11

Tracks: / Shifting sands / 1985.

Note: Featuring Peter Sellers, Spike Milligan, Harry Secombe.

Album: Released Oct '85, on BBC by BBC Records. Deleted '88. Catalogue no: **REB 565**

Cass: Released Oct '85, on BBC by BBC Records. Deleted '88. Catalogue no: **ZCF 565**

GOON SHOW GREATS

Tracks: / Tales of old Dartmoor / Dishonoured (parts 1 & 2) / Six Charlies in search of an author.

Cass: Released Oct '79, on Parlophone by EMI Records. Catalogue no: **TCPMC 7179**

Album: Released Oct '79, on Parlophone by EMI Records. Deleted Nov '88. Catalogue no: **PMC 7179**

GOON SHOW, THE

Tracks: / White man burden / China story, The.

Note: Featuring two episodes - "White man burden" and "The china story", staring Peter Sellers, Harry Secombe and Spike Milligan.

Album: Released Jan '84, on MFP by EMI Records. Deleted Jan '87. Catalogue no: **MFP 415650-1**

Cass: Released Jan '84, on MFP by EMI Records. Deleted Jan '87. Catalogue no: **TCMFP 415650-4**

HOW TO WIN AN ELECTION

Album: Released Dec '81, on Philips by Phonogram Ltd. Deleted Dec '86. Catalogue no: **AL 3464**

I'M WALKING BACKWARDS FOR CHRISTMAS

Tracks: / I'm walking backwards for Christmas / Bluebottle blues.

7" Single: Released May '56, on Decca by Decca International. Deleted '59. Catalogue no: **F 10756**

LAST GOON SHOW OF ALL

Note: The last Goon show of all from the radio 4 broadcast with Peter Sellers, Harry Secombe, Spike Milligan, Ray Ellington, Max Geldray and Andrew Timothy - Orchestra conducted by Peter Knight. Script by Spike Milligan.

Cass: Released Oct '77, on BBC by BBC Records. Catalogue no: **REMC 142**

Album: Released Oct '77, on BBC by BBC Records. Catalogue no: **REB 142**

RASPBERRY SONG

Tracks: / Raspberry song / Rhymes.

7" Single: Released Apr '78, on Decca by Decca International. Deleted '80. Catalogue no: **F 13769**

WORLD OF THE GOONS

Tracks: / Ying tong song / I love you / Ehh ah oh ooh / Bloodnocks rock 'n' roll / Whistle your cares away / Raspberry song, The / Blue bottle blues / Russian love song, A / Rhymes / I'm walking backwards for Christmas.

Album: Released Jan '80, on Decca by Decca International. Deleted '88. Catalogue no: **SPA 569**

Cass: Released Jan '80, on Decca by Decca International. Catalogue no: **KCSP 569**

YING TONG SONG

Tracks: / Ying tong song / I'm walking backwards for Christmas.

7" Single: Released Jul '73, on Decca by Decca International. Deleted '88. Catalogue no: **F 13414**

Gorillas In The Mist

GORILLAS IN THE MIST (Film soundtrack) (Various artists)

Note: The life story of anthropologist Diane Fossey, starring Sigourney Weaver (Aliens) and Bryan Brown. Original music by Maurice Jarre.

CD: Released Jan '89, on MCA by MCA Records. Catalogue no: **MCAD 6255**

Album: Released Jan '89, on MCA by MCA Records. Catalogue no: **MCA 6255**

Cass: Released Jan '89, on MCA by MCA Records. Catalogue no: **MCAC 6255**

Gorky Park

GORKY PARK (Film soundtrack) (Various artists)

Tracks: / Main title: *Various artists* / Following Kirwill: *Various artists* / Irina's theme: *Various artists* / Following KGB: *Various artists* / Chase through the park: *Various artists* / Arkady and Irina: *Various artists* / Faceless bodies: *Various artists* / Irina's chase: *Various artists* / Sable shed, The: *Various artists* / Airport farewell: *Various artists* / Releasing the sables/ End title: *Various artists*.

Note: Composed by James Horner.

CD: Released Jan '89, on Silva Screen by Silva Screen Records. Catalogue no: **VCD 47260**

Cass: Released Jan '89, on Silva Screen by Silva Screen Records.

Deleted Feb '90. Catalogue no: **CTV 81206**
Album: Released Jan '84, on T. E. R. by That's Entertainment Records. Catalogue no: **TER 1086**

Gospel At Colonus

GOSPEL AT COLONUS, THE (Original Broadway cast) (Various artists)
Tracks: / Live where you can: *Various artists* / Stop do not go on: *Various artists* / How shall I see you through my tears: *Various artists* / Voice foretold prayer, A: *Various artists* / Never drive you away: *Various artists* / Numberless are the world's wonders: *Various artists* / Lift me up (like a dove): *Various artists* / Sunlight of no light: *Various artists* / Eternal sleep: *Various artists* / Lift him up: *Various artists* / Now let the weeping cease: *Various artists*.
Album: Released Nov '84, on Warner Bros. by WEA Records. Catalogue no: **925182 1**
Cass: Released Nov '84, on Warner Bros. by WEA Records. Catalogue no: **925182 4**

GOSPEL AT COLONUS (VIDEO) (Various artists)
VHS: Released Mar '90, on Castle Hendring Video by Castle Communications Records. Catalogue no: **HEN 2 159**

Gospel Road

GOSPEL ROAD, THE (Film soundtrack) (Cash, Johnny)
2 LP Set: Released '73, on CBS by CBS Records & Distribution. Catalogue no: **CBS 68253**

Gothic

GOTHIC (Film Soundtrack) (See under Dolby, Thomas)

Gouldman, Graham

ANIMALYMPICS (Film Soundtrack)
Album: Released Apr '80, on Mercury by Phonogram Ltd. Catalogue no: **9109 630**
Cass: Released Apr '80, on Mercury by Phonogram Ltd. Catalogue no: **7231 443**

Gowers, Patrick

SIGN OF FOUR (Film Soundtrack) (See under Sign Of Four)

Goya

LIFE IN A SONG, A (Stage show) (Various artists)
Tracks: / Overture: *Various artists* / Espana: *Various artists* / Astounding romantic adventures of Goya, The: *Various artists* / In the middle of the 18th century: *Various artists* / Girl with a smile: *Various artists* / Till I loved you: *Various artists* / Picture it: *Various artists* / I will paint sounds: *Various artists* / Viva Espana: *Various artists* / Once a time I loved you: *Various artists* / I stand alone: *Various artists* / Dog in the quicksand: *Various artists* / Moving on: *Various artists* / Bon soir: *Various artists* / Finale: *Various artists*.
Album: Released 5 Jun '89, on CBS by CBS Records & Distribution. Catalogue no: **463294 1**
Cass: Released 5 Jun '89, on CBS by CBS Records & Distribution. Catalogue no: **463294 4**
CD: Released 5 Jun '89, on CBS by CBS Records & Distribution. Catalogue no: **463294 2**

Grab Me A Gondola

GRAB ME A GONDOLA (Original London cast) (Various artists)
Album: Released Jan '89, on Silva Screen by Silva Screen Records. Catalogue no: **AEI 1119**

Graduate

GRADUATE (Film Soundtrack) (See under Simon & Garfunkel)

Graffitti Bridge

GRAFFITTI BRIDGE (Film Soundtrack) (See under Prince)

Grainer, Ron

TALES OF THE UNEXPECTED & OTHER THEMES (Grainer, Ron Orchestra)
Tracks: / Tales of the unexpected / I've danced with a man / Born and bred / Malice aforethought / Joe 90 / Touch of velvet / Swing of brass / Doctor Who / Rebecca (love theme from) / When love grows cold / Paul Temple / Six by six.
Album: Released Apr '80, on RK by RK Records. Deleted '85. Catalogue no: **RKLB 103**

TALES OF THE UNEX-

PECTED THEME (Grainer, Ron Orchestra)
Tracks: / Tales of the unexpected / Malice aforethought.
7" Single: Released May '82, on RK by RK Records. Deleted '84. Catalogue no: **RK 1021**

TOUCH OF VELVET-A STING OF BRASS (Grainer, Ron Orchestra)
Tracks: / Touch of velvet, a sting of brass, A / Joe 90 theme.
7" Single: Released Dec '78, on Casino Classics by RK Records. Deleted '81. Catalogue no: **CC 5**

Grand Prix

GRAND PRIX (Film soundtrack) (Various artists)
Note: Maurice Jarre score for the John Frankenheimer spectacular about Formula One Motor Racing.
Cass: Released Jan '89, on MCA by MCA Records. Catalogue no: **MCAC 25101**
Album: Released Jan '89, on MCA by MCA Records. Catalogue no: **MCA 25101**

Grand Slam

GRAND SLAM (AD OGNI COSTO) (Film soundtrack) (Various artists)
Note: Rare Ennio Morricone score.
Album: Released Jan '89, on Silva Screen by Silva Screen Records. Catalogue no: **SP 8021**

Grange Hill Cast

GRANGE HILL - THE ALBUM
Tracks: / You know the teacher (smash head) / Girls like to do it too / School love / No supervision at break / Biology / Just say no / Don't stop / Lad's medley / I don't like Monday's / Girl's medley / Girls just wanna have fun / Greatest love of all, The / That's what friends are for.
Cass: Released Dec '86, on BBC by BBC Records. Catalogue no: **ZCF 609**
Album: Released Dec '86, on BBC by BBC Records. Catalogue no: **REB 609**

JUST SAY NO
Tracks: / Just say no.
7" Single: Released Apr '86, on BBC by BBC Records. Deleted '89. Catalogue no: **RESL 183**

YOU KNOW THE TEACHER (SMASH HEAD)
Tracks: / You know the teacher

(smash head) / Don't stop.

7" Single: Released Nov '86, on BBC by BBC Records. Deleted Sep '87. Catalogue no: **RESL 205**

12" Single: Released Nov '86, on BBC by BBC Records. Deleted Sep '87. Catalogue no: **12 RSL 205**

Grant, Eddy

ELECTRIC AVENUE

Tracks: / Electric Avenue / Walking on sunshine.

Note: Used as the theme to the BBC programme *Electric Avenue*

12" Single: Released Jan '83, on Ice by Ice Records. Catalogue no: **ICET 57**

7" Single: Released Jan '83, on Ice by Ice Records. Catalogue no: **ICE 57**

Grantham, Leslie

WINNERS AND LOSERS (TV theme) (Grantham, Leslie/ Craig Armstrong)

Tracks: / Winners and losers.

7" Single: Released Mar '89, on Lismor by Lismor Records. Catalogue no: **LINI 001**

12" Single: Released Mar '89, on Lismor by Lismor Records. Catalogue no: **LINI 001T**

Gray, Barry

JOE 90

Tracks: / Joe 90 (86 Dance mix) / Captain Scarlet / Joe 90 (original version) (On 12" version only.).

7" Single: Released May '86, on PRT by Castle Communications Records. Catalogue no: **7PX 345**

12" Single: Released May '86, on PRT by Castle Communications Records. Catalogue no: **12 PX 345**

NO STRINGS ATTACHED

Tracks: / Thunderbird / Captain Scarlet / Hijacked / Aqua Marina / Stingray / Mysterons / Joe 90 / Parker - well done.

Album: Released Sep '81, on PRT by Castle Communications Records. Catalogue no: **DOW 3**

Cass: Released Sep '81, on PRT by Castle Communications Records. Catalogue no: **ZCDOW 3**

THUNDERBIRDS

Tracks: / Thunderbirds / Joe 90 / Parker well done.

7" Single: Released Jun '81, on PRT by Castle Communications Records. Catalogue no: **7P 216**

Grease

GREASE (Film soundtrack) (Various artists) (See panel below)

Tracks: / Grease: *Valli, Frankie* / Summer nights: *Travolta, John & Olivia Newton John* / Hopelessly devoted to you: *Newton-John, Olivia* / Sandy: *Travolta, John* / Look at me, I'm Sandra Dee: *Channing, Stockard* / Greased lightning: *Travolta, John* / It's raining on prom night: *Bullens, Cindy* / You're the one that I want: *Travolta, John & Olivia Newton John* / Beauty school drop-out: *Avalon, Frankie* / Alone at the drive in movie: *Watts, Ernie* / Blue moon: *Sha Na Na* / Rock 'n' roll is here to stay: *Sha Na Na* / Those magic changes: *Sha Na Na* / Hound dog: *Sha Na Na* / Born to hand jive: *Sha Na Na* / Tears on my pillow: *Sha Na Na* / Mooning: *Bullens, Cindy* / Freddy my love: *Bullens, Cindy* / Rock 'n' roll party queen: *St. Louis, Louis* / There are worst things I could do: *Channing, Stockard* / Look at me I'm Sandra Dee (reprise): *Newton-John, Olivia* / We go together: *Travolta, John & Olivia Newton John* / Love is a many splendoured thing: *Studio Orchestra* / Grease (re-prise): *Valli, Frankie*.

Cass set: Released Apr '90, on Polydor by Polydor Ltd. Catalogue no: **351 701 5**

2 LP Set: Released Jan '84, on RSO by Polydor Ltd. Catalogue no: **SPDLP 4**

2 LP Set: Released Jul '78, on RSO by Polydor Ltd. Deleted '84. Catalogue no: **RSD 1001**

GREASE 2 (Film soundtrack) (Various artists)

Tracks: / Back to school again: *Four Tops* / Cool rider: *Pfeiffer, Michelle* / Score tonight: *T-Birds & Pink Ladies* / Girl for all seasons: *Teefy, Maureen/Lorna Luft/Alison Price/Michelle Pfeiffer* / Do it for our country: *Frechette, Peter* / Who's that guy?: *Cast* / Prowlin': *T-Birds* / Reproduction: *Hunter, Tab* / Charades: *Caulfield, Maxwell* / Turn back the hands of time: *Caulfield, Maxwell & Michelle Pfeiffer* / Rock a hula: *Cast* / We'll be together: *Caulfield, Maxwell*.

Album: Released Jun '82, on RSO by Polydor Ltd. Deleted '87. Catalogue no: **RSD 5020**

Cass: Released Jun '82, on RSO by Polydor Ltd. Deleted '87. Catalogue no: **TRSD 5020**

Grease - starring John Travolta and Olivia Newton John.

GREASE 2 (VIDEO) (Various artists)
Note: Cert: PG. Running time: 110 mins.
VHS: Released '87, on CIC Video Catalogue no: **VHR 2066**

GREASED LIGHTNIN' (SINGLE) (See under Travolta, John)

GREASE (STAGE VERSION) (Original Broadway cast) (Various artists)
CD: Released Feb '90, on Silva Screen by Silva Screen Records. Catalogue no: **827548.2**

GREASE (VIDEO) (Various artists)
Note: Cert: PG. Running time: 110 mins.
VHS: Released Apr '87, on CIC Video Catalogue no: **VHR 2003**

SANDY (SINGLE) (See under Travolta, John)

YOU'RE THE ONE THAT I WANT (SINGLE) (See under Travolta, John)

Great Balls Of Fire

GREAT BALLS OF FIRE (Film soundtrack) (Various artists)
Album: Released Nov '89, on Polydor by Polydor Ltd. Catalogue no: **839 516 1**
Cass: Released Nov '89, on Polydor by Polydor Ltd. Catalogue no: **839 516 4**
CD: Released Nov '89, on Polydor by Polydor Ltd. Catalogue no: **839 516 2**

GREAT BALLS OF FIRE (SINGLE) (See under Lewis, Jerry Lee)

Great Caruso

GREAT CARUSO (Film Soundtrack) (See under Lanza, Mario)

GREAT CARUSO / STUDENT PRINCE (Film Soundtracks) (See under Lanza, Mario)

GREAT CARUSO, THE (VIDEO) (Various artists)
Note: Mario Lanza is Caruso from humble beginnings to his triumph. 104 minutes: Cert: U.
VHS: Released Jun '89, on MGM/UA (Video) by MGM/UA Video. Catalogue no: **SMV 10067**

Great Cinema Themes

GREAT CINEMA THEMES (Various artists)
Tracks: / '2001': *Various artists* / Clockwork orange, A: *Various artists* / La traviata: *Various artists* / Apocalypse now: *Various artists* / Death in Venice: *Various artists* / Elvira Madigan: *Various artists*.
Note: Classical music more than ever features in the cinematic art. Words, vision and music are inextricable fused, and on this comprehensive selection the full gamut of human emotion is musically bared.
LP Set: Released Mar '85, on Deutsche Grammophon by PolyGram Classics. Catalogue no: **413 873-1**

Great Egg Race

GREAT EGG RACE (TV Programme) (See under Denton, Richard

Great Escape

GREAT ESCAPE (Film Soundtrack) (Various artists)
Tracks: / Main title: *Various artists* / Premature plans: *Various artists* / Cooler and Mole: *Various artists* / Blythe: *Various artists* / Discovery: *Various artists* / Various troubles: *Various artists* / On the road: *Various artists* / Betrayal: *Various artists* / Hendley's risk: *Various artists* / Road's end: *Various artists* / More action: *Various artists* / Chase: *Various artists* / Finale: *Various artists*.
Album: Released '73, on Sunset (Liberty) by EMI Records. Deleted '78. Catalogue no: **SLS 50177**

GREAT ESCAPE, THE (Film soundtrack) (Various artists)
Album: Released '85, on Liberty (import) by EMI Records. Catalogue no: **LN 10284**
Cass: Released '85, on Liberty (import) by EMI Records. Catalogue no: **L4N 10284**

Great Film Classics

GREAT FILM CLASSICS VOL.2 (Various artists)
Album: Released '82, on DG Special Catalogue no: **2535469**

Great Film Composers

GREAT FILM COMPOSERS (Various artists)
Album: Released Jan '77, on Polydor by Polydor Ltd. Deleted

'80. Catalogue no: **2489 123**

Great Film Music

GREAT FILM MUSIC (Various artists)
Tracks: / Spitfire prelude & fugue: *Various artists* / Henry V: *Various artists* / Richard II: *Various artists* / Escape me never: *Various artists* / Oliver Twist: *Various artists* / 49th parrallel: *Various artists* / Things to come: *Various artists*.
Album: Released Oct '84, on Decca by Decca International. Catalogue no: **411 837 1**

Great Film Themes

GREAT FILM THEMES
CD: Released Feb '88, on London Records by London Records Ltd. Catalogue no: **820 040-2**

Great Hitchcock

GREAT HITCHCOCK MOVIE THRILLERS (London Philharmonic Orchestra)
Tracks: / Psycho / Marnie / North by Northwest / Vertigo / Trouble with Harry, The: Portrait of Hitch.
Cass: Released '86, on Decca by Decca International. Catalogue no: **417 847-4**

Great Hollywood ...

GREAT HOLLYWOOD MUSICALS (Various artists)
Note: Selections From 42nd Street, Gold Diggers Of 1933, Footlight Parade, Go Into Your Dance, Dames And Rhapsody In Blue etc
Album: Released Jan '89, on Silva Screen by Silva Screen Records. Catalogue no: **ACH 023**
Cass: Released Jan '89, on Silva Screen by Silva Screen Records. Catalogue no: **CCH 023**

Great Moghuls

GREAT MOGHULS (Film soundtrack) (Various artists)
CD: Released Feb '90, on Silva Screen by Silva Screen Records. Catalogue no: **FILMCD 064**
Album: Released Feb '90, on Silva Screen by Silva Screen Records. Catalogue no: **FILM 064**
Cass: Released Feb '90, on Silva Screen by Silva Screen Records. Catalogue no: **FILMC 064**

Great Movie

GREAT MOVIE SOUNDTRACKS (Various artists)

Tracks: / Aliens: *Various artists* / Star wars: *Various artists* / Rambo: *Various artists* / Escape from New York: *Various artists.*
CD: Released Jan '89, on Pickwick by Pickwick Records. Catalogue no: **PWK 055**

GREAT MOVIE SOUNDTRACKS VOL II (Various artists)

Tracks: / Empire strikes back, The: *Various artists* / White mischief: *Various artists* / Running man, The: *Various artists* / Robocop: *Various artists* / Master of the Universe: *Various artists* / Final conflict, The: *Various artists* / Fly, The: *Various artists* / Hope and glory: *Various artists* / Wall Street: *Various artists* / Brainstorm: *Various artists* / Prince of darkness: *Various artists* / Seventh voyage of Sinbad: *Various artists* / No way out: *Various artists* / Boy who could fly, The: *Various artists* / Xtro: *Various artists* / Zed and two noughts, A: *Various artists* / Secret of N.Y.M.P.H., The: *Various artists.*
CD: Released May '89, on Pickwick by Pickwick Records. Catalogue no: **PWK 110**

Great Outdoors

GREAT OUTDOORS (Film soundtrack) (Various artists)
Tracks: / Land of a thousand dances: *Elwood Blues Revue/Wilson Pickett* / Hot fun in the summertime: *Elwood Blues Revue/Sam Moore/Oren Roberts* / Big country: *Walsh, Joe* / Unbearable: *Wonder Stuff* / Cabin fever: *Wilcox, David* / Big bear: *Bomb The Bass* / Beaver patrol: *Pop Will Eat Itself* / Hot weasel: *Elwood Blues Revue/Peter Aykroyd* / Hey cowboy: *Newman, Thomas & The Lazy* / Dragboat: *Elwood Blues Revue.*
CD: Released Sep '88, on Atlantic by WEA Records. Catalogue no: **781 859-2**
Album: Released Aug '88, on Atlantic by WEA Records. Catalogue no: **781 859-1**
Cass: Released Aug '88, on Atlantic by WEA Records. Catalogue no: **781 859-4**

Great Rock 'N' Roll...

GREAT ROCK 'N' ROLL SWINDLE (Film Soundtrack) (See under Sex Pistols)

Great Screen Lovers

GREAT SCREEN LOVERS COLLECTION (Various artists)
Tracks: / Who is there among...?: *Nicholson, Jack* / Chattanooga choo choo: *Power, Tyrone* / Louise: *Chevalier, Maurice* / Manhattan: *Rooney, Mickey* / Let's do it: *Coward, Noel* / Foolish pride: *Mitchum, Robert* / Puttin' on the Ritz: *Gable, Clarke* / Two of us, The: *Curtis, Tony & Gloria De Haven* / Let's make love: *Montand, Yves* / Day after day: *Stewart, James* / Did I remember?: *Grant, Cary* / Kashmiri love song: *Valentino, Rudolph* / Pillow talk: *Hudson, Rock* / Mary's a grand old name: *Cagney, James* / Woman in love: *Brando, Marlon & Jean Simmons* / As long as there is music: *Sinatra, Frank* / Chico's choo choo: *Wagner, Robert & Debbie Reynolds* / Lover come back to me: *Various artists* / All I do is dream of you: *Kelly, Gene* / Gotta bran' new suit: *Astaire & Fabray.*
Album: Released Dec '87, on Deja Vu Catalogue no: **DVLP 2117**
CD: Released Jun '88, on Deja Vu Catalogue no: **DVCD 2117**
Cass: Released Dec '87, on Deja Vu Catalogue no: **DVMC 2117**

Great Songs...

GREAT SONGS FROM DISNEY MOVIES (Various artists)
Tracks: / Funny little bunnies: *Various artists* / Penguin is a very funny creature: *Various artists* / Pied piper: *Various artists* / Grasshopper and the ants: *Various artists* / Rockabye baby: *Various artists* / Wise little hen, The: *Various artists* / Who's afraid of the big bad wolf?: *Various artists* / Ferdinand the bull: *Various artists* / Give a little whistle: *Various artists* / When you wish upon a star: *Various artists* / When I see an elephant fly: *Various artists* / Heigh-ho: *Various artists* / I'm wishing: *Various artists* / With a smile and a song: *Various artists* / One song: *Various artists* / Little wooden head: *Various artists* / Whistle while you work: *Various artists* / Some day my prince will come: *Various artists* / Turn on the old music box: *Various artists* / Love is a song: *Various artists.*
Album: Released Jun '78, on Retrospect by EMI Records.

Catalogue no: **SH 268**

GREAT SONGS FROM MGM CLASSIC FILMS, VOL 1 (Various artists)
CD: Released Jun '88, on MCA (USA) by MCA Records (USA). Catalogue no: **31056**

GREAT SONGS FROM MGM CLASSIC FILMS, VOL 2 (Various artists)
CD: Released Jun '88, on MCA (USA) by MCA Records (USA). Catalogue no: **31130**

GREAT SONGS FROM MGM CLASSIC FILMS, VOL 3 (Various artists)
CD: Released Jun '88, on MCA (USA) by MCA Records (USA). Catalogue no: **31131**

Great Train Robbery

GREAT TRAIN ROBBERY, THE (1978 film soundtrack) (Various artists)
Album: Released Jan '89, on MCA by MCA Records. Catalogue no: **MCA 25102**
Cass: Released Jan '89, on MCA by MCA Records. Catalogue no: **MCAC 25102**

Great Waltz

GREAT WALTZ, THE (Original London Cast) (Various artists)
Tracks: / Overture: *Various artists* / Waltz with wings: *Various artists* / I'm in love with Vienna: *Various artists* / My philsophy of life: *Various artists* / Love and gingerbread: *Various artists* / Teeter-totter me: *Various artists* / Where would I be: *Various artists* / Of men and violins: *Various artists* / Artist's life, An: *Various artists* / Enchanted wood: *Various artists* / At Dommayer's: *Various artists* / Gypsy told me: *Various artists* / Tritschtratsch polka: *Various artists* / No two ways: *Various artists* / I hate music: *Various artists* / Blue Danube: *Various artists.*
Album: Released '73, on Columbia by EMI Records. Deleted '78. Catalogue no: **SCX 6429**

GREAT WALTZ (1934 US cast recording)
Album: Released Jan '89, on Silva Screen by Silva Screen Records. Catalogue no: **AEI 1153**

GREAT WALTZ, THE (Film Soundtrack) (Various artists)

Tracks: / Crystal and gold: *Various artists* / Nightfall: *Various artists* / Warm: *Various artists* / Wine, women and song: *Various artists* / Love is music: *Various artists* / Louder and faster: *Various artists* / With you gone: *Various artists* / Through Jetty's eyes: *Various artists* / Say yes: Various artists / Six drinks: *Various artists* / Schani gives chase: *Various artists* / Who are you: *Various artists* / Great Waltz in Boston (Blue Danube): *Various artists*.

Cass: Released '73, on MGM (Polydor) by Polydor Ltd. Deleted '78. Catalogue no: **3110 090**

Album: Released '73, on MGM (Polydor) by Polydor Ltd. Deleted '78. Catalogue no: **2315 130**

Album: Released Jan '89, on Silva Screen by Silva Screen Records. Catalogue no: **STK 109**

Great Western...

GREAT WESTERN FILM THEMES (Various artists)
Tracks: / Magnificent seven: *Various artists* / March of the horse soldiers: *Various artists* / Joe Bass and the scalphunters: *Various artists* / Big country: *Various artists* / High noon: *Various artists* / Duel at Diablo: *Various artists* / Return of the seven: *Various artists* / Way west: *Various artists* / Wonderful country: *Various artists* / Hour of the gun: *Various artists* / Unforgiven: *Various artists* / Green leaves of summer: *Various artists* / McLintock: *Various artists* / Hallelujah trail: *Various artists*.

Album: Released Mar '79, on Sunset (Liberty) by EMI Records. Deleted '84. Catalogue no: **SLS 50425**

Cass: Released Mar '79, on Sunset (Liberty) by EMI Records. Deleted '84. Catalogue no: **TCT 50425**

GREAT WESTERN FILM THEMES COLLECTION (Various artists)
Tracks: / Magnificent Seven, The: *Various artists* / Big Country, The: *Various artists* / Scalphunters, The: *Various artists* / One-eyed Jacks: *Various artists* / High Noon: *Various artists* / Way West, The: *Various artists* / Duel at Diabola: *Various artists* / Wonderful country, The: *Various artists* / Hour of the gun: *Various artists* / Unfor-

given, The: *Various artists* / Alamo, The: *Various artists* / McLintock: *Various artists* / Katherine: *Various artists* / Good, the bad and the ugly, The: *Various artists* / How the West was won: *Various artists* / Big Gundown: *Various artists* / Hang 'em high: *Various artists* / Young Billy Young: *Various artists* / Fistful of dollars: *Various artists* / For a few dollars more: *Various artists* / Misfits, The: *Various artists* / True Grit: *Various artists* / Navajo Joe: *Various artists* / Professional gun: *Various artists* / Streets of Laredo: *Various artists*.

2 LP Set: on United Artists by EMI Records. Deleted '85. Catalogue no: **UAD 60079/80**

GREAT WESTERN MOVIE THEMES (Various artists)
Cass: Released May '85, on VFM Cassettes by VFM Cassettes. Catalogue no: **VCA 102**

GREAT WESTERN THEMES (Various artists)
Tracks: / Gunlaw: *Various artists* / Maverick: *Various artists* / Rawhide: *Various artists* / Laramie: *Various artists* / Bonanza: *Various artists* / Boots and saddles: *Various artists* / Call of the faraway hills, The: *Various artists* / Last round-up: *Various artists* / Wagon train: *Various artists* / Bronco: *Various artists* / Deputy, The: *Various artists* / Cheyenne: *Various artists* / Wells Fargo: *Various artists* / High noon: *Various artists* / Wyatt Earp: *Various artists* / Sugarfoot: *Various artists* / Chaquito: *Various artists* / Good, the bad and the ugly, The: *Various artists* / Big country, The: *Various artists* / Cascading strings: *Various artists* / Raindrops keep fallin' on my head: *Various artists*.

Cass set: Released '88, on Ditto by Pickwick Records. Catalogue no: **DTO 10200**

GREATEST WESTERN THEMES,THE (Various artists)
Tracks: / Good, the bad and the ugly, The: *Various artists* / Ghost riders in the sky: *Various artists* / Fistful of dollars, A: *Various artists* / Man who shot Liberty Valance, The: *Various artists* / Hanging tree, The: *Various artists* / Streets of Laredo: *Various artists* / Hang 'em high: *Various artists* / High chaparral: *Various artists* / Bonanza: *Various artists* / For a few dollars more:

Various artists / Big country, The: *Various artists* / Magnificent seven: *Various artists* / Shenandoah: *Various artists* / Red River Valley: *Various artists* / Once upon a time in the west: *Various artists*.

CD: Released Nov '86, on K-Tel by K-Tel Records. Catalogue no: **ONCD 3279**

Cass: Released Nov '86, on K-Tel by K-Tel Records. Catalogue no: **OCE 2279**

Album: Released Nov '86, on K-Tel by K-Tel Records. Catalogue no: **ONE 1279**

Greatest Movie Themes

GREATEST MOVIE THEMES (Various artists)
Cass: Released Feb '83, on AIM (Budget Cassettes) Catalogue no: **AIM 38**

Greatest Recordings Of

GREATEST RECORDINGS OF THE BROADWAY MUSICAL THEATRE (Archive collection) (Various artists)
LP Set: Released '84, on Franklin Mint Record Society Catalogue no: **UNKNOWN**

Greatest Story Ever

GREATEST STORY EVER TOLD, THE (Film soundtrack) (Various artists)
Note: Composed by Alfred Newman.

Album: Released Jan '89, on MCA by MCA Records. Catalogue no: **MCA 39057**

Cass: Released Jan '89, on MCA by MCA Records. Deleted Feb '90. Catalogue no: **MCAC 39057**

GREATEST STORY EVER TOLD / KING OF KINGS (Film soundtracks) (See under King Of Kings) (Various artists)

Greed In The Sun

GREED IN THE SUN/PAUL GAUGUIN (Original soundtrack) (Various artists)
Note: First ever release of these 2 scores by Georges Delerue. Greed in the sun (aka Cent-Mille Dollars Au Soleil) was a thriller directed by Henri Verneuil with Jean Paul Belmondo. Lino Ventura and Gert Frobe. Paul Gauguin was a 1974 TV series in France.

CD: Released Jan '89, on Silva Screen by Silva Screen Records.

Catalogue no: **PCD 101**

Green Ice

GREEN ICE (Original film soundtrack)
Tracks: / Si si / Beach chase / Holbrooks house (green ice theme) / Floating (Cloudhoppers theme) / Emerald guitars / Emerald vault / Water bottle, The / Noche de amour / Colombia / Tenderness / Showdown / Showdown / Cloudhoppers / Churchyard / Mines, The / Sol y sombra / Miomi arrival / Emerald waltz / Si si reprise.
Album: Released May '81, on Polydor by Polydor Ltd. Catalogue no: **POLS 1031**
Cass: Released May '81, on Polydor by Polydor Ltd. Catalogue no: **POLSC 1031**

Greenwillow

GREENWILLOW (Original Broadway cast) (Various artists)
Cass: Released Jan '89, on Silva Screen by Silva Screen Records. Catalogue no: **BT 13974**
Album: Released Jan '89, on Silva Screen by Silva Screen Records. Catalogue no: **P 13974**

Gregory, John

DETECTIVES, THE (Gregory, John Orchestra)
Tracks: / Banacek / Cannon / Columbo / Griff / Harry O / Kojak / McCloud / McMillan and wife / Policewoman / Rockford files / Six million dollar man / Streets of San Francisco / S.W.A.T. / Sweeney.
Album: Released Feb '77, on Sonic Deleted '80. Catalogue no: **SON 030**

Gremlins

GREMLINS (Film soundtrack) (Various artists)
Album: Released Oct '84, on Buena Vista by Walt Disney Productions. Deleted '88. Catalogue no: **RESLD 1**
Album: Released Dec '84, on Geffen by Geffen Records (USA). Deleted '89. Catalogue no: **GEF 54685**
Cass: Released Dec '84, on Geffen by Geffen Records (USA). Deleted '89. Catalogue no: **40 54685**

GREMLINS 2 (Film soundtrack) (Various artists) (See panel below)
Album: Released Aug '90, on Varese Sarabande Records(USA) by Varese Sarabande Records (USA). Catalogue no: **VS 5269**
Cass: Released Aug '90, on Varese Sarabande Records(USA) by Varese Sarabande Records (USA). Catalogue no: **VSC 5269**
CD: Released Aug '90, on Varese Sarabande Records(USA) by Varese Sarabande Records (USA). Catalogue no: **VSD 5269**

Grey Fox

GREY FOX, THE (Film soundtrack) (Various artists)
Tracks: / Main titles: *Chieftains* / Oyster bed sequence: *Chieftains* / Country store sequence: *Chieftains* / Ride to Kamloops: *Chieftains* / Meeting tram at Ducks Siding: *Chieftains* / Chase, The: *Chieftains* / End title: *Chieftains* / Sweet Betsy from Pike: *Farnsworth, Richard.*
Note: Original soundtrack recording composed & conducted by Michael Conway Baker. Traditional Irish music composed & performed by the Chieftains.
Cass: Released '88, on DRG (USA) by DRG Records (USA). Catalogue no: **SLC 9515**
Album: Released '88, on DRG (USA) by DRG Records (USA). Deleted Jan '89. Catalogue no: **SL 9515**
CD: Released Apr '87, on DRG (USA) by DRG Records (USA). Deleted Jan '89. Catalogue no: **CDSL 9515**

Greystoke...

GREYSTOKE - LEGEND OF TARZAN (Film soundtrack) (Various artists)
Album: Released Aug '84, on Warner Bros. by WEA Records. Deleted Aug '89. Catalogue no: **925120 1**

Griffiths, Derek

HEADS & TAILS
Album: Released Feb '80, on BBC by BBC Records. Deleted '87. Catalogue no: **REC 379**
Cass: Released Feb '80, on BBC by BBC Records. Deleted '88. Catalogue no: **ZCM 379**

Griffiths, Joe

BREAKAWAY, THEME FROM
Tracks: / Breakaway, Theme from / Red ice.
7" Single: Released Jan '80, on BBC by BBC Records. Deleted Jan '83. Catalogue no: **RESL 74**

Grind

GRIND (Original Broadway cast) (Various artists)
Tracks: / This must be the place: *Various artists* / Cadava: *Various artists* / Sweet thing like me, A: *Various artists* / I get myself out: *Various artists* / My daddy always taught me to share: *Various artists* / All things to one man: *Various artists* / Line, The: *Various artists* / Katie, my love: *Various artists* / Grind, The: *Various artists* / Yes, ma'am: *Various artists* / Why, mama, why: *Various artists* / This crazy place: *Various artists* / From

The Brain Gremlin from *Gremlins 2 (The new batch)*

the ankles down: *Various artists* / Who is he: *Various artists* / Never put it in writing: *Various artists* / I talk, you talk: *Various artists* / Timing: *Various artists* / These eyes of mine: *Various artists* / New man: *Various artists* / Down: *Various artists* / Century of progress, A: *Various artists* / Finale: *Various artists*.
Cass: Released Sep '85, on T. E. R. by That's Entertainment Records. Catalogue no: **ZCTER 1103**
CD: Released May '89, on T. E. R by That's Entertainment Records. Catalogue no: **CDTER 1103**
Album: Released Sep '85, on T. E. R. by That's Entertainment Records. Catalogue no: **TER 1103**

Grumbleweeds

BEST OF THE GRUMBLE-WEEDS
Cass: Released '80, on BBC by BBC Records. Deleted Apr '89. Catalogue no: **ZCR 372**
Album: Released '80, on BBC by BBC Records. Deleted Apr '89. Catalogue no: **REH 372**

Grusin, Dave

CINEMAGIC
Tracks: / Actor's life, An / It might be you / Heaven can wait / On golden pond / Condor (three days of the Condor) / Heart is a lonely hunter, The / Opening theme (From Goonies) / Champ, The / Mountain dance (CD only) / Letting go (CD only) / PLO camp entrance / Little drummer girl (Bonus track on CD only).
Note: A digital showcase of all Dave Grusin's most memorable motion picture film themes. Recorded with the London Symphony Orchestra and musicians such as Tom Scott, Lee Ritenour, Harvey Mason, Ernie Watts.
Album: Released May '87, on GRP by GRP Records (USA). Catalogue no: **GRP 91037**
Cass: Released May '87, on GRP by GRP Records (USA). Catalogue no: **GRPM 91037**
DAT: Released Jul '88, on GRP by GRP Records (USA). Catalogue no: **GRT 9547**
CD: Released May '87, on GRP by GRP Records (USA). Catalogue no: **GRD 9547**

FABULOUS BAKER BOYS, THE (1989 film soundtrack) (Various artists)

Tracks: / Makin' whoopee: *Pfeiffer, Michelle* / My funny valentine: *Pfeiffer, Michelle* / Do nothin' till you hear from me: *Ellington, Duke* / Moonglow: *Goodman, Benny*.
Cass: Released Jan '90, on GRP by GRP Records (USA). Catalogue no: **GRP 20024**
CD: Released Oct '89, on GRP by GRP Records (USA). Catalogue no: **GRP 20022**
Album: Released Oct '89, on GRP by GRP Records (USA). Catalogue no: **GRP 20021**

MIGRATION (Film Soundtrack)
Note: Includes the suite from The Milagro Beanfield War, for which Dave Grusin won an Oscar for best film score in 1989. CD version features three bonus tracks.
Album: Released Sep '89, on GRP by GRP Records (USA). Catalogue no: **GRP 95921**
Cass: Released Sep '89, on GRP by GRP Records (USA). Catalogue no: **GRP 95924**
CD: Released Sep '89, on GRP by GRP Records (USA). Catalogue no: **GRP 95922**

Guns For San Sebastian

GUNS FOR SAN SEBASTIAN (Film soundtrack) (Various artists)
Note: Western score by Ennio Morricone for the film starring Anthony Quinn and Charles Bronson.
Cass: Released Jan '89, on MCA by MCA Records. Deleted Feb '90. Catalogue no: **MCAC 25103**
Album: Released Jan '89, on MCA by MCA Records. Catalogue no: **MCA 25103**

Guns 'N' Roses

WELCOME TO THE JUNGLE
Tracks: / Welcome to the jungle / Whole lotta Rosie / It's so easy (12" only) / Knockin' on heavens door.
Note: Welcome To The Jungle is feaured in the Dirty Harry film 'The Dead Pool'. Knockin' on heaven's door is featured in the film 'Days Of Thunder'.
12" Single: Released Sep '87, on Geffen by Geffen Records (USA). Deleted Jul '88. Catalogue no: **GEF 30 T**
7" Single: Released Sep '87, on Geffen by Geffen Records (USA). Catalogue no: **GEF 30**

Guns Of Navarone

GUNS OF NAVARONE (Film soundtrack) (Tiomkin, Dimitri)
CD: Released Feb '90, on Silva Screen by Silva Screen Records. Catalogue no: **VSD 5236**

GUNS OF NAVARONE & OTHER FILM SOUNDTRACKS (Various artists)
Tracks: / First of the few, The: *Various artists* / Bridge on the river Kwai, The: *Various artists* / Guns of Navarone: *Various artists* / Victory at sea: *Various artists* / 633 Squadron: *Various artists* / Longest day, The: *Various artists* / Western approaches: *Various artists* / Great escape, The: *Various artists* / Mrs. Miniver: *Various artists*.
Cass: Released '86, on Decca by Decca International. Catalogue no: **417 853-4**
CD: Released Aug '88, on Decca by Decca International. Catalogue no: **417 853-2**

Guthrie, Arlo

ALICE'S RESTAURANT (See under Alice's Restaurant)

Guys & Dolls

GUYS AND DOLLS (VIDEO) (Various artists)
VHS: Released '88, on Video Gems Catalogue no: **R 1144**

GUYS & DOLLS (Film soundtrack) (Various artists)
Note: Starring Marlon Brando and Frank Sinatra.
Album: Released Jan '89, on Silva Screen by Silva Screen Records. Catalogue no: **MPT 3**

GUYS & DOLLS (Reprise Repertory Theatre) (Various artists)
Tracks: / Overture: *Reprise Repertory Theatre* / Fugue for tinhorns: *Sinatra, Frank* / *Bing Crosby* / *Dean Martin* / I'll know: *Stafford, Jo* / Oldest established craps game in New York: *Sinatra, Frank* / *Bing Crosby* / *Dean Martin* / Bushel and a peck, A: *Reprise Repertory Theatre* / Guys and dolls: *Sinatra, Frank* / *Bing Crosby* / *Dean Martin* / If I were a bell: *Shore, Dinah* / I've never been in love before: *Sinatra, Frank* / Take back your mink: *Reynolds, Debbie* / More I cannot wish you: *Dennis, Clark* / Adelaide's la-

ment: *Reynolds, Debbie* / Luck be a lady: *Sinatra, Frank* / Sue me: *Reynolds, Debbie & Alan Sherman* / Sit down you're rockin' the boat: *Reprise Repertory Theatre* / Guys and dolls (reprise): *Sinatra, Frank & Dean Martin.*

Album: Released Aug '81, on Reprise (USA) Catalogue no: **K 54113**

GUYS & DOLLS (London revival cast) (Various artists)

Tracks: / Runyonland music: *Various artists* / Fugue for tinhorns: *Various artists* / Follow the fold: *Various artists* / Oldest established craps game in the New York: *Various artists* / I'll know: *Various artists* / Bushel and a peck, A: *Various artists* / Adelaide's lament: *Various artists* / Guys and dolls: *Various artists* / If I were a bell: *Various artists* / My time of day: *Various artists* / I've never been in love before: *Various artists* / Take back your mink: *Various artists* / Adelaide's lament (reprise): *Various artists* / More I cannot wish you: *Various artists* / Crap shooters ballet, The: *Various artists*

Album: Released May '82, on Chrysalis by Chrysalis Records. Catalogue no: **CDL 1388**

Cass: Released May '82, on Chrysalis by Chrysalis Records. Catalogue no: **ZCDL 1388**

GUYS & DOLLS (Original Broadway Cast) (Various artists)

Tracks: / Runyonland music: *Various artists* / Fugue for tinhorns: *Various artists* / Follow the fold: *Various artists* / Oldest established craps game in New York: *Various artists* / I'll know: *Various artists* / Bushel and a peck, A: *Various artists* / My time of day: *Various artists* / Adelaides lament: *Various artists* / Guys and dolls: *Various artists* / If I were a bell: *Various artists* / I've never been in love before: *Various artists* / Take back your mink: *Various artists* / More I cannot wish you: *Various artists* .

Cass: Released Sep '86, on MCA by MCA Records. Catalogue no: **MCLC 1659**

Album: Released Sep '86, on MCA by MCA Records. Catalogue no: **MCL 1659**

Album: Released Sep '86, on Hallmark by Pickwick Records. Deleted '88. Catalogue no: **SHM 3201**

Cass: Released Sep '86, on Hallmark by Pickwick Records. Deleted '88. Catalogue no: **HSC 3201**

H

The following information was taken from the Music Master database on September 25th, 1990.

Hackney Empire

ON STAGE PLEASE AT THE HACKNEY EMPIRE (Various artists)
Tracks: / Overtures and beginners: That's entertainment: *Royal Artillery Orchestra* / One of the ruins (that Cromwell knocked about a bit): *Mansfield, Elizabeth* / Flanagan: *Manners, Margery* / Only a bird in a gilded cage: *Manners, Margery* / (Last of the) Gaiety Girls, The: *Wells, Billy* / Joshua: *Windsor, Barbara* / London medley, A: *Kane, Joy/Sylvia Young's Young 'uns* (Any old iron\Maybe it's because I'm a Londoner\Lambeth Walk) / Burlington Bertie: *Stables, Maggie* / Sand of the desert (medley): *Cox Twins and Pauline* (Sand dance, The\Sheik of Araby \ Egyptian ballet) / Underneath the arches: *Crowther, Leslie & Bernie Winters* / Sally: *Pollard, Su* / Songs from the shows (medley): *Arden-Griffith, Paul* (Dames \ You're getting to be a habit from me \ On the street where you live\Tonight\Thats entertainment.) / Cavatina (Stanley Myers): *Weedon, Bert* / Rock 'n' roll medley: *Weedon, Bert* (Guitar boogie shuffle\What'd I say\Shake rattle\Blue suede shoes\&2) / Songs from Broadway: *Howard, Joyce* (Broadway baby\Nobody does it like me\Razzle dazzle\If my friends could see me now) / What is a mummy, daddy?: *Trinder, Tommy* / There's no business like show business (Finale): *Royal Artillery Orchestra*.
Cass: Released Oct '89, on President by President Records. Catalogue no: **TC-PRCV 138**
Album: Released Oct '89, on President by President Records. Catalogue no: **PRCV 138**

ON STAGE AT THE HACKNEY EMPIRE (VIDEO) (Various artists)
VHS: Released Oct '89, on President by President Records. Deleted Aug '90. Catalogue no: **LVV 342**

Hair

HAIR (Original Off Broadway Cast) (Various artists)
Tracks: / Ain't got no... I got life: *Various artists* / Air: *Various artists* / Going down: *Various artists* / Hair: *Various artists* / Dead end: *Various artists* / Frank Mills: *Various artists* / Hare Krishna: *Various artists* / Where do I go: *Various artists* / Electric blues: *Various artists* / Easy to be hard: *Various artists* / Manchester: *Various artists* / White boys: *Various artists* / black boys: *Various artists* / Walking in space: *Various artists* / Aquarius: *Various artists* / Good morning starshine: *Various artists* / Exanplanetooch: *Various artists* / Climax: *Various artists*.
Album: Released '73, on RCA by BMG Records (UK). Deleted '78. Catalogue no: **INTS 1133**

HAIR (Film Soundtrack) (Various artists)
Tracks: / Aquarius: *Various artists* / Sodomy: *Various artists* / Donna: *Various artists* / Hashish: *Various artists* / Coloured spade: *Various artists* / Manchester, England: *Various artists* / Abie baby: *Various artists* / Fourscore: *Various artists* / I'm black: *Various artists* / Ain't got no air: *Various artists* / Party music: *Various artists* / My conviction: *Various artists* / I got life: *Various artists* / Frank Mills: *Various artists* / Hair: *Various artists* / L.J.B.: *Various artists* / Hare Krishna: *Various artists* / Electric blues: *Various artists* / Old fashioned melody: *Various artists* / Where do I go: *Various artists* / Black boys: *Various artists* / White boys: *Various artists* / Walking in space: *Various artists* / Easy to be hard: *Various artists* / 3-5-0-0: *Various artists* / Good morning starshine: *Various artists* / What a piece of work is man: *Various artists* / Somebody to love: *Various artists* / Don't put it down: *Various artists* / Flesh failures: *Various artists* / Let

the sunshine in: *Various artists*.
2 LP Set: Released '79, on RCA by BMG Records (UK). Deleted '84. Catalogue no: **BL 83274**
Cass set: Released '79, on RCA by BMG Records (UK). Deleted '84. Catalogue no: **BK 83274**

HAIR (London Cast) (Various artists)
Tracks: / Aquarius: *Edward, Vince & The Company* / Donna: *Tobias, Oliver & The Company* / Sodomy: *Feast, Michael & The Company* / Coloured spade: *Straker, Peter & The Company* / No air: *Various artists* / I got life: *Various artists* / Hair: *Various artists* / My Conviction: *Forray, Andy* / Easy to be hard: *Leventon, Annabel* / Frank Mills: *Kristina, Sonja* / Where do I go?: *Nicholas, Paul & The Company* / Electric blues: *Gulliver, John/Rohan McCullous* / Black boys: *Kelly, Colette/Rohan McCullous* / White boys: *Various artists* / Walking in space: *Company* / Able baby: *Straker, Peter/Limbert Spencer* / Three five zero zero: *Company* / What a piece of work is man: *Edward, Vince & Leighton Spencer* / Good morning, starshine: *Various artists* / Bed, The: *Company* / Let the sun shine in: *Various artists*.
Album: Released Dec '68, on Polydor by Polydor Ltd. Catalogue no: **583 043**
Album: Released Feb '85, on Polydor (Import) by Polydor Ltd. Catalogue no: **2459361**

HAIR (Original Broadway cast) (Various artists)
Tracks: / Aquarius: *Various artists* / Donna: *Various artists* / Hashish: *Various artists* / Sodomy: *Various artists* / Coloured spade: *Various artists* / Manchester, England: *Various artists* / I'm black: *Various artists* / Ain't got no: *Various artists* / Air: *Various artists* / Initials: *Various artists* / I got life: *Various artists* / Hair: *Various artists* / My conviction: *Various artists* / Don't put it

Rikki Lake, Divine (Pictured left) and Debbie Harry starred in the cult film *Hairspray*

down: *Various artists* / Frank Mills: *Various artists* / Be in: *Various artists* / Where did I go?: *Various artists* / Black boys: *Various artists* / White boys: *Various artists* / Easy to be hard: *Various artists* / Walking in space: *Various artists* / Abie baby: *Various artists* / Three five zero zero: *Various artists* / What a piece of work is man: *Various artists* / Good morning starshine: *Various artists* / Flesh failures (let the sunshine in): *Various artists*.
Cass: Released Jan '89, on RCA by BMG Records (UK). Catalogue no: **BK 89084**
Album: Released Jan '89, on RCA by BMG Records (UK). Catalogue no: **BL 89084**
CD: Released Jan '89, on RCA by BMG Records (UK). Catalogue no: **1150.2**
Album: Released '79, on RCA by BMG Records (UK). Deleted '84. Catalogue no: **SF 7959**

HAIR (Various artists)
Tracks: / Hair: *Various artists* / Sodomy: *Various artists* / I got life: *Various artists* / Aquarius: *Various artists* / Let the sunshine in: *Various artists* / Where do I go?: *Various artists* / Frank Mills: *Various artists* / Donna: *Various artists* / Coloured spade: *Various artists* / Black boys: *Various artists* / White boys: *Various artists* / My conviction: *Various artists*.
Album: Released Dec '79, on Boulevard by Boulevard Records. Deleted '84. Catalogue no: **BD 3008**

HAIR (VIDEO) (Various artists)
Note: Cert: 15.
VHS: Released '88, on Warner Home Video by WEA Records. Catalogue no: **PES 99230**

Hairspray

HAIRSPRAY (Film soundtrack) (Various artists) (See panel above)
Tracks: / Hairspray: *Sweet, Rachel* / Madison time, The: *Bryant, Ray* / I'm blue (the gong-gong song): *Ikettes* / Mama didn't lie: *Bradley, Jan* / Town without pity: *Pitney, Gene* / Roach, The: *Gene & Wendell* / Foot stompin': *Flares* / Shake a tail feather: *Five Du-Tones* / Bug, The: *Dallman, Jerry/Knightcaps* / You'll lose a good thing: *Lynn, Barbara* / I wish I were a...: *March, Peggy* / Nothing takes the place of you: *McCall, Toussaint.*
CD: Released Jul '88, on MCA by MCA Records. Catalogue no: **MCAD 6228**
Cass: Released Jul '88, on MCA by MCA Records. Catalogue no: **IMCAC 6228**
Album: Released Jul '88, on MCA by MCA Records. Catalogue no: **IMCA 6228**

Haley, Bill

DON'T KNOCK THE ROCK (Haley, Bill & The Comets)
Tracks: / Don't knock the rock.
7" Single: Released Feb '57, on Brunswick by Decca Records.

Deleted '60. Catalogue no: **05640**

ROCK AROUND THE CLOCK (SINGLE) (Haley, Bill & The Comets)
Tracks: / Rock around the clock.
7" Single: Released '68, on MCA by MCA Records. Deleted '71. Catalogue no: **MU 1013**
7" Single: Released Feb '81, on MCA by MCA Records. Catalogue no: **MCA 128**
7" Single: Released Jan '55, on Brunswick by Decca Records. Deleted '58. Catalogue no: **05317**

Half A Sixpence

HALF A SIXPENCE (Original London cast) (Various artists)
Tracks: / Overture: *Various artists* / All in the cause of ecomony: *Various artists* / Half a sixpence: *Various artists* / Money to burn: *Various artists* / Oak and the ash, The: *Various artists* / She's too far above me: *Various artists* / I'm not talking to you: *Various artists* / If the rain's got to fall: *Various artists* / Old military canal, The: *Various artists* / One that's run away, The: *Various artists* / Long ago: *Various artists* / Flash, bang, wallop: *Various artists* / I know what I am: *Various artists* / I'll build a palace: *Various artists* / I only want a little house: *Various artists* / Finale: *Various artists*.
Album: Released Aug '83, on T. E. R. by That's Entertainment Records. Catalogue no: **TER 1041**
Cass: Released Aug '83, on T. E. R. by That's Entertainment Records. Catalogue no: **ZCTER 1041**

HALF A SIXPENCE (ORIGINAL ISSUE) (London cast) (Various artists)
Album: Released Mar '63, on Decca by Decca International. Deleted '68. Catalogue no: **LK 4521**

Half Moon Street

HALF MOON STREET (Film soundtrack) (Various artists)
Note: Composed by Richard Harvey for the Michael Caine thriller.
Album: Released Sep '86, on SPI Milan (France) Catalogue no: **A 282**
Cass: Released Sep '86, on SPI Milan (France) Deleted Mar '90. Catalogue no: **C 282**

HALF MOON STREET (VIDEO) (Various artists)

VHS: Released Mar '90, on Channel 5 by Channel 5 Video. Catalogue no: **CFV 08692**

Halle Orchestra

INCIDENTAL MUSIC TO PEER GYNT

Note: Conducted by Sir John Barbirolli.

Cass: Released '88, on H.M.V. by EMI Records. Catalogue no: **EG 7690394**

CD: Released '88, on H.M.V. by EMI Records. Catalogue no: **CDM 769 039 2**

Hallelujah Trail

HALLELUJAH TRAIL, THE (Original soundtrack) (Various artists)

Note: Elmer Bernstein western score.

Album: Released Jan '89, on Silva Screen by Silva Screen Records. Catalogue no: **AUSLP 1017**

Halloween

HALLOWEEN (Film soundtrack) (Carpenter, John)

CD: Released Jan '89, on Silva Screen by Silva Screen Records. Catalogue no: **VCD 47230**

Album: Released Jan '89, on Silva Screen by Silva Screen Records. Catalogue no: **STV 81176**

Cass: Released Jan '89, on Silva Screen by Silva Screen Records. Catalogue no: **CTV 81176**

HALLOWEEN 2 (Film soundtrack) (Various artists)

Note: Composed by: John Carpenter.

Album: Released Jan '90, on Colosseum (West Germany) Catalogue no: **CST 8040**

CD: Released Jan '89, on Silva Screen by Silva Screen Records. Catalogue no: **VCD 47152**

Cass: Released Jan '90, on Colosseum (West Germany) Catalogue no: **CTV 81152**

Album: Released Jan '89, on Silva Screen by Silva Screen Records. Catalogue no: **STV 81152**

Album: Released Jan '86, on Celine (West Germany) by Celine Records (West Germany). Catalogue no: **CL 0009**

HALLOWEEN 2 (SINGLE) (Film soundtrack) (Various artists)

12" Single: Released Jul '86, on Blast First by Blast First Records.

Deleted '88. Catalogue no: **BFFP 3P**

HALLOWEEN 3 (Film soundtrack) (Howarth, Alan)

CD: Released Feb '90, on Silva Screen by Silva Screen Records. Catalogue no: **VSD 5243**

Cass: Released Feb '90, on Silva Screen by Silva Screen Records. Catalogue no: **VSC 5243**

Album: Released '83, on MCA by MCA Records. Catalogue no: **MCA 6115**

Album: Released Feb '90, on Silva Screen by Silva Screen Records. Catalogue no: **VS 5243**

HALLOWEEN 4 (film soundtrack) (Various artists)

Note: Music by Alan Howarth. Theme by John Carpenter.

Cass: Released Jan '89, on Take 7 Catalogue no: **VSC 5205**

CD: Released Dec '88, on Take 7 Catalogue no: **VSD 5205**

Album: Released Dec '88, on Take 7 Catalogue no: **VS 5205**

HALLOWEEN 5 (film soundtrack) (Various artists)

Tracks: / Romeo Romeo: *Becca* / Dancin' on Churchill: *Churchill* / Sporting woman: *Diggy/Chosak/Clark* / Shape also rises, The: *Howarth, Alan* / First victim: *Howarth, Alan* / Tower farm: *Howarth, Alan* / Trapped: *Howarth, Alan* / Jail break: *Howarth, Alan* / Anything for money: *DVB* / Second time around: *Rhythm Tribe* / Halloween 5 - the revenge: *Howarth, Alan* / Evil child must die: *Howarth, Alan* / Stranger in the house: *Howarth, Alan* / Stop the rage: *Howarth, Alan* / Attic, The: *Howarth, Alan* / Halloween finale: *Howarth, Alan*.

CD: Released Dec '89, on Colosseum (West Germany) Catalogue no: **VSCD 5239**

Cass: Released Dec '89, on Colosseum (West Germany) Catalogue no: **VSC 5239**

Album: Released Dec '89, on Colosseum (West Germany) Catalogue no: **VS 5239**

Hamill, Claire

DOOMSDAY, THE (EP)

Tracks: / Doomsday, The / Glastonbury / Tides / Spring awaken, lark rise / Stars.

Note: Used as the theme to the BBC *Doomsday*

7" Single: Released Nov '86, on

Coda by Coda Records. Catalogue no: **CODS 21**

VOICES

Note: Featured in the TV Prog Doomsday.

CD: Released Apr '86, on Coda by Coda Records. Catalogue no: **NAGE 8 CD**

Album: Released Apr '86, on Coda by Coda Records. Catalogue no: **NAGE 8**

Cass: Released Apr '86, on Coda by Coda Records. Catalogue no: **NAGEC 8**

Hamilton, Lynne

ON THE INSIDE

Tracks: / On the inside / Prisoner cell block H love theme.

7" Single: Released Apr '89, on A.1 by A.1 Records. Deleted Apr '90. Catalogue no: **A1 311**

Hamlisch, Marvin

BOND '77

Tracks: / Bond '77 / James Bond theme / Ride to Atlantis.

7" Single: Released Aug '77, on United Artists by EMI Records. Deleted '79. Catalogue no: **UP 36301**

ENTERTAINER, THE

Tracks: / Entertainer, The.

Note: From the film *The Sting*.

7" Single: Released Jun '83, on MCA by MCA Records. Catalogue no: **MCA 812**

ENTERTAINER, THE

Tracks: / Entertainer, The.

Note: From the film *The Sting*.

7" Single: Released Mar '74, on MCA by MCA Records. Deleted '77. Catalogue no: **MCA 121**

ORDINARY PEOPLE THEME

Tracks: / Ordinary people / Cannon in D.

7" Single: Released Apr '81, on Planet by BMG Records (UK). Catalogue no: **K 12497**

WAY WE WERE (See under Way We Were)

Hammer, Jan

CHANCER THEME

Tracks: / Chancer theme.

CD Single: Released May '90, on MCA by MCA Records. Catalogue no: **DMCAT 1415**

7" Single: Released May '90, on MCA by MCA Records. Deleted Sep '90. Catalogue no: **MCA 1415**

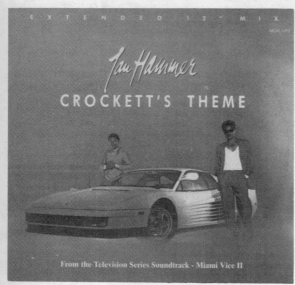

Jan Hammer - 'Crockett's Theme' from *Miami Vice*

CROCKETT'S THEME (See panel above)
Tracks: / Crockett's theme.
Note: Used in TV Series Miami Vice.
7" Single: Released Aug '87, on MCA by MCA Records. Deleted Dec '89. Catalogue no: **MCA 1193**
12" Single: Released Aug '87, on MCA by MCA Records. Catalogue no: **MCAT 1193**
12" Single: Released Oct '87, on MCA by MCA Records. Catalogue no: **MCAX 1193**

ESCAPE FROM TV
Tracks: / Crocketts theme / Theresa / Colombia / Rum cay / Trial and the search, The / Tubbs & Valerie / Forever tonight / Last flight / Rico's blues / Before the storm / Night talk / Miami Vice theme.
Album: Released Oct '87, on MCA by MCA Records. Catalogue no: **MCF 3407**
Cass: Released Oct '87, on MCA by MCA Records. Catalogue no: **MCFC 3407**
CD: Released Oct '87, on MCA by MCA Records. Catalogue no: **DMCF 3407**

MIAMI VICE THEME
Tracks: / Miami Vice theme.

12" Single: Released Nov '85, on MCA by MCA Records. Deleted Nov '88. Catalogue no: **MCAT 1000**
7" Single: Released Sep '85, on MCA by MCA Records. Catalogue no: **MCA 1000**

TUBBS & VALERIE
Tracks: / Tubbs & Valerie / Rico's blues / Tubbs & Valerie (extended) (Available on 12" only) / Crockett's theme (CD only).
7" Single: Released Oct '87, on MCA by MCA Records. Deleted 1 Jul '89. Catalogue no: **MCA 1200**
12" Single: Released Oct '87, on MCA by MCA Records. Catalogue no: **MCAT 1200**
Cassingle: Released Nov '87, on MCA by MCA Records. Catalogue no: **MCAA 1200**
CD Single: Released Nov '87, on MCA by MCA Records. Catalogue no: **DMCA 1200**

Hancock, Tony

BEST OF TONY HANCOCK
Tracks: / Blood donor / Radio ham, The.
Album: Released Jan '72, on Hallmark by Pickwick Records. Deleted '88. Catalogue no: **HMA**

228

BLOOD DONOR/RADIO HAM
Tracks: / Blood donor / Radio ham.
Cass: Released Jul '89, on PRT by Castle Communications Records. Catalogue no: **PYM 22**
Album: Released Jul '89, on PRT by Castle Communications Records. Catalogue no: **PYL 22**
CD: Released Jul '89, on PRT by Castle Communications Records. Catalogue no: **PYC 22**

GOLDEN HOUR OF TONY HANCOCK
Cass: Released Jun '90, on Knight by Knight Records Ltd.. Catalogue no: **KGHMC 115**
CD: Released Jun '90, on Knight by Knight Records Ltd.. Catalogue no: **KGHCD 115**

HANCOCK
Album: Released Mar '62, on Pye Deleted '67. Catalogue no: **NPL 18068**
Cass: Released Nov '71, on Marble Arch Catalogue no: **ZCMA 872**

HANCOCK'S HALF HOUR (Various artists)
Tracks: / Americans hit town, The: *Various artists* / Poetry society: *Various artists* / Unexploded bomb, The: *Various artists* / Sid's mystery tours: *Various artists*.
Cass set: Released Sep '88, on BBC by BBC Records. Catalogue no: **ZBBC 1008**

HANCOCK'S HALF HOUR 2 (Various artists)
Cass set: Released Sep '88, on BBC by BBC Records. Catalogue no: **ZBBC 1018**

HANCOCK'S HALF HOUR 3 (Various artists)
Tracks: / Hancock's war: *Various artists* / Christmas club, The: *Various artists* / Lift, The: *Various artists* / Twelve angry men: *Various artists*.
Cass set: Released Mar '89, on BBC by BBC Records. Catalogue no: **ZBBC 1069**

HANCOCK'S HALF HOUR VOL 1 (Poetry Society / Sid's Mystery Tours)
Tracks: / Poetry society, The / Sid's mystery tours.
Album: Released Nov '80, on BBC by BBC Records. Deleted 31 Aug '88. Catalogue no: **REB 394**

Cass: Released Nov '80, on BBC by BBC Records. Deleted 31 Aug '88. Catalogue no: **ZCF 394**

HANCOCK'S HALF HOUR VOL 2 (American Hit Town / Unexploded Bomb)

Tracks: / American hit town, The / Unexploded bomb, The.

Cass: Released Oct '81, on BBC by BBC Records. Deleted 31 Aug '88. Catalogue no: **ZCF 423**

Album: Released Oct '81, on BBC by BBC Records. Deleted 31 Aug '88. Catalogue no: **REB 423**

HANCOCK'S HALF HOUR VOL 3 (Scandal Magazine/last Of The McHancocks)

Tracks: / Scandal magazine, The / Last of the McHancocks.

Cass: Released Oct '82, on BBC by BBC Records. Deleted 31 Aug '88. Catalogue no: **ZCF 451**

Album: Released Oct '82, on BBC by BBC Records. Deleted 31 Aug '88. Catalogue no: **REB 451**

HANCOCK'S HALF HOUR VOL. 4 (Sleepless Night, The/ Fred's Pie stall)

Tracks: / Sleepless night / Fred's pie stall.

Album: Released Oct '83, on BBC by BBC Records. Deleted 31 Aug '88. Catalogue no: **REB 485**

Cass: Released Oct '83, on BBC by BBC Records. Deleted 31 Aug '88. Catalogue no: **ZCF 485**

HANCOCKS HALF HOUR VOL 5 (Hancock's War / Christmas Club)

Tracks: / Hancock's war / Christmas club, The.

Cass: Released Oct '84, on BBC by BBC Records. Catalogue no: **ZCF 526**

Album: Released Oct '84, on BBC by BBC Records. Catalogue no: **REB 526**

LIFT & TWELVE ANGRY MEN, THE (Soundtracks from two TV programmes)

Tracks: / Lift, The / Twelve angry men.

Cass: Released Nov '76, on BBC by BBC Records. Catalogue no: **RMC 4055**

Album: Released Nov '76, on BBC by BBC Records. Catalogue no: **REB 260**

PIECES OF HANCOCK

Album: Released Nov '60, on Pye Deleted '65. Catalogue no: **NPL**

18054

THIS IS HANCOCK

Album: Released Apr '60, on Pye Deleted '65. Catalogue no: **NPL 18045**

Album: Released Sep '63, on Pye Deleted '68. Catalogue no: **GGL 0206**

UNIQUE HANCOCK

Tracks: / Almost a gentlemen / Christmas East Cheam style / P.C. Hancock have feet will travel / Hancockelo / Doctor's dilemma, The / Like a dog's dinner / Is that your car outside / With my woogle I thee worship / Hospital or Hancock revisited, The.

Cass: Released Jan '79, on BBC by BBC Records. Deleted '88. Catalogue no: **REMC 150**

Album: Released Jan '74, on BBC by BBC Records. Catalogue no: **REB 150**

WORLD OF TONY HANCOCK, THE

Album: Released Oct '75, on Decca by Decca International. Catalogue no: **PA 417**

Cass: Released Jan '79, on Decca by Decca International. Catalogue no: **KCPA 417**

Handful Of Dust

HANDFUL OF DUST (Original soundtrack) (Various artists)

Tracks: / Handful of dust, A: *Various artists* / Cafe de Paris: *Various artists* / Talking pips: *Various artists* / Weekend episodes: *Various artists* / Moving over: *Various artists* / Memories: *Various artists* / Fans, The: *Various artists*.

Note: Beautiful score by George Fenton (Cry Freedom) for the recent adaptation of the Evelyn Waugh story starring James Wilby, Angelica Huston & Alec Guiness.

Cass: Released Jan '89, on DRG (USA) by DRG Records (USA). Deleted Mar '90. Catalogue no: **DRGC 6110**

CD: Released Jan '89, on DRG (USA) by DRG Records (USA). Catalogue no: **CDRG 6110**

Album: Released Jan '89, on DRG (USA) by DRG Records (USA). Catalogue no: **DRG 6110**

Hang 'Em High

HANG 'EM HIGH (film soundtrack) (Various artists)

Note: Music from the Clint East-

wood western by Dominic Frontiere.

Cass: Released Jan '89, on MCA by MCA Records. Deleted Mar '90. Catalogue no: **MCAC 1435**

Album: Released Jan '89, on MCA by MCA Records. Catalogue no: **MCA 1435**

HANG 'EM HIGH/THE SCALPHUNTERS/THE WAY WEST (Original Soundtrack Highlights) (Various artists)

Tracks: / Scalphunters, The prologue: *Various artists* / Square dance for loco horses: *Various artists* / Scalphunters, The theme: *Various artists* / Forced march: *Various artists* / Moving on: *Various artists* / Hang 'em high: *Various artists* / Rachel (love theme): *Various artists* / Tumbleweed wagon: *Various artists* / I'll get 'em myself: *Various artists* / Rachel (love theme): *Various artists* / It's no deal: *Various artists* / Hang 'em high: *Various artists* / Way west, The: *Various artists* / Way west, The overture (main title): *Various artists* / Lige celebrates: *Various artists* / We're crossing first: *Various artists* / Flowers for Mr. Mack: *Various artists* / Water and Billy's death: *Various artists* / Mercy McBee: *Various artists* / Buffaloes and indians: *Various artists* / Becky's theme: *Various artists* / One to Crystal City: *Various artists* / Tadlock's end: *Various artists* / Reluctant mercy: *Various artists* / Way west, The finale: *Various artists*.

CD: Released Sep '90, on MGM (EMI) Catalogue no: **CDP 794 946 2**

Cass: Released Sep '90, on MGM (EMI) Catalogue no: **TCMGM 27**

CD: Released Sep '90, on MGM (EMI) Catalogue no: **CDMGM 27**

Album: Released Sep '90, on MGM (EMI) Catalogue no: **LPMGM 27**

Hannah & Her Sisters

HANNAH AND HER SISTERS (Original soundtrack) (Various artists)

CD: Released '86, on MCA by MCA Records. Catalogue no: **MCAD 6190**

Cass: Released '86, on MCA by MCA Records. Catalogue no: **IMCAC 6190**

Album: Released '86, on MCA by MCA Records. Deleted Sep '90. Catalogue no: **IMCA 6190**

HANNAH AND HER SISTERS / SEPTEMBER (Film soundtracks) (Various artists)
Cass: Released Nov '88, on Entertainers Catalogue no: **ENT MC 13057**
Album: Released Nov '88, on Entertainers Catalogue no: **ENT LP 13057**

Hannibal Brooks

HANNIBAL BROOKS (Original soundtrack) (Various artists)
Note: The Michael Winner film starring Oliver Reed, Michael J Pollard & an elephant. Music by Francis Lai.
Cass: Released Jan '89, on MCA by MCA Records. Catalogue no: **MCAC 25104**
Album: Released Jan '89, on MCA by MCA Records. Deleted Mar '90. Catalogue no: **MCA 25104**

Hansson, Bo

LORD OF THE RINGS (Film Soudtrack)
Tracks: / Leaving shire / Old forest, The / Tom Bombardil / Fog on the barrow / Downs / Black riders, The / Flight to the ford / At the house of Elrond / Ring goes South, The / Journey in the dark, A / Lothlorien / Horns of Rohan, The / Shadowfax / Battle of the Pelennor Fields, The / Dreams in the house of healing / Homeward bound / Scouring of the Shire, The / Grey havens, The.
Album: Released Mar '90, on M.N.W. by M.N.W. Records. Catalogue no: **SR 4600**
CD: Released Mar '90, on M.N.W. by M.N.W. Records. Catalogue no: **SRCD 4600**
Cass: Released Mar '90, on M.N.W. by M.N.W. Records. Catalogue no: **SRS 4600**
Album: Released Sep '83, on Charisma by Virgin Records. Deleted May '88. Catalogue no: **CAS 1059**

Happy Ending

HAPPY ENDING (Film Soundtrack) (Various artists)
Tracks: / What are you doing the rest of your life: *Various artists* / Collage: *Various artists* / Diamonds are forever: *Various artists* / What are you doing the rest of your life: *Various artists* / Floating time: *Various artists* / Hurry up 'n' hurry down: *Various artists* / Whistle while you swing: *Various artists* / What are you doing the rest of your life: *Various artists* / Something for everyone: *Various artists* / Pause that refreshes: *Various artists* / It ought to be forever: *Various artists* / Smooth sailing: *Various artists* / What are you doing the rest of your life: *Various artists*.
Album: Released '73, on United Artists by EMI Records. Deleted '78. Catalogue no: **UAS 29084**

HAPPY ENDING, THE (Original soundtrack) (Various artists)
Note: Composed by: Michel Legrand.
Album: Released Jan '89, on MCA by MCA Records. Catalogue no: **MCA 25105**
Cass: Released Jan '89, on MCA by MCA Records. Catalogue no: **MCAC 25105**

Hard Cases

HARD CASES (T.V. theme) (Robinson, Tom)
Tracks: / Hard cases.
7" Single: Released '88, on Castaway by BMG Records (UK). Catalogue no: **TR 27**

Hard Days Night

HARD DAYS NIGHT (See under Beatles)

Hard To Hold

HARD TO HOLD (VIDEO) (Various artists) (See also under Sprigfield, Rick)
VHS: Released '88, on CIC Video Catalogue no: **VHT 1135**

Hardcastle, Paul

WIZARD, THE (See panel below)
Tracks: / Wizard, The (part 1) / Wizard, The (part 2).
Note: Used as the theme to Top Of The Pops.
7" Single: Released Sep '86, on Chrysalis by Chrysalis Records. Deleted Jun '90. Catalogue no: **PAUL 3**
12" Single: Released Sep '86, on Chrysalis by Chrysalis Records. Deleted Jun '90. Catalogue no: **PAULX 3**

Harder They Come

HARDER THEY COME (Film soundtrack) (Various artists) (See also under Cliff, Jimmy)

Paul Hardcastle - 'The Wizard' theme from *Top of the Pops*

Tracks: / You can get it if you really want: *Cliff, Jimmy* / Many rivers to cross: *Cliff, Jimmy* / Harder they come, The: *Cliff, Jimmy* / Sitting in limbo: *Cliff, Jimmy* / Draw your brakes: *Cliff, Jimmy* / Rivers of Babylon: *Melodians* / Sweet and Dandy: *Maytals* / Pressure drop: *Maytals* / Johnny too bad: *Slickers* / Shanty-town: *Dekker, Desmond*.
Album: Released '79, on Island by Island Records. Deleted '84. Catalogue no: **ILPS 9202**
CD: Released '88, on Island by Island Records. Catalogue no: **CCD 9202**
CD: Released Sep '90, on Mango by Island Records. Catalogue no: **RRCD 11**
Album: Released Sep '90, on Mango by Island Records. Catalogue no: **RRCT 11**
Cass: Released Sep '86, on Island by Island Records. Catalogue no: **ICM 9202**
Album: Released Sep '86, on Island by Island Records. Catalogue no: **ILPM 9202**

Harding, Mike

FOO FOO SHUFFLEWICK AND HER EXOTIC BANANA
Tracks: / Foo Foo Shufflewick and her exotic banana / I am dancing alone in the night / Dracula and the trendies / Hotel Transylvania, The / Ronald Reagan, my hero / God meets Ronnie / Son et lumiere / Sao Bras Albuferia.
Note: Mike's latest comedy album recorded live at the Leeds Grand Theatre on Mike's 'One For The Road' tour 1985. A volume seller for Christmas.
Album: Released Nov '86, on Moonraker by Moonraker Records. Catalogue no: **MOO 8**
Cass: Released Nov '86, on Moonraker by Moonraker Records. Catalogue no: **MOOC 8**

ONE MAN SHOW
Tracks: / Arnold my frog / Beaky knucklewart / Bogey man / Crumpsall cream cracker corned beef, The / Kamikaze cubs go to camp / Down our street / Irwell Delta blues / Jimmy Spoons / King Cotton / My dad the weatherman / Napoleon's retreat from Wigan / Polka off / Polka on / Talking Blackpool blues / Top of the Pops / Unlucky Uncle Arthur / Wedding at 18 Clegg Street, The.
Album: Released Jul '76, on Philips by Phonogram Ltd. Deleted

'81. Catalogue no: **6625 022**
Cass: Released Jun '76, on Philips by Phonogram Ltd. Catalogue no: **7581617**
Album: Released Sep '84, on Philips by Phonogram Ltd. Catalogue no: **PRID 4**
Cass: Released Sep '84, on Philips by Phonogram Ltd. Catalogue no: **PRIDC 4**

Harem Holiday

HAREM HOLIDAY (FILM) (Various artists) (See also under Prsley, Elvis)
Note: Elvis brings the big beat to Baghdad. Running time: 84 minutes. Cert: U.
VHS: Released May '88, on Screen Legends (video) by Pickwick Video. Catalogue no: **SMV 10486**

Harlequin

HARLEQUIN (Film soundtrack) (Various artists)
Album: Released Mar '90, on Silva Screen by Silva Screen Records. Catalogue no: **MM22002**

Harmageddon

HARMAGEDDON (See under Emerson, Keith)

Harris, Jet

MAN WITH THE GOLDEN ARM, THEME FROM
Tracks: / Man with the golden arm, Theme from.
7" Single: Released Aug '62, on Decca by Decca International. Deleted '65. Catalogue no: **F 11488**

Harris, Rolf

CARTOON TIME FAVOURITES (TV theme)
Tracks: / Heigh ho/Whistle while you work / He's a tramp / Little April showers / I wan'na be like you / Siamese cat song / Ugly bug ball, The / Zip-a-dee-doo-dah / Never smile at a crocodile / I'm late / Dream is a wish your heart makes, A / When you wish upon a star / Who's afraid of the big bad wolf / Bare necessities.
Album: Released Oct '87, on BBC by BBC Records. Catalogue no: **REH 642**
Cass: Released Oct '87, on BBC by BBC Records. Catalogue no: **ZCR 642**

Harrison, Noel

WINDMILLS OF YOUR MIND
Tracks: / Windmills of your mind / Leitch on the beach.
Note: Theme from the film 'The Thomas Crown Affair'.
7" Single: Released Jul '81, on Reprise (USA) Catalogue no: **K 14004**
7" Single: Released Feb '69, on Reprise by WEA Records. Deleted '72. Catalogue no: **RS 20758**

WINDMILLS OF YOUR MIND (Old Gold)
7" Single: Released Jul '82, on Old Gold by Old Gold Records. Catalogue no: **OG 9090**

Harry's Game

HARRY'S GAME (See under Clannad)

Hartley, Richard

SOURSWEET (See under Soursweet)

Harvey, Jane

OTHER SIDE OF SONDHEIM, THE
CD: Released Jan '89, on Silva Screen by Silva Screen Records. Catalogue no: **781 833-2**

Harvey, Richard

GAME SET AND MATCH
Tracks: / Game set and match / Goodbye codes.
Note: From the TV Series *Game Set and Match*.
7" Single: Released Nov '88, on Chrysalis by Chrysalis Records. Catalogue no: **CHS 3324**

Hatari

HATARI (Film soundtrack) (Various artists)
CD: Released Feb '90, on Silva Screen by Silva Screen Records. Catalogue no: **2559.2**
Album: Released Jan '89, on Silva Screen by Silva Screen Records. Catalogue no: **2559.1**
Album: Released Jan '89, on RCA by BMG Records (UK). Catalogue no: **NL 43595**

Hatch, Tony

NEIGHBOURS (See under Neighbours)

SWEENEY II (Hatch, Tony Orchestra, The)
Tracks: / Sweeney II / Regan's

key.
Note: Theme from the ITV series 'The Sweeney'
7" Single: Released Apr '78, on EMI by EMI Records. Deleted '80. Catalogue no: **EMI 2780**

Haunted Summer

HAUNTED SUMMER (Film soundtrack) (Various artists)
Tracks: / Haunted summer: *Various artists* / Menage: *Various artists* / Villa diodati: *Various artists* / Night was made for loving, The: *Various artists* / Polidori's potions: *Various artists* / Ariel: *Various artists* / Confreres: *Various artists* / Geneva: *Various artists* / Alby: *Various artists* / Unquiet dream, An: *Various artists* / Hauntings: *Various artists*.
Note: Beautiful score from Christopher Young (composer of Hellraiser, Hellbound, Bat-21, The Fly 2, and Nightmare on Elm St 2) for the movie from Cannon films which is directed by Award winning Ivan Passer and stars Eric Stolz (Mask), Alex Winter (The Lost Boys) and Laura Dern (Blue Velvet) and is based on the lives of Lord Byron, Percy Shelley and Mary Shelley.
Album: Released Mar '90, on Cerebus (USA) Catalogue no: **C'BUS 0215**
Album: Released Jan '89, on Silva Screen by Silva Screen Records. Deleted Jun '89. Catalogue no: **FILM 037**
CD: Released Jan '89, on Silva Screen by Silva Screen Records. Catalogue no: **FILMCD 037**

Have Gun Will Travel

HAVE GUN WILL TRAVEL Original soundtrack (Various artists)
Note: American TV scores by Bernard Herrmann.
Album: Released Jan '89, on Cerebus (USA) Catalogue no: **C'BUS 209**

Hawk The Slayer

HAWK THE SLAYER (Film Soundtrack) (Robertson, Harry)
Album: Released Nov '80, on Chips Deleted '83. Catalogue no: **CHILP 1**

Hawkins, Screamin' Jay

I PUT A SPELL ON YOU

(SOUNDTRACK) (Hawkins, Screamin' Jay/John Lurie)
Tracks: / I put a spell on you / Stranger than paradise.
Note: Featured in the film Stranger Than Paradise.
12" Single: on Crammed Discs by Crammed Discs. Catalogue no: **CRAM 052**

Hawks

HAWKS (Film soundtrack) (Gibb, Barry)
Tracks: / System of love / Childhood days / My eternal love / Moonlight madness / Where tomorrow is / Celebration de la vie (theme) / Chain reaction / Cover you / Not in love at all / Letting Go.
Album: Released 23 Sep '88, on Polydor by Polydor Ltd. Catalogue no: **POLD 5234**
Cass: Released 23 Sep '88, on Polydor by Polydor Ltd. Catalogue no: **POLDC 5234**
CD: Released Nov '88, on Polydor by Polydor Ltd. Catalogue no: **837 264-4**
Album: Released Apr '85, on Pathe Marconi (France) Catalogue no: **PM 156 137 1**

Hawks & Doves

HAWKS & DOVES (SVEGLIATI E UCCIDI) (Original soundtrack) (Various artists)
Note: Composed by Ennio Morricone.
Album: Released Jan '89, on Silva Screen by Silva Screen Records. Catalogue no: **SP 8018**

Hayes, Billy

BALLAD OF DAVY CROCKETT
Tracks: / Ballad of Davy Crockett, The.
7" Single: Released Jan '56, on London-American by Decca Records. Deleted '59. Catalogue no: **HLA 8220**

Hayes, Isaac

BEST OF SHAFT (Highlights)
Tracks: / Shaft, Theme from / Walk from Regio's / Ellie's love theme / Cafe Regio's / Early Sunday morning / Soulsville / Bumpy's blues / Do your thing / End theme, The.
Note: From the man who invented 'symphonic soul' and influenced a whole generation of 70's soul

acts, as well as countless TV and movie soundtracks, Isaac Hayes is an enduring force. The title track from this album reached the number one spot in the US singles chart and number three in the UK. Theme from 'Shaft' was also successfully covered by Eddie & The Soul Band last year and reached number 13 in the UK charts.
Cass: Released Oct '81, on Stax by Fantasy Inc (USA). Catalogue no: **STAXK 5012**
Album: Released Oct '81, on Stax by Fantasy Inc (USA). Catalogue no: **STAXL 5012**
Album: Released Jun '86, on Stax by Fantasy Inc (USA). Catalogue no: **1052504**

SHAFT (Original Soundtrack)
Tracks: / Shaft, Theme from / Bumpy's lament / Walk from Regio's / Ellie's love theme / Shaft's cab ride / Cafe regio's / Early Sunday morning / Be yourself / Friend's place, A / Soulsville / No name bar / Bumpy's blues / Shaft strikes again / Do your thing / End theme, The.
CD: Released Oct '89, on Stax by Fantasy Inc (USA). Catalogue no: **CDSXD 021**
Album: Released Dec '71, on Polydor by Polydor Ltd. Deleted '76. Catalogue no: **2659 007**
2 LP Set: Released Oct '89, on Stax by Fantasy Inc (USA). Catalogue no: **SX2 021**
Cass: Released Oct '89, on Stax by Fantasy Inc (USA). Catalogue no: **SXC2 021**

SHAFT, THEME FROM (Original issue)
Tracks: / Shaft, Theme from.
7" Single: Released Dec '71, on Stax by Fantasy Inc (USA). Deleted '74. Catalogue no: **2025 069**

SHAFT, THEME FROM (Reissue)
Tracks: / Shaft, Theme from
7" Single: Released Mar '82, on Stax by Fantasy Inc (USA). Catalogue no: **STAX 1009**
CD Single: Released May '89, on South Bound by Ace Records. Catalogue no: **CDSEWT 701**
7" Single: Released May '89, on South Bound by Ace Records. Catalogue no: **SEWS 701**
12" Single: Released May '89, on

South Bound by Ace Records. Catalogue no: **SEWT 701**
7" Single: Released Aug '87, on Stax by Fantasy Inc (USA). Catalogue no: **STAX 810**

Hayward, Justin

STAR COPS (It won't be easy)
Tracks: / Star cops / Outer space.
12" Single: Released Jul '87, on BBC by BBC Records. Deleted Apr '89. Catalogue no: **12RSL 208**
7" Single: Released Jul '87, on BBC by BBC Records. Deleted Apr '89. Catalogue no: **RESL 208**

Hayworth, Rita

SELECTIONS FROM HER FILMS
Album: Released Jan '89, on Silva Screen by Silva Screen Records. Catalogue no: **CC 100.22**

Hazelhurst, Ronnie

LAUREL & HARDY'S MUSIC BOX (See under Laurel & Hardy)

Hazell

HAZELL (See under Bell, Maggie)

He Died With His ...

HE DIED WITH HIS EYES OPEN (Original soundtrack) (Various artists)
Note: French film starring Charlotte Rampling. Music by Claude Bolling.
Album: Released Jan '89, on Silva Screen by Silva Screen Records. Catalogue no: **A 275**

Head, Murray

ONE NIGHT IN BANGKOK
Tracks: / One night in Bangkok / Merano.
Note: From the stage show *Chess*
12" Single: Released Oct '84, on RCA by BMG Records (UK). Deleted May '89. Catalogue no: **CHESST 1**
7" Single: Released Oct '84, on RCA by BMG Records (UK). Deleted Feb '90. Catalogue no: **CHESS 1**

Healey, Jeff

CONFIDENCE MAN (Healey, Jeff Band)
Tracks: / Confidence man / That's what they say.
Note: Featured in the film *Roadhouse blues*
CD Single: Released Jan '89, on Arista by BMG Records (UK).

Deleted Mar '90. Catalogue no: **661 872**
7" Single: Released Nov '88, on Arista by BMG Records (UK). Deleted '89. Catalogue no: **111872**
12" Single: Released Nov '88, on Arista by BMG Records (UK). Deleted '89. Catalogue no: **611 872**

Heart Of The Stag

HEART OF THE STAG (Original soundtrack) (Various artists)
CD: Released Jan '89, on Silva Screen by Silva Screen Records. Catalogue no: **SCCD 1017**

Hearts Of Fire

HEARTS OF FIRE (Film soundtrack) (Various artists)
Tracks: / Hearts of fire: *Fiona* / Usual, The: *Dylan, Bob* / I'm in it for love: *Fiona* / Tainted love: *Everett, Rupert* / Hair of the dog: *Fiona* / Night after night: *Dylan, Bob* / In my heart: *Everett, Rupert* / Nights we spent on earth, The: *Fiona* / Had a dream about you, baby: *Dylan, Bob* / Let the good times roll: *Fiona*.
Cass: Released Oct '87, on CBS by CBS Records & Distribution. Deleted Jan '89. Catalogue no: **460000 4**
CD: Released Oct '87, on CBS by CBS Records & Distribution. Deleted Jan '90. Catalogue no: **460000 2**
Album: Released Oct '87, on CBS by CBS Records & Distribution. Deleted Apr '89. Catalogue no: **460000 1**

Hearts Of Gold

HEARTS OF GOLD (T.V. Theme) (Various artists)
Tracks: / Hearts of gold / Sacks of gold.
7" Single: Released Nov '88, on CBS by CBS Records & Distribution. Deleted Apr, 89. catalogue no: **654501 7**

Heat & Dust

HEAT & DUST (Film soundtrack) (Various artists)
Album: Released Apr '83, on T. E. R. by That's Entertainment Records. Catalogue no: **TER 1032**

Heavenly Bodies

HEAVENLY BODIES (Original Soundtrack) (Various artists)
Album: Released May '85, on Epic by CBS Records & Distribution. Deleted '87. Catalogue no: **EPC**

70262
Cass: Released May '85, on Epic by CBS Records & Distribution. Catalogue no: **40 70262**

Heavy Metal

HEAVY METAL (Film Soundtrack) (Various artists)
2 LP Set: Released Nov '81, on Epic by CBS Records & Distribution. Deleted Nov '86. Catalogue no: **EPC 88558**

Hefti, Neal

BATMAN THEME (1966 version)
Tracks: / Batman theme.
7" Single: Released Mar '88, on RCA by BMG Records (UK). Deleted Sep '90. Catalogue no: **PB 49571**
7" Pic: Released Jul '89, on RCA by BMG Records (UK). Catalogue no: **PB 49571 PD**
12" Single: Released Mar '88, on RCA by BMG Records (UK). Deleted Feb '90. Catalogue no: **PT 49572**

Helen Morgan Story

HELEN MORGAN STORY, THE (Original Soundtrack) (Various artists)
CD: Released Jan '89, on Silva Screen by Silva Screen Records. Catalogue no: **1030.2**

Hell Can Be Heaven

HELL CAN BE HEAVEN (Original cast) (Various artists)
Album: Released Dec '83, on T. E. R. by That's Entertainment Records. Catalogue no: **TER 1068**
Cass: Released Dec '83, on T. E. R. by That's Entertainment Records. Catalogue no: **ZCTER 1068**

Hello Again

HELLO AGAIN (Original sound track) (Various artists)
Tracks: / Hello again: *Various artists* / Lucy's reflection: *Various artists* / Kevin and Lucy: *Various artists* / In the beginning: *Various artists* / Zelda visits the beyond: *Various artists* / Dinner party, The: *Various artists* / Transfiguration: *Various artists* / Jason's remorse: *Various artists* / Second thoughts: *Various artists* / Lucy despairs: *Various artists* / Kimmy pie: *Various artists* / Grand finale, The: *Various artists*.
Note: Music by William Goldstein from the comedy with Shelley

Long.
CD: Released Jul '88, on Silva Screen by Silva Screen Records. Deleted Apr '90. Catalogue no: **CDC 1003**
Cass: Released Jan '89, on Silva Screen by Silva Screen Records. Catalogue no: **CDS 1003**

Hello Dolly

HELLO DOLLY (Original cast recording) (Various artists)
Tracks: / Hello Dolly prologue: *Various artists* / I put my hand in: *Various artists* / It takes a woman: *Various artists* / Put on your Sunday clothes: *Varicus artists* / Ribbons down my back: *Various artists* / Motherhood: *Various artists* / Dancing: *Various artists* / Before the parade passes by: *Various artists* / Elegance: *Various artists* / Hello Dolly: *Various artists* / It only takes a moment: *Various artists* / So long dearie: *Various artists* / Hello Dolly finale: *Various artists.*
Cass: Released Oct '89, on RCA by BMG Records (UK). Catalogue no: **GK 83814**
CD: Released Oct '89, on RCA by BMG Records (UK). Catalogue no: **GD 83814**

HELLO DOLLY (Original Broadway cast) (Various artists)
Tracks: / I put my hand in: *Various artists* / It takes a woman: *Various artists* / Put on your Sunday clothes: *Various artists* / Ribbons down my back: *Various artists* / Dancing: *Various artists* / Motherhood march: *Various artists* / Before the parade passes by: *Various artists* / Elegance: *Various artists* / Hello Dolly: *Various artists* / It only takes a moment: *Various artists* / So long dearie: *Various artists* / Hello Dolly finale: *Various artists.*
Cass: Released Feb '80, on RCA by BMG Records (UK). Deleted '85. Catalogue no: **BK 42962**
Album: Released Feb '80, on RCA by BMG Records (UK). Deleted '85. Catalogue no: **BL 42962**

HELLO DOLLY (Original Film Sountrack)
Tracks: / Just leave everything to me: *Various artists* / It takes a woman: *Various artists* / Put on your Sunday clothes: *Various artists* / Ribbons down my back: *Various artists* / Dancing: *Various*

artists / Before the parade passes by: *Various artists* / Elegannce: *Various artists* / Love is only love: *Various artists* / Hello Dolly: *Various artists* / It only takes a minute: *Various artists* / So long dearie: *Various artists* / Finale: *Various artists.*
Cass: Released May '84, on Polydor (Italy) by Polydor Ltd. Catalogue no: **810 368-4**
Album: Released May '84, on Polydor (Italy) by Polydor Ltd. Catalogue no: **810 368-1**

HELLO DOLLY (FIRST ISSUE) (Film soundtrack) (Various artists)
Album: Released Mar '70, on Stateside by EMI Records. Deleted '75. Catalogue no: **SSL 10292**

HELLO DOLLY (VIDEO) (Various artists)
Note: Running time: 140 mins.
VHS: Released '88, on CBS-Fox by CBS-Fox Video. Catalogue no: **100150**

Hello Frisco Hello

HELLO FRISCO HELLO (Original soundtrack) (Various artists)
Note: Starring Alice Faye and June Havoc.
Album: on Hollywood Soundstage (USA) Catalogue no: **HS 5005**
Cass: Released Jan '89, on Silva Screen by Silva Screen Records. Catalogue no: **CSH 2070**
Album: Released Jan '89, on Silva Screen by Silva Screen Records. Catalogue no: **SH 2070**

Hello Goodbye

HELLO GOODBYE (Film Soundtrack) (Various artists)
Tracks: / Hello goodbye: *Various artists* / Danny takes a dip: *Various artists* / No need to cry: *Various artists* / Theme 3: *Various artists* / Food for cats: *Various artists* / Take the plunge: *Various artists* / Harry's return: *Various artists* / Interlude: *Various artists* / Journey to Marseilles: *Various artists* / Hello goodbye: *Various artists* / No need to cry: *Various artists* / Harry remembers: *Various artists* / Bistro waltz: *Various artists* / Theme 3 (reprise): *Various artists* / Morning departure: *Various artists* / Danny's theme: *Various artists* /

Destination Le Havre: *Various artists* / Together: *Various artists.*
Album: Released '73, on Stateside by EMI Records. Deleted '78. Catalogue no: **SSL 10309**

Hellraiser

HELLRAISER (Original Soundtrack) (Various artists)
Tracks: / Resurrection: *Various artists* / Hellbound heart: *Various artists* / Lament configuration, The: *Various artists* / Quick death, A: *Various artists* / Seduction and pursuit: *Various artists* / In love's name: *Various artists* / Cenobites: *Various artists* / Rat slice quartet, The: *Various artists* / Re-resurrection: *Various artists* / Uncle Frank: *Various artists* / Brought on by night: *Various artists* / Another puzzle: *Various artists.*
Note: Music by Christopher Young.
Album: Released 7 Nov '87, on Silva Screen by Silva Screen Records. Catalogue no: **FILM 021**
Cass: Released Jan '89, on Silva Screen by Silva Screen Records. Catalogue no: **FILMC 021**
CD: Released Jan '89, on Silva Screen by Silva Screen Records. Catalogue no: **FILMCD 021**

Hellraiser II

HELLRAISER II (Hellbound: Original soundtrack) (Various artists)
Tracks: / Hellbound: *Various artists* / Second sight seance: *Various artists* / Looking through a woman: *Various artists* / Something to think about: *Various artists* / Skin her alive: *Various artists* / Stringing the puppet: *Various artists* / Hall of mirrors: *Various artists* / Dead or living: *Various artists* / Leviathan: *Various artists* / Sketch with fire: *Various artists.*
Note: Christopher Young with the Graunke Symphony Orchestra & Chorus. The sequel to 1988's most successful Horror Film based on a story by Clive Barker.
Album: Released Jan '89, on GNP Crescendo (USA) by GNP Crescendo Records (USA). Catalogue no: **GNPS 8015**
CD: Released Jan '89, on GNP Crescendo (USA) by GNP Crescendo Records (USA). Catalogue no: **GNPD 8015**
Cass: Released Jan '89, on GNP

Crescendo (USA) by GNP Crescendo Records (USA). Catalogue no: **GNP5 8015**

Help (Film)

HELP (See under Beatles)

Hemingways Adventures

HEMINGWAYS ADVENTURES OF A YOUNG MAN (Film Soundtrack) (Various artists)
Note: Composed by Franz Waxman.
Album: Released Nov '80, on Entr'acte by Fith Continent Music Group (USA). Deleted Nov '85. Catalogue no: **ERS 6516**
Album: Released Jan '89, on Silva Screen by Silva Screen Records. Catalogue no: **LXRS 201**
CD: Released Jan '89, on Silva Screen by Silva Screen Records. Catalogue no: **LXCD 1**

Hendrix, Jimi

ALL ALONG THE WATCHTOWER (Hendrix, Jimi Experience)
Tracks: / All along the watchtower / Foxy lady / Purple haze / Manic depression.
Note: Featured in the film '1969'.
7" Single: Released Oct '68, on Track by Polydor Ltd. Deleted '71. Catalogue no: **604 025**
12" Single: Released Dec '81, on Polydor by Polydor Ltd. Deleted Dec '84. Catalogue no: **POSPX 401**

Henry, Paul

BENNY'S THEME (Henry, Paul & the Mayson Glen Orchestra)
Tracks: / Benny's Theme / Benny's theme (version).
Note: From TV programme *Crossroads*.
7" Single: Released Jan '78, on Pye Deleted '81. Catalogue no: **7N 46027**

Henry V

HENRY V (Film soundtrack) (City Of Birmingham Symphony Orchestra)
Tracks: / Oh for a muse of fire / Henry V theme / Boar's head, The / Three traitors, The / Now lords' for France / Death of Falstaff, The / Once more unto the breach / Threat to the governor of Harfleur, The / Katherine of France / March

to Calais / Death of Bardolph / Upon the king / St. Crispin's day / Battle of Agincourt, The / Day is yours, The / Non nobis domine / Wooing of Katherine, The / Let this acceptance take / End title.
Note: Music by Patrick Doyle. City of Birmingham Symphony Orchestra conducted by Simon Rattle
CD: Released Sep '89, on EMI by EMI Records. Catalogue no: **CDHENRY 5**
Album: Released Sep '89, on EMI by EMI Records. Catalogue no: **EL 7499191**
Cass: Released Sep '89, on EMI by EMI Records. Catalogue no: **EL 7499194**
CD: Released Sep '89, on EMI by EMI Records. Catalogue no: **CDC 749 919 2**

Henry's Cat

HENRY'S CAT (Stories from the TV series) (Godfrey, Bob)
Tracks: / Disco doddle / Treasure / Hypnotists / Circus / Christmas dinner / Film, The / Diet / Competition / Fortune teller / Race, The.
Album: Released Sep '83, on BBC by BBC Records. Deleted 31 Aug '88. Catalogue no: **REC 482**
Cass: Released Sep '83, on BBC by BBC Records. Deleted 31 Aug '88. Catalogue no: **ZCM 482**

Hentschel, David

EDUCATING RITA (Film music)
Cass: Released Jun '83, on Mercury by Phonogram Ltd. Catalogue no: **MERLC 23**
Album: Released Jun '83, on Mercury by Phonogram Ltd. Catalogue no: **MERL 23**

EDUCATING RITA (SINGLE)
Tracks: / Educating Rita / I can't dance.
7" Single: Released May '83, on Mercury by Phonogram Ltd. Catalogue no: **RITA 1**

Hercules

HERCULES (Original soundtrack) (Various artists)
Note: Composed by Pino Donaggio.
Album: Released Jan '89, on Silva Screen by Silva Screen Records. Catalogue no: **STV 81187**

HERCULES (ORIGINAL) (Original soundtrack) (Various artists)
Note: Score by Enzo Masetti for the early 1960's Italian epic.
Album: Released Jan '89, on Silva Screen by Silva Screen Records. Catalogue no: **PHCAM 01**

HERCULES UNCHAINED (Original soundtrack) (Various artists)
Note: The sequel to Hercules (original) by Enzo Masetti.
Album: Released Jan '89, on Silva Screen by Silva Screen Records. Catalogue no: **PHCAM 07**

Hero & The Terror

HERO AND THE TERROR (Film soundtrack) (Various artists)
Tracks: / Two can be one: *Various artists* / Obsession: *Various artists* / Workout: *Various artists* / Terror, The: *Various artists* / Hero's seduction: *Various artists* / San Pedro bust: *Various artists* / Ladies room, The: *Various artists* / Breakout: *Various artists* / Birthday wishes: *Various artists* / Discovery: *Various artists* / Showtime: *Various artists* / Angela: *Various artists* / Subterranean terror: *Various artists* / Simon's lair: *Various artists* / Search, The: *Various artists* / Living nightmare: *Various artists* / Love and obsession: *Various artists*.
CD: Released Jan '90, on Silva Screen by Silva Screen Records. Catalogue no: **EDL 2508.2**
Album: Released Jan '90, on Silva Screen by Silva Screen Records. Catalogue no: **EDL 2508.1**

Herrmann, Bernard

CLASSIC FANTASY FILM SCORES (Various artists)
Tracks: / Three worlds of Gulliver: *Various artists* / Mysterious island: *Various artists* / Seventh voyage of Sinbad: *Various artists* / Jason and the Argonauts: *Various artists*.
CD: Released Jun '88, on Cloud Nine by Cloud Nine Records. Catalogue no: **ACN 7014**

HITCHCOCK MOVIE THRILLER
CD: Released Jan '88, on London Records by London Records Ltd. Deleted May '89. Catalogue no: **820 277-2**

PSYCHO (See under Psycho)

He's My Girl

HE'S MY GIRL (Film soundtrack) (Various artists)
Tracks: / Rock revival: *Hallyday, David* / He's my girl: *Hallyday, David* / Kicks: *Revere, Paul & The Raiders* / I saw Mary: *Vartan, Sylvie* / Church of the poison spider: *Various artists* / One night in Hollywood: *Barrera, Micky* / She can dance: *Vartan, Sylvie* / Time has come today: *Chamber Brothers* / Mississippi queen: *Mountain* / Reggie's theme: *Bullard, Kim*.
Note: "Following the worldwide distribution deal between Scotti Bros and Polygram, IMS releases its first Scotti Bros production, a soundtrack from the US film He's My Girl. From the people who brought you the Rocky soundtracks, this album contains similar hard-hitting American rock music from various Scotti Bros artists." (IMS Records, May 1988.)
Album: Released May '88, on Polygram by PolyGram UK Ltd. Catalogue no: **8327641**
CD: Released May '88, on Polygram by PolyGram UK Ltd. Catalogue no: **832 764 2**
Cass: Released May '88, on Polygram by PolyGram UK Ltd. Catalogue no: **8327644**

Hess, Nigel

SCREENS AND STAGES (Hess, Nigel/London Film Orchestra)
Tracks: / Cyrano de Bergerac / Only game, The / Anna of the five towns / Woman of substance, A / All passion spent / Testament / Campion / London Embassy, The / An affair in mind / To us a child / Vidal in Venice / Summer's lease / Atlantis / Much ado about nothing / Vanity fair / Secret of Sherlock Holmes, The.
CD: Released Jan '90, on Fly by Fly Records. Catalogue no: **FLYCD 101**
Album: Released Jan '90, on Fly by Fly Records. Catalogue no: **FLYLP 101**
Cass: Released Jan '90, on Fly by Fly Records. Catalogue no: **FLYMC 101**

Hi De Hi

HI DE HI (songs from the BBC TV series) (Various artists)
Tracks: / I've always chased rainbows: *Various artists* / Easy to love: *Various artists* / Dancing in the dark: *Various artists* / I've grown accustomed to her face: *Various artists* / Make 'em laugh: *Various artists* / Tiptoe through the tulips: *Various artists* / Darktown poker club: *Various artists* / I don't know why: *Various artists* / Holiday rock: *Various artists* / Little white bull: *Various artists* / Chattanooga choo choo: *Various artists*.
Album: Released Nov '81, on BBC by BBC Records. Deleted '88. Catalogue no: **REC 436**
Cass: Released Nov '81, on BBC by BBC Records. Deleted '88. Catalogue no: **ZCM 436**

Hidden

HIDDEN, THE (Original soundtrack) (Various artists)
Note: Horror film score by Michael Convertino.
Album: Released Jan '89, on Silva Screen by Silva Screen Records. Catalogue no: **STV 81349**
Cass: Released Jan '89, on Silva Screen by Silva Screen Records. Deleted Mar '90. Catalogue no: **CTV 81349**
CD: Released Jan '89, on Silva Screen by Silva Screen Records. Catalogue no: **VCD 47349**

Hiding Out

HIDING OUT (Original soundtrack) (Various artists)
Album: Released '88, on Virgin by Virgin Records. Catalogue no: **V 2493**
CD: Released '88, on Virgin by Virgin Records. Catalogue no: **CDV 2493**
Cass: Released '88, on Virgin by Virgin Records. Catalogue no: **TCV 2493**

High Noon

HIGH NOON (See under Laine, Frankie)

High Road To China

HIGH ROAD TO CHINA (Film soundtrack) (Various artists)
Tracks: / Main title: *Various artists* / Charlie gets the knife: *Various artists* / Airborne: *Various artists* / Love theme: *Various artists* / Waxiri Village: *Various artists* / Attack and escape: *Various artists* / Farewell to Struts: *Various artists* / O'Malley and Eve: *Various artists* / Charleston: *Various artists* / Von Kern's attack: *Various artists* / Flight from Katmandu: *Various artists* / Eve finds her father: *Various artists* / Raid on Chang's camp: *Various artists* / High Road love theme and end title: *Various artists*.
Note: Music composed and conducted by John Barry.
Cass: Released '84, on Silva Screen by Silva Screen Records. Catalogue no: **FILMC 001**
Album: Released '84, on Silva Screen by Silva Screen Records. Catalogue no: **FILM 001**

High Society (Film)

HIGH SOCIETY (Film soundtrack) (Various artists)
Tracks: / Overture / High Society calypso / Little one / You're sensational / I love you Samantha / Now you has jazz / Well did you ever / Mind if I make love to you?.
Album: Released Nov '60, on Capitol by EMI Records. Deleted '65. Catalogue no: **SLCT 6116**
Cass: Released Jun '73 on Capitol by EMI Records. Catalogue no: **TC SLCT 6116**

HIGH SOCIETY (VIDEO) (Various artists)
VHS: Released '88 on MGM/UA (Video). Catalogue no: **SMV 10292**

High Society (Show)

HIGH SOCIETY (Broadway cast) (Various artists)
Album: Released '89 on Reality. Catalogue no: **R 108**
Cass: Released '89 on Reality. Catalogue no: **TCR 108**
CD: Released '89 on Reality. Catalogue no: **CDR 108**

HIGH SOCIETY (Original London cast) (Various artists)
Tracks: / High society overture / How do you spell Ambassador / Give him the oo-la-la / Who wants to be a millionaire? / Little one / Hey good lookin' / I love you Samantha / Ball medley / Well did you ever? / Most gentlemen don't like love / Now you has jazz / In the still of the night / You're sensational / True love / Finale
Album: Released Jan '87, on Columbia by Columbia Records. Catalogue no: **SCX 6707**
Cass: Released Jan '87, on Columbia by Columbia Records. Catalogue no: **TCSCX 6707**
CD: Released Apr '87, on Columbia by Columbia Records. Catal-

ogue no: **CDSCX 6707**
CD : Released Apr '87, on EMI by EMI Records. catalogue no: **CDP 746777 2**

High Spirits

HIGH SPIRITS (Original London cast) (Various artists)
Tracks: / Overture: *Various artists* / Was she prettier than I?: *Various artists* / Bicycle song: *Various artists* / You'd better love me: *Various artists* / Where is the man I married?: *Various artists* / Go into your trance: *Various artists* / Forever and a day: *Various artists* / Something tells me: *Various artists* / I know your heart: *Various artists* / Faster than sound: *Various artists* / If I gave you: *Various artists* / Talking to you: *Various artists* / Home sweet Heaven: *Various artists* / Something is coming to tea: *Various artists* / What in the world did you want?: *Various artists.*
Note: 1964 musical starring Cicely Courtneidge, Jan Waters, Denis Quilley and Marti Stevens. Music by Hugh Martin and Timothy Gray conducted by Michael Moores.
Album: Released Nov '85, on Flashback by Mainline Records. Catalogue no: **FBLP 8087**
Cass: Released Nov '85, on Flashback by Mainline Records. Catalogue no: **ZCFBL 8087**

High Spirits (Film)

HIGH SPIRITS (Film soundtrack) (Various artists)
Tracks: / Overture *Various artists* / Castle Plunkett: *Various artists* / Plunkett's lament: *Various artists* / Ghost bus tours: *Various artists* / Ghostly reflections: *Various artists* / She is from the far land: *Various artists* / Bumps in the knight: *Various artists* / Mary appears: *Various artists.*
Album: Released '88, on GNP Crescendo (USA) by GNP Crescendo Records (USA). Catalogue no: **GNPS 8015**
Cass: Released '88, on GNP Crescendo (USA) by GNP Crescendo Records (USA). Catalogue no: **GNP5 8015**
CD: Released '88, on GNP Crescendo (USA) by GNP Crescendo Records (USA). Catalogue no: **GNPD 8015**

Higher & Higher

HIGHER & HIGHER (Original soundtrack) (Various artists)

Note: Starring Frank Sinatra..
Album: Released Jan '89, on Silva Screen by Silva Screen Records. Catalogue no: **HS 411**

Highly Likely

WHATEVER HAPPENED TO YOU (LIKELY LADS THEME)
Tracks: / Whatever happened to you (likely lads theme):
7" Single: Released Apr '73, on BBC by BBC Records. Deleted '76. Catalogue no: **RESL 10**

Hill Street Blues

HILL STREET BLUES (Music from the TV Series) (Caine, Daniel Orchestra) (See also under Post, Mike)
Cass: Released Feb '85, on Indiana by Indiana Records. Catalogue no: **HSBC 2222**
Album: Released Feb '85, on Indiana by Indiana Records. Catalogue no: **HSBP 2222**

Hired Man

HIRED MAN (Original London cast) (Various artists)
Tracks: / Song of the hired men: *Various artists* / Say farewell: *Various artists* / Work song: *Various artists* / I wouldn't be the first: *Various artists* / Fade away: *Various artists* / What a fool I've been: *Various artists* / If I could: *Various artists* / Hired men (reprise): *Various artists* / Black rock: *Various artists* / Men of stone (Union song): *Various artists* / When next you see that smile: *Various artists* / So tell your children (War song): *Various artists.*
Cass: Released Nov '84, on Polydor by Polydor Ltd. Catalogue no: **POLHC 18**
Album: Released Nov '84, on Polydor by Polydor Ltd. Catalogue no: **POLH 18**

HIRED MAN, THE (Original London cast) (Various artists)
Album: Released 7 Nov '87, on First Night by First Night Records. Catalogue no: **SCENE 10**
Cass: Released 7 Nov '87, on First Night by First Night Records. Catalogue no: **SCENEC 10**

His Land

HIS LAND (Film Soundtrack) (Various artists)
Tracks: / His land: *Richard, Cliff* / Jerusalem: *Richard, Cliff* / New 23rd: *Richard, Cliff* / His land: Ri-

chard, *Cliff* / Keep me where love is: *Richard, Cliff* / Ezekiel's vision: *Barrows, Cliff* / Hallelujah chorus: *Barrows, Cliff* / Over in Bethlehem: *Richard, Cliff/ Barrows, Cliff* / He's everything to me: *Richard, Cliff/ Barrows, Cliff* / Dry bones: *Carmichael, Ralph Orchestra & Chorus* / Hava nagila: *Carmichael, Ralph Orchestra & Chorus.*
Album: Released '73, on Columbia by EMI Records. Deleted '78. Catalogue no: **SCX 6443**

His Monkey Wife

HIS MONKEY WIFE (Original cast) (Various artists)
Tracks: / Emily's waltz: *Various artists.*/ Home and beauty and you: *Various artists* / Marriage: *Various artists* / In Boboma tonight: *Various artists* / Haverstock Hill: *Various artists* / Don't rush me: *Various artists* / Who is she?: *Various artists* / Dear human race: *Various artists* / Leave it all to Smithers: *Various artists* / Mad about your mind: *Various artists* / His monkey wife: *Various artists* / Girl like you, A: *Various artists* / Doing the chimpanzee: *Various artists* / Live like the blessed angels: *Various artists* / His monkey wife (reprise): *Various artists* / Who is she? (reprise): *Various artists.*
Album: Released Jan '74, on President by President Records. Catalogue no: **PTLS 1051**

History Of The World

HISTORY OF THE WORLD PART 1 (Film soundtrack) (Various artists)
Album: Released Nov '81, on Warner Bros. by WEA Records. Deleted Nov '86. Catalogue no: **K56926**

Hit (film)

HIT, THE (Film soundtrack) (De Lucia, Paco)
Tracks: / Hit 1 & 2, The / Willie's theme / Spanish sun/The funeral/Andalucia / John Lennon / Kidnap/Convoy / Braddock's theme / Windmills / To Madrid (Willy Parker) / Double indemnity / Wasteland/Cracking / Maggie's problem / Roncevalles / Canyon, The / Cojones / Waterfall / Moonlight / Hilltop / Maggie fights back /

Very lucky girl.

Album: Released '84, on Mercury by Phonogram Ltd. Catalogue no: **822 668 1**

Cass: Released '84, on Mercury by Phonogram Ltd. Catalogue no: **822 668 4**

Hit The Deck

HIT THE DECK/IN THE GOOD OLD SUMMERTIME/ROYAL WEDDING (Film Soundtrack) (Various artists)

Tracks: / Sometimes I'm happy: *Powell, Jane/Vic Damone* (Hit The Deck.) / Keepin' myself for you: *Miller, Ann/Tony Martin & Girls* (Hit The Deck.) / Kiss or two, A: *Reynolds, Debbie & Boys* (Hit The Deck.) / Chiribiribee (Ciribiribin): *Powell, Jane/Vic Damone* (Hit The Deck. With Kay Armen/Tony Martin/Debbie Reynolds/Russ Tamblyn.) / Lucky bird: *Powell, Jane* (Hit The Deck.) / Join the navy/Loo loo: *Reynolds, Debbie* (Hit The Deck.) / Why oh why: *Powell, Jane/Vic Damone* (Hit The Deck. With Tony Martin/Russ Tamblyn/Debbie Reynolds/Ann Miller.) / I know that you know: *Powell, Jane/Vic Damone* (Hit The Deck.) / More than you know: *Martin, Tony* (Hit The Deck.) / Lady from the Bayou: *Miller, Ann* (Hit The Deck.) / Sometimes I'm happy: *Powell, Jane* (Hit The Deck.) / Hallelujah: *Martin, Tony/Vic Damone/Russ Tamblyn/Jubilaires* (Hit The Deck.) / I don't care: *Garland, Judy* (In The Good Old Summertime.) / Meet me tonight in dreamland: *Garland, Judy* (In The Good Old Summertime.) / Play that barber shop chord: *Garland, Judy & The King's Men* (In The Good Old Summertime.) / Last night when we were young: *Garland, Judy* (In The Good Old Summertime.) / Put your arms around me honey: *Garland, Judy* (In The Good Old Summertime.) / Merry Christmas: *Garland, Judy* (In The Good Old Summertime.) / Too late now: *Powell, Jane* (Royal Wedding.) / Ev'ry night at seven: *Astaire, Fred* (Royal Wedding.) / Happiest day of my life: *Powell, Jane* (Royal Wedding.) / I left my hat in Haiti: *Astaire, Fred* (Royal Wedding.) / You're the world to me: *Astaire, Fred* (Royal Wedding.) / How could you believe me when I said I loved you when you..: *Astaire, Fred/Jane Powell* (Royal Wedding.).

Note: Royal Wedding - U.K. title:

Wedding Bells.

CD: Released Apr '90, on MGM (EMI) Catalogue no: **CDMGM 15**

CD: Released Apr '90, on MGM (EMI) Catalogue no: **CDP 794 193 2**

Cass: Released Apr '90, on MGM (EMI) Catalogue no: **794 193 4**

Album: Released Apr '90, on MGM (EMI) Catalogue no: **LPMGM 15**

Album: Released Apr '90, on MGM (EMI) Catalogue no: **794 193 1**

Cass: Released Apr '90, on MGM (EMI) Catalogue no: **TCMGM 15**

HIT THE DECK/THE PIRATE/PAGAN LOVE SONG (Original Soundtracks) (Various artists)

CD: Released Jan '89, on Silva Screen by Silva Screen Records. Catalogue no: **MCAD 5950**

Hitchcock, Alfred

MUSIC FROM THE FILMS OF ALFRED HITCHCOCK (Various artists)

CD: Released Jan '89, on Silva Screen by Silva Screen Records. Catalogue no: **VCD 47225**

MUSIC TO BE MURDERED BY

Album: Released '88, on DRG (USA) by DRG Records (USA). Catalogue no: **SL 5183**

PORTRAIT OF ALFRED HITCHCOCK & OTHER FILM THEMES (London Philharmonic Orchestra)

Tracks: / Le 7 voyage Sinbad (the 7th voyage of Sinbad) / Psychose (psycho) / Pas de printemps pour Marnie / La mort aux trousses (north by northwest) / Sueurs froides / Mais qui a tue Harry (The trouble with Harry) / Voyage au centre de la terre / Le jour ou la terre s'arreta / Fahrenheit 451 / L'Ile mysterieuse / Jason et les argonautes / Voyages de Gulliver **Album:** Released Feb '85, on IMS by Polydor Ltd. Catalogue no: **414 296-1**

Hitch-Hiker's Guide...

HITCH-HIKER'S 1 (Various artists)

Album: Released May '89, on Hannibal by Hannibal Records. Catalogue no: **HNBL 2301**

Cass: Released May '89, on Hannibal by Hannibal Records. Catalogue no: **HNBC 2301**

HITCH-HIKERS GUIDE TO

THE GALAXY (See also under Adams, Douglas)

HITCH-HIKER'S GUIDE TO THE GALAXY (Original radio production) (Various artists)

Note: The original radio production on 6, one-hour cassettes in presentation box.

Cass set: Released Sep '88, on BBC by BBC Records. Catalogue no: **ZBBC 1035**

2 LP Set: Released Apr '80, on Original Catalogue no: **ORA 042**

CD Set: Released Sep '88, on BBC by BBC Records. Catalogue no: **BBC CD 6001**

HITCH-HIKERS GUIDE TO THE GALAXY (TV Soundtrack) (Various artists)

2 LP Set: Released Apr '80, on Original. Catalogue no: **ORA 042**

HITCH-HIKER'S GUIDE TO THE GALAXY VOL.2 (Various artists)

Album: Released Nov '80, on Original. Catalogue no: **ORA 054**

Hi-Tek 3

SPIN THAT WHEEL (TURTLES GET REAL) (Hi Tek 3 featuring Ya Kid K)

Tracks: / Spin that wheel (Turtles get real).

Note: Originally released in January 1990 (BORG), this track has been used in the film *Teenage Mutant Ninja Turtles*.

12" Single: Released Sep '90, on Brothers Organisation Catalogue no: **12 BORG 16**

Cassingle: Released Sep '90, on Brothers Organisation Catalogue no: **CABORG 16**

7" Single: Released Sep '90, on Brothers Organisation Catalogue no: **BORG 16**

CD Single: Released Sep '90, on Brothers Organisation Catalogue no: **CD BORG 16**

Hits From...

HITS FROM ROCK MUSICALS (Various artists)

Tracks: / Aquarius: *Various artists* / Day by day: *Various artists* / See me feel me: *Various artists* / You're the one that I want: *Various artists* / Don't cry for me Argentina: *Various artists* / I don't know how to love him: *Various artists* / Acid Queen: *Various artists* / Superstar: *Various artists* / Good morning

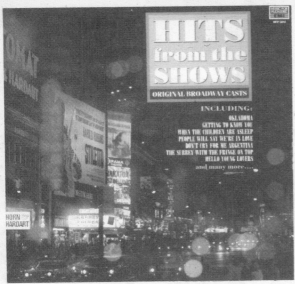

HITS from the SHOWS
ORIGINAL BROADWAY CASTS

INCLUDING:

OKLAHOMA
GETTING TO KNOW YOU
WHEN THE CHILDREN ARE ASLEEP
PEOPLE WILL SAY WE'RE IN LOVE
DON'T CRY FOR ME ARGENTINA
THE SURREY WITH THE FRINGE ON TOP
HELLO YOUNG LOVERS

and many more...

Hits from the Shows - compilation on MFP

starshine: *Various artists* / Let the sun shine in: *Various artists* / Summer nights: *Various artists* / Ain't got no....I got life: *Various artists* / Another suitcase in another hall: *Various artists* / Hopelessly devoted to you: *Various artists* / Pinball wizard: *Various artists*.
Cass: Released Feb '83, on Spot by Pickwick Records. Catalogue no: **SPC 8508**
Album: Released Feb '83, on Spot by Pickwick Records. Catalogue no: **SPR 8508**

HITS FROM THE SILVER SCREEN (Various artists)
Cass: Released Sep '81, on Ampro. Catalogue no: **AMP 010**

Hits From The Shows

HITS FROM THE SHOWS (Original Broadway Casts) (Various artists) (See panel above)
Tracks: / Oklahoma: *Various artists* / Getting to know you: *Various artists* / Doin' what comes naturally: *Various artists* / When the children are asleep: *Various artists* / Luck be a lady: *Various artists* / People will say we're in love: *Various artists* / Don't cry for me Argentina: *Various artists* / Surrey with

the fringe on top: *Various artists* / Hello young lovers: *Various artists* / Guys and dolls: *Various artists* / You can't get a man with a gun: *Various artists* / June is bustin' out all over: *Various artists* / Another suitcase in another hall: *Various artists* / Shall we dance: *Various artists* / Oldest established craps game in New York: *Various artists*.
Album: Released Nov '88, on MFP by EMI Records. Catalogue no: **MFP 5842**
Cass: Released Nov '88, on MFP by EMI Records. Catalogue no: **TCMFP 5842**

Hokey Cokey

HOKEY COKEY (TV Soundtrack) (Various artists)
Tracks: / Hokey cokey (instrumental): *Various artists* / Feeling good today: *Various artists* / Riverbank boatrace day: *Various artists* / Visiting song, The: *Various artists* / Doodly-doo: *Various artists* / Down at the bottom of the ocean: *Various artists* / Five tall rockets: *Various artists* / There was an old woman: *Various artists* / Moonwalking: *Various artists* / Rackaticky bleep: *Various artists* / One two three dancing: *Various*

artists / Bushfright: *Various artists* / We're explorers: *Various artists* / Animal fair: *Various artists* / Big bear growls, A: *Various artists* / Hot air balloon: *Various artists* / Blow the wind southerly: *Various artists* / Penguin strut, The: *Various artists* / Who goes there?: *Various artists* / Fox went out, The: *Various artists* / Hokey cokey (finale): *Various artists*.
Cass: Released May '85, on BBC by BBC Records. Catalogue no: **ZCM 557**
Album: Released May '85, on BBC by BBC Records. Deleted Apr '89. Catalogue no: **REC 557**

Holdridge, Lee

EAST OF EDEN (See under East Of Eden)

FILM MUSIC OF LEE HOLDRIDGE, THE (London Symphony Orchestra)
Tracks: / Wizards and warriors / Splash / Great whales, The / Hemingway play - Parisian sketch / Going home / Journey, The / Beastmaster suite / Music for strings / East of Eden (suite).
Note: Newly recorded suites from the Beastmaster, Splash, Wizards & Warriors, East of Eden (TV version) and Jonathan Livingstone Seagull. Conducted by Charles Gerhardt.
Album: Released Jan '89, on Varese Sarabande Records(USA) by Varese Sarabande Records (USA). Catalogue no: **704.290**
Cass: Released Jan '89, on Varese Sarabande Records(USA) by Varese Sarabande Records (USA). Catalogue no: **C704.290**
CD: Released Jan '89, on Varese Sarabande Records(USA) by Varese Sarabande Records (USA). Catalogue no: **VCD 47244**

Holiday Inn (film)

HOLIDAY INN (Original Soundtrack) (Various artists)
Note: Starring Bing Crosby and Fred Astaire.
Album: Released Jan '89, on Silva Screen by Silva Screen Records. Catalogue no: **STK 112**

Holliday, Jennifer

AND I'M TELLING YOU I'M NOT GOING
Tracks: / And I'm telling you I'm not going / Fake your way to the top.

Note: Featured in the film 'Dream-girls'.
7" Single: Released Aug '82, on Geffen by Geffen Records (USA). Catalogue no: **GEF A 2644**

Holly, Buddy

PEGGY SUE GOT MARRIED
Tracks: / Peggy Sue got married.
Note: From the film *'Peggy Sue Got Married'*
7" Single: Released Sep '59, on Coral by MCA Records. Deleted '62. Catalogue no: **Q 72376**

Hollywood...

HOLLYWOOD (London Festival Orchestra)
Tracks: / Man and a woman, A / Il silenzio / Love story / Affair to remember, An / Hello young lovers / Sound of music, The / Moon river / La ronde / Tara's theme / Three coins in the fountain / Shane / Anything goes / Dancing in the dark / Days of wine and roses / Love is a many splendoured thing / Tammy / Pennies from heaven / It's magic / Magnificent seven / High noon / Moon river
Album: Released '88, on DRG (USA) by DRG Records (USA). Catalogue no: **DS 15006**
CD: Released Apr '87, on The Collection by Object Enterprises. Catalogue no: **OP 0004**

HOLLYWOOD MUSICALS (Medley) (Hollwood musicals)
Tracks: / Hollywood musicals.
7" Single: Released Dec '83, on RCA by BMG Records (UK). Catalogue no: **RCA 381**

HOLLYWOOD MUSICALS-MGM/UA (Various artists)
Tracks: / Gold diggers of 1933: *Various artists* / Go into your dance: *Various artists* / 42nd street: *Various artists* / Dames: *Various artists* / Going places: *Various artists* / Ready willing and able: *Various artists* / Hard to get: *Various artists* / Yankee doodle boy: *Various artists* / Hollywood hotel: *Various artists* / Gold diggers of 1937: *Various artists* / Rhapsody in blue: *Various artists* / Melody for two: *Various artists* / Footlight parade: *Various artists* / Broadway gondalier: *Various artists* / 20 million sweethearts: *Various artists* / Gold diggers of 1935: *Various artists*.
Album: Released Jul '85, on SPI Milan (France) Catalogue no: **ACH**

Hollywood Hit Parade - Compilation on RCA

023
Cass: Released Jul '85, on SPI Milan (France) Catalogue no: **CCH 023**

Hollywood Cavalcade

HOLLYWOOD CAVALCADE (Various artists)
Tracks: / Sonny boy: *Jolson, Al* / Valentine: *Chevalier, Maurice* / Parlami d'amore mariu: *De Sica, Vittorio* / When April sings: *Durbin, Deanna* / I can't be bothered now: *Astaire, Fred* / Kiss: *Monroe, Marilyn* / Ich bin von caps bis fuss auf leiber eingestel: *Dietrich, Marlene* / Captain January: *Temple, Shirley* / Over the rainbow: *Garland, Judy* / Sentimental journey: *Day, Doris* / Singin' in the rain: *Kelly, Gene* / You'll never know: *Rogers, Ginger*.
Note: Legendary Hollywood Artists - Collectors Edition Series - Original recordings   Mid price release.
Album: Released Jan '86, on Meteor by Magnum Music Group. Catalogue no: **MTM 016**

Hollywood Collection

HOLLYWOOD COLLECTION (Various artists)
Tracks: / Singin' in the rain: *Kelly,*

Gene / Over the rainbow: *Garland, Judy* / Entertainer, The: *Joplin, Scott* / Cheek to cheek: *Astaire, Fred* / Mammy: *Jolson, Al* / Let's face the music and dance: *Rogers, Ginger* / Couple of swells, A: *Astaire, Fred* / Diamonds are a girl's best friend: *Monroe, Marilyn* / Night and day: *Sinatra, Frank* / In the mood: *Miller, Glenn* / Trail of the lonesome pine: *Laurel & Hardy* / Ol' man river: *Robeson, Paul* / I'm in the mood for love: *Hutton, Betty* / Hello Dolly: *Armstrong, Louis* / Zip: *Hayworth, Rita* / I've got my love to keep me warm: *Bogart, Humphrey* / Gentlemen prefer blondes: *Russell, Jane & Marilyn Monroe* / Hi lili hi lo: *Caron, Leslie & Mel Ferrer* / Who's sorry now?: *De Haven, Gloria* / It had to be you: *Lamour, Dorothy*.
CD: Released Jun '88, on Deja Vu Catalogue no: **DVCD 2054**
Album: Released May '86, on Deja Vu Catalogue no: **DVLP 2054**
Cass: Released May '86, on Deja Vu Catalogue no: **DVMC 2054**

Hollywood Hit Parade

HOLLYWOOD HIT PARADE (Various artists) (See panel above)

above)
Tracks: / We're in the money: *Studio Orchestra* / I've got to sing a torch song: *Studio Orchestra* / We're in the money: *Rogers, Ginger* / She's a Latin from Manhattan: *Jolson, Al* / Shuffle off to Buffalo: *Keeler, Ruby/Clarence Nordstrom* / 42nd Street: *Keeler, Ruby/Dick Powell* / I only have eyes for you: *Powell, Dick/Ruby Keeler* / Jeepers Creepers: *Armstrong, Louis* / Too marvellous for words: *Shaw, Winifred/Ross Alexander/Ruby Keeler/Lee Dixson* / You must have been a beautiful baby: *Powell, Dick* / About a quarter to nine: *Jolson, Al* / Yankee doodle boy: *Cagney, James* / Hooray for Hollywood: *Goodman, Benny & His Orchestra* / With plenty of money and you: *Powell, Dick*/ Let's put our heads together: *Studio Orchestra* / Life insurance song: *Studio Orchestra* / You're getting to be a habit with me: *Daniels, Bebe* / Swanee: *Jolson, Al* / September in the rain: *Melton, James* / Shanghai Lil: *Cagney, James/Ruby Keeler* / Lulu's back in town: *Powell, Dick* / By a waterfall: *Powell, Dick/Ruby Keeler* / I'll string along with you: *Powell, Dick/Ginger Rogers* / Lullaby of Broadway: *Shaw, Winifred*.
Note: Hollywood Hit Parade takes you back to the golden years of the Hollywood musical and specifically, the Warner Bros. studio. Having pioneered sound movies with *The Jazz Singer* in 1927, Warners set the tone for the thirties and the years that followed, with *42nd Street*, the grandfather of all backstage musicals.
Among the the stars on this album are such members of the Warners repertory company as Dick Powell (who later became a major dramatic actor and also a film director), Ruby Keeler (still dancing in the 1970 stage revival of *No, No, Nanette*), Ginger Rogers (who made 42nd Street prior to commencing her legendary dancing partnership with Fred Astaire at RKO), and Winifred Shaw (the singer who toured with Jack Benny during the war years, and whose single record of *Lullaby Of Broadway* entered the British pop charts in 1976).
The 42nd Street numbers (and many of the others featured here) were choreographed by Busby

Berkely, the flamboyant dance director whose use of overhead cameras peering down on scores of beautiful girls spread out in ever-changing geometric patterns, created a revolutionary look for screen musicals. The tunes that these routines accompanied were, for the most part, the work of Harry Warren and Al Dubin, probably the finest songwriting team in the history of Hollywood. Almost all of the songs in this collection have long been standards and they will undoubtedly live on forever.
Album: Released Feb '84, on RCA by BMG Records (UK). Catalogue no: **ZL 70136**
Cass: Released Feb '84, on RCA by BMG Records (UK). Catalogue no: **ZK 70136**

Hollywood Hits

BEST OF TV AND FILM THEMES VOL 1
Tracks: / Crazy for you / Stand by me / Take my breath away / Miami vice / Falcon Crest / Nobody does it better / Against all odds / Dynasty / L.A. Law / Power of love / Moonlighting / Dallas / Say you say me / Glory of love / Adagio / Up where we belong / I just called ... / Color purple / Arthur's theme.
CD: Released '89, on Spectrum (CD) by M.S.D.. Catalogue no: **U 3012 2**
CD: Released '89, on Spectrum (CD) by M.S.D.. Catalogue no: **CRC 3024 2**

HOLLYWOOD HITS
Tracks: / White knights / Karate kid 2 / Cheers / Out of Africa / Dynasty / Goodbye again / Stand by me / Crazy for you / Cosby show, The / Platoon / Softly and tenderly / American tale, An / Woman in red / Officer and a gentleman / Wizard of Oz / Terms of endearment / Latin Afternoon.
CD: Released '88, on Spectrum (CD) by M.S.D.. Catalogue no: **U 4090**

Hollywood Ladies Sing

HOLLYWOOD LADIES SING (I'm Ready For My Close Up) (Various artists)
CD: Released Feb '90, on Silva Screen by Silva Screen Records. Catalogue no: **8597.2**

Hollywood Magic

HOLLYWOOD MAGIC VOL 1

(1950's, The) (Various artists)
Note: Compilation of some of the greatest themes and songs from films of the fifties including Bus Stop, Secret Love, A Star Is Born, A Summer Place, Bridge On The River Kwai etc.
CD: Released Jan '89, on CBS (import) by CBS Records & Distribution. Catalogue no: **CK 44374**
Cass: Released Jan '89, on Silva Screen by Silva Screen Records. Catalogue no: **JST 44374**

HOLLYWOOD MAGIC VOL 2
1960's, The (Various artists)
Note: Themes and songs from The Alamo, The Guns Of Navarone, Sons of Katie Elder, Bonnie & Clyde, To Sir With Love, The Graduate, The Lion In Winter.
Cass: Released Jan '89, on Silva Screen by Silva Screen Records. Catalogue no: **JST 44373**
CD: Released Jan '89, on CBS (import) by CBS Records & Distribution. Catalogue no: **CK 44373**

Hollywood Musicals

HOLLYWOOD MUSICALS (Various artists)
Tracks: / Mammy: *Jolson, Al* / Cheek to cheek: *Astaire, Fred* / Over the rainbow: *Garland, Judy* / I'm a yankee doodle dancy: *Cagney, James* / Road to Morocco: *Hope, Bob/Bing Crosby/Judy Garland* / Put the blame on mame: *Hayworth, Rita* / White Christmas: *Crosby, Bing* / Best things in life are free: *Allyson, June/Peter Lawford* / Johnny one note: *Garland, Judy* / Couple of swells, A: *Garland, Judy & Fred Astaire* / Who's sorry now: *De Haven, Gloria* / S'wonderful: *Kelly, Gene* / Diamonds are a girls best friend: *Monroe, Marilyn* / Bye bye baby: *Monroe, Marilyn & Jane Russell* / Too darn hot: *Miller, Arthur* / Hi Lilli hi lo: *Caron, Leslie & Mel Ferrer* / Indian love call: *Blyth, Ann/Fernando Lamas* / Rose Marie: *Keel, Howard* / Stranger in paradise: *Blyth, Ann/Vic Damone* / Thank heaven for little girls: *Chevalier, Maurice* / Hello Dolly: *Armstrong, Louis* / There's no business like show business: *Merman, Ethel* / Move over darling: *Day, Doris* / Oh what a beautiful morning: *McRae, Gordon*.
CD: Released '89, on Deja Vu Catalogue no: **CVRECD 26**

Hollywood Sings

HOLLYWOOD SINGS (Stars of the silver screen) (Various artists)
Tracks: / Happy feet: *Whiteman, Paul & Rhythm Boys* / Toot toot Tootsie goodbye: *Jolson, Al* / Johnny: *Dietrich, Marlene* / Day after day: *Stewart, James* / Can Broadway do without me?: *Clayton, Jackson & Durante* / If you haven't got love: *Swanson, Gloria* / Doin' the new low down: *Robinson, Bill 'Bojangles'* / Keep your sunny side up: *Gaynor, Janet* / Kashmiri love song: *Valentino, Rudolph* / Broadway melody: *King, Charles* / Puttin' on the ritz: *Richman, Harry* / How long will it last?: *Crawford, Joan* / Hooray for Captain Spaulding: *Marx, Groucho & Zeppo* / Just like a butterfly (that's caught in the rain): *Morgan, Helen* / I love Louisa: *Astaire, Fred* / Can't get along: *Rogers, Ginger* / You've got that thing: *Chevalier, Maurice* / Beyond the blue horizon: *MacDonald, Jeanette* / White dove: *Tibbett, Lawrence* / Yes yes (my baby says yes): *Cantor, Eddie.*
CD: Released Feb '87, on Living Era by Academy Sound & Vision Records. Catalogue no: **CD AJA 5011**
Cass: Released 1 Feb '82, on Living Era by Academy Sound & Vision Records. Catalogue no: **ZC AJA 5011**
Album: Released 1 Feb '82, on Living Era by Academy Sound & Vision Records. Catalogue no: **AJA 5011**

Hollywood Studio

BROADWAY MEMORIES (22 unforgettable melodies)
CD: Released Sep '87, on Compact Collection Catalogue no: **1510**

Hollywood To Las Vegas

HOLLYWOOD TO LAS VEGAS (Film Soundtracks) (Various artists)
Tracks: / Cheek to cheek: *Astaire, Fred* / Let's call the whole thing off: *Astaire, Fred* / Top hat, white tie and tails: *Astaire, Fred* / Let's face the music and dance: *Astaire, Fred* / Fine romance, A: *Astaire, Fred* / World weary: *Coward, Noel* / Room with a view, A: *Coward,*

Noel / Mad dogs and Englishmen: *Coward, Noel* / Let's do it: *Coward, Noel* / Party's over now, The: *Coward, Noel* / Speaking confidentially: *Faye, Alice* / I'm shooting high: *Faye, Alice* / I've got my love to keep me warm: *Faye, Alice* / Slumming on Park Avenue: *Faye, Alice* / There's a lull in my life: *Faye, Alice* / Taking a chance on love: *Dietrich, Marlene* / I couldn't sleep a wink last night: *Dietrich, Marlene* / Lili Marlene: *Dietrich, Marlene* / Miss Otis regrets: *Dietrich, Marlene* / Mean to me: *Dietrich, Marlene.*
Cass set: Released '88, on Ditto by Pickwick Records. Catalogue no: **DTO 10266**

Hollywood (TV)

HOLLYWOOD (TV Soundtrack) (Various artists)
Tracks: / Hollywood: *Various artists* / In the beginning: *Various artists* / Tango di Valentino: *Various artists* / Hollywood scandal: *Various artists* (Fatty Arbuckle.) / Swashbuckler, The: *Various artists* (Douglas Fairbanks Snr.) / Kid, The: *Various artists* / Wagon's roll: *Various artists* / Harold Lloyd's glasses: *Various artists* / Stuntmen: *Various artists* / Stoic, The: *Various artists* (Buster Keaton's Rag.) / Garbo: *Various artists* / Great chariot race, The: *Various artists* (Ben Hur).
Note: Arranged by Carl Davis. Produced by Keith Grant.
CD: Released Nov '88, on EMI by EMI Records. Catalogue no: **CZ 146**
CD: Released Nov '88, on EMI by EMI Records. Catalogue no: **CDP 791 199 2**
Cass: Released Nov '88, on EMI by EMI Records. Deleted May '90. Catalogue no: **TCEMS 1308**
Album: Released Mar '83, on EMI by EMI Records. Deleted Mar '88. Catalogue no: **INA 1504**
Album: Released Nov '88, on EMI by EMI Records. Deleted May '90. Catalogue no: **EMS 1308**

Home Movies

HOME MOVIES Original soundtrack (Various artists)
Note: Composed by Pino Donaggio.
Album: Released Jan '89, on Silva Screen by Silva Screen Records. Catalogue no: **STV 81139**

Homeboy

HOMEBOY (Film soundtrack) (Various artists)
Tracks: / I want to love you baby: *Benson, Jo* / Home boy: *Clapton, Eric* / Call me if you need me: *Magic Sam* / Final fight: *Clapton, Eric* / Travelling east: *Clapton, Eric* / Bridge: *Clapton, Eric.*
Cass: Released Dec '88, on Virgin by Virgin Records. Catalogue no: **TCV 2574**
CD: Released Dec '88, on Virgin by Virgin Records. Catalogue no: **CDV 2574**
Album: Released Dec '88, on Virgin by Virgin Records. Catalogue no: **V 2574**

Homer

HOMER (Film Soundtrack) (Various artists)
Tracks: / Turn turn turn: *Byrds* / Bluebird: *Buffalo Springfield* / For what it's worth: *Buffalo Springfield* / Nashville cats: *Lovin' Spoonful* / Rock 'n' roll woman: *Buffalo Springfield* / How many more times: *Led Zeppelin* / Brave new world: *Miller, Steve Band* / Man of music: *Scardino, Don* / Rock 'n' roll gypsies: *Various artists* / Spoonful: *Cream.*
Album: Released '73, on Polydor by Polydor Ltd. Deleted '78. Catalogue no: **2400 137**

Honeysuckle Rose

HONEYSUCKLE ROSE (See under Nelson, Willie)

Honey Pot

HONEY POT, THE (Original Soundtrack) (Various artists)
Note: 1967 Comedy starring Rex Harrison. Score by John Addison.a
Cass: Released Jan '89, on MCA by MCA Records. Catalogue no: **MCAC 25106**
Album: Released Jan '89, on MCA by MCA Records. Catalogue no: **MCA 25106**

Honky

HONKY (See under Emerson, Keith)

Hoorah For Daisy

HOORAH FOR DAISY (Original London cast) (Various artists)
Album: Released Jan '89, on Silva Screen by Silva Screen Records. Catalogue no: **AEI 118**

Hooray For Hollywood

HOORAY FOR HOLLYWOOD (Original soundtrack) (Various artists)
Tracks: / I used to be colour blind / Ich bin die fesche Lola / Alone / I never knew heaven could speak / Got a bran' new suit / All I want is just one / Paradise / When April sings / Something's gotta give / I'm gonna file my claim / Mary's a grand old name / It's oh so quiet / That certain feeling / Saga of Jenny / Stardust / I couldn't be more in love
Cass: Released Oct '80, on RCA International by BMG Records (UK). Catalogue no: **INTK 5045**
Album: Released Oct '80, on RCA International by BMG Records (UK). Catalogue no: **INTS 5045**

HOORAY FOR HOLLYWOOD (COMPILATION) (Various artists)
CD: Released Jun '88, on Compact Selection Catalogue no: **TQ 157**
Cass: Released Mar '90, on Silva Screen by Silva Screen Records. Catalogue no: **MRT 40046**

Hope, Bob

RADIO SHOWS
Album: Released Jan '89, on Silva Screen by Silva Screen Records. Catalogue no: **MR 1153**

ROAD TO MOROCCO (VIDEO) (See under Road To Morocco)

ROAD TO SINGAPORE (VIDEO) (See under Road To Singapore)

ROAD TO ZANZIBAR (VIDEO) (See under Road To Zanzibar)

Horne, Kenneth

BEYOND OUR KEN (Excerpts From BBC Radio Series)
Album: Released '80, on Note by EMI Records. Catalogue no: **NTSM 195**

ROUND THE HORNE (See under Round The Horne)

Horner, James

AMERICAN TAIL, AN (See under American Tail)

RED HEAT (See under Red Heat)

WILLOW (See under Willow)

Horovitz (composer)

ALICE IN WONDERLAND
Album: Released Jan '85, on MSR Catalogue no: **MSCE 1**

RUMPOLE OF THE BAILEY
Tracks: / Rumpole of the Bailey / Soft-shoe shuffle / Les girls.
7" Single: Released Jan '87, on Columbia by EMI Records. Deleted Oct '87. Catalogue no: **DB 9143**

Horror & Sci-Fi

HORROR & SCI-FI VOL 2 (Various artists)
Tracks: / Escape from New York: *Various artists* / Mad Max: *Various artists* / Phantasm: *Various artists* / Day after Halloween, The: *Various artists* / Tourist trip: *Various artists* / Day time ended, The: *Various artists* / Maniac: *Various artists* / Videodrome: *Various artists* / Evil Dead, The: *Various artists* / Hunger, The: *Various artists* / Friday 13th: *Various artists* / Forbidden zone: *Various artists* / Liquid sky: *Various artists* / Red Sonja: *Various artists* / Lifeforce: *Various artists* / Elephant man: *Various artists*.
CD: Released Feb '90, on SPI Milan (France) Catalogue no: **CDCH 157**

Hot Rod Rumble

HOT ROD RUMBLE (Original Soundtrack) (Various artists)
Note: 1950's Jazz score by Alexander Courage.
Album: Released Jan '89, on Silva Screen by Silva Screen Records. Catalogue no: **LRP 3048**

Hotel New Hampshire

HOTEL NEW HAMPSHIRE (Original Soundtrack)
Cass: Released Nov '84, on EMI by EMI Records. Catalogue no: **EJ 2401694**
Album: Released Nov '84, on EMI by EMI Records. Catalogue no: **EJ 2401691**

House (film)

HOUSE/HOUSE II (Film Soundtracks) (Various artists)
Note: Music by Harry Manfredini for the 2 horror films.
Album: Released Jan '89, on Silva Screen by Silva Screen Records. Catalogue no: **STV 81324**

CD: Released Jan '89, on Silva Screen by Silva Screen Records. Catalogue no: **VCD 47295**

House Of Flowers

HOUSE OF FLOWERS (Original Broadway Cast) (Various artists)
Album: Released Jan '89, on Silva Screen by Silva Screen Records. Catalogue no: **COS 2320**

House Party

HOUSE PARTY (Various artists)
Tracks: / Why you get funky on me: *Today* / What a feeling: *Arts & Crafts* / Jive time sucker: *Force M.D.'s* / House party: *Full Force Family featuring Lisa Lisa & Cult Jam* / U.T.F.O.: *Riley, Cheryl Pepsii* / Doctor Ice: *Ex-Girlfriend and E-Crof* / I can't do nothing for you man!: *Flavor Flav* / Fun house: *Kid 'N Play* / To da break of dawh: *LL Cool J* / Kid vs Play (the battle): *Kid 'N Play* / Surely: *Arts & Crafts* / This is love: *Vaughan, Kenny & The Art Of Love.*
CD: Released Apr '90, on Motown by BMG Records (UK). Catalogue no: **ZD 72699**
Album: Released Apr '90, on Motown by BMG Records (UK). Catalogue no: **ZL 72699**
Cass: Released Apr '90, on Motown by BMG Records (UK). Catalogue no: **ZK 72699**

HOUSE PARTY (2) (Film Soundtrack) (Various artists)
Cass: Released Dec '88, on Low Fat Vinyl by Low Fat Vinyl Records. Catalogue no: **ZCTER 0023**
Album: Released Dec '88, on Low Fat Vinyl by Low Fat Vinyl Records. Catalogue no: **XTER 0023**
CD: Released Dec '88, on Low Fat Vinyl by Low Fat Vinyl Records. Catalogue no: **CDTER 0023**

Houseboat

HOUSEBOAT (Film soundtrack) (Various artists)
Note: Composed by George Duning.
Album: Released Jan '89, on Silva Screen by Silva Screen Records. Catalogue no: **LAALP 003**

Housekeeping

HOUSEKEEPING (Original soundtrack) (Various artists)
Note: Music by Michael Gibbs for

the recent Bill Forsyth film.
CD: Released Jan '89, on Silva Screen by Silva Screen Records. Catalogue no: **VCD 47308**
Cass: Released Jan '89, on Silva Screen by Silva Screen Records. Catalogue no: **CTV 81338**
Album: Released Jan '89, on Silva Screen by Silva Screen Records. Catalogue no: **STV 81338**

How The West Was Won

HOW THE WEST WAS WON (Film soundtrack) (Various artists)
Tracks: / Overture: *Various artists* / How the west was won: *Various artists* / Bereavement and fulfilment: *Various artists* / River pirates, The: *Various artists* / Home in the meadow: *Various artists* / Cleve and the mule: *Various artists* / Raise a ruckus tonight: *Various artists* / Come share my life: *Various artists* / Marriage proposal, The: *Various artists* / Entr'acte: *Various artists* / Cheyennes: *Various artists* / He's Linus' boy: *Various artists* / Climb a higher hill: *Various artists* / What was your name in the states: *Various artists* / No, goodbye: *Various artists* / Finale: *Various artists*.
Note: Film soundtrack composed and conducted by Alfred Newman. Featuring Debbie Reynolds.
CD: Released Apr '87, on CBS by CBS Records & Distribution. Deleted Jan '89. Catalogue no: **CD 70284**
Album: Released '73, on MGM (Polydor) by Polydor Ltd. Deleted '78. Catalogue no: **2353 029**
Cass: Released Jul '86, on CBS by CBS Records & Distribution. Deleted Aug '87. Catalogue no: **40 70284**
Cass: Released Jan '89, on MCA by MCA Records. Deleted Mar '90. Catalogue no: **MCAC 39043**
Album: Released Jul '86, on CBS by CBS Records & Distribution. Catalogue no: **CBS 70284**
Album: Released Jan '89, on MCA by MCA Records. Catalogue no: **MCA 39043**

How To Get Ahead ...

HOW TO GET AHEAD IN ADVERTISING/WITHNAIL AND I (Various artists)
Tracks: / Boilbusters: *Various artists* / Barbara Simmons: *Various artists* / It looks just like me: *Vari-*

ous artists / Julia: *Various artists* / Sit down: *Various artists* / After the dinner party: *Various artists* / Boil in a bag: *Various artists* / Bandages come off, The: *Various artists* / Get out of the bloody bath: *Various artists* / Range rover: *Various artists* / Going for the briefcase: *Various artists*.
Album: Released Sep '89, on Silva Screen by Silva Screen Records. Deleted Apr '90. Catalogue no: **FILM 091**
Cass: Released Sep '89, on Silva Screen by Silva Screen Records. Catalogue no: **FILMC 091**
CD: Released Sep '89, on Silva Screen by Silva Screen Records. Catalogue no: **FILMCD 091**

How To Make Love...

HOW TO MAKE LOVE WITH A BLACK MAN WITHOUT BEING TIRED (Original soundtrack) (Various artists)
Album: Released Feb '90, on Silva Screen by Silva Screen Records. Catalogue no: **A 513**
CD: Released Feb '90, on SPI Milan (France) Catalogue no: **CDCH 513**
Cass: Released Feb '90, on Silva Screen by Silva Screen Records. Catalogue no: **AC 513**

How To Steal A Diamond

HOW TO STEAL A DIAMOND IN FOUR UNEASY LESSONS (Film Soundtrack) (Various artists)
Tracks: / Listen to the melody: *Various artists* / Main title: *Various artists* / Talking drums: *Various artists* / Seldom seen Sam: *Various artists* / Parole party: *Various artists* / When you believe: *Various artists* / Hot rock theme: *Various artists* / Miasmo: *Various artists* / Sahara stone: *Various artists* / Slam city: *Various artists* / Listen to the melody/Dixie tag: *Various artists* / End title: *Various artists*.
Album: Released '73, on Atlantic by WEA Records. Deleted '78. Catalogue no: **K 40371**

Howard The Duck

HOWARD THE DUCK (Various artists)
Tracks: / Howard the duck: *Dolby's Cube* / Don't turn away: *Dolby's Cube*.
12" Single: Released Nov '86, on MCA by MCA Records. Cata-

logue no: **MCAT 1092**
7" Single: Released Nov '86, on MCA by MCA Records. Catalogue no: **MCA 1092**

HOWARD THE DUCK (Original Soundtrack) (Various artists)
Tracks: / Hunger city: *Dolby's Cube* / Howard the duck: *Dolby's Cube* / It don't come cheap: *Dolby's Cube* / Don't turn away: *Dolby's Cube* / I'm on my way: *Dolby's Cube* / Lullaby of duckland: *Various artists* / Journey to Earth: *Various artists* / You're the duckiest: *Various artists* / Ultraflight: *Various artists* / Beddy-bye for Howard: *Various artists* / Dark overload: *Various artists*.
Album: Released Nov '86, on MCA by MCA Records. Deleted Jan '88. Catalogue no: **MCF 3342**
Cass: Released Nov '86, on MCA by MCA Records. Deleted Jan '88. Catalogue no: **MCFC 3342**

Howling

HOWLING, THE (Original soundtrack)
Album: Released '80, on Silva Screen by Silva Screen Records. Catalogue no: **STV 81150**

HOWLING II, THE (Original Soundtrack) (Various artists)
Cass: Released Nov '85, on Filmtrax by Filmtrax Records. Deleted Apr '90. Catalogue no: **HOWC 01**
Album: Released Nov '85, on Filmtrax by Filmtrax Records. Catalogue no: **HOWL 01**

Huckleberry Finn

BIG RIVER (See under Big River)

Huckleberry Hound

HUCKLEBERRY HOUND (TV soundtracks) (Various artists)
Album: Released Mar '61, on Pye Deleted '66. Catalogue no: **GGL 0004**

Humanoids From ...

HUMANOIDS FROM THE DEEP (Original Soundtrack) (Various artists)
Note: Early score from James Horner (Krull, Willow, Name Of The Rose).
Album: Released Jan '89, on Cerebus (USA) Catalogue no: **C'BUS 203**

Hunger

HUNGER, THE (Original soundtrack) (Various artists)
Album: Released '84, on IMS by Polydor Ltd. Catalogue no: **ACH 005**

CD: Released Feb '90, on SPI Milan (France) Catalogue no: **CDCH 004**

HUNGER, THE/YEAR OF LIVING DANGEROUSLY (Original soundtrack) (Various artists)
Note: Music from the David Bowie film.

Cass: Released Jan '89, on Silva Screen by Silva Screen Records. Catalogue no: **CTV 81184**

CD: Released Jan '89, on Silva Screen by Silva Screen Records. Catalogue no: **VCD 47261**

Album: Released Jan '89, on Silva Screen by Silva Screen Records. Catalogue no: **STV 81184**

Hunting Of The Snark

HUNTING OF THE SNARK (Various artists)
Tracks: / Introduction: *Batt, Mike* / Children of the sky: *Batt, Mike* / Bellman's speech, The: *Batt, Mike* / Escapade, The: *Batt, Mike* / Midnight smoke: *Batt, Mike* / Snooker song, The: *Batt, Mike* / Pig must die, The: *Batt, Mike* / Beaver's lesson, The: *Batt, Mike* / Delicate combination, A: *Batt, Mike* / As long as the moon can shine: *Batt, Mike* / Dancing towards disaster: *Batt, Mike* / Vanishing, The: *Batt, Mike*.

Album: Released Apr '88, on Trax by Filmtrax Records. Deleted Feb '90. Catalogue no: **MODEM 1007**

Album: Released Nov '86, on Starblend by Starblend Records. Catalogue no: **SNARK 1**

Cass: Released Apr '88, on Trax by Filmtrax Records. Deleted Feb '90. Catalogue no: **MODEMC 1007**

CD: Released Apr '88, on Trax by Filmtrax Records. Deleted Apr '90. Catalogue no: **MODEMCD 1007**

CD: Released Jun '86, on Starblend by Starblend Records. Deleted '88. Catalogue no: **CDSNARK 01**

Cass: Released Nov '86, on Starblend by Starblend Records. Catalogue no: **SNARKK 1**

Hyman, Dick

PURPLE ROSE OF CAIRO (See under Purple Rose Of Cairo)

The following information was taken from the Music Master database on September 25th, 1990.

I & Albert

I & ALBERT (Original London cast) (Various artists)
Tracks: / Draw the blinds: *Various artists* / I and Albert: *Various artists* / Leave it alone: *Various artists* / I've 'eard the bloody 'indoos: *Various artists*.
Album: Released May '89, on T. E. R. by That's Entertainment Records. Catalogue no: **TERS 1004**

I Put A Spell On You

I PUT A SPELL ON YOU (See under Hawkins, Screamin' Jay)

I Remember Mama

I REMEMBER MAMA (Studio Cast recordings) (Various artists)
Tracks: / I remember mama: *Various artists* / Little bit more, A: *Various artists* / Writer writes at night, A: *Various artists* / Ev'ry day (comes something beautiful): *Various artists* / You could not please me more: *Various artists* / Most disagreeable man, A/Uncle Chris: *Various artists* / Lullaby: *Various artists* / Easy come, easy go: *Various artists* / It is not the end of the world: *Various artists* / Entr'acte: *Various artists* / Mama always makes it better: *Various artists* / When: *Various artists* / Fair trade: *Various artists* / I write, you read (fair trade): *Various artists* / It's going to be good to be gone: *Various artists* / Time: *Various artists* / I remember mama finale: *Various artists*.
Note: Original Broadway score.
Album: Released Oct '85, on T. E. R. by That's Entertainment Records. Deleted Mar '90. Catalogue no: **TER 1102**
CD: Released Oct '85, on T. E. R. by That's Entertainment Records. Catalogue no: **CDTER 1102**
Cass: Released Oct '85, on T. E. R. by That's Entertainment Records. Catalogue no: **ZCTER 1102**

I Walk The Line

I WALK THE LINE (Film Soundtrack) (Cash, Johnny)
Tracks: / Flesh and blood / I walk the line / Hungry / This town / This side of the law / Flesh and blood (instrumental) / Cause I love you / Cause I love you (string instrumental) / World's gonna fall on you / Face of despair / Standing on the promise / Amazing grace.
Album: Released '73, on CBS by CBS Records & Distribution. Deleted '78. Catalogue no: **700 83**

Ice Castles

ICE CASTLES (Original soundtrack) (Various artists)
Note: Music by Marvin Hamlisch.
Album: Released '79, on Arista by BMG Records (UK). Deleted '84. Catalogue no: **ARTY 168**
Cass: Released '79, on Arista by BMG Records (UK). Deleted '84. Catalogue no: **TC ARTY 168**
Album: Released Jan '89, on Silva Screen by Silva Screen Records. Catalogue no: **ALB 6 8317**
Cass: Released Jan '89, on Silva Screen by Silva Screen Records. Catalogue no: **ACB 6 8317**

If They Could See ...

IF THEY COULD SEE ME NOW (Original London cast) (Various artists)
Tracks: / If they could see.. (introduction): *Sherrin, Ned/Ian Ogilvy/Margaret Courtney* / I remember it well: *Courtney, Margaret/Joss Ackland* / I wish I was in love again: *Soper, Gay/James Warwick* / Why him: *Robertson, Liz/Alan Jay Lerner* / My gift: *March, Elspeth* / Overhead: *Morley, Sheridan* / That is the end of the news: *Douglas, Angela/David Kernan* / Ladies who lunch, The: *Karlin, Miriam* / Physician, The: *Brook, Faith* / Oldest established, The: *Pringle, Bryan/George Sewell* / Send in the clowns: *Kennedy, Cheryl/Robert Meadmore* / Sonny boy: *Finlay, Frank/Simon Callow* / Why must the show go on?: *Matthews, Francis* / Opening second half: *Dallas, Lorna* / Introduction: *Frost, David/Alan Jay Lerner* / Typically English: *McKenna, Virginia & Louise* / Boy from..., The: *Phillips, Sian* / Oh how to be lovely: *Tindall, Hilary/Victoria Burgoyne* / Introduction: *Nimmo, Derek* / 42nd Street: *Marsh, Jean/Eileen Atkins* / You remind me of you: *Lapotaire, Jane/Tim Curry* / Ed Sullivan stories: *Frost, David* / Introduction: *McGowan, Alec* / I'll never been jealous again: *Hordern, Michael/Joan Plowright* / Happy birthday sweet sixteen/Sixteen candles: *Reeve, Christopher* / Standing on the corner: *Various artists* / Finale: *Various artists*.
Note: A unique event in London's theatre history has been captured on disc by That's Entertainment Records. On February 26th 1984, over 100 celebrities from film, radio and TV gathered at the Theatre Royal, Drury Lane for a gala charity show called 'If they could see me now'. The event was to raise funds for ASBAH, a charity devoted to the cause of spina bifida and hydrocephalus. These celebrities performed a number of well-known show songs from such writers as Lerner & Loewe, Rodgers & Hart, Noel Coward, Stephen Sondheim, Cole Porter and Frank Loesser. Some of the shows represented are Guys & Dolls, 42nd. Street, Stop the World I Want To Get Off and A Little Night Music. This LP release presents highlights from the evening and is a lovely recording featuring artists such as Joss Ackland/ Margaret Courtney/ Liz Robertson/ Sheridan Morley/ Miriam Karlin/ George Sewell/ Frank Finlay/ Simon Callow/ Virginia McKenna/ Tim Curry & Christopher Reeve.
Album: Released Jan '86, on T. E. R. by That's Entertainment Records. Catalogue no: **TERX 1087**

If You Feel Like Singing

IF YOU FEEL LIKE SINGING (Film Soundtrack)(Various artists)
Tracks: / (Howdy neighbour) Happy harvest: *Various artists* / You wonderful you: *Various artists* / Friendly star: *Various artists* / If you feel like singing, sing: *Various artists* / Get happy: *Various artists* / Dig dig dig for your dinner: *Various artists*.
Album: Released '73, on MGM (Polydor) by Polydor Ltd. Deleted '78. Catalogue no: **2353 038**

I'm Getting My Act...

I'M GETTING MY ACT TOGETHER AND TAKING IT ON THE...(Original London cast) (Various artists)
Tracks: / Natural high: *Various artists* / Smile: *Various artists* / In a simple way I love you: *Various artists* / Miss Africa: *Various artists* / Strong woman number: *Various artists* / Dear Tom: *Various artists* / Old friend: *Various artists* / Put in a package and sold: *Various artists* / If only things were different: *Various artists* / Feel the love: *Various artists* / Lonely lady: *Various artists* / Happy birthday: *Various artists*.
Album: Released Apr '83, on T. E. R. by That's Entertainment Records. Catalogue no: **TER 1006**
Cass: Released May '89, on T. E. R. by That's Entertainment Records. Catalogue no: **ZCTER 1006**

Imaginations

IMAGINATIONS - FURTHER REFLECTIONS (Various artists)
Tracks: / American gigolo: *Various artists* / To the unknown man: *Various artists* / Harry's game: *Various artists* / Ordinary people: *Various artists* / Picnic at hanging rock: *Various artists* / Local hero: *Various artists* / Facades: *Various artists* / Song for Guy: *Various artists* / Stranger: *Various artists* / Once upon a time in the west: *Various artists* / Merry Christmas Mr. Lawrence: *Various artists* / Officer and a gentleman: *Various artists* / Kari: *Various artists* / Ballad for Adeline: *Various artists* / Reily: *Various artists* / Flight of the condor: *Various artists* / Focus 1: *Various artists* / Concerto de Aranjuez: *Various artists* / Belladonna: *Various artists*.
Album: Released Oct '83, on CBS by CBS Records & Distribution. Catalogue no: **CBS 10044**

Cass: Released Oct '83, on CBS by CBS Records & Distribution. Catalogue no: **40 10044**

In Search Of The...

IN SEARCH OF THE TROJAN WAR (See under Oldfield, Terry)

In Sickness & In Health

IN SICKNESS & IN HEALTH (See under Chas & Dave)

In The Good Old...

IN THE GOOD OLD SUMMERTIME/GOOD NEWS/2 WEEKS (Original cast recordings) (Various artists)
Album: Released Jan '89, on Silva Screen by Silva Screen Records. Catalogue no: **450 230-1**
Cass: Released Jan '89, on Silva Screen by Silva Screen Records. Catalogue no: **450 230-4**
CD: Released Jan '89, on Silva Screen by Silva Screen Records. Catalogue no: **MCAD 5951**

Indiana Jones

INDIANA JONES & THE LAST CRUSADE (Original soundtrack) (Various artists)
CD: Released Jun '89, on Warner Bros. by WEA Records. Catalogue no: **K 925883 2**
Cass: Released Jun '89, on Warner Bros. by WEA Records. Catalogue no: **K 925883 4**
Album: Released Jun '89, on Warner Bros. by WEA Records. Catalogue no: **K 925883 1**

INDIANA JONES & THE TEMPLE OF DOOM (Film soundtrack) (Various artists)
Tracks: / Anything goes: *Various artists* / Fast streets of Shanghai: *Various artists* / Nocturnal activities: *Various artists* / Shortround's theme: *Various artists* / Children in chains: *Various artists* / Slalom on mountain: *Various artists* / Humol: *Various artists* / Temple of doom, The: *Various artists* / Bug tunnel and death trap: *Various artists* / Slave children's crusade: *Various artists* / Mine car chase, The: *Various artists* / Finale: *Various artists*.
Note: Score by John Williams.
Cass: Released Jul '84, on Polydor by Polydor Ltd. Catalogue no: **POLHC 8**
Album: Released Jan '89, on Silva Screen by Silva Screen Records.

Deleted Mar '90. Catalogue no: **821592.1**
CD: Released Aug '84, on Polydor by Polydor Ltd. Deleted Mar '88. Catalogue no: **821 592-2**
Cass: Released Jan '89, on Silva Screen by Silva Screen Records. Catalogue no: **821592.4**
Album: Released Jul '84, on Polydor by Polydor Ltd. Deleted '87. Catalogue no: **POLH 8**

INDIANA JONES & THE TEMPLE OF DOOM (Various artists)
Note: Story of the film with music & dialogue from the Original Soundtrack: Narrated by Chuck Riley.
Cass: Released Oct '84, on BBC by BBC Records. Deleted '88. Catalogue no: **ZCR 543**
Album: Released Oct '84, on BBC by BBC Records. Deleted '88. Catalogue no: **REH 543**

Inferno

INFERNO (See under Emerson, Keith)

Innerspace

INNERSPACE (Original soundtrack) (Various artists)
Tracks: / Twistin' the night away: *Stewart, Rod* / Hypnotize me: *Wang Chung* / Is it really love: *Walden, Narada Michael* / Will I ever understand you: *Berlin* / Cupid: *Cooke, Sam* / Let's get small: *Various artists* / Environmental adjust: *Various artists* / Space is a flop: *Various artists* / Gut reaction: *Various artists* / Air supply: *Various artists*.
Album: Released Jan '88, on Geffen by Geffen Records (USA). Catalogue no: **460223 1**
CD: Released Jan '88, on Geffen by Geffen Records (USA). Catalogue no: **24161.2**
Cass: Released Jan '88, on Geffen by Geffen Records (USA). Deleted Jan '90. Catalogue no: **460223 4**

Innocent

INNOCENT, THE (Film soundtrack) (Various artists)
Album: Released '85, on Cinevox by Cinevox Italy. Catalogue no: **CIA 5023**
Cass: Released '85, on Cinevox by Cinevox Italy. Catalogue no: **CIAK 75023**

Insignificance

INSIGNIFICANCE (Film soundtrack) (Various artists)

Tracks: / Wild hearts(time): *Orbison, Roy* / When your heart runs out of time: *Gregory, Glen and Claudia Brucken* / Life goes on: *Russell, Theresa* / Dog of a night, A: *Myers, Stanley* / Relativity 1,2 & 3: *Myers, Stanley* / Forever(what the hell): *Myers, Stanley*/ Remember, remember: *Zimmer, Hans* / B29 (shape of the universe): *Zimmer, Hans* / World of theory: *Zimmer, Hans*.

Cass: Released Aug '85, on ZTT by ZTT Records. Deleted '87. Catalogue no: **ZCIQ 4**

Album: Released Aug '85, on ZTT by ZTT Records. Deleted Apr '88. Catalogue no: **ZTTIQ 4**

Intervista

INTERVISTA (Film soundtrack) (Piovani, Nicola)
Tracks: / Prologo / Cincetta ore nova / Ritornello dell intervista / Clowns / Slow dell intervista / Il tranvetto azzurro / Swing dell intervista / Il bidone / La marcetta di nino rota / Lo sceicco bianco / Cerco la titinia / La cioria di cinecitta / Rock mimesis / Anita e marchello / La dolce vita / Dia salgariana / El mercato persiano / Il tango dell capinere / Imperial / Tea for two / Rock mimesis / Tuttie al trucco / Oh akariu / Dove sta zaza / Toro seduto / Smack smack smacchiatut / Il bidone / Epilogo.

Album: Released Dec '87, on Virgin by Virgin Records. Deleted 13 Feb '89. Catalogue no: **V 2443**

CD: Released Dec '88, on Virgin by Virgin Records. Deleted 13 Feb '89. Catalogue no: **CDV 2443**

Cass: Released Dec '87, on Virgin by Virgin Records. Deleted 13 Feb '89. Catalogue no: **TCV 2443**

Into The Night

INTO THE NIGHT (Film soundtrack) (Various artists) (See also under King, B.B.)
Tracks: / Into the night: *Various artists* / My Lucille: *Various artists* / In the midnight hour: *Various artists* / Enter Shaheen: *Various artists* / Century city chase: *Various artists* / Don't make me sorry: *Labelle, Patti* / Keep it light: *Houston, Thelma* / Let's get it on: *Gaye, Marvin* / I can't help myself: *Four Tops*.

Album: Released Oct '87, on MCA by MCA Records. Deleted Jan '88. Catalogue no: **MCL 1828**

Album: Released May '85, on MCA by MCA Records. Catalogue no: **MCF 3269**

Cass: Released May '85, on MCA by MCA Records. Catalogue no: **MCFC 3269**

Cass: Released Oct '87, on MCA by MCA Records. Deleted Jan '88. Catalogue no: **MCLC 1828**

Into The Woods

INTO THE WOODS (Original Broadway cast) (Various artists)
Tracks: / Act 1 prologue: *Various artists* / Into the woods: *Various artists* / Cinderella at the grave: *Various artists* / Hello little girl: *Various artists* / I guess this is goodbye: *Various artists* / Maybe they're magic: *Various artists* / I know things now: *Various artists* / Very nice prince, A: *Various artists* / First midnight: *Various artists* / Giants in the sky: *Various artists* / Agony: *Various artists* / It takes two: *Various artists* / Stay with me: *Various artists* / On the steps of the palace: *Various artists* / Ever after: *Various artists* / Act 2 prologue: *Various artists* / So happy: *Various artists* / Lament: *Various artists* / Any moment: *Various artists* / Moments in the woods: *Various artists* / Your fault: *Various artists* / Last midnight: *Various artists* / No more: *Various artists* / No one is alone: *Various artists* / Finale: *Various artists*.

Note: Sondheim's musical stars Bernadette Peters, Joanna Gleason, Chip Zien, Tom Aldredge and Robert Westenberg.

Cass: Released Apr '88, on RCA by BMG Records (UK). Deleted Jul '90. Catalogue no: **BK 86796**

CD: Released Apr '88, on RCA by BMG Records (UK). Deleted Sep '90. Catalogue no: **BD 86796**

Album: Released Apr '88, on RCA by BMG Records (UK). Deleted Jul '90. Catalogue no: **BL 86796**

Invasion U.S.A

INVASION U.S.A (Film soundtrack) (Various artists)
Note: Chuck Norris adventure film with music by Jay Chattaway.

Cass: Released Jan '89, on Silva Screen by Silva Screen Records. Catalogue no: **C 285**

Album: Released Jan '89, on Silva Screen by Silva Screen Records. Catalogue no: **A 285**

Investigation Of A...

INVESTIGATION OF A CITIZEN ABOVE SUSPICION (Film soundtrack) (Various artists)
Note: Score by Ennio Morricone.

Album: Released Jan '89, on Silva Screen by Silva Screen Records. Catalogue no: **803036**

Irish R.M.

IRISH RM, THE (TV soundtrack) (Various artists)
Tracks: / Major Yeates' fancy: *Various artists* / Teetotaller, The: *Various artists* / Sally's lament: *Various artists* / Mrs Cadogan's waltz: *Various artists* / Sheehy's runaway foal: *Various artists* / Fire at the Aussolas: *Various artists* / Phillipa's dance: *Various artists* / Sultan wins the race: *Various artists* / Lady Knox and Mrs Knox: *Various artists*.

Cass: Released '83, on Ritz by Ritz Records. Catalogue no: **RITZLC 0011**

Album: Released '83, on Ritz by Ritz Records. Catalogue no: **RITZLP 0011**

Irma La Douce

IRMA LA DOUCE (Original Broadway Cast) (Various artists)
Album: Released Jan '89, on Silva Screen by Silva Screen Records. Catalogue no: **AOS 2029**

CD: Released Jan '89, on Silva Screen by Silva Screen Records. Catalogue no: **MCAD 6178**

IRMA LA DOUCE (Film Soundtrack) (Various artists)
Tracks: / Dis-donc, dis-donc: *Various artists* / Meet Irma: *Various artists* / Irma La Douce: *Various artists* / Nestor the honest policeman: *Various artists* / Our language of love, The: *Various artists* / Market: *Various artists* / Easy living the hard way: *Various artists* / Escape: *Various artists* / Return of Lord, The: *Various artists* / In the tub with fieldglasses: *Various artists* / Goodbye Lord: *Various artists* / I'm sorry Irma: *Various artists* / But that's another story: *Various artists*.

Cass: Released Feb '87, on CBS by CBS Records & Distribution. Deleted Jun '88. Catalogue no: **450225 4**

Album: Released Feb '87, on

CBS by CBS Records & Distribution. Deleted Jun '88. Catalogue no: **450225 1**

Iron Eagle

IRON EAGLE (Film soundtrack) (Various artists)
Tracks: / One vision: *Queen* / Iron eagle (never say die): *King Kobra* / These are the good times: *Martin, Eric* / Maniac house: *Katrina & The Waves* / Intense: *Clinton, George* / Hide in the rainbow: *Dio* / It's too late: *Helix* / Love can make you cry: *Urgent* / This ragin' fire: *Axis, Jon Butcher* / Road of the gypsy: *Adrenalin.*
Cass: Released May '86, on Capitol by EMI Records. Deleted '88. Catalogue no: **TCEST 2013**
Album: Released May '86, on Capitol by EMI Records. Catalogue no: **EST 2013**

Is Paris Burning?

IS PARIS BURNING? (Film soundtrack) (Jarre, Maurice)
CD: Released Feb '90, on Varese Sarabande Records(USA) by Varese Sarabande Records (USA). Catalogue no: **VSD 5222**

Isabel's A Jezebel

ISABEL'S A JEZEBEL (Original London Cast) (Various artists)
Tracks: / More than earth: *Various artists* / More than air: *Various artists* / Down by the ocean: *Various artists* / All fish in the sea: *Various artists* / On the sand by the sea: *Various artists* / Isabel's a Jezebel: *Various artists* / In another life: *Various artists* / Nothing: *Various artists* / Sand: *Various artists* / Oh mummy darling: *Various artists* / God, it matters now: *Various artists* / Saddest moon: *Various artists* / Mama don't want no baby: *Various*

artists / These are the things: *Various artists* / Stanley Irritability: *Various artists* / Use your name: *Various artists* / Moon should be rising soon/ Weeds in the wind: *Various artists* / My God when I think: *Various artists* / Hah: *Various artists* / Love knows no season: *Various artists* / So ends our night: *Various artists.*
Album: Released '73, on United Artists by EMI Records. Deleted '78. Catalogue no: **UAG 29148**

It Happened At The...

IT HAPPENED AT THE WORLD FAIR (See under Presley, Elvis)

It Happened In Brooklyn

IT HAPPENED IN BROOKLYN (Film soundtrack) (Various artists)
Note: Starring Frank Sinatra and Jimmy Durante.
Album: Released Jan '89, on Silva Screen by Silva Screen Records. Catalogue no: **HS 5006**

It Started In Naples

IT STARTED IN NAPLES (Film soundtrack) (Various artists)
Note: Clark Gable/Sophia Loren film, music by A.Cicognini and Carlo Savina.
Album: Released Jan '89, on Silva Screen by Silva Screen Records. Catalogue no: **STV 81122**

It's Always Fair ...

IT'S ALWAYS FAIR WEATHER (Film soundtrack) (Various artists)
Note: Starring Gene Kelly and Dan Dailey.
Album: Released May '74, on MGM (Polydor) by Polydor Ltd. Catalogue no: **2353 036**
Cass: Released Jan '89, on MCA

by MCA Records. Catalogue no: **MCAC 25018**
Album: Released Jan '89, on MCA by MCA Records. Catalogue no: **MCA 25018**

It's Trad Dad

IT'S TRAD DAD (Film soundtrack) (Various artists)
Album: Released Apr '62, on Columbia by EMI Records. Deleted '66. Catalogue no: **33SX 1412**

Ivan The Terrible

IVAN THE TERRIBLE (Film Soundtrack) (Various artists)
Cass: on EMI by EMI Records. Catalogue no: **EG 7695844**
CD: on EMI by EMI Records. Catalogue no: **CDM 7695842**

IVAN THE TERRIBLE (VIDEO) (see under Rimsky Korsakov (composer)) (Bolshoi Ballet)
VHS: Released '88, on Entertainment In Video Catalogue no: **EVC 004**

Ivor The Engine

IVOR THE ENGINE (Stories from the BBC TV childrens series) (Various artists)
Tracks: / Railway, The: *Various artists* / Egg, The: *Various artists* / Proper container, The: *Various artists* / Alarm, The: *Various artists* / Retreat, The: *Various artists* / Unidentified objects: *Various artists* / Gold?: *Various artists* / Mrs. Porty: *Various artists* / Cold: *Various artists* / Endowment, The: *Various artists.*
Album: Released Jul '84, on BBC by BBC Records. Deleted Apr '89. Catalogue no: **REC 517**
Cass: Released Jul '84, on BBC by BBC Records. Catalogue no: **ZCM 517**

J

The following information was taken from the Music Master database on September 25th, 1990.

Jackanory

JACKANORY:STORIES FROM LITTLENOSE (Grant, John)
Album: Released '79, on BBC by BBC Records. Deleted '88. Catalogue no: **REB 229**

Jackson

JACKSON (Original Soundtrack) (Various artists)
Album: Released Apr '88, on Atlantic by WEA Records. Catalogue no: **K 790 886 1**
Cass: Released Apr '88, on Atlantic by WEA Records. Catalogue no: **K 790 886 4**
CD: Released Apr '88, on Atlantic by WEA Records. Catalogue no: **790 886 2**

Jackson, Jermaine

DO WHAT YOU DO
Tracks: / Do what you do / Tell me I'm not dreaming / When the rain begins to fall (Only on 12" single.).
Note: Used in the film version of *Miami Vice*
12" Single: Released Jan '85, on Arista by BMG Records (UK). Catalogue no: **ARIST 12609**
7" Single: Released Jan '85, on Arista by BMG Records (UK). Catalogue no: **ARIST 609**

Jackson, Joe

TUCKER (Original Soundtrack)
Tracks: / Captain of industry (overture) / Car of tomorrow - today / No chance blues / (He's a shape) In a drape / Factory / Vera / It pays to advertise / Tiger rag / Showtime in Chicago / Lone bank loan blues / Speedway / Marilee / Hangin' in Howard Hughes' hangar / Toast of the town, The / Abe's blues / Trial, The / Freedom swing / Rhythm delivery.
Note: "Tucker" (a soundtrack) is a major motion picture directed by Francis Ford Coppola, who chose Joe to create a score of 40's era music for this new drama from

Paramount Pictures.
CD: Released Nov '88, on A&M by A&M Records. Catalogue no: **CDA 3917**
Album: Released Nov '88, on A&M by A&M Records. Catalogue no: **AMA 3917**
Cass: Released Nov '88, on A&M by A&M Records. Catalogue no: **AMC 3917**

Jackson, Michael

MAKING OF THRILLER
Note: Cert: 15.
VHS: Released Oct '86, on Vestron Music Catalogue no: **MA 11000**

MOONWALKER (VIDEO)
VHS: Released Apr '90, on Guild Home Video by Guild Home Video. Catalogue no: **GH 8580**

Jacky

WHITE HORSES
Tracks: / White horses.
Note: Theme tune to the TV programme of the 1960's *White Horses*
7" Single: Released Apr '68, on Philips by Phonogram Ltd. Deleted '71. Catalogue no: **BF 1674**

WHITE HORSES (OLD GOLD)
Tracks: / White horses / Come what may.
7" Single: Released Jan '90, on Old Gold by Old Gold Records. Catalogue no: **OG 9928**

Jagged Edge (Film)

JAGGED EDGE (Film Soundtrack) (Various artists)
Note: 'Jagged Edge' directed by Richard Marquand, who was responsible for 'Eye Of The Needle' and 'Return Of The Jedi'. The film stars Jeff Bridges and Glenn Close and has music composed by John Barry.
Cass: Released Jan '89, on Silva Screen by Silva Screen Records. Deleted Mar '90. Catalogue no: **CTV 81252**
Cass: Released Feb '86, on T. E.

R. by That's Entertainment Records. Catalogue no: **ZCTER 1107**
Album: Released Feb '86, on T. E. R. by That's Entertainment Records. Catalogue no: **TER 1107**

Jagger, Mick

PERFORMANCE (Film Soundtrack) (Jagger, Mick & James Fox)
Tracks: / Gone dead train / Performance / Get away / Powis Square / Rolls Royce / Dyed, dead, red / Harry Flowers / Memo from Turner / Hashishin, The / Wake up, niggers / Poor white hound dog / Natural magic / Turner's murder.
Album: Released '88, on Warner Bros. by WEA Records. Catalogue no: **K 46075**

Jailhouse Rock

JAILHOUSE ROCK (See under Presley, Elvis)

Jake Speed

JAKE SPEED (Film soundtrack) (Various artists)
Note: Composed by Mark Snow.
Cass: Released Jan '89, on Silva Screen by Silva Screen Records. Catalogue no: **CTV 81285**
Album: Released Jan '89, on Silva Screen by Silva Screen Records. Catalogue no: **STV 81285**

Jam Session (film)

JAM SESSION/REVEILLE WITH BEVERLY (Original Soundtrack) (Various artists)
Note: Starring Ann Miller, Duke Ellington, Count Basie and Louis Armstrong.
Album: Released Jan '89, on Silva Screen by Silva Screen Records. Catalogue no: **HS 5014**

Jamaica

JAMAICA (Original Broadway Cast) (Various artists)
Album: on Varese Sarabande Records (USA) by Varese Sarabande Records (USA). Catalogue no: **LOC 1036**

Jamboree (Film)

JAMBOREE (Various session artists) (Various artists)
Cass: Released Feb '83, on AIM (Budget Cassettes) Catalogue no: **AIM 74**

James, Bob

TAXI, THEME FROM
Tracks: / Taxi, Theme from / Caribbean nights.
Note: This track is more commonly known as *Angela*
12" Single: Released Apr '82, on CBS by CBS Records & Distribution. Deleted Apr '85. Catalogue no: **CBSA 132176**
7" Single: Released May '80, on CBS by CBS Records & Distribution. Deleted '83. Catalogue no: **CBS 8540**

James Bond

JAMES BOND:13 ORIGINAL THEMES (Various artists)
Tracks: / James Bond theme: *Norman, Monty & Studio Orchestra* / From Russia with love: *Monro, Matt* / Goldfinger: *Bassey, Shirley* / Thunderball: *Jones, Tom* / You only live twice: *Sinatra, Nancy* / We have all the time in the world: *Armstrong, Louis* / Diamonds are forever: *Bassey, Shirley* / Live and let die: *McCartney, Paul & Wings* / Man with the golden gun, The: *Lulu* / Nobody does it better: *Simon, Carly* / Moonraker: *Bassey, Shirley* / For your eyes only: *Easton, Sheena* / All time high: *Coolidge, Rita.*
CD: Released Apr '87, on EMI by EMI Records. Catalogue no: **CDP 746 079 2**

JAMES BOND SINGLES ALBUM (Original soundtrack recordings) (Various artists)
Tracks: / James Bond theme: *Various artists* / From Russia with love: *Various artists* / You only live twice: *Various artists* / Goldfinger: *Various artists* / Thunderball: *Various artists* / We have all the time in the world: *Various artists* / Diamonds are forever: *Various artists* / Live and let die: *Various artists* / Man with the golden gun: *Various artists* / Nobody does it better: *Various artists* / Bond 77": *Various artists* / Moonraker: *Various artists.*
Album: Released Jan '81, on United Artists by EMI Records. Catalogue no: **BOND 007**
Cass: Released Jan '81, on United

Artists by EMI Records. Catalogue no: **TCBOND 007**

JAMES BOND:GREATEST HITS (Various artists)
Tracks: / James Bond theme: *Norman, Monty & Studio Orchestra* / Kingston calypso: *Norman, Monty & Studio Orchestra* / Under the mango tree: *Norman, Monty & Studio Orchestra* / From Russia with love: *Monro, Matt* / Goldfinger: *Bassey, Shirley* / 007: *Barry, John & Studio Orchestra* / Thunderball: *Jones, Tom* / You only live twice: *Sinatra, Nancy* / On her Majesty's secret service: *Barry, John & Studio Orchestra* / We have all the time in the world: *Armstrong, Louis* / Diamonds are forever: *Bassey, Shirley* / Live and let die: *McCartney, Paul & Wings* / Just a closer walk with thee: *Dejan, Harold A. "Duke" & The Olympia Brass Band* / New second line: *Dejan, Harold A. "Duke" & The Olympia Brass Band* / Bond meets Solitaire: *Martin, George & Studio Orchestra* / Man with the golden gun, The: / Bond '77: *Hamlisch, Marvin & Studio Orchestra* / Moonraker: *Bassey, Shirley* / For your eyes only: *Easton, Sheena* / Nobody does it better: *Simon, Carly.*
Album: Released Mar '82, on EMI by EMI Records. Catalogue no: **EMTV 007**
Cass: Released Mar '82, on EMI by EMI Records. Catalogue no: **TCEMTV 007**

LIVING DAYLIGHTS, THE (18 James Bond themes) (Living Daylights)
CD: Released Dec '88, on Laser Catalogue no: **CD 86018**

Jane Eyre

JANE EYRE (Film soundtrack) (Various artists)
Tracks: / Jane Eyre theme: *Various artists* / Overture (main title): *Various artists* / Lowood: *Various artists* / To Thornfield: *Various artists* / String quartet - Festivity at Thornfield: *Various artists* / Grace Pools and Mason's arrival: *Various artists* / Trrio - The meeting: *Various artists* / Thwarted wedding: *Various artists* / Across the Moors: *Various artists* / Restoration: *Various artists* / Reunion: *Various artists.*
Album: Released '73, on Capitol by EMI Records. Deleted '78. Catalogue no: **EST 749**

CD: Released Sep '88, on Silva Screen by Silva Screen Records. Catalogue no: **FILMCD 031**

Jarre, Jean Michel

CALYPSO
Tracks: / Calypso.
Note: Used as the theme tune to ITV's *Sportsmasters*
7" Single: Released Jul '90, on Polydor by Polydor Ltd. Catalogue no: **PO 84**
12" Single: Released Jul '90, on Polydor by Polydor Ltd. Catalogue no: **PZ 84**
CD Single: Released Jul '90, on Polydor by Polydor Ltd. Catalogue no: **PZCD 84**

OXYGENE PART IV
Tracks: / Oxygene (part IV).
Note: Used as the theme tune to ITV's *Where there's life*
7" Single: Released Aug '77, on Polydor by Polydor Ltd. Deleted '80. Catalogue no: **2001 721**

Jarre, Maurice

JARRE BY JARRE (Royal Philharmonic Orchestra)
Tracks: / Lawrence of Arabia: suite / Ryan's daughter: Rosy's theme / Doctor Zhivago: Prelude / Doctor Zhivago: Lara's theme / Passage to India, A: Adela's theme / Witness: Building the barn / Is Paris burning? / Damned, The / Mad Max: Beyond the thunderdome: Fanfare / Thunderdome music / Villa Rides! Main title.
Note: New digital selection of Maurice Jarre's film music
Album: Released Jan '89, on Silva Screen by Silva Screen Records. Catalogue no: **FM 42307**
CD: Released Jan '89, on Silva Screen by Silva Screen Records. Catalogue no: **MK 42307**
Cass: Released Jan '89, on Silva Screen by Silva Screen Records. Catalogue no: **FMT 42307**

JESUS OF NAZARETH (See under Jesus Of Nazareth)

JULIA & JULIA (See under Julia & Julia)

LION OF THE DESERT (Film soundtrack) (Jarre, Maurice & London Philharmonic Orchestra)
Tracks: / Lion of the desert: *Various artists* / Message, The (Mohammed messenger of God): *Various artists.*

CD: Released Feb '90, on Silva Screen by Silva Screen Records. Catalogue no: **FILMCD060**

LION OF THE DESERT (Film Soundtrack) (Jarre, Maurice & London Philharmonic Orchestra)

Cass: Released Jul '81, on RK by RK Records. Deleted '83. Catalogue no: **ZCRK 100**

Album: Released Jul '81, on RK by RK Records. Deleted '83. Catalogue no: **RKLP 5005**

LION OF THE DESERT (SINGLE) (Jarre, Maurice & London Symphony Orchestra)

Tracks: / Lion of the desert / March of freedom.

7" Single: Released Aug '81, on RK by RK Records. Deleted '84. Catalogue no: **RK 1034**

PASSAGE TO INDIA (See under Passage To India)

Jarreau, Al

MOONLIGHTING

Tracks: / Moonlighting / Golden girl (Lp version)

12" Single: Released Feb '87, on WEA (International). Deleted Jul '88. Catalogue no: **U 8407 T**

7" Single: Released Feb '87, on WEA (International). Deleted Jul '88. Catalogue no: **U 8407**

Jaws

JAWS (Film Soundtrack) (Various artists)

Note: Classic horror film music composed by John Williams.

Cass: Released Jan '89, on MCA by MCA Records. Catalogue no: **MCAC 1660**

Album: Released Jan '76, on MCA by MCA Records. Deleted '81. Catalogue no: **MCF 2716**

Album: Released Jan '89, on MCA by MCA Records. Catalogue no: **MCA 1660**

JAWS 3-D (Film Soundtrack Music) (Various artists)

Album: Released Jan '84, on MCA by MCA Records. Deleted Jan '89. Catalogue no: **MCF 3194**

JAWS II (Film soundtrack) (Various artists)

Note: Composed by John Williams.

Album: Released Jan '89, on Silva Screen by Silva Screen Records. Catalogue no: **MCA 2045**

Jazz & Country...

JAZZ AND COUNTRY IN THE MOVIES (Film Soundtrack) (Various artists)

Tracks: / Pourin' whiskey blues: Labelle, Patti / Low down dirty shame: Labelle, Patti & Larry Riles / Cotton-eyed Joe: Watson, Doc & Merle / Ida Red: Barnes, Roosevelt / Faded love: Barnes, Roosevelt / Lovesick blues: Barnes, Roosevelt / Down home blues: Barnes, Roosevelt / Every time she goes by: Oxford Community Choir / I want to go home: Oxford Community Choir / Liberty: Oxford Community Choir.

Note: Blues and country music from the films A Soldier's Story, Places in the Heart and Mississippi Blues.

Cass: Released Aug '85, on SPI Milan (France) Catalogue no: **CCH 030**

Album: Released Aug '85, on SPI Milan (France) Catalogue no: **ACH 030**

Jazz On A Summer's Day

JAZZ ON A SUMMER'S DAY (VIDEO) (Various artists)

VHS: Released May '90, on Hendring Catalogue no: **HEN 2239**

Jazz Singer

JAZZ SINGER (See under Diamond, Neil)

Jenatsch

JENATSCH (Film Soundtrack) (Various artists)

Note: Score by Pino Donaggio (Dressed to Kill etc.)

Album: Released Jan '89, on SPI Milan (France) Catalogue no: **ACH 036**

CD: Released Jan '89, on SPI Milan (France) Catalogue no: **CDCH 036**

Jerome Kern Goes To...

JEROME KERN GOES TO HOLLYWOOD (Original Cast Recording) (Various artists)

Tracks: / Song is you, The/ I've told every little star: Various artists / I'll be hard to handle: Various artists / Smoke gets in your eyes: Various artists / Yesterdays: Various artists / I won't dance: Various artists / I'm old fashioned: Various artists / Dearly beloved: Various artists / Pick yourself up: Various artists / She didn't say no: Various

artists / Folks who live on the hill, The: Various artists / Long ago and far away: Various artists / Lovely to look at/ Just let me look at you: Various artists / Remind me: Various artists / Last time I saw Paris: Various artists / Ol' man river: Various artists / Why was I born?: Various artists / Bill/ Can't help lovin' dat man of mine: Various artists / All things you are/ They don't believe me: Various artists.

Cass: Released Aug '85, on First Night by First Night Records. Catalogue no: **JEROME C 1**

Album: Released Aug '85, on First Night by First Night Records. Catalogue no: **JEROME 1**

Jerry's Girls

JERRY'S GIRLS (Original Broadway cast) (Various artists)

Tracks: / Jerry's girls: Various artists / Put on your Sunday clothes: Various artists / It only takes a moment: Various artists / Wherever he ain't: Various artists / We need a little Christmas: Various artists / I won't send roses: Various artists / Tap your troubles away: Various artists / Two a day: Various artists / Bosom buddies: Various artists / Man in the moon, The: Various artists / So long dearie: Various artists / Take it all off: Various artists / Shalom: Various artists / Milk and honey: Various artists / Showturn: Various artists / If he walked into my life: Various artists / Hello, Dolly: Various artists / Nelson: Various artists / Just go to the movies: Various artists / Movies were movies: Various artists / Look what happened to Mabel: Various artists / Time heals everything: Various artists / It's today: Various artists / Mame: Various artists / Kiss her now: Various artists / That's how young I feel: Various artists / Gooch's song: Various artists / Before the parade passes: Various artists / I don't want to know: Various artists / La cage aux folles: Various artists / Song on the sand: Various artists / I am what I am: Various artists / Best of times, The: Various artists / Jerry's turn: Various artists.

Cass set: Released Mar '85, on T. E. R. by That's Entertainment Records. Catalogue no: **ZCTER 1093**

2 LP Set: Released Mar '85, on T.

E. R. by That's Entertainment Records. Catalogue no: **TER 2 1093**

CD Set: Released Mar '85, on T. E. R. by That's Entertainment Records. Catalogue no: **CDTER 1093**

Jesus Christ Superstar

JESUS CHRIST SUPERSTAR (Various artists)

Tracks: / Overture: *Various artists* / Heaven on their minds: *Various artists* / What's the buzz: *Various artists* / Everything's alright: *Various artists* / Hosanna: *Various artists* / Simon Zealotes: *Various artists* / Pilate's dream: *Various artists* / I don't know how to love him: *Various artists* / Damned for all time: *Various artists* / I only want to say: *Various artists* / King Herod's song: *Various artists* / Superstar: *Various artists*.

Album: Released '73, on Philips by Phonogram Ltd. Deleted '78. Catalogue no: **6382 060**

JESUS CHRIST SUPERSTAR (Stage show) (Various artists)

Tracks: / Overture: *Various artists* / Heaven on their minds: *Various artists* / What's the buzz?: *Various artists* / Strange thing mystifying: *Various artists* / Then we are decided: *Various artists* / Everything's alright: *Various artists* / This Jesus must die: *Various artists* / Hosanna: *Various artists* / Simon Zealotes: *Various artists* / Poor Jerusalem: *Various artists* / Pilate's dream: *Various artists* / Temple, The: *Various artists* / I don't know how to love him: *Various artists* / Damned for all time: *Various artists* / Blood money: *Various artists* / Last Supper, The: *Various artists* / Gethsemane: *Various artists* / Arrest: *Various artists* / Peter's denial: *Various artists* / Pilate and Christ: *Various artists* / King Herod's song: *Various artists* / Could we start again please?: *Various artists* / Judas's death: *Various artists* / Trial before Pilate: *Various artists* / John 19:41: *Various artists* / Forty one: *Various artists*.

Album: Released '72, on MCA by MCA Records. Catalogue no: **MKPS 2011/2**

CD: Released Apr '87, on MCA by MCA Records. Catalogue no:

DMCX 501

2 LP Set: Released '74, on MCA by MCA Records. Catalogue no: **MCX 501**

Cass: Released '74, on MCA by MCA Records. Catalogue no: **MCXC 501**

JESUS CHRIST SUPERSTAR (Stage Show) (Various artists)

Tracks: / Overture: *Various artists* / Heaven on their mind: *Various artists* / What's the buzz: *Various artists* / Strange thing mystifying: *Various artists* / Everything's alright: *Various artists* / This Jesus must die: *Various artists* / Hosanna: *Various artists* / Simon Zealotes: *Various artists* / Pilate's dream: *Various artists* / Temple: *Various artists* / I don't know how to love him: *Various artists* / Damned for all time: *Various artists* / Blood money: *Various artists* / Gethsemane (Ionly want to say): *Various artists* / King Herod's song: *Various artists* / Trial before Pilate: *Various artists* / Crucifixion: *Various artists* / John Nineteen: *Various artists* / Forty one: *Various artists*.

Album: Released '73, on Starline

(EMI) by EMI Records. Deleted '78. Catalogue no: **SRS 5125**

JESUS CHRIST SUPERSTAR (Original London cast) (Various artists) (See panel below)

Tracks: / Heaven on their minds: *Various artists* / Everything's alright: *Various artists* / This Jesus must die: *Various artists* / Hosanna: *Various artists* / Simon Zealotes: *Various artists* / I don't know how to love him: *Various artists* / Gethsemane: *Various artists* / Pilate's dream: *Various artists* / King Herod's song: *Various artists* / Could we start again please?: *Various artists* / Trial before Pilate: *Various artists* / Superstar: *Various artists* / John 19:41: *Various artists*.

Cass: Released '70, on MCA by MCA Records. Deleted '74. Catalogue no: **MKPC 8008**

Cass: Released '74, on MCA by MCA Records. Catalogue no: **MCFC 2503**

CD: Released Aug '85, on MCA by MCA Records. Catalogue no: **DMCF 2503**

Album: Released '74, on MCA by MCA Records. Catalogue no: **MCF 2503**

Jesus Christ Superstar - **Original London Cast Recording (MCA)**

Album: Released '70, on MCA by MCA Records. Deleted '74. Catalogue no: **MDKS 8008**

JESUS CHRIST SUPERSTAR (Excerpts) (Various artists)
Album: Released '73, on Deram by Decca International. Catalogue no: **SML 1088**

JESUS CHRIST SUPERSTAR (1973) (Film soundtrack) (Various artists)
Tracks: / Overture: *Various artists* / Heaven on their minds: *Various artists* / What's the buzz?: *Various artists* / Strange thing mystifying: *Various artists* / Then we decided: *Various artists* / Everything's alright: *Various artists* / This Jesus must die: *Various artists* / Hosanna: *Various artists* / Simon Zealotes: *Various artists* / Poor Jerusalem: *Various artists* / Pilate's dream: *Various artists* / Temple, The: *Various artists* / I don't know how to love him: *Various artists* / Damned for all time: *Various artists* / Blood money: *Various artists* / Last supper, The: *Various artists* / Gethsemane (I only want to say): *Various artists* / Arrest, The: *Various artists* / Peter's denial: *Various artists* / Pilate and Christ: *Various artists* / King Herod's song: *Various artists* / Could we start again please: *Various artists* / Judas's death: *Various artists* / Trial before Pilate: *Various artists* / Superstar: *Various artists* / Crucifixion: *Various artists* / John 19:41: *Various artists*.
Cass: Released '73, on MCA by MCA Records. Catalogue no: **MCXC 502**
2 LP Set: Released '73, on MCA by MCA Records. Catalogue no: **MCX 502**

JESUS CHRIST SUPERSTAR / GODSPELL (Stage highlights) (Various artists)
Tracks: / Overture - Heaven on their minds: *Various artists* / Everything's alright: *Various artists* / Pilate's dream: *Various artists* / I don't know how to love him: *Various artists* / Last supper: *Various artists* / Arrest: *Various artists* / Superstar: *Various artists* / Crucifixion: *Various artists* / Conclusion: *Various artists* / Prepare ye: *Various artists* / Save the people: *Various artists* / Day by day: *Various artists* / O bless the Lord my soul: *Various artists* / All for the best:

Kathleen Turner and Michael Douglas in *Jewel of the Nile*

Various artists / All good gifts: *Various artists* / Turn back o' man: *Various artists* / By my side: *Various artists* / On the willows: *Various artists* / Finale: *Various artists*.
Album: Released '73, on Golden Hour Deleted '78. Catalogue no: **GH 551**

JESUS CHRIST SUPERSTAR (VIDEO) (Various artists)
VHS: Released '88, on CIC Video Catalogue no: **VHR 1008**
VHS: Released '88, on CIC Video Catalogue no: **CIC 100825**

Jesus Of Nazareth

JESUS OF NAZARETH (TV Film Soundtrack) (Various artists)
Note: Maurice Jarre score for the Franco Zeffirelli TV film/mini series.
Cass: Released Jan '89, on Silva Screen by Silva Screen Records. Catalogue no: **AV 5102**
Cass: Released Apr '79, on PRT by Castle Communications Records. Catalogue no: **ZCP 28504**
Album: Released Jan '89, on Silva Screen by Silva Screen Records. Catalogue no: **AV 4102**

Jewel In The Crown

JEWEL IN THE CROWN (TV soundtrack) (Various artists)
Tracks: / Jewel in the crown main theme: *Various artists* / Lakes, The: *Various artists* / Triangle: *Various artists* / Crossing the river: *Various artists* / Imprisoned: *Various artists* / Death by fire: *Various*

artists / Chillingborough School song: *Various artists* / Butterflie caught in a web: *Various artists* Daphne & Hari: *Various artists* Mirat: *Various artists* / Princel state: *Various artists* / Kedara an waltz dedara: *Various artists* / Ba bie leaves Rose Cottage: *Variou artists* / Champagne Charlie: *Vari ous artists* / Guy Perrons march *Various artists* / Pankot - the hills *Various artists* / Jewel in the crow - end titles: *Various artists*.
Cass: Released Feb '84, on Chry salis by Chrysalis Records. Cata logue no: **ZCDL 1465**
Album: Released Feb '84, o Chrysalis by Chrysalis Records Catalogue no: **CDL 1465**

Jewel Of The Nile

JEWEL OF THE NILE, THE (Film soundtrack) (Various ar tists) (See panel above)
Tracks: / When the going get tough (the tough get going: *Ocean Billy* / I'm in love: *Turner, Ruby* African breeze: *Masekela, Hugh* Johnathan Butler* / Party: *Willes den Dodgers* / Freaks come out a night: *Whodini* / Jewel of the Nile The: *Wilson, Precious* / Legion (here I come): *Shreeve, Mark* / Nu bian dance: *Nubians* / Love theme *Nitzsche, Jack* / Plot thickens, The *Nitzsche, Jack*.
Note: Artists include: Bill Ocean/Ruby Turner/Precious Wil son.
Album: Released Feb '86, on Jiv by Zomba Records. Catalogue no

HIP 33

Cass: Released Jul '86, on Jive by Zomba Records. Deleted '88. Catalogue no: **HIPC 33**

CD: Released Jul '86, on Jive by Zomba Records. Deleted '88. Catalogue no: **CHIP 33**

Jingle Jangle

JINGLE JANGLE (Original Broadway cast) (Various artists)

Album: Released May '83, on T. E. R. by That's Entertainment Records. Catalogue no: **JJ 001**

Joe

JOE (Original Soundtrack) (Various artists)

Tracks: / Butler, Jerry / Expiration of Frank: Butler, Jerry / You can fly: Butler, Jerry / It's a crock: Butler, Jerry / When in Rome: Butler, Jerry / Send the hippies to hell: Butler, Jerry / Hej Joe: Michaels, Dean / Compton's hangout: Exuma / You don't know what's going on: Exuma.

Album: Released '70, on Mercury by Phonogram Ltd. Deleted '75. Catalogue no: **6338 029**

Joe 90

JOE 90 (See under Gray, Barry)

John, Elton

PINBALL WIZARD

Tracks: / Pinball wizard / Harmony.

Note: From the rock-opera Tommy

7" Single: Released '82, on DJM Catalogue no: **DJS 10652**

7" Single: Released Mar '76, on DJM Deleted '77. Catalogue no: **DJS 65**

John, Paul...

JOHN, PAUL, GEORGE, RINGO & BERT (London cast) (John, Paul, Ringo & Bert)

Album: Released '74, on RSO by Polydor Ltd. Catalogue no: **2394 141**

John Wayne Westerns

JOHN WAYNE WESTERNS (See under Wayne, John)

Johnny Be Good

JOHNNY BE GOOD (Original Soundtrack) (Various artists)

Tracks: / Johnny B. Goode: Judas Priest / Caviar: Goodwin, Myles / No ring around Rosie: Kix / If there's any justice: Fiona / Been there, done that: Astley, John / Perfect stranger: Saga / Skintight: Nugent, Ted / Rock still rolls me: Frozen Ghost & Friends / No place like home: Various artists / It's not the way you rock: Dirty Looks.

Cass: Released 30 Apr '88, on Atlantic by WEA Records. Catalogue no: **K 781 837 4**

Album: Released 30 Apr '88, on Atlantic by WEA Records. Catalogue no: **K 781 837 1**

CD: Released 30 Apr '88, on Atlantic by WEA Records. Catalogue no: **781 837-2**

Johnny Handsome

JOHNNY HANDSOME (See under Cooder, Ry)

Johnny The Priest

JOHNNY THE PRIEST (Original London cast) (Various artists)

Tracks: / Doin' the burp: Various artists / Little box, The: Various artists / Vicarage tea: Various artists / Be not afraid: Various artists / I'm your girl: Various artists / Beyond these narrow streets: Various artists / Rooftops: Various artists / Foggy foggy blues, The: Various artists / He'll let you down: Various artists / Ping pong: Various artists / Johnny earn peanuts: Various artists / Tanner's worth of tunes, A: Various artists / Charge me: Various artists / Boy called Johnny, A: Various artists / Stormy evening: Various artists / Finale: Various artists.

Album: Released Apr '83, on T. E. R. by That's Entertainment Records. Catalogue no: **TER 1044**

Johnson, Laurie

AVENGERS (See under the Avengers)

FILM MUSIC OF LAURIE JOHNSON

Tracks: / First men in the moon / Hedda / Captain Kronos / Dr. Strangelove.

Album: Released May '81, on Unicorn-Kanchana by Unicorn - Kanchana Records. Catalogue no:

DKP 9001

MUSIC FROM THE AVENGERS, THE NEW AVENGERS & THE PROFESSIONALS (With the London Studio Orchestra)

Tracks: / Avengers, The / Joker / Pandora / New avengers, The / Obsession / Cat amongst the pigeons / Tale of the big why / Professionals, The / Sleuthing / On the scent / In pursuit / Interlude / Waiting and ambush / On target.

Album: Released Oct '80, on KPM by KPM Records International. Catalogue no: **KPM 7009**

PROFESSIONALS MAIN THEME (Johnson, Laurie Orchestra)

Tracks: / Professionals (main theme) / New avengers.

7" Single: Released Mar '85, on Unicorn-Kanchana by Unicorn - Kanchana Records. Catalogue no: **C15**

SUCU SUCU

Tracks: / Sucu sucu.

Note: Theme tune to the TV Series 'Top Secret'

7" Single: Released Sep '61, on Pye Deleted '64. Catalogue no: **7N 15383**

Jolson, Al

JAZZ SINGER, THE

Tracks: / California here I come / Pasadena / I'm sitting on top of the world / Blue river / Golden gate / Back in your own back yard / My Mammy / Dirty hands, Dirty face / There's a rainbow round my shoulder / Sonny boy / I'm in seventh heaven / Little pal / Used to you / Why can't you / Liza / Let me sing and I'm happy / April showers / Rockabye your baby with a Dixie melody.

Note: Eighteen tracks covering Al Jolson the performer, the writer and the star. Brian Rust has given us some excellent sleeve notes which really say it all.

Cass: Released Nov '85, on Halcyon (USA) by Submarine Records. Catalogue no: **CHDL 102**

Album: Released Nov '85, on Halcyon (USA) by Submarine Records. Catalogue no: **HDL 102**

CD: Released Nov '89, on Halcyon

(USA) by Submarine Records. Catalogue no: **DHDL 102**

ON THE AIR
Album: Released Jan '89, on Silva Screen by Silva Screen Records. Catalogue no: **SH 2003**
Cass: Released Jan '89, on Silva Screen by Silva Screen Records. Catalogue no: **CSH 2003**

SWANEE RIVER 1945 BROADCAST (Jolson, Al / Dennis Morgan)
Tracks: / Oh Susannah / De Camptown races / My old Kentucky home / Ring ring the banjo / I dream of Jeannie with the light brown hair / Old black Joe / Old folks at home / April showers.
Album: Released May '79, on Totem Catalogue no: **TOTEM 1028**

Jolson Revue

JOLSON REVUE (Original London cast) (Various artists)
Tracks: / Shaking the blues away: *Various artists* / Let me sing and I'm happy: *Various artists* / My mammy: *Various artists* / Alabama jubilee: *Various artists* / I only have eyes for you: *Various artists* / Can't help loving that man: *Various artists* / Rock a bye your baby with a Dixie melody: *Various artists* / Sonny boy: *Various artists* / Swanee: *Various artists* / Give my regards to Broadway: *Various artists* / I'm looking over a four leaf clover: *Various artists* / Baby face: *Various artists* / Toot toot tootsie goodbye: *Various artists* / Thoroughly modern Millie: *Various artists* / Anniversary song: *Various artists* / There's a rainbow round my shoulder: *Various artists* / Pretty baby: *Various artists* / April showers: *Various artists* / American trilogy: *Various artists* / He's got the whole world in his hands: *Various artists* / Carolina in the morning: *Various artists* / You made me love you: *Various artists* / Bye bye blackbird: *Various artists* / When you're smiling: *Various artists* / California here I come: *Various artists* / When the saints go marching: *Various artists*.
Album: Released '79, on Sunset (Liberty) by EMI Records. Deleted '84. Catalogue no: **SLS 50426**

Jonathan Livingstone

JONATHAN LIVINGSTONE SEAGULL (Original sound-

track)(See also under Diamond, Neil)

Jones, Aled

ALED (Music from the TV series)
Tracks: / O worship the king / Sheep may safely graze / King of love my shepherd is, The / Alleluja (Exsultate jubiltate) / O my saviour lifted / Thy hand, o God, has guided / How lovely are thy dwellings / Love divine / Bist du bei mir / All thanks to thee / Benedictus (Little organ mass) / Let there be peace on earth.
Album: Released Feb '87, on 10 Records by Virgin Records. Deleted May '90. Catalogue no: **AJ 3**
Cass: Released Feb '87, on 10 Records by Virgin Records. Catalogue no: **CAJ 3**
CD: Released Feb '87, on 10 Records by Virgin Records. Catalogue no: **AJCD 3**

WINTER STORY, A (TV theme)
Tracks: / Winter story, A / Sion blewych coch.
7" Single: Released Nov '86, on H.M.V. by EMI Records. Deleted Oct '87. Catalogue no: **ALED 2**
12" Single: Released Nov '86, on H.M.V. by EMI Records. Deleted Jul '87. Catalogue no: **12 ALED 2**

Jones, John Paul

SCREAM FOR HELP (Film soundtrack)
Tracks: / Spaghetti Junction / Bad child / Take it or leave it / Chilli sauce / Silver train / Christie / Here I am / Crackback.
Cass: Released Apr '85, on Atlantic by WEA Records. Deleted Aug '87. Catalogue no: **780 190-4**
Album: Released Apr '85, on Atlantic by WEA Records. Deleted Aug '87. Catalogue no: **780 190-1**

Journey Into Space

JOURNEY INTO SPACE (Various artists)
2 LP Set: Released Jul '86, on Avon by Avon Records. Catalogue no: **ADL 519**
Cass set: Released Jul '86, on Avon by Avon Records. Catalogue no: **ADK 519**

JOURNEY INTO SPACE-OPERATION LUNA (6 hours

of space adventure) (Various artists)
Cass set: Released May '89, on BBC by BBC Records. Catalogue no: **ZBBC 4002**

Julia

JULIA (Film soundtrack) (Various artists)
Album: Released '80, on DRG (USA) by DRG Records (USA). Catalogue no: **DRG 9514**

RETURN OF MARTIN GUERRE / JULIA (See under Return Of Martin Guerre)

Julia & Julia

JULIA & JULIA (Film soundtrack) (Various artists)
Note: Score by Maurice Jarre for the film starring Kathleen Turner and Sting.
CD: Released Jan '89, on Silva Screen by Silva Screen Records. Catalogue no: **VCD 47327**
Album: Released Jan '89, on Silva Screen by Silva Screen Records. Catalogue no: **STV 81327**

Jumpin' Jack Flash

JUMPIN' JACK FLASH (Film soundtrack) (Various artists) (See also under Rolling Stones)
Tracks: / Set me free: *Rene & Angela* / Trick of the night, A: *Bananarama* / Misled: *Kool & The Gang* / Rescue me: *Various artists* / Jumpin' Jack Flash: *Rolling Stones* / You can't hurry love: *Supremes* / Hold on: *Branigan, Laura* / Window to the world: *Face To Face* / Breaking the code: *Newman, Thomas* / Love music: *Newman, Thomas.*
Album: Released Apr '87, on Mercury by Phonogram Ltd. Deleted Mar '88. Catalogue no: **830 545-1**
Cass: Released Apr '87, on Mercury by Phonogram Ltd. Deleted Mar '88. Catalogue no: **830 545-4**
CD: Released Apr '87, on Mercury by Phonogram Ltd. Deleted Mar '88. Catalogue no: **830 545-2**

Jungle Book

JUNGLE BOOK (Original Film Soundtrack) (Various artists) (See panel on next page)
Tracks: / Main title: *Various artists* / Trust in me: *Various artists* / Colonel Hathi's march: *Various artists*

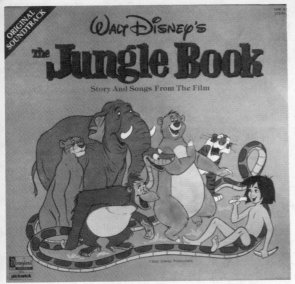

Soundtrack to Disney's *Jungle Book* on Hallmark

/ Bare necessities: *Various artists* / I wan'na be like you: *Various artists* / Colonel Hathi's march: *Various artists* / That's what friends are for: *Various artists* / My own home: *Various artists* / Bare necessities: *Various artists*.
Album: Released '67, on Hallmark by Pickwick Records. Deleted '72. Catalogue no: **SHM 937**

JUNGLE BOOK (ORIGINAL ISSUE) (Film soundtrack) (Various artists)
Album: Released Mar '68, on Disneyland by Disneyland-Vista Records (USA). Deleted '70. Catalogue no: **ST 3948**

JUNGLE BOOK, THE (Original soundtrack)
Album: Released Dec '87, on Walt Disney Catalogue no: **WD 019**
Cass: Released Oct '84, on Walt Disney Deleted '88. Catalogue no: **ZCM 536**
Cass: Released Dec '87, on Walt Disney Catalogue no: **WDC 019**
Album: Released Oct '84, on Walt Disney Deleted '88. Catalogue no: **REC 536**

JUNGLE BOOK/THIEF OF BAGHDAD (Film soundtrack) (Various artists)
Note: New recordings of 2 Miklos Rozsa scores.
Album: Released Jan '89, on Silva Screen by Silva Screen Records. Catalogue no: **CL 0017**
CD: Released Jan '89, on Silva Screen by Silva Screen Records. Catalogue no: **VCD 47258**

Just A Gigolo

JUST A GIGOLO (Film soundtrack) (Various artists)
Tracks: / Just a gigolo: *Dietrich, Marlene* / Don't let it be too long: *Rome, Sydne* / Johnny: *Manhattan Transfer* / I kiss your hand: *Manhattan Transfer* / Jealous eyes: *Manhattan Transfer* / Salome: *Pasadena Roof Orchestra* / Black bottom: *Pasadena Roof Orchestra* / Charmaine: *Pasadena Roof Orchestra* / Easy winners: *Ragtimers* / Just a gigolo: *Village People*.
Cass: Released '79, on Pye Deleted '84. Catalogue no: **ZCJAM 1**
VHS: Released Sep '86, on Cinema Features Deleted '88. Catalogue no: **F 019 C**
Album: Released '79, on Pye Deleted '84. Catalogue no: **JAM 1**

Just For Fun

JUST FOR FUN (Film soundtrack) (Various artists)
Album: Released Jun '63, on Decca by Decca International. Deleted '68. Catalogue no: **LK 4524**

K

The following information was taken from the Music Master database on September 25th, 1990.

Kamen, Michael

RITA, SUE AND BOB TOO

Tracks: / Rita, Sue and Bob too / Silly tune / Gang bang (On 12" only.).

7" Single: Released Sep '87, on RCA by BMG Records (UK). Catalogue no: **109377**

12" Single: Released Sep '87, on RCA by BMG Records (UK). Catalogue no: **609377**

WATCHING YOU (DUTY MEN) (Original T V theme)

Tracks: / Watching you (duty men.)

7" Single: Released Oct '87, on BBC by BBC Records. Deleted Apr '89. Catalogue no: **RESL 215**

12" Single: Released Oct '87, on BBC by BBC Records. Deleted Apr '89. Catalogue no: **12RSL 215**

Kaper, Bronislaw

BRONISLAW KAPER PLAYS HIS FILM MUSIC

Note: Selections from Mutiny on the Bounty, Lili, Butterfield 8, Auntie Mame, Lord Jim etc.

CD: Released Jan '89, on Silva Screen by Silva Screen Records. Catalogue no: **FCD 8101**

Karas, Anton

HARRY LIME THEME (THE THIRD MAN) (An Evening With Anton Karas)

Note: Zither player Karas with 28 numbers beginning with the title track, which he wrote for the film The Third Man.

Album: Released Jun '88, on Telefunken (Teldec (BRD)) Catalogue no: **6.21295**

Cass: Released Jun '88, on Telefunken (Teldec (BRD)) Catalogue no: **4.21295**

CD: Released Jun '88, on Telefunken (Teldec (BRD)) Catalogue no: **8.26751**

THIRD MAN, THE

CD: Released Feb '90, on Zeta Catalogue no: **ZET 526**

WORLD OF ANTON KARAS

Album: Released '71, on Decca by Decca International. Catalogue no: **SPA 118**

Karate Kid

KARATE KID (Film Soundtrack) (Various artists)

Tracks: / Moment of truth, The: Survivor / On the beach: Flirts & Jan & Dean Bop Bop / No shelter: Broken Edge / It takes two to tango: Davis, Paul / Tough love: Shandi / Rhythm man: St. Regis / Feel the night: Robertson, Baxter / Desire: Gang Of Four / You're the best: Esposito, Joe.

Album: Released Aug '84, on Casablanca by PolyGram UK Ltd. Catalogue no: **CANH 10**

Cass: Released Jan '89, on Silva Screen by Silva Screen Records. Catalogue no: **822213.4**

Cass: Released Aug '84, on Casablanca by PolyGram UK Ltd. Catalogue no: **CANHC 10**

Album: Released Jan '89, on Silva Screen by Silva Screen Records. Deleted Mar '90. Catalogue no: **822213.1**

KARATE KID PART II, THE (Film Soundtrack) (Various artists)

Tracks: / Glory of love: Various artists / Rock 'n' roll over you: Various artists / Fish for life: Various artists / Rock around the clock: Various artists / Let me at 'em: Various artists / This is the time: Various artists / Earth angel: Various artists / Love theme: Various artists / Two looking at one: Various artists / Storm The: Various artists.

Album: Released Jun '86, on Warner Bros. by WEA Records. Catalogue no: **925489 1**

Cass: Released Jun '86, on Warner Bros. by WEA Records. Catalogue no: **925489 4**

KARATE KID PART III, THE (Original Soundtrack) (Various artists)

Tracks: / Listen to your heart: Little River Band / This could take all night: Boy's Club / Summer in the city: Pointer Sisters / 48 hours: P.B.F. / Karate Kid (love theme): Conti, Bill / Under any moon: Medeiros, Glenn / I can't help myself: Medeiros, Glenn / Out for the count: Winger / In a trance: Money Talks.

CD: Released 18 Aug '89, on MCA by MCA Records. Deleted Sep '90. Catalogue no: **DMCF 6061**

Album: Released 18 Aug '89, on MCA by MCA Records. Deleted Jul '90. Catalogue no: **MCD 6061**

Cass: Released 18 Aug '89, on MCA by MCA Records. Catalogue no: **MCDC 6061**

Katmandu

DYNASTY, THEME FROM

Tracks: / Dynasty (theme from).

12" Single: Released Mar '86, on Lovebeat Int. Catalogue no: **COLBY 121**

7" Single: Released Mar '86, on Lovebeat Int. Catalogue no: **COLBY 1**

Katrina & The Waves

WALKING ON SUNSHINE

Tracks: / Walking on Sunshine / Red wine & Whisky / Do you want Crying / Que te quiero / Sun street / Is that it.

Note: featured in the film 'Look Who's Talking'

12" Single: Released Apr '85, on Capitol by EMI Records. Deleted '88. Catalogue no: **12CL 354**

7" Single: Released Apr '85, on Capitol by EMI Records. Deleted '88. Catalogue no: **CL 354**

Kay, Janet

NO EASY WALK TO FREEDOM (TV theme)

Tracks: / No easy walk to freedom.

7" Single: Released Aug '87, on Local Catalogue no: **7LR 012**

12" Single: Released Aug '87, on Local Catalogue no: **LR 012**

Kaye, Danny

HANS CHRISTIAN ANDER-

SEN (Film Soundtrack)
Tracks: / Anywhere I wander /
Ugly duckling / King's new clothes
/ Thumbelina / Wonderful Copen-
hagen / I'm Hans Christian Ander-
sen / No two people / Tubby the tuba.
Cass: Released Dec '79, on MFP
by EMI Records. Deleted '84.
Catalogue no: **TC 50456**
Album: Released Dec '79, on
MFP by EMI Records. Deleted
'84. Catalogue no: **MFP 50456**

Keating, Johnny
THEME FROM 'Z CARS'
Tracks: / 'Z Cars', Theme from.
7" Single: Released Mar '62, on
Piccadilly Deleted '65. Catalogue
no: **7N 35032**

Kelly, Gene
**AMERICAN IN PARIS, AN
(Film Soundtrack) (See under
American In Paris, An)**

**ANCHORS AWEIGH (Film
Soundtrack) (See under Anchors Aweigh)**

**BEST OF GENE KELLY —
FROM MGM FILMS**
Album: Released Jan '89, on
MCA by MCA Records. Cata-
logue no: **MCA 25166**
CD: Released Jun '88, on MCA (USA)
by MCA Records (USA). Deleted Mar
'90. Catalogue no: **31177**
Cass: Released Jan '89, on MCA
by MCA Records. Catalogue no:
MCAC 25166

**BRIGADOON (Film Sound-
track) (See under Brigadoon)**

**COVER GIRL (Film Sound-
track) (See under Cover Girl)**

**FOR ME AND MY GIRL (Film
Soundtrack) (See under For
Me & My Girl)**

GENE KELLY ON THE AIR
Album: Released Feb '88, on
Totem Catalogue no: **TOTEM 1034**

**IT'S   ALWAYS   FAIR
WEATHER (Film Soundtrack)
(See under It's Always Fair...)**

**MARJORIE MORNINGSTAR
(Film Soundtrack) (See under
Marjorie Morningstar)**

**ON THE TOWN (Film Sound-
track) (See under On The Town)**

SINGIN' IN THE RAIN
Album: Released Sep '78, on
Decca by Decca International.
Catalogue no: **SKL 5265**

CD: Released Jan '89, on Decca
by Decca International. Catalogue
no: **820 488 2**

**SOUNDTRACKS, VOICES
AND THEMES (See under As-
taire, Fred)**

Kelly, Kris
**PRISONER CELL BLOCK H
(THEME FROM)**
Tracks: / Prisoner cell block H
(theme from).
7" Single: Released Jan '89, on
Silver Heart by Silver Heart Rec-
ords. Catalogue no: **HEART 2**

Kelly's Heroes
**KELLY'S HEROES (Film
Soundtrack) (Various artists)**
Tracks: / Kelly's heroes: Various artists / All for the love of sunshine:
Various artists / Burning bridges: Various artists / Tiger tank: Various artists
/ Clairmont waltz: Various artists /
Battle hymn of the republic: Various
artists / Burning bridges: Various artists / Quick draw Kelly: Various artists
/ All for the love of sunshine: Various
artists / I've been working on the railroad: Various artists / Commando
opus: Various artists.
Album: Released '73, on Polydor
by Polydor Ltd. Deleted '78. Catalogue no: **2315 019**

Kenton, Stan
**STAGE DOOR SWINGS, 1958
(Kenton, Stan & His Orchestra)**
Tracks: / Lullaby of Broadway /
Party's over, The / Baubles, ban-
gles and beads / Every time we say
goodbye / Whatever Lola wants
(Lola gets) / Bali ha'i / Hey there
/ Younger than Springtime / On the
street where you live / I love Paris
/ All at once you love her / I've
never been in love before .
Cass: Released Jun '86, on Capi-
tol by EMI Records. Deleted Nov
'88. Catalogue no: **TCEMS 1159**
Album: Released Jul '86, on Capitol by EMI Records. Deleted May
'90. Catalogue no: **EMS 1159**
Album: Released '85, on Creative
World USA) by GNP Crescendo Records (USA). Catalogue no: **ST 1044**

Kentuckian
**KENTUCKIAN, THE AND
OTHER FILM THEMES (Vari-
ous artists)**
Tracks: / Kentuckian, The: Various
artists / Down to the sea in ships:

Various artists / Day the earth stood
still: Various artists / In love and war:
Various artists / Sunrise at Campo-
bello: Various artists.
Album: Released Jan '89, on
Silva Screen by Silva Screen Rec-
ords. Catalogue no: **ERS 6506**
CD: Released Sep '87, on Silva
Screen by Silva Screen Records.
Catalogue no: **PRCD 1777**

Kern, Jerome
**OVERTURES & MUSIC FROM
SWING TIME (National Phil-
harmonic Orchestra)**
Tracks: / Cat and the fiddle, The /
Girl from Utah, The / Leave it to
Jane / Have a heart / Sweet
Adeline / O lady lady / Sitting pretty
/ Very warm for May / Swing time
main title and pick yourself up /
Way you look tonight.
Note: National Philharmonic Orches-
tra conducted by John McGlinn.
CD: Released Jun '89, on EMI by
EMI Records. Catalogue no: **CDC
749 630 2**
Cass: Released Jun '89, on EMI
by EMI Records. Catalogue no: **EL
749 630 4**
Album: Released Jun '89, on EMI
by EMI Records. Catalogue no: **EL
749 630 1**

Ketcham, Charles
**4   ALFRED   HITCHCOCK
FILMS (Ketcham, Charles &
Utah Symphony Orchestra)**
Tracks: / Family plot end credits /
Strangers on a train / Suspicion /
Notorious.
Album: Released Sep '86, on T.
E. R. by That's Entertainment
Records. Catalogue no: **TER 1109**
Cass: Released Sep '86, on T. E.
R. by That's Entertainment Rec-
ords. Catalogue no: **ZCTER 1109**
CD: Released Sep '86, on T. E. R.
by That's Entertainment Records.
Catalogue no: **VCD 47225**

Key
**KEY, THE (Film soundtrack)
(Various artists)**
Album: Released '82, on Ariola
by BMG Records (UK). Catalogue
no: **206 253**

Khatchaturian, Aram
**SPARTACUS (Khatchaturian,
Aram & Vienna Philharmonic
Orchestra)**
Album: Released Jan '72, on
Decca by Decca International.

Deleted Jan '77. Catalogue no:
SXL 6000

Kid Galahad

**KID GALAHAD (See under
Presley, Elvis)**

Kid Millions

**KID MILLIONS / ROMAN
SCANDALS (Original Sound-
tracks) (Various artists)**
Note: Starring Eddie Cantor and
Ethel Merman.
Album: Released Jan '89, on
Silva Screen by Silva Screen Rec-
ords. Catalogue no: **SH 2039**

Kidnapped

**KIDNAPPED (Film Sound-
track) (Various artists)**
Tracks: / Overture: *Various artists*
/ Main title: *Various artists* / David
and Catriona: *Various artists* /
Mungo Campbell: *Various artists* /
Fugitives from the redcoats: *Vari-
ous artists* / Alan Breck: *Various
artists* / Shipwreck: *Various artists*
/ Cluny's cave: *Various artists* /
Edinburgh Castle: *Various artists* /
Highlands and the Lowlands: *Vari-
ous artists* / Moors and heather:
Various artists / For all my days:
Various artists.
Album: Released '73, on Polydor
by Polydor Ltd. Deleted '78. Cata-
logue no: **2383 102**

**KIDNAPPED (Story of the TV
Serial) (Various artists)**
2 LP Set: Released '79, on Decca
by Decca International. Deleted
'84. Catalogue no: **DPA 3067/2**

Kids Are Alright

**KIDS ARE ALRIGHT, THE
(Film Soundtrack) (See under
Who)**

**KIDS ARE ALRIGHT, THE
(VIDEO) (Various artists)**
VHS: Released '88, on Channel 5
by Channel 5 Video. Catalogue no:
CFV 00072

**KIDS ARE ALRIGHT, THE
(Various artists)**
CD: Released '88, on Ironic by
Ironic Records. Catalogue no:
IRONIC 5CD

Kids From Fame (TV)

BEST OF FAME
Tracks: / Starmaker / We got the
power / Rock 'n' roll world / Take
that first step / Body language / Hi
fidelity / Life is a celebration / Be

Compilation from the popular TV series *Kids from Fame*

your own hero / Friday night /
Fame.
CD: Released Oct '84, on RCA by
BMG Records (UK). Deleted May
'89. Catalogue no: **PD 84961**

BODY LANGUAGE
Tracks: / Body language / Life is a
celebration.
12" Single: Released Jun '83, on
RCA by BMG Records (UK).
Catalogue no: **RCAT 343**
7" Single: Released Jun '83, on
RCA by BMG Records (UK).
Catalogue no: **RCA 343**

**FAME (TV series) (See panel
above)**
Tracks: / Starmaker / I can do
anything better than you can / I still
believe in me / Life is a celebration
/ Step up to the mike / Hi fidelity /
We got the power / It's gonna be a
long night / Desdemona / Be my
music.
Album: Released Jun '82, on BBC
by BBC Records. Deleted '88.
Catalogue no: **REP 447**
Cass: Released Jun '82, on BBC
by BBC Records. Deleted '88.
Catalogue no: **ZCH 447**

FRIDAY NIGHT
Tracks: / Friday night / Could we
be magic like you.

7" Single: Released Feb '83, on
RCA by BMG Records (UK).
Catalogue no: **RCA 320**

FROM FAME AGAIN
Tracks: / Mannequin / Carnival / I
was only trying to help / Alone in a
crowd / You're the real music / Sho
sho Shorofsky / Special place, A /
Do the gimme that / It's sonata
Mozart / Come what may / Show
must go on.
Album: Released Jan '84, on RCA
by BMG Records (UK). Catalogue
no: **PL 89079**
Album: Released Oct '82, on RCA
by BMG Records (UK). Deleted
Oct '87. Catalogue no: **RCALP
6057**
Cass: Released Jan '84, on RCA
by BMG Records (UK). Catalogue
no: **PK 89079**

HI FIDELITY
Tracks: / Hi fidelity / I still believe
in you.
7" Single: Released Jul '82, on
RCA by BMG Records (UK).
Catalogue no: **RCA 254**

KIDS FROM FAME EP
Tracks: / Hi fidelity / Desdemona /
Starmaker / It's gonna be a long
night.
Cassingle: Released May '83, on

RCA by BMG Records (UK). Catalogue no: **RCXK 002**

KIDS FROM FAME (VIDEO)

Note: At the movies 'Fame' was a smash. On TV 'The Kids From Fame' - a sensation. Then the 'Kids From Fame' were live, a sell out concert at London's Royal Albert Hall. If you were there this is your chance to recapture the magic; if you missed it then this has to be the next best thing. Featuring your favourite kids, your favourite songs and some of the most spectacular dance routines the Albert Hall stage has ever seen, 'The Kids From Fame' is non stop entertainment and includes toe tapping and hand clapping versions of Kids From Fame classics. Running time: 75 mins. (MGM/UA Home Video)

VHS: Released Feb '88, on MGM/UA (Video) by MGM/UA Video. Catalogue no: **SMV 10205**

LIVE: KIDS FROM FAME (T.V. soundtrack)

Tracks: / Body language / Could we be magic like you / Friday night / We got the power / Desdemona / Starmaker / Hi fidelity / Mannequin / Life is a celebration / Fame / Special place, A / It's gonna be a long night / I still believe in me / Secret / Be my music.

Cass: Released Jan '84, on RCA by BMG Records (UK). Deleted '88. Catalogue no: **PK 89257**

Album: Released Feb '83, on BBC by BBC Records. Deleted Feb '88. Catalogue no: **KIDLP 003**

Album: Released Jan '84, on RCA by BMG Records (UK). Deleted '88. Catalogue no: **PL 89257**

MANNEQUIN

Tracks: / Mannequin / Come what may.

7" Single: Released Nov '82, on RCA by BMG Records (UK). Catalogue no: **RCA 299**

SING FOR YOU

Album: Released Aug '83, on BBC by BBC Records. Deleted Aug '88. Catalogue no: **KIDLP 005**

SONGS

Tracks: / Be your own hero / Just like you / There's a train / Could we be magic like you / Lay back and be cool / Songs / Body language / Beautiful dreamer / Dancing endlessly / Bet your life it's me.

Album: Released May '83, on

BBC by BBC Records. Deleted '87. Catalogue no: **KIDLP 004**

Cass: Released May '83, on BBC by BBC Records. Deleted '87. Catalogue no: **KIDK 004**

SONGS (SINGLE)

Tracks: / Songs / Just like you.

7" Single: Released Aug '83, on RCA by BMG Records (UK). Catalogue no: **RCA 353**

STARMAKER

Tracks: / Starmaker / Step up to the mike.

7" Single: Released Sep '82, on RCA by BMG Records (UK). Catalogue no: **RCA 280**

STARMAKER (OLD GOLD)

Tracks: / Starmaker / Hi fidelity.

7" Single: Released Nov '86, on Old Gold by Old Gold Records. Catalogue no: **OG 9643**

Kill Or Be Killed

KILL OR BE KILLED/GOD FORGIVES - I DON'T (Original Soundtracks) (Various artists)

Note: 2 Spaghetti western scores by Carlo Rustichelli.

Album: Released Jan '89, on Silva Screen by Silva Screen Records. Catalogue no: **PHCAM 08**

Killing Fields

KILLING FIELDS (See under Oldfield, Mike)

Kindred

KINDRED, THE (Original Soundtrack) (Various artists)

Note: Horror score by David Newman.

Album: Released Jan '89, on Silva Screen by Silva Screen Records. Catalogue no: **STV 81308**

King, Ben E.

STAND BY ME (SINGLE)

Tracks: / Stand By Me / Yakety yak.

Note: Used as the title song to the film *Stand by Me*

7" Single: Released Jan '87, on Atlantic by WEA Records. Catalogue no: **A 9361**

7" Single: Released Jun '61, on London-American by Decca Records. Deleted '64. Catalogue no: **HLK 9358**

12" Single: Released Jan '87, on Atlantic by WEA Records. Deleted Jul '88. Catalogue no: **A 9361 T**

King Creole

KING CREOLE (See under Presley, Elvis)

King, Denis

DICK TURPIN (King, Denis Orchestra)

Tracks: / Dick Turpin / Belinda.

7" Single: Released Jan '79, on Columbia by EMI Records. Deleted '83. Catalogue no: **DB 9061**

REGAN'S THEME (King, Denis & His Orchestra)

Tracks: / Regan's theme / F.J.'s tune.

7" Single: Released Jan '77, on EMI by EMI Records. Deleted '80. Catalogue no: **EMI 2578**

WE'LL MEET AGAIN (King, Denis Orchestra)

Tracks: / We'll meet again.

7" Single: Released Jun '83, on Multi-Media Catalogue no: **MMT 6**

King & I

KING AND I (Original London Cast) (Various artists)

Album: on DRG (USA) by DRG Records (USA). Catalogue no: **DS 15014**

KING AND I (1977 Broadway Cast) (Various artists)

Tracks: / Arrival at Bangkok: *Various artists* / I whistle a happy tune: *Various artists* / My lord and master: *Various artists* / Hello, young lovers: *Various artists* / March of the Siamese children: *Various artists* / Puzzlement, A: *Various artists* / Royal Bangkok Academy: *Various artists* / Getting to know you: *Various artists* / So big a world: *Various artists* / We kiss in a shadow: *Various artists* / Shall I tell you what I think of you?: *Various artists* / Something wonderful: *Various artists* / Western people funny: *Various artists* / Dance of Anna and Sir Edward: *Various artists* / I have dreamed: *Various artists* / Song of the king: *Various artists* / Shall we dance?: *Various artists.*

Cass: Released '79, on RCA by BMG Records (UK). Deleted '84. Catalogue no: **BK 12610**

CD: Released Jan '89, on RCA by BMG Records (UK). Catalogue no: **RCD 1 2610**

Album: Released Jan '79, on RCA by BMG Records (UK). Catalogue

Soundtrack from *The King and I* on the Capitol label. Features Yul Brynner and Deborah Kerr.

no: **BL 12610**

KING AND I (Original Broadway cast) (Various artists)
Tracks: / Overture: *Various artists* / I whistle a happy tune: *Various artists* / My lord and master: *Various artists* / Hello, young lovers: *Various artists* / March of the Siamese children: *Various artists* / Puzzlement, A: *Various artists* / Getting to knoe you: *Various artists* / We kiss in a shadow: *Various artists* / I tell you what I think of you?: *Various artists* / Something wonderful: *Various artists* / I have dreamed: *Various artists* / Shall we dance: *Various artists*
Album: Released '79, on Chrysalis by Chrysalis Records. Deleted '84. Catalogue no: **CDL 8026**
Cass: Released Mar '82, on MCA by MCA Records. Catalogue no: **MCLC 1663**
Album: Released Mar '82, on MCA by MCA Records. Catalogue no: **MCL 1663**
Cass: Released '79, on Chrysalis by Chrysalis Records. Deleted '84. Catalogue no: **TC CDL 8026**

KING AND I (Film Soundtrack)

(Various artists) (See panel above)
Tracks: / I whistle a happy tune: *Various artists* / My lord and master: *Various artists* / Hello, young lovers: *Various artists* / March of the Siamese children: *Various artists* / Puzzlement, A: *Various artists* / Getting to knoe you: *Various artists* / We kiss in a shadow: *Various artists* / I have dreamed: *Various artists* / Shall we tell you what I think of you?: *Various artists* / Something wonderful?: *Various artists* / Song of the king: *Various artists* / Shall we dance?: *Various artists*.\
CD: Released Mar '87, on Capitol by EMI Records. Catalogue no: **CDP 746 632 2**
Cass: Released '70, on Capitol by EMI Records. Catalogue no: **TCSW 740**
Album: Released Aug '58, on Capitol by EMI Records. Catalogue no: **SLCT 6108**
CD: Released Mar '87, on Capitol by EMI Records. Catalogue no: **CZ 75**

King, Jonathan
I'LL SLAP YOUR FACE

Tracks: / I'll slap your face / No speed limit.
Note: Used as the theme to the BBC 2 programme *Entertainment USA*, presented by Jonathan King.
7" Single: Released Jul '87, on BBC by BBC Records. Deleted Apr '89. Catalogue no: **RESL 218**

King Kong (Film)
KING KONG (See under Steiner, Max)

KING KONG (Original Soundtrack) (National Philharmonic Orchestra)
Tracks: / Main theme, a boat in the fog / Jungle Dance / Sea at night, The / Aboriginal Sacrificial Dance / Entrance of Kong / Log sequence, The / Cryptic Shadow / Cave, The / Sailors waiting / Return of Kong / King Kong Theatre march / Aeroplanes, Finale.
Note: Newly recorded the original score from the 1933 film with music by Max Steiner. Conductor: Fred Steiner.
Album: Released Mar '88, on Silva Screen by Silva Screen Records. Deleted Apr '90. Catalogue no: **FILM 013**
CD: Released Jun '88, on Silva Screen by Silva Screen Records. Catalogue no: **SCCD 901**

King Kong Lives
KING KONG LIVES (Original Soundtrack) (Various artists)
Note: The more recent of the King Kong's with a symphonic score by John Scott.
Album: Released Jan '89, on MCA by MCA Records. Catalogue no: **MCA 6203**
Cass: Released Jan '89, on MCA by MCA Records. Catalogue no: **MCAC 6203**

King Of Comedy
KING OF COMEDY (Original Soundtrack) (Various artists)
Note: Songs from the Martin Scorsese Film.
Album: Released Jan '89, on Silva Screen by Silva Screen Records. Catalogue no: **23765.1**

King Of Kings
KING OF KINGS (Film Soundtrack) (Various artists)
Tracks: / King of Kings theme - prelude: *Various artists* / Holy of holies: *Various artists* / Pontius Pilate's arrival in Jerusalem: *Vari-*

ous artists / Virgin Mary: *Various artists* / Nativity: *Various artists* / Temptation of Christ: *Various artists* / John the Baptist: *Various artists* / Miracles of Christ: *Various artists* / Salome's dance: *Various artists* / Mount Galilee and the sermon on the mount: *Various artists* / Prayer of Our Lord: *Various artists* / Christ's entry into Jerusalem: *Various artists* / Tempest in Judea: *Various artists* / Way of cross: *Various artists* / Scourging of Christ: *Various artists* / Mary at the sepulcher: *Various artists* / Resurrection: *Various artists* / Finale: *Various artists*.

Album: Released '73, on MGM (Polydor) by Polydor Ltd. Deleted '78. Catalogue no: **2353 035**

Cass: Released Jan '89, on MCA by MCA Records. Catalogue no: **MCAC 39056**

Album: Released Jan '89, on MCA by MCA Records. Catalogue no: **MCA 39056**

KING OF KINGS/GREATEST STORY EVER TOLD (MGM Original Soundtrack Album) (Various artists)

Tracks: / King of kings theme - prelude: *Various artists* / Holy of holies: *Various artists* / Pontius Pilate's arrival into Jerusalem: *Various artists* / Virgin Mary, The: *Various artists* / Nativity: *Various artists* / Temptation of Christ, The: *Various artists* / John the Baptist: *Various artists* / Miracles of Christ, The: *Various artists* / Salome's dance: *Various artists* / Mount Galilee and the sermon on the mount: *Various artists* / Prayer of Our Lord: *Various artists* / Christ's entry into Jerusalem and tempest in Judea: *Various artists* / Scourging of Christ, The: *Various artists* / Way of the cross, The: *Various artists* / Mary at the Sepulcher: *Various artists* / Resurrection - finale: *Various artists* / Jesus of Nazareth (main theme): *Various artists* / Prophesy, A: *Various artists* / Voice in the wilderness, A: *Various artists* / Great journey, The: *Various artists* / Time of wonders, A: *Various artists* / There shall come a time to enter: *Various artists* / New commandment, A: *Various artists* / Hour has come, The: *Various artists* / Into thy hands: *Various artists*.

CD: Released Sep '90, on MGM (EMI) Catalogue no: **CDP 794 987 2**

Album: Released Sep '90, on MGM (EMI) Catalogue no: **794 987 1**

Album: Released Sep '90, on MGM (EMI) Catalogue no: **LPMGM 25**

CD: Released Sep '90, on MGM (EMI) Catalogue no: **CDMGM 25**

Cass: Released Sep '90, on MGM (EMI) Catalogue no: **TCMGM 25**

Cass: Released Sep '90, on MGM (EMI) Catalogue no: **794 987 4**

King Solomon's Mines

KING SOLOMON'S MINES (Film Soundtrack) (Various artists)

Tracks: / Main title: *Various artists* / Upside down people: *Various artists* / Crocodiles: *Various artists* / Pot luck: *Various artists* / Forced flight: *Various artists* / Dancing shots: *Various artists* / Good morning: *Various artists* / No pain: *Various artists* / Ritual, The: *Various artists* / No diamonds - Generique fin: *Various artists*.

Album: Released Apr '86, on SPI Milan (France). Catalogue no: **A 259**

Cass: Released Apr '86, on SPI Milan (France). Catalogue no: **C 259**

CD: Released Feb '90, on Silva Screen, by Silva Screen records. Catalogue no: **CDCH 290**

King's Story...

KING'S STORY, A (Film Soundtrack) (Various artists)

Album: Released '88, on DRG (USA) by DRG Records (USA). Catalogue no: **SL 5185**

CD: Released '88, on DRG (USA) by DRG Records (USA). Catalogue no: **SLC 5185**

Kings's Row

KING'S ROW (Film Soundtrack) (Various artists)

CD: Released Jul '84, on T. E. R. by That's Entertainment Records. Catalogue no: **CDTER 9001**

CD: Released Jan '89, on Silva Screen by Silva Screen Records. Catalogue no: **VCD 47203**

Album: Released Aug '80, on Chalfont (USA) by Varese Sarabande Records (USA). Catalogue no: **SDG 305**

Kinks

PERCY (See under Percy)

Kismet

KISMET (Studio Cast) (Various artists)

Tracks: / Overture: *Various artists* / Sands of time: *Various artists* /

Rhymes have I: *Various artists* / Fate: *Various artists* / Not since Nineveh: *Various artists* / Baubles, bangles and beads: *Various artists* / Stranger in paradise: *Various artists* / Night of my nights: *Various artists* / And this is my beloved: *Various artists* / Olive tree: *Various artists* / Zubbediya - Samaris' dance: *Various artists* / Finale: *Various artists*.

Note: Featuring :- Gordon MacRae, Dorothy Kirsten, Salli Terri, Bunny Bishop, Richard Levitt & Muezzins, Roger Wagner Chorale & Orchestra conducted by Van Alexander.

Album: Released '73, on Starline (EMI) by EMI Records. Deleted '78. Catalogue no: **SRS 5054**

KISMET (Stage Show) (Various artists) (See panel on next page)

Tracks: / Overture: *Various artists* / Sands of time: *Various artists* / Rhymes have I: *Various artists* / Fate: *Various artists* / Hand of fate, The: *Various artists* / Fate (reprise): *Various artists* / Bazaar of the caravans: *Various artists* / Entrance of Lalume: *Various artists* / Not since Ninevah: *Various artists* / Not since Ninevah dance: *Various artists* / Exit of lalume: *Various artists* / Stolen oranges: *Various artists* / Baubles, bangles and beads: *Various artists* / Paradise garden: *Various artists* / Stranger in paradise: *Various artists* / He's in love: *Various artists* / Gesticulate: *Various artists* / Finale act one: *Various artists* / Entr'acte: *Various artists* / Night of my nights: *Various artists* / Stranger in paradise (reprise): *Various artists* / Was I Wazir?: *Various artists* / Rahadlakum: *Various artists* / Rahadlakum dance: *Various artists* / And this is my beloved: *Various artists* / Poets meet, The: *Various artists* / Olive tree, The: *Various artists* / Zubbediya: *Various artists* / Samaris' dance: *Various artists* / Finale act two: *Various artists* / Bored: *Various artists*.

Album: Released Jun '90, on T. E. R. by That's Entertainment Records. Catalogue no: **TER2 1170**

CD: Released Jun '90, on T. E. R. by That's Entertainment Records. Catalogue no: **CDTER2 1170**

Cass: Released Jun '90, on T. E. R. by That's Entertainment Records. Catalogue no: **ZCTED 1170**

KISMET (Original Broadway Cast) (Various artists)

WRIGHT & FORREST'S

KISMET

based on themes of Alexandr Borodin

Valerie **MASTERSON**
Donald **MAXWELL**
David **RENDALL**
Richard **VAN ALLAN**
Rosemary **ASHE**
Bonaventura **BOTTONE**
and
Judy **KAYE**

AMBROSIAN CHORUS
and the
PHILHARMONIA ORCHESTRA
Conducted by John
OWEN EDWARDS

Soundtrack to *Kismet* on the TER label. Based on Themes of Alexandr Borodin.

Cass: Released Jan '89, on CBS (import) by CBS Records & Distribution. Catalogue no: **PST 32605**
Album: Released Jan '89, on CBS (import) by CBS Records & Distribution. Deleted Mar '90. Catalogue no: **PS 32605**
CD: Released Jan '89, on CBS (import) by CBS Records & Distribution. Catalogue no: **CK 32605**

KISMET (Film Soundtrack) (Various artists)
Tracks: / Fate: *Keel, Howard* / Not since Niniveh: *Gray, Dolores* / Baubles, bangles and beads: *Blyth, Ann* / Stranger in paradise: *Blyth, Ann/Vic Damone* / Gesticulate: *Keel, Howard* / Night of my nights: *Damone, Vic* / Bored: *Gray, Dolores* / Olive tree: *Keel, Howard* / Rahadlakum: *Keel, Howard/Dolore Gray* / And this is my beloved: *Keel, Howard/Anne Blyth/Vic Damone* / Sands of time: *Keel, Howard*.
CD: Released Aug '90, on MGM (EMI) Catalogue no: **CDMGM 22**
Cass: Released Aug '90, on MGM (EMI) Catalogue no: **TCMGM 22**
CD: Released Aug '90, on MGM

(EMI) Catalogue no: **CDP 794 866 2**
Album: Released Aug '90, on MGM (EMI) Catalogue no: **LPMGM 22**
Album: Released Jul '86, on CBS by CBS Records & Distribution. Deleted Jun '88. Catalogue no: **CBS 70287**
Album: Released Aug '90, on MGM (EMI) Catalogue no: **794 866 3**
Cass: Released Aug '90, on MGM (EMI) Catalogue no: **794 866 4**
Cass: Released Jul '86, on CBS by CBS Records & Distribution. Deleted Jan '89. Catalogue no: **40 70287**
CD: Released May '87, on CBS by CBS Records & Distribution. Deleted Jan '89. Catalogue no: **CD 70287**
Album: Released '73, on MGM (Polydor) by Polydor Ltd. Deleted '78. Catalogue no: **2353 057**

KISMET (VIDEO) (Various artists)
VHS: Released Mar '88, on Screen Legends (video) by Pickwick Video. Catalogue no: **SMV 10130**

KISS ME KATE (Original Broadway Cast) (Various artists)
Note: Starring Alfred Drake and Patricia Morrison.
Album: Released Jan '89, on CBS (import) by CBS Records & Distribution. Deleted Mar '90. Catalogue no: **PS 32609**
Cass: Released Jan '89, on CBS (import) by CBS Records & Distribution. Catalogue no: **PST 32609**
Cass: Released Jan '89, on CBS (import) by CBS Records & Distribution. Catalogue no: **JST 04140**
CD: Released Jan '89, on CBS (import) by CBS Records & Distribution. Catalogue no: **CK 04140**

KISS ME KATE (Royal Shakespeare Cast) (Various artists)
Album: Released Sep '87, on First Night by First Night Records. Catalogue no: **CAST 10**
CD: Released Oct '87, on First Night by First Night Records. Catalogue no: **CASTCD 10**
Cass: Released Sep '87, on First Night by First Night Records. Catalogue no: **CASTC 10**

KISS ME KATE (Film Soundtrack) (Various artists)
Tracks: / Too darn hot: *Various artists* / So in love: *Various artists* / We open in Venice: *Various artists* / Why can't you behave?: *Various artists* / Were thine that special face: *Various artists* / Tom, Dick or Harry: *Various artists* / I've come to wive it wealthily in Padua: *Various artists* / From this moment on: *Various artists* / Always true to you in my fashion: *Various artists* / I hate men: *Various artists* / Where is the life that late I led?: *Various artists* / Brush up your Shakespear: *Various artists* / Kiss me Kate: *Various artists*.
Cass: Released Jul '86, on CBS by CBS Records & Distribution. Deleted Jan '89. Catalogue no: **40 70278**
Album: Released Jul '86, on CBS by CBS Records & Distribution. Deleted Jan '89. Catalogue no: **CBS 70278**
Cass: Released '73, on MGM (Polydor) by Polydor Ltd. Deleted '78. Catalogue no: **3110 069**

CD: Released Mar '87, on CBS by CBS Records & Distribution. Deleted Jan '89. Catalogue no: **CD 70278**

Album: Released '73, on MGM (Polydor) by Polydor Ltd. Deleted '78. Catalogue no: **2353 062**

KISS ME KATE: REPRISE REPERTORY THEATRE (Original Cast) (Various artists)

Tracks: / Another opening, another show: *Various artists* / Too darn hot: *Various artists* / I hate men: *Various artists* / Bianca: *Various artists* / Where is the life that late I led: *Various artists* / Wunderbar: *Various artists* / So in love: *Various artists* / Were thine that special face: *Various artists* / Always true to you in my fashion: *Various artists* / So in love: *Various artists* / We open in Venice: *Various artists* / Overture: *Various artists*.

Album: Released Aug '81, on Reprise (USA) Catalogue no: **K 54114**

KISS ME KATE (VIDEO) (Various artists)

VHS: Released Feb '88, on MGM/UA (Video) by MGM/UA Video. Catalogue no: **SMV 10307**

KISS ME KATE/BRIGADOON (Various artists)

Tracks: / Too darn hot: *Miller, Ann* (Kiss Me Kate) / So in love: *Keel, Howard/Kathryn Grayson* (Kiss Me Kate) / We open in Venice: *Grayson, Kathryn/Howard Keel/Ann Miller/Tommy Rall* (Kiss Me Kate) / Why can't you behave: *Miller, Ann* (Kiss Me Kate) / Were thine that special face: *Keel, Howard* (Kiss Me Kate) / Tom, Dick or Harry: *Miller, Ann/Bobby Van/Tommy Rall/Bob Fosse* (Kiss Me Kate) / Wunderbar: *Keel, Howard/Kathryn Grayson* (Kiss Me Kate) / Always true to you in my fashion: *Miller, Ann/Tommy Rall* (Kiss Me Kate) / I hate men: *Grayson, Kathryn* (Kiss Me Kate) / I've come to wive it wealthily in Padua: *Keel, Howard* (Kiss Me Kate) / From this moment on: *Miller, Ann/Bobby Van/Tommy Rall/Bob Fosse* (Kiss Me Kate) / Where is the life that late I led?: *Keel, Howard* (Kiss Me Kate) / Brush up your Shakespeare: *Wynn, Keenan/James Whitmore* (Kiss Me Kate) / Kiss me Kate: *Keel, Ho-*

ward/Kathryn Grayson (Kiss Me Kate) / Prologue: *Various artists* (Brigadoon) / Down on MacConnachy Square: *Various artists* (Brigadoon) / Heather on the hill, The: *Kelly, Gene* (Brigadoon) / Waitin' for my dearie: *Richards, Carol* (Brigadoon) / I'll go home with my bonnie Jean: *Johnson, Van/John Gustafson* (Brigadoon) / Come to me, bend to me: *Gustafson, John* (Brigadoon) / Almost like being in love: *Kelly, Gene* (Brigadoon) / Heather on the hill, The: *Various artists* (Brigadoon) / There but for you go I: *Various artists* (Brigadoon) / Brigadoon: *Various artists* (Brigadoon).

Album: Released Jan '90, on MGM (EMI) Catalogue no: **LPMGM 2**

Cass: Released Jan '90, on MGM (EMI) Catalogue no: **TCMGM 2**

CD: Released Jan '90, on MGM (EMI) Catalogue no: **CDMGM 2**

Album: Released Jan '90, on MGM (EMI) Catalogue no: **793 297 1**

Cass: Released Jan '90, on MGM (EMI) Catalogue no: **793 297 4**

CD: Released Jan '90, on MGM (EMI) Catalogue no: **CDP 792 297 2**

Kiss Of The Spiderwoman

KISS OF THE SPIDERWOMAN (Film Soundtrack) (Badarou, Wally)

Tracks: / Overture / Most ravishing woman, The / Visions of the ultra-rhine / Kabaret / Je me moque de l'amour / Molina's fantasies / Lunapark / Novel das nove / Spider Island / Pavihao IV / Avocado scene, The / Theme / Call, The / Valentin's message / Blue for you / Goodbye mama / Finale.

Note: The soundtrack to William Hurt's critically acclaimed movie. The album includes new music from Wally Badarou, recently in the charts with the club favourite "Chief Inspector".

Album: Released Jan '86, on Island by Island Records. Deleted Jun '88. Catalogue no: **ISTA 12**

Cass: Released Jan '86, on Island by Island Records. Deleted Jul '87. Catalogue no: **ICT 12**

Kissin' Cousins

KISSIN' COUSINS (See under Presley, Elvis)

Knack (film)

KNACK, THE (Film Soundtrack) (Various artists)

Note: John Barry score for the 1965 Richard Lester film.

Album: Released Jan '89, on MCA by MCA Records. Catalogue no: **MCA 25109**

Cass: Released Jan '89, on MCA by MCA Records. Deleted Mar '90. Catalogue no: **MCAC 25109**

Knight, Gladys

LICENCE TO KILL

Tracks: / Licence to kill.

7" Single: Released May '89, on MCA by MCA Records. Catalogue no: **MCA 1339**

12" Single: Released May '89, on MCA by MCA Records. Catalogue no: **MCAT 1339**

CD Single: Released May '89, on MCA by MCA Records. Catalogue no: **DMCA 1339**

Cassingle: Released May '89, on MCA by MCA Records. Deleted Dec '89. Catalogue no: **MCAC 1339**

7" Single: Released Jun '89, on MCA by MCA Records. Deleted Dec '89. Catalogue no: **MCASP 1339**, on Buddah by Buddah Records Inc.(USA). Deleted '81. Catalogue no: **BDS 470**

7" Single: Released Apr '83, on CBS by CBS Records & Distribution. Catalogue no: **A 3314**

Knights & Emeralds

KNIGHTS AND EMERALDS (Film Soundtrack) (Various artists)

Tracks: / Tell me tomorrow: *Princess* / Strollin' on: *Priest, Maxi* / Life of crime: *Arrowsmith, Eugenie* / Ready or not: *Thompson, Carroll* / Tremblin': *Smith, Mel* / We won't give in: *Slade* / I'm the one who really loves you: *Howard, Austin* / Wild wild party: *Slade* / Something special: *Duffy, Stephen & Sandii* / Modern girl: *Astley, Rick* / Bubble (We ah go bubble): *Priest, Maxi* / Stand by the word: *Joubert Singers*.

Cass: Released Jun '88, on 10 Records by Virgin Records. Deleted Jun '90. Catalogue no: **CXID 11**

Album: Released Oct '86, on 10 Records by Virgin Records. Catalogue no: **DIX 28**

Album: Released Jun '88, on 10

Records by Virgin Records. Deleted May '90. Catalogue no: **XID 11**

Knights Of The ...

KNIGHTS OF THE ROUND TABLE (Film Soundtrack) (Various artists)
Album: Released Jan '89, on Silva Screen by Silva Screen Records. Catalogue no: **STV 81128**
CD: Released Jan '89, on Silva Screen by Silva Screen Records. Catalogue no: **VCD 47269**

Knopfler, Mark

CAL (See under Cal)

GOING HOME
Tracks: / Going home (theme from Local Hero) / Wild theme / Smooching (Extra track on 12" version only.).
7" Single: Released Feb '83, on Vertigo by Phonogram Ltd. Deleted '85. Catalogue no: **DSTR 4**
12" Single: Released Sep '86, on Vertigo by Phonogram Ltd. Deleted Mar '88. Catalogue no: **DSTR 1412**
7" Single: Released Sep '86, on Vertigo by Phonogram Ltd. Deleted Mar '88. Catalogue no: **DSTR 14**

LAST EXIT TO BROOKLYN (See under Last Exit To Brooklyn)

PRINCESS BRIDE (See under Princess Bride)

STORYBOOK LOVE (Theme From The Princess Bride) (Knopfler, Mark/Willy Deville)
Tracks: / Storybook love.
12" Single: Released 7 Mar '88, on Vertigo by Phonogram Ltd. Deleted Oct '88. Catalogue no: **VERX 37**
CD Single: Released Mar '88, on Vertigo by Phonogram Ltd. Deleted Oct '88. Catalogue no: **VERCD 37**
7" Single: Released 7 Mar '88, on Vertigo by Phonogram Ltd. Deleted Oct '88. Catalogue no: **VER 37**

Koller, Dagmar

DAGMAR KOLLER ON BROADWAY (Koller, Dagmar & Opus Studio Orchestra)
Tracks: / New York, New York /

People / Don't cry for me Argentina / Hello Dolly / If my friends could see me now / Send in the clowns / Memory / Impossible dream, The / On a clear day / I've grown accustomed to his face / What I did for love / I am what I am.
CD: Released Jul '89, on Opus by Opus Records. Catalogue no: **9356 2060**

Kongos, John

C.A.T.S. EYES
Tracks: / C.A.T.S eyes.
7" Single: Released May '85, on Sierra by Sierra Records. Catalogue no: **FED 11**

Koyaanisqatsi

KOYAANISQATSI (See under Glass, Philip)

Kraftwerk

TOUR DE FRANCE
Tracks: / Tour de France.
Note: Used in the film *Breakdance*
Cassingle: Released Aug '83, on EMI by EMI Records. Deleted '88. Catalogue no: **TC EMI 5413**
7" Single: Released Aug '84, on EMI by EMI Records. Deleted '88. Catalogue no: **EMI 5413**
12" Single: Released Aug '84, on EMI by EMI Records. Deleted Aug '90. Catalogue no: **12EMI 5413**

Kramer vs Kramer

KRAMER VS KRAMER (Film Soundtrack) (Various artists)
Tracks: / Mandolin and harpsichord concerto: *Various artists* /

Scott Kuney: *Various artists* / Frederick Hand: *Various artists* / New York: *Various artists* / Trumpet sonata: *Various artists* / Gordion knot untied: *Various artists*.
Cass: on CBS by CBS Records & Distribution. Catalogue no: **40 73945**
CD: Released Feb '90, on Silva Screen by Silva Screen Records. Catalogue no: **MK35873**
Album: on CBS by CBS Records & Distribution. Catalogue no: **CBS 73945**

Krays (film)

KRAYS (Film Soundtrack) (Various artists) (See panel below)
CD: Released May '90, on Parkfield Catalogue no: **PMCD 5018**
Album: Released May '90, on Parkfield Catalogue no: **PMLP 5018**
Cass: Released May '90, on Parkfield Catalogue no: **PMMC 5018**

Kronos

KRONOS (Film Soundtrack) (Various artists)
Note: Sci-fi score by Paul Sawtell & Bert Shefter.
Album: Released Jan '89, on Silva Screen by Silva Screen Records. Catalogue no: **CLP 1001**

Krull

KRULL (Film Soundtrack) (London Symphony Orchestra)

Spandau Ballet's Martin and Gary Kemp with Billie Whitelaw in *The Krays*

Tracks: / Riding the fire mares / Slayer's attack / Widow's web / Widows's lullaby / Destruction of the black fortress / Epilogue.

Note: London Symphony Orchestra perform one of James Horner's finest scores.

CD: Released '86, on Silva Screen by Silva Screen Records. Catalogue no: **FILMCD 05**

CD: Released Nov '86, on Silva Screen by Silva Screen Records. Catalogue no: **SCCD 1004**

Album: Released Nov '86, on Silva Screen by Silva Screen Records. Deleted Apr '90. Catalogue no: **FILM 005**

KRULL (JAMES HORNER) (Film Soundtrack) (London Symphony Orchestra)

Album: Released Mar '84, on Ades by Ades Records (France). Catalogue no: **ADE 2108**

Krush Groove

KRUSH GROOVE (Film Soundtrack) (Various artists)

Tracks: / Can't stop the street: *Khan, Chaka* / I can't live without my radio: *LL Cool J* / If I ruled the world: *Blow, Kurtis* / All you can eat: *Fat Boys* / Feel the spin: *Harry, Debbie* / Holly rock: *Sheila E* / She's on it: *Beastie Boys* / Love triangle: *Gap Band* / Tender love: *Force M.D.'s* / Krush groovin': *Fat Boys/Run DMC/Sheila E/Kurtis Blow.*

Album: Released Mar '86, on Warner Bros. by WEA Records. Catalogue no: **925295 1**

Cass: Released Mar '86, on Warner Bros. by WEA Records. Deleted Aug '87. Catalogue no: **925295 4**

L

The following information was taken from the Music Master database on September 25th, 1990.

La Bamba

LA BAMBA (Film soundtrack) (Various artists)
Tracks: / La Bamba: *Los Lobos* / Come on: *Los Lobos* / Ooh my head: *Los Lobos* / We belong together: *Los Lobos* / Framed: *Los Lobos* / Donna: *Los Lobos* / Lonely teardrops: *Huntsberry, Howard* / Crying, waiting, hoping: *Crenshaw, Marshall* / Summertime blues: *Setzer, Brian* / Who do you love: *Diddley, Bo* / Goodnight my love, pleasant dreams: *Various artists*.
CD: Released Aug '87, on London Records by London Records Ltd. Catalogue no: **828 058 2**
Album: Released Aug '87, on London Records by London Records Ltd. Catalogue no: **LONLP 36**
Cass: Released Aug '87, on London Records by London Records Ltd. Catalogue no: **LONC 36**

LA BAMBA (2) (More music from the film) (Various artists)
Tracks: / Ready Teddy: *Little Richard* / Chantilly lace: *Big Bopper* / Tweedlee dee: *Various artists* / Don't you just know it?: *Smith, Huey & The Clowns* / Betty Jean: *Berry, Chuck* / La Bamba: *Valens, Ritchie* / Sleepwalk: *Santo & Johnny* / Over the mountain across the sea: *Johnnie & Joe* / For your precious love: *Butler, Jerry & The Impressions* / This I swear: *Skyliners* / Smoke gets in your eyes: *Platters* / Donna: *Valens, Ritchie*.
CD: Released May '88, on London Records by London Records Ltd. Deleted Apr '89. Catalogue no: **828 097 2**
Album: Released May '88, on London Records by London Records Ltd. Deleted Apr '89. Catalogue no: **LONLP 56**
Cass: Released May '88, on London Records by London Records Ltd. Deleted Apr '89. Catalogue no: **LONC 56**

LA BAMBA (SINGLE) (See under Los Lobos) (See panel)
LA BAMBA (VIDEO) (Various artists)
Note: Cert: 15.
VHS: Released Jun '89, on RCA/Columbia (video) by BMG Records (UK). Catalogue no: **CVT 21285**

La Cage Aux Folles

LA CAGE AUX FOLLES (Original Broadway cast) (Various artists)
Tracks: / La Cage Aux Folles: Prelude / We are what we are / Little bit more mascara, A / With Anne on my arm / With you on my arm / Song on the sand(La da da da) / La Cage aux folles/ I am what I am / Masculinity / Look over there / Cocktail counterpoint / Best times, The / La Cage aux folles, Finale
Album: Released '84, on RCA by BMG Records (UK). Catalogue no: **BL 84824**

CD: Released '84, on RCA by BMG Records (UK). Catalogue no: **BD 84824**
Cass: Released '84, on RCA by BMG Records (UK). Catalogue no: **BK 84824**

LA CAGE AUX FOLLES (Film soundtrack) (Various artists)
Note: Music by Ennio Morricone for the original French/Italian film.
Album: on Cerebus (USA) Catalogue no: **803 003**
Album: Released Jan '89, on Cerebus (USA) Catalogue no: **C'BUS 102**

La Gabbia

LA GABBIA (Film soundtrack) (Various artists)
Note: Composed by Ennio Morricone.
Album: Released Jan '89, on Inte-

Title song from the film *La Bamba* - starring Lou Diamond Phillips

rior Music by Interior Music Records. Catalogue no: **IM 006**

La Passion Beatrice

LA PASSION BEATRICE (Film soundtrack) (Various artists)
Note: Film from Bertrand Tavernier with music by Lili Boulanger from the Pie Jesu conducted by Igor Markevitch.
CD: Released Jan '89, on Silva Screen by Silva Screen Records. Catalogue no: **CD 314**
Album: Released Jan '89, on Silva Screen by Silva Screen Records. Catalogue no: **A 314**

La Petite Voleuse

LA PETITE VOLEUSE (THE LITTLE THIEF) (Original soundtrack) (Jomy, Alain)
Album: Released Feb '90, on Silva Screen by Silva Screen Records. Catalogue no: **A399**
CD: Released Feb '90, on Silva Screen by Silva Screen Records. Catalogue no: **CDDH399**

Labyrinth

LABYRINTH (Film soundtrack) (Various artists)
Tracks: / Underground: *Bowie, David* / Into the labyrinth: *Various artists* / Magic dance: *Bowie, David* / Sarah: *Various artists* / Chilly down: *Various artists* / Hallucination: *Various artists* / As the world falls down: *Bowie, David* / Goblin battle, The: *Various artists* / Within you: *Various artists* / Thirteen o'clock: *Various artists* / Home at last: *Various artists* / Underground (reprise): *Bowie, David*.
Cass: Released Jun '86, on EMI by EMI Records. Deleted Jan '88. Catalogue no: **TCAML 3104**
Album: Released Jun '86, on EMI by EMI Records. Deleted Jan '88. Catalogue no: **AML 3104**
CD: Released Sep '86, on EMI by EMI Records. Catalogue no: **CDP 746 312 2**
CD: Released Feb '90, on EMI (Import) Catalogue no: **CDP 46312**

LABYRINTH (VIDEO) (Various artists)
VHS: Released '88, on Channel 5 by Channel 5 Video. Catalogue no: **CFV 08582**

Lady Be Good

LADY BE GOOD (Film soundtrack) (Various artists)
Note: Starring Eleanor Powell and Ann Southern.
Album: Released Jan '89, on Silva Screen by Silva Screen Records. Catalogue no: **HS 5010**

LADY BE GOOD (Original London cast) (Various artists)
Tracks: / Fascinating rhythm / Swiss maid / Lady be good / So am I / Half of it dearie blues / I'd rather Charleston / Hang on to me / After you who / Night and day / Puttin' on the ritz / Crazy feet / Flying down to Rio / Music makes me / Louisiana / Not my girl
Album: Released Oct '85, on RCA by BMG Records (UK). Catalogue no: **RL84824**
Album: Released '74, on Retrospect by EMI Records. Catalogue no: **WRCSH 124**
Cass: Released May '79, on Retrospect by EMI Records. Catalogue no: **TC SH 124**

Lady Hawke

LADY HAWKE (Film Soundtrack) (Various artists)
Tracks: / Main title: *Various artists* / Phillipe's escape: *Various artists* / Search for Phillipe, The: *Various artists* / Tavern fight: *Various artists* / Tavern fight (Navarre): *Various artists* / Phillipe describes Isabeau: *Various artists* / Navarre's ambush: *Various artists* / Chase, the fall and the transformation, The: *Various artists* / She was sad at first: *Various artists* / Navarre returns to Aquila: *Various artists* / Navarre's and Marquet's duel: *Various artists* / Marquet's

death: *Various artists* / Bishop's death: *Various artists* / End title: *Various artists*.
Album: Released Aug '85, on Atlantic by WEA Records. Catalogue no: **781 248-1**

Lady In The Dark

LADY IN THE DARK (Studio cast) (Various artists)
Album: Released Jan '89, on Silva Screen by Silva Screen Records. Catalogue no: **COS 2390**
Cass: Released Jan '89, on Silva Screen by Silva Screen Records. Catalogue no: **BT 2390**

LADY IN THE DARK (Original cast recording) (Various artists)
Album: Released Jan '89, on Silva Screen by Silva Screen Records. Catalogue no: **AEI 1146**

Lady In White

LADY IN WHITE (Film soundtrack) (Various artists)
Note: Score by the director of the film, Frank Laloggia.
CD: Released Jan '89, on Silva Screen by Silva Screen Records. Catalogue no: **VCD 47530**
Album: Released Jan '89, on Silva Screen by Silva Screen Records. Catalogue no: **704.530**

Lady Sings The Blues

LADY SINGS THE BLUES (Story of Billie Holiday) (See under Ross, Diana)

Lady & The Tramp

LADY AND THE TRAMP (Vari-

Lady & the Tramp - a very popular Disney production

ous artists) (See panel on previous page)
Cass: Released Oct '84, on Walt Disney Deleted '88. Catalogue no: **ZCM 538**
Album: Released Dec '87, on Walt Disney Catalogue no: **WD 015**
Cass: Released Dec '87, on Walt Disney Catalogue no: **WDC 015**
Album: Released Oct '84, on Walt Disney Deleted '88. Catalogue no: **REC 538**

Lai, Francis

BILITIS (Film Soundtrack) (See under Bilitis)

DARK EYES (TV Soundtrack) (See under Dark Eyes)

GREAT FILM THEMES
Tracks: / Bilitis / Blue rose, The (la rose bleue) / Happy New Year / Seduction / Par le sang des autres / Live for life / Sur notre etoile / Les unes et les autres / Solitude / Love story (theme from) / Emotion / Love in the rain / Intimate moments / Man and a woman, A / African summer / La ronde / Smic smac smoc / Whitechapel.
CD: Released Jun '90, on Prestige (BBC) by BBC Records. Catalogue no: **CDPC 5002**
Cass: Released Jun '90, on Prestige (BBC) by BBC Records. Catalogue no: **ZPREC 5002**
Album: Released Jun '90, on Prestige (BBC) by BBC Records. Catalogue no: **PREC 5002**

Laine, Frankie

HIGH NOON
From the film 'High Noon' starring Gary Cooper.
Tracks: / High noon.
78 rpm: Released Nov '52, on Columbia by EMI Records. Deleted Nov '55. Catalogue no: **DB 3113**

HIGH NOON (OLD GOLD)
Tracks: / High noon / Cool water.
7" Single: Released Nov '80, on Old Gold by Old Gold Records. Deleted '83. Catalogue no: **OG 9082**

HIGH NOON (RE-ISSUE)
Tracks: / High noon / Cool water.
7" Single: Released Apr '82, on CBS by CBS Records & Distribution. Catalogue no: **CBS 1156**

RAWHIDE (OLD GOLD)
Tracks: / Rawhide.
7" Single: Released Jan '87, on Old Gold by Old Gold Records.

Catalogue no: **OG 9665**

RAWHIDE (SINGLE)
From the 50's and 60's TV series 'Rawhide'.
Tracks: / Rawhide.
7" Single: Released Nov '59, on Philips by Phonogram Ltd. Deleted Nov '62. Catalogue no: **PB 965**

Laird, Christopher

DOGTANIAN
Tracks: / Three muskhounds, The.
Note: Theme to the cartoon series Dogtanian & The Muskhounds
Cassingle: Released Apr '85, on BBC by BBC Records. Deleted Apr '89. Catalogue no: **ZRESL 165**
7" Single: Released Apr '85, on BBC by BBC Records. Deleted 31 Aug '88. Catalogue no: **RESL 165**

Lamb, Annabelle

DAMON AND DEBBIE (His song) (Lamb, Annabelle & Dani Ali)
Tracks: / Damon and Debbie (his song) / Damon and Debbie (her song).
Note: Theme song for the Brookside spin-off Damon & Debbie
7" Single: Released Nov '87, on Ariola by BMG Records (UK). Deleted May '89. Catalogue no: **109.612**

Land Before Time

LAND BEFORE TIME (Film soundtrack) (Horner, James)
Album: Released Feb '90, on MCA by MCA Records. Catalogue no: **MCA 6266**
CD: Released Feb '90, on MCA by MCA Records. Catalogue no: **MCAD 6266**
Cass: Released Feb '90, on MCA by MCA Records. Catalogue no: **MCAC 6266**

Landlord

LANDLORD (Film Soundtrack) (Various artists)
Tracks: / Brand new day / Landlord / Car commercial / Walter G's boogaloo / Croquet game / Let me love you/ Lainie's theme / Rent party / Elgar's fantasy / Love theme / Soul hoedown/ Doin' me dirty / Brand new day/ Axe: *Various artists* / God bless the children.
Album: Released '73, on United

Artists by EMI Records. Deleted '78. Catalogue no: **UAS 29120**

Lanza, Mario

BROADWAY HITS
Tracks: / On the street where you live / You'll never walk alone / Younger than springtime / More than you know.
Album: Released '83, on RCA (Germany) by BMG Music International. Catalogue no: **CL 12847**

GREAT CARUSO (Film soundtrack)
CD: Released Sep '89, on RCA by BMG Records (UK). Catalogue no: **GD 60049**
Album: Released Jul '60, on RCA by BMG Records (UK). Deleted Jul '65. Catalogue no: **RB 16112**
Cass: Released Sep '89, on RCA by BMG Records (UK). Catalogue no: **GK 60049**

STUDENT PRINCE/GREAT CARUSO
Album: Released Dec '58, on RCA by BMG Records (UK). Deleted Dec '83. Catalogue no: **RB 16113**

Lassiter

LASSITER (Film soundtrack) (Various artists)
Album: Released Dec '84, on T. E. R. by That's Entertainment Records. Catalogue no: **TER 1092**

Last American Virgin

LAST AMERICAN VIRGIN, THE (Film Soundtrack) (Various artists)
Album: Released Nov '82, on CBS by CBS Records & Distribution. Deleted '87. Catalogue no: **CBS 70228**

Last Days Of Pompeii

LAST DAYS OF POMPEII (Film soundtrack) (Various artists)
Note: Italian epic from the early sixties. Music by Angelo F Lavagnino.
Album: Released Jan '89, on Silva Screen by Silva Screen Records. Catalogue no: **PHCAM 03**

Last Dragon

LAST DRAGON (Film soundtrack) (Various artists)
Tracks: / Last dragon, The: *Dwight, David* / 7th heaven: *Vanity* / Star: *Wood, Alfie* / Fire: *Charlene*

/ Glow, The: *Hutch, Willie* / Rhythm of the night: *DeBarge* / Upset stomach: *Wonder, Stevie* / First time on a ferris wheel: *Robinson, Smokey & Syreets* / Peeping Tom: *Rockwell* / Inside you: *Hutch, Willie & Temptations*.

Cass: Released '86, on Motown by BMG Records (UK). Catalogue no: **ZK 72363**

CD: Released May '85, on Motown by BMG Records (UK). Catalogue no: **ZD 72363**

Album: Released '86, on Motown by BMG Records (UK). Catalogue no: **ZL 72363**

Last Emperor

LAST EMPEROR, THE (Film soundtrack) (Sakamoto, Ryuichi & David Byrne)
Tracks: / First coronation / Open the door / Where is Armo? / Picking up brides / Last Emperor, The (theme) (variation 1) / Picking a bride / Bed / Wind, rain and water / Paper emperor / Rain (I want a divorce) / Baby, The (was born dead) / Last Emperor, The (theme) (variation 2) / Last Emperor, The (theme) / Main title / Lunch / Red guard / Emperor's waltz, The / Red guard dance, The.

Cass: Released Nov '87, on Virgin by Virgin Records. Catalogue no: **TCV 2485**

Album: Released Nov '87, on Virgin by Virgin Records. Catalogue no: **V 2485**

CD: Released Nov '87, on Virgin by Virgin Records. Catalogue no: **CDV 2485**

Last Exit To Brooklyn

LAST EXIT TO BROOKLYN (Film soundtrack) (Knopfler, Mark)
CD: Released Nov '89, on Vertigo by Phonogram Ltd. Catalogue no: **838 725 2**

Cass: Released Nov '89, on Vertigo by Phonogram Ltd. Catalogue no: **838 725 4**

Album: Released Nov '89, on Vertigo by Phonogram Ltd. Catalogue no: **838 725 1**

Last Metro

LAST METRO, THE (Film soundtrack) (Various artists)
Album: Released '88, on DRG (USA) by DRG Records (USA). Catalogue no: **SL 9504**

Last Night Of The Proms

LAST NIGHT OF THE PROMS (Various artists)
Note: Includes Arne :Rule Britania /Wagner :Two wesedonk lieder /Elgar :Pomp and circumstance march no 1. Performed by BBC Symphony Orchestra, Norman Davis

CD: Released Jul '89, on Philips by Phonogram Ltd. Catalogue no: **420 085-2**

Cass: Released Jul '89, on Philips by Phonogram Ltd. Catalogue no: **420 085-4**

LAST NIGHT OF THE PROMS (BBC Symphony Orchestra)
CD: Released Aug '90, on BBC by BBC Records. Catalogue no: **BBC CD 580**

Last Run

LAST RUN, THE (Film soundtrack) (Various artists)
Tracks: / Last run: *Various artists* / Main title - the last run: *Various artists* / Border crossing: *Various artists* / Spanish coast: *Various artists* / Claudie says yes: *Various artists* / Rickard escapes: *Various artists* / Last run: *Various artists* / Double cross: *Various artists* / Yo te amo: *Various artists* / Claudie's stockings: *Various artists* / Trap: *Various artists* / End title: *Various artists*.

Note: Jerry Goldsmith score for the thriller starring George C Scott.

Album: Released '73, on Polydor by Polydor Ltd. Deleted '78. Catalogue no: **2315 072**

Album: Released Jan '89, on MCA by MCA Records. Catalogue no: **MCA 25116**

Cass: Released Jan '89, on MCA by MCA Records. Deleted Mar '90. Catalogue no: **MCAC 25116**

Last Starfighter

LAST STARFIGHTER, THE (Film soundtrack) (Various artists)
Tracks: / Outer space chase: *Various artists* / Into the starscape: *Various artists* / Planet of Rylos, The: *Various artists* / Death blossom: *Various artists* / Incommunicado: *Various artists* / Never crossed my mind: *Various artists* / Return to Earth: *Various artists* / Hero's march, The: *Various artists* / Centauri dies: *Various artists*.

Note: Composed by Craig Safan.

Album: Released Jan '89, on Silva Screen by Silva Screen Records. Catalogue no: **SCRS 1007**

CD: Released May '87, on Silva Screen by Silva Screen Records. Catalogue no: **SCCD 1007**

LAST STARFIGHTER, THE (VIDEO) (Various artists)
VHS: Released Oct '89, on Spectrum (1) Catalogue no: **SPC 00332**

Last Tango In Paris

LAST TANGO IN PARIS (Film Soundtrack) (Various artists)
Tracks: / Last tango in Paris - tango: *Various artists* / Jeanne: *Various artists* / Girl in black: *Various artists* / Last tango in Paris - ballad: *Various artists* / Fake Ophelia: *Various artists* / Picture in the rain: *Various artists* / Return - tango: *Various artists* / It's over: *Various artists* / Goodbye (un largo adios): *Various artists* / Why did she choose you: *Various artists* / Last tango in Paris - jazz waltz: *Various artists*.

Album: Released '73, on United Artists by EMI Records. Deleted '78. Catalogue no: **UAS 29440**

LAST TANGO IN PARIS (Original Soundtrack) (Various artists)
Album: Released Feb '90, on Silva Screen by Silva Screen Records. Catalogue no: **1828971**

Cass: Released Jan '89, on Liberty (import) by EMI Records. Catalogue no: **L4N 10286**

Cass: Released Feb '90, on Silva Screen by Silva Screen Records. Catalogue no: **1828974**

Album: Released Jan '89, on Liberty (import) by EMI Records. Catalogue no: **LN 10286**

Last Temptation Of...

LAST TEMPTATION OF CHRIST (Film Soundtrack) (See under Gabriel, Peter 'Passion / Last Temptation')

Last Valley

LAST VALLEY (Film Soundtrack) (Various artists)
Tracks: / Main title theme: *Various artists* / Last valley: *Various artists* / Shrine: *Various artists* / Evening song, An: *Various artists* / Plague pit: *Various artists* / Village attack: *Various artists* / Children's song: *Various artists* / Attack at Rheinfelden: *Various artists* / Main title

theme, part 2: *Various artists* / Last valley: *Various artists* / Christmas song: *Various artists* / Witch burning: *Various artists* / Offertory chant: *Various artists* / Vogel leaves the valley: *Various artists* / Death of the captain/ End title: *Various artists*.
Album: Released '73, on Probe Deleted '78. Catalogue no: **SPB 1027**

Last Waltz
LAST WALTZ (Film Soundtrack) (See under Band)

Laughing Stock Of BBC
LAUGHING STOCK OF THE BBC (Various artists)
Cass: Released Apr '82, on BBC by BBC Records. Deleted '88. Catalogue no: **ZCLAF 1**
Album: Released Apr '82, on BBC by BBC Records. Deleted '87. Catalogue no: **LAF 1**

Lauper, Cyndi
GIRLS JUST WANT TO HAVE FUN
Tracks: / Girls just want to have fun / Right track, wrong train.
Note: As featured in the film of the same name.
CD 3": Released Aug '88, on Epic (import) by CBS Records & Distribution. Catalogue no: **34K 05480**
7" Single: Released Jan '84, on Portrait by CBS Records & Distribution. Deleted '86. Catalogue no: **A 3943**

Laurel & Hardy
TRAIL OF THE LONESOME PINE
Tracks: / Trail of the lonesome pine.
Note: Featured in the film *Way out West* starring Laurel & Hardy
7" Single: Released Sep '89, on Another Fine Mess Catalogue no: **MESS 001**
7" Single: Released Oct '75, on United Artists by EMI Records. Catalogue no: **UP 36026**
7" Pic: Released Sep '89, on Another Fine Mess Catalogue no: **MESS 001P**

Lawrence Of Arabia
LAWRENCE OF ARABIA (Film soundtrack) (Jarre, Maurice) (See panel opposite)
Tracks: / Overture / Main title /

Miracle / Nefud mirage / Rescue of Gasim / Bringing Gasim into camp / Arrival at Auda's camp / Voice of the guns, The / Continuation of the miracle / Suns anvil / Lawrence and body guard / That is the desert / End title.
Note: Music composed by Maurice Jarre.
Album: Released '64, on Colpix by Pye Records. Catalogue no: **NPL 28023**

LAWRENCE OF ARABIA (Golden Guinea) (Various artists)
Album: Released '74, on Golden Guinea Catalogue no: **GSGL 10389**

LAWRENCE OF ARABIA (PRT) (Various artists)
Album: Released '87, on PRT by Castle Communications Records. Catalogue no: **PYL 6040**
Cass: Released '87, on PRT by Castle Communications Records. Catalogue no: **PYM 6040**

LAWRENCE OF ARABIA (RE-RELEASE) (Film soundtrack) (Jarre, Maurice)
Tracks: / Overture / First entrance to the desert - Night and stars / Lawrence and Tafas / Miracle /

That is the desert / Nefud mirage/The Sun's anvil / Rescue of Gasim, The/Bringing Gasim into camp / Arrival at Auda's camp / On to Akaba/The beach at night / Sinai desert / Voice at the guns / Horse stampede - Ali rescues Lawrence / Lawrence and his bodyguard / End/Playoff music.
Note: A new digital recording of this classic score, released to coincide with the re-released version of Sir David Lean's film. The new recording will include extra music not on the original soundtrack release. The Philharmonia Orchestra performed the music composed and conducted by Maurice Jarre.
T.E.Lawrence, the illegitimate son of Thomas Chapman, an Irish Baronet, has fascinated film-makers ever since Lowell Thomas's *Magic Lantern* lectures during Lawrence's lifetime. In 1936 Alexander Korda had planned a film biography and had gone as far as signing the actor Walter Hudd because of his physical resemblance to Lawrence. At another time Leslie Howard was to have portrayed the enigmatic hero. In the late 1950's Rank projected a version with Dirk Bogarde, written by

Lawrence of Arabia - starring Peter O'Toole, Omar Sharif and Alec Guinness in this David Lean classic

Terence Rattigan. The scenario of this formed the basis for his play *Ross* (which starred Alec Guinness) when the film was cancelled. Maurice Jarre is always good at atmospheric music, and the mystery and terror of the desert gave him plenty of opportunities in *Lawrence*. Notice the skilled use of Ondes Martenot and the zither-like cithara. But these cues are not merely formless "atmosphere". Each listening reveals more fragments of already-heard tunes in a kaleidoscope of guises. There is however a problem when performing music of this sort away from the film, in what to abridge, what to omit. Musical moments which have a significance when dubbed to picture can sound odd heard in isolation. For this reason we have departed, to a small extent from Jarre's picture tempi in some of these cues. Also, on the instructions of the composer, many revisions to the orchestration have been made by Christopher Palmer.(Tony Bremner 1989).

CD: Released Jan '89, on Silva Screen by Silva Screen Records. Catalogue no: **FILMCD 036**
Cass: Released Jan '89, on Silva Screen by Silva Screen Records. Catalogue no: **FILMC 036**
Album: Released Jan '89, on Silva Screen by Silva Screen Records. Catalogue no: **FILM 036**

Laws, Herbert

REDS, THEME FROM (Laws, Herbert & Cheryl Lynn)
Tracks: / Reds (theme from) / Reds (theme from) (part 2).
7" Single: Released Mar '82, on CBS by CBS Records & Distribution. Deleted '85. Catalogue no: **A 2052**

Lawson, Dennis

ULTRA FANTASTICO (TV Theme)
Tracks: / Ultra fantastico.
Note: Theme for Channel 4 series Kit Curran
7" Single: Released Apr '84, on EMI by EMI Records. Catalogue no: **EMI 5466**

Le Bal

LE BAL (Original Soundtrack) (Cosma, Vladimir)
Cass: Released Feb '90, on Silva Screen by Silva Screen Records.

Catalogue no: **76.078**
Album: Released Feb '90, on Silva Screen by Silva Screen Records. Catalogue no: **66.078**

Le Professional

LE PROFESSIONAL (Film soundtrack) (Various artists)
Note: Score by Ennio Morricone.
Album: Released Jan '89, on Silva Screen by Silva Screen Records. Catalogue no: **803 026**

Le Testament

LE TESTAMENT D'UN POETE JUIF ASSASSINE (Film Soundtrack) (Various artists)
Note: French film with score by Gabriel Yared.
Album: Released Jan '89, on Silva Screen by Silva Screen Records. Catalogue no: **242 261.1**

Lean On Me

LEAN ON ME (Film Soundtrack) (Various artists)
CD: Released '88, on WEA by WEA Records. Catalogue no: **925 843 2**

Leave It To Jane

LEAVE IT TO JANE (Original Broadway cast) (Various artists)
Tracks: / Just you watch my step: *Various artists* / Leave it to Jane: *Various artists* / Siren's song: *Various artists* / Cleopatterer: *Various artists* / Crickets are calling, The: *Various artists* / Sun shines brighter, The: *Various artists* / Sir Galahad: *Various artists* / Wait 'til tomorrow: *Various artists* / I'm going to find a girl etc.: *Various artists*.
Album: Released '88, on DRG (USA) by DRG Records (USA). Catalogue no: **DS 15002**

Lee, Johnny

DALLAS (MAIN THEME)
Tracks: / Dallas (Dallas dreams), Theme from / Dallas (Dallas dreams), Theme from / Loneliness in Lucy's eyes (the life Sue Ellen is living).
7" Single: Released Jan '86, on Warner Bros. by WEA Records. Catalogue no: **W 8817**

Lee, Peggy

PETE KELLY'S BLUES (Film soundtrack) (Lee, Peggy & Ella Fitzgerald)

Tracks: / Oh, didn't he ramble? / Sugar (that sugar baby of mine) / Somebody loves me / I gonna meet my sweetie now / I never knew / Bye bye blackbird / What can I say, after I say I'm sorry? / Hard hearted Hannah / Ella hums the blues / He needs me / Sing a rainbow / Pete Kelly's blues.
Album: Released Sep '83, on Jasmine by Hasmick Promotions. Catalogue no: **JASM 1024**

Legal Eagles

LEGAL EAGLES (Film Soundtrack) (Various artists)
Tracks: / Love theme: *Various artists* / Moving on: *Various artists* / Hypnotic eyes: *Various artists* / Strange birthday: *Various artists* / Tom and Kelly: *Various artists* / Scared: *Various artists* / Fire and rescue: *Various artists* / Put out the fire: *Hannah, Daryl* / Good lovin': *Rascals* / Magic carpet ride: *Steppenwolf*.
Cass: Released Oct '86, on MCA by MCA Records. Deleted Jan '88. Catalogue no: **MCFC 3344**
Album: Released Oct '86, on MCA by MCA Records. Deleted Jan '88. Catalogue no: **MCF 3344**

Legend

LEGEND (Film Soundtrack) (Various artists)
Album: Released Jan '90, on Silva Screen by Silva Screen Records. Catalogue no: **FILM 045**
Cass: Released Jan '90, on Silva Screen by Silva Screen Records. Catalogue no: **FILMC 045**
CD: Released Jan '90, on Silva Screen by Silva Screen Records. Catalogue no: **FILMCD 045**

LEGEND (Film Soundtrack) (National Philharmonic Orchestra)
Tracks: / My true love's eyes: *National Philharmonic Orchestra* / Riddle, The: *National Philharmonic Orchestra* / Sing the wee: *National Philharmonic Orchestra* / Goblins, The: *National Philharmonic Orchestra* / Dress waltz, The: *National Philharmonic Orchestra* / Ring, The: *National Philharmonic Orchestra* / Unicorns, The: *National Philharmonic Orchestra* / Bumps and hollows: *National Philharmonic Orchestra* / Forgive me: *National Philharmonic Orchestra* / Reunited: *National Philharmonic Orchestra*.

Album: Released Jan '89, on Silva Screen by Silva Screen Records. Catalogue no: **MOMENT 100**
Cass: Released Jan '89, on Silva Screen by Silva Screen Records. Catalogue no: **MOMENTC 100**
CD: Released Jan '89, on Silva Screen by Silva Screen Records. Catalogue no: **MOMENTCD 100**

LEGEND (AMERICAN) (Film Soundtrack) (Tangerine Dream)
Note: The score for the American release of the Tom Cruise film.
Album: Released Jan '89, on MCA by MCA Records. Catalogue no: **MCA 6165**
Cass: Released Jan '89, on MCA by MCA Records. Catalogue no: **MCAC 6165**

Legend Of Billie Jean
LEGEND OF BILLIE JEAN (See under Pat Benatar 'Invincible' for title track)

Legend Of Glass ...
LEGEND OF GLASS MOUNTAIN (See under Goodwin, Ron)

Legions Last Patrol
LEGIONS LAST PATROL (Theme from) (See under Thorne, Ken)

Legrand, Michel
LOVE SONGS (Film Soundtrack) (See under Love Songs)

TROIS PLACES POUR LE 26 (Film Soundtrack) (See under Trois places pour le 26)

UMBRELLAS OF CHERBOURG, THE/GO-BETWEEN, THE (Film soundtracks) (Legrand, Michel & London Symphony Orchestra)
Tracks: / Umbrellas of Cherbourg / Symphonic suite / Go - between / Variations for two pianos and orchestra.
Album: Released '79, on CBS by CBS Records & Distribution. Deleted '84. Catalogue no: **CBS 73886**

Legs Diamond
LEGS DIAMOND (Original Broadway cast) (Allen, Peter)
CD: Released Feb '90, on Silva Screen by Silva Screen Records. Catalogue no: **7983.2**

Album: Released Mar '90, on Silva Screen by Silva Screen Records. Catalogue no: **7983.1**
Cass: Released Feb '90, on Silva Screen by Silva Screen Records. Catalogue no: **7983.4**

Lemon Popsicle...
LEMON POPSICLE 5 (Film Soundtrack) (See under Baby Love) (Various artists)

LEMON POPSICLE 6 (Film soundtrack) (Various artists)
Tracks: / Sea cruise: *Ford, Frankie* / You got what it takes, it's just a matter of: *Benton, Brook* / Surf city: *Jan & Dean* / Because they're young: *Eddy, Duane* / Tutti frutti: *Little Richard* / Bama lama bama loo: *Little Richard* / Green onions: *Cortez, Dave 'Baby'* / For your love: *Yardbirds* / Still I'm sad: *Yardbirds* / Mashed potato time: *Sharp, Dee* / Peppermint twist: *Dee, Joey & The Starlighters* / Shout: *Dee, Joey & The Starlighters* / Great balls of fire: *Lewis, Jerry Lee* / Slow twistin': *Checker, Chubby* / Coma prima: *Dallera, Tony* / Teen beat: *Nelson, Sandy* / Hippy hippy shake: *Swinging Blue Jeans* / Why don't they understand: *Hamilton, George IV.*
Cass: Released Oct '85, on Red Bus by Red Bus Records. Catalogue no: **ZCRBM 8471**
Album: Released Oct '85, on Red Bus by Red Bus Records. Catalogue no: **RBMP 8471**

Lenin:The Train
LENIN:THE TRAIN (TV Series) (Piovani, Nicola)
CD: Released Feb '90, on SPI Milan (France) Catalogue no: **CDCH 381**

Lennon, John
IMAGINE - THE MOVIE (Original soundtrack) (Lennon, John/Beatles)
Tracks: / Real love / Twist and shout / Help / In my life / Strawberry fields forever / Day in the life, A / Revolution / Ballad of John and Yoko / Julia / Don't let me down / Give me a chance / How? / Imagine / God / Mother / Stand by me / Jealous guy / Woman / Beautiful boy / Just like starting over / Imagine.
Cass set: Released Oct '88, on Parlophone by EMI Records. Catalogue no: **TCPCSP 722**

CD: Released Oct '88, on Parlophone by EMI Records. Catalogue no: **CDPCSP 722**
CD: Released Oct '88, on Parlophone by EMI Records. Catalogue no: **CDP 790 803 2**
2 LP Set: Released Oct '88, on Parlophone by EMI Records. Catalogue no: **PCSP 722**

IMAGINE (VIDEO) (Documentary)
Note: Cert: 15.
VHS: Released May '89, on Warner/Parkfield Catalogue no: **PES 11819**

IMAGINE-THE FILM
VHS: Released Jun '86, on PMI by EMI Records. Catalogue no: **MVP 99 1101 2**
Beta: Released Jun '86, on PMI by EMI Records. Catalogue no: **MXP 99 1101 4**

Lennon, Julian
TIME WILL TELL (From the show 'Time') (See under Time)

Lennox, Annie
PUT A LITTLE LOVE IN YOUR HEART (Lennox, Annie & Al Green)
Tracks: / Put a little love in your heart / Great big piece of love, A.
Note: This Jackie de Shannon/Randy Myers/Jimmy Holiday composition was produced by Dave Stewart and features on the forthcoming soundtrack to the new Bill Murray fim 'Scrooged' which includes tracks by Natalie Cole and Miles Davies.
7" Single: Released Oct '88, on A&M by A&M Records. Catalogue no: **AM 484**
12" Single: Released Oct '88, on A&M by A&M Records. Catalogue no: **AMY 484**

Leopard
LEOPARD, THE (Film Soundtrack) (Various artists)
Note: Nino Rota score for the Visconti film starring Burt Lancaster.
Album: Released Jan '89, on Silva Screen by Silva Screen Records. Catalogue no: **STV 81190**

Les Girls
LES GIRLS (VIDEO) (Various artists)
VHS: Released Sep '89, on MGM/UA (Video) by MGM/UA

Video. Catalogue no: **SMV 10308**

LES GIRLS/LILI (Film Soundtracks) (Various artists)
Note: Starring Gene Kelly and Mitzi Gaynor.
Cass: Released Jan '89, on MCA by MCA Records. Catalogue no: **MCAC 1426**
Album: Released Jan '89, on MCA by MCA Records. Catalogue no: **MCA 1426**

LES GIRLS/SILK STOCKINGS (Film Soundtracks) (Various artists)
Album: Released Jan '89, on Silva Screen by Silva Screen Records. Catalogue no: **MCAD 6177**

Les Miserables

5 OUTSTANDING PERFORMANCES FROM LES MISERABLES (Various artists)
Tracks: / Empty chairs at empty tables: *Various artists* / Stars: *Various artists* / One day more: *Various artists* / I dreamed a dream: *Various artists* / On my own: *Various artists*.
Album: Released Apr '89, on First Night by First Night Records. Catalogue no: **SCOREL 17**

LES MISERABLES (Original Broadway cast) (Various artists)
Album: Released Jan '89, on Silva Screen by Silva Screen Records. Catalogue no: **924151.1**
Cass: Released Jan '89, on Silva Screen by Silva Screen Records. Catalogue no: **924151.4**
CD: Released Jan '89, on Silva Screen by Silva Screen Records. Catalogue no: **924151.2**

LES MISERABLES (Original London Cast) (Various artists) (See panel above)
Tracks: / At the end of the day: *Various artists* / I dreamed a dream: *Various artists* / Lovely ladies: *Various artists* / Who am I: *Various artists* / Come to me: *Various artists* / Confrontation: *Various artists* / Castle on a cloud: *Various artists* / Master of the house: *Various artists* / Stars: *Various artists* / Look down: *Various artists* / Little people: *Various artists* / Red and black: *Various artists* / Do you hear the people sing: *Various artists* / I saw him once in my life: *Various artists* / Heart full of love, A: *Various artists* / One day more: *Various*

Les Miserables - Original London Cast (First Night)

artists / On my own: *Various artists* / Attack, The: *Various artists* / Little fall of rain, A: *Various artists* / Drink with me: *Various artists* / Bring him home: *Various artists* / Dog eat dog: *Various artists* / Soliloquy: *Various artists* / Empty chairs at empty tables: *Various artists* / Wedding chorale: *Various artists* / Beggars at the feast: *Various artists* / Finale: *Various artists*.
Album: Released Dec '85, on First Night by First Night Records. Catalogue no: **ENCORE 1**
Cass: Released Dec '85, on First Night by First Night Records. Catalogue no: **ENCOREC 1**
CD: Released '86, on First Night by First Night Records. Catalogue no: **ENCORECD 1**

LES MISERABLES (Complete symphonic recording) (Various artists)
Album: Released Dec '88, on First Night by First Night Records. Catalogue no: **MIZ 1**
Cass: Released Dec '88, on First Night by First Night Records. Catalogue no: **MIZC 1**
CD: Released Feb '89, on First Night by First Night Records. Catalogue no: **MIZCD 1**

LES MISERABLES (Original Paris Cast) (Various artists)
Tracks: / La journee est finie: *Various artists* / J'ai reve d'une autre vie: *Various artists* / La volonte du peuple: *Various artists* / L'air de la misere: *Various artists* / La devise du cabaretier: *Various artists* / Le coeur au bon heur: *Various artists* / Donnez donnez: *Various artists* / Mon prince est en chemin: *Various artists* / Demain: *Various artists* / La faute a voltaire: *Various artists* / Noir ou blanc: *Various artists* / La luminere: *Various artists* .
Album: Released Jan '86, on First Night by First Night Records. Catalogue no: **SCENE 2**
Cass: Released Jan '86, on First Night by First Night Records. Catalogue no: **SCENEC 2**
CD: Released '89, on First Night by First Night Records. Catalogue no: **SCENE CD 2**

LES MISERABLES (VIDEO) (Various artists)
CD Video: Released Nov '89, on Polygram Music Video by Polygram Video. Catalogue no: **080 6461**
VHS: Released '88, on Channel 5 by Channel 5 Video. Catalogue no:

CFV 02872

Les Morfalous

LES MORFALOUS (Film Soundtrack) (Various artists)
Note: Georges Delerue score for the French action film starring Jean Paul Belmondo.
Album: Released Jan '89, on Silva Screen by Silva Screen Records. Catalogue no: **A 243**

Les Parapluies ...

LES PARAPLUIES DE CHERBOURG (Film Soundtrack) (Various artists)
Note: A Jacques Demy film starring Catherine Deneuve and Nino Castelnuovo. Music composed by Michel Legrand.
CD: Released Feb '89, on Polygram (France) by PolyGram UK Ltd. Catalogue no: **834139 2**

Les Uns Et Les Autres

LES UNS ET LES AUTRES (Film Soundtrack) (Various artists)
Note: Composed by Michel Legrand and Francis Lai.
Cass: Released Jan '89, on Silva Screen by Silva Screen Records. Catalogue no: **BK 70713**
2 LP Set: Released Jan '89, on Silva Screen by Silva Screen Records. Catalogue no: **BL 70713**
CD: Released '83, on RCA by BMG Records (UK). Deleted Jul '89. Catalogue no: **PD 70033**

Less Than Zero

LESS THAN ZERO (Film Soundtrack) (Various artists)
Tracks: / Rockin' pneumonia and the boogie woogie flu: *Aerosmith* / Life fades away: *Orbison, Roy* / Rock and roll all nite: *Poison* / Going back to Cali: *L.L.Cool J.* / You and me (less than zero): *Danzig, Glenn & The Power & Fury Orchestra* / In a gadda-da-vida: *Slayer* / Bring the noise: *Public Enemy* / Are you my woman: *Black Flames* / She's lost you: *Jett, Joan & The Blackhearts* / How to love again: *Jones, Oran "Juice"* / Hazy shade of winter: *Bangles.*
Cass: Released Nov '87, on CBS by CBS Records & Distribution. Deleted Jan '90. Catalogue no: **460449 4**
Album: Released Nov '87, on CBS by CBS Records & Distribution. Deleted 17 Apr '89. Catalogue no: **460449 1**
CD: Released Nov '87, on CBS by CBS Records & Distribution. Deleted Jan '90. Catalogue no: **460449 2**

LESS THAN ZERO (Theme from) (See under Bangles 'Hazy shade of winter')

Lethal Weapon

LETHAL WEAPON (Film soundtrack) (Various artists)
Tracks: / Lethal weapon: *Various artists* / Amanda: *Various artists* / Meet Martin Riggs: *Various artists* / Roger: *Various artists* / Coke deal: *Various artists* / Mr. Joshua: *Various artists* / They've got my daughter: *Various artists* / Desert, The: *Various artists* / Nightclub: *Various artists* / Weapon, The: *Various artists.*
CD: Released Aug '87, on Warner Bros. by WEA Records. Catalogue no: **925551 2**
Album: Released Aug '87, on Warner Bros. by WEA Records. Deleted Jan '90. Catalogue no: **925551 1**
Cass: Released Aug '87, on Warner Bros. by WEA Records. Catalogue no: **925551 4**

LETHAL WEAPON II (Film Soundtrack) (Various artists)
Cass: Released Sep '89, on Warner Bros. by WEA Records. Catalogue no: **K 925985 4**
CD: Released Sep '89, on Warner Bros. by WEA Records. Catalogue no: **K 925985 2**
Album: Released Sep '89, on Warner Bros. by WEA Records. Catalogue no: **K 925985 1**

Let's Get Harry

LET'S GET HARRY (Film soundtrack) (Various artists)
Note: Composed by Brad Fiedel (The Terminator).,
Album: Released Jan '89, on Silva Screen by Silva Screen Records. Catalogue no: **STV 81301**

Let's Go To The Movies

LET'S GO TO THE MOVIES VOL.1 (Various artists)
CD: Released '88, on Denon Catalogue no: **C32 7074**

LET'S GO TO THE MOVIES VOL.2 (Various artists)
Tracks: / Tara's theme: *Various artists* / Over the rainbow: *Various artists* / Love is a many splendoured thing: *Various artists* / Summertime in Venice: *Various artists* / East of Eden: *Various artists* / Plein soliel: *Various artists* / Raindrops keep falling on my head: *Various artists* / Speak softly love: *Various artists* / Man and a woman, A: *Various artists* / Live for life: *Various artists* / Romeo and Juliet: *Various artists* / Love story: *Various artists* / Sunflower: *Various artists* / Way we were, The: *Various artists.*
CD: Released '88, on Denon Catalogue no: **C32 7099**

Let's Make Love

LET'S MAKE LOVE (Film Soundtrack) (Various artists)
Note: Starring Marilyn Monroe and Yves Montand.
Album: Released Jan '89, on Silva Screen by Silva Screen Records. Catalogue no: **ACS 8327**
Cass: Released Jan '89, on Silva Screen by Silva Screen Records. Catalogue no: **BT 8327**
CD: Released Feb '90, on Silva Screen by Silva Screen Records. Catalogue no: **8369842**

Letter To Brezhnev

LETTER TO BREZHNEV (Film soundtrack) (Various artists)
Tracks: / Don't ask me to choose: *Fine Young Cannibals* / Bring it down (this insane thing): *Redskins* / How long: *Carmel* / Always something there to remind me: *Shaw, Sandie* / Letter to Brezhnev theme: *Gill, Alan* / Hit that perfect beat: *Bronski Beat* / You can't help (sentimental Sunday): *Flesh* / Wild party: *A Certain Ratio* / Ain't that always the way: *Quinn, Paul* / Lockets and stars: *Clarke, Marie.*
Album: Released Nov '85, on London Records by London Records Ltd. Catalogue no: **LONLP 8**
Cass: Released Nov '85, on London Records by London Records Ltd. Deleted Sep '87. Catalogue no: **LONC 8**

Leviathan

LEVIATHAN (Film soundtrack) (Goldsmith, Jerry)
Album: Released Feb '90, on Silva Screen by Silva Screen Records. Catalogue no: **VS 5226**
Cass: Released Feb '90, on Silva Screen by Silva Screen Records. Catalogue no: **VSG 5226**

CD: Released Feb '90, on Silva Screen by Silva Screen Records. Catalogue no: **VSD 5226**

Lewis, Huey

POWER OF LOVE (Lewis, Huey & The News)
Tracks: / Power of love, The / Do you believe in love.
Note: From the film 'Back To The Future'.
12" Single: Released Aug '85, on Chrysalis by Chrysalis Records. Catalogue no: **HUEYX 1**
7" Single: Released Aug '85, on Chrysalis by Chrysalis Records. Catalogue no: **HUEY 1**

Lewis, Jerry Lee

BREATHLESS (2)
Note: Used in the film 'Breathless' starring Richard Gere.
Tracks: / Breathless.
7" Single: Released Apr '58, on London-American by Decca Records. Deleted Apr '61. Catalogue no: **HLS 8592**

GREAT BALLS OF FIRE (OLD GOLD)
Tracks: / Great balls of fire / Whole lotta shakin' goin' on / What'd I say ('What'd I say' extra track on 12" only.).
CD Single: Released 27 Feb '89, on Old Gold by Old Gold Records. Catalogue no: **OG 6115**
7" Single: Released Jul '82, on Old Gold by Old Gold Records. Catalogue no: **OG 9110**

GREAT BALLS OF FIRE (SINGLE)
Tracks: / Great balls of fire.
Note: Used as the theme to the film Great balls of fire starring Dennis Quaid as Jerry Lee Lewis.
7" Single: Released Dec '57, on London-American by Decca Records. Deleted Dec '60. Catalogue no: **HLS 8529**

Licence To Kill

LICENCE TO KILL (Single) (See under Knight, Gladys)
LICENCE TO KILL (Film soundtrack) (Various artists)
Tracks: / Licence to kill: Various artists / Dirty love: Various artists / If you asked me to: Various artists / His funny valentine: Various artists / Ninja: Various artists / Wedding party: Various artists / Pam: Various artists / James & Felix on their way to church: Various artists

/ Sanchez is in the Bahamas (Shark fishing): Various artists / Licence revoked: Various artists.
Album: Released Jul '89, on MCA by MCA Records. Catalogue no: **MCG 6051**
CD: Released Jul '89, on MCA by MCA Records. Catalogue no: **DMCG 6051**
Cass: Released Jul '89, on MCA by MCA Records. Catalogue no: **MCGC 6051**

Licence To Drive

LICENCE TO DRIVE (Original Soundtrack) (Various artists)
CD: Released Feb '90, on MCA by MCA Records. Catalogue no: **MCAD 6241**

Lick The Tins

CAN'T HELP FALLING IN LOVE
Tracks: / Can't help falling in love / Bad dreams.
Note: From the film 'Some Kind Of Wonderful'.
7" Single: Released Feb '87, on Sedition by Sedition Records. Catalogue no: **EDIT 3308**
12" Single: Released Feb '87, on Sedition by Sedition Records. Catalogue no: **EDITL 3308**

Life & Loves Of A...

LIFE AND LOVES OF A SHE DEVIL (Original TV soundtrack) (Various artists)
Tracks: / Revenge: Various artists / Warm love variations: Various artists / Commercial break - vista rose: Various artists / For Lucille: Various artists / Eden Grove: Various artists / Devil groove: Various artists / Ways to say goodbye: Various artists / Warm love gone cold: Various artists / All because of you: Various artists / It's all just talk: Various artists / Cavatina: Various artists / Some enchanted evening: Various artists / Cavatina (sequenced version): Various artists.
Note: Brilliant new music from the BBC serial starring Dennis Waterman. Includes the title song "Warm love gone cold" sung by Christine Collister.
Cass: Released Oct '86, on BBC by BBC Records. Deleted Apr '89. Catalogue no: **ZCF 615**
Album: Released Oct '86, on BBC by BBC Records. Deleted Apr '89. Catalogue no: **REB 615**

Life & Times Of ...

LIFE AND TIMES OF JUDGE ROY BEAN (Original Soundtrack) (Various artists)
Tracks: / Judge Roy Bean's theme: Various artists / Marshall's: Various artists / Marias fashion show: Various artists / Matchmaker (yellow rose of Texas): Various artists / Bear: Various artists / Marmalade, molasses and honey: Various artists / On the way to the opera: Various artists / Old ragtime: Various artists / Bad Bob: Various artists / Justice: Various artists / Miss Lillie Langtry: Various artists.
Album: Released '73, on CBS by CBS Records & Distribution. Deleted '78. Catalogue no: **70118**

Lifeforce

LIFEFORCE (Film soundtrack) (London Symphony Orchestra)
Tracks: / Lifeforce / Spacewalk / Into the alien craft / Exploration / Sleeping vampires / Evil visitations / Carson's story / Girl in the raincoat / Web of destiny (parts 1-3).
Note: Sci/fi film with music by Henry Mancini.
CD: Released Feb '90, on Milan Catalogue no: **CDFM 256**
Album: Released Jan '89, on SPI Milan (France) Catalogue no: **A 56**
Album: Released Mar '86, on Red Bus by Red Bus Records. Catalogue no: **RBMP 8472**

Light Of Day

LIGHT OF DAY (Film soundtrack) (Various artists)
Tracks: / Light of day: Barbusters / This means war: Barbusters / Twist it off: Fabulous Thunderbirds / Cleveland rocks: Hunter, Ian / Stay with me tonight: Edmunds, Dave / It's all coming down tonight: Barbusters / Rude mood: Barbusters / Only lonely: Bon Jovi / Rabbit's got the gun: Hunzz / You got no place to go: Fox, Michael J / Elegy (instrumental): Cox, Rick, Chas Smith, Jon C Clarke & Michael Boddicker.
Cass: Released Dec '88, on Epic by CBS Records & Distribution. Deleted Apr '90. Catalogue no: **450501 4**
Album: Released Dec '88, on Epic by CBS Records & Distribution. Deleted Apr '90. Catalogue no: **450501 1**

CD: Released May '87, on Epic by CBS Records & Distribution. Deleted Apr '90. Catalogue no: **450501 2**

Lighthorsemen

LIGHTHORSEMEN/SHAME (Film soundtrack) (Various artists)
Note: 2 Australian film scores by Mario Millo. The Lighthorsemen is a first world war epic with a large orchestral score performed by the Victorian Philharmonic Orchestra.
Album: Released Jan '89, on DRG (USA) by DRG Records (USA). Catalogue no: **SL 9521**
Cass: Released Jan '89, on DRG (USA) by DRG Records (USA). Catalogue no: **SLC 9521**

Li'l Abner

LI'L ABNER (Original Broadway Cast) (Various artists)
Cass: Released Jan '89, on Silva Screen by Silva Screen Records. Catalogue no: **BT 5150**
Album: Released Jan '89, on Silva Screen by Silva Screen Records. Catalogue no: **AOL 5150**

L'ile

L'ILE (THE ISLAND) (Original Soundtrack) (Various artists)
Note: Score for the French film by Jean Claude Petit (composer of Jean De Florette & Manon Des Sources).
CD: Released Jan '89, on Silva Screen by Silva Screen Records. Catalogue no: **CD 340**
Album: Released Jan '89, on Silva Screen by Silva Screen Records. Catalogue no: **A 340**

Lili

LILI / LES GIRLS (Film Soundtracks) (See under Les Girls)

Lili Marlene

LILI MARLENE (Original Soundtrack) (Various artists)
Album: Released '88, on DRG (USA) by DRG Records (USA). Catalogue no: **SL 9506**

Lindsay, Julian

NETWORK 7 (Theme from the TV series) (Lindsay, Julian & Steve Levine)
Tracks: / Network 7 / Straight in straight out / 808 (Extra track on 12").
12" Single: Released Jul '87, on

Sierra by Sierra Records. Catalogue no: **FED 36T**
7" Single: Released Jul '87, on Sierra by Sierra Records. Catalogue no: **FED 36**

Link

LINK (Film soundtrack) (Various artists)
Note: Composed by Jerry Goldsmith.
CD: Released Jan '89, on Silva Screen by Silva Screen Records. Catalogue no: **VCD 47276**
Album: Released Jan '89, on Silva Screen by Silva Screen Records. Catalogue no: **STV 81294**
Cass: Released Jan '89, on Silva Screen by Silva Screen Records. Catalogue no: **CTV 81294**

Lion In Winter

LION IN WINTER (Original Soundtrack) (Barry, John)
CD: Released Feb '90, on Silva Screen by Silva Screen Records. Catalogue no: **VSD5217**

Lion Of The Desert

LION OF THE DESERT (Film Soundtrack) (See under Jarre, Maurice)

Lionheart

LIONHEART (Film soundtrack) (Various artists)
Note: Jerry Goldsmith score for the Franklin J Schaffner film set in the times of the Crusades.
Cass: Released Jan '89, on Silva Screen by Silva Screen Records. Catalogue no: **CTV 81304**
CD: Released Jan '89, on Silva Screen by Silva Screen Records. Catalogue no: **VCD 47282**
Album: Released Jan '89, on Silva Screen by Silva Screen Records. Catalogue no: **STV 81304**

LIONHEART VOL 2 (Film soundtrack) (Various artists)
Note: Composed by Jerry Goldsmith.
CD: Released Jan '89, on Silva Screen by Silva Screen Records. Catalogue no: **VCD 47288**
Album: Released Jan '89, on Silva Screen by Silva Screen Records. Catalogue no: **STV 81311**
Cass: Released Jan '89, on Silva Screen by Silva Screen Records. Catalogue no: **CTV 81311**

Lipman, Maureen

RE-JOYCE (Stage Show)
CD: Released Oct '89, on Legacy by Legacy Records. Deleted Jul '90. Catalogue no: **LLCD 129**
Album: Released Oct '89, on Legacy by Legacy Records. Deleted Jul '90. Catalogue no: **LLP 129**
Cass: Released Oct '89, on Legacy by Legacy Records. Deleted Jul '90. Catalogue no: **LLK 129**

Liquid Sky

LIQUID SKY (Film soundtrack) (Various artists)
Note: Music by Slava Tsukerman..
CD: Released Jan '89, on Silva Screen by Silva Screen Records. Catalogue no: **VCD 47181**
Album: Released Jan '89, on Silva Screen by Silva Screen Records. Catalogue no: **STV 81181**

Liquidator

LIQUIDATOR, THE (Film soundtrack) (Various artists)
Note: Lalo Schifrin score for the thriller starring Rod Taylor.
Album: Released Jan '89, on Silva Screen by Silva Screen Records. Catalogue no: **MCA 25137**
Cass: Released Jan '89, on Silva Screen by Silva Screen Records. Deleted Mar '90. Catalogue no: **MCAC 25137**

Little Dorrit

LITTLE DORRIT (Film soundtrack) (Various artists)
Cass: Released '87, on Filmtrax by Filmtrax Records. Catalogue no: **MOMENTC 117**
Album: Released '87, on Filmtrax by Filmtrax Records. Catalogue no: **MOMENT 117**

Little Mary Sunshine

LITTLE MARY SUNSHINE (Original London Cast) (Various artists)
Album: Released Jan '89, on Silva Screen by Silva Screen Records. Catalogue no: **AEI 1105**

Little Me

LITTLE ME (London cast recording) (Various artists)
Tracks: / Overture: *Various artists* / Truth, The: *Various artists* / On the other side of the tracks: *Various artists* / Rich kids rag: *Various*

artists / I love you: *Various artists* / Deep down inside: *Various artists* / To be a performer: *Various artists* / Le grand boom-boom: *Various artists* / I've got your number: *Various artists* / Real live girl: *Various artists* / Poor little Hollywood star: *Various artists* / Little me: *Various artists* / Goodbye: *Various artists* / Here's to us: *Various artists*.
Cass: Released Nov '85, on Flashback by Mainline Records. Catalogue no: **ZCFBL 8077**
Album: Released Nov '85, on Flashback by Mainline Records. Catalogue no: **FBLP 8077**

Little Night Music

LITTLE NIGHT MUSIC, A (Original Broadway cast) (Various artists)
Album: Released Jan '89, on CBS (import) by CBS Records & Distribution. Deleted Mar '90. Catalogue no: **JS 32265**
Cass: Released Mar '90, on CBS (import) by CBS Records & Distribution. Catalogue no: **PST 32265**
CD: Released Jan '89, on CBS (import) by CBS Records & Distribution. Catalogue no: **CK 32265**

LITTLE NIGHT MUSIC (Original London cast) (Various artists)
Tracks: / Overture and night waltz: *Various artists* / Now: *Various artists* / Soon: *Various artists* / Glamourous life, The: *Various artists* / You must meet my wife: *Various artists* / In praise of women: *Various artists* / Every day a little death: *Various artists* / Weekend in the country: *Various artists* / Sun won't set, The: *Various artists* / I would have been wonderful: *Various artists* / Perpetual anticipation: *Various artists* / Send in the clowns: *Various artists* / Miller's son, The: *Various artists* / Night waltz: *Various artists* / Finale - send in the clowns (reprise): *Various artists* .
Album: Released Jan '73, on Silva Screen by Silva Screen Records. Deleted '78. Catalogue no: **LRL 1 5090**
CD: Released Jan '73, on Silva Screen by Silva Screen Records. Deleted '78. Catalogue no: **RCD 1 5090**
Cass: Released Jan '73, on Silva Screen by Silva Screen Records. Deleted '78. Catalogue no: **LRK 1 5090**

Album: Released Apr '90, on RCA by BMG Records (UK). Catalogue no: **GL 85090**
Cass: Released Apr '90, on RCA by BMG Records (UK). Catalogue no: **GK 85090**
CD: Released Apr '90, on RCA by BMG Records (UK). Catalogue no: **GD 85090**
Cass: Released '79, on RCA by BMG Records (UK). Deleted '84. Catalogue no: **RK 11687**

Little Richard

GIRL CAN'T HELP IT, THE
Tracks: / Girl can't help it, The / She's got it.
Note: From the film of the same name.
7" Single: Released Dec '80, on Speciality (USA) by Speciality Records (USA). Deleted Dec '85. Catalogue no: **SON 5018**
7" Single: Released Mar '57, on London-American by Decca Records. Deleted Mar '60. Catalogue no: **HLO 8382**

GREAT GOSH A'MIGHTY
Tracks: / Great gosh a'mighty / Ride, The / Down and out in Beverly Hills (Extra track available on 12" version only).
Note: From the film 'Down And Out In Beverly Hills'.
12" Single: Released May '86, on MCA by MCA Records. Catalogue no: **MCAT 1049**
7" Single: Released May '86, on MCA by MCA Records. Catalogue no: **MCA 1049**

Little Shop Of Horrors

LITTLE SHOP OF HORRORS (Broadway cast recording) (Various artists)
Album: Released Dec '83, on Geffen by Geffen Records (USA). Deleted '88. Catalogue no: **GEF70244**

LITTLE SHOP OF HORRORS (Film Soundtrack) (Various artists)
Tracks: / Prologue (Little shop of horrors): *Various artists* / Skid row (down town): *Various artists* / Da doo: *Various artists* / Grow for me: *Various artists* / Somewhere that's green: *Various artists* / Some fun now: *Various artists* / Dentist: *Various artists* / Feed me: *Various artists* / Suddenly Seymour: *Various artists* / Suppertime: *Various artists* / Meek shall inherit, The: *Vari-*

ous artists / Mean green mother from outer space: *Various artists* / Finale: *Various artists*.
Note: Film starring Rick Moranis as Seymour. With guest appearances by Bill Murray and Steve Martin. Levi Stubbs from The Four Tops provides the voice for Audrey II.
Album: Released Mar '87, on Geffen by Geffen Records (USA). Catalogue no: **K 924125 1**
CD: Released Oct '87, on WEA by WEA Records. Catalogue no: **924125 2**
Cass: Released Mar '87, on Geffen by Geffen Records (USA). Catalogue no: **K 924125 4**

Little Thief

LITTLE THIEF,THE (LA PETITE VOLEUSE) (Film Soundtrack) (Jomy,Alain) (See under La Petite Voleuse)

Little Vera

LITTLE VERA (film soundtrack) (Various artists)
CD: Released Apr '90, on SPI Milan (France) Catalogue no: **CDCH 368**

Live & Let Die

LIVE & LET DIE (Film soundtrack) (Various artists)
Tracks: / Live and let die: *McCartney, Paul & Wings* / Just a closer walk with thee: *Various artists* / New second line: *Dejan, Harold A.* "Duke" & The Olympia Brass Band / Bond meets Solitaire: *Various artists* / Whisper who dares: *Various artists* / Snakes alive: *Various artists* / Baron Samedi's dance of death: *Various artists* / San Monique: *Various artists* / Fillet of soul: *Various artists* / Live and let die: *Arnau, BJ* / Fillet of soul: *Various artists* / Bond drops in: *Various artists* / If he finds it, kill him: *Various artists* / Trespassers will be eaten: *Various artists* / Solitaire gets her cards: *Various artists* / Sacrifice: *Various artists* / James Bond theme: *Various artists*.
Note: Produced by Harry Saltzman & Cubby Broccoli.
Album: Released '73, on United Artists by United Artists. Catalogue no: **UAS 29475**
Cass: Released Jul '87, on Liberty by EMI Records. Deleted Jan '90. Catalogue no: **TCEMS 1269**
CD: Released Jan '89, on Silva

Screen by Silva Screen Records. Catalogue no: **CD 90629**

Album: Released Jul '87, on Liberty by EMI Records. Deleted Aug '90. Catalogue no: **EMS 1269**

Living Daylights

LIVING DAYLIGHTS, THE (Film soundtrack) (Various artists)

Tracks: / Living daylights, The: *A-Ha* / Necros attacks: *Various artists* / Sniper was a woman, The: *Various artists* / Ice chase: *Various artists* / Kara meets Bond: *Various artists* / Koskov escapes: *Various artists* / Where has every body gone: *Various artists* / Into Vienna: *Various artists* / Hercules takes off: *Various artists* / Mujahadin and Opium: *Various artists* / Inflight flight: *Various artists* / If there was a man: *Various artists.*

Album: Released Aug '87, on Warner Bros. by WEA Records. Catalogue no: **WX 111**

Cass: Released Aug '87, on Warner Bros. by WEA Records. Catalogue no: **WX 111 C**

CD: Released Aug '87, on Warner Bros. by WEA Records. Catalogue no: **925616 2**

LIVING DAYLIGHTS (Theme from) (See under Aha)

Living Desert...

LIVING DESERT/ VANISHING PRAIRIE (Film Soundtracks) (Various artists)

Tracks: / Main title: *Various artists* / Denizens of the desert: *Various artists* / Scorpion square dance: *Various artists* / Sidewinder crawl: *Various artists* / More desert characters: *Various artists* / Wasp and the tarantula: *Various artists* / Desert bloom: *Various artists* / End title: *Various artists* / Buffalo theme: *Various artists* / Prairie home: *Various artists* / Bird's homecoming: *Various artists* / Bird dances: *Various artists* / Buffalo: *Various artists* / Coyote and the prairie dog: *Various artists* / Stampede: *Various artists* / Prairie fire: *Various artists* / Rains: *Various artists* / Winter finale: *Various artists.*

Album: Released '73, on Disneyland by Disneyland-Vista Records (USA). Deleted '78. Catalogue no: **DQ 1198**

Living Free

LIVING FREE (Original

Soundtrack Recording) (Various artists)

Tracks: / Living free - main title: *Various artists* / Trek to the Serengeti: *Various artists* / Playing for cups: *Various artists* / Life and death in the bush, part 1: *Various artists* / Big lions go hunting: *Various artists* / Little lions get lost: *Various artists* / Living free theme: *Various artists* / Jespah, Gopa and little Elsa: *Various artists* / Joy's theme: *Various artists* / Life and death in the bush, part 2: *Various artists* / Enticement, frustration and hope: *Various artists* / Caress and the kill: *Various artists* / Vigil and victory: *Various artists* / Living free - end title: *Various artists.*

Album: Released '73, on RCA by BMG Records (UK). Deleted '78. Catalogue no: **SER 5637**

Living Sound

SPIDERMAN (TV theme)

Tracks: / Spiderman / Iceman and Firestar.

7" Single: Released Nov '87, on Dulcima by Dulcima Records. Catalogue no: **DLCS 102**

Lloyd Webber, Andrew

70'S SHOWS (Limited Edition) (Various artists)

Album: Released Oct '81, on MCA by MCA Records. Catalogue no: **MBOX 1**

ANDREW LLOYD WEBBER - A TRIBUTE (Various artists)

CD: Released '89, on K-Tel by K-Tel Records. Catalogue no: **ONCD 3441**

ANDREW LLOYD WEBBER'S CLASSIC MUSICALS (Royal Philharmonic Pops Orchestra)

Tracks: / Think of me (prelude) / Phantom of the opera / Think of me / Angel of music / Phantom (reprise) / Music of the night / Masquerade / Think of me (reprise) / All I ask of you / Wishing you were somehow here again / Overture / Heaven their minds / What's the buzz / Everything's alright / I don't know how to love him / Damned for all time/Blood money / Last supper, The / Pilate and Herod / Trial before Pilate.

Note: The Phantom Of The Opera and Jesus Christ Superstar. Selection conducted by Paul Geminani.

Album: Released 6 Aug '88, on Pickwick by Pickwick Records. Catalogue no: **SHM 3237**

CD: Released 6 Aug '88, on Pickwick by Pickwick Records. Catalogue no: **PWKS 506**

Cass: Released 6 Aug '88, on Pickwick by Pickwick Records. Catalogue no: **HSC 3237**

JOSE CARRERAS SINGS THE SONGS OF ANDREW LLOYD WEBBER (See under Carreras, Jose)

MEMORY

Tracks: / Memory / Lost variation. Note: From the show 'Cats'.

7" Single: Released Apr '81, on MCA by MCA Records. Deleted '85. Catalogue no: **MCA 698**

MUSIC OF ANDREW LLOYD WEBBER (Various artists)

Tracks: / Music of the night: *Various artists* / Memory: *Various artists* / Jesus Christ superstar: *Various artists* / Take that look off your face: *Various artists* / Don't cry for me Argentina: *Various artists* / All I ask of you: *Various artists.*

Note: Artists include Paul Nicholas, Stephanie Lawrence, Jacqueline Barron, James Rainbird, The Stephen Hill Singers and The Royal Philharmonic Orchestra conducted by Michael Reed.

Cass: Released Sep '88, on First Night by First Night Records. Catalogue no: **LLOYDC 1**

Album: Released Sep '88, on First Night by First Night Records. Catalogue no: **LLOYD 1**

CD: Released Sep '88, on First Night by First Night Records. Catalogue no: **LLOYDCD 1**

PREMIERE COLLECTION (See under Premier Collection)

RICHARD CLAYDERMAN PLAYS THE SONGS OF ANDREW LLOYD WEBBER (See under Clayderman, Richard)

Local Hero

GOING HOME (Theme to Local Hero) (See under Knopfler, Mark)

MUSIC FROM LOCAL HERO (Film soundtrack) (Knopfler, Mark)

Tracks: / Rocks and the water, The / Wild theme / Freeway flyer / Boomtown / Way it always starts,

The / Rocks and the thunder, The / Ceilidh and the Northern lights, The / Mist covered mountain, The / Ceilidh, The / Louis favourite Billy tune / Whistle, Theme from / Smooching / Stargazer / Rocks and the thunder, The / Going home (theme from Local Hero) .

Cass: Released Apr '83, on Vertigo by Phonogram Ltd. Catalogue no: **VERLC 4**

Album: Released Apr '83, on Vertigo by Phonogram Ltd. Catalogue no: **VERL 4**

Lock Up Your Daughters

LOCK UP YOUR DAUGHTERS (Original London cast) (Various artists)
Tracks: / All's well: *Various artists* / Proper man, A: *Various artists* / It must be true: *Various artists* / Red wine and a wench: *Various artists* / On the side: *Various artists* / When does the ravishing begin: *Various artists* / Lovely lover: *Various artists* / Lock up your daughters: *Various artists* / There's a plot afoot: *Various artists* / Mr. Jones: *Various artists* / On a sunny Sunday morning: *Various artists* / If I'd known you: *Various artists* / 'Tis plain to see: *Various artists* / Kind fate: *Various artists* / I'll be there: *Various artists* / Finale: *Various artists*.
Album: Released Apr '83, on T. E. R. by That's Entertainment Records. Catalogue no: **TER 1049**
Cass: Released Apr '83, on T. E. R. by That's Entertainment Records. Catalogue no: **ZCTER 1049**

Loggins, Kenny

DANGER ZONE
Tracks: / Danger zone / I'm gonna do it right.
Note: Used in the film *Top Gun*
7" Single: Released Sep '86, on CBS by CBS Records & Distribution. Catalogue no: **A 7188**

FOOTLOOSE
Tracks: / Footloose / Swear your love.
Note: Title track of the film *Footloose*
7" Single: Released Apr '84, on CBS by CBS Records & Distribution. Deleted '87. Catalogue no: **A 4101**
12" Single: Released Apr '84, on CBS by CBS Records & Distribution. Deleted '87. Catalogue no: **TA 4101**

Lolita

LOLITA (Film soundtrack) (Various artists)
Note: Nelson Riddle score for the Stanley Kubrick film starring James Mason and Peter Sellers.
Cass: Released Jan '89, on MCA by MCA Records. Deleted Mar '90. Catalogue no: **MCAC 39067**
Album: Released Jan '89, on MCA by MCA Records. Catalogue no: **MCA 39067**

London Calling

LONDON CALLING (Famous Themes: Vol.3) (Various artists)
Tracks: / London calling: *Coates, Eric* (Theme for BBC radio overseas service) / On the sea shore (players cigarettes TV commercial): *Farnon, Robert* / Shadow waltz: *Dubois, Paul* (from "the Teckman biography") / Picture parade: *Beaver, Jack* / Swiftly (from 'a place in the sun'): *Arel, Jack/Jean-Claude Petit* / Rippling waters (BBC-TV angel fish interlude): *Thorne, Donald* / Royal review: *Steck, Arnold* / Shopping centre: *Green, Philip* / Seascape: *Lowry, Tony* (From 'the windjammers') / Jamboree (from 'Out of the blue'): *Richardson, Clive* / Openings and endings: *Farnon, Robert* / Trapeze waltz: *Torch, Sidney* (From Guy De Maupassant) / Jockey on the carousel (from 'Mainly for women'): *Farnon, R./Buchel,P.* / Dalilia (the desperadoes): *Roger, Roger* (From 'Desperate People') / Autumn love: *Lewis, Paul* (from 'Spring and Autumn') / Bring on the girls (from 'time for titch'): *Torch, Sidney* / Proscenium (from 'armchair theatre'): *Farnon, Robert* / Pastoral montage:BBC-TV windmill interlude: *Fagan, Gideon* / Jolly juggler: *Ellis, Vivian* / Sentimental: *Foley, Adrian/Daley, Ronnie* (Theme from "Richard Attenborough presents".) / Metropolitan march(from 'calling all sportsmen'): *Barsotti, Roger.*
Album: Released 15 Aug '88, on Grasmere by Grasmere Records. Catalogue no: **GRALP 30**
Cass: Released 15 Aug '88, on Grasmere by Grasmere Records. Catalogue no: **GRTC 30**

London Festival ...

GREAT MUSICALS (London Festival Orchestra)
Tracks: / Sound of music, The / My fair lady / South Pacific / West side story / Oklahoma / Mary Poppins / Fiddler on the roof / Gigi.
CD: Released '88, on Decca Classics by PolyGram Classics. Catalogue no: **421 262 2**

London Film Orchestra

ANNA OF THE FIVE TOWNS
Tracks: / Anna of the five towns / Atlantis.
7" Single: Released Jan '85, on Sierra by Sierra Records. Catalogue no: **FED 8**

London Philharmonic

ACADEMY AWARD THEMES
CD: Released '88, on Pickwick by Pickwick Records. Catalogue no: **PWK 037**

AN AMERICAN IN PARIS
Tracks: / American in Paris, An / Porgy and Bess suite / El salon Mexico .
Album: Released Apr '88, on Classics For Pleasure by EMI Records. Deleted Apr '90. Catalogue no: **CFP 4537**
CD: Released Apr '88, on Classics For Pleasure by EMI Records. Catalogue no: **CDCFP 9019**
Cass: Released Apr '88, on Classics For Pleasure by EMI Records. Catalogue no: **TCCFP 4537**
CD: Released Apr '88, on Classics For Pleasure by EMI Records. Catalogue no: **CDB 762 037 2**

CHARIOTS OF FIRE (Film Soundtrack)
Tracks: / Chariots of fire / 2001 / Elvira Madigan.
Cass: Released Jun '82, on Hallmark by Pickwick Records. Deleted '88. Catalogue no: **HSC 3112**
Album: Released Jun '82, on Hallmark by Pickwick Records. Catalogue no: **SHM 3112**

London Shows...

LONDON SHOWS (The War years) (Various artists)
Tracks: / Are you havin any fun?: *Flanagan & Allen* / Run rabbit run: *Flanagan & Allen* / How beautiful you are: *Ambrose & His Orchestra* / My heart belongs to daddy: *Hall, Adelaide* / Crash, bang, I wanna go home: *Stones, Lew & His Band* / Have you met Miss Jones: *Hall, Adelaide* / Who's taking you home tonight: *Lynn, Vera* / Start the day

right: *Daniels, Bebe & Ben Lyon* / As round and round we go-Your company's requested: *Daniels, Bebe* / This can't be love: *Hall, Adelaide* / Let the people sing: *Payne, Jack & His Band/Billy Scott Coomber/* You done something to my heart: *Davis, Beryl* / They call me a dreamer: *Rabin, Oscar & His Band* / We'll go smiling along: *Rabin, Oscar & His Band* / Cheerio': *Daniels, Bebe* / Let's be buddies: *Flanagan & Allen* / But in the morning no!: *Day, Francis & Bud Flanagan* / Lambeth walk: *Ambrose & His Orchestra* / Me & my girl: *Cotton, Billy & His Band* / Waiting for Sally: *Stones, Lew & His Band* / Wrap yourself in cotton wool: *Hatchett's Swingtette* / Tahiti rendezvous: *Hatchett's Swingtette* / It's a million to one: *Mantovani* / Smiths and the Jones, The: *Flanagan & Allen* / Yankee doodle came to town: *Cotton, Billy & His Band*. Note: A definite "Hits Of The Blitz" compilation, featuring unforgettable songs from a host of London shows at theatres who kept the "Business As Usual" notices up while the bombs dropped all around. A bevy of top composers are represented   including Irving Berlin, Cole Porter, Noel Gaye, Richard Rodgers and Lorenz Hart. Among the contributing shows are "The Little Dog Laughed", "Black Velvet", "Haw Haw" and "Gangway"; a perfect way to lift the gloom by raising the blackout curtains...... Recorded in mono.
Cass set: Released May '87, on Recollections (Decca) by Decca Records. Catalogue no: **RECDC 1**
2 LP Set: Released May '87, on Recollections (Decca) by Decca Records. Deleted Feb '89. Catalogue no: **RECDL 1**

London Studio ...
NORTH BY NORTHWEST (See under London Studio Symphony Orchestra)
WESTERN WORLD OF DIMITRI TIOMKIN (See under Tiomkin, Dimitri)

London Symphony...
E.T., THEME FROM (London Symphony Orchestra)
Tracks: / E.T., Theme from / Escort theme.
7" Single: Released Nov '82, on MFP by EMI Records. Catalogue

no: **FP 907**
7" Single: Released Dec '82, on Towerbell Catalogue no: **TOW 31**
FANTASY MOVIE THEMES (London Symphony Orchestra)
Note: With Roy Budd. Full orchestral scores of *Raiders of the Lost Ark, Indiana Jones, Wild Geese, Final Conflict* etc.
CD: Released Jan '86, on Hermes by Nimbus Records. Catalogue no: **HRM 7002**
MOVIE MUSIC (London Symphony Orchestra/Stanley Black)
Tracks: / Raiders of the lost ark / Big country / Superman / Star wars / 2001, a space odyssey / Magnificent 7 / Lawrence of Arabia / Deer hunter (Cavatina) / 633 squadron / James Bond medley.
Cass: Released '88, on Hallmark by Pickwick Records. Catalogue no: **HSC 3408**
CD: Released '88, on Pickwick by Pickwick Records. Catalogue no: **PCD 887**
MUSIC FROM EDWARD VII (London Symphony Orchestra)
Album: Released Jul '75, on Polydor by Polydor Ltd. Deleted Jul '80. Catalogue no: **2659 041**
PINBALL WIZARD (London Symphony Orchestra)
Tracks: / Pinball wizard / American trilogy.
Note: From 'Tommy'.
7" Single: Released '79, on Warner Bros. by WEA Records. Deleted '82. Catalogue no: **K 11315**
SPACE MOVIE THEMES (London Symphony Orchestra)
Note: Full orchestral scores of 'Star Wars', 'The Empire Strikes Back', 'Return of the Jedi', 'Superman' etc.
CD: Released Jan '86, on Hermes by Nimbus Records. Catalogue no: **HRM 7001**
STAR WARS (ORIGINAL SOUNDTRACK) (London Symphony Orchestra)
Tracks: / Mouse robot and blasting off.
Cass: Released Nov '79, on 20th Century by Phonogram Ltd. Catalogue no: **CT 541**
THEME FROM SUPERMAN

(London Symphony Orchestra)
Tracks: / Superman, Theme from / Superman, Love theme.
7" Single: Released Jan '79, on Warner Bros. by WEA Records. Deleted '82. Catalogue no: **K 17292**
TOP T.V. THEMES (London Symphony Orchestra)
Album: Released Mar '72, on Studio 2 Deleted Mar '77. Catalogue no: **STWO 372**

Lone Ranger
LEGEND OF THE LONE RANGER (Film Soundtrack) (Various artists)
Note: Composed by John Barry.
Album: Released Jan '89, on MCA by MCA Records. Catalogue no: **MCA 1564**
Cass: Released Jan '89, on MCA by MCA Records. Catalogue no: **MCAC 1564**

Lone Wolf McQuade
LONE WOLF MCQUADE (Film Soundtrack) (De Masi, Francesco)
Album: Released Nov '83, on T. E. R. by That's Entertainment Records. Catalogue no: **TER 1071**

Lonely Guy
LONELY GUY (Original Soundtrack) (Various artists)
Note: Songs and music by Jerry Goldsmith from the Steve Martin comedy.
Album: Released Jan '89, on MCA by MCA Records. Catalogue no: **MCA 36010**
Cass: Released Jan '89, on MCA by MCA Records. Catalogue no: **MCAC 36010**

Lonely Passion Of ...
LONELY PASSION OF JUDITH HEARNE (Film soundtrack) (Various artists)
CD: Released Sep '88, on AVM by AVM Records. Deleted May '90. Catalogue no: **AVMCD 2001**
Cass: Released Sep '88, on AVM by AVM Records. Deleted Mar '90. Catalogue no: **AVMC 2001**
Album: Released Sep '88, on AVM by AVM Records. Catalogue no: **AVM 2001**

Long Day Of Vengeance
LONG DAY OF VENGE-

ANCE/SARTANA (Original Soundtracks) (Various artists)

Note: 2 Spaghetti western scores from Piero Piccioni & Armando Trovajoli.
Album: Released Jan '89, on Silva Screen by Silva Screen Records. Catalogue no: **IMGM 003**

Long Good Friday

LONG GOOD FRIDAY (Film soundtrack) (Various artists)
Tracks: / Long good Friday, The: *Various artists* / Overture: *Various artists* / Scene is set, The: *Various artists* / At the pool: *Various artists* / Discovery: *Various artists* / Icehouse, The: *Various artists* / Talking to the police: *Various artists* / Guitar interludes: *Various artists* / Realization: *Various artists* / Fury: *Various artists* / Taken: *Various artists.*
Note: Classic British thriller starring Bob Hoskins. Music by Francis Monkman.
Cass: Released Sep '89, on Silva Screen by Silva Screen Records. Catalogue no: **FILMC 020**
Album: Released Sep '84, on C.E.S. Catalogue no: **CES 1001**
CD: Released Sep '89, on Silva Screen by Silva Screen Records. Catalogue no: **FILMCD 020**
Album: Released Jan '89, on Silva Screen by Silva Screen Records. Catalogue no: **FILM 020**

Long Riders

LONG RIDERS (See under Cooder, Ry)

Longthorne, Joe

JOE LONGTHORNE SONG BOOK, THE (Songs from the TV series)
Tracks: / You're my world / My prayer / Always on my mind / My mother's eyes / Just loving you / It's only make believe / To all the girls I've loved before / End of the world / It was almost like a song / Hurt / Answer me / Danny boy / Don't laugh at me / When your old wedding ring was new.
Album: Released Nov '88, on Telstar by Telstar Records (UK). Catalogue no: **STAR 2353**
CD: Released Nov '88, on Telstar by Telstar Records (UK). Catalogue no: **TCD 2353**
Cass: Released Nov '88, on Telstar by Telstar Records (UK).

Catalogue no: **STAC 2353**

Look Who's Talking

LOOK WHO'S TALKING (See under Katrina & The Waves 'Walking on Sunshine')

L'Orchestre

SOUND WAVES
Tracks: / Heaven & hell / Chariots of fire / Oxygene / Missing / Westway / Chung Kuo (the long march) / Magnetic fields / Equinoxe / Pulstar / Carillon / Bladerunner / Prelude to earthrise / To the unknown man / Close encounters of the third kind / Star Wars.
CD: Released '86, on Nouveau Music Catalogue no: **CDNML 1005**
CD: Released Sep '87, on Trax by Filmtrax Records. Catalogue no: **MODCD 1003**
Album: Released Nov '83, on Nouveau Music Catalogue no: **NML 1005**
Cass: Released '83, on Nouveau Music Catalogue no: **ZCNML 1005**

Lord, Jon

COUNTRY DIARY OF AN EDWARDIAN LADY (T.V. soundtrack)

Album: Released Mar '84, on Safari by Safari Records. Catalogue no: **DIARY 1**
Cass: Released Mar '84, on Safari by Safari Records. Catalogue no: **DIARYC 1**

COUNTRY DIARY OF AN EDWARDIAN LADY (Theme from) (Lord, Jon)

Tracks: / Country diary of an Edwardian lady: *Lord, Jon*
7" Single: Released Mar '84, on Safari by Safari Records. Catalogue no: **SAFE 60**

Lord Of The Flies

LORD OF THE FLIES (Film soundtrack) (Sarde, Philippe) (See panel below)
Tracks: / Lord of the flies / Island, The / Demons / Fire on the mountain / Cry of the hunters / Last hope / Savages / After the storm / Bacchanalia / Lord Of The Flies - finale.
Note: Lord Of The Flies begins as an adventure story but soon develops into a gripping drama of survival. Set on a deserted island, a group of schoolboys find themselves stranded after a plane crash. Bereft of adult supervision, 24 young men are forced to protect

Soundtrack to the film version of William Golding's novel, *Lord of the Flies*

themselves against one another as two rival factions are formed - one embodying the values of the civilization left behind, the other embracing the savagery of their new environment until ultimately, one young man stands alone against an entire band of boy savages. Filmed in Jamaica, the movie is based on Nobel laureate Sir William Golding's classic novel.
CD: Released Jun '90, on Silva Screen by Silva Screen Records. Catalogue no: **FILMCD 067**
Cass: Released Jun '90, on Silva Screen by Silva Screen Records. Catalogue no: **FILMC 067**

Lord Of The Rings

LORD OF THE RINGS (Film soundtrack) (Various artists)
Note: Composed by Leonard Rosenman.
2 LP Set: Released '79, on Fantasy by Ace Records. Deleted '84. Catalogue no: **LORD 11/12**
2 LP Set: Released Jan '89, on Silva Screen by Silva Screen Records. Catalogue no: **LOR 1**

Los Lobos

LA BAMBA
Tracks: / La Bamba / Charlena / Rip it up (Extra track on 12").
Note: Title track of the film La Bamba starring Lou Diamond Phillips as Richie Valens.
7" Single: Released Jul '87, on Slash by London Records Ltd. Deleted Oct '88. Catalogue no: **LASH 13**
Cassingle: Released Jul '87, on Slash by London Records Ltd. Deleted May '89. Catalogue no: **LASCS 13**
12" Single: Released Jul '87, on Slash by London Records Ltd. Deleted Oct '88. Catalogue no: **LASHX 13**

Loss, Joe

MAIGRET THEME (TV Theme)
Tracks: / Maigret theme.
7" Single: Released Mar '62, on H.M.V. by EMI Records. Deleted '65. Catalogue no: **POP 995**

Lost Boys

LOST BOYS (Film soundtrack) (Various artists)
Tracks: / To the shock of Miss Louise: Various artists / Good times: Various artists / Lost in the shadows: Various artists / Don't let

the sun go down on me: Various artists / Laying down the law: Various artists / People are strange: Various artists / Cry little sister: Various artists / Power play: Various artists / I still believe: Various artists / Beauty has her way: Various artists.
CD: Released Aug '87, on Atlantic by WEA Records. Catalogue no: **781 767-2**
Album: Released Aug '87, on Atlantic by WEA Records. Catalogue no: **781 767-1**
Cass: Released Aug '87, on Atlantic by WEA Records. Catalogue no: **781 767-4**

LOST BOYS (Title track 'People are strange) (See under Echo & The Bunnymen)

Lost Empires

LOST EMPIRES (TV soundtrack) (Various artists)
Tracks: / Lost empires theme, The: Various artists / Army of today's alright, The: Various artists / Your king and country: Various artists / Pure white rose, A: Various artists / Somewhere: Various artists / Oh Flo: Various artists / They didn't believe me: Various artists / Wedding glide, The: Various artists / Cigar girl, The: Various artists / Honeysuckle and the bee, The: Various artists / Mother Machree: Various artists / Alexander's ragtime band: Various artists / Land of hope and glory: Various artists / Rule Britannia: Various artists / I don't want to play in your yard: Various artists / Yankee doodle boy: Various artists / Shine on harvest moon: Various artists / Love's old sweet song: Various artists / Trombone song, The: Various artists / Take me on the flip flap: Various artists / Nobody knows, nobody cares: Various artists / Mr. Knick Knock: Various artists / Poor little Dolly: Various artists / Waiting for the Robert E Lee: Various artists / Catari catari: Various artists / Nightingale and the star, The: Various artists / Julia's theme: Various artists.
Album: Released Nov '86, on T. E. R. by That's Entertainment Records. Catalogue no: **TER 1119**
Cass: Released Nov '86, on T. E. R. by That's Entertainment Records. Catalogue no: **ZCTER 1119**
CD: Released Nov '86, on T. E. R. by That's Entertainment Records.

Catalogue no: **CDTER 1119**

Lost In The Stars

LOST IN THE STARS (Original Broadway cast) (Various artists)
Cass: Released Jan '89, on MCA by MCA Records. Catalogue no: **MCAC 1535**
Album: Released Jan '89, on MCA by MCA Records. Catalogue no: **MCA 1535**

Louisiana (Film)

LOUISIANA (Original Soundtrack) (Various artists)
Cass: Released May '84, on CBS (import) by CBS Records & Distribution. Catalogue no: **40 71127**
Album: Released May '84, on CBS (import) by CBS Records & Distribution. Catalogue no: **CBS 71127**

Love At First Bite

LOVE AT FIRST BITE (Film soundtrack) (Various artists)
Album: Released '79, on Parachute (USA) Deleted '84. Catalogue no: **RRL 2008**

Love, Geoff

20 EXPLOSIVE TV THEMES (Love, Geoff & His Orchestra)
Tracks: / Theme from "Lillie" / Starsky and Hutch / Dick Barton / Crossroads / Muppet Show / Who pays the ferryman / Hawaii Five-O / Poldark / Charlie's Angels / All creatures great and small / Coronation Street / Nationwide.
Album: Released Apr '79, on EMI by EMI Records. Deleted Apr '84. Catalogue no: **NTS 168**

BIG BAND MOVIE THEMES (Love, Geoff & His Orchestra & Singers)
Album: Released Sep '75, on MFP by EMI Records. Deleted '80. Catalogue no: **MFP 50227**

BIG BIG MOVIE THEMES (Love, Geoff & His Orchestra & Singers)
Album: Released Apr '77, on MFP by EMI Records. Deleted '82. Catalogue no: **MFP 50321**

BIG LOVE MOVIE THEMES
Album: Released Sep '71, on MFP by EMI Records. Deleted '86. Catalogue no: **MFP 5221**

BIG TV THEMES ALBUM (Love, Geoff & His Orchestra)

Tracks: / Dynasty / Onedin Line / Chi Mai / Brideshead revisited / Hill Street Blues / Coronation Street / Eye level / Reilly / Edwardians / Dallas / Winds of war / Match of the day / Pink Panther / Thorn birds, The.

Album: Released Oct '84, on MFP by EMI Records. Deleted Oct '87. Catalogue no: **MFP 41 5684-1**

Cass: Released Oct '84, on MFP by EMI Records. Deleted Oct '87. Catalogue no: **MFP 41 5684 4**

BIG WAR MOVIE THEMES (Love, Geoff & His Orchestra)

Tracks: / Colonel Bogey / Lawrence of Arabia / Guns of Navarone / Battle of Britain theme / Longest Day, The / Where eagles dare, Theme from / 633 Squadron / Dambusters / Great escape, The / Green berets, The / Cavatina (From The Deer Hunter.) / Winds of war / Victory at sea extracts / We'll meet again / Is Paris burning? / Reach for the Sky.

Cass: Released Aug '86, on Hour Of Pleasure by EMI Records. Catalogue no: **HR 8140**

Album: Released Aug '71, on MFP by EMI Records. Deleted Aug '76. Catalogue no: **MFP 5171**

CD: Released May '88, on Compacts For Pleasure by Music For Pleasure Records. Catalogue no: **CDB 752 037 2**

CD: Released May '88, on Compacts For Pleasure by Music For Pleasure Records. Catalogue no: **CC 211**

BIG WESTERN MOVIE THEMES

Album: Released Aug '71, on MFP by EMI Records. Deleted Aug '76. Catalogue no: **MFP 5204**

CLASSIC T.V. THEMES (Love, Geoff & His Orchestra & Singers)

Tracks: / Colditz: *Love, Geoff & His Orchestra & Singers* / Edwardians, the: *Love, Geoff & His Orchestra & Singers* / Galloping home (Theme from Black Beauty): *Love, Geoff & His Orchestra & Singers* / Ironside: *Love, Geoff & His Orchestra & Singers* / Alias Smith and Jones: *Love, Geoff & His Orchestra & Singers* / Brothers, The: *Love, Geoff & His Orchestra & Singers* / World of sport: *Love, Geoff & His Orchestra & Singers* / Cheyenne..: *Love, Geoff & His Orchestra & Singers* / Sucu Sucu (Top Secret): *Love,*

Geoff & His Orchestra & Singers / Hawaii Five-O: *Love, Geoff & His Orchestra & Singers* / Bless this house: *Love, Geoff & His Orchestra & Singers* / Sleepy shores: *Love, Geoff & His Orchestra & Singers* / Crossroads: *Love, Geoff & His Orchestra & Singers* / Onedin line: *Love, Geoff & His Orchestra & Singers* / Match of the day: *Love, Geoff & His Orchestra & Singers* / Persuaders, The: *Love, Geoff & His Orchestra & Singers* / Bonanza: *Love, Geoff & His Orchestra & Singers* / We'll meet again: *Love, Geoff & His Orchestra & Singers* / Eye level: *Love, Geoff & His Orchestra & Singers* / Pink panther: *Love, Geoff & His Orchestra & Singers* / Dick Barton: *Love, Geoff & His Orchestra & Singers* / Return of the Saint: *Love, Geoff & His Orchestra & Singers* / Good word, The: *Love, Geoff & His Orchestra & Singers*.

Love In Las Vegas

LOVE IN LAS VEGAS (Film soundtrack) (See under Presley, Elvis)

Love Is A Funny Thing

LOVE IS A FUNNY THING (Original Soundtrack) (Various artists)

Note: Claude Lelouch (a man & a woman) film with Francis Lai score.

Cass: Released Jan '89, on MCA by MCA Records. Catalogue no: **MCAC 25111**

Album: Released Jan '89, on MCA by MCA Records. Catalogue no: **MCA 25111**

Love Me Or Leave Me

LOVE ME OR LEAVE ME (Original Soundtrack) (Various artists)

Note: Starring Doris Day.

Cass: Released Jan '89, on Silva Screen by Silva Screen Records. Catalogue no: **BT 8773**

Album: Released Jan '89, on Silva Screen by Silva Screen Records. Catalogue no: **ACS 8773**

Love Me Tender

LOVE ME TENDER (Film Soundtrack) (See under Presley, Elvis)

Love Songs

LOVE SONGS FROM THE SIL-

VER SCREEN (Various artists)

Tracks: / Gigi: *Jourdan, Louis* (From Gigi.) / Love is here to stay: *Kelly, Gene* (From An American In Paris.) / You were meant for me: *Kelly, Gene* (From Singing In The Rain.) / All I do is dream of you: *Kelly, Gene* (From Singing In The Rain.) / Almost like being in love: *Kelly, Gene* (From Birgadoon.) / So in love: *Keel, Howard/Kathryn Grayson* (From Kiss Me Kate.) / Why do I love you: *Keel, Howard/Kathryn Grayson* (From Show Boat.) / Make believe: *Keel, Howard/Kathryn Grayson* (From Show Boat.) / And this is my beloved: *Keel, Howard/Anne Blyth/Vic Damone* (From Kismet.) / Indian love call: *Blyth, Ann/Fernando Lamas* (From Rose Marie.) / When you're in love: *Keel, Howard, Jane Powell* (From Seven Brides for Seven Brothers.) / Stranger in paradise: *Blyth, Ann/Vic Damone* (From Kismet.) / Can't help lovin' dat man: *Gardner, Ava* (From Show Boat. CD only.) / Love of my life: *Garland, Judy* (From The Pirate. CD only.).

Cass: Released Oct '89, on MFP by EMI Records. Catalogue no: **TCMFP 5877**

Album: Released Oct '89, on MFP by EMI Records. Catalogue no: **MFP 5877**

CD: Released Oct '89, on MFP by EMI Records. Catalogue no: **CDB 793 247 2**

CD: Released Oct '89, on MFP by EMI Records. Catalogue no: **CDMFP 6081**

Love Songs

LOVE SONGS (Original Soundtrack) (Various artists)

Note: French film starring Christopher Lambert and Catherine Deneuvre. Music by Michel Legrand.

Album: Released Jan '89, on Silva Screen by Silva Screen Records. Catalogue no: **STV 81258**

Love Story

LOVE STORY (Original soundtrack) (Various artists)

Tracks: / Love story theme: *Various artists* / Snow frolic: *Various artists* / Sonata No.12 in F major: *Various artists* / I love you Phil: *Various artists* / Christmas tree, The: *Various artists* / Search for Jenny: *Various artists* / Bozo Bar-*

rett: *Various artists* / Skating in Central Park: *Various artists* / Long walk home: *Various artists* / Concerto No.3 in D major: *Various artists* / Love story finale (theme from Love Story: *Various artists* .
Note: Composed by Francis Lai.
Album: Released Feb '84, on MCA by MCA Records. Catalogue no: **MCL 1782**
Cass: Released Feb '84, on MCA by MCA Records. Catalogue no: **MCLC 1782**
Album: Released Jan '89, on MCA by MCA Records. Catalogue no: **MCA 27017**
Cass: Released Jan '89, on MCA by MCA Records. Catalogue no: **MCAC 27017**

LOVE STORY (ORIGINAL ISSUE) (Film Soundtrack) (Various artists)
Album: Released Apr '71, on Paramount Deleted '76. Catalogue no: **SPFL 267**

Lovely To Look At

LOVELY TO LOOK AT/SUMMER STOCK (Original Soundtrack) (Various artists)
Note: Starring Judy Garland, Kathryn Grayson, and Ann Miller. Summer Stock stars Harry Warren and Jerome Kern.
Album: Released Jan '89, on MCA by MCA Records. Catalogue no: **MCA 39084**
Cass: Released Jan '89, on MCA by MCA Records. Catalogue no: **MCAC 39084**

Loving You

LOVING YOU (Film soundtrack) (Presley, Elvis)
Tracks: / Mean woman blues / Teddy bear / Got a lot of livin' to do / Lonesome cowboy / Hot dog / Party / Blueberry Hill / True love / Don't leave me now / Have I told you lately that I love you? / I need you so / Loving you
Album: on RCA by BMG Records (UK). Catalogue no: **NL 81515**
Cass: on RCA by BMG Records (UK). Catalogue no: **NK 81515**
CD: on RCA by BMG Records (UK). Catalogue no: **ND 81515**
Album: Released Sep '77, on

RCA by BMG Records (UK). Catalogue no: **PL 42358**
Album: Released '57, on RCA by BMG Records (UK). Deleted '62. Catalogue no: **RC 24001**
Album: Released May '84, on RCA (Germany). Catalogue no: **130 251**
Album: Released Oct '81, on RCA International. Catalogue no: **INTS 5109**
Cass: Released 77, on RCA. Deleted 82. Catalogue no: **PK 42358**

LOVING YOU (VIDEO) (Various artists)
Note: Running time: 97 mins.
VHS: Released Sep '89, on Video Collection by Video Collection. Catalogue no: **VC 3311**

Lucky Luke

LUCKY LUKE (Film Soundtrack) (Various artists)
Tracks: / I'm a poor lonesome cowboy (Lucky Luke theme): *Various artists* / Lucky Luke special: *Various artists* / Daisy town theme: *Various artists* / Town comes to life: *Various artists* / Daisy town saloon song: *Various artists* / Way West: *Various artists* / Daisy town march: *Various artists* / Dalton theme: *Various artists* / Stamp your feet: *Various artists* / Duel: *Various artists* / Far West choo choo: *Various artists* / City life: *Various artists* / Battle: *Various artists* / I'm a poor lonesome cowboy (Lucky Luke theme): *Various artists*.
Album: Released '73, on United Artists by EMI Records. Deleted '78. Catalogue no: **UAS 29290**

Lullaby of Broadway

LULLABY OF BROADWAY (Various artists)
Tracks: / Lullaby of Broadway: *Various artists* / I found a million dollar baby: *Various artists* / Dancing in the dark: *Various artists* / You're the cream in my coffee: *Various artists* / Body and soul: *Various artists* / Exactly like you: *Various artists* / Broadway melody: *Various artists* / Black bottom: *Various artists* / Sleepy time girl:

Various artists / It had to be you: *Various artists* / I'm just wild about Harry: *Various artists* / September song: *Various artists* / Chinatown my Chinatown: *Various artists* / San Francisco: *Various artists*.
Album: Released Apr '87, on Meteor by Magnum Music Group. Catalogue no: **MTLP 1009**

LULLABY OF BROADWAY (VIDEO) (Various artists)
Note: Famous songs from Doris Day at her best. Running time: 89 minutes.
VHS: Released Jun '89, on Warner Home Video by WEA Records. Catalogue no: **PES 11866**

Lulu

MAN WITH THE GOLDEN GUN (See under 'Man with the golden gun')

Lurie, John

DOWN BY LAW (1987 film soundtrack)
Album: Released 30 May '87, on Made To Measure by Crammed Discs. Catalogue no: **MTM 14**
Cass: Released '87, on Made To Measure by Crammed Discs. Catalogue no: **MTM 14C**
CD: Released '87, on Made To Measure by Crammed Discs. Catalogue no: **MTM 14CD**

STRANGER THAN PARADISE (Film soundtrack)
Album: Released Mar '86, on Made To Measure by Crammed Discs. Catalogue no: **MTM 7**
CD: Released '88, on Made To Measure by Crammed Discs. Catalogue no: **MTM 7CD**

Lynott, Phil

YELLOW PEARL
Tracks: / Yellow pearl / Girls.
Note: Intro music to 'Top Of The Pops' during the early 80's.
7" Single: Released Dec '81, on Vertigo by Phonogram Ltd. Catalogue no: **SOLO 3**
12" Single: Released Dec '81, on Vertigo by Phonogram Ltd. Deleted '85. Catalogue no: **SOLO 312**

M

The following information was taken from the Music Master database on September 25th, 1990.

MacArthur

MACARTHUR (Film Soundtrack) (Various artists)
Note: Jerry Goldsmith score for the Gregory Peck film.
Album: Released Jan '89, on Silva Screen by Silva Screen Records. Catalogue no: **255088 1**

MacBeth

MACBETH (VIDEO) (Various artists)
VHS: Released '88, on Screen Legends (video) by Pickwick Video. Catalogue no: **SLL 7017**
VHS: Released '88, on Virgin by Virgin Records. Catalogue no: **VVD 384**

McCartney, Paul

GIVE MY REGARDS TO BROAD STREET (Film Soundtrack)
Tracks: / No more lonely nights / Good day sunshine / Corridor music / Yesterday / Here there and everywhere / Wanderlust / Ballroom dancing / Silly love songs / Silly love songs (Reprise) / Not such a bad boy / So bad / No values / No more lonely nights (reprise) / For no one / Eleanor Rigby / Eleanor's dream / Long and winding road, The / No more lonely nights (play out version) / Goodnight princess.
Note: Digital stereo recording.
CD: Released Oct '84, on Parlophone by EMI Records. Catalogue no: **CDP 746 043 2**
Cass: Released Oct '84, on Parlophone by EMI Records. Catalogue no: **EL 2602780**
Album: Released Oct '84, on Parlophone by EMI Records. Catalogue no: **PCTC 2**
Cass: Released Oct '84, on Parlophone by EMI Records. Catalogue no: **TC PCTC 2**
Album: Released Oct '84, on Parlophone by EMI Records. Catalogue no: **EL 2602781**

GIVE MY REGARDS TO

BROAD STREET (VIDEO)
VHS: Released '88, on CBS-Fox by CBS-Fox Video. Catalogue no: **144850**

NO MORE LONELY NIGHTS
Tracks: / No more lonely nights.
Note: From the film 'Give My Regards To Broad Street'.
7" Single: Released Sep '84, on Parlophone by EMI Records. Catalogue no: **R 6080**
12" Single: Released Sep '84, on Parlophone by EMI Records. Catalogue no: **12R 6080**

RUPERT AND THE FROG SONG
Beta: Released '88, on Virgin Vision by Virgin Records. Catalogue no: **VVC 109 B**
VHS: Released '88, on Virgin Vision by Virgin Records. Catalogue no: **VVC 109**

SPIES LIKE US
Tracks: / Spies like us.
Note: Theme tune to the film of the same name starring Chevy Chase and Dan Ackroyd.
7" Single: Released Nov '85, on Parlophone by EMI Records. Deleted Oct '87. Catalogue no: **R 6118**
7" Pic: Released Dec '85, on Parlophone by EMI Records. Deleted Oct '87. Catalogue no: **RP 6118**
12" Pic: Released Dec '85, on Parlophone by EMI Records. Catalogue no: **12RP 6118**
12" Single: Released Nov '85, on Parlophone by EMI Records. Deleted Oct '87. Catalogue no: **12R 6118**

WE ALL STAND TOGETHER (McCartney, Paul & The Frog Chorus)
Tracks: / We all stand together / We all stand together (humming version).
Note: From the animated featurette Rupert and the Frog Chorus.
7" Single: Released Nov '85, on

Parlophone by EMI Records. Catalogue no: **R 6086**
7" Single: Released Nov '85, on Parlophone by EMI Records. Deleted '88. Catalogue no: **RP 6086**

McDonald, Michael

OUR LOVE
Tracks: / Our love / Don't let me down / Bad times (Extra track on 12" version).
Note: From the film 'No Mercy' starring Richard Gere and Kim Basinger.
7" Single: Released Mar '87, on Warner Bros. by WEA Records. Deleted Jan '88. Catalogue no: **W 8596**
12" Single: Released Mar '87, on Warner Bros. by WEA Records. Deleted Jan '88. Catalogue no: **W 8596T**

SWEET FREEDOM
Tracks: / Sweet freedom / Freedom lights,The.
Note: From the film *Running Scared*.
7" Single: Released Aug '86, on MCA by MCA Records. Catalogue no: **MCA 1073**

McFerrin, Bobby

DON'T WORRY BE HAPPY
Tracks: / Don't worry be happy (LP version) / Simple pleasures / From me to you (CD single only.) / Don't worry be happy (7" version).
Note: From the film 'Cocktail' starring Tom Cruise.
12" Single: Released Sep '88, on EMI-Manhattan by EMI Records. Deleted Oct '89. Catalogue no: **12MT 56**
7" Single: Released Sep '88, on EMI-Manhattan by EMI Records. Deleted May '90. Catalogue no: **MT 56**
CD Single: Released Sep '88, on EMI-Manhattan by EMI Records. Deleted Jun '89. Catalogue no: **CDMT 56**

McHugh, David

THREE FUGITIVES (See under Three Fugitives)

McHugh, Jimmy

JACK THE RIPPER (Original Film Soundtrack) (McHugh, Jimmy & Pete Rugolo)
Album: Released Jun '88, on Fresh Sounds (Spain) by Fresh Sounds Records (Spain). Catalogue no: **FS 334**

MacJunior, Peter

WATER MARGIN, THE
Tracks: / Water margin, The.
7" Single: Released Oct '77, on BBC by BBC Records. Deleted '80. Catalogue no: **RESL 50**

Mack & Mabel

MACK & MABEL (Original Broadway cast) (Various artists)
Tracks: / Overture: Orchestra / Movies were movies: Preston, Robert / Look what happened to Mabel: Mack & Mabel / Big time: Kirk, Lisa / I won't send roses: Preston, Robert / I wanna make the world laugh: Preston, Robert / Wherever he ain't: Peters, Bernadette / Hundreds of girls: Preston, Robert & The Bathing Beauties / When Mabel comes in the room: Simmonds, Stanley / My heart leaps up: Preston, Robert / Time heals everything: Peters, Bernadette / Tap your troubles away: Kirk, Lisa / I promise you a happy ending: Preston, Robert.
Cass: Released Oct '82, on MCA by MCA Records. Catalogue no: **MCLC 1728**
Album: Released Oct '82, on MCA by MCA Records. Catalogue no: **MCL 1728**

MACK & MABEL IN CONCERT (Various artists)
Cass: Released May '88, on First Night by First Night Records. Catalogue no: **CASTC 13**
Album: Released May '88, on First Night by First Night Records. Catalogue no: **CAST 13**
CD: Released May '88, on First Night by First Night Records. Catalogue no: **CASTCD 13**

MacRae, Gordon

MOTION PICTURE SOUND-STAGE
Tracks: / Singin' in the rain / Danc-ing in the dark / You're a swee-theart / Cabin in the sky / Hooray for love / Love is a many splen-doured thing / Jealousy / Pennies from Heaven / Laura / Easy to love / Flirtation walk / Goodnight Swee-theart.
Note: Orchestra conducted by: Van Alexander
Cass: Released Oct '86, on Capitol by EMI Records. Deleted Aug '89. Catalogue no: **TCEMS 1183**
Album: Released Oct '86, on Capitol by EMI Records. Deleted Aug '89. Catalogue no: **EMS 1183**

McTell, Ralph

BEST OF ALPHABET ZOO
Tracks: / Zoo zoo zoo / Albert the albatross / Fergus the frog / Gor-don the goat / Holly the hedgehog / Impala song / Kenny the kanga-roo / Maurice the mole / Nigel the Nightingale / Ollie the otter / Peter the parrot / Sally the seal / Tammy the tortoise / Victor the vulture / X ray fish / Yuri the yak / Zoe the zebra.
Album: Released Sep '84, on MFP by EMI Records. Deleted Sep '87. Catalogue no: **MFP 4156741**
Cass: Released Sep '84, on MFP by EMI Records. Deleted Sep '87. Catalogue no: **MFP 4156744**

TICKLE ON THE TUM (TV soundtrack) (McTell, Ralph & Jacqui Redding)
Album: Released Nov '86, on Mays by Mays Records. Cata-logue no: **TPG 008**
Cass: Released Nov '86, on Mays by Mays Records. Catalogue no: **TPGC 008**

McVicar

(See also under Daltrey, Roger)

MCVICAR (VIDEO) (Various artists)
VHS: Released Oct '89, on Spec-trum (1) Catalogue no: **SPC 00252**

Mad Max (Film)

MAD MAX (Film soundtrack) (Various artists)
Note: Composed by Brian May.
CD: Released Jan '89, on Silva Screen by Silva Screen Records. Catalogue no: **VCD 47144**
Album: Released Jan '89, on Silva Screen by Silva Screen Rec-ords. Catalogue no: **STV 81144**

MAD MAX 2 (Film soundtrack) (Various artists)
Tracks: / Opening titles: Various artists / Montage: Various artists / Confrontation: Various artists / Ma-rauder's massacre: Various artists / Max enters compound: Various artists / Feral boy strikes: Various artists / Gyro saves Max: Various artists / Gyro flight: Various artists / Break out: Various artists / Chase continues, The: Various artists / Finale and largo: Various artists / End titles: Various artists.
Album: Released Mar '82, on T. E. R. by That's Entertainment Records. Catalogue no: **TER 1016**
CD: Released Jan '89, on Silva Screen by Silva Screen Records. Catalogue no: **VCD 47262**

MAD MAX - BEYOND THE THUNDERDOME (Film soundtrack) (Various artists)
Tracks: / We don't need another hero: Turner, Tina / One of the living: Turner, Tina / We don't need another hero (inst): Turner, Tina / Batertown: Various artists / Child-ren, The: Various artists / Coming home: Various artists.
Cass: Released Aug '85, on Capi-tol by EMI Records. Catalogue no: **EJ 240380 4**
Album: Released Aug '85, on Capitol by EMI Records. Cata-logue no: **DOME 1**
Album: Released Aug '85, on Capitol by EMI Records. Cata-logue no: **EJ 240380 1**
Cass: Released Aug '85, on Capi-tol by EMI Records. Catalogue no: **TCDOME 1**

Madame Sousatzka

MADAME SOUSATZKA (Film soundtrack) (Various artists)
Note: Music by Gerald Gouriet. Film starring Shirley MacLaine.
Album: Released Dec '88, on Take 7 Catalogue no: **VS 5204**
Cass: Released Jan '89, on Take 7 Catalogue no: **VSC 5204**
CD: Released Dec '88, on Take 7 Catalogue no: **VSD 5204**

Made In Heaven (film)

MADE IN HEAVEN (Film soundtrack) (Various artists)
Note: Composed by Mark Isham.
CD: Released Jan '89, on Silva Screen by Silva Screen Records. Catalogue no: **960729.2**
Cass: Released Jan '89, on Silva

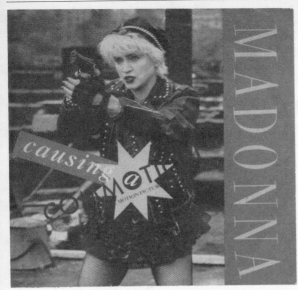

Madonna - 'Causing a Commotion' from *Who's that Girl* (Sire)

Screen by Silva Screen Records. Catalogue no: **960729.4**
Album: Released Jan '89, on Silva Screen by Silva Screen Records. Catalogue no: **960729.1**

Madness

IT MUST BE LOVE
Tracks: / It must be love / Shadow on the house.
Note: Featured in the film 'The Tall Guy' starring Jeff Goldblum/Rowan Atkinson/Emma Thompson.
7" Single: Released Nov '81, on Stiff by Stiff Records. Catalogue no: **BUY 134**

Madonna

CAUSING A COMMOTION
(See picture above)
Tracks: / Causing a commotion / Jimmy Jimmy / Causing a commotion (silver screen mix) (Only on 12" single.) / Causing a commotion (movie house mix) (Only on 12" single.).
Note: From the film *Who's That Girl*.
Cassingle: Released Sep '87, on Warner Bros. by WEA Records. Deleted Jul '88. Catalogue no: **W 8224C**

12" Pic: Released Sep '87, on Warner Bros. by WEA Records. Deleted Jul '88. Catalogue no: **W 8224TP**
Cassingle: Released Nov '87, on Sire (import) Catalogue no: **207624**
7" Single: Released Sep '87, on Warner Bros. by WEA Records. Deleted Jan '90. Catalogue no: **W 8224**
12" Single: Released Sep '87, on Warner Bros. by WEA Records. Deleted Jan '90. Catalogue no: **W 8224T**

CRAZY FOR YOU
Tracks: / Crazy for you / Gambler, The.
Note: From the film *Vision Quest*.
7" Single: Released Nov '87, on Geffen (USA import) by Geffen Records (USA). Catalogue no: **GGEF 0540**
12" Single: Released Jun '85, on Geffen by Geffen Records (USA). Deleted '85. Catalogue no: **WA 6323P**
7" Single: Released Jun '85, on Geffen by Geffen Records (USA). Catalogue no: **A 6323**

GAMBLER
Tracks: / Gambler, The / Gambler,

The (instrumental).
Note: From the film *Vision Quest*.
12" Single: Released Oct '85, on Geffen by Geffen Records (USA). Deleted '88. Catalogue no: **TA 6585**
7" Single: Released Oct '85, on Geffen by Geffen Records (USA). Deleted '88. Catalogue no: **QA 6585**
7" Single: Released Oct '85, on Geffen by Geffen Records (USA). Deleted '88. Catalogue no: **A 6585**

HANKY PANKY
Tracks: / Hanky panky / More.
Note: From the film *Dick Tracy*.
7" Single: Released Jul '90, on Sire by Sire Records. Catalogue no: **W 9789**
CD Single: Released Jul '90, on Sire by Sire Records. Catalogue no: **W 9789 CD**
12" Single: Released Jul '90, on Sire by Sire Records. Catalogue no: **W 9789 T**
Cassingle: Released Jul '90, on Sire by Sire Records. Catalogue no: **W 9789 C**
12" Pic: Released Jul '90, on Sire by Sire Records. Catalogue no: **W 9789 TP**

I'M BREATHLESS
Note: From the film *Dick Tracy*.
CD: Released May '90, on Sire by Sire Records. Catalogue no: **7599262092**
Cass: Released May '90, on Sire by Sire Records. Catalogue no: **WX 351 C**
CD: Released May '90, on Sire by Sire Records. Catalogue no: **WX 351 CD**
Album: Released May '90, on Sire by Sire Records. Catalogue no: **WX 351**

INTO THE GROOVE
Tracks: / Shoo-bee-doo / Into the groove / Everybody (Only on 12" single.).
Note: Featured in the film 'Desperately Seeking Susan' starring Madonna and Rosanna Arquette.
12" Single: Released Sep '87, on Sire by Sire Records. Catalogue no: **920352 0**
7" Pic: Released Jul '85, on Sire by Sire Records. Deleted '85. Catalogue no: **W 8934P**
7" Single: Released Jul '85, on Warner Bros. by WEA Records. Catalogue no: **W 8934**

12" Single: Released Jul '85, on Warner Bros. by WEA Records. Deleted Jan '88. Catalogue no: **W 8934 T**

Special: Released Jul '85, on Warner Bros. by WEA Records. Catalogue no: **W 9405 T**

LIVE TO TELL

Tracks: / Live to tell / Live to tell (inst) / Live to tell (Edit).

Note: From the film *At Close Range*.

12" Pic: Released '86, on Sire by Sire Records. Deleted Jun '87. Catalogue no: **W 8717 TP**

12" Single: Released Jul '88, on Sire by Sire Records. Catalogue no: **920461 0**

12" Single: Released '86, on Sire by Sire Records. Deleted Jan '90. Catalogue no: **W 8717 T**

7" Single: Released '86, on Sire by Sire Records. Deleted Jan '90. Catalogue no: **W 8717**

LOOK OF LOVE

Tracks: / Look of love, The / I know it / Love don't live here anymore.

12" Pic: Released Nov '87, on Sire by Sire Records. Catalogue no: **W 8115TP**

12" Single: Released Nov '87, on Sire by Sire Records. Catalogue no: **W 8115T**

7" Single: Released Nov '87, on Sire by Sire Records. Deleted Jan '90. Catalogue no: **W 8115**

WHO'S THAT GIRL

Tracks: / Who's that girl / White heat.

Note: From the film of the same name.

Cassingle: Released Nov '87, on Sire by Sire Records. Catalogue no: **206924**

12" Single: Released Jul '87, on Sire by Sire Records. Deleted Jan '90. Catalogue no: **W 8341T**

7" Single: Released Jul '87, on Sire by Sire Records. Deleted Jan '90. Catalogue no: **W 8341**

12" Pic: Released Jul '87, on Sire by Sire Records. Deleted '87. Catalogue no: **W 8341TP**

Maggie May

MAGGIE MAY (Original London cast) (Various artists)

Tracks: / Overture: *Various artists* / Ballad of the Liver bird, The: *Various artists* / Lullaby: *Various artists* / I love a man: *Various artists* /

Casey: *Various artists* / Dey don't do dat t'day: *Various artists* / I told you so: *Various artists* / Right of way: *Various artists* / Land of promises, The: *Various artists* / Maggie Maggie May: *Various artists* / Stroll on: *Various artists* / Leave her, Johnny leave her: *Various artists* / I told you so: *Various artists* / Shine, you swine: *Various artists* / World's a lovely place, The: *Various artists* / I'm me: *Various artists* / It's yourself: *Various artists* / We don't all wear d'same size boots: *Various artists* / Finale: *Various artists*.

Album: Released Apr '83, on T. E. R. by That's Entertainment Records. Catalogue no: **TER 1046**

Cass: Released Apr '83, on T. E. R. by That's Entertainment Records. Catalogue no: **ZCTER 1046**

Maggots

MAGGOTS (See under O'Williams, Wendy)

Magic of Lassie

MAGIC OF LASSIE (film soundtrack) (Various artists)

Tracks: / When you're loved: *Various artists* / There'll be other Friday nights: *Various artists* / Brass rings and daydreams: *Various artists* / Nobody's property: *Various artists* / I can't say goodbye: *Various artists* / Banjoy song: *Various artists* / Rose is not a rose, A: *Various artists* / Travelin' music: *Various artists* / That hometown feeling: *Various artists* / Thanksgiving prayer: *Various artists* / Nobody's property: *Various artists*.

Cass: Released May '79, on Pickwick by Pickwick Records. Catalogue no: **HSC 370**

Album: Released May '79, on Hallmark by Pickwick Records. Catalogue no: **SHM 992**

Magic Toyshop

MAGIC TOYSHOP, THE (Film soundtrack) (Various artists)

Cass: Released Aug '87, on T. E. R. by That's Entertainment Records. Catalogue no: **ZCTER 1138**

Album: Released Aug '87, on T. E. R. by That's Entertainment Records. Catalogue no: **TER 1138**

Magical Mystery Tour

MAGICAL MYSTERY TOUR

(See under Beatles)

Magnificent Obsession

MAGNIFICENT OBSESSION (Film Soundtrack) (Various artists)

Note: Composed by Frank Skinner.

Album: Released Jan '89, on Varese Sarabande Records(USA) by Varese Sarabande Records (USA). Catalogue no: **STV 81118**

Magnificent Seven

(See also under Bernstein, Elmer)

MAGNIFICENT SEVEN / RETURN OF THE SEVEN (Film soundtrack) (Various artists)

Tracks: / Magnificent Seven, The: *Various artists* / Bandidos: *Various artists* / Return of the seven: *Various artists* / Defeat: *Various artists* / Mariachis de Mexico: *Various artists* / El toro: *Various artists* / Journey, The: *Various artists* / Council: *Various artists* / Petra's declaration: *Various artists* / In the trap: *Various artists* / Battle: *Various artists* / Finale: *Various artists*.

Album: Released May '85, on EMI by EMI Records. Deleted Nov '88. Catalogue no: **EG 2605811**

Cass: Released May '85, on EMI by EMI Records. Deleted Nov '88. Catalogue no: **EG 2605814**

Album: Released '73, on Sunset (Liberty) by EMI Records. Deleted '78. Catalogue no: **SLS 50171**

MAGNIFICENT SEVEN, THE (Various artists)

Tracks: / Loan shark: *Various artists* / King rat: *Various artists* / Piledriver boogie: *Various artists* / PVC chair: *Various artists* / Pervy in the park: *Stingrays* / June rhyme: *Various artists* / Gimme the drugs: *Various artists* / Whip it up: *Various artists* / Blue sunshine: *Various artists* / Axe attack: *Various artists* / Johnny remember me: *Various artists* / I see red: *Various artists* / Mexican radio (Frenzy): *Various artists* / Girl invisible, The (Restless): *Various artists* / Vanish without a trace: *Various artists* / After midnight (Restless): *Various artists*.

Album: Released '87, on ABC (indie) Catalogue no: **ABCLP 9**

Magnum P.I.
(See also under Post, Mike)
MAGNUM P.I. (The American TV hits album) (Caine, Daniel Orchestra)
Tracks: / Mike Hammer / Lou Grant / Cagney and Lacey / Rockford files, The / Taxi / Bill Cosby show / Cheers / Hill Street blues / Hollywood wives / St. Elsewhere / Simon and Simon.
Cass: Released Nov '86, on Indiana by Indiana Records. Catalogue no: **ATVC 5555**
Album: Released Nov '86, on Indiana by Indiana Records. Catalogue no: **ATVP 5555**

Mahabharata
MAHABHARATA (Film soundtrack) (Various artists)
Tracks: / Nibiro ghono andare: Various artists / Draupadi: Various artists / Ontoro momo: Various artists / Satvati: Various artists / Virata: Various artists / Bushi ok sudure: Various artists / Cities: Various artists / Bhima: Various artists / Markandeya (part 1): Various artists / Duryodhana: Various artists / Dhire: Various artists / Markandeya (part 2): Various artists / Svetasvatara upanisad: Various artists.
Album: Released Jan '90, on Real World Catalogue no: **RWLP 9**
Cass: Released Jan '90, on Real World Catalogue no: **RWMC 9**
CD: Released Jan '90, on Real World Catalogue no: **RWCD 9**

Mahogany
MAHOGANY (Film soundtrack) (Various artists)
Tracks: / Do you know where you're going to?: Ross, Diana / Feeling again: Various artists / You don't ever have to be alone: Various artists / Can you hear it in my music ?: Various artists / Christian's theme: Various artists / After you: Various artists / My hero is a gun: Various artists / Cat fight: Various artists / Erucu: Various artists / Let's go back to day one: Various artists / Tracy: Various artists / She's the ideal girl: Various artists / Sweets (and other things): Various artists / Mahogany suite: Various artists.
Cass: Released Nov '82, on Motown by BMG Records (UK). Catalogue no: **CSTMS 5082**

Album: Released Nov '82, on Motown by BMG Records (UK). Catalogue no: **STMS 5082**
MAHOGANY (SINGLE) (See under Ross, Diana)

Maigret
MAIGRET (See under Loss, Joe)

Main Event (Film)
MAIN EVENT (Film Soundtrack) (Various artists)
Tracks: / Main event: Various artists / Fight: Various artists / Body shop: Various artists / Copeland meets the Coasters: Various artists / Get a job: Various artists / Big girls don't cry: Various artists / It's your foot again: Various artists / Angry eyes: Various artists / I'd clean a fish for you: Various artists.
Note: Music from the Barbra Streisand film.
Album: Released Sep '79, on CBS by CBS Records & Distribution. Deleted '84. Catalogue no: **CBS 70171**
Cass: Released Jan '89, on Silva Screen by Silva Screen Records. Catalogue no: **JST 36115**
Cass: Released Sep '79, on CBS by CBS Records & Distribution. Deleted '84. Catalogue no: **CBS 40 70171**
Album: Released Jan '89, on Silva Screen by Silva Screen Records. Catalogue no: **JS 36115**
Album: Released May '79, on K-Tel by K-Tel Records. Catalogue no: **NE 1046**

Majella
ON THE INSIDE (TV theme)
Tracks: / On the inside / Amazing grace.
7" Single: Released Nov '88, on Igus by Klub Records. Catalogue no: **KLUB 55**

Majestics (TV)
TUTTI FRUTTI (Songs from the TV series)
Tracks: / Almost grown / Rockin' through the rye / No particular place to go / Promised land / Rip it up / Bye, bye love / Great balls of fire / Tutti frutti / Love is strange / That'll be the day / You're sixteen / Love hurts / Almost grown/ Tutti frutti.
Note: From the BBC TV Series.
Cass: Released Mar '87, on BBC by BBC Records. Catalogue no:

ZCN 629
Album: Released Mar '87, on BBC by BBC Records. Catalogue no: **REN 629**

Major League
MAJOR LEAGUE (Film Soundtrack) (Various artists)
Tracks: / Wild thing: X / Cryin' shame: Lovett, Lyle / Walkaway: Snakes / Hideaway: Beat Farmers / How can the girl refuse: Beckett / U.S. male: Lonesome Romeos / Trial & error (inst. score): Various artists / Pennant fever (inst. score): Various artists / Most of all you: Medley, Bill.
Cass: Released Sep '89, on RCA by BMG Records (UK). Catalogue no: **ZK 74277**
Album: Released Sep '89, on RCA by BMG Records (UK). Catalogue no: **ZL 74277**
CD: Released Sep '89, on RCA by BMG Records (UK). Catalogue no: **ZD 74277**

Majors, Lee
UNKNOWN STUNTMAN
Tracks: / Unknown stuntman / Lust in a lady's eyes.
Note: From the TV series 'The Fall Guy'.
7" Single: Released Feb '83, on Scotti Bros (USA) by WEA Records. Catalogue no: **SCT A 3117**

Make Me An Offer
MAKE ME AN OFFER (Original London Cast) (Various artists)
Album: Released Jan '89, on Silva Screen by Silva Screen Records. Catalogue no: **AEI 1112**

MAKE ME AN OFFER (ORIGINAL ISSUE) (London cast) (Various artists)
Album: Released May '60, on H.M.V. by EMI Records. Deleted '65. Catalogue no: **CLP 1333**

Making Of Thriller
MAKING OF THRILLER, THE (See under Jackson, Michael)

Making The Grade
MAKING THE GRADE (Film soundtrack) (Various artists)
Note: Composed by Basil Poledouris.'
Album: Released Jan '89, on Varese Sarabande Records(USA) by Varese Sarabande Records

(USA). Catalogue no: **STV 81204**

Maltese Falcon (Film)

MALTESE FALCON, THE (Film Soundtrack) (Various artists)
Album: Released Jan '89, on Silva Screen by Silva Screen Records. Catalogue no: **MR 1091**

Mame

MAME (Original Broadway cast) (Various artists)
Album: Released Jan '89, on CBS (import) by CBS Records & Distribution. Deleted Mar '90. Catalogue no: **PS 3000**
Cass: Released Jan '89, on CBS (import) by CBS Records & Distribution. Catalogue no: **PST 3000**
CD: Released Jan '89, on CBS (import) by CBS Records & Distribution. Catalogue no: **CK 03000**

MAME (VIDEO) (Various artists)
Note: Lucille Ball as the eccentric Auntie Mame. Running time: 127 minutes. Cert: PG.
VHS: Released Jun '89, on Warner Home Video by WEA Records. Catalogue no: **PES 61100**

Man & A Woman

MAN AND A WOMAN (Film Soundtrack) (Various artists)
Tracks: / Man and a woman, A: *Various artists* / Stronger than us: *Various artists* / Today it's you: *Various artists* / 124 miles an hour: *Various artists* / Samba: *Various artists* / Today it's you (aujourd'hui c'est toi): *Various artists* / Shadows of our love: *Various artists*.
Cass: Released Feb '90, on Silva Screen by Silva Screen Records. Catalogue no: **1831844**
Album: Released '76, on Sunset (Liberty) by EMI Records. Deleted '79. Catalogue no: **SLS 50409**
Album: Released Jul '67, on United Artists by EMI Records. Deleted '72. Catalogue no: **SULP 1155**
Album: Released Feb '90, on Silva Screen by Silva Screen Records. Catalogue no: **1831841**

Man From Snowy River

MAN FROM SNOWY RIVER (Film soundtrack) (Various artists)
Note: Australian western with

music by Bruce Rowland.
CD: Released Jan '89, on Silva Screen by Silva Screen Records. Catalogue no: **VCD 47217**
Cass: Released Jan '89, on Silva Screen by Silva Screen Records. Catalogue no: **CTV 81167**
Album: Released Jan '89, on Silva Screen by Silva Screen Records. Catalogue no: **STV 81167**

Man In Love

MAN IN LOVE, A (UN HOMME AMOUREUX) (Original Soundtrack) (Various artists)
Note: Composed by Georges Delerue.
Album: Released Jan '89, on Silva Screen by Silva Screen Records. Catalogue no: **240801.1**

Man In The Wilderness

MAN IN THE WILDERNESS (Film Soundtrack) (Various artists)
Tracks: / Main title (Capt. Henry theme): *Various artists* / Zach discovers water: *Various artists* / Shadows of Reckerys: *Various artists* / Zach makes his bed: *Various artists* / Zach's music box: *Various artists* / Zach bass theme: *Various artists* / Zach meets Redthorn: *Various artists* / Zach goes for Henry: *Various artists* / Finale (Zach bass theme): *Various artists*.
Album: Released '73, on Atlantic by WEA Records. Deleted '78. Catalogue no: **K 46126**

Man Of A Thousand

MAN OF A THOUSAND FACES (Film soundtrack) (Various artists)
Album: Released '88, on Varese Sarabande Records(USA) by Varese Sarabande Records (USA). Catalogue no: **STV 81121**

Man Of La Mancha

MAN OF LA MANCHA (Original London Cast) (Various artists)
2 LP Set: on MCA by MCA Records. Catalogue no: **MCA 2 10010**
MAN OF LA MANCHA (Film soundtrack) (Various artists)
Tracks: / Overture: *Various artists* / Man of La Mancha (I, Don Quixote): *Various artists* / It's all the same: *Various artists* / Dulcinea: *Various artists* / I'm only thinking of him: *Various artists* / I really like

him: *Various artists* / Barber's song: *Various artists* / Golden helmet of Mambrino: *Various artists* / Little bird, little bird: *Various artists* / Impossible dream: *Various artists* / Dubbing: *Various artists* / Life as it really is: *Various artists* / Man of La Mancha: *Various artists* / Aldonza: *Various artists* / Little gossip: *Various artists* / Dulcinea: *Various artists* / Impossible dream (reprise): *Various artists*.
CD: Released Jun '88, on MCA (USA) by MCA Records (USA). Catalogue no: **31065**
Album: Released '73, on United Artists by EMI Records. Deleted '78. Catalogue no: **UAG 29422**
Album: Released Nov '82, on MCA by MCA Records. Catalogue no: **MCL 1722**

MAN OF LA MANCHA (VIDEO) (Various artists)
Note: Cert: PG.
VHS: Released Jun '89, on Warner Home Video by WEA Records. Catalogue no: **PES 99456**

Man On Fire

MAN ON FIRE (Film soundtrack) (Graunke Symphony Orchestra)
Note: Composed by John Scott.m
Album: Released Jan '89, on Silva Screen by Silva Screen Records. Catalogue no: **STV 81343**
CD: Released Jan '89, on Silva Screen by Silva Screen Records. Catalogue no: **VCD 47314**
Cass: Released Jan '89, on Silva Screen by Silva Screen Records. Catalogue no: **CTV 81343**

Man Who Loved

MAN WHO LOVED CAT DANCING (Various artists)
VHS: Released '88, on MGM/UA (Video) by MGM/UA Video. Catalogue no: **SMV 103638**

Man With Golden Arm

MAN WITH THE GOLDEN ARM, THE (Original soundtrack) (Various artists) (See also under Harris, Jet)
Note: Composed by Elmer Bernstein.
CD: Released Aug '88, on Trax by Filmtrax Records. Deleted Jan '90. Catalogue no: **MODEMCD 1013**
Album: Released Jan '89, on

MCA by MCA Records. Catalogue no: **MCA 1526**

Cass: Released Jan '89, on MCA by MCA Records. Catalogue no: **MCAC 1526**

Cass: Released Aug '88, on Trax by Filmtrax Records. Deleted Jan '90. Catalogue no: **MODEMC 1013**

Album: Released Aug '88, on Trax by Filmtrax Records. Deleted Jan '90. Catalogue no: **MODEM 1013**

Man With Golden Gun

MAN WITH THE GOLDEN GUN, THE (Film Soundtrack) (Various artists)

Note: Score by John Barry featuring Lulu.

Cass: Released Jan '89, on EMI (Import) Catalogue no: **E 41 E 90619**

CD: Released Jan '89, on EMI (Import) Catalogue no: **CDP 90619**

Mancini, Henry

ARABESQUE (See under Arabesque)

AT THE MOVIES

Tracks: / Moon river / Pink panther / Peter Gunn / Good, the bad and the ugly, The / Midnight cowboy / Magnificent seven, The / How soon / Shot in the dark / Dear heart / Seventy-six trombones / Days of wine and roses / Shaft, Theme from / Raindrops keep falling on my head.

Album: Released Sep '86, on MFP by EMI Records. Deleted '88. Catalogue no: **MFP 5778**

Cass: Released Sep '87, on MFP by EMI Records. Deleted Apr '90. Catalogue no: **TCMFP 5778**

BEST OF HENRY MANCINI (Mancini, Henry & His Orchestra)

Tracks: / You'll never know / Stella by starlight / Love is a many splendoured thing / Charade / Mona Lisa / Moonlight serenade / Whatever will be will be / Raindrops keep falling on my head / As time goes by / Over the rainbow / Romeo and Juliet love theme / Midnight cowboy / Gigi / Peter Gunn.

Cass: Released Jan '84, on RCA/Camden by BMG Records (UK). Catalogue no: **770 4065**

Album: Released Jan '84, on RCA/Camden by BMG Records (UK). Catalogue no: **107 4065**

MOON RIVER

Tracks: / Moon river.

Note: From the film ' Breakfast At Tiffany's'.

7" Single: Released Dec '61, on RCA by BMG Records (UK). Deleted '64. Catalogue no: **RCA 1256**

NIGHT VISITOR (Film Soundtrack)

Album: Released Mar '79, on Citadel (USA) by Varese Sarabande Records (USA). Catalogue no: **CT 6015**

PINK PANTHER (See under Pink Panther)

RETURN OF THE PINK PANTHER, THE (Mancini, Henry & His Orchestra)

Tracks: / Pink Panther, Theme from / Greatest gift (instrumental), The / Here's looking at you, kid / Summer in Gstaad / So smooth / Return of the Pink Panther, The / Greatest gift (vocal), The / Orange float, The / Dreamy / Disco / Navel manoeuvre / Belly belly, bum bum / Wet look, The.

Album: Released '79, on RCA by BMG Records (UK). Deleted '84. Catalogue no: **RS 1010**

THEME SCENE (Mancini, Henry & His Orchestra)

Tracks: / Heaven can wait / Battlestar Galactica / Little house on the prairie / Fantasy Island / Star Trek / Three's company / Children of Sanchez / Cheap detective / NBC nightly news theme / Once is not enough.

Album: Released '79, on RCA by BMG Records (UK). Deleted '84. Catalogue no: **PL 13052**

THORN BIRDS (Mancini, Henry & His Orchestra)

Tracks: / Thorn birds / Thorn Birds - love theme (Double A-side).

7" Single: Released Aug '86, on WEA by WEA Records. Deleted Jun '87. Catalogue no: **YZ 83**

7" Single: Released Feb '84, on Warner Bros. by WEA Records. Deleted '87. Catalogue no: **9677**

TOUCH OF EVIL, A (Original Soundtrack)

Album: Released Feb '88, on Fresh Sounds (Spain) by Fresh Sounds Records (Spain). Catalogue no: **FS 293**

TRAIL OF THE PINK PANTHER (See under Trail Of...)

TWO FOR THE ROAD (See under Two For The Road)

Mandel, Johnny

RUSSIANS ARE COMING (See under Russians Are Coming)

Manhattan (Film)

MANHATTAN (Film soundtrack) (Various artists)

Tracks: / Rhapsody in blue: *Various artists* / Someone to watch over me: *Various artists* / I've got a crush on you: *Various artists* / Embraceable you: *Various artists* / Land of the gay cabellaro: *Various artists* / Do do do: *Various artists* / S'wonderful: *Various artists* / Mine: *Various artists* / He loves and she loves: *Various artists* / Bronco busters: *Various artists* / Lady be good: *Various artists* / Love is here to stay: *Various artists* / Sweet and low down: *Various artists* / Blue blue blue: *Various artists* / But not for me: *Various artists* / Strike up the band: *Various artists* / Love is sweeping the country: *Various artists*.

Cass: Released '79, on CBS by CBS Records & Distribution. Catalogue no: **40 73875**

Album: Released '79, on CBS by CBS Records & Distribution. Catalogue no: **73875**

CD: Released Jun '87, on CBS by CBS Records & Distribution. Catalogue no: **MK 36020**

Mantovani

AT THE THEATRE

Tracks: / C'est magnifique (Not on CD.) / I feel pretty (Not on CD.) / Hey there / Out of my dreams / I've grown accustomed to her face / Almost like being in love / Hello, Dolly / They say it's wonderful / I've never been in love before / Edelweiss / What kind of fool am I / Do-ra-me / Whatever Lola wants / Shall we dance / Stranger in Paradise / Tonight / Maria / Somewhere / As long as he needs me / Ascot gavotte (Not on CD.) / Where is love / Mr. Wonderful (Not on CD.) / 76 trombones / Wunderbar / Embraceable you (Not on CD.) / Climb every mountain / If I were a rich man (Not on CD.) / Windmills of your mind / Summertime / Sunrise sunset (Not on CD.) / You'll never walk alone / How are things in Glocca Morra / Carousel waltz,

The.

Cass: Released Oct '89, on Horatio Nelson by Horatio Nelson Records & Tapes Ltd.. Catalogue no: **CSIV 1108**

CD: Released Oct '89, on Horatio Nelson by Horatio Nelson Records & Tapes Ltd.. Catalogue no: **CDSIV 6108**

2 LP Set: Released Oct '89, on Horatio Nelson by Horatio Nelson Records & Tapes Ltd.. Catalogue no: **SIV 1108**

FAVOURITE SCREEN THEMES (Mantovani & His Orchestra)

Tracks: / Tara's theme / Secret love / True love / Exodus theme / Days of wine and roses, The / Alfie / Wand'rin star / On a clear day you can see forever / Over the rainbow / Edelweiss / Moon river / When you wish upon a star / As long as he neede me / Gigi / Lara's theme / As time goes by.

Cass: Released Apr '90, on Pickwick by Pickwick Records. Catalogue no: **CN4 2106**

CD: Released Apr '90, on Pickwick by Pickwick Records. Catalogue no: **PWK128**

FILM ENCORES

Cass: Released May '71, on Decca by Decca International. Deleted '88. Catalogue no: **KSKC 4002**

FILM FAVOURITES

Cass set: Released May '80, on Decca by Decca International. Deleted '88. Catalogue no: **KDKC 2 8114**

2 LP Set: Released May '80, on Decca by Decca International. Deleted '88. Catalogue no: **DKL 105**

FILM THEMES

Tracks: / Moon river (Not on CD) / Love is a many splendoured thing / Never on a Sunday / Laura / Born free / Limelight / Over the shadow / Gigi (Not on CD) / On a clear day / Man and a woman / Hello young lovers / Que sera sera / Secret love / High and mighty / Days of wine and roses / Exodus / True love / High noon / Be my love / Hi-lilli hi-lo / Tammy (Not on CD) / I could have danced all night / Moulin Rouge theme / This is my song / Around the world / September song / Intermezzo / When you wish upon a star (Not on CD).

CD: Released Oct '89, on Horatio Nelson by Horatio Nelson Records & Tapes Ltd.. Catalogue no: **CDSIV 6105**

Cass: Released Oct '89, on Horatio Nelson by Horatio Nelson Records & Tapes Ltd.. Catalogue no: **CSIV 105**

2 LP Set: Released Oct '89, on Horatio Nelson by Horatio Nelson Records & Tapes Ltd.. Catalogue no: **SIV 105**

KISMET

Tracks: / Overture / Sands of time / Rhymes have I / Fate / Baubles, bangles and beads / Not since Nineveh / Stranger in paradise / He's in love / Night of my nights / Gesticulate / Was I Wazir / Rahadiakum / And this is my beloved / Olive tree / Zubbediya / Samaris dance / Kismet (finale).

Cass: Released Sep '79, on Decca by Decca International. Deleted May '82. Catalogue no: **KDGC 3**

Album: Released Sep '79, on Gold Crown by Decca Records. Deleted May '82. Catalogue no: **DGS 3**

MORE MANTOVANI FILM ENCORES

CD: Released Oct '87, on London Records by London Records Ltd. Deleted 1 Mar '89. Catalogue no: **820 469-2**

MUSIC FILMS

CD: Released Nov '87, on London Records by London Records Ltd. Catalogue no: **820 462-2**

Cass: Released Oct '70, on Decca by Decca International. Catalogue no: **KSKC 4014**

THEATRE FAVOURITES

Tracks: / C'est magnifique / I feel pretty / Hey there / Out of my dreams / I've grown accustomed to her face / Almost like being in love / Till there was you / Hello Dolly / They say it's wonderful / Maria / Somewhere / As long as he needs me / Sunrise, sunset / Where is love / Mr. Wonderful / Seventy-six trombones / Wunderbar / I've never been in love before / Gigi / Edelweiss / Hello young lovers / What kind of fool am I / Do-re-mi / Whatever Lola wants (Lola gets) / I could have danced all night / Shall we dance / Stranger in paradise / Tonight / Climb every mountain.

Cass set: Released Jan '80, on

Decca by Decca International. Deleted '88. Catalogue no: **KDKC2 8115**

2 LP Set: Released Jan '80, on Decca by Decca International. Deleted '88. Catalogue no: **DKL 106**

MOVIE HITS (Manuel & The Music of the Mountains)

Tracks: / Cavatina / You light up my life / As time goes by / Princess Leia's theme / Way we were / Evergreen / Moon river / Love story / What are you doing the rest of your life? / Romance / Can you read my mind / Raindrops keep fallin'.

Album: Released '79, on EMI by EMI Records. Deleted '84. Catalogue no: **NTS 172**

NEVER ON SUNDAY (Manuel & The Music of the Mountains)

Tracks: / Never on Sunday.

7" Single: Released Oct '60, on Columbia by EMI Records. Deleted '63. Catalogue no: **DB 4515**

PRINCESS LEIA'S THEME (Manuel & The Music of the Mountains)

Tracks: / Princess Leia's theme / Mountain fire.

7" Single: Released Jan '78, on EMI International by EMI Records. Deleted '81. Catalogue no: **EMI 2743**

THEME FROM HONEYMOON (Manuel & The Music of the Mountains)

Tracks: / Honeymoon, Theme from.

7" Single: Released Aug '59, on Columbia by EMI Records. Deleted '62. Catalogue no: **DB 4323**

MARIE WARD (Film Soundtrack) (Various artists)

Note: Composed by Elmer Bernstein.

Album: Released Jan '89, on Varese Sarabande Records(USA) by Varese Sarabande Records (USA). Catalogue no: **STV 81268**

Album: Released Sep '86, on Colosseum (West Germany) Catalogue no: **CST 8015**

MARIGOLD (Original London Cast) (Various artists)

Album: Released Jan '89, on Silva Screen by Silva Screen Records. Catalogue no: **AEI 1120**

Marjorie Morningstar

MARJORIE MORNINGSTAR (Film soundtrack) (Various artists)
Note: Score by Max Steiner.
Album: Released Jan '89, on Silva Screen by Silva Screen Records. Catalogue no: **LOC 1005**

Markopoulos, Yannis

WHO PAYS THE FERRYMAN
Cass: Released May '78, on BBC by BBC Records. Deleted '85. Catalogue no: **ZCF 315**
Album: Released Aug '78, on BBC by BBC Records. Deleted Aug '83. Catalogue no: **REB 315**
WHO PAYS THE FERRYMAN (SINGLE)
Tracks: / Who pays the ferryman.
7" Single: Released Dec '77, on BBC by BBC Records. Deleted '80. Catalogue no: **RESL 51**

Married To The Mob

MARRIED TO THE MOB (Film soundtrack) (Various artists)
Album: Released Jul '89, on WEA by WEA Records. Deleted Jul '90. Catalogue no: **925 163 1**
Cass: Released Jul '89, on WEA by WEA Records. Deleted Jul '90. Catalogue no: **925 163 4**
CD: Released Jul '89, on WEA by WEA Records. Catalogue no: **925 163 2**

M/A/R/R/S

PUMP UP THE VOLUME
Tracks: / Pump up the volume / Anitina (first time I see she dance).
Note: Featured in the film 'My Stepmother Is An Alien' starring Dan Ackroyd and Kim Basinger.
12" Single: Released Sep '87, on 4AD by 4AD Records. Deleted Jul '88. Catalogue no: **BAD 707**
7" Single: Released Sep '87, on 4AD by 4AD Records. Deleted Jul '88. Catalogue no: **AD 707**
12" Single: Released Sep '87, on 4AD by 4AD Records. Deleted Jul '88. Catalogue no: **BAD 707R**

CD Single: Released Oct '87, on 4AD by 4AD Records. Deleted Jul '88. Catalogue no: **BAD 707 CD**

Marry Me A Little

MARRY ME A LITTLE (Original Broadway Cast) (Various artists)
Tracks: / Saturday night: *Various artists* / Two fairy tales: *Various artists* / Can that boy foxtrot: *Various artists* / All things bright and beautiful: *Various artists* / Bang: *Various artists* / All things bright and beautiful (part 2): *Various artists* / Girls of summer, The: *Various artists* / Uptown, downtown: *Various artists* / So many people: *Various artists* / Your eyes are blue: *Various artists* / Moment with you, A: *Various artists* / Marry me a little: *Various artists* / Happily ever after: *Various artists* / Pour le sport: *Various artists* / Silly people: *Various artists* / There won't be trumpets: *Various artists* / It wasn't mean't to happen: *Various artists* / Who could be blue: *Various artists* / Little white house: *Various artists*.
Album: Released Jan '89, on Silva Screen by Silva Screen Records. Catalogue no: **AGL 1 7142**
CD: Released Apr '90, on RCA by BMG Records (UK). Catalogue no: **GD 87142**
Cass: Released Jan '89, on Silva Screen by Silva Screen Records. Catalogue no: **AGK 1 7142**
Cass: Released Apr '90, on RCA by BMG Records (UK). Catalogue no: **GK 87142**

Martin, Dean

RIO BRAVO
Tracks: / Rio Bravo.
Note: Taken from the film *Rio Bravo*
7" Single: Released Apr '83, on EMI (France) by EMI Records. Catalogue no: **2C 008 81168**

Martin, Juan

THORN BIRDS - LOVE THEME (Martin, Juan & Royal Philharmonic Orchestra)
Tracks: / Thorn Birds - love theme / Last farewell.

7" Single: Released Jan '84, on WEA by WEA Records. Deleted '87. Catalogue no: **X 9518**

Martin, Steve

DENTIST
Tracks: / Dentist.
Note: From the film '*The Little Shop Of Horrors*' starring Rick Moranis, Steve Martin, James Belushi, Bill Murray and the voice of Levi Stubbs.
7" Single: Released Jan '84, on Geffen by Geffen Records (USA). Deleted Jan '88. Catalogue no: **GEF 20**

Martinez, Cliff

SEX, LIES AND VIDEOTAPE (See under Sex, Lies & Videotape)

Marvin

MARVIN (Marvin The Paranoid Android)
Tracks: / Marvin / Metal man.
Note: Marvin is a character from the popular TV comedy series by Douglas Adams, "*The Hitch-Hikers Guide To The Galaxy*".
7" Single: Released May '81, on Polydor by Polydor Ltd. Deleted '84. Catalogue no: **POSP 261**

Marvin, Lee

WAND'RIN STAR
Tracks: / Wand'rin' star / I talk to the trees.
Note: From the film 'Paint Your Wagon'.
7" Single: Released Jul '80, on MCA by MCA Records. Catalogue no: **MCA 703**
7" Single: Released Feb '70, on Paramount Deleted '73. Catalogue no: **PARA 3004**

Marvin & Tige

MARVIN AND TIGE (Film Soundtrack) (Various artists)
Album: Released Dec '83, on Capitol by EMI Records. Catalogue no: **EST 7123071**
Cass: Released Dec '83, on Capitol by EMI Records. Catalogue no: **TCEST 7123074**

Mary Poppins featuring Julie Andrews (HMV)

Marx Brothers

3 HOURS, 59 MINUTES, 51 SECONDS
LP Set: Released Oct '79, on Record & Tape Sales* Deleted '85. Catalogue no: **931680**

EVERYONE SAYS I LOVE YOU
Tracks: / Everyone says I love you.
7" Single: Released Dec '81, on MCA by MCA Records. Deleted Dec '84. Catalogue no: **MCA 758**

MOVIE MADNESS (Selections from their films)
Album: Released Jan '89, on Silva Screen by Silva Screen Records. Catalogue no: **MR 1097**

Marx, Groucho

ON THE RADIO
Album: Released Jan '89, on Silva Screen by Silva Screen Records. Catalogue no: **MR 1072**

Mary Poppins

MARY POPPINS (Film soundtrack) (Various artists) (See picture above)
Tracks: / Overture: *Various artists* / Perfect nanny, The: *Various artists* / Sister suffragette: *Various artists* / Life I lead, The: *Various artists* / Spoonful of sugar, The: *Various artists* / Pavement artist: *Various artists* / Jolly holiday: *Various artists* / Supercallifragilisticexpiallidocious: *Various artists* / Stay awake: *Various artists* / I love to laugh: *Various artists* / British bank, A: *Various artists* / Feed the birds (tuppence a bag): *Various artists* / Fidelity fiduclay bank: *Various artists* / Chim chim cher ee: *Various artists* / Step in time: *Various artists* / Man has dreams, A: *Various artists* / Let's go fly a kite: *Various artists*.
Album: Released Oct '84, on Walt Disney Deleted '88. Catalogue no: **REH 535**
Album: Released Dec '82, on Disneyland by Disneyland-Vista Records (USA). Catalogue no: **D 3922**
LP Pic: Released Dec '82, on Disneyland by Disneyland-Vista Records (USA). Catalogue no: **D 3104**
Cass: Released Dec '82, on Disneyland by Disneyland-Vista Records (USA). Catalogue no: **D 12DC**
Mini-LP: Released Dec '82, on Disneyland by Disneyland-Vista Records (USA). Catalogue no: **D 302**

Cass: Released Oct '84, on Walt Disney Deleted '88. Catalogue no: **ZCR 535**

MARY POPPINS (Film soundtrack) (Various Artists)
Tracks: / Overture: *Various artists* / Perfect nanny: *Various artists* / Sister suffragette: *Various artists* / Life I lead, The: *Various artists* / Spoonful of sugar, A: *Various artists* / Pavement artist, The: *Various artists* / Jolly holiday: *Various artists* / Super-cali-fragil-istic-expi-ali-docious: *Various artists* / Stay awake: *Various artists* / I love to laugh: *Various artists* / British bank, A: *Various artists* / Feed the birds: *Various artists* / Fidelity fiduciary bank: *Various artists* / Chim chim cheree: *Various artists*.
Cass: Released Dec '87, on Walt Disney Catalogue no: **WDC 100**
Album: Released Aug '82, on Disneyland by Disneyland-Vista Records (USA). Catalogue no: **D 5005**
Album: Released Dec '87, on Walt Disney Catalogue no: **WD 100**

MARY POPPINS (ORIGINAL ISSUE) (Film soundtrack) (Various artists)
Album: Released Jan '65, on H.M.V. by EMI Records. Deleted '67. Catalogue no: **CLP 1794**

Mary Queen Of Scots

MARY QUEEN OF SCOTS (Film soundtrack) (Various artists)
Tracks: / Mary's theme: *Various artists* / Vivre et mourir: *Various artists* / But not through my realm: *Various artists* / Journey to Scotland: *Various artists* / Black knight: *Various artists* / Escape with Bothwell: *Various artists* / Mary's theme: *Various artists* / Journey to England: *Various artists* / Death at Kirk O'Fields: *Various artists* / March to the castle: *Various artists* / Mary at Chartley: *Various artists* / Execution: *Various artists* / Reprise - Vivre et Mourir: *Various artists* / Mary's theme: *Various artists*.
Note: Score by John Barry.
Album: Released Jan '89, on Silva Screen by Silva Screen Records. Catalogue no: **255 099.1**
Album: Released '73, on MCA by MCA Records. Deleted '78. Catalogue no: **MUPS 441**
CD: Released Nov '89, on Trax by

Filmtrax Records. Deleted Apr '90. Catalogue no: **NVLCD 108**

M.A.S.H.

M*A*S*H* (Original Soundtrack) (Various artists)
Cass: Released Mar '90, on Silva Screen by Silva Screen Records. Catalogue no: **PST 32753**
Album: Released '84, on CBS by CBS Records & Distribution. Catalogue no: **31842**
Cass: Released '84, on CBS by CBS Records & Distribution. Catalogue no: **40 31842**

M.A.S.H. (SUICIDE IS PAINLESS) (OLD GOLD)
Tracks: / M.A.S.H., Theme / MASH march.
7" Single: Released Jan '88, on Old Gold by Old Gold Records. Catalogue no: **OG 9759**

M.A.S.H., THEME FROM
Tracks: / M.A.S.H., Theme from.
7" Single: Released Apr '80, on CBS by CBS Records & Distribution. Catalogue no: **CBS 8536**

Massey, Howard

(POP QUIZ) SATURN STOMP
Tracks: / (Pop quiz) Saturn stomp / Red hot.
7" Single: Released Jul '81, on EMI by EMI Records. Deleted '84. Catalogue no: **EMI 5214**

Master Of The Game

MASTER OF THE GAME (Television Soundtrack) (Various artists)
Album: Released Sep '84, on BBC by BBC Records. Deleted '88. Catalogue no: **REB 521**

Master Of The Islands

MASTER OF THE ISLANDS (Original Film Soundtrack) (Various artists)
Tracks: / Theme from Master of the islands: *Various artists* / Auntie's theme: *Various artists* / Pineapple pirates: *Various artists* / Music for a Japanese bath: *Various artists* / Quiet thoughts: *Various artists* / Fumiko: *Various artists* / Molaka: *Various artists* / Street of Chinatown: *Various artists* / Theme from Master of the islands: *Various artists* / Auntie's theme (end title): *Various artists*.
Album: Released '73, on United Artists by EMI Records. Deleted '78. Catalogue no: **UAS 29122**

Mata Hari

MATA HARI (Film soundtrack) (Various artists)
Note: Wilfred Joseph's score for the Sylvia Kristel film.
Album: Released May '85, on SPI Milan (France) Catalogue no: **ACH 020**

Matador (Film)

MATADOR (Original soundtrack) (Various artists)
Tracks: / Overture: *Various artists* / There's no way out of here: *Various artists* / To be a Matador: *Various artists* / I was born to me: *Various artists* / Only other people: *Various artists* / Manolete, Belmonte, Joselito.: *Various artists* / Boy from nowhere, A: *Various artists* / Wake up Madrid: *Various artists* / I'll take you out to dinner: *Various artists* / This incredible journey: *Various artists* / Don't be deceived: *Various artists* / I'll dress you in mourning: *Various artists* / Dance with death: *Various artists* / Panama hat, A: *Various artists*.
Cass: Released Jun '87, on Epic by CBS Records & Distribution. Catalogue no: **VIVA C 1**
Album: Released Jun '87, on Epic by CBS Records & Distribution. Catalogue no: **VIVA 1**
CD: Released Jun '87, on Epic by CBS Records & Distribution. Catalogue no: **VIVA CD 1**

Maurice (Film)

MAURICE (Original soundtrack) (Various artists)
Album: Released Nov '87, on RCA by BMG Records (UK). Deleted Jul '89. Catalogue no: **BL 86618**
CD: Released Nov '87, on RCA by BMG Records (UK). Deleted Jul '89. Catalogue no: **BD 86618**
Cass: Released Nov '87, on RCA by BMG Records (UK). Deleted Jul '89. Catalogue no: **BK 86618**

Maximum Overdrive

MAXIMUM OVERDRIVE (See under AC/DC)

May, Billy

MAN WITH THE GOLDEN ARM, THEME FROM
Tracks: / Man with the golden arm, Theme from.
7" Single: Released Apr '56, on Capitol by EMI Records. Deleted

'59. Catalogue no: **CL 14551**

May, Simon

EASTENDERS
Tracks: / Eastenders / Julia's theme.
7" Single: Released Feb '85, on BBC by BBC Records. Deleted '87. Catalogue no: **RESL 160**

GLORY BE (Eastenders' hymn) (May, Simon Orchestra & Choir)
Tracks: / Glory be.
7" Single: Released Nov '88, on Polydor by Polydor Ltd. Deleted 30 May '89. Catalogue no: **RUR 2**

HOWARDS WAY
Tracks: / Howards way.
7" Single: Released Oct '85, on BBC by BBC Records. Deleted '88. Catalogue no: **RESL 174**

OLYMPIC THEME, THE
Tracks: / Olympic theme, The (ITV).
7" Single: Released 16 Sep '88, on Polydor by Polydor Ltd. Catalogue no: **RUR 1**
12" Single: Released 16 Sep '88, on Polydor by Polydor Ltd. Catalogue no: **RURX 1**

THEMES (May, Simon Orchestra)
CD: Released Feb '89, on Polydor by Polydor Ltd. Catalogue no: **837 613-2**
Cass: Released Feb '89, on Polydor by Polydor Ltd. Catalogue no: **837 613-4**

Mayfield, Curtis

SUPERFLY (Film soundtrack)
Tracks: / Little child runnin' wild / Freddie's dead / Give me your love / No thing on me / Superfly / Pusherman / Junkie chase / Eddie you should know / Think.
Album: Released Jun '88, on Ichiban by Ichiban Records (UK). Catalogue no: **CUR 2002**
Album: Released Sep '79, on RSO by Polydor Ltd. Deleted '84. Catalogue no: **RSS 5**
CD: Released Jun '88, on Ichiban by Ichiban Records (UK). Catalogue no: **CDCUR 2002**
Album: Released Mar '73, on Buddah by Buddah Records Inc.(USA). Deleted Mar '78. Catalogue no: **2318 065**
Cass: Released Jun '88, on Ichiban by Ichiban Records (UK). Catalogue no: **ZCCUR 2002**

Original London Cast Recording of *Me and my Girl* (Columbia)

Maytime

MAYTIME (Radio soundtrack) (Various artists)
Note: Starring Jeanette MacDonald and Nelson Eddy.
Cass: Released Jan '89, on Silva Screen by Silva Screen Records. Catalogue no: **CSH 2008**
Album: Released Jan '89, on Silva Screen by Silva Screen Records. Catalogue no: **SH 2008**

Me & My Girl

ME AND MY GIRL (London stage cast) (Various artists) (See picture above)
Tracks: / Overture: *Various artists* / Weekend at Hareford, A: *Various artists* / Thinking of no one but me: *Various artists* / Family solicitor, The: *Various artists* / Me and my girl: *Various artists* / English gentleman, An: *Various artists* / You would if you could: *Various artists* / Lambeth walk: *Various artists* / Sun has got his hat on, The: *Various artists* / Once you lose your heart: *Various artists* / Take it on the chin: *Various artists* / Song of Hareford: *Various artists* / Love makes the world go round: *Various artists*.
Album: Released Feb '85, on Columbia. Catalogue no: **EJ 2403011**
Cass: Released Feb '85, on Columbia. Catalogue no: **EJ 2403014**
CD: Released Apr '88, on MFP. Catalogue no: **CDMFP 6024**

ME AND MY GIRL (Original Broadway Cast) (Various artists)
Album: Released Nov '87, on T. E. R. Catalogue no: **TER 1145**
Cass: Released Nov '87, on T. E. R. Catalogue no: **ZCTER 1145**
CD: Released Oct '87, on T. E. R. Catalogue no: **CDTER 1145**

Me & The Colonel

ME AND THE COLONEL (Film Soundtrack) (Various artists)
Note: George Duning score for the Danny Kaye film.
Album: Released Jan '89, on Silva Screen by Silva Screen Records. Catalogue no: **LOC 1046**

Meatballs

MEATBALLS (Film soundtrack) (Various artists)
Tracks: / Are you ready for the summer?: *Camp North Star Kids Chorus* / Makin' it: *Naughton, David* / Moondust: *Black, Terry* / Good friend: *MacGregor, Mary* / Meatballs: *Dees, Rick* / CIT song: *Various artists* / Rudy and tripper: *Various artists* / Olympiad: *Various artists*.
Album: Released '80, on Polydor by Polydor Ltd. Deleted '85. Catalogue no: **RSS 11**

Meco

CLOSE ENCOUNTERS, THEME FROM
Tracks: / Close encounters, Theme from / Roman nights.
7" Single: Released '79, on RCA by BMG Records (UK). Deleted '82. Catalogue no: **XB 1039**

STAR WARS THEME
Tracks: / Star wars / Cantina Band / Funk.
7" Single: Released Oct '77, on RCA by BMG Records (UK). Deleted '80. Catalogue no: **XB 1028**

SUPERMAN AND OTHER GALLACTIC HEROES
Tracks: / Superman, Theme from / Boy wonder, The / Caped crusader, The / Lord of the jungle / Amazing Amazon.
Album: Released '79, on RCA by BMG Records (UK). Deleted '84. Catalogue no: **XL 13070**

SUPERMAN THEME
Tracks: / Superman theme / Superman love theme.
7" Single: Released Mar '79, on RCA by BMG Records (UK). Deleted Mar '82. Catalogue no: **XB 1073**

Medley, Bill

HE AIN'T HEAVY HE'S MY BROTHER
Tracks: / He ain't heavy he's my brother / Bridge, The / It's our destiny (Available on 12").
Note: From the film "*Rambo III*"
12" Single: Released 15 Aug '88, on Polydor by Polydor Ltd. Catalogue no: **PZ 10**
CD Single: on Polydor by Polydor Ltd. Catalogue no: **PZCD 10**
7" Single: Released 15 Aug '88, on Polydor by Polydor Ltd. Catalogue no: **PO 10**

I'VE HAD THE TIME OF MY LIFE (Medley, Bill & Jennifer Warnes)
Tracks: / I've had the time of my life / Love is strange.
Note: Featured in the film 'Dirty Dancing'.
7" Single: Released Oct '87, on

Megadeth - "No More Mr Nice Guy" from the film *Shocker* **(SBK)**

RCA by BMG Records (UK). Catalogue no: **PB 49625**

Medwin, Michael

SIGNATURE TUNE OF THE ARMY GAME (Medwin/Bresslaw/Bass/Fyson)
Tracks: / Army Game, signature tune.
7" Single: Released May '58, on H.M.V. by EMI Records. Deleted '61. Catalogue no: **POP 490**

Megadeth

NO MORE MR. NICE GUY (See picture above)
Tracks: / No more Mr. Nice Guy / Different breed / Demon bell (The ballad of Horace Pinker) (12",'s & CD single only.).
Note: Featured in the film 'Shocker' directed by Wes Craven.
12" Pic: Released Nov '89, on SBK by SBK Records. Deleted May '90. Catalogue no: **12SBKP 4**
12" Single: Released Nov '89, on SBK by SBK Records. Deleted May '90. Catalogue no: **203 620 6**
Cassingle: Released Nov '89, on SBK by SBK Records. Deleted May '90. Catalogue no: **203 620 4**
7" Single: Released Nov '89, on SBK by SBK Records. Deleted May '90. Catalogue no: **SBK 4**
Cassingle: Released Nov '89, on SBK by SBK Records. Deleted May '90. Catalogue no: **TCSBK 4**
CD Single: Released Nov '89, on SBK by SBK Records. Deleted May '90. Catalogue no: **CDSBK 4**
CD Single: Released Nov '89, on SBK by SBK Records. Deleted May '90. Catalogue no: **203 620 2**
7" Pic: Released Nov '89, on SBK by SBK Records. Deleted May '90. Catalogue no: **203 620 0**
12" Single: Released Nov '89, on SBK by SBK Records. Deleted May '90. Catalogue no: **12SBK 4**
7" Single: Released Nov '89, on SBK by SBK Records. Deleted May '90. Catalogue no: **203 620 7**
12" Pic: Released Nov '89, on SBK by SBK Records. Deleted May '90. Catalogue no: **203 620 8**
7" Pic: Released Nov '89, on SBK by SBK Records. Deleted May '90. Catalogue no: **SBKPD 4**

Mehmed My Hawk

MEHMED MY HAWK (Original Soundtrack) (Various artists)
Album: Released Mar '84, on T. E. R. by That's Entertainment Records. Catalogue no: **TER 1088**

Cass: Released Mar '84, on T. E. R. by That's Entertainment Records. Catalogue no: **ZCTER 1088**

Mehta, Zubin

STAR WARS (Los Angeles Philharmonic Orchestra)
Tracks: / Star Wars suite / Close encounters of the third kind (John Williams).
CD: Released Jun '88, on Decca by Decca International. Catalogue no: **CD 417 846 2**

Melancholia

MELANCHOLIA (Original Soundtrack) (Turner, Simon)
Tracks: / Holiday snaps and raincoat / Wrench and pull and blue / Flirt / Drinking at a stream / Butcher and Musak, The / Sergio electro / Bom, bom, bom / Sarah / Runner, The.
CD: Released Dec '89, on Silva Screen by Silva Screen Records. Catalogue no: **FILMCD 061**

Melody

MELODY (Film Soundtrack) (Various artists)
Tracks: / In the morning: *Various artists* / In the morning (reprise): *Various artists* / Melody fair: *Various artists* / Melody fair (reprise): *Various artists* / Spicks and specks: *Various artists* / Romance: *Various artists* / Theme in F: *Various artists* / Give your best: *Various artists* / To love somebody: *Various artists* / Working on it night and day: *Various artists* / First of May: *Various artists* / First of May (reprise): *Various artists* / Seaside banjo: *Various artists* / Teachers chase: *Various artists* / Teach your children: *Various artists*.
Cass: Released '73, on Polydor by Polydor Ltd. Deleted '78. Catalogue no: **3170 032**
Album: Released '73, on Polydor by Polydor Ltd. Deleted '78. Catalogue no: **2383 043**

PEOPLE LIKE YOU (TV theme) (Melody (and the Simon May orchestra))
Tracks: / People like you.
Note: Theme from the BBC TV program 'People'
7" Single: Released Jul '88, on BBC by BBC Records. Catalogue no: **RESL 225**

Original soundtrack to *Merry Christmas Mr Lawrence* (Virgin)

Melody Of Broadway
MELODY OF BROADWAY (Various artists)
Album: Released Jan '89, on Silva Screen by Silva Screen Records. Catalogue no: **AEI 1154**

Men In War
MEN IN WAR (Original Soundtrack) (Various artists)
Note: Elmer Bernstein score.
Album: Released Jan '89, on Silva Screen by Silva Screen Records. Catalogue no: **NA 240**

Mental As Anything
LIVE IT UP
Tracks: / Live it up / Good Friday.
Note: From the film *Crocodile Dundee*.
12" Single: Released Jan '87, on Epic by CBS Records & Distribution. Deleted Aug '87. Catalogue no: **ANUT 1**
12" Single: Released Mar '86, on Epic by CBS Records & Distribution. Deleted '87. Catalogue no: **TX 6797**
7" Pic: Released Mar '86, on Epic by CBS Records & Distribution. Deleted '86. Catalogue no: **WA 6797**

7" Single: Released Mar '86, on Epic by CBS Records & Distribution. Deleted '86. Catalogue no: **A 6797**
7" Single: Released Jan '87, on Epic by CBS Records & Distribution. Deleted Aug '87. Catalogue no: **ANY 1**

Mephisto
MEPHISTO (Film Soundtrack) (Various artists)
Album: Released Feb '89, on Wishbone Catalogue no: **WM 8850**

Mercury, Freddie
TIME (See under Time)

Merrill, Helen
RODGERS & HAMMERSTEIN ALBUM
Tracks: / It might as well be Spring / Hello young lovers / I have dreamed / People will say we're in love / Getting to know you / My lord and master / If I loved you / My favourite things / Sound of music, The.
Note: All songs written by: Richard Rogers & Oscar Hammerstein II.
Album: Released Apr '87, on DRG (USA) by DRG Records

(USA). Deleted Jan '89. Catalogue no: **SL 5204**
Cass: Released Apr '87, on DRG (USA) by DRG Records (USA). Catalogue no: **SLC 5204**

Merrily We Roll ..
MERRILY WE ROLL ALONG (Original Broadway Cast) (Various artists)
CD: Released Jan '89, on Silva Screen by Silva Screen Records. Catalogue no: **RCD 1 5840**
Album: Released Jan '89, on Silva Screen by Silva Screen Records. Catalogue no: **CBL 1 4197**
Cass: Released Jan '89, on Silva Screen by Silva Screen Records. Catalogue no: **CBK 1 4197**

Merry Christmas Mr...
MERRY CHRISTMAS MR. LAWRENCE (Original Soundtrack) (Sakamoto, Ryuichi & David Sylvian) (See picture on left)
Tracks: / Batavia / Germination / Hearty breakfast, A / Before the war / Seed and the sower, The / Brief encounter, A / Ride, ride, ride / Flight / Father Christmas / Dismissed / Assembly / Beyond reason / Sowing the seed / 23rd Psalm / Last regrets / Ride, ride, ride (reprise) / Seed, The / Forbidden colours / Merry Christmas Mr. Lawrence.
CD: Released Jul '86, on Virgin by Virgin Records. Catalogue no: **CDV 2276**
Album: Released Oct '83, on Virgin by Virgin Records. Deleted Feb '89. Catalogue no: **V 2276**
Cass: Released Oct '83, on Virgin by Virgin Records. Deleted Feb '89. Catalogue no: **TCV 2276**
Album: Released Apr '90, on Virgin by Virgin Records. Catalogue no: **OVED 237**
Cass: Released Apr '90, on Virgin by Virgin Records. Catalogue no: **OVEDC 237**

Merry Widow
MERRY WIDOW (Various artists)
Album: Released Jun '81, on Teldec (1) by ASV (Academy Sound & Vision). Catalogue no: **6.22992**
Cass: Released Jun '81, on Teldec (1) by ASV (Academy Sound & Vision). Catalogue no: **CH4 22992**

Metropolis - **Original London Cast (TER)**

MERRY WIDOW (Film soundtrack) (Various artists)
Tracks: / Merry widow waltz: *Various artists* / Maxim's: *Various artists* / Vilia: *Various artists* / Girls, girls, girls: *Various artists* / Night: *Various artists* / Gypsy music: *Various artists* / Can-can: *Various artists*.
Album: Released Feb '87, on CBS by CBS Records & Distribution. Deleted Jun '88. Catalogue no: **450231 1**
Cass: Released Feb '87, on CBS by CBS Records & Distribution. Deleted Jun '88. Catalogue no: **450231 4**

MERRY WIDOW, THE (Original Soundtrack) (Various artists)
Album: Released Jan '89, on Hollywood Soundstage (USA) Catalogue no: **HS 5015**

MERRY WIDOW, THE (Musical Operetta 86) (New Sadler's Wells Cast)
CD: Released Sep '86, on T. E. R. by That's Entertainment Records. Catalogue no: **CDTER 1111**

Album: Released Sep '86, on T. E. R. by That's Entertainment Records. Catalogue no: **TER 1111**
Cass: Released Sep '86, on T. E. R. by That's Entertainment Records. Catalogue no: **ZCTER 1111**

MERRY WIDOW, THE (Original Cast Recording) (Various artists)
Album: Released Oct '76, on Note by EMI Records. Deleted '79. Catalogue no: **NTS 103**

MERRY WIDOW, THE (Highlights) (Various artists)
CD: Released '89, on Classics For Pleasure by EMI Records. Catalogue no: **CDCFP 4485**
CD: Released '89, on Classics For Pleasure by EMI Records. Catalogue no: **CDB 762 630 2**
Cass: Released '89, on Classics For Pleasure by EMI Records. Catalogue no: **TCCFP 4485**

MERRY WIDOW, THE (VIDEO) (Various artists)
VHS: Released '88, on Virgin Vision by Virgin Records. Catalogue no: **VVD 390**

Message (Film)

MESSAGE, THE (Film soundtrack) (Jarre, Maurice)
CD: Released Feb '90, on Silva Screen by Silva Screen Records. Catalogue no: **FILMCD 060**

Metal Mickey

DO THE FUNKY ROBOT
Tracks: / Do the funky robot.
7" Single: Released Oct '82, on Mickeypops Catalogue no: **MET-MIK 3**

I WANT TO HOLD YOUR HAND
Tracks: / I want to hold your hand / Eugene machino.
7" Single: Released Mar '83, on Hollywood by Hollywood Records. Catalogue no: **HWD 008**

LOLLIPOP
Tracks: / Lollipop / Eugene Hollywood monster movie friend.
7" Single: Released Dec '78, on EMI by EMI Records. Deleted '81. Catalogue no: **EMI 2895**

METAL MICKEY MAGIC
Tracks: / Metal Mickey magic.
7" Single: Released Oct '82, on Mickeypops Catalogue no: **MET-MIK 1**

METAL MICKEY THEME
Tracks: / Metal Mickey theme / Fruit bat rap.
7" Single: Released Jan '83, on Hollywood by Hollywood Records. Catalogue no: **HWD 004**

SILLYCON CHIP
Tracks: / Sillycon chip.
7" Single: Released Oct '82, on Mickeypops Catalogue no: **MET-MIK 2**

Metropolis

METROPOLIS (Original London cast) (Various artists) (See picture above left)
Tracks: / One hundred and one point eleven / Hold back the night / Machines are beautiful, The / He's distant from me now / Elitist's dance / Oh my, what a beautiful city / This is the vision we're forbidden / Children of Metropolis / Fifty thousand pounds of power / One more morning / It's only love / Bring on the night / Pressure chant / Day after day / When Maria comes / You are the light / Girl is a witch, The / It's only love (reprise) /

Sun, The / Almost done / I don't need help from you / There's a girl down below / Futura / We're the cream / I've seen a nightmare / This is life / Look at this girl who stands before you / Futura's dance / Where do you think she's gone your precious / If that was love / Listen to me / Learning song / Old friends / When Maria wakes / Futura's promise / Maria's insane / Perfect face / Haven't you finished with me? / Let's watch the world go to the devil / One of those nights / Requiem / Metropolis / Finale.

2 LP Set: Released Jul '89, on T. E. R. Catalogue no: **TER2 1168**
Cass set: Released Jul '89, on T. E. R. Catalogue no: **ZCTER2 1168**
CD Set: Released Jul '89, on T. E. R. Catalogue no: **CDTER2 1168**

MGM Musicals

GREAT MGM HOLLYWOOD MUSICALS (Film Soundtracks) (Various artists)
CD: Released Jan '89, on Silva Screen by Silva Screen Records. Catalogue no: **CD 023**

THOSE MAGNIFICENT MGM MUSICALS Vol. 1 (1939-1952) (Various artists)
Tracks: / Over the rainbow: *Garland, Judy* (Wizard of Oz.) / Ol' man river: *Peterson, Caleb* (Till the clouds roll by.) / Look for the silver lining: *Garland, Judy* (Till the clouds roll by.) / Leave it to Jane and Cleopatra: *Allyson, June* (Till the clouds roll by.) / Can't help lovin' dat man: *Horne, Lena* (Till the clouds roll by.) / Who?: *Garland, Judy* (Till the clouds roll by.) / Best things in life are free: *Allyson, June/Peter Lawford* (Good news.) / Pass that peace pipe: *McCracken, Joan* (Good news.) / Lucky in love: *Marshall, Pat/Peter Lawford/June Allyson* (Good news.) / Varsity drag, The: *Allyson, June/Peter Lawford* (Good news.) / Steppin' out with my baby: *Astaire, Fred* (Easter parade) / Fella with an umbrella, A: *Garland, Judy/Peter Lawford* (Easter Parade.) / Shaking the blues: *Miller, Ann* (Easter Parade.) / Couple of swells, A: *Garland, Judy & Fred Astaire* (Easter Parade.) / Easter parade: *Garland, Judy & Fred As-taire* (Easter Parade.) / Manhattan: *Rooney, Mickey* (Words and music.) / Johnny one note: *Garland, Judy* (Words and music.) / Lady is a tramp, The: *Horne, Lena* (Words and music.) / I wish I were in love again: *Rooney, Mickey/Judy Garland* (Words and music.) / Where or when: *Horne, Lena* (Words and music.) / Thou swell: *Allyson, June* (Words and music.) / Be a clown: *Garland, Judy/Gene Kelly* (The Pirate.) / Love of my life: *Garland, Judy* (The Pirate.) / I don't care: *Garland, Judy* (In the good old summertime.) / Meet me tonight in dreamland: *Garland, Judy* (In the good old summertime.) / Play that barber shop chord: *Garland, Judy & The King's Men* (In the good old summertime.) / Last night when we were young: *Garland, Judy* (In the good old summertime.) / Put your arms around me honey: *Garland, Judy* (In the good old summertime.) / Merry Christmas: *Various artists* (In the good old summertime.) / Pagan love song: *Keel, Howard* (Pagan love song.) / House of singing bamboo: *Keel, Howard* (Pagan love song.) / Who's sorry now?: *De Haven, Gloria* (Three little words.) / I wanna be loved by you: *Kane, Helen* (Three little words.) / Nevertherless (I'm in love with you): *Astaire, Fred/Red Skelton/Anita Ellis* (Three little words.) / I love you so much: *Dahl, Arlene* (Three little words.) / Where did you get that girl: *Astaire, Fred/Anita Ellis* (Three little words.) / Get happy: *Garland, Judy* (Summer Stock (UK: If you feel like singing)) / Howdy neighbour happy harvest: *Garland, Judy* (Summer Stock (UK: If you feel like singing)) / You wonderful you: *Kelly, Gene* (Summer Stock (UK: If you feel like singing)) / Friendly star: *Garland, Judy* (Summer Stock (UK: If you feel like singing)) / Heavenly music: *Kelly, Gene/Phil Silvers* (Summer Stock (UK: If you feel like singing)) / If you feel like singing, sing: *Garland, Judy* (Summer Stock (UK: If you feel like singing)) / Dig-dig-dig-dig for your dinner: *Kelly, Gene/Phil Silvers* (Summer Stock (UK: If you feel like singing)) / Aba daba honeymoon: *Car-penter, Carleton/Debbie Reynolds* (Two weeks with love.) / By the light of the silvery moon: *Powell, Jane* (Two weeks with love.) / Row, row, row: *Carpenter, Carleton/Debbie Reynolds* (Two weeks with love.) / My hero: *Powell, Jane* (Two weeks with love.) / Ol' man river: *Warfield, William* (Showboat.) / Make believe: *Keel, Howard/Kathryn Grayson* (Showboat.) / I might fall back on you: *Champion, Marge & Gower* (Showboat.) / Can't halp lovin' dat man: *Gardner, Ava* (Showboat.) / Why do I love you: *Keel, Howard/Kathryn Grayson* (Showboat.) / Bill: *Gardner, Ava* (Showboat.) / Life upon the wicked stage: *Champion, Marge & Gower* (Showboat.) / You are love: *Keel, Howard/Kathryn Grayson* (Showboat.) / Wonder why?: *Powell, Jane* (Rich, young and pretty.) / Paris: *Lamas, Fernando* (Rich, young and pretty.) / I can see you: *Powell, Jane* (Rich, young and pretty.) / There's danger in your eyes, cherie: *Darrieux, Danielle* (Rich, young and pretty.) / Too late now: *Powell, Jane* (Royal wedding (UK: Wedding bells).) / Ev'ry night at seven: *Astaire, Fred* (Royal wedding (UK: Wedding bells).) / Happiest day of my life: *Powell, Jane* (Royal wedding (UK: Wedding bells).) / I left my hat in Haiti: *Astaire, Fred* (Royal wedding (UK: Wedding bells).) / You're all the world to me: *Astaire, Fred* (Royal wedding (UK: Wedding bells).) / How could you believe me when I said I love you: *Astaire, Fred/Jane Powell* (Royal wedding (UK: Wedding bells).) / 'S wonderful: *Kelly, Gene/Georges Guetary* (An American in Paris.) / Love is here to stay: *Kelly, Gene* (An American in Paris.) / I'll build a stgairway to paradise: *Guetary, Georges* (An American in Paris.) / I got rhythm: *Kelly, Gene* (An American in Paris.) / Singin' in the rain: *Kelly, Gene* (Singin' in the rain.) / Fit as a fiddle: *Kelly, Gene/Donald O'Connor* (Singin' in the rain.) / You were meant for me: *Kelly, Gene* (Singin' in the rain.) / Make 'em laugh: *O'Connor, Donald* (Singin' in the rain.) / Good morning: *Kelly, Gene/Donald O'Connor* (Singin' in

the rain.) / All I do is dream of you: *Kelly, Gene* (Singin' in the rain.) / Moses: *Kelly, Gene/Donald O'Connor* (Singin' in the rain.) / You are my lucky star: *Kelly, Gene/Debbie Reynolds* (Singin' in the rain.) / Oops: *Astaire, Fred* (Belle of New York.) / Naughty but nice: *Ellis, Anita* (Belle of New York.) / Seeing's believing: *Astaire, Fred* (Belle of New York.) / I wanna be a dancin' man: *Astaire, Fred* (Belle of New York.) / Everything I have is yours/Seventeen thousand telephones: *Astaire, Fred* (Everything I have is yours.) / Maxim's: *Lamas, Fernando/Richard Haydn* (Merry widow.) / Vilia: *Lamas, Fernando* (Merry widow.) / Girls, girls, girls: *Various artists* (Merry widow.) / Night: *Lamas, Fernando* (Merry widow.) / Merry widow waltz: *Lamas, Fernando/Trudy Erwin* (Merry widow.).
Note: Medleys contained in box set: (1) I love a piano/Snooky ookums/When the midnight choo choo leaves for Alabam' (Judy Garland/Fred Astaire - Easter Parade). (2) My sunny Tennessee/So long! oo-long (how long you gonna be gone) (Fred Astaire/Red Skelton - Three Little Words).
LP Set: Released May '90, on MGM (EMI) Catalogue no: **MGB 1**
CD Set: Released May '90, on MGM (EMI) Catalogue no: **CDP 793 603 2**
LP Set: Released May '90, on MGM (EMI) Catalogue no: **793 603 1**
CD Set: Released May '90, on MGM (EMI) Catalogue no: **CDMGB 1**

THOSE MAGNIFICENT MGM MUSICALS (Vol. 2 1952-1971) (Various artists)

Tracks: / Shine of your shoes, A: *Astaire, Fred* / By myself: *Astaire, Fred* / Triplets: *Astaire, Fred/Nanette Fabray* / New sun in the sky: *Adams, India* / I guess I'll have to change my plans: *Astaire, Fred/Jack Buchanan* / I love Louisa: *Astaire, Fred & Chorus* / That's entertainment: *Astaire, Fred/Nanette Fabray* / Smoke gets in your eyes: *Grayson, Kathryn* / I'll be hard to handle: *Miller, Ann* / Yesterdays: *Grayson, Kathryn* / Touch of your hand, The: *Keel, Howard/Kathryn Grayson* / Lovely to look at: *Keel, Howard/Kathryn Grayson* / Hi Lili, hi lo: *Caron, Leslie & Mel Ferrer* / Too darn hot: *Miller, Ann* / So in love: *Keel, Howard/Kathryn Grayson* / Tom, Dick or Harry: *Miller, Ann/Bobby Van* / Were thine that special face: *Keel, Howard* / Why can't you behave: *Miller, Ann* / Wunderbar: *Keel, Howard/Kathryn Grayson* / Always true to you in my fashion: *Miller, Ann/Tommy Rall* / I hate men: *Grayson, Kathryn* / From this moment on: *Rall, Tommy/Ann Miller* / Brush up your Shakespear: *Wynn, Keenan/James Whitmore* / Spring, spring, spring: *Various artists* / Bless your beautiful hide: *Keel, Howard* / Wonderful, wonderful day: *Powell, Jane* / Goin' co'tin': *Various artists* / Sobin' women: *Keel, Howard & Brothers* / Sometimes I'm happy: *Powell, Jane/Vic Damone* / Chiribiribee: *Variousartists* / More than you know: *Martin, Tony* / I know that you know: *Powell, Jane/Vic Damone* / Rose Marie: *Keel, Howard* / I'm a montie who never got his man: *Lahr, Bert* / Indian love call: *Blyth, Ann/Fernando Lamas* / Softly as in a morning sunrise: *Traubel, Helen* / Serenade: *Olvis, William* / Lover come back to me: *Martin, Tony* / Road to paradise: *Damone, Vic* / Will you remember (sweetheart): *Damone, Vic/Powell, Jane* / Once in the highlands: *Various artists* / Brigadoon: *Various artists* / Heather on the hill, The: *Kelly, Gene* / Waitin' for my dearie: *Richards, Carol* / I'll go home with Bonnie Jean: *Johnson, Van/John Gustafson* / Come to me, bend to me: *Gustafson, John* / Fate: *Keel, Howard* / Not since Nineveh: *Gray, Dolores* / Baubles, bangles and beads: *Blyth, Ann* / Gesticulate: *Keel, Howard* / Night of my nights: *Damone, Vic* / Bored: *Gray, Dolores* / Olive tree, The: *Keel, Howard* / Rahadlakum: *Keel, Howard* / And this is my beloved: *Keel, Howard/Anne Blyth* / March, march: *Kelly, Gene/Dan Dailey* / Thanks alot, but no thanks: *Gray, Dolores* / Blue Danube (Why are we here): *Kelly, Gene/Dan Dailey* / Music is better than words: *Gray, Dolores* / I like myself: *Kelly, Gene* / Les girls: *Kelly, Gene/Kay Kendall* / You're just too too: *Kelly, Gene/Kay Kendall* / Ca, c'est l'amour: *Elg, Tania* / Ladies in waiting: *Gaynor, Mitzi/Kay Kendall* /

Why am I so gone (about the girl): *Kelly, Gene* / Thank heaven for little girls: *Chevalier, Maurice* / Say a prayer for me tonight: *Caron, Leslie* / I remember it well: *Chavalier, Maurice* / Gaston's soliloquy: *Jordan, Louis* / I'm glad I'm not young any more: *Chevalier, Maurice* / Night they invented Champagne, The: *Caron, Leslie/Louis Jordan* / Paris loves lovers: *Astaire, Fred/Cyd Charisse* / All of you: *Astaire, Fred* / Fated to be mated: *Charisse, Cyd/Fred Astaire* / Siberia: *Various artists* / Ritz roll and rock, The: *Astaire, Fred* / I ain't down yet: *Reynold, Debbie* / I'll never say no: *Presnell, Harve/Debbie Reynolds* / Belly up to the bar, boys: *Reynolds, Debbie* / London is London: *Clark, Petula & Chorus* / You and I: *Clark, Petula* / I could be happy with you: *Twiggy/Christopher Gable* / It's never too late to fall in love: *Adrian, Max/Georgina Hale* / Room in Bloomsbury, A: *Twiggy/Christopher Gable* / Riviera: *Various artists* / Boy friend finale, The: *Various artists.*
CD Set: Released May '90, on MGM (EMI) Catalogue no: **CDMGB 2**
LP Set: Released May '90, on MGM (EMI) Catalogue no: **794 081 1**
LP Set: Released May '90, on MGM (EMI) Catalogue no: **MGB 2**
CD Set: Released May '90, on MGM (EMI) Catalogue no: **CDP 794 081 2**

Miami Vice

BEST OF MIAMI VICE (Various artists)

CD: Released Mar '90, on MCA by MCA Records. Catalogue no: **241 746 2**
Album: Released Mar '90, on MCA by MCA Records. Catalogue no: **241 746 1**
Cass: Released Mar '90, on MCA by MCA Records. Catalogue no: **241 746 4**

MIAMI VICE (TV soundtrack) (Various artists) (Also see under Hammer, Jan)

Tracks: / Original Miami Vice theme, The (instrumental): Hammer, Jan / Smuggler's blues: Frey, Glenn / Own the night: Khan, Chaka / You belong to the city: Frey, Glen / In the air tonight: Collins, Phil / Miami Vice (instrumental): *Hammer, Jan* / Vice: *Hammer, Jan* / Better be good to me: *Turner, Tina* / Flashback (instrumental): *Hammer, Jan* / Chase (instrumental): *Hammer, Jan* / Evan (instrumental): *Hammer, Jan*.

Album: Released Oct '85, on MCA-BBC by MCA Records. Catalogue no: **REMV 584**

Cass: Released Oct '85, on MCA-BBC by MCA Records. Catalogue no: **ZCMV 584**

CD: Released Jul '88, on MCA by MCA Records. Catalogue no: **DMCL 1871**

Album: Released Jul '86, on MCA by MCA Records. Catalogue no: **MCF 3287**

Cass: Released Jul '86, on MCA by MCA Records. Catalogue no: **MCFC 3287**

CD: Released '88, on MCA-BBC by MCA Records. Catalogue no: **DMCF 3287**

MIAMI VICE II (TV soundtrack) (Various artists)

Tracks: / Mercy: *Jones, Steve* / Last unbroken heart, The: *Labelle, Patti* / Crockett's theme: *Hammer, Jan* / Lives in the balance: *Browne, Jackson* / Original Miami Vice theme, The: *Hammer, Jan* / Send it to me: *Knight, Gladys & The Pips* / When the rain comes down: *Taylor, Andy* / Lover: *Roxy Music* / In dulce decorum: *Damned*.

Cass: Released Dec '86, on MCA by MCA Records. Catalogue no: **MCGC 6019**

CD: Released Feb '87, on MCA by MCA Records. Catalogue no: **DMCG 6019**

Album: Released Dec '86, on MCA by MCA Records. Catalogue no: **MCG 6019**

MIAMI VICE III (Various artists)

Cass: Released Sep '88, on MCA by MCA Records. Catalogue no: **MCGC 6033**

Album: Released Sep '88, on MCA by MCA Records. Catalogue no: **MCG 6033**

CD: Released Sep '88, on MCA by MCA Records. Catalogue no: **DMCG 6033**

MIAMI VICE THEME (See under Hammer, Jan)

Midas Run

MIDAS RUN (See under Bernstein, Elmer)

Midler, Bette

BEACHES (Film soundtrack)

Tracks: / Under the boardwalk / I've still got my health / Otto Titsling / Glory of love / Oh industry / Wind beneath my wings / I think it's going to rain today / I know you by heart / Baby mine / Friendship theme.

Album: Released May '89, on WEA by WEA Records. Catalogue no: **K 781933-1**

Cass: Released May '89, on WEA by WEA Records. Catalogue no: **K 781933-4**

CD: Released May '89, on WEA by WEA Records. Catalogue no: **K 781933-2**

DIVINE MADNESS (Original soundtrack)

Tracks: / Big noise from Winnetka / Paradise / Shiver me timbers / Fire down below / Stay with me / My other's eyes / Chapel of love / Boogie woogie bugle boy / E. street shuffle, The / Summer / Leader of the pack / You can't always get what you want / I shall be released.

Album: Released Jan '81, on Atlantic by WEA Records. Deleted Jan '86. Catalogue no: **K 50760**

ROSE, THE (Film soundtrack)

Tracks: / Whose side are you on? / Midnight in Memphis / Concert monologue / When a man loves a woman / Sold my soul to rock'n'roll / Keep on rockin' / Love me with a feeling / Camellia / Homecoming monologue / Stay with me / Let me call you sweetheart / Rose, The.

Cass: Released Jan '80, on Atlantic by WEA Records. Catalogue no: **K4 50681**

CD: Released Jan '84, on Atlantic by WEA Records. Catalogue no: **K 250 681**

Album: Released Jan '80, on Atlantic by WEA Records. Deleted Sep '87. Catalogue no: **K 50681**

ROSE, THE (SINGLE)

Tracks: / Rose, The / Stay with me.

Note: From the film *The Rose*.

7" Single: Released Apr '80, on Atlantic by WEA Records. Deleted Apr '83. Catalogue no: **K 11459**

Midney, Boris

MUSIC FROM THE EMPIRE STRIKES BACK

Tracks: / Yoda's theme / Imperial

march / Han Solo & the princess / Star wars.

Album: Released Aug '80, on RSO by Polydor Ltd. Deleted '85. Catalogue no: **2394 268**

Midnight Cowboy

MIDNIGHT COWBOY (Film soundtrack) (Various artists)

Tracks: / Everybody's talkin': *Various artists* / Joe Buck rides again: *Various artists* / Famous myth, A: *Various artists* / Fun City: *Various artists* / He quit me man: *Various artists* / Jungle gym at the zoo: *Various artists* / Midnight cowboy: *Various artists* / Old man Willow: *Various artists* / Florida fantasy: *Various artists* / Tears and joys: *Various artists* / Science fiction: *Various artists* / Everybody's talkin': *Various artists*.

CD: Released Sep '88, on EMI by EMI Records. Catalogue no: **CZ 64**

CD: Released Sep '88, on EMI by EMI Records. Catalogue no: **CDP 748 409 2**

Album: Released Oct '80, on Liberty by EMI Records. Catalogue no: **LBR 1036**

MIDNIGHT COWBOY (SINGLE)

Tracks: / Midnight cowboy.

Note: From the film "*Midnight Cowboy*".

7" Single: Released Nov '80, on United Artists by EMI Records. Deleted '83. Catalogue no: **UP 634**

Midnight Express

MIDNIGHT EXPRESS (Original Soundrack) (Various artists)

Tracks: / Chase: *Various artists* / Love's theme: *Various artists* / Midnight express, Theme from: *Various artists* / Istanbul blues: *Various artists* / Wheel, The: *Various artists* / Istanbul opening: *Various artists* / Cacaphony: *Various artists* / Billy's theme: *Various artists*.

Album: Released Nov '81, on Casablanca by PolyGram UK Ltd. Catalogue no: **9128 018**

Cass: Released '79, on Casablanca by PolyGram UK Ltd. Deleted '84. Catalogue no: **ZCCAN 2030**

Album: Released Apr '86, on Casablanca by PolyGram UK Ltd. Catalogue no: **PRICE 91**

Cass: Released Nov '81, on Casablanca by PolyGram UK Ltd. Catalogue no: **7268 014**
CD: Released Apr '85, on Casablanca by PolyGram UK Ltd. Catalogue no: **824 206 2**
Cass: Released Apr '86, on Casablanca by PolyGram UK Ltd. Catalogue no: **PRIMC 91**
Album: Released '79, on Casablanca by PolyGram UK Ltd. Deleted '84. Catalogue no: **CAL 2030**

Midnight Run

MIDNIGHT RUN (Original Soundtrack) (Various artists)
Cass: Released Mar '90, on MCA (USA) by MCA Records (USA). Catalogue no: **MCAC 6250**
CD: Released Jan '89, on MCA (USA) by MCA Records (USA). Catalogue no: **MCAD 6250**
Album: Released Mar '90, on MCA (USA) by MCA Records (USA). Catalogue no: **MCA 6250**

Midsummer Night's...

MIDSUMMER NIGHT'S SEX COMEDY (Original Soundtrack)
Cass: Released Oct '82, on CBS by CBS Records & Distribution. Catalogue no: **40 73673**
Album: Released Oct '82, on CBS by CBS Records & Distribution. Catalogue no: **CBS 73673**

Mighty Quinn

MIGHTY QUINN, THE (Original Soundtrack) (Various artists)
CD: Released Jun '89, on A&M by A&M Records. Catalogue no: **393 924-2**
Album: Released Jun '89, on A&M by A&M Records. Catalogue no: **393 924-1**
Cass: Released Jun '89, on A&M by A&M Records. Catalogue no: **393 924-4**

Mikado

MIKADO (VIDEO) (Various artists)
VHS: Released '88, on Thames Video Col Catalogue no: **TV 8061**

Milestone Of Memory

MILESTONE OF MEMORY (Berlin, Irving)
Album: Released Jun '89, on Reid Catalogue no: **RD 3**

Miller, Glenn

GLENN MILLER STORY (Film soundtrack)
Cass: Released Jul '85, on MCA by MCA Records. Deleted Jan '88. Catalogue no: **MCFC 3273**
Album: Released Jul '85, on MCA by MCA Records. Deleted Jan '88. Catalogue no: **MCF 3273**

GLENN MILLER STORY (VIDEO)
VHS: Released '88, on CIC Video Catalogue no: **VHR 1187**

HITS FROM THE GLENN MILLER STORY
Tracks: / Moonlight serenade / American patrol / Pennsylvania 6 5000 / In the mood / I've got a gal in Kalamazoo / Boulder buff / Tuxedo Junction / St. Louis blues / String of pearls / Little brown jug / Farewell blues / King Porter stomp.
Album: Released May '76, on RCA by BMG Records (UK). Catalogue no: **LSA 3274**

IN HOLLYWOOD
Album: Released '88, on Mercury by Phonogram Ltd. Deleted 28 Feb '90. Catalogue no: **826 635 1**
CD: Released Jan '87, on Phonogram by Phonogram Ltd. Deleted Mar '88. Catalogue no: **826 635 2**
Cass: Released '88, on Mercury by Phonogram Ltd. Deleted 28 Feb '90. Catalogue no: **826 635 4**

Minerbi, Marcello

ZORBA'S DANCE
Tracks: / Zorba's dance.
Note: From the film 'Zorba The Greek'.
7" Single: Released Jul '82, on Old Gold by Old Gold Records. Catalogue no: **OG 9055**
7" Single: Released Jul '65, on Durium Deleted '68. Catalogue no: **DRS 54001**

Minipops

SONGS FOR CHRISTMAS '88
7" Single: Released Dec '88, on Bright by Bright Records. Catalogue no: **BUB 12**
12" Single: Released Dec '88, on Bright by Bright Records. Catalogue no: **BULB 12**

Minor Miracle

MINOR MIRACLE, A (Original Soundtrack) (Various artists)
Note: Composed by Rik Patterson.
Album: Released Jan '89, on

Silva Screen by Silva Screen Records. Catalogue no: **STV 81193**

Mishima

MISHIMA (Original Soundtrack) (Various artists)
Tracks: / Opening: *Various artists* / November 25: *Various artists* / Morning 1934: *Various artists* / Grandmother and Kimitake: *Various artists* / Temple of the golden pavillion: *Various artists* / Osamu's theme: *Various artists* / Kyoko's house: *Various artists* / 1937: *Various artists* / Saint Sebastian: *Various artists* / Kyoko's house: *Various artists* / November 25th: *Various artists* / Ichigaya: *Various artists* / 1957: *Various artists* / Award montage: *Various artists* / Runaway horses: *Various artists* / 1962: *Various artists* / Body building: *Various artists* / November 25: *Various artists* / Last day, The: *Various artists* / F 104: *Various artists* / Epilogue from sun and steel: *Various artists*.
CD: Released Nov '85, on Elektra by Elektra Records (UK). Catalogue no: **979 113 2**
Album: Released Nov '85, on Elektra by Elektra Records (UK). Catalogue no: **EKT 23**
Cass: Released Nov '85, on Elektra by Elektra Records (UK). Catalogue no: **EKT 23 C**

Miss Saigon

MISS SAIGON (Film soundtrack) (Various artists)
Album: Released Dec '89, on Warner Bros. by WEA Records. Catalogue no: **WX 329**
Cass: Released Dec '89, on Warner Bros. by WEA Records. Catalogue no: **WX 329C**
CD: Released Feb '90, on Warner Bros. by WEA Records. Catalogue no: **759 9242712**

Mission (Film)

MISSION (See under Morricone, Ennio)

Mission Impossible

MISSION IMPOSSIBLE (Original soundtrack) (Various artists)
Note: Music from the 1960's TV series by Lalo Schifrin.
Album: Released Jan '89, on Silva Screen by Silva Screen Records. Catalogue no: **250674.1**
Album: Released Jun '87, on

Film soundtrack to *Mississippi Burning* (Island)

Power House. Catalogue no: **DSR 8618**

Mississippi Burning

MISSISSIPPI BURNING (Original Soundtrack) (Various artists) (See picture above)
Tracks: / Take my hand precious Lord: *Jackson, Mahalia* / Murder in Mississippi (Part 1): *Jones, Trevor* / Some things are worth dying for: *Jones, Trevor* / Murder in Mississippi (Part 2): *Jones, Trevor* / Anderson and Mrs Pell: *Jones, Trevor* / When we all get to heaven: *Choral* / Try Jesus: *Williams, Vesta* / Abduction: *Jones, Trevor* / You live it, you breathe it, you marry it: *Jones, Trevor* / Murder in Mississippi (Part 3): *Jones, Trevor* / Requiem for three young men: *Jones, Trevor* / Burning cross: *Jones, Trevor* / Justice in Mississippi: *Jones, Trevor* / Walk on by faith (vocal): *McBride, Lannie* / Walk on by faith: *McBride, Lannie*.
Album: Released 6 Mar '89, on Antilles/New Directions by Island Records. Catalogue no: **AN 8745**
Cass: Released 6 Mar '89, on Antilles/New Directions by Island Records. Catalogue no: **ANC 8745**
CD: Released 6 Mar '89, on Antilles/New Directions by Island Records. Catalogue no: **ANCD 8745**

Missouri Breaks

MISSOURI BREAKS, THE (Original Soundtrack) (Various artists)
Note: Western score by John Williams for the Arthur Penn film starring Marlon Brando and Jack Nicholson.
Album: Released Jan '89, on Silva Screen by Silva Screen Records. Catalogue no: **MCA 25113**
Cass: Released Jan '89, on Silva Screen by Silva Screen Records. Deleted Mar '90. Catalogue no: **MCAC 25113**

Mistrals Daughter

MISTRALS DAUGHTER (Soundtrack theme) (Various artists)
Tracks: / Teddy's theme: *Various artists* / Mistral's theme: *Various artists*.
7" Single: Released Feb '86, on Carrere Catalogue no: **CAR 382**
MISTRALS DAUGHTER, THE (TV soundtrack) (Various artists)
Tracks: / Only love: *Mouskouri, Nana* / Cavaillion series, The: *Various artists* / I remember Mistral: *Various artists* / Teddy's theme: *Various artists* / Flower market, The: *Various artists* / Surrealist ball, The: *Various artists* / Maggy's theme: *Various artists* / Paula's theme: *Various artists* / Model's fair, The: *Various artists* / Mistral's daughter, The: *Various artists* / La Rue Hebraique: *Various artists* / La tourello: *Various artists* / Death of Teddy, The: *Various artists* / Mistral theme: *Various artists* / War: *Various artists* / Last Mistral, The: *Various artists* / Fade: Mistral's daughter, The: *Various artists*.
Album: Released May '85, on Carrere (France) Catalogue no: **66180**
Album: Released Mar '86, on Carrere Catalogue no: **CAL 221**
Cass: Released Mar '86, on Carrere Catalogue no: **CAC 221**

Mitford Girls

MITFORD GIRLS (London Cast Album) (Various artists)
Album: Released Jan '82, on Philips by Phonogram Ltd. Deleted Jan '87. Catalogue no: **635 908 8**

Mocky, Jean Pierre

MUSIC FROM THE FILMS OF JEAN-PIERRE MOCKY (Various artists)
CD: Released Jan '89, on Silva Screen by Silva Screen Records. Catalogue no: **CD 361**

Modern Times (film)

MODERN TIMES (Film soundtrack-Charlie Chaplin) (Various artists)
Album: Released '89, on Liberty (import) by EMI Records. Catalogue no: **LN 10288**
Album: Released '83, on EMI (Germany) by EMI Records. Catalogue no: **IC 064 82892**

Moderns

MODERNS, THE (Original Soundtrack) (Isham, Mark)
Tracks: / Les modernes / Cafe Selavy / Paris la nuit / Really the blues / Madame Valentin / Dada je suis / Parlez-moi d'amour / La valse moderne / Les peintres / Death of Irving Fagelman / Je ne veux pas de tes chocolats / Parlez-

moi d'amour / Selavy.

Note: The Moderns recreates the boldness and colour of Paris in the 1920's amid luminaries like Hemingway, Stein and Picasso. The soundtrack was written, performed and produced by Mark Isham.

CD: Released May '88, on Virgin by Virgin Records. Catalogue no: **CDV 2530**

Cass: Released May '88, on Virgin by Virgin Records. Catalogue no: **TCV 2530**

Album: Released May '88, on Virgin by Virgin Records. Catalogue no: **V 2530**

Moliere

MOLIERE (Film Soundtrack) (Various artists)
Album: Released May '80, on Harmonia Mundi (France) by Harmonia Mundi (UK). Deleted '85. Catalogue no: **HM 1020**

Molly Maguires (film)

MOLLY MAGUIRES (Film soundtrack) (Various artists)
Tracks: / Theme from the Molly Maguires: *Various artists* / Molly's strike: *Various artists* / Main title: *Various artists* / Fiddle and fife: *Various artists* / Work montage: *Various artists* / Jamie and Mary (the hills of yesterday): *Various artists* / Room and board (theme from the Molly Maguires): *Various artists* / Hills of yesterday: *Various artists* / Penny whistle jig: *Various artists* / Sandwiches and tea: *Various artists* / Trip to town: *Various artists* / Molly's strike again: *Various artists* / Brew with the boys: *Various artists* / Suit for Grandpa: *Various artists* / End: *Various artists*.
Note: One of Henry Mancini's greatest scores for the Martin Ritt film starring Sean Connery and Richard Harris.
Album: Released Jan '89, on Silva Screen by Silva Screen Records. Catalogue no: **255065.1**
Album: Released '73, on Paramount Deleted '78. Catalogue no: **SPFL 259**

Moment By Moment

MOMENT BY MOMENT (Film soundtrack) (Various artists)
Tracks: / Moment to moment: *Various artists* / Lady wants to know: *Various artists* / Everybody needs love: *Various artists* / You

know I love you: *Various artists* / Your heart never lies: *Various artists* / Sometimes when we touch: *Various artists* / For you and I: *Various artists* / Hollywood Boulevard: *Various artists*.
Album: Released Dec '79, on RSO by Polydor Ltd. Deleted '84. Catalogue no: **RSD 5004**
Cass: Released Dec '79, on RSO by Polydor Ltd. Deleted '84. Catalogue no: **TRSD 5004**

Mon Oncle Americain

MON ONCLE AMERICAIN (Film soundtrack) (Various artists)
Album: on DRG (USA) by DRG Records (USA). Catalogue no: **SL 9505**

Mona Lisa

MONA LISA (Film soundtrack) (Various artists)
Tracks: / When I fall in love: *Cole, Nat "King"* / Introduction (When I fall in love): *Various artists* / Story, The: *Kamen, Michael* / George: *Kamen, Michael* / Elevator attack and after: *Kamen, Michael* / Slap you back: *Exception* / Mona Lisa: *Cole, Nat "King"* / Kings Cross/follow Anderson: *Kamen, Michael* / Pimp: *Kamen, Michael* / Simone's story: *Kamen, Michael* / Daughters of Babylon: *Lindsay, Jimmy* / Love duet from Madame Butterfly & Puccini: *Tibaldi, Renata/Carlo Bergonzi*.
Note: Original score composed and arranged by Michael Kamen.
Cass: Released Sep '86, on Columbia by EMI Records. Deleted 31 Jul '88. Catalogue no: **TCSCX 6705**
Album: Released Sep '86, on Columbia by EMI Records. Deleted Nov '88. Catalogue no: **SCX 6705**

Monkees

HEAD (Film soundtrack) (See also under Head)
Album: Released Jan '86, on Rhino (USA) by Rhino Records (USA). Catalogue no: **RNLP 145**

MONKEES, THE VOL 1 (VIDEO)
VHS: Released Jun '89, on Hollywood Collection Catalogue no: **CVT 11082**

MONKEES, THE VOL 2 (VIDEO)
VHS: Released Jun '89, on Holly-

wood Collection Catalogue no: **CVT 11083**

MONKEES, THE VOL 3 (VIDEO)
VHS: Released Jun '89, on Hollywood Collection Catalogue no: **CVT 11084**

MONKEES, THE VOL 4 (VIDEO)
VHS: Released Jun '89, on Hollywood Collection Catalogue no: **CVT 11085**

Monkey

MONKEY (See under Godiego)

MONKEY MAGIC (See under Godiego)

Monroe, Marilyn

COLLECTION: MARILYN MONROE (20 golden greats)
Tracks: / Diamonds are a girl's best friend / River of no return / Heatwave / Do it again / Kiss / My heart belongs to daddy / I'm gonna file my claim / This is a fine romance / Little girl from Little Rock, A / Happy birthday, Mr. President / After you get what you want you don't want it / You'd be surprised / She acts like a woman should / Lazy / When love goes wrong nothing goes right / One silver dollar / When I fall in love / Things / Bye bye duet (With Jane Russell.) / Bye bye baby.
Album: Released Aug '85, on Deja Vu Catalogue no: **DVLP 2001**
CD: Released Jul '87, on Deja Vu Catalogue no: **DVCD 2001**
Cass: Released Aug '85, on Deja Vu Catalogue no: **DVMC 2001**

COMPLETE RECORDINGS, THE: MARILYN MONROE
Tracks: / Ladies of the chorus / Every baby needs a da da daddy / Anyone can see I love you / Kiss / Do it again / She acts like a woman should / Two little girls from Little Rock / Bye bye baby / Diamonds are a girl's best friend / When love goes wrong / Fine romance, A / River of no return / I'm gonna file my claim / One silver dollar / Down in the meadow / Man chases a girl, A / After you get what you want you don't want it / There's no business like show business / Heatwave / Lazy / You'd be surprised / Rachmaninov & Chopsticks / That old black magic / I found a dream / I'm through with love / I wanna be

loved by you / Running wild / Some like it hot / My heart belongs to daddy / Let's make love / Incurably romantic / Specialization / When I fall in love / Happy birthday Mr.President / Thanks for the memory.

CD Set: Released '88, on Rare Catalogue no: **RARECD 06/07**
LP Set: Released '88, on Rare Catalogue no: **RARELP 06/07**

FINE ROMANCE, A
2 LP Set: Released Mar '87, on Legends by Pantheon Music Intl.(USA). Catalogue no: **LEGENDS 1000/1**

GOODBYE NORMA JEAN
Tracks: / My heart belongs to daddy / Diamonds are a girl's best friend / River of no return / I'm gonna file my claim / Bye bye baby / After you get what you want you don't want it / One silver dollar / Heatwave / When I fall in love / Specialisation.
CD: Released Aug '87, on Zuma Catalogue no: **CDZUMA 1**
Cass: Released May '87, on Zuma Catalogue no: **ZUMAC 1**
Album: Released May '87, on Zuma Catalogue no: **ZUMA 1**

GOODBYE PRIMADONNA
Album: Released Apr '84, on Telefunken (Germany) Catalogue no: **6.24800**
Album: Released May '85, on Zuma Catalogue no: **ZUMA 1001**
2 LP Set: Released Sep '84, on Teldec (1) by ASV (Academy Sound & Vision). Catalogue no: **6 23430**
Album: Released Aug '84, on Disc AZ (France) by Musidisc Records (France). Catalogue no: **AZ 2372**
Cass: Released May '85, on Zuma Catalogue no: **ZUMAK 1001**
CD: Released Dec '85, on Musidisc by Musidisc Records (France). Catalogue no: **339 372**
Cass: Released Aug '84, on Disc AZ (France) by Musidisc Records (France). Catalogue no: **C 372**

I WANNA BE LOVED BY YOU
Tracks: / I wanna be loved by you / I'm thru with love / Running wild.
7" Single: Released Feb '79, on United Artists by EMI Records. Catalogue no: **UP 36484**
7" Single: Released Apr '83, on EMI (France) by EMI Records. Catalogue no: **2C 008 83377**

I WANNA BE LOVED BY YOU

(ALBUM)
CD: Released Oct '86, on Solid Gold (1) by Creole Records. Deleted '86. Catalogue no: **CD 8602**

LEGEND, THE
Album: Released Jan '89, on Silva Screen by Silva Screen Records. Catalogue no: **LEGENDS 1000.1**

LET'S MAKE LOVE
LP Pic: Released 7 Nov '87, on Exclusive Picture Discs Catalogue no: **AR 30077**

MAGIC OF MARILYN MONROE, THE (BOX SET)
VHS: Released Oct '89, on Warner Home Video by WEA Records. Catalogue no: **PES 35181**

MARILYN
CD: Released Jul '88, on Entertainers Catalogue no: **ENTCD 262**

MARILYN MONROE
Cass: Released Aug '86, on Lotus Catalogue no: **LCS 14119**
Album: Released Aug '86, on Lotus Catalogue no: **LOP 14 119**

MARILYN MONROE (PIC DISC)
Album: Released 6 Nov '87, on Counterpoint Catalogue no: **PD 83003B**

MARILYN MONROE STORY, THE
Tracks: / Every baby needs a da da daddy / Anyone can see I love you / Kiss / Do it again / She acts like a woman should / Two little girls from little rock / Bye bye baby / Diamonds are a girl's best friend / (This is) a fine romance / River of no return / I'm gonna file my claim / One silver dollar / Down in the meadow / After you get what you want you don't want it / Heatwave / Lazy / You'd be surprised / That old black magic / I'm through with love / I wanna be loved by you / Running wild / My heart belongs to Daddy / Incurably romantic / When I fall in love / Happy birthday Mr. President / Thanks for the memory.
Cass: Released May '89, on Deja Vu Catalogue no: **DVREMC 01**
CD: Released May '89, on Deja Vu Catalogue no: **DVRECD 01**

NEVER BEFORE AND NEVER AGAIN (Compilation of songs from Marilyn Monroe films)
Tracks: / Gentlemen prefer blondes / Diamonds are a girl's best friend / Little girl from little rock, A / Ain't there anyone here for love? / When love goes wrong / Bye bye baby / Do it again / Kiss / You'd be surprised / Fine romance, A / She acts like a woman should / Heatwave / Happy birthday Mr. President.
Cass: Released Feb '87, on DRG (USA) by DRG Records (USA). Catalogue no: **DSC 15005**
Album: Released Feb '87, on DRG (USA) by DRG Records (USA). Deleted Jan '89. Catalogue no: **DS 15005**
CD: Released Mar '87, on DRG (USA) by DRG Records (USA). Deleted Jan '89. Catalogue no: **CDXP 15005**

PORTRAIT: MARILYN MONROE
Tracks: / I wanna be loved by you / Diamond's are a girl's best friend / Little girl from little rock, A / When love goes wrong / Bye bye baby / My heart belongs to Daddy / I'm gonna file my claim / River of no return / Do it again / Kiss / You'd be surprised / This is a fine romance / I'm through with love / Heat wave / Running wild / Lazy / Happy birthday to John F Kennedy / That old black magic / I'm through with love / I wanna be loved by you / Heat wave / Running wild / Lazy / Happy birthday to John F Kennedy /
CD: Released Dec '88, on Platinum Music by Prism Leisure. Catalogue no: **PLATCD 3905**
Album: Released Dec '88, on Platinum Music by Prism Leisure. Catalogue no: **PLAT 3905**
Cass: Released Dec '88, on Platinum Music by Prism Leisure. Catalogue no: **PLAC 3905**

RARE RECORDINGS (1948-62)
Tracks: / Some like it hot / Diamonds are a girl's best friend / Like a woman should.
Album: on Sandy Hook (USA) Catalogue no: **SH 2013**
Cass: Released Jan '89, on Sandy Hook (USA) Catalogue no: **CSH 2013**

REMEMBER MARILYN
Album: Released Apr '74, on Pye Catalogue no: **NSPH 28500**

SOME LIKE IT HOT (Film soundtrack)
Tracks: / Runnin' wild / Sugar blues / Down among the sheltering palms / Randolph street rag / I wanna be loved by you / Park Avenue fantasy / I'm through with

love / Play it again Charlie / Tell the whole darn world.
Album: Released Mar '79, on United Artists by EMI Records. Catalogue no: **UAS 30226**
Album: Released '83, on EMI (Germany) by EMI Records. Catalogue no: **IC 064 82894**

VERY BEST OF MARILYN MONROE, THE
Tracks: / My heart belongs to Daddy / Diamonds are a girl's best friend / Specialisation.
Album: Released Sep '88, on Fun (Holland) Catalogue no: **FUN 9001**
Cass: Released Sep '88, on Fun (Holland) Catalogue no: **FUNC 9001**

VOICE SONGS AND FILMS, THE
Album: Released Oct '85, on RCA (France) by BMG Records (France). Catalogue no: **NL 89345**
Cass: Released Oct '85, on RCA (France) by BMG Records (France). Catalogue no: **NK 89345**

WHEN I FALL IN LOVE
Tracks: / Heatwave / Diamonds are a girl's best friend / When I fall in love.
12" Single: Released Feb '87, on Zuma Catalogue no: **ZOOMT 6**
7" Pic: Released Feb '87, on Zuma Catalogue no: **ZOOMP 6**
7" Single: Released Feb '87, on Zuma Catalogue no: **ZOOM 6**

Monsieur Beaucaire
MONSIEUR BEAUCAIRE (Original 1919 Cast) (Various artists)
Album: Released Oct '83, on Opal Catalogue no: **OPAL 817**

Monster Club
MONSTER CLUB, THE (Original soundtrack) (Various artists)
Album: on Chips Catalogue no: **CHILP 2**

Montenegro, Hugo
BEST OF BROADWAY
Album: Released Nov '77, on Golden Hour Catalogue no: **GH 866**

BEST OF HUGO MONTENEGRO
Tracks: / Good, the bad and the ugly, The / Valley of the dolls, Theme from / Fox, The (theme from) / Fistful of dollars / Hang 'em

high / Good vibrations / Love is blue / For a few dollars more / Happy together / Classical gas.
Cass: Released Apr '80, on RCA International by BMG Records (UK). Catalogue no: **INTK 5004**
Album: Released Apr '80, on RCA International by BMG Records (UK). Catalogue no: **INTS 5004**

BROADWAY MELODIES 1
Tracks: / Lady be good / Man I love / Tea for two / Girl Friend / Who / Thou swell / Hallelujah / I got rhythm / Of thee I sing / Song is you / Yesterdays / Night & day / Varsity drag / Make believe / Easter parade.
Cass: Released '83, on Everest (Premier) by Everest Records. Catalogue no: **KCBR 1003**
Album: Released '83, on Everest (Premier) by Everest Records. Catalogue no: **CBR 1003**

GOOD, THE BAD AND THE UGLY, THE (Theme from the film)
Tracks: / Good, the bad and the ugly, The / Fistful of dollars.
7" Single: Released Sep '68, on RCA by BMG Records (UK). Deleted '71. Catalogue no: **RCA 1727**
7" Single: Released Jul '81, on RCA Golden Grooves by BMG Records (UK). Deleted May '89. Catalogue no: **GOLD 518**
7" Single: Released Oct '86, on Old Gold by Old Gold Records. Catalogue no: **OG 9604**

HANG 'EM HIGH
Tracks: / Hang 'em high.
7" Single: Released Jan '69, on RCA by BMG Records (UK). Deleted '72. Catalogue no: **RCA 1771**

MUSIC FROM THE GOOD, THE BAD & THE UGLY (Original Soundtrack)
Tracks: / Good bad and the ugly, The / Marcia (march) with hope / Story of a soldier, The / Ecstasy of gold / Fistful of dollars, A / Square dance / Titoli - man with no name / Aces high / Vice of killing / Sixty seconds to what / For a few dollars more.
Cass: Released '74, on RCA by BMG Records (UK). Deleted '80. Catalogue no: **VCS 67200**
Album: Released '74, on RCA by BMG Records (UK). Catalogue no: **SF 7994**

PLAYS FOR LOVERS

Cass: Released Sep '81, on Ampro Catalogue no: **AMP 018**

Monty Python
ALWAYS LOOK ON THE BRIGHT SIDE OF LIFE (Monty Python's Flying Circus)
Tracks: / Always look on the bright side of things / Brian.
Note: From the film "*Life of Brian*"
7" Single: Released Dec '88, on Warner Bros. by WEA Records. Deleted Jan '90. Catalogue no: **W 7653**

ANOTHER MONTY PYTHON RECORD (Monty Python's Flying Circus)
Tracks: / Trondheim hammer dance / Liberty bell / Fanfare opening / Formal presentation / Contesana padwana / Man of power / Gold lame / Southern breeze / Spam song / Man of power / Bahama parakeet / House of fashion / Circus tumble / Fanfare / Mystery drums, / Mystery place / Ode to Edward / In step with Johann / Knees up Mother Brown.
CD: Released Jan '90, on Virgin by Virgin Records. Catalogue no: **CASCD 1049**
Album: Released Oct '71, on Charisma by Virgin Records. Deleted Oct '76. Catalogue no: **CAS 1049**
Album: Released Apr '87, on Charisma by Virgin Records. Catalogue no: **CHC 79**
Cass: Released Apr '87, on Charisma by Virgin Records. Catalogue no: **CHCMC 79**

BRIAN
Tracks: / Brian / Always look on the bright side of life.
7" Single: Released '79, on Warner Bros. by WEA Records. Deleted '82. Catalogue no: **K 17495**

CONTRACTUAL OBLIGATION (Monty Python's Flying Circus)
Tracks: / Henry Kissinger / Never be rude to an Arab / I like Chinese / Medical love song / Finland / I'm so worried / I bet you they won't play this song on the rad / Here comes another one / Do wot John / Muddy knees / Traffic lights / All things dull and ugly / Scottish farewell, A / Sing as we go / Polygon / Sportstrack / Decomposing composers.

Album: Released '83, on Charisma by Virgin Records. Deleted '88. Catalogue no: **CAS 1152**

Cass: Released Apr '87, on Charisma by Virgin Records. Catalogue no: **CHCMC 34**

CD: Released Nov '89, on Charisma by Virgin Records. Catalogue no: **CASCD 1152**

Album: Released Apr '87, on Charisma by Virgin Records. Catalogue no: **CHC 34**

FINAL RIP OFF, THE (Highlights compilation album) (Monty Python's Flying Circus)

Tracks: / Introduction / Constitutional peasants / Fish licence / Eric the half bee / Finland song / Travel agent / Are you embarrassed easily? / Australian table wines / Argument / Henry Kissinger / Parrot (Oh not again) / I like Chinese / Spanish inquisition (parts 1/2/3) / Cheese soup / Cherry orchard / Architect's sketch / Spam / Comfy chair / Famous person quiz / You be the actor / Nudge nudge / Cannibalism / Spanish inquisition revisited / Sit on my face / Undertaker / Novel writing (Live from Wessex) / String / Bells / Traffic lights / Cocktail bar / Four Yorkshiremen / Election special / Lumberjack song... / I bet you they won't play this song... / Bruces / Do wot John / Rock notes / I'm so worried / Crocodile / French taunter / Marylin Monroe / Swamp castle / Last word, The / Bookshop / French taunter (part 2).

Album: Released 21 Nov '87, on Virgin by Virgin Records. Catalogue no: **MPD 1**

Cass: Released '87, on Virgin by Virgin Records. Catalogue no: **MPDC 1**

CD: Released '87, on Virgin by Virgin Records. Catalogue no: **CDMP 1**

GALAXY SONG (Monty Python's Flying Circus)

Tracks: / Galaxy song / Every sperm is sacred.

7" Single: Released Jun '83, on CBS by CBS Records & Distribution. Catalogue no: **A 3495**

7" Single: Released Jun '83, on CBS by CBS Records & Distribution. Catalogue no: **WA 3495**

I LIKE CHINESE

Tracks: / I like chinese / I bet they won't play this song on the radio.

7" Single: Released Oct '80, on

Charisma by Virgin Records. Deleted Oct '83. Catalogue no: **CB 374**

INSTANT RECORD COLLECTION (Monty Python's Flying Circus)

Tracks: / Introductions / Alastair Cooke / Nudge nudge / Mrs. Nigger Baiter / Constitutional peasants / Fish licence / Eric the half bee / Australian table wines / Silly noises / Novel writing / Elephantoplasty / How to do it / Gumby cherry orchard / Oscar Wilde / Introduction / Argument / French taunter / Summarized Proust competition / Cheese emporium / Funerals at Prestatyn / Camelot / Word association / Bruces / Parrot / Monty Python.

Album: Released Apr '87, on Charisma by Virgin Records. Catalogue no: **CAS 1134**

CD: Released Nov '89, on Charisma by Virgin Records. Catalogue no: **CASCD 1134**

Cass: Released Apr '87, on Charisma by Virgin Records. Catalogue no: **CASMC 1134**

LIFE OF BRIAN (Film soundtrack) (Monty Python's Flying Circus)

Album: Released Oct '79, on WEA by WEA Records. Catalogue no: **K 56751**

Cass: Released Oct '79, on WEA by WEA Records. Deleted '84. Catalogue no: **K4 56751**

LIVE AT DRURY LANE (Monty Python's Flying Circus)

Tracks: / Introduction / Llamas / Gumby / Flower arranging / Secret service / Wrestling / Communist quiz / Idiot song / Albatross / Colonel / Nudge nudge / Cocktail bar / Travel agent / Spot the brain cell / Bruces / Argument / Four Yorkshiremen / Election special / Lumberjack song / Parrot sketch.

CD: Released Sep '89, on VIP (1) Catalogue no: **VVIPD 104**

Album: Released Apr '87, on Charisma by Virgin Records. Catalogue no: **CLASS 4**

Cass: Released Sep '89, on VIP (1) Catalogue no: **VVIPC 104**

Album: Released Sep '89, on VIP (1) Catalogue no: **VVIP 104**

MATCHING TIE AND HANDKERCHIEF (Monty Python's Flying Circus)

Note: Continuous track-spurious

titles!

Album: Released Apr '87, on Charisma by Virgin Records. Catalogue no: **CHC 81**

CD: Released Nov '89, on Charisma by Virgin Records. Catalogue no: **CASCD 1080**

Cass: Released Sep '83, on Charisma by Virgin Records. Catalogue no: **CHCMC 81**

Album: Released Feb '74, on Charisma by Virgin Records. Deleted Feb '79. Catalogue no: **CAS 1080**

MONTY PYTHON (Monty Python's Flying Circus)

Album: Released Aug '75, on Charisma by Virgin Records. Deleted Aug '80. Catalogue no: **CAS 1003**

MONTY PYTHON AND THE HOLY GRAIL (Film soundtrack) (Monty Python's Flying Circus)

Tracks: / Jeunesse / Honours list / Big country / Homeward bound / God choir / Fanfare / Camelot song, The / Sunrise music / Magic finger / Sir Robin's song / In the shadows / Desperate moment / Knights of Ni / Circle of danger / Love theme / Magenta / Starlet in the starlight / Monk's chat / Promised land, The.

Note: Continuous track-spurious titles!

CD: Released Nov '89, on Charisma by Virgin Records. Catalogue no: **CASCD 1103**

Cass: Released Mar '83, on Charisma by Virgin Records. Catalogue no: **CHCMC 17**

Album: Released Mar '83, on Charisma by Virgin Records. Catalogue no: **CHC 17**

MONTY PYTHON'S FLYING CIRCUS (Monty Python's Flying Circus)

Tracks: / Flying sheep / Television interviews / Trades descriptions act / Nudge nudge / Mouse problem / Buying a bed / Interesting people / Barber, The / Interviews / More television interviews / Children's stories / Visitors, The / Cinema / North Minehead by-election / Me, doctor / Pet shop / Self defence.

CD: Released Jun '85, on BBC by BBC Records. Catalogue no: **BBC CD 73**

Cass: Released Jun '85, on BBC

Music from the TV series *Moonlighting* (MCA)

by BBC Records. Catalogue no: **REMC 73**

Album: Released '74, on BBC by BBC Records. Catalogue no: **REB 73**

MONTY PYTHON'S MEANING OF LIFE (Film soundtrack) (Monty Python's Flying Circus)

Album: Released Jun '83, on CBS by CBS Records & Distribution. Deleted Aug '87. Catalogue no: **CBS 70239**

Cass: Released Jun '83, on CBS by CBS Records & Distribution. Deleted Aug '87. Catalogue no: **40 70239**

PREVIOUS ALBUM (Monty Python's Flying Circus)

Tracks: / Fashion parade / Alla handel / Sporting news / Money song / Dennis Moore (Robin Hood theme) / Happy movement / Eric the half a bee / Holiday time / Beethoven's 5th / Comic giggles / Beachy head / Yangtse music / Medieval fanfares / Great adventure suite / Fairytale music / Ya de bucketty / Television tensions.

Note: Continuous track-spurious titles!

Album: Released Jan '73, on Charisma by Virgin Records. Deleted Jan '78. Catalogue no: **CAS 1063**

Cass: Released Sep '83, on Charisma by Virgin Records. Catalogue no: **CHCMC 80**

CD: Released Nov '89, on Charisma by Virgin Records. Catalogue no: **CASCD 1063**

Album: Released Apr '87, on Charisma by Virgin Records. Catalogue no: **CHC 80**

SINGS (Monty Python's Flying Circus)

Tracks: / Always look on the bright side of life / Sit on my face / Lumberjack song / Penis song (not the Noel Coward song) / Oliver Cromwell / Money song / Accountancy shanty / Finland / Medical love song / I'm so worried / Every sperm is sacred / Never be rude to an arab / I like Chinese / Eric the half a bee / Brian song / Bruce's philosophers song / Meaning of life / Knights of the Round Table / All things dull and ugly / Decomposing compers / Henry Kissinger / I've got two legs / Christmas in heaven / Galaxy song / Spam song.

Album: Released Dec '89, on Virgin by Virgin Records. Catalogue

no: **MONT 1**

CD: Released Dec '89, on Virgin by Virgin Records. Catalogue no: **MONTD 1**

Cass: Released Dec '89, on Virgin by Virgin Records. Catalogue no: **MONTC 1**

Moon In The Gutter

MOON IN THE GUTTER, THE (Original Soundtrack) (Various artists)

Album: Released Jan '89, on DRG (USA) by DRG Records (USA). Catalogue no: **SL 9516**

CD: Released Jan '89, on DRG (USA) by DRG Records (USA). Catalogue no: **CDFMC 2**

Cass: Released Jan '89, on DRG (USA) by DRG Records (USA). Catalogue no: **SLC 9516**

Moon Over Parador

MOON OVER PARADOR, THE (Original Soundtrack) (Various artists)

Note: Score by Maurice Jarre for the Richard Dreyfuss film.

CD: Released Jan '89, on MCA (USA) by MCA Records (USA). Catalogue no: **MCAD 6249**

Album: Released Jan '89, on MCA (USA) by MCA Records (USA). Catalogue no: **MCA 6249**

Cass: Released Jan '89, on MCA (USA) by MCA Records (USA). Catalogue no: **MCAC 6249**

Moonlight Moods

THEMES & DREAMS

Tracks: / Chi mai / Chariots of fire / Xanadu / Imagine / For your eyes only / Bermuda triangle / Riders in the sky / Sukiyaki / Sailing / MASH / To love the lord / Bright eyes / Fantasy / Magic / Waterfalls / North star / I made it through the rain / Angel of the morning / Give us shelter / Cavatina.

Cass set: Released Mar '85, on Pickwick by Pickwick Records. Catalogue no: **IMPC 103**

Album: Released Feb '82, on Hallmark by Pickwick Records. Catalogue no: **SHM 3102**

Cass: Released Feb '82, on Hallmark by Pickwick Records. Catalogue no: **HSC 3102**

Album: Released Mar '85, on Pickwick by Pickwick Records. Catalogue no: **IMP 103**

CD: Released '86, on Pickwick by

Pickwick Records. Catalogue no: **PCD 815**

THEMES & DREAMS, VOL.2
CD: Released '88, on Pickwick by Pickwick Records. Catalogue no: **PWK 013**
Album: Released Sep '84, on Hallmark by Pickwick Records. Catalogue no: **SHM 3148**
Cass: Released Sep '84, on Hallmark by Pickwick Records. Catalogue no: **HSC 3148**

Moonlighting

MOONLIGHTING (Television soundtrack) (Various artists) (See picture on previous page)
Tracks: / Moonlighting: *Jarreau, Al* / Limbo rock: *Checker, Chubby* / This old heart of mine: *Isley Brothers* / I told ya I love ya, now get out: *Sheperd, Cybill* / Good lovin': *Willis, Bruce* / Since I fell for you: *James, Bob & David Sanborn* / When a man loves a woman: *Sledge, Percy* / Someone to watch over me: *Ronstadt, Linda* / Stormy weather: *Holiday, Billie*.
Album: Released Jul '87, on MCA by MCA Records. Catalogue no: **MCF 3386**
CD: Released Jul '87, on MCA by MCA Records. Catalogue no: **DMCF 3386**
Cass: Released Jul '87, on MCA by MCA Records. Catalogue no: **MCFC 3386**
CD: Released Jul '88, on MCA by MCA Records. Catalogue no: **DMCL 1873**
CD: Released Nov '88, on WEA by WEA Records. Catalogue no: **241 438-2**

Moonraker

MOONRAKER (SINGLE) (See under Bassey, Shirley)

MOONRAKER (Original Soundtrack) (Various artists)
Note: Score by John Barry with Shirley Bassey.
Album: Released Mar '90, on Silva Screen by Silva Screen Records. Catalogue no: **1826961**
Cass: Released Mar '90, on Silva Screen by Silva Screen Records. Catalogue no: **1826964**
Cass: Released Jan '89, on EMI (Import) Catalogue no: **E 41 E**

90620
CD: Released Jan '89, on EMI (Import) Catalogue no: **CD 90620**

MOONRAKER (Film soundtrack) (Various artists)
Tracks: / Moonraker (main title): *Various artists* / Space laser battle: *Various artists* / Miss Goodhead meets Bond: *Various artists* / Cable car and snake fight: *Various artists* / Bond lured to pyramid: *Various artists* / Flight into space: *Various artists* / Bond arrives in Rio and boat chase: *Various artists* / Centrifuge and Corrine put down: *Various artists* / Bond smells a rat: *Various artists* / Moonraker (end title): *Various artists*.
Cass: Released Dec '86, on Conifer Catalogue no: **1C 064 82696**
Album: Released Sep '79, on United Artists by EMI Records. Deleted '84. Catalogue no: **UAG 30247**
Cass: Released '79, on United Artists by EMI Records. Deleted '84. Catalogue no: **TCK 30247**
Album: Released Dec '86, on Conifer Catalogue no: **3C 054 82696**

Moonstruck

MOONSTRUCK (Original soundtrack) (Various artists)
Tracks: / That's amore: *Martin, Dean* / Canzone per Loretta: *Various artists* / Addio, Mulberry Street: *Various artists* / Mr. Moon: *Various artists* / It must be him: *Various artists* / Old man Mazurka: *Various artists* / Lament for Johnny's mama: *Various artists* / La boheme: *Various artists* / Che gelida manina: *Various artists* / Donde lieta usci: *Various artists* / O soave fanciulla: *Various artists* / Musettas waltz: *Various artists* / Musettas entrance: *Various artists* / Instrumental excerpts: *Various artists* / Getting ready: *Various artists* / Brooklyn heights stroll: *Various artists* / Beautiful senorita: *Various artists* / Moonglow: *Various artists* / Gioventu mia, tu non sei morta: *Various artists*.
CD: Released May '88, on Capitol by EMI Records. Catalogue no: **CDEST 2060**
CD: Released May '88, on Capitol by EMI Records. Catalogue no:

CDP 790 231 2
Album: Released May '88, on Capitol by EMI Records. Catalogue no: **EST 2060**
Cass: Released May '88, on Capitol by EMI Records. Catalogue no: **TCEST 2060**

Moonwalker

MOONWALKER (See under Jackson, Michael)

Moore, Sam

SOUL MAN (Moore, Sam & Lou Reed)
Tracks: / Soul man / Sweet Sarah.
7" Single: Released Jan '87, on A&M by A&M Records. Deleted Mar '88. Catalogue no: **AM 364**

Mop & Smiff

MOP AND SMIFF (Various artists)
Tracks: / Two of a kind: *Various artists* / Happy birthday Mop and Smiff: *Various artists* / Special day: *Various artists* / Big top travelling show: *Various artists* / Sniffin': *Various artists* / Trackin' through the bracken: *Various artists* / Wooly friends: *Various artists* / Flower floats and beauty queens: *Various artists* / With the May Queen: *Various artists* / Down by the lakeside: *Various artists* / Bumpity bang: *Various artists* / Fluttering by: *Various artists* / Home for gnomes, A: *Various artists* / Mop's no Sherlock Holmes: *Various artists* / Painting song, The: *Various artists*.
Note: From the BBC children's TV programme.
Album: Released May '85, on BBC by BBC Records. Deleted Apr '89. Catalogue no: **REC 558**
Cass: Released May '85, on BBC by BBC Records. Deleted Apr '89. Catalogue no: **ZCM 558**

Moran, Diana

GET FIT WITH THE GREEN GODDESS
Tracks: / Introduction - Breakfast time / Morning dance (Legs and ankles.) / Wake up everybody (the great stretch) / Chi Mai (Neck and shoulders) / Hill Street blues / I heard it through the grapevine (Boobs, Chest & Underarms) / (They long to be) close to you / Daybreak (Hips) / I'm not in love

(Back.) / Rise / Whiter shade of pale, A / Green goddess, The (tummy) / In the summertime (exercises for legs) / Who pays the ferryman? ((back and leg exercises)) / Relax.
Album: Released '83, on BBC by BBC Records. Deleted Apr '89. Catalogue no: **REH 479**
Cass: Released '83, on BBC by BBC Records. Catalogue no: **ZCR 479**

More Dirty Dancing

MORE DIRTY DANCING (1987 film soundtrack) (Various artists)
Tracks: / I've had the time of my life: *Morris, John Orchestra, The* / Big girls don't cry: *Four Seasons* / Merengue: *Lloyd, Michael & Le Disc* / Some kind of wonderful: *Drifters* / Johnny's mambo: *Lloyd, Michael & Le Disc* / Do you love me: *Contours* / Love man: *Redding, Otis* / Wipe out: *Surfaris, The* / These arms of mine: *Redding, Otis* / De todo un poco: *Lloyd, Michael & Le Disc* / Cry to me: *Burke, Solomon* / Trot the fox: *Lloyd, Michael & Le Disc* / Will you love me tomorrow: *Shirelles* / Kellerman's anthem: *Emile Bergstein Chorale, The.*
Album: Released 30 Apr '88, on RCA by BMG Records (UK). Catalogue no: **BL 86965**
CD: Released 30 Apr '88, on RCA by BMG Records (UK). Catalogue no: **BD 86965**
Cass: Released 30 Apr '88, on RCA by BMG Records (UK). Catalogue no: **BK 86965**

Morecambe & Wise

BBC TV SHOWS
Tracks: / Here you are / 45 minutes of fun and laughter / Eric Morecambe, you'll do anything for a laugh / There's a lot of flu about / Diamond ring in the window, The / Ern, you have got a magnificent body / Carry on Ern / Visit from the police, A / Are you Mrs. T Potter / Welcome to the show / I'm going to be Bob Hope's chief scriptwriter / Finale.
Cass: Released Oct '84, on BBC by BBC Records. Deleted 31 Aug '88. Catalogue no: **ZCM 534**
Album: Released Oct '84, on BBC by BBC Records. Deleted 31 Aug

'88. Catalogue no: **REC 534**

IT'S MORECAMBE & WISE
Cass: Released Nov '76, on BBC by BBC Records. Deleted '87. Catalogue no: **MRMC 052**

MUSICAL EXTRAVAGANZA
VHS: Released '88, on BBC Video by BBC Video. Catalogue no: **BBCV 4005**

SO WHAT DO YOU THINK OF THE SHOW SO FAR
Tracks: / Overture and beginners / Byron and Keats / Marriage with licence, A / Pilchards / Bath time for Ernie / Spy with the cold nose, The.
Cass: Released Sep '75, on BBC by BBC Records. Deleted '88. Catalogue no: **RMC 4020**
Album: Released Sep '75, on BBC by BBC Records. Deleted '87. Catalogue no: **REB 210**

Moroder, Giorgio

DUEL
Tracks: / Duel / Madeline's theme. Note: From the film *Electric Dreams.*
7" Single: Released Dec '84, on Virgin by Virgin Records. Deleted '87. Catalogue no: **VS 732**

NOW YOU'RE MINE (Moroder, Giorgio & Helen Terry)
Tracks: / Now you're mine.
Note: From the film 'Electric Dreams'.
12" Single: Released Nov '84, on Virgin by Virgin Records. Deleted '89. Catalogue no: **VS 710-12**
7" Single: Released Nov '84, on Virgin by Virgin Records. Deleted '89. Catalogue no: **VS 710**

PAUL'S THEME
Tracks: / Paul's theme / Cat people.
Note: From the film 'Cat People' starring Malcolm McDowell and Nastassia Kinski.
7" Single: Released Jul '82, on MCA by MCA Records. Catalogue no: **MCA 770**
12" Single: Released Jul '82, on MCA by MCA Records. Catalogue no: **MCAT 770**

Morons From Outer...

MORONS FROM OUTER SPACE
Tracks: / Morons from outer space.

12" Single: Released Mar '85, on EMI by EMI Records. Deleted '86. Catalogue no: **12 MORON 1**
7" Single: Released Mar '85, on EMI by EMI Records. Deleted '86. Catalogue no: **MORON 1**

Morricone, Ennio

ASSOLUTO NATURALE (See under Assoluto Naturale)

CHI MAI (OLD GOLD) (TV theme)
Tracks: / Chi mai / Who pays the ferryman.
Note: Theme from BBC TV series The Life and Times of David Lloyd George
7" Single: Released Jan '85, on Old Gold by Old Gold Records. Catalogue no: **OG 9413**

ENDLESS GAMES, THE (T.V. soundtrack)
Tracks: / Endless game, The / Alec's journey / Game goes on, The / Summer solitude / Caroline's song / From Russia / Love game, The / Anif / Silvia's game / Just a game / Chess game.
Cass: Released Sep '89, on Virgin by Virgin Records. Catalogue no: **TCV 2602**
Album: Released Sep '89, on Virgin by Virgin Records. Catalogue no: **V 2602**
CD: Released Sep '89, on Virgin by Virgin Records. Catalogue no: **CDV 2602**

ENNIO MORRICONE 1 (The greatest film music of) (Various artists)
Cass: Released Jan '89, on Silva Screen by Silva Screen Records. Catalogue no: **240576.4**
Album: Released Jan '89, on Silva Screen by Silva Screen Records. Catalogue no: **240576.1**

ENNIO MORRICONE 2 (The greatest film music of) (Various artists)
Album: Released Jan '89, on Silva Screen by Silva Screen Records. Catalogue no: **240577.1**
Cass: Released Jan '89, on Silva Screen by Silva Screen Records. Catalogue no: **240577.4**

ENNIO MORRICONE 3 (The greatest film music of) (Various artists)
Album: Released Jan '89, on Silva Screen by Silva Screen Rec-

ords. Catalogue no: **240077.1**
Cass: Released Jan '89, on Silva Screen by Silva Screen Records. Catalogue no: **240077.4**

ENNIO MORRICONE 4 (The greatest film music of) (Various artists)

Album: Released Jan '89, on Silva Screen by Silva Screen Records. Catalogue no: **242049.1**
Cass: Released Jan '89, on Silva Screen by Silva Screen Records. Catalogue no: **242049.4**

ENNIO MORRICONE 5 (The greatest film music of) (Various artists)

Cass: Released Jan '89, on Silva Screen by Silva Screen Records. Catalogue no: **242052.4**
Album: Released Jan '89, on Silva Screen by Silva Screen Records. Catalogue no: **242052.1**

FILM HITS

Tracks: / Once upon a time in the west / For a few dollars more / Moses theme / Bye bye Colonel / Fistful of dollars / Gun for Ringo / Ballad of Sacco and Vanzetti / Here's to you / Vice of killing / Paying off scores / Adventurer / What have you done to Solange / Violent city / Mertello.
Cass: Released '86, on RCA by BMG Records (UK). Catalogue no: **NK 70091**
CD: Released May '90, on RCA by BMG Records (UK). Catalogue no: **ND 70091**
Album: Released '86, on RCA by BMG Records (UK). Deleted Jun '90. Catalogue no: **NL 70091**
Album: Released Jan '81, on RCA International by BMG Records (UK). Deleted Jan '86. Catalogue no: **INTS 5059**

FILM MUSIC 1966-1987

Tracks: / Good, the bad and the ugly, The / Sicilian clan, The / Chi Mai / Investigation of a citizen above suspicion / Mosca Addio / Marche en la / Battle of Algiers, The / Infernal trio, The / Dedicace / Sacco and Vanzetti / La tragedia di un uomo ridicolo / Once upon a time in the west (Main theme.) / Mission, The (remix) / Once upon a time in America (Cokey's song.) / Gabriel's oboe / Atto di dolore / Baci dopo il tramonto / Le marginal / Estate 1943 / Falls, The / Man

with the harmonica, The / Lontano / My name is Nobody / Peur sur la ville / Le vent, le cri / Once upon a time in America (Deborah's theme.).
Cass: Released 15 Jan '88, on Virgin by Virgin Records. Catalogue no: **TCVD 2516**
CD Set: Released '88, on Virgin by Virgin Records. Catalogue no: **CDVD 2516**
2 LP Set: Released 15 Jan '88, on Virgin by Virgin Records. Catalogue no: **VD 2516**

GREATEST FILM THEMES

CD: Released Aug '90, on Musidisc by Musidisc Records (France). Catalogue no: **402222**
Cass: Released Aug '90, on Musidisc by Musidisc Records (France). Catalogue no: **402224**

GREATEST MOVIE THEMES

CD: Released '86, on Accord (France) by Musidisc Records (France). Catalogue no: **139 220**

HAWKS AND DOVES (See under Hawks & Doves)

MISSION, THE (Original Soundtrack) (Morricone, Ennio & The London Philharmonic Orch)

Tracks: / On earth as it is in Heaven / Mission, The / Falls, The / River / Gabriel's oboe / Ave Maria Guarani / Te Deum Guarani / Brothers / Refusal / Carlotta / Asuncion / Vita nostra / Alone / Climb / Guarani / Remorse / Sword, The / Penance / Miserere.
Cass: Released Oct '86, on Virgin by Virgin Records. Catalogue no: **TCV 2402**
CD: Released Oct '86, on Virgin by Virgin Records. Catalogue no: **CDV 2402**
Album: Released Oct '86, on Virgin by Virgin Records. Catalogue no: **V 2402**

MOSES (Original Soundtrack)

Album: Released Jan '77, on Pye International Catalogue no: **NSPH 28503**

MY NAME IS NOBODY (See under My Name Is Nobody)

ONCE UPON A TIME IN THE WEST (SINGLE)

Tracks: / Once upon a time in the west / Finale.
7" Single: Released '79, on RCA

by BMG Records (UK). Deleted '82. Catalogue no: **PB 6197**

ONCE UPON A TIME IN THE WEST (SINGLE)

Tracks: / Once upon a time in the west / Secret.
7" Single: Released Jun '81, on BBC by BBC Records. Deleted Jun '84. Catalogue no: **RESL 93**

ONCE UPON A TIME IN THE WEST (Film soundtrack)

Tracks: / Once upon a time in the West / As a judgement / Farewell to Cheyenne / Transgression, The / First tavern, The / Second tavern, The / Man with a harmonica / Dimly lit room, A / Bad orchestra / Man, The / Jill's America.
Cass: Released '79, on RCA by BMG Records (UK). Deleted '84. Catalogue no: **PK 31387**
Cass: Released Oct '83, on Deja Vu Catalogue no: **NK 70032**
Album: Released '79, on RCA by BMG Records (UK). Deleted '84. Catalogue no: **PL 31387**
CD: Released Feb '90, on Silva Screen by Silva Screen Records. Catalogue no: **4736.2**
CD: Released Jun '88, on RCA by BMG Records (UK). Catalogue no: **ND 71704**
Album: Released Oct '83, on Deja Vu Catalogue no: **NL 70032**

OUT WEST WITH MORRICONE'S HIT FILM THEMES

Tracks: / For a few dollars more / My name is Nobody / Once upon a time in the West / L'homme a l'harmonica / Good, the bad and the ugly, The / Professional gun, A / Il etait une fois la revolution / Mercenary / La liberted / Exorcist 2 theme.
Cass: on Biba Catalogue no: **BBM 57**

RAMPAGE (Film Soundtrack)

Tracks: / Rampage / Son / Findings / Over to the jury / Run, Run, Run / Since childhood / Magma / Gruesome discovery / Carillon / District attorney / Mother / Recollections.
Cass: Released '88, on Virgin by Virgin Records. Deleted Jun '90. Catalogue no: **TCV 2491**
CD: Released Jun '88, on Virgin by Virgin Records. Catalogue no: **CDV 2491**
Album: Released '88, on Virgin

by Virgin Records. Deleted May '90. Catalogue no: **V 2491**

TEPEPA (See under Tepepa)

TIME OF DESTINY (See under Time Of Destiny)

SAHARA (See under Sahara)

UNTOUCHABLES, THE (Original soundtrack)
Tracks: / Untouchables, The (end title) / Al Capone / Waiting at the border / Death theme / On the rooftops / Victorious / Man with the matches, The / Strength of the righteous, The (main title) / Ness and his family / False alarm / Untouchables, The / Four friends / Machine gun lullaby.
Cass: Released Oct '87, on A&M by A&M Records. Catalogue no: **393 909-4**
Album: Released Oct '87, on A&M by A&M Records. Catalogue no: **393 909-1**
CD: Released Oct '87, on A&M by A&M Records. Catalogue no: **393 909-2**

Morrison, Diana

FIRST MAN YOU REMEMBER, THE (See under Ball, Michael)

Morton, Mike

WINDS OF WAR LOVE THEME (Morton, Mike Orchestra)
Tracks: / Winds of war (Love theme.) / Berlin beat.
Note: From the TV mini series *Winds Of War.*
7" Single: Released Oct '83, on M&H Catalogue no: **MH 1002**

WINDS OF WAR (THEME)
Tracks: / Winds of war / Berlin heat.
Note: From the TV mini series of the same name.
7" Single: Released Jul '85, on Sounds Right Catalogue no: **MSBW 2**

Moses

MOSES (Film soundtrack) (See under Morricone, Ennio)

Mosquito Coast

MOSQUITO COAST (Film soundtrack) (Various artists)
Tracks: / Mosquito Coast: *Jarre, Maurice* / Goodbye America:

Jarre, Maurice / Gimme soca: *Lee, Byron & The Dragonaires* / Up the river: *Jarre, Maurice* / Jeronimo: *Jarre, Maurice* / Fat boy: *Jarre, Maurice* / Destruction: *Jarre, Maurice* / Storm, The: *Jarre, Maurice* / Allie's theme: *Jarre, Maurice.*
Note: Mosquito Coast, starring Harrison Ford and Helen Mirren, features music composed and conducted by Maurice Jarre, plus one track, Gimme Soca, by Byron Lee and the Dragonaires.
CD: Released Mar '87, on London Records by London Records Ltd. Deleted '88. Catalogue no: **902 210-4**
CD: Released Jan '89, on Silva Screen by Silva Screen Records. Catalogue no: **FCD 21005**
Album: Released Mar '87, on London Records by London Records Ltd. Deleted Oct '88. Catalogue no: **LONLP 30**
Album: Released Feb '90, on Silva Screen by Silva Screen Records. Catalogue no: **FSP21005**
CD: Released Mar '87, on London Records by London Records Ltd. Deleted '88. Catalogue no: **FCD 210 052**
Cass: Released Feb '90, on Silva Screen by Silva Screen Records. Catalogue no: **FSPC21005**
Cass: Released Mar '87, on London Records by London Records Ltd. Deleted Oct '88. Catalogue no: **LONC 30**

Most Happy Fella

MOST HAPPY FELLA (Original Broadway cast) (Various artists)
Album: Released Jan '89, on Silva Screen by Silva Screen Records. Catalogue no: **ACS 2330**

MOST HAPPY FELLA (ORIGINAL ISSUE) (Broadway cast) (Various artists)
Album: Released May '60, on Philips by Phonogram Ltd. Deleted '65. Catalogue no: **BBL 7374**
Album: Released Jul '60, on H.M.V. by EMI Records. Deleted '65. Catalogue no: **CLP 1365**

Mother Wore Tights

MOTHER WORE TIGHTS/THE

SHOCKING MISS PILGRIM (Film soundtrack) (Various artists)
Note: Starring Betty Grable.
Album: Released Jan '89, on CIF Catalogue no: **CIF 3008**

Motley Crue

GIRLS, GIRLS, GIRLS (SINGLE)
Tracks: / Girls, girls, girls / Sumthin' for nuthin' / Smokin' in the boys room (live) (Extra track on 12").
Note: From the film *Like Father Like Son.*
12" Single: Released Jul '87, on Elektra by Elektra Records (UK). Deleted Jan '90. Catalogue no: **EKR 59 T**
7" Single: Released Jul '87, on Elektra by Elektra Records (UK). Deleted Jul '88. Catalogue no: **EKR 59**

WILD SIDE
Tracks: / Wild side / Five years dead.
Note: From the film *Like Father Like Son.*
7" Single: Released Nov '87, on Elektra (Import) by Elektra/Asylum/Nonesuch Records (USA). Catalogue no: **769449**

Motorhead

ACE OF SPADES (SINGLE)
Tracks: / Ace of spades.
Note: Featured in the film 'Supergrass'.
7" Single: Released Nov '80, on Bronze by Bronze Records. Deleted '83. Catalogue no: **BRO 106**

EAT THE RICH
Tracks: / Eat the rich / Cradle to the grave.
Note: From the film of the same name.
12" Single: Released '89, on Road Runner (1) by Road Runner Records. Catalogue no: **RR 125468**
12" Single: Released 31 Oct '87, on GWR by GWR Records. Catalogue no: **GWR 6**

Mouskouri, Nana

SONGS FROM HER T.V. SERIES
Tracks: / I have a dream / Blow the wind Southerly / Open the door /

Morning has broken / Imagine / My colouring book / And I love her so / Let it be / Loch Lomond / Milisse Mou.

Cass: Released Sep '80, on Philips by Phonogram Ltd. Deleted '85. Catalogue no: **7206 069**

Album: Released Oct '80, on Philips by Phonogram Ltd. Deleted '85. Catalogue no: **6395 069**

Album: Released Apr '73, on Fontana by Phonogram Ltd. Deleted Apr '78. Catalogue no: **6312 036**

Movie Busters

MOVIE BUSTERS (Various artists)

Tracks: / Ghostbusters: *Various artists* / Footloose: *Various artists* / Chariots of fire: *Various artists* / Arthur's theme: *Various artists* / Flashdance... what a feeling: *Various artists* / Love on the rocks: *Various artists* / E.T.: *Various artists* / It might be you: *Various artists* / Eye of the tiger: *Various artists* / Maniac: *Various artists* / Against all odds: *Various artists* / Let's hear it for the boy: *Various artists* / Up where we belong: *Various artists* / For your eyes only: *Various artists* / Carol Anne's theme: *Various artists* / Terms of endearment: *Various artists*.

Album: Released Nov '84, on Emerald by Emerald Records. Catalogue no: **BER 001**

Cass: Released Nov '84, on Emerald by Emerald Records. Catalogue no: **KBER 001**

Movie Collection

MOVIE COLLECTION (Various artists)

2 LP Set: Released '79, on Polydor by Polydor Ltd. Deleted '84. Catalogue no: **2675178**

Movie Greats

MOVIE GREATS (Various artists)

Tracks: / Jaws, Theme from: *Various artists* / Flying (theme from E.T.): *Various artists* / Axel F: *Various artists* / Back to the future: *Various artists* / Somewhere in time: *Various artists* / Fletch theme: *Various artists* / Entertainer, The: *Various artists* (from "The Sting") / Overture (from: Jesus Christ Superstar): *Various artists* / Love story theme: *Various artists* / River, The: *Various artists* / Main title: *Various artists* (From

the film 'Out of Africa'.) / Over the moon (E.T. the Extra-Terrestial): *Various artists*.

Album: Released Oct '87, on MCA by MCA Records. Catalogue no: **MCL 1860**

Cass: Released Oct '87, on MCA by MCA Records. Catalogue no: **MCLC 1860**

Movie Masters

MOVIE MASTERS (16 original soundtrack recordings) (Various artists)

Tracks: / Godfather: *Various artists* / Great Gatsby: *Various artists* / Oh what a lovely war: *Various artists* / Odd couple: *Various artists* / Chinatown: *Various artists* / Borsalino: *Various artists* / Nashville: *Various artists* / Love story: *Various artists* / Serpico: *Various artists* / Song of Norway: *Various artists* / Ten commandments: *Various artists* / Dove: *Various artists* / Easy rider: *Various artists* / Shaft in Africa: *Various artists*.

Album: Released Jan '77, on ABC Records by MCA Records. Deleted '81. Catalogue no: **ABCL 5205**

Movie Musicals

MOVIE MUSICALS (Various artists)

CD: Released 6 Feb '88, on BBC by BBC Records. Catalogue no: **BBC CD 546**

MOVIE MUSICALS 1927-1936 (Classic years vol 7) (Various artists)

Tracks: / Fine romance: *Astaire, Fred & Ginger Rogers* / Three little words: *Ellington, Duke* / My mammy: *Jolson, Al* / My man: *Brice, Fanny* / What would you do: *Chevalier, Maurice* / Beyond the blue horizon: *McDonald, Joe* / I love you so much that I hate you: *Swan Song* / It's only a paper moon: *Edwards, Cliff* / I'm no angel: *West, Mae* / 42nd Street: *Keeler, Ruby/Dick Powell* / Learn to croon: *Crosby, Bing* / On the good ship lollipop: *Temple, Shirley* / Okay toots: *Cantor, Eddie* / Lulu's back in town: *Powell, Dick* / Old man river: *Robeson, Paul* / Bojangles of Harlem: *Astaire, Fred*.

CD: Released '86, on BBC by BBC Records. Catalogue no: **BBC CD 654**

Cass: Released '86, on BBC by BBC Records. Catalogue no: **ZCF**

654

Album: Released '86, on BBC by BBC Records. Catalogue no: **REB 654**

MOVIE MUSICALS VOL.2 (Various artists)

Tracks: / Broadway melody: *Various artists* / Everybody sing: *Various artists* / Let's sing again: *Various artists* / Rose Marie: *Various artists* / Some of these days: *Various artists* / I'm putting all my eggs in one basket: *Various artists* / About a quarter to nine: *Various artists* / Lullaby of Broadway: *Various artists* / Swing me an old fashioned song: *Various artists* / Yours and mine: *Various artists* / Little Broadway: *Various artists* / Dear Mr. Gable: *Various artists*.

Cass: Released Mar '90, on BBC by BBC Records. Catalogue no: **ZCF 767**

Album: Released Mar '90, on BBC by BBC Records. Catalogue no: **REB 767**

CD: Released Mar '90, on BBC by BBC Records. Catalogue no: **BBCCD 767**

Movie Themes

MOVIE THEMES (Various artists)

Tracks: / Way we were, The: *Webb, Roger* / Honeymoon song: *Manuel & The Music of the Mountains* / Miss Marples theme: *Goodwin, Ron & His Orchestra* / Beyond tomorrow: *King, Denis & His Orchestra* / Princess Leia's theme: *Love, Geoff & His Orchestra* / James Bond theme: *Pourcel, Franck & His Orchestra* / 633 Squadron: *Goodwin, Ron & His Orchestra* / It's only a paper moon: *Webb, Roger* / Close encounters of the third kind: *Love, Geoff & His Orchestra* / Evergreen: *Manuel & The Music of the Mountains* / Chinatown theme: *King, Denis & His Orchestra* / You're the one that I want: *Love, Geoff & His Orchestra*.

Cass: Released Jul '84, on Ideal Tapes Deleted Jul '87. Catalogue no: **EE 260 093 4**

MOVIES GO TO THE OPERA (Various artists)

Tracks: / Madame Butterfly: *Various artists* (Fatal Attraction.) / Turandot: *Various artists* (The Witches Of Eastwick) / Lakme: *Various artists* (Someone to Watch Over Me.) / La boheme:

Various artists (Moonstruck.) / Barber of Seville: *Various artists* (Dark Eyes.) / De Walkure: *Various artists* (Apocalypse Now.) / La forza del destino: *Various artists* (Jean De Florette, Manon Of The Spring.) / La wally: *Various artists* (Diva.) / Les Pecheurs de Perles: *Various artists* (Gallipoli.) / Manon Lescaut: *Various artists* (Hannah & Her Sisters.) / Gianni Schicchi: *Various artists* (A Room With A View.) / La rondine: *Various artists* (A Room With A View.) / Cavalleria rusticana: *Various artists* (Raging Bull.).

CD: Released Oct '88, on EMI by EMI Records. Catalogue no: **CDM 769 596 2**

Movie Wonderland

MOVIE WONDERLAND (Various artists)
Cass: Released Feb '80, on Bravo by Pickwick Records. Deleted '88. Catalogue no: **BRC 2512**

Movin' Dream Orchestra

BOX OFFICE BLASTS
Tracks: / Color purple (Main title) / Round midnight / Take my breath away / Living in America / Surprise, surprise / Left of centre / So far so good / Earth angel / Absolute beginners / Say you, say me / Separate lives / Ghostbusters / Goonies 'r' good enough / Young Sherlock Holmes (Love theme from) / Tonight is what it means to be young.
CD: Released '88, on Denon Catalogue no: **DC-8501**

FLIGHT INTO FANTASY
Tracks: / Danger zone / Howard the duck / Power of love, The / E.T., Theme from / Star wars / Close encounters of the third kind / Superman / Convoy / We may never love like this again / Jaws 2 (Theme from) / View to a kill, A / From Russia with love / Speak softly love / Stranger in the night / Exodus / Laurence of Arabia.
CD: Released '88, on Denon Catalogue no: **DC-8502**

YESTERDAY'S DREAM (Movie theme classics)
Tracks: / Moon river / Way we were, The / Shadow of your smile / Time for us, A / Over the rainbow / Melody fair / East of Eden / To love again / Windmills of your mind / Third, man, Theme from / Sunflower / Where do I begin / Both sides now / Sound of silence, The

/ Let it be / Raindrops keep falling on my head / Born free / Tara's theme.
CD: Released '88, on Denon Catalogue no: **DC-8503**

Mr. Cinders

MR. CINDERS (London revival cast) (Various artists)
Tracks: / Tennis: *Various artists* / Blue blood: *Various artists* / True to two: *Various artists* / I want the world to know: *Various artists* / One man girl: *Various artists* / On with the dance: *Various artists* / At the ball: *Various artists* / Spread a little happiness: *Various artists* / Entracte: *Various artists* / 18th century dance: *Various artists* / She's my lovely: *Various artists* / Please Mr. Cinders: *Various artists* / On the Amazon: *Various artists* / Every little moment: *Various artists* / I've got you, you've got me: *Various artists* / Honeymoon for four: *Various artists* / Finale: *Various artists*.
Cass: Released Sep '83, on T. E. R. by That's Entertainment Records. Catalogue no: **ZCTER 1069**
Album: Released Sep '83, on T. E. R. by That's Entertainment Records. Catalogue no: **TER 1069**

MR. CINDERS (ORIGINAL) (Original London cast 1983) (Various artists)
Cass: on T. E. R. by That's Entertainment Records. Deleted May '89. Catalogue no: **ZCTER 1037**
Album: on T. E. R. by That's Entertainment Records. Deleted May '89. Catalogue no: **TER 1037**

Mr Men

MR MEN SONGS (Various artists)
Tracks: / Mr. Men theme: *Various artists* / Mr. Sneeze: *Various artists* / Mr. Bump: *Various artists* / Mr. Small: *Various artists* / Mr. Tickle: *Various artists*.
Cass: Released May '79, on BBC by BBC Records. Deleted 31 Aug '88. Catalogue no: **ZCM 345**
Album: Released May '79, on BBC by BBC Records. Deleted 31 Aug '88. Catalogue no: **REC 345**

PARTY TIME WITH THE MR MEN (Original Cast) (Various artists)
Album: Released Nov '85, on Stylus by Stylus Music Records.

Deleted '88. Catalogue no: **SMR 8510**
Cass: Released Nov '85, on Stylus by Stylus Music Records. Deleted '88. Catalogue no: **SMC 8510**

Muppet Babies

MUPPET BABIES (Various artists)
Tracks: / Muppet babies theme, The: *Various artists* / Merry go round: *Various artists* / Sleep rockin': *Various artists* / Dream for you inspiration: *Various artists* / Good things happen in the dark: *Various artists* / Camilla: *Various artists* / Rocket to the stars: *Various artists* / Practice makes perfect: *Various artists* / It's up to you: *Various artists* / I can't help being a star: *Various artists*.
Cass: Released Oct '86, on BBC by BBC Records. Deleted Apr '89. Catalogue no: **ZCR 613**
Album: Released Oct '86, on BBC by BBC Records. Deleted Apr '89. Catalogue no: **REH 613**

Muppets

GREAT MUPPET CAPER, THE (Original soundtrack)
Tracks: / Main title / Hey, a movie / Big red bus / Happiness hotel / Lady Holiday / Steppin' out with a star / Apartment / Night life / First time it happens / Couldn't we ride? / Piggy's fantasy / Great muppet caper / Homeward bound / Finale.
Note: Feature film based on the characters from the Jim Henson TV series.
Album: Released Sep '81, on Warner Bros. by WEA Records. Deleted Sep '86. Catalogue no: **K56942**

HALFWAY DOWN THE STAIRS
Tracks: / Halfway down the stairs.
7" Single: Released May '77, on PRT by Castle Communications Records. Catalogue no: **7N 45698**

MUPPET MOVIE (Film Soundtrack) (Various artists)
Tracks: / Rainbow connection: *Various artists* / Movin' right along: *Various artists* / Never before never again: *Various artists* / I hope that something better comes along: *Various artists* / Can you picture that: *Various artists* / I'm going to go back there someday: *Various artists* / God bless America: *Various artists* / Come back

animal: *Various artists* / Magic stone: *Various artists*.

Cass: Released '79, on CBS by CBS Records & Distribution. Deleted '84. Catalogue no: **CBS 40 70170**

Album: Released '79, on CBS by CBS Records & Distribution. Deleted '84. Catalogue no: **CBS 70170**

MUPPET SHOW-2, THE
Tracks: / Muppet show theme, The / Baby face / There's a new sound / Monologue by Fozzie Bear, A / Cuento le gusta / Who / Time in a bottle / Editorial by Sam the eagle, An / Borneo / At the dance / Upidee / Just one person / Happy feet / Pigs in space / I'm five / Sea shanty / New York state of mind / Pig calypso, The / When Gypsy's violin, A / Wishing song / Animal sings Gershwin / For what it's worth / We got us.

Album: on Pye Catalogue no: **NSPH 21**

MUPPET SHOW MUSIC ALBUM, THE
Tracks: / Muppet show theme, The / Hawaiian war chant / Rhyming song / Blue skies / Eight little notes / Do wah diddy diddy / Jamboree / Henrietta's wedding / Jam / Magic garden / Macho man / Mad about the frog / Pennsylvania 6-5000 / Lime and coconut / Frog kissin' / Dog walk / While my guitar gently weeps / Sixty seconds / It was a very good year.

Album: Released Nov '79, on Pye Catalogue no: **NSPL 18613**

Cass: Released Nov '79, on PRT by Castle Communications Records. Catalogue no: **ZCP 18613**

MUPPET SHOW MUSIC HALL
Tracks: / Don't dilly dally on the way / Waiting at the church / Boy in the gallery / Wotcher (knocked 'em in the Old Kent Road).

7" EP: Released Dec '77, on Pye Deleted '80. Catalogue no: **7NX 8004**

7" Single: Released Sep '80, on IMS by Polydor Ltd. Catalogue no: **LR 4375**

MUPPET SHOW, THE
Tracks: / Muppet show theme, The / Mississippi mud / Mahnamahna (with lullaby of birdland) / Flight of the bumble bee / Mr. Bass man / Cottleston pie / Muppaphones / Lady of Spain / Pachalafaka / Lydia the tattooed lady /

Halfway down the stairs / Tenderly / I'm in love with a big blue frog / Tit willow / Soap opera / Vetenarian's hospital / Simon Smith and the amazing dancing bear / What now my love / Fozzie monologue / Hugga wugga / Trees / Sax and violence / Being green.

Cass: Released Jun '77, on PRT by Castle Communications Records. Catalogue no: **ZCP 19**

Album: Released Jun '77, on Pye Catalogue no: **NSPH 19**

MUPPET SHOW THEME
Tracks: / Muppet show theme / Bein' green.

7" Single: Released Jun '77, on Pye Deleted '79. Catalogue no: **7N 45705**

MUPPETS TAKE MANHATTAN (Film soundtrack)
Album: Released Jun '85, on Warner Bros. by WEA Records. Catalogue no: **9251141**

Murder On The...

MURDER ON THE ORIENT EXPRESS/LADY CAROLINE LAMB (Original soundtrack) (Various artists) (See also under Lady Caroline Lamb)
Tracks: / Overture: *Various artists* / Stamboul Ferry: *Various artists* / Orient Express: *Various artists* / Princess Dragomiroff: *Various artists* / Finale: *Various artists* / Entr'acte: *Various artists* / Caroline: *Various artists* / Honeymoon In Italy: *Various artists* / Caroline & Byron: *Various artists* / Byron's March: *Various artists* / Banquet, The: *Various artists* / William returns home: *Various artists* / Temple, The: *Various artists* / Caroline's ride: *Various artists* / William and Caroline: *Various artists* / End music: *Various artists*.
Note: 2 of Richard Rodney Bennett's finest score.

CD: Released Feb '90, on Silva Screen by Silva Screen Records. Catalogue no: **FILMCD 019**

Album: Released Mar '88, on Silva Screen by Silva Screen Records. Deleted May '90. Catalogue no: **FILM 019**

Murderock
MURDEROCK (See under Emerson, Keith)

Murphy, Walter
THEMES FROM ET AND

MORE (Murphy, Walter & His Orchestra)
Tracks: / E.T. / Jaws / Poltergeist / Superman / Close encounters of the third kind / Star trek / Raiders of the lost ark.

Album: Released '83, on MCA by MCA Records. Deleted '88. Catalogue no: **MCF 3134**

Music Box
MUSIC BOX (Film Soundtrack) (Various artists)
Tracks: / Ann's theme: *Various artists* / Federal building: *Various artists* / Ann studies documents: *Various artists* / Scar, The: *Various artists* / Mirror, The: *Various artists* / Music box: *Various artists* / Blood red Danube: *Various artists* / Departure from court: *Various artists* / Journey to Budapest: *Various artists* / Ann and Georgina in Talbot: *Various artists* / Remembering: *Various artists* / Newspaper, The: *Various artists*.

Cass: Released Apr '90, on Varese Sarabande Records(USA) by Varese Sarabande Records (USA). Catalogue no: **VSC 5248**

Album: Released Apr '90, on Varese Sarabande Records(USA) by Varese Sarabande Records (USA). Catalogue no: **VS 5248**

CD: Released Apr '90, on Varese Sarabande Records(USA) by Varese Sarabande Records (USA). Catalogue no: **VSD 5248**

Music For Films
MUSIC FOR FILMS (Various artists)
CD: Released Sep '88, on Land by Land Records. Catalogue no: **LANDCD 004**

Album: Released Sep '88, on Land by Land Records. Catalogue no: **LAND 004**

Album: Released Oct '88, on Land by Land Records. Catalogue no: **LAND 004**

Music From...
MUSIC FROM JACQUES TATI FILMS (Tati, Jacques)
CD: Released Feb '90, on Silva Screen by Silva Screen Records. Catalogue no: **836983.2**

MUSIC FROM STREETS OF FIRE (Music from Streets of Fire)
Note: With the film imminent in cinemas, this EP contains three of

its song sequences, plus a behind-the-scenes look at the production in the making. Running time: 26 mins.

VHS: Released Sep '84, on CIC Video Catalogue no: **FIREVH 1**

MUSIC FROM THE ANDRE TECHINE FILMS (Sarde, Philippe)

CD: Released Feb '90, on SPI Milan (France) Catalogue no: **CDCH 343**

MUSIC FROM THE FILMS OF FRANCOIS TRUFFAUT (Jaubert, Maurice)

CD: Released Feb '90, on SPI Milan (France) Catalogue no: **CDCH 220**

MUSIC FROM THE HAMMER FILMS (Philharmonia Orchestra)

Tracks: / Dracula suite / Dracula, prince of darkness suite / Hands of the ripper suite / Taste the blood of Dracula suite / Vampire circus suite.

Note: February 1949 marked the offical birth of a small, unremarkable English film production company. They were registered as Hammer Film Productions Ltd. Within ten years, they had achieved great success worldwide by rescuing the Dracula and Frankenstein characters from the Hollywood doldrums; within twenty they had produced over fifty films featuring all manner of vampires, werewolves, mummys, zombies, reptiles, gorgons, psychos, witches, aliens and a series of man made monsters. They were all colourfully depicted in Hammer's own richly-textured gothic romances. This recording is a celebration of 40 years of Hammer film production. But more than that, it is also a celebration of a style of horror film that seems to have gone out of fashion. In an age when it customary to approach this genre with banks of electronic keyboards, the selections presented here in newly recorded digital sound serve to remind us that, although the budgets may have been low, the music, always an essential tool in helping to create and sustain atmosphere, was always symphonic in approach; an approach that can perhaps be best described as full-blooded.

CD: Released Jan '90, on Silva

Screen by Silva Screen Records. Catalogue no: **FILMCD 066**
Cass: Released Jan '90, on Silva Screen by Silva Screen Records. Catalogue no: **FILMC 066**
Album: Released Jan '90, on Silva Screen by Silva Screen Records. Catalogue no: **FILM 066**

MUSIC FROM THE HORROR FILMS OF DARIO ARGENTO (Various artists)

Note: Music by Ennio Morricone and Goblin.

Cass: Released Jan '89, on Cinevox by Cinevox Italy. Catalogue no: **CIAK 75009**
Album: Released Jan '89, on Cinevox by Cinevox Italy. Catalogue no: **CIA 5009**

MUSIC FROM THE PASOLINI FILMS (Various artists)

Album: Released May '85, on General Music (France) Catalogue no: **803 072**

MUSIC FROM THE REPUBLIC STUDIO SERIALS (Various artists)

Note: Newly recorded the music of William Lava.o

Album: Released Jan '89, on Silva Screen by Silva Screen Records. Catalogue no: **STV 81250**

Music From Great ...

MUSIC FROM GREAT AUSTRALIAN FILMS (Australian Broadcasting Comm. Philharmonic Orch.)

Tracks: / Newsfront / Gallipoli / My brillant career / Tall timbers / Cathy's child / Eliza Frazer / Breaker morant / Chant of Jimmy Blacksmith / Picture show man / Picnic at Hanging Rock / Mango tree, The / Dimboola / Caddie.

Note: Arranged and conducted by William Motzing, featuring Mark Isaacs, Bob Barnard, Tony Ansell, Erroll Buddle. Orchestra leader, Robert Ingram; producer, Peter Wall.

Album: Released Jun '83, on DRG (USA) by DRG Records (USA). Deleted Jan '89. Catalogue no: **SBL 12582**
Cass: Released '88, on DRG (USA) by DRG Records (USA). Catalogue no: **SBLC 12582**
CD: Released May '87, on DRG (USA) by DRG Records (USA). Deleted '88. Catalogue no: **CDSBL 12582**

Music From The Movies

MUSIC FROM THE MOVIES (Various artists)

Tracks: / Warsaw concerto: Various artists / Dream of Olwen: Various artists / Spellbound concerto: Various artists / Cornish rhapsody: Various artists / Rhapsody in blue: Various artists.

Cass: Released '85, on Classics For Pleasure by EMI Records. Catalogue no: **CFP4 14493 4**
Album: Released '85, on Classics For Pleasure by EMI Records. Catalogue no: **CFP4 14493 1**
Album: Released Jun '80, on H.M.V. by EMI Records. Deleted '85. Catalogue no: **ASD 3862**

Music Lovers

MUSIC LOVERS (Film Soundtrack) (Various artists)

Tracks: / Overture - Russian fair: Various artists / Piano concerto performance: Various artists / Tchaikovsky playing his new opera: Various artists / Ballet in St. Petersburg Park: Various artists / Night train to Moscow: Various artists / Canal sequence: Various artists / Dreams at Brailov: Various artists / Firework sequence: Various artists / Success: Various artists / Nina's madness and Tchaikovsky's death: Various artists.

Album: Released '73, on United Artists by EMI Records. Deleted '78. Catalogue no: **UAS 29134**

Music Machine

MUSIC MACHINE (Film soundtrack) (Various artists)

Tracks: / Let me feel your heartbeat: Various artists / Disco dancer: Various artists / Dilly: Various artists / Get the feel right: Various artists / Jumping the gun: Various artists / Music machine: Various artists / Move with the beat: Various artists / Music's my thing: Various artists / Ready for love: Various artists.

Album: Released '79, on Pye Deleted '84. Catalogue no: **NH 106**
Cass: Released '79, on Pye Deleted '84. Catalogue no: **ZC 106**

MUSIC MACHINE (VIDEO) Various artists (Various artists)

Note: Disco holds competition to find two new dance stars. Cert: PG.

Original soundtrack to *My Fair Lady* (CBS)

VHS: Released '88, on Phoenix Home Entertainment Catalogue no: **PB 43**
VHS: Released '87, on AVR Catalogue no: **AVR 030**

Music Man

MUSIC MAN (ORIGINAL ISSUE) (London cast) (Various artists)
Album: Released Jun '61, on H.M.V. by EMI Records. Deleted '66. Catalogue no: **CLP 1444**

MUSIC MAN, THE (Film soundtrack) (Various artists)
Album: Released Sep '62, on Warner Bros. by WEA Records. Deleted '65. Catalogue no: **WB 4066**
CD: Released Jul '87, on EMI by EMI Records. Deleted Aug '89. Catalogue no: **CDP 746 633 2**

MUSIC MAN, THE (FILM) (Original Soundtrack) (Various artists)
Note: Starring Robert Preston and Shirley Jones.
Album: Released Jan '89, on Warner Bros.(USA) by WEA Records. Catalogue no: **BS 1459**
CD: Released Jan '89, on Warner

Bros.(USA) by WEA Records. Catalogue no: **1459.2**
Cass: Released Jan '89, on Warner Bros.(USA) by WEA Records. Catalogue no: **W5 1459**

MUSIC MAN, THE (VIDEO) (Various artists)
VHS: Released Mar '88, on Warner Home Video by WEA Records. Catalogue no: **PES 11473**

Music Time

MUSIC TIME (Music from BBC Schools TV series) (Various artists)
Album: Released Nov '79, on BBC by BBC Records. Deleted '84. Catalogue no: **REC 362**

Musical Youth

NEVER GONNA GIVE YOU UP
Tracks: / Never gonna give you up / Rub'n'dub / Jim'll fix it.
Note: B side features theme tune to BBC TV's *Jim'll fix it.*
12" Single: Released Feb '83, on MCA by MCA Records. Deleted '86. Catalogue no: **YOUT 3**
7" Single: Released Feb '83, on MCA by MCA Records. Deleted '86. Catalogue no: **YOU 3**

Musique De Film

MUSIQUE DE FILM (FILM MUSIC) (Various artists)
LP Set: Released Jan '85, on Pathe Marconi (France) Catalogue no: **PM 2901573**

Mutant

MUTANT (Original soundtrack) (Various artists)
Note: Composed by Richard Band.
Album: Released Jan '89, on Varese Sarabande Records(USA) by Varese Sarabande Records (USA). Catalogue no: **STV 81209**

Mutiny!

MUTINY! (Original London cast) (Various artists) (See also under Essex, David)
Cass: Released Oct '85, on Telstar by Telstar Records (UK). Catalogue no: **STAC 2261**
Album: Released Oct '85, on Telstar by Telstar Records (UK). Catalogue no: **STAR 2261**

Mutiny On The Bounty

MUTINY ON THE BOUNTY (Original soundtrack) (Various artists)
Note: Bronislau Kaper score for the Marlon Brando version.
Cass: Released Jan '89, on MCA by MCA Records. Deleted Mar '90. Catalogue no: **MCAC 25007**
Album: Released Jan '89, on MCA by MCA Records. Catalogue no: **MCA 25007**

MUTINY ON THE BOUNTY / TARAS BULBA (Various artists)
Tracks: / Mutiny on the bounty theme: *Various artists* / Portsmouth harbour: *Various artists* / Storm at sea: *Various artists* / Girls and sailors: *Various artists* / Mutiny, The: *Various artists* / Follow me (Tahitian): *Various artists* / Leaving harbour: *Various artists* / Arrival in Tahiti: *Various artists* / Pitcairn island: *Various artists* / Follow me (English): *Various artists* / Outrigger chase: *Various artists* / Christian's death: *Various artists* / Taras bulba (overture): *Various artists* / Birth of Andrei, The: *Various artists* / Sleighride, The: *Various artists* / Chase at night: *Various artists* / No retreat: *Various artists* / Ride to Dubno,

The: *Various artists* / Wishing star, The - pastorale: *Various artists* / Black plague: *Various artists* / Taras' pledge: *Various artists* / Battle of Dubno & finale: *Various artists*.

Note: Contains medley: Native Tahitians; Te manu pukarua/Torea/Tahitian drums - Lucky star.

CD: Released Aug '90, on MGM (EMI) Catalogue no: **794 876 2**

Cass: Released Aug '90, on MGM (EMI) Catalogue no: **TCMGM 26**

Album: Released Aug '90, on MGM (EMI) Catalogue no: **LPMGM 26**

Album: Released Aug '90, on MGM (EMI) Catalogue no: **794 876 1**

CD: Released Aug '90, on MGM (EMI) Catalogue no: **CDMGM 26**

Cass: Released Aug '90, on MGM (EMI) Catalogue no: **794 876 4**

My Beautiful

MY BEAUTIFUL LAUNDERETTE (See under Woolfe, Rita)

MY BEAUTIFUL LAUNDERETTE / SAMMY AND ROSIE GET LAID (Original soundtrack) (Various artists)

Note: Music by Stanley Myers for two of the most successful recent British films.

Cass: Released Jan '89, on SPI Milan (France) Catalogue no: **C 369**

CD: Released Jan '89, on SPI Milan (France) Catalogue no: **CD 369**

Album: Released Jan '89, on SPI Milan (France) Catalogue no: **A 369**

My Demon Lover

MY DEMON LOVER (Original Soundtrack) (Various artists)

Note: Composed by David Newman.

Album: Released Jan '89, on Silva Screen by Silva Screen Records. Catalogue no: **STV 81322**

My Fair Lady

MY FAIR LADY (Original Broadway cast - 1959) (Various artists)

Cass: Released Mar '90, on CBS (import) by CBS Records & Distribution. Catalogue no: **PST 02015**

CD: Released Jan '89, on CBS (import) by CBS Records & Distribution. Catalogue no: **CK 2015**

MY FAIR LADY (Film soundtrack) (Various artists) (See picture on previous page)

Tracks: / Overture: *Various artists* / Why can't the English?: *Various artists* / Wouldn't it be lovely?: *Various artists* / I'm just an ordinary man: *Various artists* / With a little bit of luck: *Various artists* / Just you wait: *Various artists* / Rain in Spain, The: *Various artists* / I could have danced all night: *Various artists* / Ascot gavotte: *Various artists* / On the street where you live: *Various artists* / You did it: *Various artists* / Show me: *Various artists* / Get me to the Church on time: *Various artists*.

Album: Released Jun '81, on CBS by CBS Records & Distribution. Catalogue no: **CBS 32043**

Album: Released Oct '64, on CBS by CBS Records & Distribution. Deleted '67. Catalogue no: **BPG 72237**

Cass: Released Jun '81, on CBS by CBS Records & Distribution. Catalogue no: **40 32043**

CD: Released Dec '85, on CBS by CBS Records & Distribution. Catalogue no: **CD 70000**

MY FAIR LADY (Original London stage cast) (Various artists)

Tracks: / Overture: *Various artists* / Why can't the English: *Various artists* / Wouldn't it be lovely: *Various artists* / With a little bit of luck: *Various artists* / I'm an ordinary man: *Various artists* / Just you wait: *Various artists* / Rain in Spain: *Various artists* / I could have danced all night: *Various artists* / Ascot gavotte: *Various artists* / On the street where you live: *Various artists* / You did it: *Various artists* / Show me: *Various artists* / Get me to the church on time: *Various artists* / Hymn to him: *Various artists* / Without you: *Various artists*.

Album: Released Aug '85, on CBS Cameo by CBS Records & Distribution. Deleted 10 Jul '89. Catalogue no: **CBS 32671**

Cass: Released Aug '85, on CBS Cameo by CBS Records & Distribution. Deleted Aug '90. Catalogue no: **40 32671**

MY FAIR LADY (Original 1956 recording) (Various artists)

Cass: Released Jan '89, on CBS (import) by CBS Records & Distribution. Catalogue no: **JST 05090**

CD: Released Jan '89, on CBS (import) by CBS Records & Distribution. Catalogue no: **CK 05090**

MY FAIR LADY (Studio recording) (Various artists)

Tracks: / Overture...Why can't the English?: *Various artists* / Wouldn't it be lovely?: *Various artists* / With a little bit of luck: *Various artists* / I'm an ordinary man: *Various artists* / Just you wait: *Various artists* / Rain in Spain, The: *Various artists* / I could have danced all night: *Various artists* / Ascot gavotte: *Various artists* / On the street where you live: *Various artists* / Embassy waltz, The: *Various artists* / You did it: *Various artists* / Show me: *Various artists* / Get me to the church on time: *Various artists* / Hymn to him: *Various artists*.

CD: Released Nov '87, on Decca by Decca International. Deleted '88. Catalogue no: **421 200-2**

Cass: Released Nov '87, on Decca by Decca International. Deleted '88. Catalogue no: **MFLC 1**

Album: Released Nov '87, on Decca by Decca International. Deleted '88. Catalogue no: **MFL 1**

MY FAIR LADY (ORIGINAL ISSUE) (Broadway cast) (Various artists)

Album: Released Nov '58, on Philips by Phonogram Ltd. Deleted '63. Catalogue no: **RBL 1000**

Album: Released Jan '64, on CBS by CBS Records & Distribution. Deleted '69. Catalogue no: **BPG 68001**

MY FAIR LADY (VIDEO) (Various artists)

Note: Running time: 164 mins.

VHS: Released Aug '88, on CBS-Fox by CBS-Fox Video. Catalogue no: **7038 50**

My Left Foot

MY LEFT FOOT (See under Da/My Left Foot)

My Name Is Nobody

MY NAME IS NOBODY (Film soundtrack) (Various artists)

Note: Spaghetti western score by Ennio Morricone.

Album: Released Jan '89, on Cerebus (USA) Catalogue no: **C'BUS 101**

My Square Laddie

MY SQUARE LADDIE (Original cast recording) (Various artists)
Album: Released Jan '89, on Silva Screen by Silva Screen Records. Catalogue no: **AEI 1132**

My Stepmother Is ...

MY STEPMOTHER IS AN ALIEN (Film soundtrack) (Various artists)
Tracks: / Pump up the volume: *M/A/R/R/S* / Room to move: *Animotion* / Be the one: *Jackson, Jackie* / One good lover: *Siren* / Klystron, The: *Various artists* / Not just another girl: *Neville, Ivan* / I like the world: *Cameo* / Hot wives: *Aykroyd, Dan* / Enjoy: *Various artists* / Celeste: *Various artists.*
CD: Released Apr '89, on Polydor

by Polydor Ltd. Catalogue no: **837 798-2**
Album: Released Apr '89, on Polydor by Polydor Ltd. Deleted Sep '90. Catalogue no: **837 798-1**
Cass: Released Apr '89, on Polydor by Polydor Ltd. Catalogue no: **837 798-4**

Mystery Of Edwin Drood

MYSTERY OF EDWIN DROOD (Original Broadway cast) (Various artists)
Tracks: / There you are: *Various artists* / Man could go quite mad, A: *Various artists* / Two kinsmen: *Various artists* / Moonfall: *Various artists* / Wages of sin, The: *Various artists* / Ceylon: *Various artists* / Both sides of the coin: *Various artists* / Perfect strangers: *Various artists* / No good can come from

bad: *Various artists* / Never the luck: *Various artists* / Name of love, The: *Various artists* / Setting up the score: *Various artists* / Off to the races: *Various artists* / Don't quit while you're ahead: *Various artists* / Garden path to hell, The: *Various artists* / Out on a limerick: *Various artists* / Jasper's confession: *Various artists* / Puffer's confession: *Various artists* / Writing on the wall, The: *Various artists.*
Cass: Released Aug '86, on Polydor by Polydor Ltd. Deleted Jan '88. Catalogue no: **POLDC 5196**
CD: Released '88, on Polydor by Polydor Ltd. Catalogue no: **827 969 2**
Album: Released Aug '86, on Polydor by Polydor Ltd. Deleted Jan '88. Catalogue no: **POLD 5196**

The following information was taken from the Music Master database on September 25th, 1990.

Name Of The Rose

NAME OF THE ROSE (Film Soundtrack) (Various artists)
Tracks: / Beta viscera: *Various artists* / First recognition: *Various artists* / Lesson, The: *Various artists* / Kyrie: *Various artists* / Scriptorium, the: *Various artists* / Veri sancti spiritus: *Various artists* / Confession, the: *Various artists* / Flashbacks: *Various artists* / Discovery, The: *Various artists* / Betrayed: *Various artists* / Epilogue: *Various artists* / End title: *Various artists*.
Note: James Horner score for film starring Sean Connery.
Album: Released Jan '87, on First Night by First Night Records. Catalogue no: **SCENE 7**
CD: Released Jan '89, on Silva Screen by Silva Screen Records. Catalogue no: **30046**
Cass: Released Jan '87, on First Night by First Night Records. Catalogue no: **SCENEC 7**

Nancy Goes To Rio

NANCY GOES TO RIO / RICH YOUNG & PRETTY / ROYAL WEDDING (Original soundtracks) (Various artists)
CD: Released Jan '89, on MCA by MCA Records. Catalogue no: **MCAD 5952**

Nanou

NANOU/CARELESS TALK (Various artists)
Album: Released '85, on Filmtrax by Filmtrax Records. Catalogue no: **MOMENT 104**
Cass: Released '85, on Filmtrax by Filmtrax Records. Catalogue no: **MOMENTC 104**

Napoleon

NAPOLEON (Film soundtrack) (See under Davis, Carl)

Nascimbene, Mario

SOLOMON & SHEBA (See under Solomon & Sheba)

Nashville Sound

WESTERN MOVIE THEMES (Nashville Sound Orchestra)
Tracks: / Good, the bad and the ugly, The / Shenandoah / Magnificent seven, The / Rawhide.
Note: These tracks and more.
CD: Released '86, on Bridge (MCS Bridge) Catalogue no: **100 003**

National Philharmonic

CLASSIC SCORES FROM HUMPHREY BOGART FILMS (National Philharmonic Orchestra)
Tracks: / Key Largo / Big sleep / Caine mutiny / Casablanca / To have and to have not / Treasure of the Sierra Madre.
Note: Conducted by Charles Gerhardt.
Album: Released May '85, on RCA by BMG Records (UK). Catalogue no: **NL 10422**
Cass: Released May '85, on RCA by BMG Records (UK). Catalogue no: **NK 10422**

CLOSE ENCOUNTERS OF THE 3RD KIND (National Philharmonic Orchestra)
Tracks: / Five tones, The / Experience begins, The (Introduction to 'Close Encounters'.) / Mountain visions / John Williams symphonic suite of 'Close Encounters...'' / Conversation, The / Appearance of the vistors, The / Restoration / First light / Sky ride / Aeromancy.
Album: Released Jan '89, on Silva Screen by Silva Screen Records. Catalogue no: **AL 9500**
Cass: Released Jan '89, on Silva Screen by Silva Screen Records. Catalogue no: **ACB 6 8365**
Album: Released Apr '78, on Damont by Damont Audio Ltd.. Catalogue no: **DMT 2002**

JESUS OF NAZARETH (Na- tional Philharmonic Orchestra)
Cass: Released Mar '79, on Pye International Deleted '84. Catalogue no: **ZCP 28504**
Album: Released Mar '79, on Pye International Catalogue no: **NSPH 28504**

LEGEND (Film Soundtrack) (See under Legend)

OVERTURES & MUSIC FROM SWING TIME (See under Kern, Gerome)

RETURN OF THE JEDI (Film soundtrack) (National Philharmonic Orchestra)
Tracks: / Approaching the death star / Parade of the Ewoks / Luke and Leia / Jabba the hutt / Return of the Jedi / Ewok battle, The / Han Solo returns / Into the trap / Fight in the dungeon / Heroic ewok / Battle in the forest / Finale.
Cass: Released Aug '83, on RCA by BMG Records (UK). Catalogue no: **RK 14748**
CD: Released May '83, on RCA by BMG Records (UK). Deleted Nov '88. Catalogue no: **RCD 14748**
Album: Released Aug '83, on RCA by BMG Records (UK). Catalogue no: **RL 14748**

SUNSET BOULEVARD (Classic film scores of Franz Waxman) (National Philharmonic Orchestra)
Tracks: / Prince Valiant / To have and have not / Peyton Place / Place in the sun, A / Bride of Frankenstein / Two Mrs Carrolls / Sunset Boulevard / Mr. Skeffington / Objective Burma / Rebecca / Philadelphia story / Old acquaintance / Taras bulba.
CD: Released Jul '86, on RCA by BMG Records (UK). Deleted May '89. Catalogue no: **RD 87017**

Natural

NATURAL, THE (Film soundtrack) (Newman, Randy)
Note: Superb score by Randy Newman for the Robert Redford film.
Album: Released Jan '89, on Silva Screen by Silva Screen Records. Catalogue no: **925116.1**
CD: Released Feb '90, on Silva Screen by Silva Screen Records. Catalogue no: **925116.2**
Cass: Released Jan '89, on Silva Screen by Silva Screen Records. Catalogue no: **925116.4**

Naughty Marietta

NAUGHTY MARIETTA (Film soundtrack) (Various artists)
Note: Starring Jeanette MacDonald and Nelson Eddy.
Album: Released Jan '89, on Hollywood Soundstage (USA) Catalogue no: **HS 413**

Navigator

NAVIGATOR (Film soundtrack) (Various artists)
Tracks: / Forging the cross: *Various artists* / Vision: *Various artists* / Ascent, The: *Various artists* / Plainsong: *Various artists* / Queenfish: *Various artists* / Macedonian pipes: *Various artists* / Paean: The: *Various artists* / Dance: *Various artists* / Refugees: *Various artists* / Connor's return: *Various artists* / Storm: *Various artists* / Work song: *Various artists* / Escape: *Various artists* / Fall, The: *Various artists* / Celtic refrain: *Various artists*.
Album: Released Jun '89, on Silva Screen by Silva Screen Records. Deleted Apr '90. Catalogue no: **FILM 039**
Cass: Released Jun '89, on Silva Screen by Silva Screen Records. Deleted Nov '89. Catalogue no: **FILMC 039**
CD: Released Jun '89, on Silva Screen by Silva Screen Records. Catalogue no: **FILMCD 039**

Navy Lark

NAVY LARK, THE (Various artists)
Cass set: Released Nov '89, on BBC by BBC Records. Catalogue no: **ZBBC 1096**

Near Dark

NEAR DARK (See under Tangerine Dream)

Ned Kelly

NED KELLY (Film Soundtrack) (Various artists)
Tracks: / Ned Kelly: *Various artists* / Wild colonial boy: *Various artists* / Son of a scoundrel: *Various artists* / Shadow of the gallows: *Various artists* / Lonigan's widow: *Various artists* / Stoney cold ground: *Various artists* / Kelly's keep comin': *Various artists* / Ranchin' in the evenin': *Various artists* / Blame it on the Kellys: *Various artists* / Pictures of a Sunday afternoon: *Various artists* / Hey Ned: *Various artists*.
Album: Released '73, on United Artists by EMI Records. Deleted '78. Catalogue no: **UAS 29108**

Neighbours

NEIGHBOURS (See under Crocker, Barry)
NEIGHBOURS THEME (EPISODE 2001)
Tracks: /Neighbours theme (episode 2001).
7" Single: Released Jan '90, on Mushroom (Australia) Catalogue no: **MR 102**
12" Single: Released Jan '90, on Mushroom (Australia) Catalogue no: **MR 102T**

Neighbours & Lovers

NEIGHBOURS & LOVERS (Original Cast recording) (Various artists)
Tracks: / Isn't it amazing: *Jarvis, Linda & David Cope* / I love you, I really do: *Jarvis, Linda & David Cope* / You must understand: *Jarvis, Linda & David Cope* / Who cares what people think: *Jarvis, Linda* / Wouldn't it be wonderful: *Jarvis, Linda, David Cope, Alison Barry, Richard Croxford* / If only: *Jarvis, Linda & David Cope* / Yes it's true: *Cope, David* / It's a fantasy: *Cope, David* / What does he see (when he looks at me): *Barry, Alison* / Don't ask me why: *Barry, Alison* / I feel sorry for her (being married to him!): *Croxford, Richard* / Top of the tree: *Croxford, Richard*

/ It's New Year's Eve!: *Various artists* / George & Dragon, The: *Various artists* / Everyone needs to be needed (finale): *Various artists*.
Cass: Released Mar '87, on Sagittarius by Sagittarius Records. Catalogue no: **SGC 1**

Nelson, Bill

BROND (THEME FROM) (Nelson, Bill & Daryl Runswick)
Tracks: / Brond.
12" Single: Released May '87, on Cocteau by Cocteau Records. Catalogue no: **COQT 21**

Nelson, Willie

HONEYSUCKLE ROSE (Original soundtrack)
Tracks: / On the road again / Pick up the tempo / Heaven or hell / Fiddlin' around / Blue eyes crying in the rain / Working man blues / Jumpin' cotton eyed Joe / Whiskey river / Bloody Mary morning / Loving you was easier than anything / I don't do windows / Coming back to Texas / If you want me to love you I will / It's not supposed to be that way / You show me yours and I'll show you mine / If you could touch her at all / Angel flying too close to the ground / I guess I've come to live here in your eyes / Angel eyes / So you think you're a cowboy / Make the world go away / Two sides to every story / Song for you / Uncloudy day.
2 LP Set: Released Nov '80, on CBS by CBS Records & Distribution. Deleted Nov '85. Catalogue no: **CBS 22080**

Network 7

NETWORK 7 (See under Lindsay, Julian)

Never On Sunday

NEVER ON SUNDAY (Film soundtrack) (Various artists)
Album: Released Jan '61, on London-American by Decca Records. Deleted '65. Catalogue no: **HAT 2309**

Neverending Story

NEVERENDING STORY (Film soundtrack) (Various artists)
Tracks: / Neverending story, The: *Limahl* / Swamps of sadness: *Various artists* / Ivory tower: *Various artists* / Ruined landscape: *Various*

artists / Sleepy dragon: *Various artists* / Bastian's happy flight: *Various artists* / Fantasia: *Various artists* / Atreju's quest: *Various artists* / Theme of sadness: *Various artists* / Atreju meets Falkor: *Various artists* / Mirrorgate - Southern oracle: *Various artists* / Gmork: *Various artists* / Moonchild: *Various artists* / Auryn, The: *Various artists* / Happy flight: *Various artists*.
Album: Released Mar '85, on EMI by EMI Records. Catalogue no: **NES 1**
Cass: Released '85, on EMI by EMI Records. Catalogue no: **EJ 240222-4**
Album: Released '85, on EMI by EMI Records. Catalogue no: **EJ 240222-1**
Cass: Released Mar '85, on EMI by EMI Records. Catalogue no: **TC NES 1**

New American Orchestra
MUSIC FROM BLADE RUNNER
Tracks: / Love theme / Main title / One more kiss dear / Memories of green / End title / Blade runner blues / Farewell / End title.
Cass: Released Sep '82, on Full Moon (USA) Catalogue no: **K 499262**
Album: Released Sep '82, on Full Moon (USA) Catalogue no: **K 99262**

New Avengers
NEW AVENGERS (See under Avengers)

New Moon
NEW MOON/ROSE MARIE (Original cast recordings) (Various artists)
Album: Released Jan '89, on Silva Screen by Silva Screen Records. Catalogue no: **P 13878**
Cass: Released Jan '89, on Silva Screen by Silva Screen Records. Catalogue no: **BT 13878**

New Order
ROUND AND ROUND
Tracks: / Round and round / Best & Marsh.
Note: Theme from the TV Series 'Makin' Out'.
CD Single: Released Mar '89, on Factory by Factory Records. Catalogue no: **FACD 263**
12" Single: Released Mar '89, on

Factory by Factory Records. Catalogue no: **FAC 263 R**
CD 3": Released Mar '89, on Factory by Factory Records. Catalogue no: **FACD 263 R**
7" Single: Released Mar '89, on Factory by Factory Records. Catalogue no: **FAC 2637**
12" Single: Released Mar '89, on Factory by Factory Records. Catalogue no: **FAC 263**

SHELLSHOCK
Tracks: / Shellshock.
Note: Featured in the film *Pretty in pink*
12" Single: Released Mar '86, on Factory by Factory Records. Catalogue no: **FAC 143T**
7" Single: Released Mar '86, on Factory by Factory Records. Catalogue no: **FAC 143**

New Orleans (Film)
NEW ORLEANS (Film soundtrack) (Various artists)
Tracks: / Free as a bird: *Various artists* / When the saints go marching in: *Various artists* / West End blues: *Various artists* / Do you know what it means to miss New Orleans?: *Various artists* / Brahms' lullaby: *Various artists* / Tiger rag: *Various artists* / Buddy Bolden blues: *Various artists* / Basin Street blues: *Various artists* / Raymond Street blues: *Various artists* / Melenberg joys: *Various artists* / Where the blues were born in New Orleans: *Various artists* / Farewell to Storyville: *Various artists* / Beale Street stomp: *Various artists* / Dippermouth blues (slow and fast versions): *Various artists* / Shimme sha wobble: *Various artists* / Ballin' the jack: *Various artists* / King Porter stomp: *Various artists* / Mahogany Hall stomp: *Various artists* / Endie: *Various artists* / Blues are brewin': *Various artists*.
Cass: Released Jul '84, on Giants of Jazz by Hasmick Promotions. Catalogue no: **GOJC 1025**
Album: Released Jul '84, on Giants of Jazz by Hasmick Promotions. Catalogue no: **GOJ 1025**

NEW ORLEANS - TIL BUTCHER (VIDEO) (Various artists)
VHS: Released '88, on Kay Jazz (video) by Kay Jazz. Catalogue no: **KJ 009**

New World Philharmonic
ACE OF THEMES VOL. 1 (See

under Reilly Ace Of Themes)
ACE OF THEMES VOL 2
Tracks: / Dynasty / Terms of endearment / No matter what happens / Thorn birds / Hill St. blues / Up where we belong / Bolero / Body walk / Only he has the power to move me / Almost paradise / Seduction / Memory / Sometimes.
Album: Released Jun '84, on Red Bus by Red Bus Records. Catalogue no: **RBD 1102**
Cass: Released Jun '84, on Red Bus by Red Bus Records. Catalogue no: **ZCRBD 1102**

DYNASTY, THEME FROM
Tracks: / Dynasty (theme from).
7" Single: Released Sep '84, on Red Bus by Red Bus Records. Catalogue no: **RBUS 100**

FAMOUS THEMES
Tracks: / Reilly, ace of spies - theme (Olympic Orchestra) / Terms of endearment / Thorn birds / No matter what happens (From Yentl) / Hill Street blues / Up where we belong (From An Officer And A Gentleman) / Bolero / Body talk / Only He (From Starlight Express) / Dynasty / Almost paradise / Memory (From Cats) / Seduction, The (From American Gigolo) / Sometimes (From Champions).
Note: Conducted by Iain Sutherland and Alyn Ainsworth.
CD: Released '86, on Red Bus by Red Bus Records. Catalogue no: **CDRBL 7782**

New York New York
NEW YORK NEW YORK (Original soundtrack) (Various artists)
Album: Released Jan '89, on Silva Screen by Silva Screen Records. Catalogue no: **154 99290.1**
CD: Released Jan '89, on EMI by EMI Records. Catalogue no: **CDP 46090**
Cass: Released Jan '89, on Silva Screen by Silva Screen Records. Catalogue no: **254 99290.1**

NEW YORK, NEW YORK VOL.1 (Original Soundtrack) (Various artists)
Tracks: / Main title: *Various artists* / You brought a new kind of love to me: *Minnelli, Liza* / Flip the dip: *Auld, Georgie* / V.J. stomp: *Various artists* / Opus one: *Various artists* / Once in a while: *Minnelli, Liza* / You are my lucky star: *Min-*

nelli, Liza / Game over: *Auld, Georgie* / It's a wonderful world: *Various artists* / Man I love, The: *Minnelli, Liza* / Hazoy: *Various artists* / Just you, just me: *Minnelli, Liza.*
Note: Burns, Ralph: Arranger, conductor & album producer.
Cass set: Released Sep '86, on EMI (Italy) by EMI Records. Catalogue no: **3C 254 99290**

NEW YORK, NEW YORK VOL.2 (Original Soundtrack) (Various artists)
Tracks: / There goes the ball game: *Minnelli, Liza* / Blue Moon: *Place, Mary Kay & Robert De Niro* / Don't be that way: *Various artists* / Happy endings: *Minnelli, Liza & Larry Kert* / But the world goes round: *Minnelli, Liza* / New York, New York: *Auld, Georgie* / New York, New York: *Minnelli, Liza* / New York, New York (orchestral reprise): *Various artists* / Honeysuckle Rose: *Abbott, Diahnne* / Once again right away: *Auld, Georgie.*
Note: Ralph Burns: Arranger, conductor, album producer. Track 4 (Happy Endings) was originally recorded for the film but deleted during final editing.
Cass: Released Sep '86, on DRG (USA) by DRG Records (USA). Catalogue no: **3C 254 99291**

New York Stories
NEW YORK STORIES (Film soundtrack) (Various artists)
CD: Released '89, on Elektra by Elektra Records (UK). Catalogue no: **960 857 2**
Cass: Released Nov '89, on Elektra by Elektra Records (UK). Catalogue no: **960 857 4**
Album: Released Nov '89, on Elektra by Elektra Records (UK). Catalogue no: **960 857 1**

Newley, Anthony
IDLE ON PARADE
Tracks: / I've waited so long / Idle rock a boogie / Idle on parade / Saturday night rock a boogie.
Note: Theme from film *Idle on parade*
7" EP: Released May '59, on Decca by Decca International. Deleted '62. Catalogue no: **DFE 6566**

STOP THE WORLD I WANT TO GET OFF (Original cast)
Album: Released Jan '61, on

Decca by Decca International. Deleted '88. Catalogue no: **SKL 4142**

WHAT KIND OF FOOL AM I
Tracks: / What kind of fool am I.
Note: Taken from the show *Stop the world I want to get off*
7" Single: Released Aug '61, on Decca by Decca International. Deleted '64. Catalogue no: **F 11376**

Newman, Randy
NATURAL, THE (See under Natual, The)

PARENTHOOD (See under Parenthood)

Newton-John, Olivia
HOPELESSLY DEVOTED TO YOU
Tracks: / Hopelessly devoted to you / Love is a many splendoured thing.
Note: Taken from the film *Grease*
7" Single: Released Nov '78, on RSO by Polydor Ltd. Deleted '81. Catalogue no: **RSO 17**

XANADU (Newton-John, Olivia & ELO)
Tracks: / Xanadu / Fool country.
Note: Theme to the film *Xanadu*
7" Single: Released Jun '80, on Jet by Jet Records. Deleted '83. Catalogue no: **JET 185**

Next Of Kin
NEXT OF KIN (Film soundtrack) (Various artists)
Tracks: / Brother to brother: *Various artists* / Hillbilly heart: *Various artists* / Paralyzed: *Various artists* / My sweet baby's gone: *Various artists* / Brothers: *Various artists* / On a Spanish Highway (revised): *Various artists* / Hey backwoods: *Various artists* / Straight and narrow: *Various artists* / Yard sale, The: *Various artists* / Pyramids of cans: *Various artists* / Wailing sax: *Various artists.*
Album: Released May '90, on Epic by CBS Records & Distribution. Catalogue no: **466240 1**
CD: Released May '90, on Epic by CBS Records & Distribution. Catalogue no: **466240 2**
Cass: Released May '90, on Epic by CBS Records & Distribution. Catalogue no: **466240 4**

Nicholas Nickleby
NICHOLAS NICKLEBY (Orig-

inal cast soundtrack) (Various artists)
Tracks: / London: *Various artists* / Home in Devonshire: *Various artists* / Dotheboys' Hall: *Various artists* / Journey to Portsmouth: *Various artists* / Farewell waltz, The: *Various artists* / Mantalini chase, The: *Various artists* / Wedding anthem: *Various artists* / Patriotic song: *Various artists* / Milliners' sewing room, The: *Various artists* / Sir Mulberry Hawk: *Various artists* / Mrs. Grudden's goodbye: *Various artists* / Wititterly gavotte, The: *Various artists* / At the opera: *Various artists* / Cheerybyble brothers, The: *Various artists* / Christmas carol: *Various artists.*
Cass: Released May '89, on T. E. R. by That's Entertainment Records. Catalogue no: **ZCTER 1029**
Album: Released Apr '83, on T. E. R. by That's Entertainment Records. Catalogue no: **TER 1029**

Nicholas, Paul
JUST GOOD FRIENDS (SINGLE) (Theme from the TV series)
7" Single: Released Dec '84, on Flying by Flying Records. Deleted '86. Catalogue no: **FLY 109**

MAGICAL MR. MISTOFFELEES
Tracks: / Magical Mr. Mistoffelees / Old Deuteronomy.
Note: From the musical 'Cats'.
7" Single: Released Jan '81, on Polydor by Polydor Ltd. Deleted Jan '84. Catalogue no: **POSP 204**

YESTERDAY'S HERO
Tracks: / Yesterday's hero / Shooting star.
Note: From the film of the same name.
7" Single: Released Nov '79, on RSO by Polydor Ltd. Deleted '82. Catalogue no: **RSO 50**

Night Crossing
NIGHT CROSSING (Film soundtrack) (Various artists)
Tracks: / Main title: *Various artists* / All in vain: *Various artists* / Picnic: *Various artists* / Plans: *Various artists* / Success: *Various artists* / First flight: *Various artists* / Patches, The: *Various artists* / Tomorrow we go: *Various artists* / No time to wait: *Various artists* / Final flight:

Elizabeth Shue in *A Night on the Town*

Various artists / In the west: *Various artists*.
Note: Score by Jerry Goldsmith.
CD: Released Jan '89, on Intrada (USA) Catalogue no: **RVFD 6004**
Album: Released Jan '89, on Intrada (USA) Catalogue no: **RVF 6004**

Night & Day (Film)

NIGHT AND DAY (VIDEO) (Various artists)
VHS: Released Jun '89, on Warner Home Video by WEA Records. Catalogue no: **PES 99465**

Night Of The Comet

NIGHT OF THE COMET (Film soundtrack) (Various artists)
Tracks: / Unbelievable: *Revolver* / Learn to: *Farren, Chris & Army Holland* / Strong heart: *Townsend, John* / Let my fingers do the talking: *Stallion* / Whole: *Farren, Chris / Wayne Crawford* / Hard act to follow: *Night of the Comet* / Virgin in love: *Thom Pace* / Yell me yourself: *Revolver* / Trouble: *SKP Adams* / Lady in love: *Revolver*.
Note: Includes free 7" single
Cass: Released May '86, on Chord by Chord Records. Deleted '88. Catalogue no: **TCMRC 900**
Album: Released May '86, on Chord by Chord Records. Deleted '88. Catalogue no: **CHORD 006**
Album: Released May '86, on Chord by Chord Records. Deleted

'88. Catalogue no: **MRC 900**

Night On The Town

NIGHT ON THE TOWN, A (Original soundtrack) (Various artists) (See panel above)
Tracks: / Then he kissed me: *Crystals, The* / Blues and they..., The: *Waters, Muddy* / What does it take (to win your love): *Collins, Albert* / Albert's Smokin' Ice: *Collins, Albert* / What does it take (to win your love): *Walker, Junior* / Future in your..: *Southside Johnny & The Jukes* / Twenty five miles: *Starr, Edwin* / Expressway to your heart: *Southside Johnny & The Jukes* / Evil: *Taylor, Koko* / Bring it on home to me: *Cooke, Sam* / Just can't stop...: *Sledge, Percy* / Babysitting blues: *Collins, Albert*.
Note: Released on video as 'Adventures In Babysitting'.
Album: Released 12 Feb '88, on Aeroplane by Sonet Records. Catalogue no: **SNTF 999**

Night Visitor

NIGHT VISITOR (See under Mancini, Henry)

Nighthawks (film)

NIGHTHAWKS (Film soundtrack) (Emerson, Keith)
Note: Keith Emerson score for the Sylvester Stallone film.
Album: Released May '81, on MCA by MCA Records. Deleted '86. Catalogue no: **MCF 3107**
Album: Released Jan '89, on

MCA by MCA Records. Catalogue no: **MCA 1521**
Cass: Released Jan '89, on MCA by MCA Records. Catalogue no: **MCAC 1521**
Cass: Released May '81, on MCA by MCA Records. Deleted '86. Catalogue no: **MCFC 3107**

Nightmare On Elm St

NIGHTMARE ON ELM STREET 1 & 2 (Film soundtracks) (Various artists)
CD: Released Jan '89, on Colosseum (West Germany) Catalogue no: **VCD 47255**

NIGHTMARE ON ELM STREET 2 (FREDDIES REVENGE) (Film soundtrack) (Various artists)
Note: Music by Christopher Young.
Cass: Released Jan '89, on Varese Sarabande Records(USA) by Varese Sarabande Records (USA). Catalogue no: **CTV 81275**
CD: Released Jan '89, on Varese Sarabande Records(USA) by Varese Sarabande Records (USA). Catalogue no: **VCD 47275**
Album: Released Jan '89, on Varese Sarabande Records(USA) by Varese Sarabande Records (USA). Catalogue no: **STV 81275**

NIGHTMARE ON ELM STREET 3 (DREAM WARRIORS) (Film soundtrack) (Various artists)
Note: Music by Angelo Badalamenti.
Album: Released Jan '89, on Varese Sarabande Records(USA) by Varese Sarabande Records (USA). Catalogue no: **STV 81314**
CD: Released Jan '89, on Colosseum (West Germany) Catalogue no: **VCD 47293**
Cass: Released Jan '89, on Varese Sarabande Records(USA) by Varese Sarabande Records (USA). Catalogue no: **CTV 81314**

NIGHTMARE ON ELM STREET 4 (Film soundtrack) (Various artists)
Tracks: / Under the night stars: *Sea Hags* / Don't be afraid of your dreams: *Go West* / My way or the highway: *Davis, Jimmie* / Therapist: *Vigil* / Angel: *Love Hate* / Standing over you: *Angels From*

Angel City / Back to the wall: *Divinyls* / Love kills: *Vincent, Vinnie* / Rip her to shreds: *Blondie* / Resurrection: *Safan, Craig.*
CD: Released Apr '89, on Chrysalis by Chrysalis Records. Catalogue no: **CCD 1673**
Cass: Released Apr '89, on Chrysalis by Chrysalis Records. Catalogue no: **ZCHR 1673**
Album: Released Apr '89, on Chrysalis by Chrysalis Records. Catalogue no: **CHR 1673**

NIGHTMARE ON ELM STREET 4 (INSTRUMENTAL) (Film Soundtrack) (Various artists)
Note: Craig Safan's chilling instrumental score to Freddy Krueger's box office smash makes this the perfect companion to the song album available on Chrysalis Records.
Cass: Released Jan '89, on Take 7 Catalogue no: **VSC 5203**
CD: Released Jan '89, on Take 7 Catalogue no: **VCD 5203**
Album: Released Jan '89, on Take 7 Catalogue no: **VS 5203**

NIGHTMARE ON ELM STREET 5 (Film soundtrack) (Various artists)
Tracks: / Bring your daughter: *Dickinson, Bruce* / Savage: *W.A.S.P.* / What do you know: *Slave Raider* / Now I lay me down to sleep: *Fox, Samantha* / Word up doc: *Doctor Ice* / Heaven in the back seat: *Romeo's Daughter* / Can't take the hurt: *Mammoth* / Any way I gotta swing it: *Whodini* / Let's go: *Kool Moe Dee* / Livin' in the jungle: *Schoolly D.*
Album: Released May '90, on Jive by Zomba Records. Deleted Sep '90. Catalogue no: **HIP 87**
Cass: Released Oct '89, on Varese Sarabande Records(USA) by Varese Sarabande Records (USA). Catalogue no: **VSC 5238**
CD: Released May '90, on Jive by Zomba Records. Deleted Sep '90. Catalogue no: **CHIP 87**
CD: Released Oct '89, on Varese Sarabande Records(USA) by Varese Sarabande Records (USA). Catalogue no: **VSD 5238**
Album: Released Oct '89, on Varese Sarabande Records(USA) by Varese Sarabande Records (USA). Catalogue no: **VS 5238**
Cass: Released May '90, on Jive by Zomba Records. Deleted Sep

'90. Catalogue no: **HIPC 87**

NIGHTMARE ON ELM STREET (DREAM CHILD) (Film soundtrack) (Various artists)
Album: Released '85, on Varese Sarabande Records(USA) by Varese Sarabande Records (USA). Catalogue no: **STV 81238**
Cass: Released '85, on Varese Sarabande Records(USA) by Varese Sarabande Records (USA). Catalogue no: **CTV 81238**

Nijinsky

NIJINSKY (Film soundtrack) (Various artists)
Tracks: / Invitation to the dance: *Various artists* / Jeux: *Various artists* / Prelude a l'apres midi d'un faune: *Various artists* / Scheherazade: *Various artists* / Carnival: *Various artists* / Le sacre du printemps: *Various artists* / Petrushka: *Various artists.*
Album: Released '80, on CBS by CBS Records & Distribution. Deleted '85. Catalogue no: **CBS 73885**
Cass: Released '80, on CBS by CBS Records & Distribution. Deleted '85. Catalogue no: **CBS 40 73885**

Nine & A Half Weeks

NINE & A HALF WEEKS (Film soundtrack) (Various artists)
Tracks: / I do what I do: *Taylor, John* / Best is yet to come, The: *Luba* / Slave to love: *Ferry, Bryan* / Black on black: *Dalbello* / Eurasian eyes: *Hart, Corey* / You can leave your hat on: *Cocker, Joe* / Bread and butter: *Devo* / This city never sleeps: *Eurythmics* / Cannes: *Copeland, Stewart* / Let it go: *Luba.*
Album: Released Mar '86, on Capitol by EMI Records. Catalogue no: **EST 2003**
CD: Released Feb '90, on EMI (Import) Catalogue no: **CDP 46722**
Cass: Released Mar '86, on Capitol by EMI Records. Catalogue no: **TCEST 2003**
CD: Released '88, on Capitol by EMI Records. Catalogue no: **CDP 746 722 2**

Nine (show)

NINE (Original Broadway cast) (Various artists)

CD: Released Jan '89, on CBS (import) by CBS Records & Distribution. Catalogue no: **CK 38325**
Cass: Released Jan '89, on Silva Screen by Silva Screen Records. Catalogue no: **JST 38325**
Album: Released Jan '89, on Silva Screen by Silva Screen Records. Deleted Mar '90. Catalogue no: **JS 38325**

Nine To Five

9 TO 5 (See under Parton, Dolly)

9 TO 5 (Film soundtrack) (Various artists)
Album: Released Apr '81, on 20th Century by Phonogram Ltd. Catalogue no: **T 627**
Cass: Released Apr '81, on 20th Century by Phonogram Ltd. Catalogue no: **C 627**

Nineteen Sixty Nine

1969 (Film soundtrack) (Various artists)
CD: Released May '89, on Polydor by Polydor Ltd. Catalogue no: **837 362-2**
Cass: Released May '89, on Polydor by Polydor Ltd. Catalogue no: **837 362-4**
Album: Released May '89, on Polydor by Polydor Ltd. Catalogue no: **837 362-1**

No Easy Walk To...

NO EASY WALK TO FREEDOM (See under Kay, Janet)

No Honestly

NO HONESTLY (See under De Paul, Lynsey)

No Man's Land (film)

NO MAN'S LAND (Film soundtrack) (Various artists)
Tracks: / Jewel movement: *Various artists* / Medusa's refrain (part 1): *Various artists* / Medusa's refrain (part 2): *Various artists* / Spark from the infinite, A (part 1): *Various artists* / Spark from the infinite, A (part 2): *Various artists* / Return of the dream collector: *Various artists* / Jaipur local: *Various artists* / Blue anthem: *Various artists.*
Note: Recent score by Basil Poledouris.
CD: Released Jan '89, on Silva Screen by Silva Screen Records. Catalogue no: **VCD 47352**

Album: Released '85, on Plainisphare Catalogue no: **PL 1267 17**
Cass: Released Jan '89, on Silva Screen by Silva Screen Records. Catalogue no: **CTV 81352**
Album: Released Jan '89, on Silva Screen by Silva Screen Records. Catalogue no: **STV 81352**

No Mercy

NO MERCY (Film soundtrack) (Silvestri, Alan)
Tracks: / Main title / Barge, The / Delivery, The / River crush / Afterglow / Like your friends / Lasado's woman / Michel arrives / Tailed / Blue parrot / I was late / What do you say / No mercy reprise.
Note: Music by Alan Silvestri (Back To The Future, Predator, Who Framed Roger Rabbit) for the Richard Gere and Kim Basinger thriller.
Album: Released May '87, on Silva Screen by Silva Screen Records. Catalogue no: **FILM 015**
Cass: Released May '87, on Silva Screen by Silva Screen Records. Catalogue no: **FILMC 015**

No No Nanette

NO NO NANETTE (1971 Revival cast) (Various artists)
Album: Released Jan '89, on Silva Screen by Silva Screen Records. Deleted Mar '90. Catalogue no: **PS 30563**
Cass: Released Jan '89, on Silva Screen by Silva Screen Records. Catalogue no: **PST 30563**
CD: Released Jan '89, on CBS (import) by CBS Records & Distribution. Catalogue no: **CK 30563**

NO NO NANETTE (Original London cast) (Various artists)
Album: Released '73, on Retrospect by EMI Records. Catalogue no: **SH 176**

No Strings

NO STRINGS (London cast recording) (Various artists)
Tracks: / How sad: *Various artists* / Man who has everything: *Various artists* / Orthodox fool: *Various artists* / Loads of love: *Various artists* / You don't tell me: *Various artists* / Love makes the world go: *Various artists* / Eager beaver: *Various artists* / La la la: *Various artists* / Look no further: *Various artists* / Maine:

Various artists / No strings: *Various artists* / Nobody told me: *Various artists* / Sweetest sounds: *Various artists.*
Album: Released Jul '79, on DRG (USA) by DRG Records (USA). Deleted Jan '89. Catalogue no: **DS 15013**

No Surrender

NO SURRENDER (Film soundtrack) (Various artists)
Album: Released Dec '87, on Compact Catalogue no: **PACT 12**

No Way Out

NO WAY OUT/THE YEAR OF LIVING DANGEROUSLY (Film soundtrack) (Jarre, Maurice) (See also under Jarre, Maurice)
Tracks: / No way out / National security / Cover-up / In the Pentagon / We can interface / Susan.
Cass: Released Feb '88, on T. E. R. by That's Entertainment Records. Catalogue no: **ZCTER 1149**
Album: Released Feb '88, on T. E. R. by That's Entertainment Records. Catalogue no: **TER 1149**
CD: Released 30 Jan '88, on T. E. R. by That's Entertainment Records. Catalogue no: **CDTER 1149**

Noble House

NOBLE HOUSE (TV soundtrack) (Various artists)
Note: TV Mini series based on the James Clavell book. Music by Paul Chihara.
Cass: Released Jan '89, on Silva Screen by Silva Screen Records. Catalogue no: **CTV 81360**
Album: Released Jan '89, on Silva Screen by Silva Screen Records. Catalogue no: **STV 81360**
CD: Released Jan '89, on Silva Screen by Silva Screen Records. Catalogue no: **VCD 47360**

Nocturna

NOCTURNA (Film soundtrack) (Various artists)
Album: Released Feb '80, on MCA by MCA Records. Deleted '85. Catalogue no: **MCG 4004**

Noel & Gertie

NOEL AND GERTIE (Original London cast) (Various artists)
Tracks: / Overture / Some day I'll

find you / Mrs. Worthington / Touring days / Parisian pierrot / Dance little lady / Play, orchestra, play / We were dancing / Man about town / I travel alone / Sail away / Why must the show go on? / Come the wild, wild weather / I'll remember her / I'll see you again / Curtain music.
Cass: Released Jan '87, on T. E. R. by That's Entertainment Records. Catalogue no: **ZCTER 1117**
Album: Released Jan '87, on T. E. R. by That's Entertainment Records. Catalogue no: **TER 1117**

Norman, Neil

GREATEST SCIENCE FICTION HITS, VOL 1 (Norman, Neil & his Orchestra)
Tracks: / Alien / Moonraker / Star wars / Superman / 2001 / Battlestar galactica / Space 1999 / Star trek / Black hole, The.
Album: Released Jan '82, on PRT by Castle Communications Records. Catalogue no: **NCP 1003**
Album: Released Jan '89, on GNP Crescendo (USA) by GNP Crescendo Records (USA). Catalogue no: **GNPS 2128**
CD: Released Jan '89, on GNP Crescendo (USA) by GNP Crescendo Records (USA). Catalogue no: **GNPD 2128**
Cass: Released Jan '89, on GNP Crescendo (USA) by GNP Crescendo Records (USA). Catalogue no: **GNP 5 2128**
Album: Released '87, on PRT by Castle Communications Records. Catalogue no: **PYL 6042**
Cass: Released '87, on PRT by Castle Communications Records. Catalogue no: **PYM 6042**

GREATEST SCIENCE FICTION HITS, VOL 2 (Norman, Neil & his Orchestra)
Tracks: / Empire strikes back, The / Twilight zone / Buck Rogers / Time tunnel, The / Doctor who / Voyage to the bottom of the sea / Dark star / Sinbad and the eye of the tiger.
CD: Released Jan '89, on GNP Crescendo (USA) by GNP Crescendo Records (USA). Catalogue no: **GNPD 2133**
Cass: Released Jan '89, on GNP Crescendo (USA) by GNP Crescendo Records (USA). Cata-

logue no: **GNP5 2133**
Cass: Released '87, on PRT by Castle Communications Records. Catalogue no: **PYM 6043**
Cass: Released Mar '84, on PRT by Castle Communications Records. Catalogue no: **ZCNP 702**
Album: Released Jan '89, on GNP Crescendo (USA) by GNP Crescendo Records (USA). Catalogue no: **GNPS 2133**
Album: Released '87, on PRT by Castle Communications Records. Catalogue no: **PYL 6043**
Album: Released Mar '84, on PRT by Castle Communications Records. Catalogue no: **NCP 702**

GREATEST SCIENCE FICTION HITS, VOL 3 (Norman, Neil & his Orchestra)
Tracks: / E.T. / War of the worlds / Lost in space / Bladerunner / Flash Gordon / Thing, The / Prisoner, The / Land of giants / Space 1999 / Angry red planet / Capricorn one / Raiders of the lost ark / Invaders / UFO / Vena's dance / Return of the jedi.
Cass: Released Jan '89, on GNP Crescendo (USA) by GNP Crescendo Records (USA). Catalogue no: **GNP5 2163**
CD: Released Jan '89, on GNP Crescendo (USA) by GNP Crescendo Records (USA). Catalogue no: **GNPD 2163**
Album: Released Jan '89, on GNP Crescendo (USA) by GNP Crescendo Records (USA). Catalogue no: **GNPS 2163**

INDIANA JONES AND THE TEMPLE OF DOOM (Norman, Neil & his Orchestra)
Tracks: / Indiana Jones and the Temple of Doom / Raiders of the Lost Ark / Blade Runner.
7" Single: Released Aug '84, on PRT by Castle Communications Records. Catalogue no: **7P 315**

NOT OF THIS EARTH (Norman, Neil & his Orchestra)
Note: Various themes based on science fiction stories.
Album: Released Jan '89, on GNP Crescendo (USA) by GNP Crescendo Records (USA). Catalogue no: **GNPS 2111**

SECRET AGENT FILE (Norman, Neil & his Orchestra)

Tracks: / Reilly, ace of spies - theme / Octopussy / I spy / Rockford files, The / Man from Uncle, The / Casino Royale / Ipcress file, The / Get smart / Thunderball / Spy who came in from the cold.
Cass: Released Jan '89, on GNP Crescendo (USA) by GNP Crescendo Records (USA). Catalogue no: **GNP 5 2166**
CD: Released '88, on GNP Crescendo (USA) by GNP Crescendo Records (USA). Catalogue no: **GNPD 2166**
Album: Released Jan '89, on GNP Crescendo (USA) by GNP Crescendo Records (USA). Catalogue no: **GNPS 2166**

SOUND OF THE UNIVERSE (Norman, Neil & his Orch.)
Tracks: / Return of the Jedi / Star wars / Star trek / E.T. / Battlestar galactica / 2001 / Radar.
CD: Released '86, on Delta (1) by Delta Records. Deleted '88. Catalogue no: **11 007**

North, Alex
SPARTACUS (See under Spartacus)

North By Northwest
NORTH BY NORTHWEST (Film soundtrack) (London Studio Symphony Orchestra)
Album: Released Sep '80, on Kanchana Catalogue no: **DKP 9000**
CD: Released Nov '84, on T. E. R. by That's Entertainment Records. Catalogue no: **CDVCD 47205**

North, Nicky
JAMES BOND 21ST ANNIVERSARY (North, Nicky Orchestra)
Tracks: / Goldfinger / 007 theme / Diamonds are forever / Thunderball / We have all the time in the world / Live and let die / From Russia with love.
Album: Released Jul '83, on VCL Deleted '88. Catalogue no: **VCLP 007**

North Of Hollywood
FILM MUSIC OF ALEX NORTH (North, Alex)
CD: Released Feb '90, on Silva Screen by Silva Screen Records. Catalogue no: **1445.2**

North & South
NORTH AND SOUTH / RIGHT STUFF, THE (Film soundtracks) (Various artists)
Note: Music from the TV series by Bill Conti plus his Oscar Winning film score performed by the London Symphony Orchestra.
Cass: Released Jan '89, on Varese Sarabande Records(USA) by Varese Sarabande Records (USA). Deleted Jun '90. Catalogue no: **C 704.310**
CD: Released Jan '89, on Varese Sarabande Records(USA) by Varese Sarabande Records (USA). Catalogue no: **VCD 47250**
Album: Released Jan '89, on Varese Sarabande Records(USA) by Varese Sarabande Records (USA). Catalogue no: **704.310**

Norwood (Film)
NORWOOD (Film Soundtrack) (Various artists)
Tracks: / Ol' Norwood comin' home: *Various artists* / Country girl: *Various artists* / Marie: *Various artists* / Brass ensemble of Ralph: *Various artists* / Texas: *Various artists* / Repo man: *Various artists* / Hot wheels: *Various artists* / I'll paint you a song: *Various artists* / Norwood (me and my guitar): *Various artists* / Fring thing: *Various artists* / Down home: *Various artists* / Chicken out: *Various artists* / I'll paint you a song: *Various artists* / Different kind of rock: *Various artists* / Everything a man could ever need: *Various artists.*
Album: Released '73, on Capitol by EMI Records. Deleted '78. Catalogue no: **ESW 457**

Nosferatu
NOSFERATU (Film soundtrack) (Vuh, Popol)
Note: Music by Popol Vuh.
Album: Released Jan '89, on Silva Screen by Silva Screen Records. Catalogue no: **PLDM 7005**
Cass: Released Jan '89, on Silva Screen by Silva Screen Records. Catalogue no: **PMM 705**

Not Quite Jerusalem
NOT QUITE JERUSALEM (Film soundtrack) (Rondo Veneziano) (See also under

Rondo Veneziano)
Cass: Released Apr '85, on Fanfare by Captain Billy's Music. Catalogue no: **ZCRON 4**
Album: Released Apr '85, on Fanfare by Captain Billy's Music. Catalogue no: **RON 4**

Not The Nine O'Clock

AYATOLLAH SONG
Tracks: / Ayatollah song / Gob on you.
7" Single: Released Dec '80, on BBC by BBC Records. Deleted '87. Catalogue no: **RESL 88**

HEDGEHOG SANDWICH (TV soundtrack) (Various artists)
Tracks: / Loyal apology: *Various artists* / News summary: *Various artists* / Constable Savage: *Various artists* / Baronet Ernold Oswald Mosley: *Various artists* / University challenge: *Various artists* / (I like) trucking: *Various artists* / Sir Robert Mark: *Various artists* / Hi-fi shop: *Various artists* / England my leotard: *Various artists* / Divorce: *Various artists* / Main points again, The: *Various artists* / Bad language: *Various artists* / Gift shop: *Various artists* / Hedgehog apology: *Various artists* / Supa dupa: *Various artists* / Soccer violence: *Various artists* / (Because I'm) wet and lonely: *Various artists* / That's lies: *Various artists* / Creed (The new revised version): *Various artists* / I believe: *Various artists* / Aide, The: *Various artists* / Main points again, The: *Various artists* / Not the parrot sketch: *Various artists* / Open marriage: *Various artists* / Lager: *Various artists* / And finally: *Various artists*.
Album: Released Oct '81, on BBC by BBC Records. Deleted 31 Aug '88. Catalogue no: **REB 421**
Cass: Released Oct '81, on BBC by BBC Records. Deleted 31 Aug '88. Catalogue no: **ZCF 421**

MEMORY KINDA LINGERS, THE/NOT IN FRONT OF THE AUDIENCE (TV soundtrack & Live at Drury Lane) (Various artists)
Tracks: / Spy who came in from the cold, The: *Various artists* / News, The: *Various artists* / Budget: *Various artists* / Question: *Various artists* / Headbangers: *Various artists* / Rock interview: *Various artists* / Game for a laugh: *Various artists* / Typical bloody

Not The Nine O' Clock News **(MFP)**

typical: *Various artists* / Well, Mr. Glossop: *Various artists* / Financial times: *Various artists* / Hey Bob: *Various artists* / New glea: *Various artists* / Holiday habits: *Various artists* / Pizza moment: *Various artists* / Failed in Wales: *Various artists* / Rinbley's pies: *Various artists* / Made from whales: *Various artists* / Brain death: *Various artists* / Swedish chemists: *Various artists* / Hey wow: *Various artists* / Nice video, shame about the song: *Various artists* / Jackanory: *Various artists* / Golf trousers: *Various artists* / News, The: *Various artists* / Two ninnies song: *Various artists* / Aussie pilot: *Various artists* / Does God exist: *Various artists* / Re-altered images: *Various artists* / McEnroe's breakfast: *Various artists* / Ah come in Rawlinson: *Various artists* / Ask the family: *Various artists* / Polish show: *Various artists* / Aleebee: *Various artists* / Main points again, The: *Various artists* / What a load of willies: *Various artists* / Kinda lingers, (The memory): *Various artists* / Grow up you bastards: *Various artists* / Confrontation song: *Various artists* / American improv: *Various artists* / Duke of Kent: *Various artists* /

Alien: *Various artists* / Oh oh oh means I respect you: *Various artists* / Simon and Garfunkel: *Various artists* / Awards: *Various artists* / S.A.S.: *Various artists* / Prompt: *Various artists* / Barry Manilow: *Various artists* / Return of Constable Savage, The: *Various artists* / Gob on you: *Various artists* / The pope's visit: *Various artists*.
Note: The pope's visit: Including: a) Introduction by the Dean, b) A Word from the sponsors, c) Papal tee shirt offer, d) Address by his Holiness, e) Tasty wafer time, f) Miracle / Laker. Interruptions: Including: a) Insulting the audience b) Main sketch rant 4.
Cass: Released Oct '82, on BBC by BBC Records. Catalogue no: **ZCD 453**
2 LP Set: Released Oct '82, on BBC by BBC Records. Catalogue no: **REF 453**

NOT THE DOUBLE ALBUM (TV soundtrack) (Various artists)
Cass: Released Oct '84, on BBC by BBC Records. Deleted 31 Aug '88. Catalogue no: **ZCR 516**
Album: Released Oct '84, on BBC by BBC Records. Deleted 31 Aug

'88. Catalogue no: **REH 516**

NOT THE NINE O'CLOCK NEWS (Various artists)
Cass set: Released Mar '89, on BBC by BBC Records. Catalogue no: **ZBBC 1009**

NOT THE NINE 'O' CLOCK NEWS (TV Soundtrack) (Various artists) (See panel on previous page)
Tracks: / Death of a princess (apology to the Saudis): *Rhys Jones, Griff* / Gorilla interview, The: *Atkinson, Rowan/Mel Smith/Pamela Stephenson* / Confrontation (song): *Smith, Mel* / Airline safety: *Stephenson, Pamela* / National wealth beds: *Smith, Mel* / Simultaneous translation: *Atkinson, Rowan* / Pamela Stephenson / General synod's, The: "Life of Monty Python": *Atkinson, Rowan/Mel Smith/Pamela Stephenson* / There's a man (in Iran)...: *Stephenson, Pamela* / Closedown: *Rhys Jones, Griff/Rowan Atkinson* / Point of view: *Rhys Jones, Griff/Rowan Atkinson* / Rowan's rant: *Rhys Jones, Griff/Rowan Atkinson* / Stout life: *Rhys Jones, Griff/Rowan Atkinson* / Gob on you: *Smith, Mel* / Gay Christian: *Smith, Mel* / Bouncin' (song): *Atkinson, Rowan & Sox* / Oh Bosanquet (song): *Stephenson, Pamela* / I believe: *Rhys Jones, Griff / Rowan Atkinson*.
Cass: Released Oct '87, on MFP by EMI Records. Catalogue no: **TCMFP 5810**
Album: Released Oct '87, on MFP by EMI Records. Deleted '89. Catalogue no: **MFP 5810**

NOT THE NINE 'O' CLOCK NEWS (Original Cast) (Various artists)
Album: Released Oct '80, on BBC by BBC Records. Deleted '88. Catalogue no: **REB 400**
Cass: Released Oct '80, on BBC by BBC Records. Deleted '88. Catalogue no: **ZCF 400**

Nothing In Common
NOTHING IN COMMON (Film soundtrack) (Various artists)
Tracks: / Nothing in common: *Thompson Twins* / Burning of the heart: *Marx, Richard* / If it wasn't love: *Simon, Carly* / Over the weekend: *Heyward, Nick* / Loving strangers: *Cross, Christopher* /

Until you say you love me: *Franklin, Aretha* / Don't forget to dance: *Kinks* / No one's gonna love you: *Real To Reel* / 7 summers: *Cruzados* / Instrumental theme: *Leonard, Pat.*
Cass: Released Mar '87, on Arista by BMG Records (UK). Catalogue no: **407 010**
Album: Released Mar '87, on Arista by BMG Records (UK). Catalogue no: **207.010**
CD: Released Mar '87, on Arista by BMG Records (UK). Catalogue no: **ARCD 8438**

Nova
BLACK HOLE (Theme from Over The Moon)
Tracks: / Black hole.
7" Single: Released Jan '80, on Epic by CBS Records & Distribution. Deleted Jan '85. Catalogue no: **EPC 8145**

Now Voyager
NOW VOYAGER (See under Gibb, Barry)

Nowhere To Hide
NOWHERE TO HIDE (Film soundtrack) (Various artists)
Note: Music by Brad Fiedel.
Album: Released Jan '89, on Varese Sarabande Records(USA) by Varese Sarabande Records (USA). Catalogue no: **STV 81336**

Nun Of Monza
NUN OF MONZA / UN BELLISSIMO NOVEMBRE (Original soundtrack) (Various artists)
Note: Re-issue of 2 rare Ennio Morricone scores.
Album: Released Jan '89, on Interior Music by Interior Music Records. Catalogue no: **IM 001**

Nuns On The Run
NUNS ON THE RUN (Original soundtrack) (Various artists)
Tracks: / Race, The: *Yello* / Comin' to you: *Hidden Faces* / Roll with it: *Winwood, Steve* / Moon on ice: *Yello* / Sacred heart: *Shakespear's Sister* / On the run: *Yello* / Hawaiian chance: *Yello* / Blow away: *Harrison, George* / Tied up: *Yello* / Dr Van Steiner: *Yello* / Gold rush: *Yello* / Nun's medley: *Hidden Faces.*
CD: Released Jun '90, on Mercury by Phonogram Ltd. Catalogue no:

8460432
Album: Released Jun '90, on Mercury by Phonogram Ltd. Catalogue no: **8460431**
Cass: Released Jun '90, on Mercury by Phonogram Ltd. Catalogue no: **8460434**

Nunsense
NUNSENSE (Original 1987 London cast) (Various artists)
Tracks: / Nunsense is habit-forming: *Various artists* / Difficult transition, A: *Various artists* / Benedicte: *Various artists* / Biggest ain't the best, The: *Various artists* / Playing second fiddle: *Various artists* / So you want to be a nun: *Various artists* / Turn up the spotlight: *Various artists* / Lilacs bring back memories: *Various artists* / Tackle that temptation with a time step: *Various artists* / Growing up Catholic: *Various artists* / We've got to clean out the freezer: *Various artists* / Just a coupl'a sisters: *Various artists* / Soup's on: *Various artists* / I just want to be a star: *Various artists* / Drive in, The: *Various artists* / I could've gone to Nashville: *Various artists* / Gloria in excelsis deo: *Various artists* / Holier than thou: *Various artists* / Finale: *Various artists.*
Cass: Released Jun '87, on T. E. R. by That's Entertainment Records. Catalogue no: **ZCTER 1132**
Album: Released Jun '87, on T. E. R. by That's Entertainment Records. Catalogue no: **TER 1132**

NUNSENSE (Original Broadway Cast) (Various artists)
Tracks: / Nunsense is habit-forming: *Various artists* / Difficult transition, A: *Various artists* / Benedicte/Biggest ain't best: *Hubert & Leo* / Playing second fiddle: *Anne, Robert* / So you want to be a Nun: *Amnesia, Mary* / Turn up the spotlight: *Cardelia, Mary* / Lilacs bring back memories: *Various artists* / Tackle that temptation with a time-step: *Various artists* / Growing up Catholic: *Various artists* / Drive-in: *Saint Andrew's, Sister* / I could've gone to Nashville: *Amnesia, Mary* / Holier than thou: *Various artists* / Finale: *Various artists.*
CD: Released '88, on DRG (USA) by DRG Records (USA). Catalogue no: **CDSBL 12589**
Album: Released Apr '87, on

DRG (USA) by DRG Records (USA). Deleted Jan '89. Catalogue no: **SBL 12589**

Cass: Released Apr '87, on DRG (USA) by DRG Records (USA). Deleted Jan '89. Catalogue no: **SBLC 12589**

Nyman, Michael

DROWNING BY NUMBERS (Film Soundtrack)

Tracks: / Trysting fields / Sheep and tides / Great death game / Drowning by number 3 / Wheelbarrow walk / Dead man's catch / Drowning by number 2 / Bees in trees / Fish beach / Wedding tango / Crematorium conspiracy / Knowing the ropes / End game.

CD: Released 22 Aug '88, on Venture (2) by Virgin Records. Catalogue no: **CDVE 23**

Cass: Released Aug '88, on Venture (2) by Virgin Records. Catalogue no: **TCVE 23**

Album: Released Aug '88, on Venture (2) by Virgin Records. Catalogue no: **VE 23**

ZED AND TWO NOUGHTS (See under Zed & Two Noughts)

The following information was taken from the Music Master database on September 25th, 1990.

O Lucky Man

O LUCKY MAN (Film Soundtrack) (Price, Alan)
Tracks: / O Lucky man / Poor people / Sell sell / Pastoral / Arrival / Look over your shoulder / Justice / My home town / Changes.
Album: Released '77, on Warner Bros. by WEA Records. Deleted '82. Catalogue no: **K 46227**

Oakey, Philip

TOGETHER IN ELECTRIC DREAMS (Oakey, Philip & Giorgio Moroder)
Tracks: / Together in electric dreams (7" only) / Together in electric dreams (instrumental) / Together in electric dreams (extended) (12" only).
Note: From the film 'Electric Dreams'.
7" Single: Released Sep '84, on Virgin by Virgin Records. Deleted May '90. Catalogue no: **VS 713**
12" Single: Released Sep '84, on Virgin by Virgin Records. Catalogue no: **VS 713-12**

Oberammergau...

OBERAMMERGAU PASSION PLAY (1634-1984 - Highlights from 1984 production) (Various artists)
2 LP Set: Released Apr '85, on Polydor (Germany) by Polydor Ltd. Catalogue no: **821 123 1**
Cass: Released Apr '85, on Polydor (Germany) by Polydor Ltd. Catalogue no: **821 123 4**

OBERAMMERGAU PASSION PLAY (1980 Production) (Various artists)
Album: Released Mar '81, on IMS by Polydor Ltd. Catalogue no: **243 782 0**

O'Brien, Virginia

SONGS FROM HER MGM FILMS
Album: Released Jan '89, on Silva Screen by Silva Screen Records. Catalogue no: **AEI 2117**

Obsession (film)

OBSESSION (Film Soundtrack) (Various artists)
Note: Re-issue of the Bernard Herrmann score for the 1976 Brian De Palma horror film.
Album: Released Jan '89, on Silva Screen by Silva Screen Records. Catalogue no: **16.45029**

Ocean, Billy

WHEN THE GOING GETS TOUGH (THE TOUGH GET GOING)
Tracks: / When the going gets tough (the tough get going).
Note: From the film 'Jewel In The Nile'.
7" Set: Released Jun '86, on Jive by Zomba Records. Deleted '88. Catalogue no: **JIVED 114**
7" Single: Released Jan '86, on Jive by Zomba Records. Deleted '88. Catalogue no: **JIVE 114**
12" Single: Released Jan '86, on Jive by Zomba Records. Catalogue no: **JIVER 114**
7" Pic: Released Jan '86, on Jive by Zomba Records. Deleted '87. Catalogue no: **JIVES 114**
12" Single: Released Jan '86, on Jive by Zomba Records. Deleted '87. Catalogue no: **JIVET 114**

O'Connor, Hazel

BREAKING GLASS (See under Breaking Glass)

CALLS THE TUNE
Tracks: / Calls the tune / Eighth day / Give me an inch.
Note: From the film *'Breaking Glass'*.
7" Single: Released Jan '82, on A&M by A&M Records. Deleted '85. Catalogue no: **AMS 8203**

EIGHTH DAY
Tracks: / Eighth day / Monster in disguise.
Note: From the film 'Breaking Glass'.
7" Single: Released Aug '80, on A&M by A&M Records. Deleted '83. Catalogue no: **AMS 7553**

FIGHTING BACK (O'Connor, Hazel And The Arts Freedom Singers)
Tracks: / Fighting back / Reach.
Note: Theme from the BBC TV series of the same name.
7" Single: Released Jul '86, on BBC by BBC Records. Deleted 31 Aug '88. Catalogue no: **RESL 182**
12" Single: Released Jul '86, on BBC by BBC Records. Deleted 31 Aug '88. Catalogue no: **12 RSL 182**

GIVE ME AN INCH
Tracks: / Give me an inch.
Note: From the film 'Breaking Glass'.
7" Single: Released Oct '80, on A&M by A&M Records. Deleted '83. Catalogue no: **AMS 7569**

WILL YOU?
Tracks: / Will you? / Sons and lovers.
Note: From the film Breaking Glass.
7" Single: Released May '81, on A&M by A&M Records. Deleted May '84. Catalogue no: **AMS 8131**

WILL YOU? (OLD GOLD)
Tracks: / Will you? / Eighth day.
Note: From the film Breaking Glass.
7" Single: Released Jun '88, on Old Gold by Old Gold Records. Catalogue no: **OG 9544**

WRITING ON THE WALL
Tracks: / Writing on the wall / Big brother.
Note: From the film 'Breaking Glass'.
7" Single: Released Jun '80, on A&M by A&M Records. Deleted '83. Catalogue no: **AMS 7530**

Octopussy

OCTOPUSSY (Film soundtrack) (Various artists)
Tracks: / All-time high: *Coolidge, Rita* / Bond look-alike: *Various artists* / 009 gets the knife: *Various artists* / Gobinda attacks: *Various artists* / That's my little Octopussy: *Various artists* / Arrival at the island of Octopussy: *Various artists* /

Bond at the Monsoon Palace: *Various artists* / Bond meets Octopussy: *Various artists* / Yo-yo fight: *Various artists* / Death of Vijay: *Various artists* / Chase bomb theme, The: *Various artists* / Palace fight, The: *Various artists*.
Album: Released Jun '83, on A&M by A&M Records. Deleted '88. Catalogue no: **AMLX 64967**
Cass: Released Jun '83, on A&M by A&M Records. Deleted '88. Catalogue no: **CXM 64967**

'Off Limits

OFF LIMITS (SAIGON) (Film Soundtrack) (Various artists)
Note: Composed by James Newton Howard.
CD: Released Jan '89, on Silva Screen by Silva Screen Records. Catalogue no: **VCD 70445**

Off The Record With...

OFF THE RECORD WITH... THEMES (TV themes) (Various artists)
Tracks: / Cats' eyes: *Kongos, John* / Me and my girl: *Skellern, Peter* / Deer hunter, Theme from the: *Williams, John (Guitarist)* / Waltons - theme: *Giltrap, Gordon* / Tales from...: *Grainer, Ron Orchestra* / Onedin line: *Keating John* / Song of freedom: *Mansell Chorale* / Love for Lydia: *London Film Orchestra* / Bouquet of flowers: *South Bank Orchestra* / Paris was made for...: *Legrand, Michel* / Mapp & Lucia: *South Bank Orchestra* / Married man, A: *South Bank Orchestra* / Drummonds: *South Bank Orchestra* / Dempsey & Makepeace: *South Bank Orchestra* / Atlantis: *South Bank Orchestra* / Upstairs....: *South Bank Orchestra* / Black beauty: *King, Denis* / Lillie: *South Bank Orchestra* / Dick Turpin: *King, Denis Orchestra* / Love story: *Lai, Frances Orchestra* / Man and a...., A: *Lai, Frances Orchestra* / Windmills of your mind: *Legrand, Michel*.
Cass set: Released Aug '87, on Sierra by Sierra Records. Catalogue no: **CFEDD 1010**
2 LP Set: Released Aug '87, on Sierra by Sierra Records. Catalogue no: **FEDD 1010**

Officer & A Gentleman

OFFICER AND A GENTLEMAN, AN (Film soundtrack) (Various artists)

Tracks: / Officer and a gentleman, An: *Ritenour, Lee* / Up where we belong: *Cocker, Joe & Jennifer Warnes* / Hungry for you love: *Morrison, Van* / Tush: *ZZ Top* / Treat me right: *Benatar, Pat* / Be real: *Sir Douglas Quintet* / Tunnel of love: *Dire Straits*.
Cass: Released '90, on Island by Island Records. Catalogue no: **ICM 2041**
Cass: Released Jan '83, on Island by Island Records. Deleted '90. Catalogue no: **ICT 3**
CD: Released '89, on Island by Island Records. Catalogue no: **IMCD 77**
Cass: Released '90, on Island by Island Records. Catalogue no: **842 715 4**
CD: Released '88, on Island by Island Records. Catalogue no: **CIDST 3**
Album: Released Jan '83, on Island by Island Records. Deleted Jun '88. Catalogue no: **ISTA 3**

Oh Boy

OH BOY (TV soundtracks) (Various artists)
Album: Released Dec '58, on Parlophone by EMI Records. Deleted '63. Catalogue no: **PMC 1072**

OH BOY (Jack Good's TV Show) (Various artists)
Album: Released Jul '78, on EMI by EMI Records. Catalogue no: **NUTM 13**

Oh Calcutta

OH CALCUTTA (Original Australian Cast) (Various artists)
Tracks: / Oh Calcutta: *Various artists* / Coming together, going together: *Various artists* / Sincere replies: *Various artists* / Dick and Jane: *Various artists* / Clarence and Mildred: *Various artists* / Exchanges of information: *Various artists* / I like the look: *Various artists* / Jack and Jill: *Various artists* / Green pants: *Various artists* / Much too soon: *Various artists* / Reprise: *Various artists*.
Album: Released '73, on RCA International by BMG Records (UK). Deleted '78. Catalogue no: **INTS 1178**

Oh Captain

OH CAPTAIN (Original Broadway cast) (Various artists)

Album: Released Jan '89, on Silva Screen by Silva Screen Records. Catalogue no: **AOS 2002**

Oh What A Lovely War

OH WHAT A LOVELY WAR (Original London Cast) (Various artists)
Tracks: / Overture: *Various artists* / Row row row: *Various artists* / Your king and country want you: *Various artists* / Belgium put the kibosh on the Kaiser: *Various artists* / Are we downhearted? No: *Various artists* / Hold your hand out you naughty boy: *Various artists* / I'll make a man of you: *Various artists* / Pack up your troubles: *Various artists* / Hitchy koo: *Various artists* / Heillige nacht: *Various artists* / Christmas day in the cookhouse: *Various artists* / Goodbyee: *Various artists* / Oh it's a lovely war: *Various artists* / Gassed last night: *Various artists* / There's a long long trail: *Various artists* / Hush here comes a whizzbang: *Various artists* / They were only playing leapfrog: *Various artists* / I wore a tunic: *Various artists* / Forward, Joe Soap's army: *Various artists* / When this lousy war is over: *Various artists* / Wash me in the water: *Various artists* / I want to go home: *Various artists* / Bells of hell, The: *Various artists* / Keep the home fires burning: *Various artists* / La chanson de Craonne: *Various artists* / I don't want to be a soldier: *Various artists* / They didn't believe me: *Various artists*.
Cass: Released Apr '83, on T. E. R. by That's Entertainment Records. Catalogue no: **ZCTER 1043**
Album: Released Apr '83, on T. E. R. by That's Entertainment Records. Catalogue no: **TER 1043**

Oil City Symphony

OIL CITY SYMPHONY (Stage Show Soundtrack) (Various artists)
Note: Original New York cast. 1988 winner of the Critics Award for Best Musical.
CD: Released Jan '89, on Silva Screen by Silva Screen Records. Catalogue no: **CDSBL 12594**
Cass: Released Jan '89, on Silva Screen by Silva Screen Records. Catalogue no: **SBLC 12594**
Album: Released Jan '89, on Silva Screen by Silva Screen Records. Catalogue no: **SBL**

Soundtrack to *Oklahoma* on Capitol featuring Gordon McCrae & Shirley Jones

12594

Oklahoma

OKLAHOMA (Revival Broadway Cast) (Various artists)
Cass: Released Aug '80, on RCA Red Seal by BMG Records (UK). Deleted '85. Catalogue no: **BK 13572**
Album: Released Aug '80, on RCA Red Seal by BMG Records (UK). Deleted '85. Catalogue no: **BL 13572**
Album: Released Jan '89, on Silva Screen by Silva Screen Records. Catalogue no: **CBL 1 3572**
Cass: Released Jan '89, on Silva Screen by Silva Screen Records. Catalogue no: **CBK 1 3572**
CD: Released Jan '89, on Silva Screen by Silva Screen Records. Catalogue no: **RCD 1 3572**
CD: Released Aug '90, on Silva Screen by Silva Screen Records. Catalogue no: **RD 83572**

OKLAHOMA (London Stage Cast) (Various artists)
Tracks: / Overture: *Various artists* / Oh what a beautiful morning: *Various artists* / Surrey with the fringe on top: *Various artists* / Kansas city: *Various artists* / I can't say no: *Various artists* / Many a new day: *Various artists* / People will say we're in love: *Various artists* / Poor Jud is dead: *Various artists* / Lonely room: *Various artists* / Out of my dreams: *Various artists* / Farmer and the cowman: *Various artists* / All er nothin': *Various artists* / Oklahoma: *Various artists* / Finale: *Various artists*.
Cass: Released Nov '80, on Stiff by Stiff Records. Catalogue no: **ZOAK 1**
Album: Released Nov '80, on Stiff by Stiff Records. Catalogue no: **OAK 1**

OKLAHOMA (Film Soundtrack) (Various artists) (See panel)
Tracks: / Oklahoma overture: *Various artists* / Oh what a beautiful morning: *Various artists* / Surrey with the fringe on top: *Various artists* / Kansas city: *Various artists* / I can't say no: *Various artists* / Many a new day: *Various artists* / People will say we're in love: *Various artists* / Poor Jud is dead: *Various artists* / Out of my dreams: *Various artists* / Farmer and the cowman: *Various artists* / All er' nothin': *Various artists* / Oklahoma: *Various artists*.
Album: Released May '59, on Capitol by EMI Records. Deleted Aug '90. Catalogue no: **SLCT 6100**
Cass: Released Sep '70, on Capitol by EMI Records. Catalogue no: **TCSW 595**
CD: Released May '87, on Capitol by EMI Records. Catalogue no: **CDP 746 631 2**

OKLAHOMA (Original Broadway Stage Cast) (Various artists)
Tracks: / Oh what a beautiful morning: *Various artists* / Surrey with the fringe on top: *Various artists* / Out of my dreams: *Various artists* / Kansas City: *Various artists* / I can't say no: *Various artists* / People will say we're in love: *Various artists* / Farmer dance, The: *Various artists* / Poor Jud is dead: *Various artists* / It's a scandal, it's an outrage: *Various artists* / Many a new day: *Various artists* / All er' nothin': *Various artists* / Oklahoma: *Various artists*.
Cass: Released Mar '82, on MCA by MCA Records. Catalogue no: **MCLC 1658**
Album: Released Mar '82, on MCA by MCA Records. Catalogue no: **MCL 1658**
CD: Released Aug '90, on MCA by MCA Records. Catalogue no: **DMCL 1658**
Album: Released Feb '81, on Retrospect by EMI Records. Catalogue no: **SH 393**

OKLAHOMA (VIDEO) (Various artists)
Note: Running time: 119 mins.

VHS: Released May '88, on CBS-Fox by CBS-Fox Video. Catalogue no: **7020 50**

Old Grey Whistle Test

OLD GREY WHISTLE TEST
Album: Released Feb '81, on BBC by BBC Records. Deleted '85. Catalogue no: **BELP 017**

OLD GREY WHISTLE TEST TAKE 2 (Various artists)
2 LP Set: Released Jan '77, on Beeb by BBC Records. Catalogue no: **BEEDP 001**

Old Gringo

OLD GRINGO (Film soundtrack) (Various artists)
Tracks: / Ride to the hacienda: *Various artists* / Battle, The: *Various artists* / Harriet's theme: *Various artists* / Bitter's last ride: *Various artists* / Mirrors, The: *Various artists* / Night time: *Various artists* / Bell tower, The: *Various artists* / Sigh, The: *Various artists* / Battle (resolution), The: *Various artists* / Bitter's destiny: *Various artists* / Finale: *Various artists*.
CD: Released Nov '89, on GNP Crescendo (USA) by GNP Crescendo Records (USA). Catalogue no: **GNPD 8017**
Album: Released Nov '89, on Silva Screen by Silva Screen Records. Catalogue no: **GNPS 8017**
Cass: Released Nov '89, on Silva Screen by Silva Screen Records. Catalogue no: **GNP5 8017**

Old Man Of Lochnagar

OLD MAN OF LOCHNAGAR (Original cast recording) (Various artists)
Cass: Released Nov '86, on First Night by First Night Records. Catalogue no: **SCENE C 5**

Old Man & The Sea

OLD MAN & THE SEA, THE (Film Soundtrack) (Various artists)
Note: Composed by Dimitri Tiomkin.
Album: Released Jan '89, on Silva Screen by Silva Screen Records. Catalogue no: **ACS 8013**

OLD MAN & THE SEA, THE (Film soundtrack) (Tiomkin, Dimitri)
CD: Released Feb '90, on Silva Screen by Silva Screen Records. Catalogue no: **VSD 5232**

Oldfield, Mike

BLUE PETER
Tracks: / Blue Peter / Woodhenge.
7" Single: Released Dec '79, on Virgin by Virgin Records. Deleted '82. Catalogue no: **VS 317**

KILLING FIELDS, THE (Film Soundtrack)
Tracks: / Pran's theme / Requiem for a city / Evacuation / Capture / Execution / Bad news / Pran's departure / Work site / Year zero / Blood sucking / Pran's escape / Trek, The / Boy's burial, The/Pran sees the red cross / Good news / Etude / Pran's theme - 2 / Year zero (2).
CD: Released Nov '84, on Virgin by Virgin Records. Catalogue no: **CDV 2328**
Cass: Released Nov '84, on Virgin by Virgin Records. Deleted Aug '87. Catalogue no: **TCV 2328**
Album: Released Jun '88, on Virgin by Virgin Records. Catalogue no: **OVED 183**
Cass: Released Jun '88, on Virgin by Virgin Records. Catalogue no: **OVEDC 183**
Album: Released Nov '84, on Virgin by Virgin Records. Deleted Aug '87. Catalogue no: **V 2328**

KILLING FIELDS, THE (SINGLE)
Tracks: / Killing fields, The / Etude / Evacuation.
12" Single: Released Nov '84, on Virgin by Virgin Records. Deleted May '88. Catalogue no: **VS 731-12**
7" Single: Released Nov '84, on Virgin by Virgin Records. Deleted '85. Catalogue no: **VS 731**

Oldfield, Terry

IN SEARCH OF THE TROJAN WAR (TV soundtrack)
Tracks: / Trojan War, The / Mycenae / Journey to war, The / Troy / Trojan theme / Epitaph / Sea people / Nesas waspas / Hittites / Great railway journeys:Boy on a bicycle / Great river journeys:Maji mengi / Great river journeys:Leaving Kishasa / Helen's song.
Album: Released Mar '85, on BBC by BBC Records. Deleted 31 Aug '88. Catalogue no: **REB 553**
Cass: Released Mar '85, on BBC by BBC Records. Deleted 31 Aug '88. Catalogue no: **ZCF 553**

MAIN THEME FROM JOHN SILVER'S TREASURE ISLAND (TV Theme) (Oldfield, Terry & Tom McGuinness)
Tracks: / John Silver's return to Treasure Island (main theme) / Isabella / Island of dreams.
7" Single: Released Jul '86, on Towerbell Catalogue no: **TVP 8**

Oliver

OLIVER (Various artists)
Tracks: / Oliver: *Various artists* / I'd do anything: *Various artists* / Food glorious food: *Various artists* / Oom pah pah: *Various artists* / Boy for sale: *Various artists* / Who will buy?: *Various artists* / It's a fine life: *Various artists* / You've got to pick a pocket or two: *Various artists* / As long as he needs me: *Various artists* / Reviewing the situation: *Various artists* / Consider yourself: *Various artists*.
Album: Released Dec '79, on Boulevard by Boulevard Records. Deleted '84. Catalogue no: **BD 3012**

OLIVER (Original Broadway Cast) (Various artists)
Tracks: / Food, glorious food: *Various artists* / Oliver: *Various artists* / I shall scream: *Various artists* / Boy for sale: *Various artists* / Where is love: *Various artists* / Consider yourself: *Various artists* / You've got to pick a pocket or two: *Various artists* / It's a fine life: *Various artists* / I'd do anything: *Various artists* / Be back soon: *Various artists* / Oom-pah-pah: *Various artists* / My name: *Various artists* / As long as he needs me: *Various artists* / Who will buy: *Various artists* / Reviewing the situation: *Various artists* / As long as he needs me (reprise): *Various artists* / Reviewing the situation (reprise): *Various artists* / Oliver (finale): *Various artists*.
CD: Released Oct '89, on RCA by BMG Records (UK). Catalogue no: **GD 84113**
Cass: Released Oct '89, on RCA by BMG Records (UK). Catalogue no: **GK 84113**

OLIVER (Film Soundtrack) (various artists)
Tracks: / Overture: Various artists / Food, glorious food: Various artists / Boy for sale: Various artists / Where is love: Various artists /

You've got to pick a pocket or two: Various artists / Consider yourself: Various artists / I'd do anything: Various artists / Be back soon: Various artists / As long as he needs me: Various artists / Who will buy: Various artists / It's a fine life: Various artists / Reviewing the situation: Various artists / Oom-pah-pah: Various artists / Finale: Various artists.

Album: Released Mar '89, on RCA by BMG Records (UK). Catalogue no: **NL 90311**

CD: Released Mar '89, on RCA by BMG Records (UK). Catalogue no: **ND 90311**

CD: Released Jan '89, on Silva Screen by Silva Screen Records. Catalogue no: **5501.2**

Cass: Released Mar '89, on RCA by BMG Records (UK). Catalogue no: **NK 90311**

Cass: Released '79, on RCA by BMG Records (UK). Deleted '84. Catalogue no: **VCS 67277**

Album: Released Nov '68, on RCA by BMG Records (UK). Deleted '73. Catalogue no: **SB 6777**

Cass: Released Jan '89, on Silva Screen by Silva Screen Records. Catalogue no: **OKCG 1003**

Album: Released Jan '89, on Silva Screen by Silva Screen Records. Catalogue no: **COSD 5503**

Album: Released '84, on RCA by BMG Records (UK). Catalogue no: **PL 85501**

Cass: Released '84, on RCA by BMG Records (UK). Catalogue no: **PK 85501**

OLIVER (Film Soundtrack) (Various artists)

Tracks: / Food, glorious food: *Various artists* / Oliver: *Various artists* / I shall scream: *Various artists* / Boy for sale: *Various artists* / That's your funeral: *Various artists* / Where is love?: *Various artists* / Consider yourself: *Various artists* / You've got to pick a pocket or two: *Various artists* / It's a fine life: *Various artists* / Be back soon: *Various artists* / Oom pah pah: *Various artists* / My name: *Various artists* / As long as he needs me: *Various artists* / I'd do anything: *Various artists* / Who will buy?: *Various artists* / Reviewing the situation: *Various artists* / Finale: *Various artists*.

Cass: Released Apr '83, on T. E.

R. by That's Entertainment Records. Catalogue no: **ZCTER 1042**

Album: Released Apr '83, on T. E. R. by That's Entertainment Records. Catalogue no: **TER 1042**

OLIVER (Original Cast) (Various artists)

Cass: Released '79, on Decca by Decca International. Catalogue no: **KCSP 30**

CD: Released Jan '89, on London by London Records Ltd. Catalogue no: **820 590 2**

OLIVER (ORIGINAL ISSUE) (London cast) (Various artists)

Album: Released Sep '60, on Decca by Decca International. Deleted '65. Catalogue no: **LK 4359**

OLIVER (RE-ISSUE) (London cast) (Various artists)

Album: Released Nov '69, on Decca by Decca International. Deleted '74. Catalogue no: **SPA 30**

OLIVER (VIDEO) (Various artists)

VHS: Released Oct '88, on RCA by BMG Records (UK). Catalogue no: **CVT 20048**

Oliver (Artist)

GOOD MORNING STAR-SHINE

Tracks: / Good morning starshine.
Note: From the musical 'Hair'.
7" Single: Released Aug '69, on CBS by CBS Records & Distribu-

tion. Deleted '72. Catalogue no: **CBS 4435**

Oliver & Company

OLIVER AND COMPANY (Film Soundtrack)

Album: Released Jul '90, on Pickwick by Pickwick Records. Catalogue no: **PDL 450**

CD: Released Jul '90, on Pickwick by Pickwick Records. Catalogue no: **PWKD 450**

Cass: Released Jul '90, on Pickwick by Pickwick Records. Catalogue no: **PBC 450**

Olivier, Laurence

TIME, THEME FROM

Tracks: / Time, Theme from.
10" Single: Released Nov '85, on EMI by EMI Records. Deleted Oct '87. Catalogue no: **10 EMI 5539**

7" Single: Released Nov '85, on EMI by EMI Records. Catalogue no: **EMI 5539**

Oliver Twist

OLIVER TWIST/MALTA G.C. (Film soundtracks) (Royal Philharmonic Orchestra)

Tracks: / Prelude / Storm, The / Fight, The / Oliver's sleepless night / Oliver and the Artful Dodger / Fagin's romp / Chase, The / Oliver and Brownlow / Nancy and Brownlow / Finale / Prelude / Convoy / Old valletta / Air raid / Ruins / Quick march / Intermezzo / Work and play / Finale.

Oliver & Company - a 1988 Disney production

Note: 2 Classic 1940's film scores by Sir Arnold Bax, newly recorded.
Album: Released Jan '89, on Silva Screen by Silva Screen Records. Catalogue no: **CN 7012**
CD: Released Jan '89, on Silva Screen by Silva Screen Records. Catalogue no: **ACN 7012**

Oliver's Story

OLIVER'S STORY (Film soundtrack) (Various artists)
Album: Released '79, on MCA by MCA Records. Deleted '84. Catalogue no: **MCF 3003**
Cass: Released '79, on MCA by MCA Records. Deleted '84. Catalogue no: **MCFC 3003**

Ollie & Jerry

BREAKIN' ... THERE'S NO STOPPIN' US (OLD GOLD)
Tracks: / Breakin' ... there's no stoppin' us / You can dance if you want to.
12" Single: Released 28 Aug '89, on Old Gold by Old Gold Records. Catalogue no: **OG 4131**

BREAKIN' THERE'S NO STOPPING US
Tracks: / Breakin' there's no stopping us / Breakin' there's no stopping us (instr.).
Note: From the film 'Breakdance'.
7" Single: Released Jun '84, on Polydor by Polydor Ltd. Deleted '87. Catalogue no: **POSP 690**

ELECTRIC BOOGALOO
Tracks: / Electric boogaloo / Physical clash.
Note: From the film 'Breakdance'
12" Single: Released Mar '85, on Polydor by Polydor Ltd. Deleted '88. Catalogue no: **POSPX 730**
7" Single: Released Mar '85, on Polydor by Polydor Ltd. Deleted '88. Catalogue no: **POSP 730**

Olympic Orchestra

REILLY - ACE OF SPIES
Tracks: / Reilly, ace of spies - theme / Canon in D.
7" Single: Released Sep '83, on Red Bus by Red Bus Records. Catalogue no: **RBUS 82**

Olympus On My Mind

OLYMPUS ON MY MIND (Film soundtrack) (Various artists)
Tracks: / Welcome to Greece: Chorus, The / Heaven on earth: Jupiter, Alchmene / Gods on tap, The: Delores, Jupiter / Surprise:

Sosia and Mercury / Love - what...: Jupiter, Mercury And Dolores / Enter the husband: Chorus, The / I know my wife: Amphitryon / It was me: Sosia and Amphitryon / Back so soon: Amphitryon, Sosia and orch / Wonderful: Alchmene / At liberty...: Charis and the chorus / Jupiter slept here: Jupiter and all / Something of yourself: Mercury / Star is born, A: Delores & all / Final sequence: Amphitryon, Alchmene.
Album: Released Feb '88, on T. E. R. by That's Entertainment Records. Catalogue no: **TER 1131**

Omen (Film)

DAMIEN: OMEN 2 (1978 film soundtrack) (Various artists)
Tracks: / Main title: Various artists / Runaway train: Various artists / Claws: Various artists / Thoughtful night: Various artists / Broken ice: Various artists / Fallen temple: Various artists / I love you, Mark: Various artists / Shafted: Various artists / Knife, The: Various artists / All the power (end title): Various artists.
Note: Score by Jerry Goldsmith.
CD: Released Nov '89, on Silva Screen by Silva Screen Records. Catalogue no: **FILMCD 002**
Cass: Released Nov '89, on Silva Screen by Silva Screen Records. Catalogue no: **FILMC 002**
Album: Released Nov '89, on Silva Screen by Silva Screen Records. Catalogue no: **FILM 002**

FINAL CONFLICT - OMEN III (1985 film soundtrack) (Various artists)
Note: Composed by Jerry Goldsmith.
Album: Released Sep '86, on Colosseum (West Germany) Catalogue no: **CST 8020**
Cass: Released Jan '89, on Varese Sarabande Records(USA) by Varese Sarabande Records (USA). Catalogue no: **CTV 81272**
Album: Released Jan '89, on Varese Sarabande Records(USA) by Varese Sarabande Records (USA). Catalogue no: **STV 81272**
CD: Released '86, on Varese Sarabande Records(USA) by Varese Sarabande Records (USA). Catalogue no: **VCD 47242**

Omen & Others

OMEN & OTHER THEMES,

THE (Film soundtracks: 50 Years of classic horror) (Various artists)
Tracks: / Omen suite: Various artists / She suite: Various artists / Rosemary's baby suite: Various artists / Doctor Jekyll & Mr. Hyde suite: Various artists / King Kong suite: Various artists / Vampire lovers suite, The: Various artists / Fear in the night suite: Various artists / Exorcist II suite: Various artists / Hellraiser suite: Various artists / Doctor Jekyll & Sister Hyde suite: Various artists.
Note: Composers include Jerry Goldsmith, James Bernard, Kristoff Komeda, Franz Waxman, Max Steiner, Harry Robinson, John McCabe, Ennio Morricone, Christopher Young, David Whittaker.
Album: Released Nov '89, on Silva Screen by Silva Screen Records. Catalogue no: **FILM 017**
CD: Released Nov '89, on Silva Screen by Silva Screen Records. Catalogue no: **FILMCD 017**
Cass: Released Nov '89, on Silva Screen by Silva Screen Records. Catalogue no: **FILMC 017**

On A Clear Day ...

ON A CLEAR DAY YOU CAN SEE FOREVER (Film soundtrack) (Various artists)
Note: Starring Barbra Streisand.
Cass: Released Jan '89, on Silva Screen by Silva Screen Records. Catalogue no: **BT 30086**
CD: Released Feb '90, on Silva Screen by Silva Screen Records. Catalogue no: **A 20716**
Album: Released Jan '89, on Silva Screen by Silva Screen Records. Catalogue no: **AS 30086**

On Golden Pond

ON GOLDEN POND (Film soundtrack) (Various artists)
Note: Music (Dave Grusin) and dialogue from the Henry and Jane Fonda film.
Album: Released Jan '89, on MCA by MCA Records. Catalogue no: **MCA 1497**
Cass: Released Jan '89, on MCA by MCA Records. Catalogue no: **MCAC 1497**

ON GOLDEN POND (VIDEO) (Various artists)
VHS: Released Oct '89, on Spectrum (1) Catalogue no: **SPC 00162**

On Her Majesty's...

ON HER MAJESTY'S SECRET SERVICE (Film soundtrack) (Various artists)
Note: Score by John Barry with Louis Armstrong.
Cass: Released Jan '89, on Silva Screen by Silva Screen Records. Catalogue no: **E 41 E 90618**
CD: Released Jan '89, on Silva Screen by Silva Screen Records. Catalogue no: **CD 90618**
2 LP Set: Released '88, on United Artists by EMI Records. Catalogue no: **UAD 60027/8**

On Moonlight Bay

ON MOONLIGHT BAY/TEA FOR TWO (Film Soundtrack) (Various artists)
Note: 2 Doris Day Musical soundtracks.
Album: Released Jan '89, on Silva Screen by Silva Screen Records. Catalogue no: **P 17660**
Cass: Released Jan '89, on Silva Screen by Silva Screen Records. Catalogue no: **BT 17660**

On The Air

ON THE AIR (60 years of BBC theme music) (Various artists)
Tracks: / On the air: *Various artists* / In town tonight: *Various artists* / I.T.M.A.: *Various artists* / Take it from here: *Various artists* / Much binding in the marsh: *Various artists* / In the mood: *Various artists* / You're dancing on my heart: *Various artists* / Meet the Huggets: *Various artists* / Paul Temple: *Various artists* / Dick Barton: *Various artists* / Music while you work: *Various artists* / Say it with music: *Various artists* / T.V. newsreel: *Various artists* / Toytown: *Various artists* / Muffin the mule: *Various artists* / Sooty: *Various artists* / Housewives choice: *Various artists* / Down your way: *Various artists* / Have a go: *Various artists* / Sports report: *Various artists* / Billy Cotton Band show: *Various artists* / Mrs. Dale's diary: *Various artists* / Archers, The: *Various artists* / Listen with mother theme: *Various artists* / Children's choice: *Various artists* / Top of the form: *Various artists* / Tonight: *Various artists* / Six five special: *Various artists* / Jukebox jury: *Various artists* / Sing something simple: *Various artists* / Pick of the pops: *Various artists* / Roundabout: *Various artists* / Doctor Kildare theme: *Various artists* / Grand hotel: *Various artists* / Desert island discs: *Various artists* / Nationwide: *Various artists* / Doctor Finlay's casebook: *Various artists* / Monitor: *Various artists* / Two way family favourites: *Various artists* / Dixon of Dock Green: *Various artists* / Maigret: *Various artists* / Z Cars: *Various artists* / Tomorrows world: *Various artists* / Sky at night, The: *Various artists* / Grandstand: *Various artists* / Match of the day: *Various artists* / That was the week that was: *Various artists* / Steptoe and son: *Various artists* / Monty Python: *Various artists* / Fawlty Towers: *Various artists* / Dad's army: *Various artists* / Blue Peter: *Various artists* / Magic roundabout: *Various artists* / Forsyte saga, The: *Various artists* / Onedin line: *Various artists* / All creatures great and small: *Various artists* / Juliet Bravo: *Various artists* / Dallas: *Various artists* / Here's to the next time: *Various artists*.
Cass: Released Oct '82, on BBC by BBC Records. Catalogue no: **ZCD 454**
2 LP Set: Released Oct '82, on BBC by BBC Records. Catalogue no: **REF 454**

On The Big Hill

ON THE BIG HILL (Film soundtrack) (Various artists)
Tracks: / Opening shot: *Various artists* / Best laid plans: *Various artists* / Mountain madness: *Various artists* / Thru the window: *Various artists* / Try not to fall: *Various artists* / Higher ground: *Various artists* / There are times: *Various artists* / Things look different: *Various artists* / Take a short walk: *Various artists* / Some people get hurt: *Various artists* / Long walk: *Various artists* / Across the bridge: *Various artists* / Dougie's march: *Various artists* / Each night you die a little: *Various artists* / In the back of your mind: *Various artists* / Home Dougie, home: *Various artists*.
Cass: Released Dec '88, on Silvertone Catalogue no: **OREC 501**
Album: Released Dec '88, on Silvertone Catalogue no: **ORELP 501**
CD: Released Dec '88, on Silvertone Catalogue no: **ORECD 501**

On The Town

ON THE TOWN (Original Broadway cast) (Various artists)
Album: Released Jan '89, on Silva Screen by Silva Screen Records. Catalogue no: **AS 31005**
Cass: Released Jan '89, on Silva Screen by Silva Screen Records. Catalogue no: **BT 31005**

ON THE TOWN (Film Soundtrack) (Various artists)
Album: Released '88, on DRG (USA) by DRG Records (USA). Catalogue no: **DS 15029**

ON THE TOWN (Broadway Cast) (Various artists)
Tracks: / New York, New York: *Various artists* / Dance: *Various artists* / Miss Turnstiles: *Various artists* / Taxi number: *Various artists* / Come up to my place: *Various artists* / Carried away: *Various artists* / Lonely town: *Various artists* / I can cook too: *Various artists* / Lucky to be me: *Various artists* / Times square: *Various artists* / Night club sequence: *Various artists* / Ballet: *Various artists* / Imaginary Coney Island: *Various artists* / Some other time: *Various artists* / Finale: *Various artists*.
Album: Released Jul '83, on CBS Cameo by CBS Records & Distribution. Catalogue no: **CBS 32315**
Cass: Released Jan '89, on Silva Screen by Silva Screen Records. Catalogue no: **JST 02038**
Cass: Released Jul '83, on CBS Cameo by CBS Records & Distribution. Catalogue no: **40-32315**
CD: Released Jan '89, on CBS (import) by CBS Records & Distribution. Catalogue no: **CK 02038**

ON THE TOWN (VIDEO) (Various artists)
VHS: Released '88, on MGM/UA (Video) by MGM/UA Video. Catalogue no: **SMV 10057**

On The Twentieth ...

ON THE TWENTIETH CENTURY (Original Broadway Cast) (Various artists)
Cass: Released Jan '89, on Silva Screen by Silva Screen Records. Catalogue no: **BT 35330**
Album: Released Jan '89, on Silva Screen by Silva Screen Records. Catalogue no: **ATS 35330**

On Your Toes

ON YOUR TOES (Studio Cast) (Various artists)
Album: Released Jan '89, on Silva Screen by Silva Screen Records. Catalogue no: **COS 2590**

ON YOUR TOES (1983 Original Broadway cast) (Various artists)
Tracks: / Overtures: *Various artists* / Two a day for Keith: *Various artists* / It's got to be love: *Various artists* / Too good for the average man: *Various artists* / There's a small hotel: *Various artists* / Heart is quicker than the eye, The: *Various artists* / Quiet night: *Various artists* / Questions and answers: *Various artists* / Glad to be unhappy: *Various artists* / On your toes: *Various artists* / Princess Zenobia (edited): *Various artists* / Slaughter on Tenth Avenue (edited): *Various artists*.
CD: Released '85, on T. E. R. by That's Entertainment Records. Catalogue no: **CDTER 1063**
Cass: Released Jul '83, on T. E. R. by That's Entertainment Records. Catalogue no: **ZCTER 1063**
Album: Released Jul '83, on T. E. R. by That's Entertainment Records. Catalogue no: **TER 2 1063**

Once Bitten

ONCE BITTEN (Film soundtrack) (Various artists)
Album: Released Feb '84, on Red Door by Red Door Records. Catalogue no: **RD 001**
Cass: Released '85, on MCA by MCA Records. Catalogue no: **IMCA 6154**

Once Upon A Time

ONCE UPON A TIME IN AMERICA (Film soundtrack) (Various artists)
Tracks: / Once upon a time in America: *Various artists* / Poverty: *Various artists* / Deborah's theme: *Various artists* / Childhood memories: *Various artists* / Amapola: *Various artists* / Friends: *Various artists* / Prohibition dirge: *Various artists* / Cockeye's song: *Various artists* / Childhood poverty: *Various artists* / Photographic memories: *Various artists* / Friendship and love: *Various artists* / Speakeasy: *Various artists* / Deborah's theme: *Various artists* / Amapola: *Various artists*.
CD: Released Dec '84, on Mercury by Phonogram Ltd. Catalogue no: **822 334-2**
Cass: Released Dec '84, on Mercury by Phonogram Ltd. Catalogue no: **MERHC 45**
Album: Released Dec '84, on Mercury by Phonogram Ltd. Catalogue no: **MERH 45**

One Flew Over...

ONE FLEW OVER THE CUCKOO'S NEST (Film soundtrack) (Various artists)
Note: Composed by Jack Nitzsche.
Album: Released Jan '89, on Fantasy by Ace Records. Catalogue no: **MPF 4531**

One From The Heart

ONE FROM THE HEART (Film soundtrack) (Various artists)
Tracks: / Opening montage: *Various artists* / Tom's piano: *Various artists* / Once upon a town: *Various artists* / Wages of love, The: *Various artists* / Is there any way out of this dream?: *Various artists* / Presents: *Various artists* / Picking up after you: *Various artists* / Old boy friends: *Various artists* / Broken bicycles: *Various artists* / I beg your pardon: *Various artists* / Little boy blue: *Various artists* / Instrumental montage: *Various artists* / Tango, The: *Various artists* / Circus girl: *Various artists* / You can't unring a bell: *Various artists* / This one's from the heart: *Various artists* / Take me home: *Various artists*.
Note: Artists include Tom Waits and Crystal Gayle.
Cass: Released Jan '89, on CBS by CBS Records & Distribution. Catalogue no: **40 70215**
Album: Released Feb '83, on CBS by CBS Records & Distribution. Catalogue no: **CBS 70215**

One Hundred & One...

ONE HUNDRED AND ONE DALMATIANS (Film Soundtrack) (Various artists)
Tracks: / Playful melody: *Various artists* / Kanine krunchies kommercial: *Various artists* / Cruella De Ville: *Various artists* / Dalmatian plantation: *Various artists*.
Cass: Released Dec '87, on Walt Disney Catalogue no: **WDC 017**

Album: Released Dec '87, on Walt Disney Catalogue no: **WD 017**

One Million Years BC

ONE MILLION YEARS BC (Film Soundtrack) (Various artists)
Note: Music from the Racquel Welch film by Mario Nascimbene.
Album: Released Jan '89, on Interior Music by Interior Music Records. Catalogue no: **IM 005**

One Minute To Pray

ONE MINUTE TO PRAY, ONE SECOND TO DIE (Film Soundtrack) (Various artists)
Note: Spaghetti western score by Carlo Rustichelli.
Album: Released Jan '89, on Silva Screen by Silva Screen Records. Catalogue no: **SP 8023**

One Mo' Time

ONE MO' TIME (Original cast) (Various artists)
Tracks: / Down in Honky Tonk town: *Various artists* / Kiss me sweet: *Various artists* / Miss Jenny's ball: *Various artists* / Cake-walkin' babies from home: *Various artists* / I've got what it takes: *Various artists* / CC rider: *Various artists* / Graveyard: *Various artists* / He's funny that way: *Various artists* / Kitchen man: *Various artists* / Wait till you see my baby do the Charleston: *Various artists* / Love: *Various artists* / Louise: *Various artists* / New Orleans hop scop: *Various artists* / Blues: *Various artists* / Everybody loves my baby: *Various artists* / You've got the right key but the wrong keyhole: *Various artists* / After you've gone: *Various artists* / My man blues: *Various artists* / Papa de da da: *Various artists* / Muddy water: *Various artists* / There'll be a hot time in the old town tonight: *Various artists*.
Album: Released Aug '81, on Warner Bros. by WEA Records. Deleted Aug '86. Catalogue no: **K56850**

One Moment In Time

ONE MOMENT IN TIME (American Olympic theme) (Various artists)
Note: The Christians and Whitney Houston etc.

Cass: Released Sep '88, on Arista by BMG Records (UK). Deleted Jan '90. Catalogue no: **409299**
CD: Released Sep '88, on Arista by BMG Records (UK). Deleted Jan '90. Catalogue no: **259299**
Album: Released Sep '88, on Arista by BMG Records (UK). Deleted Jan '90. Catalogue no: **209299**

One Silver Dollar

ONE SILVER DOLLAR (Film Soundtrack) (Various artists)
Note: Spaghetti western by Gianno Ferrio.
Album: Released Jan '89, on Silva Screen by Silva Screen Records. Catalogue no: **PHCAM 02**

One Touch Of Venus

ONE TOUCH OF VENUS (Original Broadway Cast) (Various artists)
Album: Released Jan '89, on Silva Screen by Silva Screen Records. Catalogue no: **AEI 1136**

Opportunity Knocks

OPPORTUNITY KNOCKS (See under Dee, Kiki)

Oranges...

ORANGES ARE NOT THE ONLY FRUIT (Various artists)
Cass set: Released Mar '90, on BBC by BBC Records. Catalogue no: **ZBBC 1152**

Ordinary People

ORDINARY PEOPLE (See under Hamlisch, Marvin)

Original...

ORIGINAL SOUNDTRACKS (Various artists)
Cass: Released '88, on EMI (Holland) by EMI Records. Catalogue no: **1A 222 1582754**

ORIGINAL TV HITS OF THE SIXTIES (Various artists)
Tracks: / Route 66: *Riddle, Nelson* / Doctor Kildare theme: *Spence, Johnny* / Human jungle, The: *Barry, John* / Saint, The: *Fahey, Brian* / Danger man theme: *Fahey, Brian* / Man from uncle, The: *Fahey, Brian* / Avengers, The: *Various artists* / Baron, The: *Various artists* / Thunderbird: *Various artists* / Dept. S: *Stapleton, Cyril & Orchestra* / Prisoner, The: *Grainer, Ron*.
Album: Released Feb '87, on

Watching Music Catalogue no: **MOMENT 105**
Cass: Released Feb '87, on Watching Music Deleted Feb '90. Catalogue no: **MOMENTC 105**

Osterman Weekend

OSTERMAN WEEKEND, THE (Film soundtrack) (Various artists)
Note: Composed by Lalo Schifrin.
Album: Released Mar '84, on T. E. R. by That's Entertainment Records. Catalogue no: **TER 1084**
Cass: Released Jan '89, on T. E. R. by That's Entertainment Records. Deleted Mar '90. Catalogue no: **CTV 81198**

Otello

OTELLO (Film soundtrack) (Various artists)
LP Set: Released '86, on H.M.V. by EMI Records. Deleted Sep '90. Catalogue no: **EX 270 461 3**
CD Set: Released '86, on H.M.V. by EMI Records. Catalogue no: **CDS 747 450 8**
Cass set: Released '86, on H.M.V. by EMI Records. Catalogue no: **EX 270 461 5**

Our Man Flint

OUR MAN FLINT (Film soundtrack) (Various artists)
Cass: Released Sep '90, on Silva Screen by Silva Screen Records. Catalogue no: **FILMC 046**
Album: Released Sep '90, on Silva Sceen by Silva Screen Records. Catalogue no: **FILM 046**

Out Of Africa

OUT OF AFRICA (Film soundtrack) (Various artists)
Tracks: / I had a farm in Africa: *Various artists* / I'm better at hello (Karen's theme): *Various artists* / Have you got a story for me: *Various artists* / Concerto for clarinet in A (K 622): *Various artists* / Safari: *Various artists* / Karen's journey: *Various artists* / Siyawe: *Various artists* / Flying over Africa: *Various artists* / I had a compass from Denys (Karen's theme II): *Various artists* / Alone on the farm: *Various artists* / Let the rest of the world go by: *Various artists* / If I know a song from Africa (Karen's theme III): *Various artists* / You are Karen (end theme): *Various artists* / Music of goodbye, The: *Various artists*.
Note: John Barry's music for Sidney

Pollack's "Out of Africa" is as timeless and hauntingly beautiful as the Kenyan landscapes that dominate this film based on the famed novels of Izak Dinesen and this Danish writer's life on an African coffee plantation in the early part of the century. Starring Meryl Streep and Robert Redford in the major roles. John Barry's emotive score is complimented by the brilliant vocal performances of Melissa Manchester and Al Jarreau in the song "The music of goodbye", the album's musical highlight.
Album: Released Mar '86, on MCA by MCA Records. Catalogue no: **MCF 3310**
CD: Released '86, on MCA by MCA Records. Catalogue no: **DMCF 3310**
CD: Released Feb '90, on MCA by MCA Records. Catalogue no: **MCAD 6158**
Cass: Released Mar '86, on MCA by MCA Records. Catalogue no: **MCFC 3310**

Out Of Order

OUT OF ORDER (ABWARTS) (Film soundtracks) (Various artists)
Note: Music by Jacques Zwart from the hit German film.
Album: Released Mar '86, on RG (West Germany) Catalogue no: **RG 1018**

Out Of The Ruins

OUT OF THE RUINS (Film soundtrack) (Various artists)
Note: Soundtrack for BBC TV's Aid for Armenia.
Cass: Released Dec '89, on Silva Screen by Silva Screen Records. Catalogue no: **FILMC 063**
CD: Released Dec '89, on Silva Screen by Silva Screen Records. Catalogue no: **FILMCD 063**

Out Of This World

OUT OF THIS WORLD (Original Broadway Cast) (Various artists)
Album: Released Jan '89, on Silva Screen by Silva Screen Records. Catalogue no: **CML 4390**

Outland

OUTLAND (Film soundtrack) (Goldsmith, Jerry)
Album: Released Jul '81, on Warner Bros. by WEA Records. Catalogue no: **K 56921**

Outlaw Blues

OUTLAW BLUES (Film Soundtrack) (Various artists)
Tracks: / Everybody's goin' on the road: *Various artists* / Jailbirds don't fly: *Various artists* / I dream of highways: *Various artists* / Outlaw on the run: *Various artists* / Beyond these walls: *Various artists* / Outlaw blues love theme: *Various artists* / Water for my horses: *Various artists* / Whisper in a velvet night: *Various artists* / Little more holy: *Various artists*
Album: Released Nov '77, on Capitol by EMI Records. Catalogue no: **EST 11691**

Outsiders (Film)

OUTSIDERS (Film soundtrack) (Various artists)
CD: Released Jan '90, on Silva Screen by Silva Screen Records. Catalogue no: **FILMCD 051**
Album: Released Jan '90, on Silva Screen by Silva Screen Records. Catalogue no: **FILM 051**

Ovchinnikov, Vyacheslav

WAR AND PEACE (See under War & Peace)

Over The Brooklyn...

OVER THE BROOKLYN BRIDGE (Film soundtrack) (Various artists)
Tracks: / Changes: *Various artists* / In the heat of the night: *Various artists* / Over a bridge: *Various artists* / Pino Donaggio: *Various artists* / Over the Brooklyn Bridge: *Various artists* / Streets of Manhattan: *Various artists* / Honey cake: *Various artists* / Alby's a blues: *Various artists* / Uncle Benjamin: *Various artists* / Brooklyn to Broadway: *Various artists* / Problems for Alby: *Various artists* / Son of the Godfather: *Various artists* / On Seventh Avenue: *Various artists* / Which way to go?: *Various artists* / I'd like to hold you through the night: *Various artists*.
Album: Released Mar '84, on Red Bus by Red Bus Records. Catalogue no: **BUST 1200**
Cass: Released Mar '84, on Red Bus by Red Bus Records. Catalogue no: **ZCBUST 1200**

Over The Moon

BLACKHOLE, THEME FROM (See under Nova)

Over The Top

OVER THE TOP (Film soundtrack) (Various artists)
Tracks: / Winner takes it all, The: *Hagar, Sammy* / In this country: *Zander, Robin* / Take it higher: *Greene, Larry* / All I need is you: *Big Trouble* / Bad nite: *Stallone, Frank* / Meet me half way: *Loggins, Kenny* / Gypsy soul: *Asia* / Fight, The: *Various artists* / Mind over matter: *Greene, Larry* / I will be strong: *Money, Eddie*.
Cass: Released Apr '87, on CBS by CBS Records & Distribution. Catalogue no: **450484 4**
CD: Released Apr '87, on CBS by CBS Records & Distribution. Deleted 17 Apr '89. Catalogue no: **450484 2**
Album: Released Apr '87, on CBS by CBS Records & Distribution. Catalogue no: **450484 1**

O'Williams, Wendy

MAGGOTS (Film soundtrack) (O'Williams, Wendy/Plasmatics)
Tracks: / Overture / Introduction (Spoken word) / You're a zombie / White's apartment, The / Four meal dinner (Spoken) / Day of the humans is gone, The / Central research laboratory, The / Valerie and Bruce on the phone / Destroyers / Bruce's bedroom / Brain dead / Propogators / White's bedroom fire escape, The / Finale.
Album: Released Mar '87, on GWR by GWR Records. Deleted May '90. Catalogue no: **GWLP 8**

REFORM SCHOOLGIRLS (See under Reform School girls)

Owl & The Pussycat

OWL & THE PUSSYCAT, THE (Film Soundtrack) (Various artists)
Note: Dialogue highlights from the Barbra Streisand/George Segal film.
Album: Released Jan '89, on Silva Screen by Silva Screen Records. Catalogue no: **AS 30401**
Cass: Released Jan '89, on Silva Screen by Silva Screen Records. Catalogue no: **BT 30401**

The following information was taken from the Music Master database on September 25th, 1990.

Pacific 1860

PACIFIC 1860 (Original London cast) (Various artists)
Tracks: / If I were a man: *Various artists* / His excellency regrets: *Various artists* / Uncle Harry: *Various artists* / Dear Madam Salvador: *Various artists* / My horse has cast a shoe: *Various artists* / Bright was the day: *Various artists* / One, two, three: *Various artists* / I never knew: *Various artists* / I saw no shadow: *Various artists* / Invitation to the waltz: *Various artists* / I wish, I wasn't quite such a big girl: *Various artists* / Pretty little bridesmaids: *Various artists* / Mothers' lament: *Various artists* / This is a changing world: *Various artists* / This is a night for lovers: *Various artists* / Fumfumbolo: *Various artists* / Toast music and finale: Various artists.
Cass: Released Apr '83, on T. E. R. by That's Entertainment Records. Catalogue no: **ZCTER 1040**
Album: Released Apr '83, on T. E. R. by That's Entertainment Records. Catalogue no: **TER 1040**

Pacific Overtures

PACIFIC OVERTURES (Original Broadway cast) (Various artists)
Cass: Released Jan '89, on Red Seal by RCA Records. Catalogue no: **BK 84407**
Album: Released Mar '90, on Red Seal by RCA Records. Catalogue no: **BL 84407**
CD: Released Feb '90, on Red Seal by RCA Records. Catalogue no: **BD 84407**

PACIFIC OVERTURES (LONDON CAST) (Various artists)
Album: Released Mar '90, on T. E. R. by That's Entertainment Records. Catalogue no: **TER2 1151** '
Cass: Released Mar '90, on T. E.

R. by That's Entertainment Records. Catalogue no: **ZCTED 1151**
CD Set: Released Feb '90, on T. E. R. by That's Entertainment Records. Catalogue no: **CD2TER1151**

Pagan Love Story

PIRATE, THE/PAGAN LOVE STORY (See under Pirate (Film))

Page, Jimmy

DEATHWISH II (Film soundtrack)
Tracks: / Who's to blame / Chase, The / City sirens / Jam sandwich / Carol's theme / Release, The / Hotel rats and photostats / Shadow in the city, A / Jill's theme / Deathwish: prelude / Big band / Sex and violence / Hypnotizing ways (Oh mamma).
Album: Released Feb '82, on Swansong Deleted Feb '87. Catalogue no: **SSK 59415**

Paige, Elaine

CINEMA
Tracks: / Windmills of your mind / Out here on my own / Prisoner, The / Sometimes / Do you know where you're going to (Theme from 'Mahogany') / Up where we belong / Unchained melody / Bright eyes / Alfie / Missing / Way we were, The / Rose, The.
CD: Released Oct '89, on Pickwick by Pickwick Records. Catalogue no: **PWKS 545**
Album: Released Oct '89, on Pickwick by Pickwick Records. Catalogue no: **SHM 3285**
Cass: Released Oct '89, on Pickwick by Pickwick Records. Catalogue no: **HSC 3285**
Album: Released Oct '84, on K-Tel by K-Tel Records. Catalogue no: **NE 1282**
Cass: Released Oct '84, on K-Tel by K-Tel Records. Catalogue no: **CE 2282**

MEMORIES
Tracks: / I don't know how to love him / Love hurts / Second time, The / Tomorrow / On my own / I know him so well / Way we were, The / Rose, The / Walking in the air / If you don't want my love for you / Missing / Another suitcase in another hall / Don't cry for me Argentina.
CD: Released Nov '87, on Telstar by Telstar Records (UK). Deleted Aug '89. Catalogue no: **TCD 2313**
Cass: Released Nov '87, on Telstar by Telstar Records (UK). Deleted Nov '89. Catalogue no: **STAC 2313**
Album: Released Nov '87, on Telstar by Telstar Records (UK). Deleted Nov '89. Catalogue no: **STAR 2313**

MEMORY
Tracks: / Memory / Overtures.
Note: From the show *'Cats'*.
7" Single: Released May '81, on Polydor by Polydor Ltd. Deleted 30 May '89. Catalogue no: **POSP 279**

MEMORY (OLD GOLD)
Tracks: / Memory / Take that look off your face.
7" Single: Released Oct '88, on Old Gold by Old Gold Records. Deleted Nov '88. Catalogue no: **OG 9797**

SOMETIMES (THEME FROM CHAMPIONS)
Tracks: / Sometimes (theme from Champions) / I'm going to live.
7" Single: Released Apr '84, on Island by Island Records. Deleted '87. Catalogue no: **IS 174**

STAGES
Tracks: / Memory / Be on your own / Another suitcase in another hall / Send in the clowns / Running back for more / Good morning, starshine / Don't cry for me Argentina / I don't know how to love him / What I did for love / One night only

/ Losing my mind / Tomorrow.
Cass: Released Nov '83, on K-Tel by K-Tel Records. Catalogue no: **CE 2262**
Cass: Released Nov '86, on WEA by WEA Records. Catalogue no: **2402284**
Album: Released Nov '86, on WEA by WEA Records. Catalogue no: **2402281**
CD: Released Nov '83, on WEA by WEA Records. Catalogue no: **C 2402282**
Album: Released Nov '83, on K-Tel by K-Tel Records. Catalogue no: **NE 1262**

TAKE ME BACK (Theme from 'Classmates')
Tracks: / Take me back (Theme from 'Classmates') / Everybody's singing love songs.
7" Single: Released Jul '88, on Siren by Virgin Records. Deleted '89. Catalogue no: **SRNP 89**
Note: Poster bag.
7" Single: Released Jul '88, on Siren by Virgin Records. Catalogue no: **SRN 89**

Paint Your Wagon

PAINT YOUR WAGON (Musical show 1951 version) (Various artists)
Tracks: / I'm on my way: *Various artists* / Rumson: *Various artists* / What's goin' on here: *Various artists* / I talk to the trees: *Various artists* / They call the wind Maria: *Various artists* / I still see Elisa: *Various artists* / How can I wait: *Various artists* / In between: *Various artists* / Whoop-ti-ay: *Various artists* / Carino mio: *Various artists* / There's a coach comin' in: *Various artists* / Hand me down that can o' beans: *Various artists* / Another autumn: *Various artists* / All for him: *Various artists* / Wandrin' star: *Various artists*.
CD: Released 2 Oct '89, on RCA by BMG Records (UK). Catalogue no: **GD 60243**
Cass: Released 2 Oct '89, on RCA by BMG Records (UK). Catalogue no: **GK 60243**

PAINT YOUR WAGON (Film Soundtrack) (Various artists)
Tracks: / I'm on my way: *Various artists* / I still see Elisa: *Various artists* / First thing you know, The: *Various artists* / Hand me down that can 'o beans: *Various artists* / They call the wind Maria: *Various*

artists / Million miles away behind the door: *Various artists* / There's a coach comin' in: *Various artists* / Whoop-ti-ay (shivaree): *Various artists* / I talk to the trees: *Various artists* / Gospel of no name city, The: *Various artists* / Best things: *Various artists* / Wand'rin' star: *Various artists* / Gold fever: *Various artists* / Finale: *Various artists*.
Album: Released Apr '82, on MCA by MCA Records. Catalogue no: **MCL 1667**
Cass: Released Apr '82, on MCA by MCA Records. Catalogue no: **MCLC 1667**

PAINT YOUR WAGON (Original London cast) (Various artists)
Tracks: / I'm on my way: *Various artists* / Rumson: *Various artists* / What's goin' on here?: *Various artists* / I talk to the trees: *Various artists* / They call the wind Maria: *Various artists* / I still see Elisa: *Various artists* / How can I wait?: *Various artists* / In between: *Various artists* / Whoop ti ay: *Various artists* / Carino mio: *Various artists* / There's a coach comin' in: *Various artists* / Hand me down that can of beans: *Various artists* / Another Autumn: *Various artists* / All for him: *Various artists* / Wanderin' star: *Various artists*.
Cass: Released Apr '83, on T. E. R. by That's Entertainment Records. Catalogue no: **ZCTER 1061**
Album: Released Apr '83, on T. E. R. by That's Entertainment Records. Catalogue no: **TER 1061**

PAINT YOUR WAGON (ORIGINAL ISSUE) (Film soundtrack) (Various artists)
Album: Released Feb '70, on Paramount Deleted '75. Catalogue no: **SPFL 257**

PAINT YOUR WAGON (VIDEO) (Various artists)
VHS: Released Jan '89, on CIC Video Catalogue no: **VHR 2044**

Pajama Game

PAJAMA GAME (Original 1955 London Cast) (Various artists)
Tracks: / Overture: *Various artists* / Pajama game, The: *Various artists* / Racing with the clock: *Various artists* / New town is a blue town, A: *Various artists* / I'm not at all in love: *Various artists* / I'll never

be jealous again: *Various artists* / Hey there: *Various artists* / Her is: *Various artists* / Once a year day: *Various artists* / Small talk: *Various artists* / There once was a man: *Various artists* / Steam heat: *Various artists* / Think of the time I save: *Various artists* / Hernando's hideaway: *Various artists* / Seven and a half cents: *Various artists* / Finale: *Various artists*.
Cass: Released Apr '83, on T. E. R. by That's Entertainment Records. Deleted Mar '90. Catalogue no: **ZCTER 1058**
Album: Released Apr '83, on T. E. R. by That's Entertainment Records. Deleted Mar '90. Catalogue no: **TER 1058**
CD: Released Feb '90, on CBS (import) by CBS Records & Distribution. Catalogue no: **CK32606**
Cass: Released Mar '90, on CBS (import) by CBS Records & Distribution. Catalogue no: **PST 32606**

PAJAMA GAME, THE (Original soundtrack) (Various artists)
Note: Starring Doris Day.
Album: Released Jan '89, on Silva Screen by Silva Screen Records. Catalogue no: **AOL 5212**
CD: Released Jan '89, on CBS (import) by CBS Records & Distribution. Catalogue no: **CK 32606**
Cass: Released Jan '89, on Silva Screen by Silva Screen Records. Catalogue no: **BT 5210**

PAJAMA GAME, THE (VIDEO) (Various artists)
Note: Doris Day in the performance of her career. Running time: 97 minutes. Cert: U.
VHS: Released Jun '89, on Warner Home Video by WEA Records. Catalogue no: **PES 35085**

Pal Joey

PAL JOEY (Original cast recording) (Various artists)
Note: Rodgers and Hart show with Harold Lang and Vivienne Segal.
Cass: Released Jan '89, on CBS (import) by CBS Records & Distribution. Catalogue no: **JST 04364**
CD: Released Jan '89, on CBS (import) by CBS Records & Distribution. Catalogue no: **CK 04364**

PAL JOEY (1981 London Revival cast) (Various artists)

Tracks: / What is a man?: *Various artists* / Chicago: *Various artists* / Flower garden of my heart: *Various artists* / Zip: *Various artists* / In out little den of iniquity: *Various artists* / I could write a book: *Various artists* / You mustn't kick it around: *Various artists* / That terrific rainbow: *Various artists* / Bewitched: *Various artists*.
Album: Released Mar '90, on T. E. R. by That's Entertainment Records. Catalogue no: **TER 1005**
Cass: Released Mar '90, on T. E. R. by That's Entertainment Records. Catalogue no: **ZCTER 1005**

PAL JOEY (ORIGINAL ISSUE) (Film soundtrack) (Various artists)
Tracks: / That terrific rainbow: *Various artists* / I didn't know what time it was: *Various artists* / Do it the hard way: *Various artists* / Great big town: *Various artists* / There's a small hotel: *Various artists* / Zip: *Various artists* / Bewitched: *Various artists* / I could write a book: *Various artists* / Lady is a tramp: *Various artists* / Plant you now, dig you later: *Various artists* / My funny valentine: *Various artists* / You mustn't kick it around: *Various artists* / Strip number: *Various artists* / What do I care for a dame: *Various artists*.
Album: Released '79, on Capitol by EMI Records. Deleted '84. Catalogue no: **T 912**
Album: Released May '60, on Capitol by EMI Records. Deleted '65. Catalogue no: **LCT 6148**

Paladin

PALADIN (See under Eddy, Duane)

Panama Hattie

PANAMA HATTIE (See under Anything Goes)

Paper House

PAPER HOUSE (Film soundtrack) (Various artists)
Note: Horror/fantasy film directed by Bernard Rose with music by Stanley (Deerhunter) Myers and Hans Zimmer (A World Apart).
Album: Released Jan '89, on SPI Milan (France) Catalogue no: **A 374**
CD: Released Feb '89, on SPI Milan (France) Catalogue no: **ACD 374**

Cass: Released Jan '89, on SPI Milan (France) Catalogue no: **AC 374**

Papillon

PAPILLON (Film soundtrack) (Various artists)
Tracks: / Papillon, Theme from: *Various artists* / Camp, The: *Various artists* / Reunion: *Various artists* / New friend: *Various artists* / Freedom: *Various artists* / Gift from the sea: *Various artists* / Antonio's death: *Various artists* / Cruel sea: *Various artists* / Hospital: *Various artists* / Survival: *Various artists*.
Note: Re-issue of one of Jerry Goldsmith's finest scores for the Steve McQueen/Dustin Hoffman film.
CD: Released Sep '88, on Silva Screen by Silva Screen Records. Catalogue no: **FILMCD 029**
Album: Released Sep '88, on Silva Screen by Silva Screen Records. Catalogue no: **FILM 029**

Paradise Club

PARADISE CLUB, THE (Various artists)
Tracks: / This boy: *Best Way To Walk* / Mercenary man: *Pride* / For KC: *Davis, Snake & The Charmers* / Wrong side of the river: *Lawson,Dave* / Seather fin and limb: *Tracey, Stan Big Band* / Circles: *Carmel* / Vegas throat: *Jack Rubies* / Roadrunner: *Gigantic Rock & Blues Band* / Rumour has it, rumour is...: *Lawson,Dave* / Paradise club, The - opening: *Lawson,Dave* / Bye bye Mr Blues: *Catastrophy* / Unbelievable: *Best Way To Walk* / Ma's funeral: *Lawson,Dave* / Oh boy: *Gigantic Rock & Blues Band* / Paradise club, The - end titles: *Tracey, Stan Big Band* / Body talk: *Junction* / Try a little tenderness: *Lotis, Dennis/Laurie Holloway* / Great crane robbery: *Lawson,Dave* / Paradise club, The: *Lawson,Dave*.
Album: Released Oct '89, on BBC by BBC Records. Catalogue no: **REB 764**
CD: Released Oct '89, on BBC by BBC Records. Catalogue no: **BBCCD 764**
Cass: Released Oct '89, on BBC by BBC Records. Catalogue no: **ZCF 764**

Paradise Hawaiian...

PARADISE HAWAIIAN STYLE (See under Presley, Elvis)

Paradise Postponed

PARADISE POSTPONED (TV Soundtrack) (Webb, Roger Orchestra)
Tracks: / Paradise postponed (Title theme from Thames TV series from Elgar cello concerto) / Main theme / In the chilterns / Meadows and streams / Romance / Pastorale / Encounters / Letter The / Lady Grace's waltz / Love theme / Journey to London / Picton Hall.
Cass: Released Oct '86, on Columbia by EMI Records. Deleted Jan '88. Catalogue no: **TC-SCX 6706**
Album: Released Oct '86, on Columbia by EMI Records. Deleted Jan '88. Catalogue no: **SCX 6706**

Paramor, Norrie

SUMMER PLACE, A
Tracks: / Summer place, A (theme from).
7" Single: Released Mar '60, on Columbia by EMI Records. Deleted '63. Catalogue no: **DB 4419**

Z CARS
Tracks: / Z cars.
7" Single: Released Mar '62, on Columbia by EMI Records. Deleted '65. Catalogue no: **DB 4789**

Parent Trap...

PARENT TRAP/ SUMMER MAGIC / IN SEARCH ... (Film Soundtrack Excerpts) (Various artists)
Tracks: / For now, for always: *Various artists* / Let's get together: *Various artists* / Whistling at the boys: *Various artists* / Cobbler, cobbler: *Various artists* / For now, for always: *Various artists* / Parent trap: *Various artists* / Enjoy it: *Various artists* / Castaway: *Various artists* / Flitterin': *Various artists* / Beautiful Beulah: *Various artists* / Ugly bug ball: *Various artists* / On the front porch: *Various artists*.
Album: Released '73, on Disneyland by Disneyland-Vista Records (USA). Deleted '78. Catalogue no: **DQ 1318**

Steve Martin in Ron Howard's *Parenthood*

Parenthood

PARENTHOOD (Film soundtrack) (Newman, Randy) (See panel above)
Tracks: / I love to see you smile / Helen and Julie / Gary's in trouble / Drag race / I love to see you smile (end title) / Kevin's graduation / Kevin's party (cowboy gil) / Father and son / Karen and Gill.
CD: Released '89, on Warner Bros. by WEA Records. Catalogue no: **K 926 001 2**
Album: Released Jan '90, on Warner Bros. by WEA Records. Catalogue no: **K 926 001 1**
Cass: Released Jan '90, on Warner Bros. by WEA Records. Catalogue no: **K 926 001 4**

PARENTHOOD (See also under Newman, Randy)

Paris, Texas

PARIS, TEXAS (Film soundtrack) (Cooder, Ry)
Tracks: / Paris, Texas / Brothers / Nothing out there / Cancion Mixteca / No safety zone / Houston in two seconds / She's leaving the bank / On the couch / I knew this people / Dark was the night.
Note: Wim Wenders' superb film, scripted by Sam Shepard, makes effective use of Ry Cooder's plaintive, atmospheric, steel guitar. The movie stars Harry Dean Stanton and Nastassia Kinski.
Album: Released Feb '85, on Warner Bros. by WEA Records. Catalogue no: **925270 1**
Cass: Released Feb '85, on Warner Bros. by WEA Records. Catalogue no: **925270 4**

Park, Simon

DANGER UXB (See under Danger UXB)

EYE LEVEL (Park, Simon Orchestra)
Tracks: / Eye level (Van der valk theme).
7" Single: Released Nov '72, on Columbia by EMI Records. Deleted '75. Catalogue no: **DB 8946**
7" Single: Released Apr '86, on Old Gold by Old Gold Records. Deleted Jun '89. Catalogue no: **OG 9600**

Parker, Charlie

BIRD (Film soundtrack)
Tracks: / Lester leaps in / I can't believe that you're in love with me / Laura / All of me / This time the dream's on me / Koko / Cool blues / April in Paris / Now's the time / Ornithology / Parker's mood.
Note: Film about Jazzman Charlie Parker produced and directed by Clint Eastwood.
Album: Released Nov '88, on CBS by CBS Records & Distribution. Catalogue no: **461002 1**
CD: Released Nov '88, on CBS by CBS Records & Distribution. Catalogue no: **461002 2**

Cass: Released Nov '88, on CBS by CBS Records & Distribution. Catalogue no: **461002 4**

Parker, Ray Jnr.

GHOSTBUSTERS
Tracks: / Ghostbusters / Ghostbusters (version).
Note: From the film *'Ghostbusters'*
7" Single: Released Nov '84, on Arista by BMG Records (UK). Catalogue no: **ARIST 580**
7" Pic: Released Nov '84, on Arista by BMG Records (UK). Catalogue no: **ARISD 580**
12" Pic: Released Nov '84, on Arista by BMG Records (UK). Deleted '85. Catalogue no: **ARIPD 12580**
12" Single: Released Nov '84, on Arista by BMG Records (UK). Catalogue no: **ARIST 12580**

GHOSTBUSTERS (OLD GOLD)
Tracks: / Ghostbusters / Jack & Jill / You can't change that.
12" Single: Released Jan '88, on Old Gold by Old Gold Records. Catalogue no: **OG 4041**

Parr, John

ST. ELMO'S FIRE
Tracks: / St. Elmo's fire / Treat me like an animal / Making love with a stranger (Only on 12" single).
Note: From the film *St. Elmo's fire.*
7" Single: Released Sep '85, on London Records by London Records Ltd. Deleted '88. Catalogue no: **LON 73**
12" Single: Released Sep '85, on London Records by London Records Ltd. Deleted '88. Catalogue no: **LONX 73**

Partners In Kryme

TURTLE POWER
Tracks: / Turtle power (single edit) / Splinter's tale I & II / Turtle power (album version) (12" only).
Note: From the film 'Teenage Mutant Ninja Turtles'.
12" Single: Released Jul '90, on SBK by SBK Records. Catalogue no: **203 933 6**
7" Single: Released Jul '90, on SBK by SBK Records. Catalogue no: **203 933 8**
Cassingle: Released Jul '90, on SBK by SBK Records. Catalogue no: **TCTURTLE 1**

7" Single: Released Jul '90, on SBK by SBK Records. Catalogue no: **TURTLEP 1**

7" Single: Released Jul '90, on SBK by SBK Records. Catalogue no: **TURTLE 1**

Cassingle: Released Jul '90, on SBK by SBK Records. Catalogue no: **203 933 4**

7" Pic: Released Jul '90, on SBK by SBK Records. Catalogue no: **203 933 0**

7" Single: Released Jul '90, on SBK by SBK Records. Catalogue no: **203 933 7**

7" Pic: Released Jul '90, on SBK by SBK Records. Catalogue no: **TURTLEPD 1**

12" Single: Released Jul '90, on SBK by SBK Records. Catalogue no: **12TURTLE 1**

Parton, Dolly

9 TO 5
Tracks: / 9 to 5 / Sing for the common man.
Note: From the film 9 to 5.
CD Single: Released Jun '89, on RCA by BMG Records (UK). Deleted Feb '90. Catalogue no: **PD 49447**
7" Single: Released Feb '81, on RCA by BMG Records (UK). Deleted '84. Catalogue no: **RCA 25**

RHINESTONE (Film Soundtrack)
Album: Released Aug '84, on RCA by BMG Records (UK). Catalogue no: **BL 85032**
Cass: Released Aug '84, on RCA by BMG Records (UK). Catalogue no: **BK 85032**

Party Party

PARTY PARTY (Film soundtrack) (Various artists)
Tracks: / Party party: *Costello, Elvis* / Run Rudolph run: *Edmunds, Dave* / No woman, no cry: *Black, Pauline* / Yakety yak: *Bad Manners* / Elizabethan reggae: *Bad Manners* / Tutti frutti: *Sting* / Need your love so bad: *Sting* / No feelings: *Bananarama* / Band of gold: *Modern Romance* / Little town flirt: *Altered Images* / Man who sold the world, The: *Ure, Midge* / Auld lang syne: *Chas & Dave*.
Cass: Released Sep '84, on Hallmark by Pickwick Records. Deleted '88. Catalogue no: **HSC**

3157
Album: Released '84, on A&M by A&M Records. Deleted '87. Catalogue no: **AMLH 68551**
Album: Released Sep '84, on Hallmark by Pickwick Records. Deleted '88. Catalogue no: **SHM 3157**

PARTY, PARTY (VIDEO) (Various artists).
VHS: Released Dec '86, on A&M by A&M Records. Catalogue no: **AM 822**

Pascali's Island

PASCALI'S ISLAND (Film soundtrack) (Dikker, Loek)
Tracks: / Pascali's theme (Pritouritze planinata) / Pasha's castle, The / Nisi by night / Jealous pursuit / Izzet effendi / Pascali's passion / Nightmares / Sultan's spy, The / Fear of Greeks / Deal complete, The / Mysterious Englishman / Discovery / Growing despair / Under cover of night / Lydia's death / Pascali's grief.
Note: Pascali's Island is the film starring Ben Kingsley, Charles Dance & Helen Mirren. The film is set in 1908 on a Turkish occupied isle. Ben Kingsley plays a local guide/interpreter/spy for the Sultan, when the Ottoman empire is about to crumble. The soundtrack is composed & produced by Loek Dikker. Directed by James Dearden (writer of Fatal Attraction).
CD: Released '88, on Virgin by Virgin Records. Catalogue no: **CDV 2557**
CD: Released Jan '89, on Capitol (import) Catalogue no: **90976.2**
Album: Released Jan '89, on Capitol (import) Catalogue no: **90976.1**
Cass: Released Jan '89, on Capitol (import) Catalogue no: **90976.4**
Cass: Released 3 Oct '88, on Virgin by Virgin Records. Deleted Jun '90. Catalogue no: **TCV 2557**
Album: Released 3 Oct '88, on Virgin by Virgin Records. Deleted May '90. Catalogue no: **V 2557**

Pask, Morgan

OVERKILL (Theme from The Bill)
Tracks: / Overkill / Rock steady.
7" Single: Released Jan '85, on Columbia by EMI Records. Deleted Jul '87. Catalogue no: **DB 9100**

Passage To India

PASSAGE TO INDIA, A (Film soundtrack) (Jarre, Maurice)
Cass: Released Mar '85, on EMI by EMI Records. Deleted Jul '87. Catalogue no: **EJ 2403024**
CD: Released Feb '90, on Capitol (import) Catalogue no: **CDP 92059**
Cass: Released Feb '90, on Capitol (import) Catalogue no: **92059.4**
Album: Released Mar '85, on EMI by EMI Records. Deleted Jul '87. Catalogue no: **EJ 2403021**

Pat Garret...

PAT GARRET AND BILLY THE KID (See under Dylan, Bob)

Patton

PATTON (Film Soundtrack) (Various artists)
Album: Released Sep '90, on Silva Screen by Silva Screen Records. Catalogue no: **FILM 047**
Cass: Released Sep '90, on Silva Screen by Silva Screen Records. Catalogue no: **FILMC 047**

PATTON (Film Soundtrack) (Various artists)
Tracks: / Patton speech: *Various artists* / Main title: *Various artists* / Battleground: *Various artists* / First battle: *Various artists* / Attack: *Various artists* / Funeral: *Various artists* / Winter march: *Various artists* / Patton march: *Various artists* / No assignment: *Various artists* / German advice: *Various artists* / Hospital: *Various artists* / Payoff: *Various artists* / End title/speech: *Various artists*.
Album: Released '73, on Stateside by EMI Records. Deleted '78. Catalogue no: **SSL 10302**
Album: Released Jan '89, on Silva Screen by Silva Screen Records. Catalogue no: **810366.1**
Cass: Released Jan '89, on Silva Screen by Silva Screen Records. Catalogue no: **810366.4**

Patty Hearst

PATTY HEARST (Film soundtrack) (Various artists)
Tracks: / Mom dad: *Various artists* / Cinque's vision: *Various artists* / My real crime: *Various artists* / Rest home: *Various artists* / Persistence of vision: *Various artists* / Pen chorale: *Various artists* / Closet: *Various artists* / Young

once: *Various artists* / Motel: *Various artists* / Pistol rope: *Various artists* / Dad mom: *Various artists*.
Cass: Released Dec '88, on Geffen by Geffen Records (USA). Catalogue no: **K 979186 4**
CD: Released Dec '88, on Geffen by Geffen Records (USA). Catalogue no: **K 979186 2**
Album: Released Dec '88, on Geffen by Geffen Records (USA). Catalogue no: **K 979186 1**

Pearson, Johnny

ALL CREATURES GREAT & SMALL (Pearson, Johnny Orchestra)
Tracks: / All creatures great & small / Love dream.
7" Single: Released Aug '78, on Rampage by Rampage Records. Deleted Aug '81. Catalogue no: **RAM 2**

ON GOLDEN POND (Pearson, Johnny Orchestra)
Album: Released May '82, on Page One by Page One Records. Deleted Jan '88. Catalogue no: **PAGS 701**

ON GOLDEN POND (Single) (Pearson, Johnny Orchestra)
Tracks: / On golden pond / Together.
7" Single: Released Mar '82, on Page One by Page One Records. Deleted Mar '85. Catalogue no: **POR 002**

SLEEPY SHORES
Note: Theme from TV series 'Owen MD'.
7" Single: Released Dec '71, on Penny Farthing by Penny Farthing Records. Deleted '74. Catalogue no: **PEN 778**

SLEEPY SHORES (OLD GOLD)
Tracks: / Sleepy shores.
7" Single: Released Jul '82, on Old Gold by Old Gold Records. Deleted Jul '88. Catalogue no: **OG 9050**

THEMES AND DREAMS (Pearson, Johnny Orchestra)
Tracks: / Godfather (theme) / House of Caradus (theme) / All creatures great and small (theme) / Love dream / Chi mai / First love / Triangle (love theme and intro) / Chariots of fire (theme) / You are the one / Seduction, The / Love dreamer / Cavatina / I wish I knew how it feels to be free / Love story (theme).

CD: Released Jun '89, on President by President Records. Catalogue no: **PRCD 132**
Cass: Released Jun '89, on President by President Records. Catalogue no: **TCPCRV 132**
Album: Released Jun '89, on President by President Records. Catalogue no: **PRCV 132**

TRIANGLE (Pearson, Johnny Orchestra)
Tracks: / Triangle (love theme) / Triangle (introduction).
7" Single: Released Mar '81, on Rampage by Rampage Records. Deleted Mar '84. Catalogue no: **RAM 49**

Pee Wee's...

PEE WEE'S BIG ADVENTURE / BACK TO SCHOOL (Film soundtrack) (Various artists)
Note: 2 scores by Danny Elfman.i
Cass: Released Jan '89, on Varese Sarabande Records(USA) by Varese Sarabande Records (USA). Catalogue no: **C 704.370**
CD: Released Jan '89, on Varese Sarabande Records(USA) by Varese Sarabande Records (USA). Catalogue no: **VCD 47281**
Album: Released Jan '89, on Varese Sarabande Records(USA) by Varese Sarabande Records (USA). Catalogue no: **704.370**

PEE WEE'S BIG TOP (Film soundtrack) (Various artists)
Note: Pee Wee Herman film. Music by Danny Elfman including dialogue highlights.
Album: Released Jan '89, on Arista (import) Catalogue no: **AL 8568**
Cass: Released Jan '89, on Arista (import) Catalogue no: **ALC 8568**
CD: Released Jan '89, on Arista (import) Catalogue no: **ARCD 8568**

Peg

PEG (Original London cast) (Various artists)
Album: Released Mar '84, on T. E. R. by That's Entertainment Records. Catalogue no: **TER 1024**
Cass: Released Mar '84, on T. E. R. by That's Entertainment Records. Catalogue no: **ZCTER 1024**

Peggy Sue Got Married

PEGGY SUE GOT MARRIED (Film soundtrack) (Various artists)
Tracks: / Did we break up?: *Various artists* / Charlie's unplayed guitar: *Peebles, Ann* / Peggy Sue's homecoming: *Peebles, Ann* / Charlie, I had the strangest experience: *Various artists* / Peggy Sue got married: *Holly, Buddy* / I wonder why: *Dion/Belmonts* / He don't love you: *Cage, Nicolas & Pride & Joy* / Teenager in love: *Dion/Belmonts* / You belong to me: *Crenshaw, Marshall*.
Cass: Released Mar '87, on T. E. R. by That's Entertainment Records. Catalogue no: **ZCTER 1126**
Album: Released Mar '87, on T. E. R. by That's Entertainment Records. Catalogue no: **TER 1126**
CD: Released Jan '89, on Varese Sarabande Records(USA) by Varese Sarabande Records (USA). Catalogue no: **VCD 47275**

Pelle The Conquerer

PELLE THE CONQUERER (Original Soundtrack) (Various artists)
Album: Released Feb '90, on Silva Screen by Silva Screen Records. Catalogue no: **A364**
CD: Released Feb '90, on Silva Screen by Silva Screen Records. Catalogue no: **CHCH364**

Penitent

PENITENT (Film soundtrack) (Various artists)
CD: Released '87, on Varese Sarabande Records(USA) by Varese Sarabande Records (USA). Catalogue no: **VCD 47299**
Album: Released '87, on Varese Sarabande Records(USA) by Varese Sarabande Records (USA). Catalogue no: **STV 81331**
Cass: Released '87, on Varese Sarabande Records(USA) by Varese Sarabande Records (USA). Catalogue no: **CTV 81331**

Penitentiary III

PENITENTIARY III (Film Soundtrack) (Various artists)
Tracks: / You and I: *Payne, Freda & Lenny Williams* / Special: *Yarbrough & Peoples* / Can't let it go: *Larue* / Bustin' out: *Franklin, Rodney* / Do the prep: *Midnight Star* / Sweeter than candy: *Gap Band* / Cold stupid: *New Choice* / No mission's impossible: *Shawnie* / I know you are: *Dotti, Lottie* / Just a touch: *Reese, James*.
Cass: Released Mar '88, on RCA by BMG Records (UK). Deleted Nov '88. Catalogue no: **PK 86663**

as featured in the BBC TV series

TV Soundtrack to *Pennies from Heaven* (World Records)

Album: Released Mar '88, on RCA by BMG Records (UK). Deleted Sep '90. Catalogue no: **PL 86663**

Pennies From Heaven

PENNIES FROM HEAVEN (TV soundtrack) (Various artists) (see panel above)
Tracks: / Roll along Prairie moon: *Various artists* / Seein' is believin': *Various artists* / Dreaming a dream : *Various artists* / You and the night and the music: *Various artists* / Nasty man: *Various artists* / Radio times: *Various artists* / I only have eyes for you: *Various artists* / It's got to be love: *Various artists* / Painting the clouds with Sunshine: *Various artists* / I found the right girl: *Various artists* / Hands across the table: *Various artists* / Moon got in my eyes, The: *Various artists* / March winds and April showers: *Various artists* / Haunting me: *Various artists* / Roll along covered wagon: *Various artists* / Pennies from Heaven: *Various artists*.
Album: Released Apr '78, on World Records by EMI Records. Deleted '83. Catalogue no: **SH 266**

PENNIES FROM HEAVEN (Film Soundtrack) (Various artists)
CD: Released May '89, on Object Enterprises Catalogue no: **ONN 18**

PENNIES FROM HEAVEN (Film Soundtrack) (Various artists)
2 LP Set: Released May '78, on Decca by Decca International. Deleted '88. Catalogue no: **DDV 5007/8**
2 LP Set: Released Sep '82, on Warner Bros. by WEA Records. Deleted Jan '88. Catalogue no: **K 66109**

Percy

PERCY (Film soundtrack) (Kinks)
Tracks: / God's children / Lola / Way love used to be, The / Completely / Running round town / Moments / Animals in the zoo / Just friends / Whip lady / Dreams / Helga / Willesden Green / End title.
CD: Released Oct '87, on PRT by Castle Communications Records. Catalogue no: **PYC 6011**
CD: Released Dec '89, on Castle Classics by Castle Communications Records. Catalogue no:

CLACD 164
Album: Released Oct '87, on PRT by Castle Communications Records. Catalogue no: **PYL 6011**
Album: Released '74, on Pye Catalogue no: **NSPL 18365**
Cass: Released Oct '87, on PRT by Castle Communications Records. Catalogue no: **PYM 6011**

Perfect

PERFECT (Film soundtrack) (Various artists)
Tracks: / (Closest thing to) Perfect: *Jackson, Jermaine* / I sweat (going through the motions): *Hendryx, Nona* / All systems go: *Pointer Sisters* / Shock me: *Houston, Whitney & Jermaine Ja* / Wham rap (enjoy what you do): *Wham* / Wear out the grooves: *Stewart, Jermaine* / Hot hips: *Reed, Lou* / Talking to the wall: *Hartman, Dan* / Masquerade: *Berlin* / Lay your hands on my: *Thompson Twins*.
CD: Released Jan '89, on Arista by BMG Records (UK). Catalogue no: **ARCD 8278**
Cass: Released Aug '85, on Arista by BMG Records (UK). Deleted May '89. Catalogue no: **407 203**
Album: Released Aug '85, on Arista by BMG Records (UK). Deleted Jun '90. Catalogue no: **207.203**

Performance

PERFORMANCE (See under Jagger, Mick)

Permanent Record

PERMANENT RECORD (Film Soundtrack) (Various artists)
Tracks: / Trash city: *Strummer, Joe* / Baby the trans: *Strummer, Joe* / Nefertiti rock: *Strummer, Joe* / Nothin' 'bout nothin': *Strummer, Joe* / Permanent record, Theme from: *Various artists* / 'Cause I said so: *Godfathers* / Waiting on love: *BoDeans* / Wishing on another lucky star: *Souther, J.D.* / All day and all of the night: *Stranglers* / Something happened: *Reed, Lou*.
Album: Released Jul '88, on Epic by CBS Records & Distribution. Deleted Oct '89. Catalogue no: **461161 1**
Cass: Released Jul '88, on Epic by CBS Records & Distribution. Deleted Oct '89. Catalogue no: **461161 4**

Peter Pan **leads his friends, the Darlings, to Never Never Land**

CD: Released Jul '88, on Epic by CBS Records & Distribution. Deleted Oct '89. Catalogue no: **461161 2**

Album: Released May '88, on Epic (import) by CBS Records & Distribution. Catalogue no: **SE 40879**

Persuaders (theme)

PERSUADERS, THE & OTHER THEMES BY JOHN BARRY (Various artists) (See also under Barry, John)
Album: Released Jan '89, on Silva Screen by Silva Screen Records. Catalogue no: **CBS 64816**

Pertwee, Jon

WURZEL'S SONG
Tracks: / Wurzel's song / Who'd be a scarecrow.
7" Single: Released Mar '80, on Decca by Decca International. Deleted '83. Catalogue no: **F 13885**

Pet Sematary

PET SEMATARY (Original soundtrack) (Goldenthal, Elliot) (See also under Goldenthal, Elliot
Cass: Released Jul '89, on Colosseum (West Germany) Catalogue no: **VSC 5227**
CD: Released Jul '89, on Colosseum (West Germany) Catalogue no: **VSD 5227**
Album: Released Jul '89, on Colosseum (West Germany) Catalogue no: **VS 5227**

Pete Kelly's Blues

PETE KELLY'S BLUES (See under Lee, Peggy)

Peter Gunn

PETER GUNN (See under Eddy, Duane)

PETER GUNN (TV Soundtrack) (Various artists)
CD: Released Jan '89, on Silva Screen by Silva Screen Records. Catalogue no: **1956.2**
Cass: Released Feb '90, on Silva Screen by Silva Screen Records. Catalogue no: **1956.4**

Peter Pan

PETER PAN (See under Barrie, J.M.)

PETER PAN (TV Cast with Jean Arthur and Boris Karloff) (Various artists)
Album: Released Jan '89, on Silva Screen by Silva Screen Records. Deleted Mar '90. Catalogue no: **AOL 4312**
Cass: Released Mar '90, on Silva Screen by Silva Screen Records. Catalogue no: **PST 4312**

PETER PAN (Original Broadway Cast) (Various artists)
Cass: Released Jan '89, on CBS (import) by CBS Records & Distribution. Catalogue no: **JST 04312**
CD: Released Jan '89, on CBS (import) by CBS Records & Distribution. Catalogue no: **CK 04312**

PETER PAN (Stage show) (Various artists)
Cass: Released Aug '90, on Silva Screen by Silva Screen Records. Catalogue no: **GK 83762**
CD: Released Aug '90, on Silva Screen by Silva Screen Records. Catalogue no: **GD 83762**

PETER PAN (Original Broadway cast) (Various artists)
Album: Released Jan '89, on Silva Screen by Silva Screen Records. Catalogue no: **AYKI 3762**

PETER PAN (Original Soundtrack) (Various artists)
Tracks: / Main title: *Various artists* / Second star to the right: *Various artists* / You can fly: *Various artists* / Pirate's life: *Various artists* / Following the leader: *Various artists* / What made the red man red: *Various artists* / Your mother and mine: *Various artists* / Elegant captain hook: *Various artists* / Following the leader: *Various artists* / Never smile at a crocodile: *Various artists*.
Cass: Released Dec '87, on Walt Disney Catalogue no: **WDC 014**
Album: Released Dec '87, on Walt Disney Catalogue no: **WD 014**
Album: Released '73, on Disneyland by Disneyland-Vista Records (USA). Deleted '78. Catalogue no: **DQ 1206**

PETER PAN/CINDERELLA (Film soundtracks) (Various artists)
Tracks: / Second star to the right, The: *Various artists* / You can fly, you can fly: *Various artists* / Pirate's life, A: *Various artists* / Never smile at a crocodile: *Various artists* / Following the leader: *Various artists* / What made the red man red?: *Various artists* / Your mother and mine: *Various artists* / Elegant Captain Hook, The: *Various artists* / Finale: *Various artists* / Cinderella: *Various artists* / Dream is a wish your heart makes, A: *Various artists* / Oh sing sweet nightingale: *Various artists* / Work song, The: *Various artists* / Bibbidilbobbidiboo: *Various artists* / Cinderella arrives at the ball: *Various artists* / So this is love: *Various artists* / Cinderella (finale): *Various artists*.
Cass: Released Oct '85, on BBC by BBC Records.. Deleted '88. Catalogue no: **ZCM 577**
Album: Released Oct '85, on BBC

by BBC Records. Deleted '88. Catalogue no: **REC 577**

Peter The Great

PETER THE GREAT (TV soundtrack) (Various artists)
Tracks: / Main title: *Various artists* / Cathedral: *Various artists* / Alexander: *Various artists* / Tartars, The: *Various artists* / Two living tears: *Various artists* / His first sail: *Various artists* / Foreign colony, The: *Various artists* / Eudoxia: *Various artists* / Peter's wedding: *Various artists* / Tsar and tsaritsa: *Various artists* / New tsarevich, The: *Various artists* / Death of Natalyda - The slap: *Various artists* / Great embassy, The: *Various artists* / Gopak: *Various artists* / Alexis and Danilo: *Various artists* / Battle of Poltova: *Various artists* / Sophia and Alexis - Ordeal - Martyrdom: *Various artists* / Requiem: *Various artists* / Peter's theme: *Various artists*.
Note: Epic score by Laurence Rosenthal for the TV mini series starring Maximillian Schell, Jan Niklas, Laurence Olivier and Vanessa Redgrave.
Album: Released Nov '86, on Silva Screen by Silva Screen Records. Deleted May '90. Catalogue no: **FILM 006**
Cass: Released Nov '86, on Silva Screen by Silva Screen Records. Deleted May '90. Catalogue no: **FILMC 006**
CD: Released '86, on Southern Cross (USA) by Fith Continent Music Group (USA). Catalogue no: **SCCD 01011**

Peterson, Oscar

FIORELLO (1959 show) (Peterson, Oscar Trio)
Tracks: / When did I fall in love? / Little tin box / Home again / 'Til tomorrow / Politics and poker / Gentleman Jimmy / Unfair / On the side of the Angela / Where do I go from here?.
Note: Peterson, piano, Ray Brown, bass, and Ed Thigpen, drums, play music from the Broadway musical by Jerry Beck and Sheldon Harnick.
Album: Released Jun '84, on Verve (France) Catalogue no: **8171 081**

Pete's Dragon

PETE'S DRAGON (Film

Soundtrack) (Various artists)
Tracks: / Pete's dragon (title): *Various artists* / Candle on the water: *Various artists* / I saw a dragon: *Various artists* / It's not easy: *Various artists* / Every little pieces: *Various artists* / Happiest home in these hills, The: *Various artists* / Brazzle dazzle day: *Various artists* / Boo bop bopbop bop (I love you too): *Various artists* / There's room for everybody: *Various artists* / Passamashloddy: *Various artists* / Bill of sale: *Various artists* / Candle on the water (reprise): *Various artists*.
Album: Released '78, on Capitol by EMI Records. Catalogue no: **EA ST 11704**

Peyton Place

PEYTON PLACE (Film soundtrack) (Various artists)
Album: Released Nov '80, on Entr'acte by Fith Continent Music Group (USA). Deleted Nov '85. Catalogue no: **ERS 6515**

Pfeiffer, Michelle

COOL RIDER
Tracks: / Cool rider / Do it for our country.
Note: From the film 'Grease II'.
7" Single: Released Jan '82, on RSO by Polydor Ltd. Deleted Jan '85. Catalogue no: **RSO 93**

Phaedra

PHAEDRA (Film Soundtrack) (Various artists)
Tracks: / Love theme from Phaedra: *Various artists* / Rendezvous: *Various artists* / Ship to shore: *Various artists* / London's fog: *Various artists* / One more time: *Various artists* / Agapimou: *Various artists* / Only you: *Various artists* / Fling: *Various artists* / Candlelight: *Various artists* / Rodostimo: *Various artists* / Love theme from Phaedra: *Various artists* / Goodbye John Sebastion: *Various artists*.
Album: Released '73, on Sunset (Liberty) by EMI Records. Deleted '78. Catalogue no: **SLS 50173**

Phantasm

PHANTASM (Songs From The Film) (Various artists)
Album: Released Feb '80, on Gem by RCA Records. Deleted '85. Catalogue no: **GEMLP 102**

PHANTASM (Film Soundtrack) (Various artists)
Album: Released Feb '80, on Gem by RCA Records. Catalogue no: **GEMLP 1**
Album: Released Jan '89, on Silva Screen by Silva Screen Records. Catalogue no: **VC 81105**

Phantom Of The Opera

ALL I ASK OF YOU (See under Richard, Cliff)

HIGHLIGHTS FROM THE PHANTOM OF THE OPERA (Various artists)
Tracks: / Overture: *Various artists* / Angel of music: *Various artists* / Mirror, The: *Various artists* / Phantom of the opera, The: *Various artists* / Music of the night: *Various artists* / Prima donna: *Various artists* / All I ask of you: *Various artists* / Masquerade: *Various artists* / Wishing you were somehow here again: *Various artists* / Point of no return: *Various artists* / Down once more: *Various artists*.
Note: The single album and cassette formats of the original cast recording of this highly successful West End musical. Features all the songs from the show without the Libretto. Album and cassette will feature brand new packaging. Contains the hit songs 'The phantom of the opera', 'All I ask of you', 'Music of the night'. Starring Michael Crawford, Sarah Brightman and Steve Barton. Produced by Andrew Lloyd Webber.
Cass: Released Nov '87, on Polydor by Polydor Ltd. Catalogue no: **POLHC 33**
Album: Released Nov '87, on Polydor by Polydor Ltd. Catalogue no: **POLH 33**
CD: Released Nov '87, on Polydor by Polydor Ltd. Catalogue no: **831 563-2**

PHANTOM OF THE OPERA (Film soundtrack) (Various artists)
CD: Released Jun '90, on Silva Screen by Silva Screen Records. Catalogue no: **FILM CD 069**
Album: Released Jun '90, on Silva Screen by Silva Screen Records. Catalogue no: **FILM 069**

PHANTOM OF THE OPERA (Original London cast) (Various artists)
Tracks: / Phamtom of the opera

(overture): *Various artists* / Think of me: *Various artists* / Angel of music: *Various artists* / Little lotte: *Various artists* / Mirror, The: *Various artists* / Phantom of the opera, The: *Various artists* / Music of the night: *Various artists* / I Remember: *Various artists* / Stranger than you dreamt it: *Various artists* / Magical lasso: *Various artists* / Prima donna: *Various artists* / Poor fool, he makes me laugh: *Various artists* / All I ask of you: *Various artists* / Entr'acte: *Various artists* / Masquerade: *Various artists* / Why so silent: *Various artists* / Twisted every way: *Various artists* / Wishing you were somehow here again: *Various artists* / Wandering child: *Various artists* / Point of no return, The: *Various artists* / Down once more: *Various artists* / Phantom of the opera (finale): *Various artists*.
2 LP Set: Released Feb '87, on Polydor by Polydor Ltd. Catalogue no: **PODV 9**
Cass: Released Feb '87, on Polydor by Polydor Ltd. Catalogue no: **PODVC 9**
CD: Released Feb '87, on Polydor by Polydor Ltd. Catalogue no: **831 273-2**

PHANTOM OF THE OPERA (1943) (Film soundtrack) (Various artists)
Note: Starring Nelson Eddy
CD: Released Jan '89, on Soun'trak (USA) by Silva Screen Records. Catalogue no: **FCD 8115**
2 LP Set: Released Jan '89, on Soun'trak (USA) by Silva Screen Records. Catalogue no: **STK 114**

Phar Lap...

PHAR LAP - HEART OF A NATION (Film soundtrack) (Various artists)
Cass: Released Apr '85, on EMI by EMI Records. Catalogue no: **EJ 2403194**
Album: Released Apr '85, on EMI by EMI Records. Catalogue no: **EJ 2403191**

Philharmonia Orch.

CHAMPIONS (Original Soundtrack) (Philharmonia Orchestra)
Album: Released Mar '84, on Island by Island Records. Catalogue no: **ISTA 7**
Cass: Released Mar '84, on Island by Island Records. Catalogue no:

ICT 7

Piazolla, Astor

TANGOS - THE EXILE OF GARDEL (See under Tangos)

Piccroni Piers

CHRONICLE OF A... (See under Chronicle Of A...)

Pickwick

PICKWICK (ORIGINAL ISSUE) (London cast) (Various artists)
Album: Released Aug '63, on Philips by Phonogram Ltd. Deleted '68. Catalogue no: **AL 3431**

Picnic

PICNIC (Film soundtrack) (Various artists)
Note: Composed by George Duning.
CD: Released Feb '90, on MCA by MCA Records. Catalogue no: **MCAD 31357**
Album: Released Jan '89, on MCA by MCA Records. Catalogue no: **MCA 1527**
Cass: Released Jan '89, on MCA by MCA Records. Deleted Mar '90. Catalogue no: **MCAC 1527**

Pine, Courtney

HIT OR MISS
Tracks: / Hit or miss / Children of the night / Songs from our underground (part 1) (12" only).
Note: Theme from BBC TV's Juke Box Jury.
7" Single: Released Mar '90, on Antilles/New Directions by Island Records. Catalogue no: **ANN 11**
12" Single: Released Mar '90, on Antilles/New Directions by Island Records. Catalogue no: **12ANN 11**

Pink Cadillac

PINK CADILLAC (Film Soundtrack) (Various artists)
CD: Released Feb '90, on Silva Screen by Silva Screen Records. Catalogue no: **925922.2**
Cass: Released Feb '90, on Silva Screen by Silva Screen Records. Catalogue no: **925922.4**

Pink Floyd

ANOTHER BRICK IN THE WALL
Tracks: / Another brick in the wall
From the film 'The Wall'
7" Single: Released Nov '79, on

Harvest by EMI Records. Catalogue no: **HAR 5194**

ANOTHER BRICK IN THE WALL (PART 2)
Tracks: / Another brick in the wall (part 2) / One of my turns.
Note: From the film 'The Wall'
CD 3": Released Aug '88, on Columbia (USA) by CBS Records (USA). Catalogue no: **38K03118**

MORE (Film Soundtrack)
Tracks: / Cirrus minor / Nile song, The / Crying song / Up the Khyber / Green is the colour / Cymbaline / Party sequence / Main theme / Ibiza bar / More blues / Quicksilver / Spanish piece, A / Dramatic theme.
Cass: Released Jun '69, on Columbia by EMI Records. Catalogue no: **TCSCX 6346**
Album: Released Jun '69, on Columbia by EMI Records. Catalogue no: **SCX 6346**
CD: Released Mar '87, on Columbia by EMI Records. Catalogue no: **CDP 746 386 2**

WALL, THE (Original Soundtrack)
Tracks: / In the flesh / Thin ice / Happiest days of our lives / Another brick in the wall (part 2) / Mother / Goodbye blue sky / Empty spaces / Young lust / One of my turns / Don't leave me now / Another brick in the wall (part 3) / Goodbye cruel world / Hey you / Is there anybody out there? / Nobody home / Comfortably numb / Show must go on / Run like hell / Waiting for the worms / Stop / Trial, The / Outside the wall.
Cass set: Released Dec '79, on Harvest by EMI Records. Catalogue no: **TC 2S HDW 411**
CD Set: Released Sep '84, on Harvest by EMI Records. Catalogue no: **CDS 746 036 8**
2 LP Set: Released Dec '79, on Harvest by EMI Records. Catalogue no: **SHDW 411**

WALL, THE (VIDEO)
Note: Running time: 91 mins. Cert: 15.
VHS: Released Sep '89, on Channel 5 by Channel 5 Video. Catalogue no: **CFV 08762**

Pink Panther

PINK PANTHER - HENRY MANCINI (Film soundtrack) (Various artists)
Tracks: / Pink Panther theme:

Pinocchio sets fire to his finger in Disney's classic 1940 cartoon

Various artists / It had better be tonight: *Various artists* / Royal blue: *Various artists* / Champagne and quail: *Various artists* / Village Inn, The: *Various artists* / Tiber twist, The: *Various artists* / It had better be tonight: *Various artists* / Cortina: *Various artists* / Lonely princess, The: *Various artists* / Something for Sellers: *Various artists* / Piano and strings: *Various artists* / Shades of Sennett: *Various artists*.
Cass: Released Apr '84, on RCA (France) by BMG Records (France). Catalogue no: **NK 80832**
CD: Released Sep '89, on RCA by BMG Records (UK). Catalogue no: **ND 80832**
CD: Released Feb '90, on Silva Screen by Silva Screen Records. Catalogue no: **2795.2**
Album: Released Apr '84, on RCA (France) by BMG Records (France). Catalogue no: **NL 80832**
RETURN OF THE PINK PANTHER (See under Return Of The...)
REVENGE OF THE PINK PANTHER (Film soundtrack) (Various artists)
Tracks: / Pink panther (theme from): *Revenge Of Pink Panther* / Simone: *Revenge Of Pink Panther* / Give me some mo'l: *Revenge Of Pink Panther* / Thar she blows: *Revenge Of Pink Panther* / Balls caprice: *Revenge Of Pink Panther* / Move 'em out: *Revenge Of Pink Panther* / Touch of red, A: *Revenge Of Pink Panther* / After

the shower: *Revenge Of Pink Panther* / Hong Kong fireworks: *Revenge Of Pink Panther* / Almond eyes: *Revenge Of Pink Panther*.
CD: Released Jan '89, on EMI-America by EMI Records. Catalogue no: **E 21 Y 91113**
Album: Released Jul '78, on United Artists by EMI Records. Catalogue no: **UAK 30176**
Cass: Released Jan '89, on EMI-America by EMI Records. Catalogue no: **E 41 E 91113**
TRAIL OF THE PINK PANTHER (See under Trail Of...)

Pinocchio

PINOCCHIO (Film Soundtrack) (Various artists) (See panel above)
Tracks: / When you wish upon a star: *Various artists* / Jiminy cricket theme: *Various artists* / Little wooden head: *Various artists* / Blue fairy theme: *Various artists* / Give a little whistle: *Various artists* / Pinocchio goes to school: *Various artists* / I've got no strings: *Various artists* / Hi diddle dee dee: *Various artists* / Whale chase, The: *Various artists* / Turn on the old music box: *Various artists* / Pinocchio (finale): *Various artists*.
Album: Released Dec '87, on Walt Disney Catalogue no: **WD 002**
Cass: Released Dec '87, on Walt Disney Catalogue no: **WDC 002**
Cass: Released '79, on Hallmark by Pickwick Records. Deleted '84.

Catalogue no: **H 8344**
Album: Released '79, on Hallmark by Pickwick Records. Catalogue no: **HSC 344**
Cass: Released '85, on BBC by BBC Records. Catalogue no: **ZCM 540**
Album: Released '73, on Disneyland by Disneyland-Vista Records (USA). Deleted '78. Catalogue no: **DQ 1202**
Album: Released '85, on BBC by BBC Records. Catalogue no: **REC 540**

Pins & Needles

PINS AND NEEDLES (Original Broadway Cast) (Various artists)
Album: Released Jan '89, on Silva Screen by Silva Screen Records. Catalogue no: **AOS 210**

Pirate (Film)

PIRATE, THE (VIDEO) (Various artists)
VHS: Released Sep '89, on MGM/UA (Video) by MGM/UA Video. Catalogue no: **SMV 10101**
PIRATE, THE/PAGAN LOVE SONG (Film Soundtrack) (Various artists)
Note: Starring Gene Kelly, Judy Garland and Howard Keel.
Album: Released Jan '89, on MCA by MCA Records. Catalogue no: **MCA 39080**
Cass: Released Jan '89, on MCA by MCA Records. Deleted Mar '90. Catalogue no: **MCAC 39080**

Pirates (Film)

PIRATES (Film soundtrack) (Philippe Sarde)
Tracks: / Pirates / Sauves mais captifs / Linares se meurt / Mutinerie a bord / C'ptain red maitre du galion / Red, la grenouille et le requin / Dolores (theme d,amour') / Don alfonso s'evade / Red, la grenouille, le tronde, boomako et le boa / C'ptain red's empare du tresor tandis que la grenouille perd / Red et la grenouille voguent vers de nouvelles aventures.
Note: From Roman Polanski's latest film starring Walter Matthau.
Cass: Released '86, on SPI Milan (France) Catalogue no: **C 233**
Album: Released '86, on SPI Milan (France) Catalogue no: **A 233**

CD: Released '86, on SPI Milan (France) Catalogue no: **CDCH 233**

Pirates Of Penzance

PIRATES OF PENZANCE (Original Broadway Cast) (Various artists)
Tracks: / Poor, o pour the pirate sherry: *Various artists* / When Frederic was a little lad: *Various artists* / Oh better far to live and die: *Various artists* / Oh false one you have deceived me: *Various artists* / Climbing over rocky mountain: *Various artists* / Stop ladies pray: *Various artists* / Oh is there not one maiden breast: *Various artists* / Poor wandering one: *Various artists* / What ought we to do: *Various artists* / How beautiful blue the sky: *Various artists* / Stay, we must not lose our senses: *Various artists* / Hold monsters: *Various artists* / I am the very model of a modern major general: *Various artists* / Oh men of dark and dismal fate: *Various artists* / Oh dry the glistening tear: *Various artists* / Then Frederic: *Various artists* / When the foreman bares his steel: *Various artists* / Now for the pirates lair: *Various artists* / When you had left our pirate fold: *Various artists* / My eyes are fully open: *Various artists* / Away away: *Various artists* / My heart's on fire: *Various artists* / All is prepared: *Various artists* / Stay: *Various artists* / Frederic stay: *Various artists* / Sorry her lot: *Various artists* / No I am brave: *Various artists* / When a felon's not engaged in his employment: *Various artists* / Rollicking band of pirates we, A: *Various artists* / With cat like treat upon our prey we steal: *Various artists* / Hush hush not a word: *Various artists* / Sighing softly to the river: *Various artists* / Pirates of Penzance (finale): *Various artists*.
2 LP Set: Released Jul '81, on Asylum by WEA Records. Deleted Aug '87. Catalogue no: **K 62035**

Places In The Heart

PLACES IN THE HEART (Film soundtrack) (Various artists)
Note: Music and songs by Doc Watson for the award winning Sally Fields film.
Album: Released Jan '89, on Varese Sarabande Records(USA) by Varese Sarabande Records (USA). Catalogue no: **STV 81229**

Cass: Released Jan '89, on Varese Sarabande Records(USA) by Varese Sarabande Records (USA). Catalogue no: **CTV 81229**
Album: Released Apr '85, on SPI Milan (France) Catalogue no: **A 269**

Plague Dogs (Film)

PLAGUE DOGS (Film Soundtrack) (Various artists)
Album: Released '83, on Polydor by Polydor Ltd. Deleted '88. Catalogue no: **POLD 5074**

Planer, Nigel

ROUGH WITH THE SMOOTH (TV Theme)
Tracks: / Rough with the smooth / Nicholas Craig and Max (Nigel Planer, Nicholas Craig and Max (Hugh Cornwall)).
Note: Theme for Thames TV series King and Castle
7" Single: Released '86, on Columbia by EMI Records. Catalogue no: **DB 9140**

Planes, Trains & ...

PLANES, TRAINS AND AUTOMOBILES (Film soundtrack) (Various artists)
Tracks: / I can take anything: *E.T.A* / Ba-na-na-bam-boo: *Westworld* / I'll show you something special: *Balaam & The Angel* / Modigliani (lost in your eyes): *Book Of Love* / Power to believe: *Dream Academy* / Six days on the road: *Earle, Steve & the Dukes* / Gonna move: *Edmunds, Dave* / Back in baby's arms: *Harris, Emmylou* / Red river rock: *Silicon Teens* / Wheels: *Stars Of Heaven*.
Note: Producer/director John Hughes has had extraordinary success at combining film and music in recent years. His motion picture The Breakfast Club yielded a best-selling soundtrack LP as well as the chart-topping single *Don't You (Forget About Me)*. The soundtrack from Hughes' latest picture Planes, Trains and Automobiles, is a creatively diverse album package showcasing both verteran and up-and-coming artists.
Planes, Trains and Automobiles stars Steve Martin (All Of Me, Roxanne) and John Candy (Armed And Dangerous, Spaceballs) as two mismatched travellers on an illfated (and hilarious) cross-

country journey. As befits the changes in locale, the film's soundtrack LP is divided into "Town" and "Country" sides.
Album: Released May '88, on MCA by MCA Records. Deleted Jul '90. Catalogue no: **IMCA 6223**
Cass: Released May '88, on MCA by MCA Records. Deleted Feb '90. Catalogue no: **IMCAC 6223**
CD: Released May '88, on MCA by MCA Records. Catalogue no: **MCAD 6223**

Planet Of The Apes

PLANET OF THE APES (Film Soundtrack) (Various artists)
Note: Music by Jerry Goldsmith.
Cass: Released Jan '89, on Silva Screen by Silva Screen Records. Catalogue no: **PRC 5023**
CD: Released Jan '89, on Silva Screen by Silva Screen Records. Catalogue no: **PRCD 5023**
Album: Released Jan '89, on Silva Screen by Silva Screen Records. Catalogue no: **PR 5023**

Platoon

NOWHERE TO RUN (See under Reeves, Martha)

PLATOON (Film soundtrack) (Various artists)
Tracks: / Village, The - Adagio for strings: *Vancouver Symphony Orchestra* / Tracks of my tears: *Robinson, Smokey* / Okie from Muskogee: *Haggard, Merle* / Hello, I love you: *Doors* / White rabbit: *Jefferson Airplane* / Barnes shoots Elias: *Vancouver Symphony Orchestra* / Respect: *Franklin, Aretha* / (Sittin' on) the dock of the bay: *Redding, Otis* / When a man loves a woman: *Sledge, Percy* / Groovin': *Rascals* / Adagio for strings: *Vancouver Symphony Orchestra*.
CD: Released Jun '87, on Atlantic by WEA Records. Catalogue no: **781 742-2**
Cass: Released Jun '87, on Atlantic by WEA Records. Catalogue no: **WX 95 C**
Album: Released Jun '87, on Atlantic by WEA Records. Catalogue no: **WX 95**

TRACKS OF MY TEARS (See under Robinson, Smokey)

Platoon Leader

PLATOON LEADER (Film soundtrack) (Various artists)

Platoon Leader

PLATOON LEADER (Film soundtrack) (Various artists)
Note: Starring Michael Dudikoff. Score by George S Clinton.
Album: Released Jan '89, on GNP Crescendo (USA) by GNP Crescendo Records (USA). Catalogue no: **GNPS 8013**
Cass: Released Jan '89, on GNP Crescendo (USA) by GNP Crescendo Records (USA). Catalogue no: **GNPS 8013**
CD: Released Jan '89, on GNP Crescendo by GNP Crescendo Records (USA). Catalogue no: **GNPD 8013**

Play...

PLAY AWAY (Various artists)
Tracks: / Party is about to begin (ding dong), The: *Various artists* / All change: *Various artists* / Superstition: *Various artists* / Say when: *Various artists* / Umbarbarumba: *Various artists* / Captain Kipper's clipper: *Various artists* / If I had a hammer: *Various artists* / Stops and starts: *Various artists* / Rabbit and pork: *Various artists* / Rain makes all things beautiful, The: *Various artists* / Words, words words: *Various artists* / Sitting by the river: *Various artists* / Hokey cokey: *Various artists* / Hippo song, The: *Various artists* / train to Glasgow, The: *Various artists* / First things: *Various artists* / Singalong: *Various artists*.
Cass: Released Oct '76, on BBC by BBC Records. Deleted '87. Catalogue no: **MRMC 003**
Album: Released Oct '76, on BBC by BBC Records. Deleted '87. Catalogue no: **REC 244**

PLAY ON (Songs from Playschool) (Various artists)
Tracks: / Play on: *Various artists* / I'm the man with the wellington boots: *Various artists* / Paddle your own canoe: *Various artists* / Tick tock, song of the clock: *Various artists* / Squash and a squeeze: *Various artists* / What's it like in the place where you live: *Various artists* / Elephants on a piece of string: *Various artists* / Funny face: *Various artists* / Insect songs: *Various artists* / Fling on a thing: *Various artists* / Two by two: *Various artists* / Little ted bear: *Various artists* / Sing a song of seashores: *Various artists* / Wiggle my ears: *Various artists* / Tortoise: *Various*

artists / King of the kingdom of song: *Various artists* / Well Jemima, let's go shopping: *Various artists* / Tea time treats: *Various artists* / Follow the bangalorey man: *Various artists* / Song a sing of Mrs Twisty: *Various artists*.
Cass: Released '78, on BBC by BBC Records. Deleted 31 Aug '88. Catalogue no: **ZCM 332**
Album: Released '78, on BBC by BBC Records. Deleted 31 Aug '88. Catalogue no: **REC 332**

Play It Again, Sam

PLAY IT AGAIN, SAM (Film Soundtrack) (Various artists)
Tracks: / Bogart - that's strictly in the movies: *Various artists* / Don't take it personal: *Various artists* / Dames are shrimple: *Various artists* / She wanted to swing: *Various artists* / Date for Allan: *Various artists* / What about Sharon: *Various artists* / You ashamed to sweat: *Various artists* / I love the rain: *Various artists* / Bogart fantasy: *Various artists* / Blues for Allan Felix: *Various artists* / One two one two: *Various artists* / How'd it go with Julie: *Various artists* / Homosexual panic: *Various artists* / Allan, did you say you love me?: *Various artists* / Slide: *Various artists* / Casablanca revisited: *Various artists*.
Album: Released '73, on Paramount. Deleted '78. Catalogue no: **SPFL 279**

Playing For Keeps

PLAYING FOR KEEPS (Film soundtrack) (Various artists)
Tracks: / Life to life: *Various artists* / It's not over: *Various artists* / Distant drums: *Various artists* / It's gettin' hot: *Various artists* / Think we're gonna make it?: *Various artists* / We said hello goodbye: *Various artists* / Here to stay: *Various artists* / Say the word: *Various artists* / Make a wish: *Various artists* / Stand by me: *Various artists*.
Album: Released Oct '86, on Parlophone by EMI Records. Deleted 31 Jul '88. Catalogue no: **PCS 7306**
CD: Released Oct '86, on Parlophone by EMI Records. Deleted 31 Jul '88. Catalogue no: **CDP 746 379 2**
Cass: Released Oct '86, on Parlophone by EMI Records. Deleted 31 Jul '88. Catalogue no: **TCPCS 7306**

Playschool

HELLO (Various artists)
Tracks: / How do you feel today: *Various artists* / Trumpet song: *Various artists* / Fool: *Various artists* / Here's juice in your eye: *Various artists* / Eggs and bacon: *Various artists* / English pud: *Various artists* / Frying tonight: *Various artists* / Getting dressed: *Various artists* / Hands feet cars and horses: *Various artists* / One day a hand went walking: *Various artists* / Jogging song: *Various artists* / Talking about my automobile: *Various artists* / Give me the old fashioned horse: *Various artists* / Talking about my automobile (reprise): *Various artists* / Talking tick tock talk: *Various artists* / How high does a fly fly: *Various artists* / I'd rather be me: *Various artists* / Million pound song, The: *Various artists* / Never song, The: *Various artists* / Summertime is over: *Various artists* / Aunty Nellie: *Various artists* / Catch it if you can: *Various artists* / Stand up sit down: *Various artists* / Footnotes: *Various artists*.
Album: Released Oct '81, on BBC by BBC Records. Deleted '88. Catalogue no: **REC 425**
Cass: Released Oct '81, on BBC by BBC Records. Deleted '88. Catalogue no: **ZCM 425**

PLAY SCHOOL AND PLAY AWAY, SONGS FROM (Various artists)
Tracks: / Early in the morning: *Scott, P.R./Peter Gosling* / Brush, brush, brush: *Gosling, Peter* / Sunbeams play: *Beebee, Graham* / I am here: *Gosling, Peter* / Caterpillars only crawl: *Charlton, Sue & Peter* / Wheels keep turning: *Beebee, Graham* / I like peace, I like quiet: *Cole, Michael/Gosling, Peter* / Building up my house: *Charlton, Peter* / I think I've caught a cold: *Horrox, Alan/Peter Gosling* / Israeli boat song, The: *Morton, Lionel* / One potato, two potato: *Charlton, Peter/Paul Reade* / Bang on a drum: *Jones, Rick* / Jump: *Morton, Lionel* / Paper song, The: *Whitfield, June/Paul Reade* / Down on the farm: *Beebee, Graham* / Come to the shops: *Carrick, Malcolm* / What do we do with this and that: *Blezard, William* / Circus is coming, The: *Charlton, Peter/Paul Reade* / Build it up: *Charlton, Peter* / Fidget: *Whitfield, June* / You can stamp your feet: *Whitfield, June* / Play away: *Morton, Lionel*

/ How do you feel today?: *Diamond* / Trumpet song: *Carrick, Malcolm* / Here's juice in your eye: *Wilson* / Eggs and bacon: *Reade/Charlton* / English pud: *Cole/Gosling* / Frying tonight: *Charlton, Peter* / Getting dressed: *Sullivan/Adams* / One day a hand went walking: *Charlton, Peter, Paul Reade* / Jogging song: *Sullivan/Adams* / Talk about my automobile: *Wilson* / Give me the old fashioned horse: *Harris/Moses* / Talk about my automobile (reprise): *Wilson* / Talking tick tock talk: *Rowe* / How high does a fly fly?: *Sarony/Holmes* / I'd rather be me: *Cole/Gosling* / Million pound song: *Atkin* / Never song, The: *Lipton* / Summertime is over: *Haldane/Omer* / Aunty Nellie: *Various artists* / Catch it if you can: *Atkin* / Stand up, sit down: *Gosling* / Footnotes: *Charlton/Le Sage*.

2 LP Set: Released Oct '87, on MFP by EMI Records. Deleted '89. Catalogue no: **DL 1114**

Cass: Released Oct '87, on MFP by EMI Records. Catalogue no: **TC-DL 1114**

PLAYSCHOOL - STORIES
Album: Released '74, on Roundabout Catalogue no: **RBT 10**

TALE OF A DONKEYS TAIL (See under Tale Of A Donkeys Tail)

VERY BEST OF PLAYSCHOOL, THE (Various artists)
Tracks: / How do you feel today?: *Various artists* / Trumpet song: *Various artists* / Hands, feet, cars and horses: *Various artists* / Million pound song, The: *Various artists* / Never song, The: *Various artists* / Simple Simon says: *Various artists* / Clapping song, The: *Various artists* / Jump up time with Floella's Carribbean medley: *Various artists* / How high does a fly: *Various artists* / I'd rather be me: *Various artists* / On the ning nang nong: *Various artists* / Three little fishes: *Various artists* / Ugly duckling, The: *Various artists* / Blue blues: *Various artists* / Stop start medley: *Various artists*.

Cass: Released May '89, on Pickwick by Pickwick Records. Catalogue no: **HSC 653**

Pogues

GOOD, THE BAD AND THE UGLY, THE
Tracks: / Good, the bad and the ugly, The / Rak at the gates of hell.
Note: From the film *Straight to Hell*.
12" Single: Released Jun '87, on Hell Catalogue no: **BLOODY 1**
7" Single: Released Jun '87, on Hell Catalogue no: **BLOOD 1**

HAUNTED
Tracks: / Haunted / Junk theme / Hot dogs with everything (Extra track on 12" version only).
Note: From the film 'Sid and Nancy'.
12" Single: Released Aug '86, on MCA by MCA Records. Catalogue no: **MCAT 1084**
7" Single: Released Aug '86, on MCA by MCA Records. Catalogue no: **MCA 1084**

Point (Show)

POINT, THE (Original Soundtrack) (Various artists)
Tracks: / Overture: everything's got 'em: *Various artists* / Me and my arrow: *Various artists* / Poli high: *Various artists* / Remember: *Various artists* / To be a king: *Various artists* / He's leaving here this morning: *Various artists* / Think about your troubles: *Various artists* / Blanket for a sail: *Various artists* / Lifeline: *Various artists* / Thursday: *Various artists* / It's a jungle out there: *Various artists* / P.O.V. waltz: *Various artists* / Are you sleeping: *Various artists* / Gotta get up: *Various artists* / Reprise overture: *Various artists*.
Album: Released Jan '78, on MCA by MCA Records. Catalogue no: **MCF 2826**

Pointer Sisters

NEUTRON DANCE
Tracks: / Neutron dance / Telegraph for your love / I feel for you.
Note: From the film 'Beverley Hills Cop'.
12" Single: Released Dec '84, on Planet by BMG Records (UK). Catalogue no: **RPST109**
7" Single: Released Dec '84, on Planet by BMG Records (UK). Catalogue no: **RPS 109**

Police Academy

POLICE ACADEMY FOUR 'CITIZENS ON PATROL' (Film soundtrack) (Various artists)

Tracks: / Rock the house: *Duncan, Daryll* / It's time to move: *S.O.S. Band* / Dancin' up a storm: *Lattisaw, Stacy* / Let's go to heaven in my car: *Wilson, Brian* / High flyers, The: *Folk, Robert* / Citizens on patrol: *Winslow, Michael & the L.A. Dream Team* / Rescue me: *Family Dream* / I like my body: *DeBarge, Chico* / Winning streak: *Glenn, Gary* / Shoot for the top: *Southern Pacific*.
CD: Released Jul '87, on Motown by BMG Records (UK). Catalogue no: **ZD 72586**
Cass: Released Jul '87, on Motown by BMG Records (UK). Deleted Jun '89. Catalogue no: **ZK 72586**
Album: Released Jul '87, on Motown by BMG Records (UK). Deleted Jun '89. Catalogue no: **ZL 72586**

Pollard, Su

STARTING TOGETHER (TV theme)
Tracks: / Starting together / Good news.
Note: From the BBC fly-on-the-wall documentary 'The Marriage'
7" Single: Released Jan '86, on Rainbow by Rainbow Records. Catalogue no: **RBR 4**

Poltergeist (Film)

POLTERGEIST (Film soundtrack) (Various artists)
Album: Released Oct '82, on MGM (Polydor) by Polydor Ltd. Deleted Oct '87. Catalogue no: **2315 439**

POLTERGEIST II (Film soundtrack) (Various artists)
Tracks: / Power, The / Late call / Smoke, The / Worm, The / Reaching out.
Note: Composed by Jerry Goldsmith.
Cass: Released Jan '89, on Varese Sarabande Records(USA) by Varese Sarabande Records (USA). Catalogue no: **ACS 2001**
Album: Released May '89, on T. E. R. by That's Entertainment Records. Catalogue no: **TER 1116**
CD: Released Jan '89, on Varese Sarabande Records(USA) by Varese Sarabande Records (USA). Catalogue no: **VCD 47266**

POLTERGEIST III (Film soundtrack) (Various artists)

Note: Music by Joe Renzetti.
Album: Released Jan '89, on Varese Sarabande Records(USA) by Varese Sarabande Records (USA). Catalogue no: **704.620**
CD: Released Jan '89, on Varese Sarabande Records(USA) by Varese Sarabande Records (USA). Catalogue no: **VCD 70462**
Cass: Released Jan '89, on Varese Sarabande Records(USA) by Varese Sarabande Records (USA). Catalogue no: **C 704.620**

Poparound

BANKING ON ORION (See under Terry & Gerry)

Popeye

POPEYE (Original soundtrack) (Various artists)
Tracks: / I yam what I yam: *Various artists* / He needs me: *Various artists* / Swee'pea's lullaby: *Various artists* / Din' we?: *Various artists* / Sweethaven: *Various artists* / Blow me down: *Various artists* / Sailin': *Various artists* / It's not easy being me: *Various artists* / He's large: *Various artists* / I'm mean: *Various artists* / Kids: *Various artists* / I'm Popeye the sailor man: *Various artists*.
Album: Released Apr '81, on Epic by CBS Records & Distribution. Catalogue no: **EPC 70203**
Cass: Released Apr '81, on Epic by CBS Records & Distribution. Catalogue no: **40-70203**

Poppie Nongena

POPPIE NONGENA (Original Cast Recording) (Various artists)
Tracks: / Amen: *Various artists* / Taru bawo: *Various artists* / Wenzeni na: *Various artists* / U Jehova: *Various artists* / Uzubale: *Various artists* / Makoti: *Various artists* / Lalasana: *Various artists* / Jerusalem: *Various artists* / Nkosi Sikela l'Afrika: *Various artists* / Zisana abantwane: *Various artists* / Bantwena besikolo: *Various artists* / Liza Lisi Dinga: *Various artists* / Mampondo mse: *Various artists*.
Note: Traditional harmony singing from the award-winning play depicting the true story of a South African woman and her family.
Album: Released Jan '87, on Hannibal by Hannibal Records. Catalogue no: **HNBL 6301**
Cass: Released May '89, on Han-

nibal by Hannibal Records. Catalogue no: **HNBC 6301**

Popul Vuh

COBRA VERDE (1988 film soundtrack) (Various artists)
Tracks: / Der tod des Cobra Verde: *Various artists* / Nachts: schnee: *Various artists* / Der marktplatz: *Various artists* / Eine Andere Welt: *Various artists* / Grab der mutter: *Various artists* / Die singenden madchen von ho, ziavi: *Various artists* / Sieh Nicht Uberm Meer Ist's: *Various artists* / Ha'mut bis dass die nacht mit ruh: *Various artists*.
Album: Released 12 Feb '88, on SPI Milan (France) Catalogue no: **A 353**
Cass: Released 12 Feb '88, on SPI Milan (France) Catalogue no: **C 353**
CD: Released 12 Feb '88, on SPI Milan (France) Catalogue no: **CD 353**

FITZCARALDO (1982 film soundtrack)
Album: Released '89, on Sync Pulse Catalogue no: **ZYX 20017**

MUSIC FROM COEUR DE VERRE
Album: Released Nov '79, on Egg by Egg Records. Catalogue no: **900536**

MUSIC FROM NOSFERATU
Tracks: / Mantra 1 and 2 / Morning sunrays / Venus principle / On the way / Through pains to heaven / To a little way / Zwiestrache der rohrsolette mit der saengerin / Die nacht derhimmel / Der rus der rohrosolette.
Album: Released Nov '79, on Egg by Egg Records. Catalogue no: **900573**

Porgy & Bess

PORGY AND BESS (See under Gershwin, George)
PORGY AND BESS (ORIGINAL ISSUE) (Film soundtrack) (Various artists)
Album: Released Oct '59, on Philips by Phonogram Ltd. Deleted '64. Catalogue no: **ABL 3282**

PORGY AND BESS (Various artists)
CD: Released '88, on RCA by BMG Records (UK). Deleted May '89. Catalogue no: **RD 82109**
CD: Released '88, on RCA by

BMG Records (UK). Catalogue no: **RD 84680**

PORGY AND BESS (Original 1942 Broadway cast) (Various artists)
Tracks: / Overture and summertime: *Various artists* / Woman is a sometime thing: *Various artists* / My man's gone now: *Various artists* / It take a long pull to get there: *Various artists* / O got plenty o' nuttin': *Various artists* / Buzzard song: *Various artists* / Bess, you is my woman: *Various artists* / It ain't necessarily so: *Various artists* / What you want wid Bess: *Various artists* / Strawberry woman's call - crab man's call: *Various artists* / I loves you, Porgy: *Various artists* / Requiem, The: *Various artists* / There's a boat that's leavin' soon for New York: *Various artists* / Porgy's lament and finale: *Various artists*.
Cass: Released Mar '82, on MCA by MCA Records. Catalogue no: **MCLC 1662**
Album: Released Mar '82, on MCA by MCA Records. Catalogue no: **MCL 1662**

PORGY AND BESS (Various artists)
LP Set: Released Apr '76, on Decca by Decca International. Deleted '88. Catalogue no: **SET 609/11**

PORGY AND BESS (Original Soundtrack) (Various artists)
Cass: Released Jan '89, on Silva Screen by Silva Screen Records. Catalogue no: **PST 2016**
Album: Released Jan '89, on Silva Screen by Silva Screen Records. Deleted Mar '90. Catalogue no: **PS 2016**
Album: Released Jun '84, on CBS (import) by CBS Records & Distribution. Catalogue no: **70007**

Porky's

PORKY'S (Original Soundtrack) (Various artists)
Cass: Released Aug '82, on Polydor by Polydor Ltd. Catalogue no: **3199 326**
Album: Released Aug '82, on Polydor by Polydor Ltd. Catalogue no: **2488 858**

PORKY'S REVENGE (Film soundtrack) (Various artists)
Album: Released Jul '85, on CBS by CBS Records & Distribution.

Catalogue no: **CBS 70265**
Cass: Released Jul '85, on CBS by CBS Records & Distribution. Catalogue no: **40 70265**

Porridge

PORRIDGE (VIDEO) (Various artists)
VHS: Released Oct '89, on Spectrum (1) Catalogue no: **SPC 00272**

Porter, Cole

ANYTHING GOES (See under Anything Goes)

NYMPH ERRANT (World premiere complete recording) (Various artists)
Note: Recorded live in concert at the Theatre Royal Drury Lane. Featuring Kaye Ballard; Emile Belcourt; Lorna Dallas; Fiona Fullerton; Patricia Hodge; Larry Kert; Lisa Kirk; Audrey Leybourn; Maureen McGovern; Virginia McKenna; Lilian Montevecchi; Patrice Munsel; Marie Santell; Alexis Smith; Derek Waring; Elisabeth Welch; Andrea McArdie; Stephen Hill Singers. Orchestra conducted by Donald Pippin & David Firman.
Cass: Released Aug '90, on EMI by EMI Records. Catalogue no: **EL 754 079 4**
CD: Released Aug '90, on EMI by EMI Records. Catalogue no: **CDC 754 079 2**

Portnoy, Gary

CHEERS THEME
Tracks: / Cheers theme / Jenny.
7" Single: Released Jan '84, on Starblend by Starblend Records. Catalogue no: **CHEER 1**

Post, Mike

A-TEAM, THE
Tracks: / St Elsewhere / Cast your fate to the wind / Think of Laura / Against all odds / Terms of endearment / A team / Like Chopin / Beat it / Do you really want to hurt me / Footloose.
Album: Released Nov '84, on RCA by BMG Records (UK). Deleted '87. Catalogue no: **PL 85183**
Cass: Released Nov '84, on RCA by BMG Records (UK). Deleted '87. Catalogue no: **PK 85183**

A-TEAM, THEME FROM
Tracks: / A Team, Theme from / 6 slash 24.
7" Single: Released Sep '84, on RCA by BMG Records (UK). Deleted '87. Catalogue no: **RCA 443**

HILL STREET BLUES
Tracks: / Hill Street blues / Aarons theme.
7" Single: Released Nov '85, on Elektra by Elektra Records (UK). Deleted Sep '87. Catalogue no: **K 12576**
7" Pic: Released Nov '85, on Elektra by Elektra Records (UK). Catalogue no: **K 12576T**

HILL STREET BLUES (OLD GOLD)
Tracks: / Hill Street Blues / Rockford Files.
7" Single: Released Sep '85, on Old Gold by Old Gold Records. Deleted Sep '88. Catalogue no: **OG 9515**

MAGNUM P.I.
Tracks: / Magnum P.I / Rockford files.
7" Single: Released Apr '82, on Elektra by Elektra Records (UK). Catalogue no: **K 13167**

ROCKFORD FILES
Tracks: / Rockford files / Dixie lullaby.
7" Single: Released Nov '77, on MGM (EMI) Deleted '79. Catalogue no: **2006 521**
7" Single: Released Mar '82, on Elektra by Elektra Records (UK). Deleted '85. Catalogue no: **K 12606**

T.V. THEME SONGS
Tracks: / Hill Street Blues / Greatest American hero / White shadow / Magnum p.i. / School's out / Rockford files.
Album: Released Mar '82, on Elektra by Elektra Records (UK). Deleted '87. Catalogue no: **K 52372**

Pourcel, Franck

CLOSE ENCOUNTERS OF THE THIRD KIND (Pourcel, Franck & His Orchestra)
Tracks: / Close encounters if the third kind / Space.
7" Single: Released Mar '78, on EMI by EMI Records. Deleted '80. Catalogue no: **EMI 2772**

Powaqqatsi

POWAQQATSI (See under Glass, Philip)

Powell, Dick

LULLABY OF BROADWAY
Tracks: / Lullaby of Broadway / I'm sitting high on a hilltop / I'm goin' shoppin' with you / Lulu's back in town / Words are in my heart, The / Don't give up the ship / Down sunshine lane / Pop goes your heart / Happiness ahead / Rose in her heart, The / Mr. & Mrs. is the name / Flirtation walk / Don't say goodnight / Wonder bar / Thanks a million / I've got a pocket full of sunshine.
Note: Star of the unforgettable Busby Berkeley musicals, Dick Powell recreated the atmosphere of glamour with this collection of his original movie hits from the early Thirties. Powell himself enjoyed a long and varied career in Hollywood on both sides of the camera, by the extravaganzas which spawned these songs created his international fame. Among the films represented are 'Gold Diggers of 1935', 'Flirtation Walk' and 'Broadway Gondolier'.
Album: Released Sep '86, on American Recollections by London Records Ltd. Catalogue no: **RECOL 6**
Cass: Released Sep '86, on American Recollections by London Records Ltd. Catalogue no: **RECMC 6**

LULLABY OF BROADWAY (LIVING ERA)
Tracks: / Fair and warmer / Young and healthy / Wonder bar / Lulu's back in town / Outside of you / Lonely gondolier / Why do I dream those dreams? / I'll string along with you / I only have eyes for you / Mr. and Mrs. is the name / Flirtation walk / Rose in her hand, The / Waterfall, A / Thanks a million / I'm going shopping with you / Lullaby of Broadway.
Cass: Released 1 Nov '86, on Living Era by Academy Sound & Vision Records. Catalogue no: **ZC AJA 5045**
Album: Released 1 Nov '86, on Living Era by Academy Sound & Vision Records. Catalogue no: **AJA 5045**

Power (film)

POWER, THE (Film soundtrack) (Various artists)
Note: Composed by Christopher Young (Hellraiser).
Album: Released Jan '89, on Cerebus (USA) Catalogue no: **C'BUS 206**

Q THE WINGED SERPENT / POWER (See under Q The Winged Serpent)

Power Pack Orchestra

'A' IS FOR ACTION

Tracks: / Superman (theme) / Hill Street blues (theme) / T.J. Hooker (theme).

Cass: Released Jul '85, on MFP by EMI Records. Catalogue no: **TCMFP 5705**

Cass: Released Jul '85, on MFP by EMI Records. Catalogue no: **MFP 4 15705 6**

Album: Released Jul '85, on MFP by EMI Records. Deleted Apr '90. Catalogue no: **MFP 5705**

Album: Released Jul '85, on MFP by EMI Records. Deleted Apr '90. Catalogue no: **MFP 4 15705 1**

CRIMEBUSTERS

Tracks: / Cagney & Lacey / Miami Vice / Scarecrow and Mrs.King / Gentle touch, The / Hunter, The / Miss Marple / Remington Steele / Hart to Hart / Mike Hammer theme / Highway patrol / Airwolf / Crazy like a fox / Murder She Wrote / Magnum / Juliet Bravo / Sweeney, The / Fall guy, The / Chinese detective, The / Bill, The (Overkill) / Z Cars.

Note: 1986 riginal Sound Recordings made by Gordon Lorenz Productions Limited.

Album: Released Jul '85, on MFP by EMI Records. Deleted Jun '89. Catalogue no: **MFP 5768**

Cass: Released Sep '86, on MFP by EMI Records. Deleted Apr '90. Catalogue no: **TCMFP 5768**

FAVOURITE SPORTS THEMES

Tracks: / Match of the day / BBC snooker theme (Drag racer) / ITV's big match live (Aztec gold) / Sportsnight / BBC golf theme (Chase side shoot up) / Ski Sunday (Pop goes Bach) / Question of sport / Sports report (Out of the blue) / Boxing (Gonna fly now) / BBC cricket theme / Wimbledon (Light and tuneful) / Saint and Greavsie theme / BBC Grandstand / Rugby special / ITV's world of sport / 1987 world championship athletic theme / Chain, The (Grand Prix) / Chariots of fire / Kick start (Be my boogie woogie baby) / Shuffle, The.

Cass: Released Feb '88, on MFP by EMI Records. Catalogue no: **TC**

MFP 5818

CD: Released Jul '88, on MFP by EMI Records. Catalogue no: **CDMFP 6028**

CD: Released Jul '88, on MFP by EMI Records. Catalogue no: **CDB 752 061 2**

Album: Released Feb '88, on MFP by EMI Records. Catalogue no: **MFP 5818**

GREAT WAR THEMES

Tracks: / Winds of war, The / Longest day, The / Where eagles dare / Six three three squadron / Dam busters, The / Operation crossbow / Cavatina / Colonel Bogey / Death before dishonor (theme) / Washington post / In the mood / Great escape march / Guns for San Sebastian (love theme) / Reach for the sky / Battle of Britain / Aces high (Luftwaffe march) (CD only).

Cass: Released Jun '90, on MFP by EMI Records. Catalogue no: **TCMFP 5885**

CD: Released Jun '90, on MFP by EMI Records. Catalogue no: **CDMFP 5885**

CD: Released Jun '90, on MFP by EMI Records. Catalogue no: **CDB 794 195 2**

MUSIC OF ANDREW LLOYD WEBBER

Tracks: / Jesus Christ superstar / Phantom of the opera / Tell me on a Sunday (from 'Song and Dance') / Starlight express (from 'Starlight Express') / Mr. Mistoffelees (from 'Cats') / Music of the night (from 'Phantom of the Opera') / Take that look off your face (from 'Song and Dance') / Another suitcase in another hall (from 'Evita') / I don't know how to love Him (from 'Jesus Christ Superstar') / Any dream will do (from 'Joseph and The Amazing Technicolour Dreamcoat') / Don't cry for me Argentina (From 'Evita') / Old Deuteronomy (from 'Cats') / All I ask of you (from 'The Phantom of the Opera') / Pumping iron (CD only.) / King Herod's song (CD only.) / One more angel in heaven (CD only.) / Love changes everything (CD only.).

Cass: Released Oct '87, on MFP by EMI Records. Catalogue no: **TCMFP 5808**

Album: Released Oct '87, on MFP by EMI Records. Deleted Apr '90. Catalogue no: **MFP 5808**

CD: Released Aug '89, on MFP by EMI Records. Catalogue no:

CDMFP 6065

CD: Released Aug '89, on MFP by EMI Records. Catalogue no: **CDB 792 374 2**

SCREEN ACTION

Tracks: / Superman / Miami vice / Magnum / Hunter, The / Professionals, The / Starsky & Hutch / Shoestring / Hawaii five-O / Dempsey & Makepeace / Indiana Jones and the Temple of Doom / T.J. Hooker / James Bond theme / New Avengers theme / Rockford files / Street hawk / Good, the bad and the ugly, The / 'A' team / Knight rider / Crazy like a fox / Mike Hammer theme / Fall guy, The / Sweeney, The / Chinese detective, The / Highway patrol / Airwolf.

CD: Released Apr '88, on MFP by EMI Records. Catalogue no: **CDB 752 011 2**

CD: Released Apr '88, on MFP by EMI Records. Catalogue no: **CDMFP 6017**

SOAPS (TV Themes)

Tracks: / Soap / Coronation Street / Eastenders / Dynasty / Crossroads / Knots Landing / Sons and daughters / Colbys, The / Brookside / Waltons - theme / Dallas / Emmerdale Farm / Falcon Crest / Alice / Albion Market / Hotel / Take the High Road / St. Elsewhere / Sullivans, The / Barwick Green.

Note: Producer/Arranger - Gordon Lorenz.

Cass: Released Aug '86, on MFP by EMI Records. Deleted Apr '90. Catalogue no: **TCMFP 5759**

Album: Released Aug '86, on MFP by EMI Records. Deleted '88. Catalogue no: **MFP 5759**

TOP T.V. THEMES

Tracks: / Eastenders / Cagney & Lacey / Dynasty / Miss Marple / Hill Street blues / Dallas / Bergerac / Crossroads / St. Elsewhere / Soap / Juliet Bravo / Colbys, The / Coronation Street / Bill, The (Overkill) / Brookside / Hart to Hart / Sons and daughters / Knots Landing / Remington Steele / Falcon Crest / Emmerdale Farm / Hotel / Scarecrow and Mrs King / Dukes of Hazzard / Waltons - theme / Gentle touch, The.

CD: Released Oct '87, on MFP by EMI Records. Deleted '89. Catalogue no: **CDMFP 6010**

CD: Released Oct '87, on MFP by EMI Records. Deleted '89. Catalogue no: **CDB 752 004 2**

Prayer For The Dying

PRAYER FOR THE DYING, A (Film soundtrack by John Scott) (Various artists)
CD: Released '88, on J.O.S. Catalogue no: **JSCD 1202**

Premiere Collection

PREMIERE COLLECTION, THE (Best of Andrew Lloyd Webber) (Various artists)
Tracks: / Phantom of the opera: *Harley, Steve & Sarah Brightman* / Take that look off your face: *Webb, Marti* / All I ask of you: *Richard, Cliff & Sarah Brightman* / Don't cry for me Argentina: *Covington, Julie* / Magical Mr. Mistoffeles: *Nicholas, Paul* / Variations 1-4: *Lloyd Webber, Julian* / Superstar: *Head, Murray* / Memory: *Paige, Elaine* / Starlight express: *Shell, Ray* / Tell me on a Sunday: *Webb, Marti* / Music of the night: *Crawford, Michael* / Another suitcase in another hall: *Dickson, Barbara* / I don't know how to love him: *Elliman, Yvonne* / Pie Jesu: *Brightman, Sarah & Paul Miles Kingston*.
Album: Released Oct '88, on Really Useful Records by Really Useful Group. Catalogue no: **ALWTV 1**
Cass: Released Oct '88, on Really Useful Records by Really Useful Group. Catalogue no: **ALWTC 1**
CD: Released Oct '88, on Really Useful Records by Really Useful Group. Catalogue no: **837 282-2**

Presenting Lily Mars

PRESENTING LILY MARS (Film soundtrack) (Various artists)
Note: Starring Judy Garland.
Album: Released Jan '89, on Soun'trak (USA) by Silva Screen Records. Catalogue no: **STK 117**

Presley, Elvis

32 FILM HITS VOL. 1
Tracks: / Fun in Acapulco / Mexico / Marguerita / Bossa nova baby / Blue Hawaii / Can't help falling in love / Rock a hula baby / Ku-u-i-po / King Creole / Hard headed woman / Trouble / Dixieland rock / Frankie and Johnny / Please don't stop loving me / Easy come, easy go / Sing you children / Tonight's alright for love / Frankfurt special / Wooden heart / G.I. blues / Blue suede shoes / Doin' the best I can / Dog's life / Charro / Roustabout / Little Egypt / Poison ivy league / Girls, girls, girls / Where do you come from / Return to sender / Follow that dream / Angel.
2 LP Set: Released Aug '84, on RCA(Special Imports Service) by BMG Records (UK). Catalogue no: **NL 89388**
Cass set: Released Aug '84, on RCA(Special Imports Service) by BMG Records (UK). Catalogue no: **NK 89388**
CD: Released Oct '84, on RCA(Special Imports Service) by BMG Records (UK). Catalogue no: **PD 89388**

32 FILM HITS VOL. 2
Tracks: / Jailhouse rock / Young and beautiful / Baby I don't care / They remind me too much of you / Beyond the bend / Relax / One broken heart for sale / I'm falling in love tonight / No more / Island of love / Moonlight swim.
Note: Tracks include the above
CD: Released Jul '85, on RCA(Special Imports Service) by BMG Records (UK). Catalogue no: **PD 89550**
2 LP Set: Released Jul '85, on RCA(Special Imports Service) by BMG Records (UK). Catalogue no: **NL 89550**
Cass set: Released Jul '85, on RCA(Special Imports Service) by BMG Records (UK). Catalogue no: **NK 89550**

ARE YOU LONESOME TO-NIGHT (See under Are you lonesome tonight)

ALOHA FROM HAWAII SAT-ELLITE
Tracks: / What now my love / Fever / Welcome to my world / Suspicious minds / See see rider / Burning love / Hound dog / I'll remember you / Long tall sally / Whole lotta shakin' goin' on / American trilogy / Big hunk o' love, A / Can't help falling in love / Burning love / Something / You gave me a mountain / Steemroller blues / My way / Love me / Johnny B. Goode / It's over / Blue suede shoes / I'm so lonesome I could cry / I can't stop loving you.
Note: From the concert recorded especially for Television.
CD: Released Nov '85 on RCA by BMG Records (UK). Catalogue no: **PD 82642**

Album: Released Nov '85 on RCA by BMG Records (UK). Deleted Sep '90. Catalogue no: **PL 82642**
Album: Released Feb '73 on RCA by BMG Records (UK). Deleted Feb '73. Catalogue no: **DPS 2040**
Cass: Released Feb '73 on RCA by BMG Records (UK). Deleted Feb '73. Catalogue no: **PK 5144**

BLUE HAWAII (1961 Film soundtrack) (See panel on next page)
Tracks: / Blue Hawaii / Almost always true / Aloha-oe / No more / Can't help falling in love / Rock a hula baby / Moonlight swim / Ku-u-i-po / Ito eats / Slicin' sand / Hawaiian sunset / Beach boy blues / Island of love / Hawaiian wedding song.
Cass: Released '84, on RCA International by BMG Records (UK). Catalogue no: **NK 83683**
Cass: Released Sep '77, on RCA by BMG Records (UK). Deleted '82. Catalogue no: **PK 11561**
Album: Released Dec '61, on RCA by BMG Records (UK). Catalogue no: **RD 27238**
Album: Released Sep '77, on RCA by BMG Records (UK). Catalogue no: **SF 8145**
Album: Released '84, on RCA International by BMG Records (UK). Catalogue no: **NL 83683**
CD: Released Oct '87, on RCA by BMG Records (UK). Catalogue no: **ND 83683**

BLUE HAWAII (SINGLE) (Film soundtrack)
7" Single: Released '80, on RCA by BMG Records (UK). Catalogue no: **LR 5194**

BLUE HAWAII (VIDEO)
VHS: Released '88, on Channel 5. Catalogue no: **CFV 01182**

BOSSA NOVA BABY
Tracks: / Bossa nova baby / Witchcraft.
Note: From the film *'Fun in Acapulco'*
7" Single: Released Oct '63, on RCA by BMG Records (UK). Deleted '66. Catalogue no: **RCA 1374**

CALIFORNIA HOLIDAY (Film Soundtrack)
Tracks: / Stop look and listen / Adam and evil / All that I am / Never say yes / Am I ready / Beach shack / Spinout / Smorgasbord / I'll be back / Tomorrow is a long time /

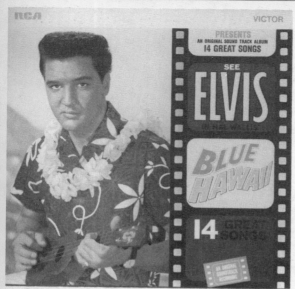

Soundtrack to the film *Blue Hawaii* starring Elvis Presley

Down in the valley / I'll remember you.
Album: Released Nov '66, on RCA by BMG Records (UK). Catalogue no: **RD 7820**
Album: Released '80, on RCA by BMG Records (UK). Catalogue no: **NL 82560**
Cass: Released Aug '80, on RCA International by BMG Records (UK). Deleted '85. Catalogue no: **INTK 5038**
Album: Released '80, on RCA International by BMG Records (UK). Deleted '85. Catalogue no: **INTS 5038**

CAN'T HELP FALLING IN LOVE & OTHER GREAT MOVIE HITS
Tracks: / Can't help falling in love / Rock a hula baby / Follow that dream / What a wonderful life / Easy come, easy go / Rubberneckin', / One broken heart for sale / Girls, girls, girls / G.I. blues / Roustabout / Frankie and Johnny / Charro / I got lucky / Home is where the heart is.
Cass: Released Apr '83, on RCA/Camden by BMG Records (UK). Deleted '88. Catalogue no: **CAM 1210**
Album: Released Apr '83, on

RCA/Camden by BMG Records (UK). Deleted '88. Catalogue no: **CDS 1210**

CLAMBAKE (Film Soundtrack)
Tracks: / Clambake / Who needs money / House that has everything / Confidence / Hey hey hey / You don't know me / Girl I never loved, The / Guitar man / How can you lose what you never had / Big boss man / Singing trees / Just call me lonesome.
Album: Released Apr '68, on RCA by BMG Records (UK). Catalogue no: **SF 7917**
Cass: Released '84, on RCA International by BMG Records (UK). Catalogue no: **NK 82565**
Album: Released Oct '80, on RCA International by BMG Records (UK). Deleted '84. Catalogue no: **INTS 5040**
Album: Released '84, on RCA International by BMG Records (UK). Catalogue no: **NL 82565**

CLAMBAKE (VIDEO)
VHS: Released Jul '88, on Warner Home Video by WEA Records. Catalogue no: **PES 99667**

CLEAN UP YOUR OWN BACK

YARD
Tracks: / Clean up your own back yard.
Note: From the film *'Trouble With Girls'*
7" Single: Released Sep '69, on RCA by BMG Records (UK). Catalogue no: **RCA 1869**

DO THE CLAM
Tracks: / Do the clam / You'll be gone.
Note: From the film *'Girl Happy'*
7" Single: Released Mar '65, on RCA by BMG Records (UK). Catalogue no: **RCA 1443**

DOUBLE TROUBLE (Film soundtrack)
Tracks: / Double trouble / Baby, if you'll give me all your love / Could I fall in love / Long legged girl / City by night / Old McDonald / I love only one girl / There is so much world to see / It won't be long / Never ending / Blue river / What now, what next, where to.
Album: Released Oct '80, on RCA International by BMG Records (UK). Deleted '85. Catalogue no: **INTS 5039**
Album: Released Oct '80, on RCA International by BMG Records (UK). Deleted '85. Catalogue no: **NL 82564**
Album: Released Sep '67, on RCA by BMG Records (UK). Deleted Sep '72. Catalogue no: **SF 7892**

DOUBLE TROUBLE (VIDEO)
VHS: Released '89, on MGM/UA (Video) by MGM/UA Video. Catalogue no: **SMSMV 10485**

ELVIS ON TOUR (VIDEO)
VHS: Released Jan '84, on MGM/UA (Video) by MGM/UA Video. Catalogue no: **SMSMV 10153**

ELVIS SINGS HITS FROM HIS MOVIES
Tracks: / Down by the riverside / When the saints go marching in / Guitar man / Frankie and Johnny / How would you like to be big boss man.
Album: Released Jan '72, on RCA/Camden by BMG Records (UK). Catalogue no: **CDS 1110**
Cass: Released Jan '72, on RCA/Camden by BMG Records (UK). Catalogue no: **CAM 423**

FILM HITS (50th anniversary album)
CD: Released '88, on RCA by

BMG Records (UK). Catalogue no: **PD 89550**

LP Set: Released Nov '85, on RCA (Germany) by BMG Music International. Catalogue no: **NL 89797**

FLAMING STAR
Tracks: / Flaming star / Wonderful night / Night life / All I needed was the rain / Too much monkey business / Yellow rose of Texas / Eyes of Texas, The / She's a machine / Do the vega / Tiger man.
Album: Released Sep '65, on RCA by BMG Records (UK). Catalogue no: **RD 7723**
Album: Released Jul '69, on RCA International by BMG Records (UK). Catalogue no: **INTS 1012**
Album: Released Jan '80, on RCA/Camden by BMG Records (UK). Catalogue no: **CDS 1185**
Cass: Released Jan '80, on RCA/Camden by BMG Records (UK). Catalogue no: **CAM 490**

FLAMING STAR (VIDEO) (See under Flaming Star)

FOLLOW THAT DREAM (EP)
Tracks: / Follow that dream / Angel / What a wonderful life / I'm not the marrying kind.
7" EP: Released Feb '82, on RCA by BMG Records (UK). Catalogue no: **RCX 7196**
7" EP: Released Jun '62, on RCA by BMG Records (UK). Deleted '65. Catalogue no: **RCX 211**

FOLLOW THAT DREAM (VIDEO) (See under Follow That Dream)

FRANKIE AND JOHNNY (Film soundtrack)
Tracks: / Frankie and Johnny / Come along / Petunia, the gardner's daughter / Chesay / What every woman lives for / Look out Broadway / Beginners luck / Down by the riverside / When the saints go marching in / Shout it out / Hard luck / Please don't stop loving me.
Album: Released Jan '84, on RCA International by BMG Records (UK). Catalogue no: **NL 82559**
Album: Released Apr '66, on RCA by BMG Records (UK). Catalogue no: **RD 7793**
Album: Released Oct '80, on RCA International by BMG Records (UK). Deleted '84. Catalogue no: **INTS 5036**
Cass: Released Jan '84, on RCA International by BMG Records

Soundtrack to the film *G.I. Blues* starring Elvis Presley

(UK). Catalogue no: **NK 82559**

FRANKIE AND JOHNNY (VIDEO)
VHS: Released Jul '88, on Warner Home Video by WEA Records. Catalogue no: **PES 99666**

FUN IN ACAPULCO (Film soundtrack)
Tracks: / Fun in Acapulco / Vino / Dinero Y amor / Mexico / El toro / Marguerita / Bullfighter was a lady / No room to rhumba in a sports car / I think I'm gonna like it here / Bossa nova baby / You can't say no in Acapulco / Guadalajara / Love me tonight / Slowly but surely.
Cass: Released '79, on RCA by BMG Records (UK). Deleted '84. Catalogue no: **PK 42357**
Album: Released '79, on RCA by BMG Records (UK). Deleted '84. Catalogue no: **NL 89014**
Album: Released Sep '81, on RCA International by BMG Records (UK). Deleted Sep '86. Catalogue no: **INTS 5106**
Album: Released Dec '63, on RCA by BMG Records (UK). Deleted Dec '68. Catalogue no: **RD 7609**
Album: Released '79, on RCA by

BMG Records (UK). Deleted '84. Catalogue no: **PL 42357**

FUN IN ACAPULCO (VIDEO)
VHS: Released '88, on Channel 5. Catalogue no: **CFV 01192**

G.I. BLUES (EP) (The alternate takes)
Tracks: / Shoppin' around / Big boots / Tonight's all right for love / Frankfurt special.
7" EP: Released '82, on RCA by BMG Records (UK). Deleted May '89. Catalogue no: **RCX 1**

G.I. BLUES (See also under G.I.Blues)

G.I.BLUES (Film soundtrack) (See panel above)
Tracks: / Tonight is so right for love / What's she really like? / Frankfurt special / Wooden heart / G.I. blues / Pocketful of rainbows / Shopping around / Big boots / Blue suede shoes / Didja ever? / Blue suede shoes / Doin' the best I can.
Cass: Released Jan '84, on RCA International by BMG Records (UK). Catalogue no: **NK 83735**
Album: Released Sep '77, on RCA by BMG Records (UK). Catalogue no: **SF 5078**
Album: Released Sep '81, on

RCA International by BMG Records (UK). Deleted Sep '86. Catalogue no: **INTS 5104**

Album: Released Dec '60, on RCA by BMG Records (UK). Catalogue no: **RD 27192**

CD: Released Oct '87, on RCA by BMG Records (UK). Catalogue no: **ND 83735**

Cass: Released '77, on RCA by BMG Records (UK). Deleted '82. Catalogue no: **PK 5078**

Album: Released Jan '84, on RCA International by BMG Records (UK). Catalogue no: **NL 83735**

GIRL HAPPY (Film Soundtrack)

Tracks: / Girl happy / Spring fever / Fort Lauderdale / Chamber of Commerce / Startin' tonight / Wolf call / Do not disturb / Cross my heart and hope to die / Meanest girl in town / Do the clam / Puppet on a string / I've got to find my baby / You'll be gone.

Cass: Released Nov '84, on RCA International by BMG Records (UK). Catalogue no: **NK 83338**

Album: Released May '65, on RCA by BMG Records (UK). Catalogue no: **RD 7714**

Album: Released Oct '80, on RCA International by BMG Records (UK). Deleted '85. Catalogue no: **INTS 5034**

Album: Released Nov '84, on RCA International by BMG Records (UK). Catalogue no: **NL 83338**

GIRLS GIRLS GIRLS (Film Soundtrack) (See under Girls Girls Girls)

GIRLS GIRLS GIRLS

Tracks: / Girls, girls, girls / I don't wanna be tied / Where do you come from / I don't want to / We'll be together / Boy like me, a girl like / Earth boy / Return to sender / Because of love / Thanks to the rolling sea / Song of the shrimp / Walls have ears / We're coming in loaded.

Album: Released Jan '84, on RCA International by BMG Records (UK). Catalogue no: **NL 89048**

Cass: Released '79, on RCA by BMG Records (UK). Deleted '84. Catalogue no: **PK 42354**

Cass: Released Jan '84, on RCA International by BMG Records (UK). Catalogue no: **AK 89048**

Album: Released Sep '81, on

RCA International by BMG Records (UK). Deleted Sep '86. Catalogue no: **INTS 5107**

Album: Released '79, on RCA by BMG Records (UK). Deleted '84. Catalogue no: **PL 42354**

Album: Released Sep '86, on RCA/Camden by BMG Records (UK). Deleted '88. Catalogue no: **CDS 1221**

Cass: Released Sep '86, on RCA / Camden by BMG Records (UK). Deleted '88. Catalogue no: **CAM 1221**

Album: Released Jan '63, on RCA by BMG Records (UK). Catalogue no: **RD 7534**

GIRLS GIRLS GIRLS (VIDEO)

VHS: Released '88 on Channel 5. Catalogue no: **CFV 01212**

HARD HEADED WOMAN

Tracks: / Hard headed woman / Don't ask me why.

Note: From the film *'King Creole'*

7" Single: Released Jul '58, on RCA by BMG Records (UK). Deleted '61 Catalogue no: **RCA 1070**

HAREM HOLIDAY (See under Harem Holiday)

HAREM HOLIDAY (Film Soundtrack)

Tracks: / Harem holiday / My desert serenade / Go west young man / Mirage / Shake that tambourine / Hey little girl / Golden coins / So close yet so far / Animal instinct / Wisdom of the ages.

Cass: Released Jan '84, on RCA International by BMG Records (UK). Catalogue no: **NK 82558**

Album: Released Jan '84, on RCA International by BMG Records (UK). Catalogue no: **NL 82558**

Album: Released Oct '80, on RCA International by BMG Records (UK). Deleted '84. Catalogue no: **INTS 5035**

Album: Released Jan '66, on RCA by BMG Records (UK). Catalogue no: **RD 7767**

IN HOLLYWOOD

Tracks: / Jailhouse rock / Rock a hula baby / GI blues / Kissin' cousins / Wild in the country / King Creole / Fun in Acapulco / Blue Hawaii / Follow that dream / Viva Las Vegas / Girls girls girls / Bossa nova baby / Flaming star / Girl happy / Frankie and Johnny / Double trouble / Roustabout / Spinout / They remind me too much of

you / Charro.

Album: Released Feb '88, on Premier by Premier Records. Catalogue no: **PMP 1011**

Cass: Released Feb '88, on Premier by Premier Records. Catalogue no: **PMPK 1011**

IT HAPPENED AT THE WORLD'S FAIR (Film soundtrack)

Tracks: / Beyond the bend / Relax / Take me to the fair / They remind me too much of you / One broken heart for sale / I'm falling in love tonight / Cotton candy land / World of our own, A / How would you like to be big boss man / Happy ending.

Cass: Released Nov '84, on RCA International by BMG Records (UK). Catalogue no: **NK 82568**

Album: Released Oct '80, on RCA International by BMG Records (UK). Deleted '84. Catalogue no: **INTS 5033**

Album: Released May '63, on RCA by BMG Records (UK). Catalogue no: **RD 7565**

Album: Released Nov '84, on RCA International by BMG Records (UK). Catalogue no: **NL 82568**

JAILHOUSE ROCK (EP)

Tracks: / Jailhouse rock / Young and beautiful / I want to be free / Don't leave me now / Baby I don't care.

7" EP: Released '58, on RCA by BMG Records (UK). Deleted '61. Catalogue no: **RCX 106**

7" EP: Released '82, on RCA by BMG Records (UK). Catalogue no: **RCX 7193**

JAILHOUSE ROCK (VIDEO)

Note: The explosion that turned Elvis loose. Running time: 92 minutes. Cert: U.,

VHS: Released '88, on MGM/UA (Video) by MGM/UA Video. Catalogue no: **SMV 100115**

KID GALAHAD AND EASY COME EASY GO

Album: Released Apr '83, on RCA by BMG Records (UK). Catalogue no: **PL 42791**

Cass: Released Apr '83, on RCA (Germany) by BMG Music International. Catalogue no: **TC PL 42791**

Cass: Released '83, on RCA by BMG Records (UK). Catalogue no: **PK 42791**

KID GALAHAD (EP)

Tracks: / King of the whole wide world / This is living / Riding the rainbow / Home is where the heart is / I got lucky / Whistling tune.

7" EP: Released '82, on RCA by BMG Records (UK). Catalogue no: **RCX 7197**

7" EP: Released '62, on RCA by BMG Records (UK). Catalogue no: **RCX 7106**

KID GALAHAD (VIDEO)
Note: Cert: PG.
VHS: Released '88, on Warner Home Video by WEA Records. Catalogue no: **PES 99335**

KING CREOLE (See under King Creole)

KING CREOLE (Film Soundtrack)
Tracks: / King Creole / As long as I have you / Hard headed woman / Trouble / Dixieland rock / Don't ask me why / Lover doll / Crawfish / Young dreams / Steadfast, loyal and true / New orleans.

Album: Released Jan '84, on RCA International by BMG Records (UK). Catalogue no: **NL 83733**
CD: Released Oct '87, on RCA by BMG Records (UK). Catalogue no: **ND 83733**
Album: Released '79, on RCA by BMG Records (UK). Deleted '84. Catalogue no: **SF 8231**
Cass: Released Aug '86, on Astan (USA) Catalogue no: **40173**
Cass: Released Jan '84, on RCA International by BMG Records (UK). Catalogue no: **NK 83733**
Album: Released Sep '81, on RCA International by BMG Records (UK). Deleted Sep '86. Catalogue no: **INTS 5013**
Album: Released Nov '58, on RCA by BMG Records (UK). Catalogue no: **RD 27086**

KING CREOLE VOL.1 (EP)
Tracks: / King Creole / New Orleans / As long as I have you / Lover doll.

7" EP: Released '82, on RCA by BMG Records (UK). Catalogue no: **RCX 7194**
7" EP: Released '58, on RCA by BMG Records (UK). Catalogue no: **RCX 117**

KING CREOLE VOL.2 (EP)
7" EP: Released '82, on RCA by BMG Records (UK). Catalogue no: **RCX 7201**
7" EP: Released '58, on RCA by

BMG Records (UK). Catalogue no: **RCX 118**

KISSIN' COUSINS (Film Soundtrack)
Tracks: / Kissin' cousins / Smokey mountain boys / Catchin' on fast / Tender feeling / Anyone could fall in love with you / Barefoot ballad / Once is enough / Echoes of love / It's a long lonely highway.

Album: Released Sep '81, on RCA International by BMG Records (UK). Deleted Sep '86. Catalogue no: **INTS 5108**
Cass: Released '79, on RCA by BMG Records (UK). Deleted '84. Catalogue no: **PK 42355**
Album: Released '79, on RCA by BMG Records (UK). Deleted '84. Catalogue no: **PL 42355**
Cass: Released Nov '84, on RCA International by BMG Records (UK). Catalogue no: **NK 84115**
Album: Released Jul '64, on RCA by BMG Records (UK). Catalogue no: **RD 7645**
Album: Released Nov '84, on RCA International by BMG Records (UK). Catalogue no: **NL 84115**

KISSIN' COUSINS (SINGLE)
Tracks: / Kissin' cousins / It hurts me.
Note: From the film 'Kissin Cousins'
7" Single: Released Jun '64, on RCA by BMG Records (UK). Deleted '67. Catalogue no: **RCA 1404**

LOVE IN LAS VEGAS (Film soundtrack)
7" EP: Released Oct '82, on RCA by BMG Records (UK). Catalogue no: **RCX 7206**
7" EP: Released '64, on RCA by BMG Records (UK). Catalogue no: **RCX 7141**

LOVE ME TENDER (EP)
Tracks: / Love me tender / We're gonna move / Let me / Poor boy.
7" EP: Released '56, on H.M.V. by EMI Records. Deleted '57. Catalogue no: **7EG 8199**
7" EP: Released '82, on RCA by BMG Records (UK). Catalogue no: **RCX 7191**

LOVE ME TENDER (SINGLE) (Original release)
Tracks: / Love me tender / Anyway you want me.
Note: From the film 'Love me ten-

der'
7" Single: Released '56, on H.M.V. Deleted '57. Catalogue no: **POP 253**

LOVING YOU (See under Loving You)

NBC TV SPECIAL
Tracks: / Trouble / Guitar man / Lawdy Miss Clawdy / Baby, what you want me to do / Medley / Love me tender / Where could I go but to the Lord / Up above my head / Saved / Blue Christmas / One might / Memories / If I can dream.

Album: Released Sep '81, on RCA International by BMG Records (UK). Deleted Sep '86. Catalogue no: **INTS 5093**
Album: Released '84, on RCA by BMG Records (UK). Catalogue no: **NL 83894**
Cass: Released '84, on RCA by BMG Records (UK). Catalogue no: **NK 83894**
Album: Released May '69, on RCA by BMG Records (UK). Catalogue no: **RD 8011**
Cass: Released Sep '78, on RCA by BMG Records (UK). Deleted Sep '83. Catalogue no: **PK 42370**
Album: Released Sep '78, on RCA by BMG Records (UK). Deleted Sep '83. Catalogue no: **PL 42370**

ONE BROKEN HEART FOR SALE
Tracks: / One broken heart for sale / They remind me too much of you.
Note: From the film 'It happened at the worlds fair'
7" Single: Released Feb '63, on RCA by BMG Records (UK) Deleted '66. Catalogue no: **RCA 1337**

PARADISE HAWAIIAN STYLE (Film Soundtrack)
Tracks: / Paradise Hawaiian style / Queenie Wamine's papaya / Scratch my back (then I'll scratch yours) / Drums of the islands / Datin' / Dog's life / House of sand / Stop where you are / This is my heaven / Sand castles.

Album: Released Aug '66, on RCA by BMG Records (UK). Catalogue no: **RD 7810**
Cass: Released Jan '84, on RCA International by BMG Records (UK). Catalogue no: **NK 89010**
Album: Released Aug '80, on RCA International by BMG Rec-

ords (UK). Deleted '84. Catalogue no: **INTS 5037**

Album: Released Jan '84, on RCA International by BMG Records (UK). Catalogue no: **NL 89010**

PICTURES OF ELVIS

Tracks: / Return to sender / Roustabout / Little Egypt / Paradise Hawaiian style / Girls, girls, girls / Double trouble / Do the clam / Fun in Acapulco / Bossa nova baby / Clambake / Girl happy / Rock a hula baby.

Cass: Released Apr '80, on RCA International by BMG Records (UK). Catalogue no: **INTK 5001**

Album: Released Apr '80, on RCA International by BMG Records (UK). Catalogue no: **INTS 5001**

PICTURES OF ELVIS (II)

Tracks: / I was the one / Blue suede shoes / Tutti frutti / Blue moon / Lawdy Miss Clawdy / Love me tender / Teddy bear / Loving you / Jailhouse rock / Trying to get to you / Anyway you want me / Just because.

LP Pic: Released Feb '83, on RCA International by BMG Records (UK). Catalogue no: **AR 30 002**

RETURN TO SENDER (SINGLE)

Tracks: / Return to sender / Where do you come from.

Note: From the film *'Girls girls girls'*

7" Single: Released '62, on RCA by BMG Records (UK) Deleted '65. Catalogue no: **RCA 1320**

ROCK A-HULA BABY

Tracks: / Rock a-hula baby / Can't help falling in love.

Note: From the film *'Blue Hawaii'*.

7" Single: Released '62, on RCA by BMG Records (UK). Deleted '65. Catalogue no: **RCA 1270**

7" Single: Released '77, on RCA by BMG Records (UK). Catalogue no: **RCA 2703**

ROUSTABOUT (Film Soundtrack)

Tracks: / Roustabout / Little Egypt / Poison ivy league / Hard knock / It's a wonderful world / Big love, big heartache / One-track heart / It's carnival time / Carny town / There's a brand new day on the horizon / Wheels on my heels.

Album: Released '79, on RCA by BMG Records (UK). Deleted '84. Catalogue no: **PL 42356**

Cass: Released Jan '84, on RCA

International by BMG Records (UK). Catalogue no: **NK 89049**

Album: Released Jan '84, on RCA International by BMG Records (UK). Catalogue no: **NL 89049**

Cass: Released '79, on RCA by BMG Records (UK). Deleted '84. Catalogue no: **PK 42356**

Album: Released Sep '81, on RCA International by BMG Records (UK). Deleted Sep '86. Catalogue no: **INTS 5110**

Album: Released Jan '65, on RCA by BMG Records (UK). Catalogue no: **RD 7678**

SPEEDWAY (Film soundtrack)

Tracks: / Speedway / There ain't nothing like a song / Your time hasn't come yet, baby / Who are you, who am I? / He's your uncle, not your dad / Let yourself go / Your groovy self / Five sleepy heads / Western Union / Mine / Going home / Suppose.

Album: Released Jan '84, on RCA International by BMG Records (UK). Catalogue no: **NL 85012**

Album: Released Oct '80, on RCA International by BMG Records (UK). Deleted '84. Catalogue no: **INTS 5041**

Cass: Released Jan '84, on RCA International by BMG Records (UK). Catalogue no: **NK 85012**

TEDDY BEAR

Tracks: / Teddy bear / Loving you.

Note: From the film *'Loving you'*

7" Single: Released on RCA by BMG Records (UK). Deleted '60. Catalogue no: **RCA 1013**

TICKLE ME (Volume 1)

7" EP: Released '64 on RCA by BMG Records (UK). Catalogue no: **RCX 7173**

TICKLE ME (Volume 2)

7" EP: Released '64 on RCA by BMG Records (UK). Catalogue no: **RCX 7174**

THAT'S THE WAY IT IS (Film soundtrack)

Tracks: / I just can't help believing / Twenty days and twenty nights / How the web was woven / Patch it up / Mary in the morning / You don't have to say you love me / You've lost that lovin' feeling / I've lost you / Just pretend / Stranger in the crowd / Next step is love, The / Bridge over troubled water.

Cass: Released Jan '84, on RCA

International by BMG Records (UK). Catalogue no: **NK 84114**

Album: Released Jan '71, on RCA by BMG Records (UK). Catalogue no: **SF 8162**

Album: Released Jan '84, on RCA International by BMG Records (UK). Catalogue no: **NL 84114**

Cass: Released Jan '71, on RCA by BMG Records (UK). Deleted '82. Catalogue no: **PK 11566**

THAT'S THE WAY IT IS (VIDEO)

Tracks: / Next step is love, The / Pork salad Annie / Stranger in the crowd / You've lost that lovin' feelin' / All shook up / Bridge over troubled water / Heartbreak Hotel / Blue suede shoes / I just can't help believing / Patch it up / Suspicious minds / Can't help falling in love with you / You don't have to say you love me / Love me tender.

Note: Directed by two time Academy Award winner Denis Sanders, the movie captures 'the king' in spectacular live performance; from the opening night of his first concert tour in 13 years to his triumphant season at the Vegas International Hotel, we see Presley deliver over 30 songs in the electrifying style that made him a legend. Elvis, too appears as never before in front of the camera without direction and without a script. It's Presley in the spotlight as he really was, coping with the fun and the frustrations of rehearsal; working day in and day out at putting together the most dynamic stage show Las Vegas has ever seen. Running time: 104 mins. (MGM/UA Home Video)

VHS: Released '86, on MGM/UA (Video) by MGM/UA Video. Catalogue no: **SMV 10373**

THIS IS ELVIS (Film soundtrack)

Tracks: / His latest flame / Moody blue / That's alright / Shake, rattle and roll / Flip flop and fly / Heartbreak hotel / Hound dog / Hy Gardner interview excerpts / My baby left me / Merry Christmas, baby / Mean woman blues / Don't be cruel / Teddy bear / Jailhouse rock / Army swearing-in / G.I. blues / Departure for Germany: press conference excerpt / Home from Germany: press conference excerpt / Too much monkey business / Love me tender / I got a thing about you, baby / I need your love

Soundtrack from *Pretty in Pink* starring Molly Ringwald (A&M)

tonight / Blue suede shoes / Viva Las Vegas / Suspicious minds / JC's award to Elvis excerpt / Promised land / Madison Square Gardens press conference excerpt / Are you lonesome tonight? / My way / American trilogy / Memories.
Cass: Released '84, on RCA by BMG Records (UK). Catalogue no: **BK 84031**
Album: Released Mar '81, on RCA by BMG Records (UK). Catalogue no: **RCALP 5029**
2 LP Set: Released '84, on RCA by BMG Records (UK). Catalogue no: **BL 84031**

THIS IS ELVIS (VIDEO)
VHS: Released '88, on Warner Home Video by WEA Records. Catalogue no: **PES 11173**

VIVA LAS VEGAS
Tracks: / Viva Las Vegas / What'd I say.
Note From the film *'Viva Las Vegas'*
7" Single: Released Mar '64 on RCA by BMG Records (UK). Deleted '67. Catalogue no: **RCA 1390**

WILD IN THE COUNTRY (Film soundtrack) (See under Wild in the country)

WILD IN THE COUNTRY (SINGLE)
Tracks: / Wild in the country / I feel so bad.
Note: From the film *'Wild in the country'*
7" Single: Released Mar '61 on RCA by BMG Records (UK). Deleted '64. Catalogue no: **RCA 1244**

WILD IN THE COUNTRY (VIDEO)
VHS: Released Jun'89 on CBS-Fox. Catalogue no: **117450**

Pretty In Pink

PRETTY IN PINK (Film soundtrack) (Various artists) (See panel above)
Tracks: / Left of centre: *Vega, Suzanne* / Get to know ya: *Johnson, Jesse* / Do wot you do: *INXS* / Pretty in pink: *Psychedelic Furs* / Shellshock: *New Order* / Round round: *Some, Belouis* / Wouldn't it be good: *Hutton, June* / Bring on the dancing horses: *Echo & The Bunnymen* / Please, please let me get what I want: *Smiths* / If you leave: *O.M.D..*

Album: Released Jul '86, on A&M by A&M Records. Catalogue no: **AMA 5113**
Cass: Released Jul '86, on A&M by A&M Records. Catalogue no: **AMC 5113**
CD: Released '88, on A&M by A&M Records. Catalogue no: **395 113-2**
CD: Released '88, on A&M by A&M Records. Catalogue no: **CDA 5113**

Pretty Woman

PRETTY WOMAN (Film soundtrack) (Various artists)
Tracks: / Wild women do: *Cole, Natalie* / Fame 90: *Bowie, David* / King of wishful thinking: *Go West* / Tangled: *Wiedlin, Jane* / It must have been love: *Roxette* / Life in detail: *Palmer, Robert* / No explanation: *Cetera, Peter* / Real wild child (wild one): *Otcasek, Christopher* / Fallen: *Wood, Lauren* / Oh pretty woman: *Orbison, Roy* / Show me your soul: *Red Hot Chili Peppers.*
CD: Released Apr '90, on EMI-Manhattan by EMI Records. Catalogue no: **CDP 793 492 2**
Cass: Released Apr '90, on EMI-Manhattan by EMI Records. Catalogue no: **TCMTL 1052**
CD: Released Apr '90, on EMI-Manhattan by EMI Records. Catalogue no: **CDMTL 1052**
Album: Released Apr '90, on EMI-Manhattan by EMI Records. Catalogue no: **MTL 1052**
Cass: Released Apr '90, on EMI-Manhattan by EMI Records. Catalogue no: **793 492 4**
Album: Released Apr '90, on EMI-Manhattan by EMI Records. Catalogue no: **793 492 1**

Previn, Andre

SOUND STAGE (Under The Direction Of Johnny Williams)
Tracks: / You oughta be in pictures / Way you look tonight, The / Zip-a-dee-doo-dah / Swinging on a star / Only have eyes for you, I / Around the world / Someday my prince will come / There will never be another you / When you wish upon a star / Stella by starlight / Summertime / That old black magic.
Album: Released '64, on CBS by CBS Records & Distribution. Deleted '69. Catalogue no: **BPG 62394**

WEST SIDE STORY (Previn, Andre/Shelly Manne/Leroy Vinnegar)

Album: Released 2 May '89, on Contemporary by Ace Records. Catalogue no: **COP 046**

CD: Released Jan '89, on JVC/Fantasy Catalogue no: **VDJ 1626**

CD: Released 2 May '89, on Contemporary by Ace Records. Catalogue no: **CDCOP 046**

Price, Alan

O LUCKY MAN (See under O Lucky Man)

PAPERS (TV theme)

Tracks: / Papers / Frozen moments.

Note: Theme for LWT's Hot Metal

7" Single: Released Mar '86, on Trojan by Trojan Records. Deleted May '88. Catalogue no: **TRO 9083**

Prick Up Your Ears

PRICK UP YOUR EARS (Film soundtrack) (Various artists)

Tracks: / Prick up your ears: *Various artists* / Song for a joke: *Various artists* / Keep your socks on: *Various artists* / This one's on me: *Various artists* / Dancing hearts: *Various artists* / We're all friends here: *Various artists* / Boys will be boys: *Various artists* / Mr. Right: *Various artists* / Love in Islington: *Various artists* / By the beautiful sea: *Various artists*.

Note: The award winning British film about Joe Orton, with music by Stanley Myers (The Deerhunter) featuring John Harle and the Berliner Band.

Cass: Released May '87, on Silva Screen by Silva Screen Records. Catalogue no: **FILMC 014**

Album: Released May '87, on Silva Screen by Silva Screen Records. Deleted Apr '90. Catalogue no: **FILM 014**

Pride & The Passion

PRIDE & THE PASSION, THE (Film Soundtrack) (Various artists)

Note: George Antheil score for the Cary Grant/Sophia Loren/Frank Sinatra film.

Album: Released Jan '89, on Silva Screen by Silva Screen Records. Catalogue no: **AUSLP 1005**

Priest Of Love

PRIEST OF LOVE (film soundtrack) (Various artists)

Tracks: / Lawrence: *Various artists* / English hotel trio: *Various artists* / Variations: *Various artists* / Mabel's tango: *Various artists* / Frieda's theme (part 1): *Various artists* / Frieda's theme (part 2): *Various artists* / Italy: *Various artists* / Cornwall: *Various artists* / Fugue: *Various artists* / Lawrence's death: *Various artists* / Priest of love (finale): *Various artists* / Way we get it together, The: *Various artists*.

Album: Released Nov '85, on D-Sharp Catalogue no: **DSLP 1003**

CD: Released Nov '85, on D-Sharp Catalogue no: **DSCD 1003**

Album: Released Feb '82, on T. E. R. by That's Entertainment Records. Deleted May '89. Catalogue no: **TER 1014**

Prince

ARMS OF ORION, THE

Tracks: / Arms of Orion, The.

Note: From the film 'Batman'.

7" Single: Released Oct '89, on Warner Bros. by WEA Records. Catalogue no: **W 2757**

CD Single: Released Oct '89, on Warner Bros. by WEA Records. Catalogue no: **W 2757 CD**

Cassingle: Released Oct '89, on Warner Bros. by WEA Records. Catalogue no: **W 2757 C**

12" Single: Released Oct '89, on Warner Bros. by WEA Records. Catalogue no: **W 2757 T**

BATDANCE

Tracks: / Batdance / 200 balloons.

Note: From the film 'Batman'.

12" Single: Released Jun '89, on Warner Bros. by WEA Records. Catalogue no: **W 2924 T**

7" Single: Released Jun '89, on Warner Bros. by WEA Records. Catalogue no: **W 2924**

Cassingle: Released Jun '89, on Warner Bros. by WEA Records. Catalogue no: **W 2924 C**

12" Pic: Released Jul '89, on Warner Bros. by WEA Records. Catalogue no: **W 2924TP**

CD 3": Released Jul '89, on Warner Bros. by WEA Records. Catalogue no: **W 2924CDX**

CD Single: Released Jun '89, on Warner Bros. by WEA Records. Catalogue no: **W 2924CD**

BATMAN (Film soundtrack)

Tracks: / Future, The / Electric chair / Arms of orion / Partyman / Vicking waiting / Trust / Lemon crush / Scandalous / Batdance.

Note: Catalogue number 925 978 2 is a Limited Edition CD in tin.

CD: Released Jun '89, on Warner Bros. by WEA Records. Catalogue no: **925 936 2**

Special: Released '89, on Warner Bros. by WEA Records. Catalogue no: **925 978 2**

Album: Released Jun '89, on Warner Bros. by WEA Records. Catalogue no: **WX 281**

CD Pic: Released Jun '89, on Warner Bros. by WEA Records. Catalogue no: **925 489 2**

Cass: Released Jun '89, on Warner Bros. by WEA Records. Catalogue no: **WX 281C**

FUTURE, THE

Tracks: / Future, The / Electric chair / Batman (U.S. mix).

Note: From the film 'Batman'.

12" Single: Released Jun '90, on Warner Bros.(USA) by WEA Records. Catalogue no: **9215700**

GRAFFITI BRIDGE (Original Soundtrack)

Cass: Released Aug '90, on WEA by WEA Records. Catalogue no: **WX 361 C**

Album: Released Aug '90, on WEA by WEA Records. Catalogue no: **WX 361**

CD: Released Aug '90, on WEA by WEA Records. Catalogue no: **7599274932**

I WOULD DIE 4 U (Prince & The Revolution)

Tracks: / I would die 4 U.

Note: From the film 'Purple Rain'.

7" Single: Released Dec '84, on Warner Bros. by WEA Records. Deleted '87. Catalogue no: **W 9121**

12" Single: Released Dec '84, on Warner Bros. by WEA Records. Deleted '87. Catalogue no: **W 9121T**

LET'S GO CRAZY (Prince & The Revolution)

Tracks: / Let's go crazy / Take me with U.

Note: From the film 'Purple Rain'.

12" Single: Released Nov '87, on Warner Bros.(USA) by WEA Records. Catalogue no: **202460**

12" Single: Released Feb '85, on Warner Bros. by WEA Records.

Deleted Feb '88. Catalogue no: **W 2000T**

7" Single: Released Feb '85, on Warner Bros. by WEA Records. Deleted Feb '88. Catalogue no: **W 2000**

PARADE (Original soundtrack) (Prince & The Revolution)

Tracks: / Christopher Tracey's parade / New position / I wonder u / Under the cherry moon / Girls and boys / Life can be so nice / Venus de Milo / Mountains / Do u lie / Kiss / Anotherloverholenyohead / Sometimes it snows in April.

CD: Released Apr '86, on Warner Bros. by WEA Records. Catalogue no: **925395 2**

Album: Released Apr '86, on Warner Bros. by WEA Records. Catalogue no: **WX 39**

Cass: Released Apr '86, on Warner Bros. by WEA Records. Catalogue no: **WX 39C**

PARTY-MAN

Tracks: / Party-man / Feel U up.

Note: From the film 'Batman'.

7" Single: Released Aug '89, on Warner Bros. by WEA Records. Catalogue no: **W 2814**

CD Single: Released Aug '89, on Warner Bros. by WEA Records. Catalogue no: **W 2814CD**

Cassingle: Released Aug '89, on Warner Bros. by WEA Records. Catalogue no: **W 2814MC**

12" Single: Released Aug '89, on Warner Bros. by WEA Records. Catalogue no: **W 2814T**

PARTY-MAN (IMPORT)

Tracks: / Purple party mix / Party-man music mix / Party-man (video mix) / Feel u up (short stroke).

12" Single: Released '89, on Warner Bros. by WEA Records. Catalogue no: **9213700**

PURPLE RAIN (Film soundtrack) (Prince & The Revolution)

Tracks: / Let's go crazy / Take me with U / Beuatiful ones / Computer blue / Darling Nikki / When doves cry / I would die 4 U / Baby I'm a star / Purple rain.

CD: Released Aug '84, on Warner Bros. by WEA Records. Catalogue no: **925110 2**

Cass: Released Jul '84, on Warner Bros. by WEA Records.

Catalogue no: **925110 4**

Album: Released Jul '84, on Warner Bros. by WEA Records. Catalogue no: **925110 1**

PURPLE RAIN (SINGLE) (Prince & The Revolution)

Tracks: / Purple rain / God.

Note: (Cat. No. 9202670 - 12" Import single, full picture disc.

7" Single: Released Sep '84, on Warner Bros. by WEA Records. Deleted '87. Catalogue no: **W 9174**

12" Single: Released Sep '84, on Warner Bros. by WEA Records. Deleted Sep '87. Catalogue no: **W 9216T**

7" Single: Released Sep '84, on Warner Bros. by WEA Records. Deleted Sep '87. Catalogue no: **W 9216**

12" Single: Released Nov '87, on Warner Bros. by WEA Records. Catalogue no: **920267 0**

PURPLE RAIN (VIDEO) (Various artists)

Note: Running time: 107 mins. Semi-autobiographical Prince movie. Sexist, macho and at times offensive/ludicrous but the concert sequences are superb. Cert: 15.

VHS: Released Jun '88, on Warner Home Video by WEA Records. Catalogue no: **PES 61398**

THIEVES IN THE TEMPLE

Tracks: / Thieves in the temple.

Note: From the film 'Grafitti Bridge'.

Cassingle: Released Aug '90, on Warner Bros. by WEA Records. Catalogue no: **W 9751 C**

7" Single: Released Aug '90, on Warner Bros. by WEA Records. Catalogue no: **W 9751**

12" Pic: Released Aug '90, on Warner Bros. by WEA Records. Catalogue no: **W 9751 TP**

12" Single: Released Aug '90, on Warner Bros. by WEA Records. Catalogue no: **W 9751 T**

CD Single: Released Aug '90, on Warner Bros. by WEA Records. Catalogue no: **W 9751 CD**

UNDER THE CHERRY MOON (VIDEO)

Note: Cert: 15. Running time: 96 mins. Prince's black and white romantic drama.

VHS: Released Jun '88, on Warner Home Video by WEA Records. Catalogue no: **PES 11605**

WHEN DOVES CRY

Tracks: / When doves cry / 17 days / 1999 (Cassingle only.) / DMSR (Cassingle only.).

Note: From the film 'Purple Rain'.

7" Single: Released Jun '84, on Paisley Park (USA) by WEA Records. Deleted Jan '88. Catalogue no: **W 9286**

Cassingle: Released Jun '84, on Warner Bros. by WEA Records. Deleted '84. Catalogue no: **W 9286C**

12" Single: Released Jun '84, on Warner Bros. by WEA Records. Deleted '86. Catalogue no: **W 9286T**

Prince Of Darkness

PRINCE OF DARKNESS (Film soundtrack) (Various artists)

Cass: Released Feb '90, on T. E. R. by That's Entertainment Records. Catalogue no: **ZCTER 1157**

CD: Released Jan '89, on Varese Sarabande Records(USA) by Varese Sarabande Records (USA). Catalogue no: **VCD 47310**

Album: Released Feb '90, on T. E. R. by That's Entertainment Records. Catalogue no: **TER 1157**

Prince Of The City

PRINCE OF THE CITY (Film soundtrack) (Various artists)

Album: Released Dec '81, on T. E. R. by That's Entertainment Records. Catalogue no: **TER 1012**

Prince Regent

PRINCE REGENT (TV Soundtrack) (Various artists)

Album: Released Oct '79, on Decca by Decca International. Deleted '84. Catalogue no: **SKL 5313**

Cass: Released '80, on Decca by Decca International. Deleted '85. Catalogue no: **KSKC 5313**

Prince & The Pauper

PRINCE & THE PAUPER (Film soundtrack) (Various artists)

CD: Released Dec '89, on Varese Sarabande Records(USA) by Varese Sarabande Records (USA). Catalogue no: **VSD 5207**

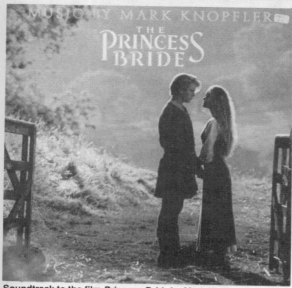

Soundtrack to the film *Princess Bride* by Mark Knopfler (Vertigo)

Princess Bride

PRINCESS BRIDE, THE (Film soundtrack) (Knopfler, Mark) (See panel above)
Tracks: / Once upon a time...storybook love / I will never love again / Florin dance / Morning ride / Friends' song, The / Cliffs of insanity, The / Sword fight, The / Guide my sword / Fire swamp and the rodents of unusual size, The / Revenge / Happy ending, A / Storybook love.
Note: Vocals on 'Storybook Love' by Willy De Ville (ex Mink DeVille). Remaining tracks are instrumental. Composed, arranged and produced by Mark Knopfler.
Album: Released '87, on Vertigo by Phonogram Ltd. Catalogue no: **VERH 53**
Cass: Released '87, on Vertigo by Phonogram Ltd. Catalogue no: **VERHC 53**
CD: Released '87, on Vertigo by Phonogram Ltd. Catalogue no: **832 864-2**
STORYBOOK LOVE (See under Knopfler, Mark)

Prior, Maddy

STOOKIE (TV theme)

Tracks: / Stookie / Stookie (version).

7" **Single:** Released Sep '85, on Making Waves by Celtic Music. Catalogue no: **SURF 108**

Prison

PRISON (Film soundtrack) (Various artists)
Note: Horror film score by Richard Band.
Album: Released Jan '89, on Varese Sarabande Records (USA) by Varese Sarabande Records (USA). Catalogue no: **STV 81361**

Prisoner

PRISONER, THE (Original TV soundtrack) (Various artists) (see panel below)
Tracks: / Arrival: *Various artists* / A,B & C: *Various artists* / Free for all: *Various artists* / General, The: *Various artists* / Many happy returns: *Various artists* / Dance of the dead: *Various artists* / Checkmate: *Various artists* / Hammer into anvil: *Various artists* / Girl who was death, The: *Various artists* / Once upon a time: *Various artists* / Closing credits: *Various artists*.
CD: Released Nov '89, on Silva Screen by Silva Screen Records. Catalogue no: **FILMCD 042**
Cass: Released Nov '89, on Silva

Soundtrack to the cult sixties TV series *The Prisoner* (Silva Screen)

Screen by Silva Screen Records. Catalogue no: **FILMC 042**

Album: Released Nov '89, on Silva Screen by Silva Screen Records. Catalogue no: **FILM 042**

PRISONER, THE (Various artists)

Tracks: / Arrival: *Various artists* / A,B & C: *Various artists* / Free for all: *Various artists* / General, The: *Various artists* / Many happy returns: *Various artists* / Dance of the dead: *Various artists* / Checkmate: *Various artists* / Hammer into anvil: *Various artists* / Girl who was death, The: *Various artists* / Once upon a time: *Various artists* / Closing credits: *Various artists*.

CD: Released '86, on Bam Caruso. Catalogue no: **WEBA 66**

Album: Released Jun '88, on Bam Caruso. Catalogue no: **KIRI 066**

Prisoner Cell Block H

PRISONER CELL BLOCK H (See under Kelly, Chris)

PRISONER CELL BLOCK H (See under Rae, Stacey)

Private Popsicle

PRIVATE POPSICLE (Film soundtrack) (Various artists)

Album: Released Jul '83, on CBS by CBS Records & Distribution. Deleted '85. Catalogue no: **CBS 70235**

Cass: Released Jul '83, on CBS by CBS Records & Distribution. Catalogue no: **40 70235**

Producers (film)

PRODUCERS, THE (Film soundtrack) (Various artists)

Cass: Released Mar '81, on RCA International by BMG Records (UK). Catalogue no: **INTK 5075**

Album: Released Mar '81, on RCA International by BMG Records (UK). Catalogue no: **INTS 5075**

Professionals

PROFESSIONALS (See under Johnson, Laurie)

PROFESSIONALS (See under Avengers)

Profundo Rosso

PROFUNDO ROSSO/ SUSPIRIA (Film soundtrack) (Various artists)

Note: Horror film score by Goblin.

Cass: Released Jan '89, on Cine-

vox by Cinevox Italy. Catalogue no: **CIAK 75005**

Album: Released Jan '89, on Cinevox by Cinevox Italy. Catalogue no: **CIA 5005**

Promised Land (Film)

PROMISED LAND (Film soundtrack) (Various artists)

CD: Released Feb '90, on Silva Screen by Silva Screen Records. Catalogue no: **2035.2**

Propaganda

DUEL

Tracks: / Duel.

Note: Theme from Channel 4's 'American Football'.

12" Single: Released Apr '85, on ZTT by ZTT Records. Catalogue no: **12 ZTAS 8**

7" Single: Released Apr '85, on ZTT by ZTT Records. Catalogue no: **ZTAS 8**

7" Single: Released May '85, on ZTT by ZTT Records. Catalogue no: **DUAL 1**

Cass: Released May '85, on ZTT by ZTT Records. Catalogue no: **CTIS 10**

Prospects

PROSPECTS (Film soundtrack) (Various artists)

Tracks: / Prospects: *Made in England* / Stay sharp: *Made in England* / Heist, The: *Glasman, Joseph* / Work hard, play hard: *Glasman, Joseph* / This is the news: *I Catch I* / My darlin': *I Catch I* / Who were you thinking of?: *Wynter, Valerie* / Today could be so good: *O'Connor, Hazel* / You gotta get up: *Chisholm, Colin* / Listen to me: *Y* / Keep on lookin': *US* / Just an illusion: *Imagination*.

Album: Released Mar '86, on Red Bus by Red Bus Records. Catalogue no: **RBLP 1011**

Cass: Released Mar '86, on Red Bus by Red Bus Records. Catalogue no: **ZCRB 1011**

Providence

PROVIDENCE (Film soundtrack) (Various artists)

Album: Released Feb '90, on DRG (USA) by DRG Records (USA). Catalogue no: **SL 9502**

Psychedelic Furs

PRETTY IN PINK

Tracks: / Pretty in pink / Love my way.

Note: From the film of the same

name.

7" Single: Released Jul '86, on CBS by CBS Records & Distribution. Deleted '87. Catalogue no: **A 7242**

12" Single: Released Jul '86, on CBS by CBS Records & Distribution. Deleted '87. Catalogue no: **TA 7242**

PRETTY IN PINK (Original version)

7" Single: Released Jun '81, on CBS by CBS Records & Distribution. Deleted '84. Catalogue no: **A 1327**

Psycho (Film)

PSYCHO (Film soundtrack) (Herrmann, Bernard)

Album: Released Feb '90, on SPI Milan (France) Catalogue no: **ACH 022**

CD: Released Feb '90, on SPI Milan (France) Catalogue no: **CDCH 022**

Cass: Released Feb '90, on SPI Milan (France) Catalogue no: **CCH 022**

PSYCHO II (Film soundtrack) (Various artists)

Cass: Released Oct '83, on MCA by MCA Records. Deleted Oct '88. Catalogue no: **MCAC 6119**

Album: Released Oct '83, on MCA by MCA Records. Deleted Oct '88. Catalogue no: **MCA 6119**

PSYCHO III (Film soundtrack) (Various artists)

Tracks: / Scream of love: *Various artists* / Maureen in the desert: *Various artists* / Dirty street: *Various artists* / Before and after shower: *Various artists* / Warm as a cry for help: *Various artists* / Mother?: *Various artists* / Sisters: *Various artists* / Catherine Mary: *Various artists* / Bad boys and body bags: *Various artists* / Revenge of the thankless child: *Various artists* / Electroshock waiting room: *Various artists*.

Cass: Released Oct '86, on MCA by MCA Records. Deleted Jan '88. Catalogue no: **IMCAC 6174**

Album: Released Oct '86, on MCA by MCA Records. Deleted Jan '88. Catalogue no: **IMCA 6174**

Public Enemy

FIGHT THE POWER

Tracks: / Fight the power / Fight the power (Radio edit) / Fight the power (12" version) (Only on 12" single.) / Fight the power (Slavor flav meets) (Only on 12 single (ZK 42878).).

Note: From the film 'Do the right thing'.

Cassingle: Released Jul '89, on Motown by BMG Records (UK). Deleted Feb '90. Catalogue no: **ZK 42877**

12" Single: Released Jun '89, on Motown by BMG Records (UK). Catalogue no: **ZT 42878**

7" Single: Released Jun '89, on Motown by BMG Records (UK). Deleted Feb '90. Catalogue no: **ZB 42877**

Pull Both Ends

PULL BOTH ENDS (Original London cast) (Various artists)
Tracks: / Prelude (Every morning): *Various artists* / What about people: *Various artists* / After all (we're women): *Various artists* / Tiny touch, A: *Various artists* / Particular woman, A: *Various artists* / Some kind of love: *Various artists* / Decisions: *Various artists* / Put a little smile: *Various artists* / Wallowers: *Various artists* / If you knew the way I feel: *Various artists* / Get the world to dance: *Various artists* / Here am I: *Various artists* / Strike: *Various artists* / Little leather book: *Various artists* / There's something about her: *Various artists* / Oh, Joe: *Various artists* / Can this be love?: *Various artists* / We're

ready: *Various artists* / Pullin' together: *Various artists*.
Note: Released May '89, on T. E. R. by That's Entertainment Records. Catalogue no: **TERS 1028**

Pump Boys & Dinettes

PUMP BOYS & DINETTES (Original Broadway cast) (Various artists)
Tracks: / Highway 57: *Various artists* / Taking it slow: *Various artists* / Serve yourself: *Various artists* / Menu song: *Various artists* / Best man, The: *Various artists* / Fishermans prayer: *Various artists* / Catfish: *Various artists* / Mamaw: *Various artists* / Be good or be gone: *Various artists* / Drinkin' shoes: *Various artists* / Pump boys: *Various artists* / Mona: *Various artists* / Night Dolly Parton was nearly mine, The: *Various artists* / Tips: *Various artists* / Sister: *Various artists* / Vacation: *Various artists* / No holds barred: *Various artists* / Farmer Tan: *Various artists* / Closing time: *Various artists*.
Cass: Released Nov '84, on CBS by CBS Records & Distribution. Catalogue no: **FMT 37790**
Album: Released Nov '84, on CBS by CBS Records & Distribution. Catalogue no: **FM 37790**

Punchline

PUNCHLINE (Film sound-

track) (Various artists)
Album: Released Mar '89, on A&M by A&M Records. Catalogue no: **SP 392 2**
Cass: Released Mar '89, on A&M by A&M Records. Catalogue no: **CS 392 2**

Purple Rain

PURPLE RAIN (See under Prince)

Purple Rose Of Cairo

PURPLE ROSE OF CAIRO (Film soundtrack) (Hyman, Dick)
Cass: Released '85, on Warner Bros. by WEA Records. Catalogue no: **252 225 4**
CD: Released '87, on Warner Bros. by WEA Records. Catalogue no: **252 225 2**
Album: Released '85, on Warner Bros. by WEA Records. Catalogue no: **252 225 1**

Pursuit

PURSUIT (Original Soundtrack) (Various artists)
Album: Released Nov '81, on Polydor by Polydor Ltd. Catalogue no: **POLS 1055**
Cass: Released Nov '81, on Polydor by Polydor Ltd. Catalogue no: **POLSC 1055**

The following information was taken from the Music Master database on September 25th, 1990.

Q The Winged Serpent

Q - THE WINGED SERPENT/ THE POWER (Original Soundtracks) (Various artists)
Note: Composed by Robert Ragland.
Album: Released Jan '89, on Cerebus (USA) Catalogue no: **C'BUS 206**

Q.B.VII

Q.B. VII (QUEENS BENCH NO.7) (Various artists)
Note: Re-issue of TV score by Jerry Goldsmith.
Album: Released Jan '89, on Warner Bros.(USA) by WEA Records. Catalogue no: **254890.1**

Quadrophenia

QUADROPHENIA (Film Soundtrack) (Various artists)
Tracks: / I am the sea: *Who* / Real me: *Who* / I'm one: *Who* / 5:15: *Who* / I've had enough: *Who* / Love reign o'er me: *Who* / Bell boy: *Who* / Helpless dancer: *Who* / Doctor Jimmy: *Who* / 4 faces: *Who* / Get out and stay out: *Who* / Joker James: *Who* / Punk and the godfather: *Who* / Louie Louie: *Kingsmen* / Zoot suit: *High Numbers* / Hi heel sneakers: *High Numbers* / Night train: *Brown, James* / Green onions: *Booker T & The MG's* / He's so fine: *Chiffons* / Rhythm of the rain: *Cascades* / Be my baby: *Ronettes* / Da doo ron ron: *Crystals.*
2 LP Set: Released Sept '79, on Polydor by Polydor Records. Catalogue no: **262 503 7**
Cass set: Released Sept '79, on Polydor, by Polydor Records. Catalogue no: **357 735 2**
CD Set: Released Sept '88, on Polydor by Polydor Records. Catalogue no; **813 074 2**

QUADROPHENIA (VIDEO) (Various artists)
Note: Cert: 18.
VHS: Released Sept '84, on Polygram Music Video. Deleted Mar '88. Catalogue no: **790 1862**

VHS: Released '88, on Channel 5 by Channel 5 Video. Catalogue no: **CFV 01412**

Queen

FLASH
Tracks: / Flash / Football fight.
Note: Title track from the film Flash Gordon.
7" Single: Released Dec '80, on EMI by EMI Records. Deleted '83. Catalogue no: **EMI 5126**

FLASH GORDON (1980 film soundtrack)
Tracks: / Flash's theme / In the space capsule (the love theme) / Ming's theme (in the court of Ming the merciless) / Ring, The (hypnotic seduction of Dale) / Football fight / In the death cell (love theme reprise) / Execution of Flash / Kiss, The (Aura resurrects Flash) / Arboria (planet of the tree men) / Escape from the swamp / Flash to the rescue / Vultan's theme (attack of the hawk men) / Battle theme / Wedding march, The / Marriage of Dale and Ming (and Flash approaching) / Crash dive on Mingo city / Flash's theme reprise (victory celebrations) / Hero, The.
CD: Released Jun '88, on EMI by EMI Records. Catalogue no: **CZ 100**
Cass: Released Dec '80, on EMI by EMI Records. Catalogue no: **TCEMC 3351**
Album: Released Dec '80, on EMI by EMI Records. Catalogue no: **ATAK 26**
CD: Released Jun '88, on EMI by EMI Records. Catalogue no: **CDP 746 214 2**

FRIENDS WILL BE FRIENDS
Tracks: / Friends will be friends / Seven seas of Rhye.
Note: From the film 'Highlander'.
12" Single: Released Jun '86, on EMI by EMI Records. Deleted Oct '87. Catalogue no: **12 QUEEN 8**
7" Pic: Released Jun '86, on EMI by EMI Records. Catalogue no: **QUEENP 8**

7" Single: Released Jun '86, on EMI by EMI Records. Deleted Oct '87. Catalogue no: **QUEEN 8**

KIND OF MAGIC, A
Tracks: / Princes of the universe / Kind of magic, A / One year of love / Pain is so close to pleasure / Friends will be friends / Who wants to live forever / Gimme the prize / Don't lose your head / One vision / Kind of a kind of magic, A (Available on CD only) / Friends will be friends... (Available on CD only) / Forever (Available on CD only).
Note: From the film 'Highlander'.
Album: Released Jun '86, on EMI by EMI Records. Catalogue no: **EU 3509**
Cass: Released Jun '86, on EMI by EMI Records. Catalogue no: **TCEU 3509**
CD: Released Jun '88, on EMI by EMI Records. Catalogue no: **CDP 746 267 2**

KIND OF MAGIC, A (CD SINGLE)
Tracks: / Kind of magic, A / Dozen red roses for my darling, A / One vision.
CD 3": Released Nov '88, on EMI by EMI Records. Catalogue no: **QUEENCD 12**
CD 3": Released Nov '88, on EMI by EMI Records. Catalogue no: **QUECD 12**

KIND OF MAGIC, A (SINGLE)
Tracks: / Kind of magic, A / Don't lose your head (instrumental) / Kind of magic, A (extended version) (12" only.) / Dozen red roses for my darling, A.
12" Single: Released Mar '86, on EMI by EMI Records. Deleted Jun '89. Catalogue no: **12 QUEEN 7**
7" Single: Released Mar '86, on EMI by EMI Records. Deleted Oct '89. Catalogue no: **QUEEN 7**
12" Pic: Released Mar '86, on EMI by EMI Records. Deleted '88. Catalogue no: **12 QUEENT 7**

KIND OF MAGIC, A (VIDEO

SINGLE)
Tracks: / Kind of magic, A / Who wants to live forever.
Note: 2 tracks. Running time: 9 mins.
VHS: Released Oct '86, on PMI by EMI Records. Catalogue no: **MVW 99 0059 2**
VHS: Released Nov '87, on PMI by EMI Records. Catalogue no: **MVP 99 1156 2**

WHO WANTS TO LIVE FOREVER

Tracks: / Who wants to live forever / Kind of magic, A / Killer queen / Forever (Track on 12" only).
Note: Taken from the film 'Highlander'.
12" Single: Released Sep '86, on EMI by EMI Records. Deleted Oct '87. Catalogue no: **12 QUEEN 9**
7" Single: Released Sep '86, on EMI by EMI Records. Deleted Oct '87. Catalogue no: **QUEEN 9**

Querelle

QUERELLE (Film soundtrack) (Raben, Peter)
Cass: Released '82, on DRG (USA) by DRG Records (USA). Catalogue no: **SLC 9509**
Album: Released '82, on DRG (USA) by DRG Records (USA). Catalogue no: **SL 9509**

Quest For Fire

QUEST FOR FIRE (Original Soundtrack) (Various artists)
CD: Released Jan '89, on Silva Screen by Silva Screen Records. Catalogue no: **CDFMC 1**
Album: Released Aug '82, on RCA by BMG Records (UK). Deleted Jan '88. Catalogue no: **RCALP 6034**

Qui C'est Ce Garcon

QUI C'EST CE GARCON (Film soundtrack) (Sarde, Philippe)
Note: Philippe Sarde score.
Album: Released Jan '89, on SPI Milan (France) Catalogue no: **A**

312
CD: Released Jan '89, on SPI Milan (France) Catalogue no: **CD 312**

Quicksilver

QUICKSILVER (Film soundtrack) (Various artists)
Tracks: / Quicksilver lightning: *Quicksilver* / Casual thing: *Quicksilver* / Nothing at all: *Quicksilver* / Shortcut to somewhere: *Quicksilver* / Love song from Quicksilver: *Quicksilver* / One sunny day/Duelling bikes from Quicksilver: *Quicksilver* / Motown song, The: *Quicksilver* / Suite streets from Quicksilver: *Quicksilver* / Quicksilver suite I-rebirth: *Quicksilver* / Quicksilver suite II-crash landing: *Quicksilver*.
Cass: Released Sep '86, on Atlantic by WEA Records. Deleted Aug '87. Catalogue no: **781 631-4**
Album: Released Sep '86, on Atlantic by WEA Records. Deleted Aug '87. Catalogue no: **781 631-1**

Quiet Earth

QUIET EARTH, THE (Film soundtrack) (Various artists)
Note: Film from New Zealand. Music by John Charles.
Album: Released Jan '89, on SPI Milan (France) Catalogue no: **ACH 028**
Cass: Released Jan '89, on SPI Milan (France) Catalogue no: **CCH 028**

Quiller Memorandum

QUILLER MEMORANDUM,THE (Film soundtrack) (Various artists)
CD: Released Feb '90, on Silva Screen by Silva Screen Records. Catalogue no: **VSD5218**

Quo Vadis

QUO VADIS (Film soundtrack) (Various artists)
Tracks: / Marcus and Lygia: *Various artists* / Fertility hymn: *Various artists* / Burning of Rome: *Various*

artists / Petronius' banquet, meditation and death: *Various artists* / Ave Caesar: *Various artists* / Chariot chase: *Various artists* / Assyrian dance: *Various artists* / Aftermath (Death of Peter): *Various artists* / Death of Poppaea, Nero's suicide: *Various artists* / Hail Galba: *Various artists* / Miracle and finale, The: *Various artists* / Epilogue: *Various artists*
Note: " Biblical and Roman-based movie spectaculars, and their appeal to cinemagoers, were well known to the Hollywood moguls long before 'Quo Vadis' hit the screens in 1951. However, this particular Metro-Goldwyn-Mayer extravaganza holds a special place in the history of talking pictures, for it marked a genuine conscious progression in the pairing of authentic music to the celluloid's subject matter. Academy Award nominated composer Miklos Rozsa spent many months in Rome preparing and researching for his task, and personally supervised the construction of all the ancient instruments which appeared in the film. At the time he decided that his handiwork must be recorded in London by The Royal Philharmonic Orchestra and BBC Chorus. Thus it was with justifiable pride that in 1977 Decca/London lured him back to faithfully re-create his score using the then current R.P.O. and Chorus, being now blessed with the technological advantages of our Phase 4 stereo sound to reveal fully Rozsa's masterpiece.
Cass: Released '86, on Decca by Decca International. Catalogue no: **421265 4**
CD: Released '86, on London Records by London Records Ltd. Deleted Jun '90. Catalogue no: **820 200-2**
Album: Released '86, on General Music (France) Catalogue no: **GM 30716**

R

The following information was taken from the Music Master database on September 25th, 1990.

Rabbitt, Eddie

EVERY WHICH WAY BUT LOOSE

Tracks: / Every which way but loose / Under the double eagle.
7" Single: Released Jan '79, on Elektra by Elektra Records (UK). Catalogue no: **K 12331**

Raben, Peter

QUERELLE (Film Soundtrack) (See under 'Querelle')

Radio Days

RADIO DAYS (Film soundtrack) (Various artists)

Tracks: / Frenesi: *Shaw, Artie & His Orchestra* / Donkey serenade, the: *Jones, Allan* / You and I: *Dorsey, Tommy Orchestra/Frank Sinatra* / Remember Pearl Harbour: *Kay, Sammy* / That old feeling: *Lombardo, Guy & His Royal Canadians* / White cliffs of Dover, The: *Miller, Glenn & His Orchestra* / I'm gettin' sentimental over you: *Dorsey, Tommy & His Orchestra* / American patrol: *Miller, Glenn & His Orchestra* / Take the 'A' train: *Ellington, Duke and his Orchestra* / One, two, three, kick blues: *Cugat, Xavier & His Waldorf-Astoria Orchestra* / Opus one: *Dorsey, Tommy & His Orchestra.*
Album: Released Jun '87, on RCA by BMG Records (UK). Catalogue no: **PL 83017**
Cass: Released Jun '87, on RCA by BMG Records (UK). Catalogue no: **PK 83017**
CD: Released Jun '87, on RCA by BMG Records (UK). Catalogue no: **PD 83017**

Radioactive

RADIO ACTIVE (Various artists)

Tracks: / Police file and shipping forecast: *Various artists* / Commercial break: *Various artists* / Radiothon: *Various artists* / S.O.S. message: *Various artists* /

Thought for the day: *Various artists* / Results service: *Various artists.*
Album: Released May '83, on BBC by BBC Records. Deleted Apr '89. Catalogue no: **REH 471**
Cass: Released May '83, on BBC by BBC Records. Deleted Apr '89. Catalogue no: **ZCR 471**

Rae, Stacey

PRISONER CELL BLOCK-H (THEME FROM)

Tracks: / Prisoner cell block H (theme from) / Goodnews (inst).
7" Single: Released Nov '87, on Humber by Humber Records. Catalogue no: **CELL-1**

Ragged Child

RAGGED CHILD, THE (Original London cast) (Various artists)

Cass: Released '89, on First Night by First Night Records. Catalogue no: **CASTC 12**
Album: Released '89, on First Night by First Night Records. Catalogue no: **CAST 12**

Raggedy Rawney

RAGGEDY RAWNEY (Film soundtrack) (Various artists)

Tracks: / Tribe, The: *Various artists* / You should see Nellie pass water: *Various artists* / Caravans: *Various artists* / Horse race, The: *Various artists* / Farmyard: *Various artists* / Rolling home: *Various artists* / Jessie and Tom: *Various artists* / Daisy chain: *Various artists* / Wedding dress: *Various artists* / Bullroarer: *Various artists* / Band of lace: *Various artists* / Peacock polka (Darky's polka): *Various artists* / Simon drowned: *Various artists* / Funeral lament: *Various artists* / Prayer: *Various artists* / Officer, The: *Various artists* / Children, The: *Various artists* / Raggedy rawney, The: *Various artists.*
Note: The film stars Bob Hoskins & Dexter Fletcher with a host of British character actors in supporting roles including Ian Dury. The ethnic based electronic score is by

Michael Kamen (Die Hard, Lethal Weapon, Highlander etc) with songs by John Tams of the Albion Band and featuring vocals from Maggie Bell.
CD: Released Sep '88, on Silva Screen by Silva Screen Records. Catalogue no: **FILMCD 033**
Cass: Released Sep '88, on Silva Screen by Silva Screen Records. Catalogue no: **FILMC 033**
Album: Released Sep '88, on Silva Screen by Silva Screen Records. Catalogue no: **FILM 033**

Raging Moon

RAGING MOON (Film Soundtrack) (Various artists)

Tracks: / Time for winning: *Various artists* / Together: *Various artists* / Disoriented: *Various artists* / Tenderness: *Various artists* / Alone: *Various artists* / Music to wake up the whole house to: *Various artists* / Loving: *Various artists* / Many loving things: *Various artists* / Playing: *Various artists* / Rage: *Various artists* / Apart: *Various artists* / Touching: *Various artists* / Remembering: *Various artists.*
Album: Released '73, on Columbia by EMI Records. Deleted '78. Catalogue no: **SCX 6447**

Ragtime

RAGTIME (Film soundtrack) (Various artists)

Note: Composed by Randy Newman..
Album: Released Jan '89, on Elektra (Import) by Elektra/Asylum/Nonesuch Records (USA). Catalogue no: **K 52342 1**
Cass: Released Jan '89, on Elektra (Import) by Elektra/Asylum/Nonesuch Records (USA). Catalogue no: **K 52342 4**

Raiders of...

RAIDERS OF THE LOST ARK (Film Soundtrack) (Various artists)

Tracks: / Raiders of the lost ark: *Various artists* / Flight from Peru:

Various artists / Map room, The: *Various artists* / Dawn: *Various artists* / Basket game, The: *Various artists* / Well of souls, The: *Various artists* / Desert chase: *Various artists* / Marion's theme: *Various artists* / Miracle of the ark, The: *Various artists* / Raiders march, The: *Various artists* .

Album: Released Aug '81, on CBS by CBS Records & Distribution. Catalogue no: **CBS 70205**

Cass: Released Aug '81, on CBS by CBS Records & Distribution. Catalogue no: **40 70205**

Cass: Released Jan '89, on Silva Screen by Silva Screen Records. Catalogue no: **821 583.4**

CD: Released Aug '84, on Polydor by Polydor Ltd. Deleted Jul '88. Catalogue no: **821 583-2**

Album: Released Aug '84, on Polydor by Polydor Ltd. Deleted '89. Catalogue no: **POLD 5146**

Album: Released Jan '89, on Silva Screen by Silva Screen Records. Deleted Mar '90. Catalogue no: **821 583.1**

Railway Children

RAILWAY CHILDREN, THE (Film soundtrack) (Various artists)

Tracks: / Overture: *Various artists* / Roberta's theme: *Various artists* / Mother's theme: *Various artists* / Robbers: *Various artists* / More than ever now: *Various artists* / Paper chase: *Various artists* / Kindly old gentleman: *Various artists* / Perks must be about it: *Various artists* / Birthday waltz: *Various artists* / Finale: *Various artists*.

Album: Released '70, on EMI by EMI Records. Deleted '77. Catalogue no: **SCX 6446**

Rain Man

RAIN MAN (Film soundtrack) (Various artists)

Tracks: / Iko Iko: *Belle Stars* / Scatterlings of Africa: *Clegg, Johnny & Savuka* / Dry bones: *Delta Rhythm Boys* / At last: *James, Etta* / Lonely Avenue: *Gillan, Ian & Roger Glover* / Nathan Jones: *Bananarama* / Leaving Wallbrook: *Zimmer, Hans* / Las Vegas (end credits): *Zimmer, Hans* / Stardust: *Wasserman, Rob/Aaron Neville* / Beyond the blue horizon: *Christie, Lou* / On the road: *Various artists*.

CD: Released Mar '89, on Capitol by EMI Records. Catalogue no: **CDEST 2091**

CD: Released Mar '89, on Capitol by EMI Records. Catalogue no: **CDP 791 866 2**

Album: Released Mar '89, on Capitol by EMI Records. Catalogue no: **791866 1**

Cass: Released Mar '89, on Capitol by EMI Records. Catalogue no: **TCEST 2091**

Album: Released Mar '89, on Capitol by EMI Records. Catalogue no: **EST 2091**

Cass: Released Mar '89, on Capitol by EMI Records. Catalogue no: **791886 4**

Rainbow Brite

RAINBOW BRITE (Various artists)

Tracks: / Rainbow Brite saves the day: *Various artists* / Rainbow Brite and the colour kids: *Various artists* / Happy birthday Twink: *Various artists* / Rainbow Brite and the blue lake: *Various artists*.

Album: Released Aug '85, on BBC by BBC Records. Deleted 31 Aug '88. Catalogue no: **REC 566**

Cass: Released Aug '85, on BBC by BBC Records. Deleted 31 Aug '88. Catalogue no: **ZCM 566**

Rainbow

RAINBOW, THE (Film soundtrack) (Davis, Carl)

Tracks: / Prelude and opening titles / Walking home / Swingboats, The / Ursula and Winifred / Seduction: The lettuce patch / Exam results / School assembly / Mr. Harby / Wedding, The / Moonlight lovers / Military two-step / Waterfull, The / Cottage Idyll / Pursuit through the forest / Ursula's dream / Rainbow, The.

Album: Released Nov '89, on Silva Screen by Silva Screen Records. Catalogue no: **FILM 040**

CD: Released Nov '89, on Silva Screen by Silva Screen Records. Catalogue no: **FILMCD 040**

Cass: Released Nov '89, on Silva Screen by Silva Screen Records. Catalogue no: **FILMC 040**

Rainbow Rhymes

RAINBOW RHYMES (TV soundtrack) (TV Cast)

Tracks: / Ride a cock horse / One two three four five once I caught a fish alive / Twinkle twinkle little star / Little Tommy Tucker / There was a crooked man / Mary, Mary, quite contrary / Cock-a-doodle-doo / Girls and boys come out to play / See-saw, Margery Daw / Little Jack Horner / Grand old Duke of York, The / Pray open your umbrella / Five little ducks / Dingle-dangle scarecrow / Here we go round the Mulberry bush / Milkman's song, The / Honey bee song, The / Doggy song, The.

Album: Released Oct '84, on Red Bus by Red Bus Records. Catalogue no: **RBBLP 7300**

Cass: Released Oct '84, on Red Bus by Red Bus Records. Catalogue no: **ZCRBB 7300**

Raintree County

RAINTREE COUNTY (Film soundtrack) (Various artists)

CD Set: Released Jan '90, on Silva Screen by Silva Screen Records. Catalogue no: **2PRCD 1781**

Raising Arizona

RAISING ARIZONA/BLOOD SIMPLE (Film soundtracks)

Album: Released Aug '87, on T. E. R. by That's Entertainment Records. Catalogue no: **TER 1140**

Cass: Released Aug '87, on T. E. R. by That's Entertainment Records. Deleted Mar '90. Catalogue no: **ZCTER 1140**

Rambo

RAMBO (Film soundtrack) (Various artists)

Cass: Released Sep '85, on T. E. R. by That's Entertainment Records. Catalogue no: **ZCTER 1104**

CD: Released Jan '89, on T. E. R. by That's Entertainment Records. Catalogue no: **VCD 47234**

Album: Released Sep '85, on T. E. R. by That's Entertainment Records. Catalogue no: **TER 1104**

RAMBO II: FIRST BLOOD (Film soundtrack) (Various artists)

Tracks: / Main title: *Various artists* / Preparation: *Various artists* / Jump, The: *Various artists* / Snake, The: *Various artists* / Stories: *Various artists* / Cage, The: *Various artists* / Betrayed: *Various artists* / Peace in our life: *Various artists* / Escape from torture: *Various artists* / Ambush: *Various artists* / Revenge: *Various artists* / Bowed down: *Various artists* / Pilot over: *Various artists* /

Home flight: *Various artists* / Day by day: *Various artists*.
CD: Released Feb '90, on Varese Sarabande Records(USA) by Varese Sarabande Records (USA). Catalogue no: **VSD 47234**
Album: Released '85, on T. E. R. by That's Entertainment Records. Catalogue no: **TER 1104**
Cass: Released '85, on T. E. R. by That's Entertainment Records. Catalogue no: **ZCTER 1104**

RAMBO III (Original soundtrack) (Various artists)
Tracks: / It's our destiny: *Medley, Bill* / Preparations: *Various artists* / Afghanistan: *Various artists* / Game, The: *Various artists* / Another time: *Various artists* / He ain't heavy, he's my brother: *Medley, Bill* / Aftermath: *Various artists* / Questions: *Various artists* / Bridge, The: *Moroder, Giorgio & Joe Pizulo* / Final battle: *Various artists*.
CD: Released Jan '90, on Intrada (USA) Catalogue no: **RVF 6006**
CD: Released 22 Aug '88, on Polydor by Polydor Ltd. Catalogue no: **834 929-2**
Album: Released 22 Aug '88, on Polydor by Polydor Ltd. Deleted Dec '89. Catalogue no: **POLD 5227**
Cass: Released 22 Aug '88, on Polydor by Polydor Ltd. Catalogue no: **POLDC 5227**

Ramones

PET SEMETARY
Note: Used as the title track to the Steven King film 'Pet semetary'
Tracks: / Pet semetary / All screwed up / Zero zero UFO (Available on 12" format only.).
7" Single: Released Nov '89, on Chrysalis by Chrysalis Records. Deleted Jul '90. Catalogue no: **CHS 3423**
12" Single: Released Nov '89, on Chrysalis by Chrysalis Records. Deleted Jul '90. Catalogue no: **CHS 123423**

ROCK 'N' ROLL HIGH SCHOOL
Note: Title track from the film '*Rock 'n' roll high school*'. (Film contains cameo appearances from the Ramones)
Tracks: / Rock 'n' roll high school / Blitzkrieg bop / Sheena is a punk rocker.
7" Single: Released Sep '79, on Sire by Sire Records. Deleted '82. Catalogue no: **SIR 4021**

Rampage

RAMPAGE (Film Soundtrack) (See under Morricone, Ennio)

Randell, Denny

E.T. MEDLEY THEME
Tracks: / E.T. medley theme / Over the moon.
7" Single: Released Nov '82, on Elektra by Elektra Records (UK). Deleted Nov '85. Catalogue no: **EET 1**
12" Single: Released Nov '82, on Elektra by Elektra Records (UK). Deleted Nov '85. Catalogue no: **EET 1T**

Rappin'

RAPPIN' (Film soundtrack) (Various artists)
Tracks: / Rappin': *Various artists* / Snack attack: *Various artists* / Fight rap, The: *Various artists* / Neighbourhood walk: *Various artists* / Itchin' for a scratch: *Various artists* / Flame in the fire: *Various artists* / Call me: *Various artists* / If you want to: *Various artists* / Golly gee: *Various artists* / First love never dies: *Various artists*.
Album: Released Oct '85, on Atlantic by WEA Records. Deleted Aug '87. Catalogue no: **781 252-1**
Cass: Released Oct '85, on Atlantic by WEA Records. Catalogue no: **781 252-4**

Rashomon

RASHOMON/7 SAMURAI (Original Soundtracks) (Various artists)
CD: Released Jan '89, on Silva Screen by Silva Screen Records. Catalogue no: **VCD 47254**

Rattle & Hum

RATTLE AND HUM (See under U2)

RATTLE & HUM (Video) (See under U2)

Raw Deal

RAW DEAL (Film soundtrack) (Various artists)
Note: Music from the Arnold Schwarzenegger film.
Album: Released Jan '89, on Varese Sarabande Records(USA) by Varese Sarabande Records (USA). Catalogue no: **STV 81286**
Cass: Released Jan '89, on Varese Sarabande Records(USA) by Varese Sarabande Records

(USA). Catalogue no: **CTV 81286**

Rawhide

RAWHIDE (TV Theme) (See under Laine, Frankie)

Rayland, Rober

TEN TO MIDNIGHT (Film Soundtrack) (See under Ten to midnight)

Razors Edge

RAZORS EDGE (Film soundtrack) (Various artists)
Note: Composed by Jack Nitzche.
Album: Released Jan '89, on Southern Cross (USA) by Fith Continent Music Group (USA). Catalogue no: **SCRS 1009**

Really Rosie

REALLY ROSIE (Broadway Cast) (Various artists)
Note: Rosie, the 10-year-old leading lady of Maurice Sendak's first theatrical venture, has the magical gift of imagination. To enliven a summer afternoon in a drab city tenement she enlists the help of her willing slave companions to "tell the story of my life": this introduces many old favourites from Sendak's Nutshell Library Tales. Music is by Carole King.
Cass: Released '82, on Caedmon (USA) by Caedmon Records (USA). Catalogue no: **CDL 5368**

Re-Animator

RE-ANIMATOR, THE (Film soundtrack) (Various artists)
Note: Horror score by Richard Band.
Cass: Released Jan '89, on Varese Sarabande Records(USA) by Varese Sarabande Records (USA). Catalogue no: **CTV 81261**
Album: Released Jan '89, on Varese Sarabande Records(USA) by Varese Sarabande Records (USA). Catalogue no: **STV 81261**

Re-Joyce

RE-JOYCE (Stage show) (See under Lipman, Maureen)

Record Breakers

RECORD BREAKERS (TV Theme) (See under Castle, Roy)

Record City

RECORD CITY (Music From The Original Soundtrack)

(Various artists)
Album: Released Mar '78, on Polydor by Polydor Ltd. Catalogue no: **2391 299**

Red Dawn

RED DAWN (Film soundtrack) (Various artists)
Tracks: / Invasion, The: *Various artists* / Drive-in, The: *Various artists* / Let it turn: *Various artists* / Woverines: *Various artists* / Flowers: *Various artists* / Eulogy, The: *Various artists* / Robert's end: *Various artists* / Death and freedom: *Various artists* / End title: *Various artists*.
Note: The Basil Poledouris score for the film directed by John Milius.
CD: Released Jan '89, on Intrada (USA) Catalogue no: **RVF 6001 D**
Album: Released Jan '89, on Intrada (USA) Catalogue no: **RVF 6001**

Red Heat

RED HEAT (Film soundtrack) (Horner, James)
Tracks: / Main title / Russian streets / Cleanhead bust / Victor escapes / Tailing kat / Hospital chase / Hotel / Bus station / End credits.
Note: Music from the film 'Red Heat' starring Arnold Schwarzenegger and James Belushi. Score by James Horner.
CD: Released Jan '89, on Silva Screen by Silva Screen Records. Catalogue no: **790989.2**
CD: Released Nov '88, on Virgin by Virgin Records. Catalogue no: **CDV 2558**
Cass: Released Jan '89, on Virgin by Virgin Records. Deleted Jun '90. Catalogue no: **TCV 2558**
Album: Released Jan '89, on Silva Screen by Silva Screen Records. Catalogue no: **790989.1**
Album: Released Jan '89, on Virgin by Virgin Records. Deleted May '90. Catalogue no: **V 2558**
Cass: Released Jan '89, on Silva Screen by Silva Screen Records. Catalogue no: **790989.4**

Red Pony

RED PONY, THE (Film soundtrack) (Various artists)
Note: Complete original score by Aaron Copland.
Cass: Released Jan '89, on Varese Sarabande Records(USA) by Varese Sarabande Records

(USA). Catalogue no: **CTV 81259**
Album: Released Jan '89, on Varese Sarabande Records(USA) by Varese Sarabande Records (USA). Catalogue no: **STV 81259**

Red Scorpion

RED SCORPION (Film soundtrack) (Various artists)
CD: Released Feb '90, on Varese Sarabande Records(USA) by Varese Sarabande Records (USA). Catalogue no: **VSD 5230**
Album: Released Sep '89, on Varese Sarabande Records(USA) by Varese Sarabande Records (USA). Catalogue no: **VS 5230**
Cass: Released Sep '89, on Varese Sarabande Records(USA) by Varese Sarabande Records (USA). Catalogue no: **VSC 5230**

Red Sonja

RED SONJA (Film soundtrack) (Various artists)
Note: Arnold Schwarzenegger and Brigette Nielson film. Score by Ennio Morricone.
Cass: Released Jan '89, on Varese Sarabande Records(USA) by Varese Sarabande Records (USA). Catalogue no: **CTV 81248**
Album: Released Jan '89, on

Varese Sarabande Records(USA) by Varese Sarabande Records (USA). Catalogue no: **STV 81248**
Album: Released Jan '86, on JMP (W.Germany) Catalogue no: **JMP 4011**

Red Tent

RED TENT (Film Soundtrack) (Various artists)
Tracks: / Love theme: *Various artists* / Do dreams go on: *Various artists* / Death at the Pole: *Various artists* / Love like the snow: *Various artists* / Message from Rome: *Various artists* / They're alive: *Various artists* / Farewell: *Various artists* / Others, who will follow us: *Various artists*.
Album: Released '73, on Paramount Deleted '78. Catalogue no: **SPFL 275**
Album: Released Jan '89, on Silva Screen by Silva Screen Records. Catalogue no: **255064.1**

Reds

REDS (Theme from) (See under Laws, Herbert)

Reeves, Martha

NOWHERE TO RUN (Reeves, Martha & The Vandellas)

Theme from *Reilly - Ace of Spies* (Red Bus)

Tracks: / Nowhere to run / Forget me not.
Note: From the films 'Platoon' and 'Good Morning Vietnam'.
7" Single: Released Apr '65, on Tamla Motown by Motown Records (UK). Deleted '68. Catalogue no: **TMG 502**
7" Single: Released Apr '69, on Tamla Motown by Motown Records (UK). Deleted '72. Catalogue no: **TMG 694**
7" Single: Released Apr '88, on Motown by BMG Records (UK). Catalogue no: **ZB 41921**

Reform Schoolgirls
REFORM SCHOOLGIRLS (Film soundtrack) (O'Williams, Wendy)
Album: Released '85, on Zebra (1) by Zebra Records (1). Catalogue no: **ZEB 7**

Reilly - Ace Of Spies
REILLY - ACE OF THEMES (Various artists) (See panel on previous page)
Tracks: / Reilly: *Various artists* / To serve them all my days: *Various artists* / Bouquet of barbed wire: *Various artists* / Onedin line: *Various artists* / Flame trees of Thika: *Various artists* / O Agatha: *Various artists* / Jennie: *Various artists* / Skorpion: *Various artists* / On the line: *Various artists* / Cavatina: *Various artists* / Walk on: *Various artists* / Who pays the ferryman: *Various artists* / Upstairs downstairs: *Various artists* / Black beauty: *Various artists* / Tales of the unexpected: *Various artists* / Winds of war: *Various artists* / Hollywood: *Various artists* / Chi mai: *Various artists*.
Cass: Released Nov '83, on Red Bus by Red Bus Records. Deleted '88. Catalogue no: **BUSK 1004**
Album: Released Nov '83, on Red Bus by Red Bus Records. Deleted '88. Catalogue no: **BUSLP 1004**

REILLY ACE OF SPIES (Theme from)
Tracks: / Reilly - ace of spies (theme): Olympic Orchestra / Canon in D: Olympic Orchestra
7" Single: Released Sept '83, on Red Bus by Red Bus Records. Catalogue no: **RBUS 82**

Rent-A-Cop
RENT-A-COP (Film soundtrack) (Various artists)
Tracks: / Rent a cop: *Various artists* / Bust, The: *Various artists* / Lonely cop: *Various artists* / Russian roulette: *Various artists* / Station, The: *Various artists* / Worth a lot: *Various artists* / Lights out: *Various artists* / This is the Guy: *Various artists* / They need me: *Various artists* / Room, The: *Various artists* / Lake forest: *Various artists* / Jump: *Various artists*.
Album: Released 30 Apr '88, on Silva Screen by Silva Screen Records. Catalogue no: **FILM 025**
CD: Released 30 Apr '88, on Silva Screen by Silva Screen Records. Catalogue no: **FILMCD 025**

Renzetti, Joe
POLTERGEIST 3 (Film Soundtrack) (See under Poltergeist 3)

Repo Man
REPO MAN (Film soundtrack) (Various artists)
Cass: Released Jun '84, on MCA by MCA Records. Deleted Sep '90. Catalogue no: **MCFC 3223**
Album: Released Jun '84, on MCA by MCA Records. Deleted Jul '90. Catalogue no: **MCF 3223**

Rescuers
RESCUERS (Film soundtrack) (Various artists) (See panel below)
Album: Released '88, on Disney-

land by Disneyland-Vista Records (USA). Catalogue no: **WD 023**
Cass: on Disneyland by Disneyland-Vista Records (USA). Catalogue no: **WDC 023**
Cass: Released Dec '82, on Disneyland by Disneyland-Vista Records (USA). Catalogue no: **D 14DC**

RESCUERS (SINGLE) (Various artists)
7" EP: Released Nov '88, on Disneyland by Disneyland-Vista Records (USA). Catalogue no: **D 367**

Residents
CENSUS TAKER (Film Soundtrack) (See under Census Taker)

Return Of...
RETURN OF MARTIN GUERRE/JULIA (Original Soundtrack) (Various artists)
Note: 2 scores by Michel Portal and Georges Delerue.
Cass: Released '88, on DRG (USA) by DRG Records (USA). Catalogue no: **SLC 9514**
Album: Released '88, on DRG (USA) by DRG Records (USA). Catalogue no: **SL 9514**

RETURN OF THE LIVING DEAD (Film soundtrack) (Various artists)
Tracks: / Surfin' dead: *Cramps* / Partytime (zombie version): *45 Grave* / Nothing for you: *T.S.O.L.* / Eyes without a face: *Flesh Eaters* / Burn the flames: *Erickson, Roky* / Dead beat dance: *Damned* / Take

A scene from Walt Disney's animated classic - *The Rescuers*.

Original Cast Recording of *Return to the Forbidden Planet*

a walk: *Tall Boys* / Love under will: *Jet Black Berries* / Tonight (we'll make love until we die): *SSQ* / Trash's theme: *SSQ*.
CD: Released Jun '88, on Big Beat by Ace Records. Catalogue no: **CDWIK 38**
Cass: Released Jun '85, on Big Beat by Ace Records. Catalogue no: **WIKC 38**
Album: Released Jul '85, on New Rose (1) by New Rose Records. Catalogue no: **ROSE 66**
Album: Released Jun '85, on Big Beat by Ace Records. Catalogue no: **WIK 38**
LP Pic: Released Jul '85, on New Rose (1) by New Rose Records. Catalogue no: **ROSE 66P**

RETURN OF THE LIVING DEAD (PART 2) (Various artists)
Tracks: / Space hopper: *Cope, Julian* / Space is the man: *Anthrax* / Monster mash: *Big O* / AD 1: *Anthrax* / Dead return: *Robinson, J Peter* / High priest of love: *Mindwarp, Zodiac* / Big band boy: *Mantronix* / Alone in the night: *Leatherwolf* / Flesh to flesh: *Lamont*.
CD: Released 13 Feb '89, on Island by Island Records. Catalogue no: **CIDST 17**

Cass: Released 13 Feb '89, on Island by Island Records. Catalogue no: **ICT 17**
Album: Released 13 Feb '89, on Island by Island Records. Catalogue no: **ISTA 17**

RETURN OF THE MUSKETEERS (Original soundtrack) (Various artists)
Album: Released Feb '90, on Silva Screen by Silva Screen Records. Catalogue no: **A383**
CD: Released Feb '90, on SPI Milan (France) Catalogue no: **CDCH 383**

RETURN OF THE PINK PANTHER (Film Soundtrack) (See under Mancini, Henry)

Return Of The Jedi

RETURN OF THE JEDI (The Ewoks Join The Fight) (Various artists)
Album: Released May '83, on RSO by Polydor Ltd. Catalogue no: **RSD 5023**
CD: Released May '83, on RSO by Polydor Ltd. Deleted Mar '88. Catalogue no: **811 767-2**
Album: Released May '83, on Polydor by Polydor Ltd. Catalogue no: **POLD 5105**

Cass: Released May '83, on Polydor by Polydor Ltd. Catalogue no: **POLDC 5105**

Return Of Superfly

RETURN OF SUPERFLY (Film soundtrack) (Various artists)
Tracks: / Superfly 1990: *Mayfield, Curtis & Ice-T* / Eazy Street: *Eazy-E* / Cheeba cheeba: *Tone Loc* / Funky in the joint: *Mellow Man Ace* / On the real tip: *Def Jef* / Showdown: *Mayfield, Curtis* / Forbidden: *Mayfield, Curtis* / Superfly 1990 (Hip hop instrumental): *Mayfield, Curtis* / For the love of you: *Mayfield, Curtis* / Take you home: *King Tee* / There's a riot jumpin' off: *King Tee* / Somethin' like dis: *C.P.O.*.
Cass: Released Aug '90, on Capitol by EMI Records. Catalogue no: **TCEST 2129**
Cass: Released Aug '90, on Capitol by EMI Records. Catalogue no: **794 244 4**
Album: Released Aug '90, on Capitol by EMI Records. Catalogue no: **EST 2129**
CD: Released Aug '90, on Capitol by EMI Records. Catalogue no: **CDP 794 244 2**
CD: Released Aug '90, on Capitol by EMI Records. Catalogue no: **CDEST 2129**
Album: Released Aug '90, on Capitol by EMI Records. Catalogue no: **794 244 1**

Return Of The Soldier

RETURN OF THE SOLDIER (Film soundtrack) (Various artists)
Tracks: / Main title (dream, The): *Various artists* / Chris and Jenny: *Various artists* / Old house, The: *Various artists* / Chris and Margaret: *Various artists* / Memories: *Various artists* / Hallucinations: *Various artists* / Anyone home: *Various artists* / After the ball: *Various artists* / Chris at the window: *Various artists* / Return to Monkey Island: *Various artists* / Chris, Jenny and Margaret: *Various artists* / Piano interlude: *Various artists* / Return of the soldier, The: *Various artists* / End titles (Love theme): *Various artists*.
Album: Released Apr '83, on T. E. R. by That's Entertainment Records. Catalogue no: **TER 1036**

Return To Oz

RETURN TO OZ (Film soundtrack) (Shire, David)
Album: Released '85, on Sonic Atmospheres (USA) by Silva Screen Records. Catalogue no: **SONIC 113**

Return To Snowy ...

RETURN TO SNOWY RIVER (Film soundtrack) (Various artists)
CD: Released Jan '89, on Varese Sarabande Records(USA) by Varese Sarabande Records (USA). Catalogue no: **VCD 70451**
Album: Released '89, on Varese Sarabande Records(USA) by Varese Sarabande Records (USA). Catalogue no: **704 510**
Cass: Released '89, on Varese Sarabande Records(USA) by Varese Sarabande Records (USA). Catalogue no: **704 510 C**

Return To The...

RETURN TO THE FORBIDDEN PLANET (Original Cast Recording) (Various artists) See panel on previous page)
Tracks: / Wipeout / It's a mans world Great balls of fire / Don't let me be misunderstood / Good vibrations / Ain't gonna wash for a week / I'm gonna change the world / Teenager in love / She's not there / All shook up / Gloria / Who's sorry now / Tell her / Robot man / Shake rattle and roll / Go now / Only the lonely / Young ones, The / We've gotta get out of this place / wipeout (reprise) / Hey Mr Spaceman / Monster mash / Great balls of fire (reprise).
Cass: Released Aug '90, on Virgin by Virgin Records. Catalogue no: **CV 2631**
CD: Released Aug '90, on Virgin by Virgin Records. Catalogue no: **CDV2631**
Album: Released Aug '90, on Virgin by Virgin Records. Catalogue no: **V2631**

Revenge

REVENGE (Film soundtrack) (Various artists)
Tracks: / Love theme / Friendship Miryea / Betrayal / Jeep ride / On the beach / Illicit love / Tibey's revenge / Whorehouse and healing / Dead Texan / Confrontation / Miryea's death
Note: It is dangerous and foolhardy, but Cochran can't help himself. He

has run off with his friend Tiburon's wife betraying the trust and hospitality of a ruthless man. Tiburon will demand satisfaction, but revenge begets revenge as two men and the woman they both love tragically discover. Kevin Costner, Anthony Quinn and Madeleine Stowe star in *Revenge*, a Columbia Pictures presentation in association with New World Entertainment of a Rastar Production. The adventure drama which also stars Sally Kirkland was directed by Tony Scott (Top Gun, Beverley Hills Cop II) from a screenplay by Jim Harrison and Jeffrey Fiskin. Hunt Lowry and Stanley Rubin are the producers, Costner is the executive producer and Jim Wilson is the associate producer.

Costner plays Cochran, a Vietnam veteran and recently retired pilot who is invited to Mexico by his long time friend Tiburon (Anthony Quinn), a wealthy, ruthless power broker. At Tiburon's palatial estate, Cochran is drawn to Tiburon's new wife, the young and beautiful Miryea (Madeleine Stowe), and finds himself torn between his loyalty to his friend and his passion for Miryea. When Tiburon - which mean's 'shark' in Spanish - discovers that his friend and wife are cheating on him, he has Cochran beaten and left for dead, and he packs Miryea off to a brothel. Cochran recovering with the help of a Mexican farmer sets out to find Miryea and settle the score with Tiburon. (Silva Screen)
CD: Released Aug '90, on Silva Screen by Silva Screen Records. Catalogue no: **FILMCD 065**
Cass: Released Aug '90, on Silva Screen by Silva Screen Records. Catalogue no: **FILMC 065**

Rhinestone

RHINESTONE (Film Soundtrack) (See under Parton, Dolly)

Rice, Tim

BLONDEL (Film Soundtrack) (See under 'Blondel')

WANDERIN' STAR (Rice, Tim & Cantabile)
Tracks: / Wanderin' star / Man from Lorraine, The.
7" Single: Released Feb '90, on First Night by First Night Records. Catalogue no: **SCORE 21**

Rich Young & Pretty

NANCY GOES TO RIO / RICH YOUNG AND PRETTY (See under Nancy Goes To Rio)

Richard, Cliff

ALL I ASK OF YOU (Richard, Cliff & Sarah Brightman)
Tracks: / All I ask of you / Phantom of the opera overture (Act II) / Only you (Extra track on 12" version only.)
Note: From the 'Phantom of the opera'.
12" Single: Released Sep '86, on Polydor by Polydor Ltd. Deleted Aug '87. Catalogue no: **POSPX 802**
7" Single: Released Sep '86, on Polydor by Polydor Ltd. Deleted Mar '88. Catalogue no: **POSP 802**

BORN TO ROCK 'N' ROLL
Tracks: / Born to rock 'n' roll / Law of the universe
Note: Taken from the show' Time'
7" Single: Released May '86, on EMI by EMI Records. Catalogue no: **EMI 5545**
12" Single: Released May '86, on EMI by EMI Records. Catalogue no: **12 EMI 5545**

CINDERELLA (Stage show)
Album: Released '83, on EMI Records (Holland). Catalogue no: **5C 052 06967**
Album: Released Jan '67, on Columbia Records. Deleted Jan '72. Catalogue no: **33CX 6103**

EXPRESSO BONGO EP (Richard, Cliff & The Shadows)
Tracks: / Love / Voice in the wilderness, A / Shrine on the second floor / Bongo blues.
7" EP: Released Jan '60, on Columbia by EMI Records. Deleted '63. Catalogue no: **SEG 7971**
12" Single: Released '83, on EMI (Holland) by EMI Records. Catalogue no: **K 052 07329**

IN THE COUNTRY
Tracks: / In the country
Note: Taken from the stage show 'Cinderella'
7" Single: Released Dec '66, on Columbia Records. Deleted '69. Catalogue no: **DB 8094**

IT'S IN EVERYONE OF US
Tracks: / It's in everyone of us
Note: Taken from the stage show 'Time'
7" Single: Released Nov '85, on

EMI by EMI Records. Catalogue no: **EMI 5537**

12" Single: Released Nov '85, on EMI by EMI Records. Catalogue no: **12 EMI 5537**

LIVING DOLL
Tracks: Living doll / Apron strings
Note: From the film 'Young ones'
7" Single: Released July '59, on Columbia Records. Deleted '64. Catalogue no: **DB 4306**

NEXT TIME, THE
Tracks: / Next time, The / Bachelor boy
Note: From the film 'Summer holiday'
7" Single: Released Dec ' 62, on Columbia Records. Deleted '67. Catalogue no: **DB 4950**

ON THE BEACH
Tracks: / On the beach
Note: From the film 'Wonderful life'
7" Single: Released July '64, on Columbia Records. Deleted '67. Catalogue no: **DB 7305**

SERIOUS CHARGE (EP) (Richard, Cliff/Drifters)
Tracks: / Serious charge.
12" Single: Released '83, on EMI (Holland) by EMI Records. Catalogue no: **K 062Z 07528**

SHE'S SO BEAUTIFUL
Tracks: / She's so beautiful / She's so beautiful (verion)
Note: Taken from the stage show 'Time'
7" Single: Released Oct '85, on EMI by EMI Records. Catalogue no: **EMI 5531**

12" Single. Released Oct '85, on EMI by EMI Records. Catalogue no: **12 EMI 5531**

SUMMER HOLIDAY (Film soundtrack) (Richard, Cliff & The Shadows)
Tracks: / Seven days to a holiday / Summer holiday / Let us take you for a ride / Les girls / Foot tapper / Round and round / Stranger in town / Orlando's mime / Bachelor boy / Swingin' affair, A / Really waltzing / All at once / Dancing shoes / Yugoslav wedding / Next time, The / Big news.
Album: Released Apr '88, on MFP by EMI Records. Catalogue no: **MFP 5824**
Cass: Released Apr '88, on MFP by EMI Records. Catalogue no: **TCMFP 5824**
CD: Released Apr '88, on MFP by

EMI Records. Catalogue no: **CDMFP 6021**
CD: Released Apr '88, on MFP by EMI Records. Catalogue no: **CDB 752 057 2**
Album: Released Jan '63, on Columbia by EMI Records. Deleted Jan '68. Catalogue no: **33SX 1472**

SUMMER HOLIDAY (VIDEO) (Various artists)
Note: Cert: U. Running time: 90 mins. Cliff Richard and the Shadows off through Europe aboard a London bus. Squeaky clean fun. Songs include 'Bachelor Boy' and 'Put on Your Dancing Shoes'. Made in 1963. Also stars Ron Moody, David Kossoff and Lauri Peters."
VHS: Released Jun '88, on Warner Home Video by WEA Records. Catalogue no: **PES 98073**

SUMMER HOLIDAY (Single) (Richard, Cliff)
7" Single: Released Feb '82, on Columbia by EMI Records. Catalogue no: **DB 4977**
12" Single: Released Jan '88, on EMI by EMI Records. Deleted Nov '88. Catalogue no: **12EMG 42**

THEME FOR YOUNG LOVERS
Tracks: / Theme for young lovers

Note: From the film 'Wonderful life'
7" Single: Released Mar '64 on Columbia Records. Deleted '67. Catalogue no: **DB 7231**

WONDERFUL LIFE (Film Soundtrack)
Album: Released Jul '64, on Columbia by EMI Records. Deleted Jul '69. Catalogue no: **33SX 1628**
Album: Released '83, on EMI (Holland) by EMI Records. Catalogue no: **5C 052 06961**

YOUNG ONES, THE (Richard, Cliff & The Shadows (Original soundtrack) (See panel below)
Tracks: / Friday night / Got a funny feeling / Peace pipe / Nothing's impossible / Young ones, The / All for one / Lessons in love / No one for me but Nicky / What d'you know, we've got a show / Vaudeville routine / Mambo / Savage.
Album: Released 5 Apr '88, on MFP by EMI Records. Catalogue no: **MFP 5823**
Cass: Released 5 Apr '88, on MFP by EMI Records. Catalogue no: **TC-MFP 5823**
CD: Released 5 Apr '88, on MFP by EMI Records. Catalogue no: **CD-MFP 6020**

Soundtrack to *The Young Ones* - Starring Cliff Richard

CD: Released 5 Apr '88, on MFP by EMI Records. Catalogue no: **CDB 752 057 2**

Album: Released '83, on MFP (Holland) by EMI Records. Catalogue no: **5C 052069 63**

YOUNG ONES, THE (Film Soundtrack) (Richard, Cliff & The Shadows)
Tracks: / Friday night / Peace pipe / Young ones, The / No one for me / but Nicky / Vaudeville routine / Living doll / When the girl in your arms / Savage / We say yeah.
Album: Released Dec '61, on Columbia by EMI Records. Deleted Dec '66. Catalogue no: **33SX 1384**
Album: Released Apr '83, on EMI by EMI Records. Deleted Apr '88. Catalogue no: **EMS 1008**
Cass: Released Apr '83, on EMI by EMI Records. Deleted Apr '88. Catalogue no: **TCEMS 1008**

YOUNG ONES (Single)
Tracks: / young Ones, The / We say yeah
7" Single: Released Jan '62, on Columbia by EMI Records. Deleted '65. Catalogue no: **DB 4761**
7" Single: Released Jan '62, on Columbia by EMI Records. Deleted '65. Catalogue no: **DB 4761**

Richard & Cosima

RICHARD AND COSIMA (Film about Richard Wagner) (Various artists)
Album: Released Mar '90, on SPI Milan (France) Catalogue no: **A 297**
Cass: Released Mar '90, on SPI Milan (France) Catalogue no: **C 297**

Richie, Lionel

SAY YOU SAY ME
Tracks: / Say you, say me.
Note: From the film 'White nights'.
12" Single: Released Nov '85, on Motown by BMG Records (UK). Catalogue no: **ZT 40421**
7" Single: Released Nov' 85 on Motown by BMG Records (UK). Catalogue no: **ZB 40421**

Ricotti, Frank

BEIDERBECKE COLLECTION (Music from the TV series) (Ricotti, Frank All Stars)
Tracks: / Connection,The / Viva le van / Tulips for Chris / Barney's walk / Boys in blue / Hobson's chase / Tiger jive / Scouting ahead / Jennie's tune / Live at the Limping Whippet / Russian over / Dormouse delights / Cryin' all day.
Cass: Released Dec '88, on Dormouse Catalogue no: **DMC 20**
CD: Released Dec '88, on Dormouse Catalogue no: **DMCD 20**
Album: Released Dec '88, on Dormouse Catalogue no: **DM 20**

Riddle, Nelson

BATMAN THEME (Riddle, Nelson & Orchestra)
Tracks: / Batman theme / Batusi a-go go.
Note: The original television soundtrack theme to Batman. The real 'duh-na-na-na-na-na Batman' music. This original and recognizable soundtrack theme was written by Neal Hefti, and then orchestrated and conducted by Nelson Riddle. (Phonogram, July 1989)
12" Pic: Released Jul '89, on Phonogram by Phonogram Ltd. Deleted Dec '89. Catalogue no: **BATPP 112**
12" Single: Released Jul '89, on Phonogram by Phonogram Ltd. Deleted Dec '89. Catalogue no: **BATSP 112**
Cassingle: Released Jul '89, on Phonogram by Phonogram Ltd. Deleted Dec '89. Catalogue no: **BATSM 1**
7" Single: Released Jul '89, on Phonogram by Phonogram Ltd. Deleted Dec '89. Catalogue no: **BATSP 1**

Rider On The Rain

RIDER ON THE RAIN (Film Soundtrack) (Various artists)
Tracks: / Rider on the rain: Various artists / Dobbs duality: Various artists / Marriage waltz: Various artists / American theme: Various artists / Mellie and the American: Various artists / Arrest: Various artists / Meeting house: Various artists / Setting the scene: Various artists / Car theme: Various artists / Mellie's theme: Various artists / Bestial theme: Various artists / Marriage: Various artists / Momento of melancholy: Various artists / Anguish: Various artists / Dobbs at the station: Various artists / Rape: Various artists / Duality and Dobbs: Various artists / Mellie's theme: Various artists.

Album: Released '73, on United Artists by EMI Records. Deleted '

Riding High

RIDING HIGH (Original soundtrack) (Various artists)
Album: on Spartan Catalogue no: **JAM 2**

Righteous Brothers

YOU'VE LOST THAT LOVIN' FEELING
Tracks: / You've lost that lovin' feeling.
7" Single: Released Nov '77, on Phil Spector Int. by Chrysalis Records. Deleted '80. Catalogue no: **2010 022**
7" Single: Released Feb '69, on London-American by Decca Records. Deleted '72. Catalogue no: **HL 10241**
7" Single: Released Jan '65, on London-American by Decca Records. Deleted '68. Catalogue no: **HLU 9943**

YOU'VE LOST THAT LOVIN' FEELING (OLD GOLD)
Tracks: / You've lost that lovin' feeling / Unchained melody.
Note: Featured in the film 'Top Gun'.
7" Single: Released Jun '88, on Old Gold by Old Gold Records. Catalogue no: **OG 9450**

Rikky & Pete

RIKKY & PETE (Original Soundtrack) (Various artists)
Album: Released Feb '90, on Silva Screen by Silva Screen Records. Catalogue no: **SBL12593**
CD: Released Feb '90, on Silva Screen by Silva Screen Records. Catalogue no: **CDSBL12593**

Ring Of Bright Water

RING OF BRIGHT WATER/GOD TOLD ME TO (Film soundtrack) (Various artists)
Album: Released '80, on Phoenix (1) by Phoenix Records. Catalogue no: **DGS 1004**

Ringo The Texan

RINGO THE TEXAN/IN A COLTS SHADOW (Original Soundtracks) (Various artists)
Note: 2 Rare spaghetti western scores by Nino Fidenco.
Album: Released Jan '89, on

Silva Screen by Silva Screen Records. Catalogue no: **SP 8014**

Rink

RINK,THE (Original Broadway Cast) (Various artists)

Tracks: / Colored lights: *Angel* / Chief cook and bottle washer: *Anna* / Don't ah ma me: *Anna* / Blue Crystal: *Dino* / Under the roller coaster: *Angel* / Not enough magic: *Various artists* / Here's to the rink: *Various artists* / We can make it: *Various artists* / After all these years: *Various artists* / Angel's rink...: *Various artists* / What...: *Various artists* / Marry me: *Various artists* / Mrs. A: *Various artists* / Rink, The: *Various artists* / Wallflower: *Various artists* / All the children in....: *Various artists* / Coda: *Various artists*.
Note: Music by John Kander, Lyrics by Fred Ebb. Starring two of Broadway's Great Stars..Liza Minnelli and Chita Rivera. Nominated for 5 Tony Awards with Chita winning the Best Actress award. Kander and Ebb wrote amongst others, the music Cabaret.Angel Antonelli (Liza Minnelli) is discovered with suitcase and knapsack at a bus station. She sings about her days of loneliness and confusion and dreams of returning to the *Coloured lights* of her childhood past.

It is the late 70's. Six Wreckers have come to begin the demolition of once a glorious Roller Rink that sits sadly at the edge of a seaside Amusement Park. They meet Anna Antonelli (Chita Rivera) who has sold the Rink and is today flying off to Rome free of the responsibilities of running the Rink (*Chief cook and bottle washer*). This is the "home" Angel returns to after fifteen years. Bad timing for a re-union of mother and daughter. Right away resentments surface. In no uncertain terms Anna tells Angel what she thinks of Angel's abandoning her for the life of a hippie (*Don't ah ma me*).

As if the Rink had ghosts of the past trapped in the high girders flashbacks unfold the story of how these two women got to this point in their lives. It is suddenly 1950 and Dino (Scott Holmes), the young charming husband and father, appears with presents of rare Venetian *Blue crystal*. In the present, one of the Wreckers of-

fers to buy the blue crystal goblets. Angel resists. She wants everything left as it was. She tries to explain that she has nowhere left to go. She has come home to find peace *Under the roller coaster*. But, how did the Rink get so run-down? Where is the mirror ball? This triggers the memory of Angel's fifth birthday, when Dino, having returned from the Korean War, comes home in the middle of the night, drunk, with his buddies and wants a party. He has a mirror ball for his little girl. His song (*Not enough magic*) turns into a dance and a toast to the Rink. But the friends disperse when Dino becomes violent and moody. Nothing is the same after the war. Alone, Anna tries to comfort him (*We can make it*).

It is only at this point that Angel becomes aware that the Rink has been sold. Mother and daughter are at it again. "This is my home. Nobody's tearing this place down. I live here." "Wrong. You used to live here". They storm upstairs into the apartment. The Wreckers make fun of the two ladies reunion (*After all these years*). Angel comes flying downstairs waving a document. In order to sell the Rink, her mother has forged her name. Angel tells of her plans for *Angels Rink and social centre*. Now Angel is waiting for the lawyer to call back. She intends to get a court order to stop the demolition. Anna tries to explain that it's not just the Rink, the whole Amusement Park is coming down. Times have changed. The boardwalk is not theirs anymore. Teenage punks carrying radios roam the park with the threat of violence. In a flashback, Anna and her friends, Mrs Silverman (Ronn Carroll) and Mrs Jackson (Mel Johnson, Jr) wonder *What happened to the old days?* and Angel learns that Anna has been brutally mugged right on the boardwalk. With great sadness, Angel stands firm. She won't give up her dream, her coloured lights. Angel offers her mother a "toke" of marijuana. At first, Anna refuses then smokes expertly, having seen it done on TV. For a "stoned" moment the two come close together, realizing they're not so very different (*The apple doesn't fall*). Angel wants to know who's going to Rome with Anna. They recall Good

Old Lenny (Jason Alexander) whoince High School has loved Anna (*Marry me*); how Anna married into the Antonelli family, although the disgusting Uncle Fausto objected; and how, after a while, Dino, trapped and restless, leaves his wife, his child and the Rink forever. But Anna tells the young Angel her father is dead. The lie, like a nightmare, evolves into a quintet. Alone, the young "widow" tries to raise her daughter and deal with her own deep emotional needs while Angel in her room hears her mother and the men in the night. (*Mrs A*). Recalling this part of the past is painful for both of them. They retreat. Angel for some ocean air, Anna to finish packing.

The Wreckers, meanwhile, frustrated that their work is on hold, find old roller skates and comically skate round and round *The Rink*. When Anna and Angel return, Angel remembers the events of her senior class spring prom. Anna had donated the Rink and gives her shy teenage daughter some pointers about boys and a dance lesson (*Wallflower*). It's a warm moment. But that is the night old Uncle Fausto, drunk and abusive, tells Angel her father is alive. Humiliated, hurt and traumatized, she packs her bags. It is the 60's and she sings of her journey to the West Coast and her ownexperience among *All the children in a row*. Anna is stunned, saddened by these revelations. The door opens and a young girl enters. It is Angel's daughter. Like her mother, Angel raised this child by herself. She named her Anna. It is now or never. Anna begs Angel to forgive her. With great difficulty they say "I love you". Forgiveness frees them. As Mother and Daughter they embrace, the past and the Rink are lifted up and away.

Cass: Released Sep '84, on T. E. R. by That's Entertainment Records. Catalogue no: **ZCTER 1091**
CD: Released '88, on Polydor by Polydor Ltd. Catalogue no: **823 125-2**
Album: Released Sep '84, on T. E. R. by That's Entertainment Records. Catalogue no: **TER 1091**
CD: Released Sep '84, on T. E. R. by That's Entertainment Records. Catalogue no: **CDTER 1091**

Rio Conchos

RIO CONCHOS (Original Soundtrack) (Goldsmith, Jerry)
CD: Released Feb '90, on Silva Screen by Silva Screen Records. Catalogue no: **RVF 6007D**

Rio Tone

RIO TONE (Original Soundtrack) (Various artists)
Note: Film with music by Brazilian star Gilberto Gil.
Album: Released Jan '89, on Silva Screen by Silva Screen Records. Catalogue no: **A 352**

Risky Business

RISKY BUSINESS (Film soundtrack) (Various artists)
Tracks: / Old time rock'n'roll: *Seger, Bob* / Dream is always the same, The: *Tangerine Dream* / No future: *Tangerine Dream* / Mannish boy: *Waters, Muddy* / Pump, The: *Beck, Jeff* / D.M.S.R.: *Prince* / After the fall: *Journey (Group)* / In the air tonight: *Collins, Phil* / Love on a real train: *Tangerine Dream* / Guido the killer pimp: *Tangerine Dream* / Lana: *Tangerine Dream.*
CD: Released 2 Apr '90, on Virgin by Virgin Records. Catalogue no: **CDV 2302**
Cass: Released Feb '84, on Virgin by Virgin Records. Deleted 13 Feb '89. Catalogue no: **TCV 2302**
Album: Released 2 Apr '90, on Virgin by Virgin Records. Catalogue no: **OVED 240**
CD: Released May '87, on Virgin by Virgin Records. Deleted 13 Feb '89. Catalogue no: **CDV 2302**
Cass: Released 2 Apr '90, on Virgin by Virgin Records. Catalogue no: **OVEDC 240**
Album: Released Feb '84, on Virgin by Virgin Records. Deleted 13 Feb '89. Catalogue no: **V 2302**

Rita, Sue & Bob Too

RITA, SUE AND BOB TOO (TV Soundtrack) (See under Kamen, Michael)

Ritenour, Lee

AMERICAN FLYERS (film soundtrack) (Ritenour, Lee & Greg Mathieson)
Tracks: / American flyers / Travelling music / Brand new day / Gone ridin' / Bad moon rising / Brothers theme (part 1) / 'J' factor, The / American flyers, Theme from / Breakaway / Brothers theme (part 2) / Treadmill / Epilogue (third race).
Cass: Released Nov '86, on GRP by GRP Records (USA). Catalogue no: **GRPC 2001**
Album: Released Jan '87, on GRP by GRP Records (USA). Catalogue no: **GRPA 2001**

River

RIVER, THE (Original Soundtrack) (Various artists)
Note: John Williams score for the Mel Gibson/Sissy Spacek film.
Album: Released Jan '89, on MCA by MCA Records. Catalogue no: **MCA 6138**
Cass: Released Jan '89, on MCA by MCA Records. Deleted Feb '90. Catalogue no: **MCAC 6138**

Roadhouse

ROADHOUSE (Film soundtrack) (Various artists)
Tracks: / Road house blues: *Healey, Jeff Band* / Blue Monday: *Seger, Bob* / I'm tore down: *Healey, Jeff Band* / These arms of mine: *Redding, Otis* / When the night comes falling from the sky: *Healey, Jeff Band* / Rad gumbo: *Little Feat* / Raising heaven (in hell tonight): *Swayze, Patrick* / Good heart, A: *McKay, Kris* / Hoochie coochie man: *Healey, Jeff Band* / Cliff's edge: *Swayze, Patrick.*
Cass: Released Jun '89, on Arista by BMG Records (UK). Catalogue no: **409 948**
Album: Released Jun '89, on Arista by BMG Records (UK). Catalogue no: **209.948**
CD: Released Jun '89, on Arista by BMG Records (UK). Catalogue no: **259 948**

Roadie

ROADIE (Film soundtrack) (Various artists)
Tracks: / Everything works if you let it: *Cheap Trick* / You better run: *Benatar, Pat* / Brainlock: *Ely, Joe* / Road rats: *Cooper, Alice* / Pain: *Cooper, Alice* / Can't we try: *Pendergrass, Teddy* / Drivin' my life away: *Rabbitt, Eddie* / Your precious love: *Bishop, Stephen* / Man needs a woman: *Ferguson, Jay* / Crystal ball: *Styx* / Double yellow line: *Saad, Su & The Next* / Ring of fire: *Blondie* / That lovin' you feelin' again: *Orbison, Roy &*
Emmylou Harris / Hot damn, I'm a one woman man: *Lewis, Jerry Lee* / Texas me and you: *Asleep At The Wheel* / American way: *Williams, Hank Jr..*
2 LP Set: Released Jun '80, on WEA by WEA Records. Catalogue no: **K 66093**
Cass: Released Jun '80, on Warner Bros. by WEA Records. Catalogue no: **K4 66093**

Roar

ROAR (Original Motion Picture Soundtrack) (Various artists)
Album: Released May '82, on GT Catalogue no: **GT 1600**
Cass: Released May '82, on GT Catalogue no: **GTC 1600**

Robe

ROBE, THE (Film Soundtrack) (Various artists)
Tracks: / Farewell to Diana: *Various artists* / Palm Sunday: *Various artists* / Carriage of the cross, The: *Various artists* / Marcellus returns to Capri: *Various artists* / Village of Cana: *Various artists* / Redemption of Marcellus, The: *Various artists* / Miriam: *Various artists* / Catacombs, The: *Various artists* / Rescue of Demetrius, The: *Various artists* / Better kingdom, The: *Various artists.*
Note: Epic score by Alfred Newman.
CD: Released Aug '88, on Trax by Filmtrax Records. Deleted Jan '90. Catalogue no: **MODEMCD 1011**
Cass: Released Aug '88, on Trax by Filmtrax Records. Deleted Jan '90. Catalogue no: **MODEMC 1011**
Album: Released Aug '88, on Trax by Filmtrax Records. Deleted Jan '90. Catalogue no: **MODEM 1011**
Cass: Released Jan '89, on MCA by MCA Records. Catalogue no: **MCAC 1529**
Album: Released Jan '89, on MCA by MCA Records. Catalogue no: **MCA 1529**

Robert & Elizabeth

ROBERT AND ELIZABETH (Chichester Festival Cast) (Various artists)
Tracks: / Here on the corner of Wimpole Street: *Various artists* / Family Moulton-Barrett, The: *Vari-*

ous artists / World outside, The: *Various artists* / Moon in my pocket, The: *Various artists* / I said love: *Various artists* / You only to love me: *Various artists* / Real thing, The: *Various artists* / In a simple way: *Various artists* / I know now: *Various artists* / Escape me never: *Various artists* / Soliloquy: *Various artists* / Pass the eau-de-cologne: *Various artists* / A'm the master here: *Various artists* / Hate me, please: *Various artists* / Girls that boys dream about, The: *Various artists* / Long ago I loved you: *Various artists* / What the world calls love: *Various artists* / Woman and man: *Various artists* / Frustration: *Various artists*.
Cass: Released Jun '87, on First Night by First Night Records. Catalogue no: **CASTC 8**
Album: Released Jun '87, on First Night by First Night Records. Catalogue no: **CAST 8**

ROBERT & ELIZABETH (Original London cast) (Various artists)
Tracks: / Robert and Elizabeth (overture): *Various artists* / Wimpole Street song: *Various artists* / Family Moulton Barrett: *Various artists* / Moon in my pocket: *Various artists* / World outside: *Various artists* / I said love: *Various artists* / Real thing: *Various artists* / You only to love: *Various artists* / In a simple way: *Various artists* / I know now: *Various artists* / Soliloquy: *Various artists* / Pass the eau de Cologne: *Various artists* / I'm the master here: *Various artists* / Escape me never: *Various artists* / Hate me please: *Various artists* / Girls that boys dream about: *Various artists* / Woman and man: *Various artists* / Frustration: *Various artists*.
Album: Released Jan '89, on Silva Screen by Silva Screen Records. Catalogue no: **AEI 1111**
Album: Released Apr '80, on Encore by EMI Records. Deleted '85. Catalogue no: **ONCR 532**

Roberta
ROBERTA (Film Soundtrack) (Various artists)
Note: A Jerome Kern film starring Astaire and Rogers.
Album: Released Jan '89, on Silva Screen by Silva Screen Records. Catalogue no: **SH 2061**

ROBERTA (Studio Cast Recording) (Various artists)

Robin Hood
ADVENTURES OF ROBIN HOOD (Film Soundtrack) (Various artists) (See under 'Adventures Of...')

Robin Of Sherwood
ROBIN OF SHERWOOD (TV Soundtrack) (See under Clannad)

Robinson Crusoe
ROBINSON CRUSOE/MAN FRIDAY (TV Soundtrack) (Various artists)
Note: TV mini series starring Michael York. Music by Maurice Jarre.
Album: Released Feb '88, on Prometheus Catalogue no: **PST 501**

Robinson, Smokey
TRACKS OF MY TEARS (Robinson, Smokey & The Miracles)
Tracks: / Tracks of my tears / I second that emotion / Going to a go-go / Shop around.
Note: Featured in the film 'Platoon'.
12" Single: Released 23 May '87, on Motown by BMG Records (UK). Catalogue no: **ZB 41374**
7" Single: Released 23 May '87, on Motown by BMG Records (UK). Catalogue no: **ZB 41373**
7" Single: Released May '69, on Tamla Motown by Motown Records (UK). Deleted '72. Catalogue no: **TMG 696**

Robocop
ROBOCOP (Film Soundtrack)
Album: Released Nov '87, on T. E. R. by That's Entertainment Records. Catalogue no: **TER 1146**
Cass: Released Nov '87, on T. E. R. by That's Entertainment Records. Catalogue no: **ZCTER 1146**
CD: Released Nov '87, on T. E. R. by That's Entertainment Records. Catalogue no: **CDTER 1146**

Rock Follies
ROCK FOLLIES (Various artists)
Album: Released Apr '76, on Island by Island Records. Deleted '81. Catalogue no: **ILPS 9362**
Album: Released '80, on E.G. by E.G. Records. Deleted '88. Cata-

logue no: **EGLP 23**
Album: Released Feb '77, on Polydor by Polydor Ltd. Catalogue no: **2302 054**

ROCK FOLLIES OF 1977
Album: Released Jun '77, on Polydor by Polydor Ltd. Catalogue no: **2302 072**
Album: Released '80, on E.G. by E.G. Records. Deleted '88. Catalogue no: **EGLP 29**

Rock It Baby Rock It
ROCK IT BABY ROCK IT (Original Soundtrack) (Various artists)
Note: Featuring: Johnny Carroll/Rosco Gordon/Preacher Smith/Etc.(MONO)
Album: Released Jan '86, on Rhino (USA) by Rhino Records (USA). Catalogue no: **RNDF 309**

Rock, Pretty Baby
PRETTY BABY (Film soundtrack) (Various artists)
Tracks: / Rock, pretty baby: *Various artists* / Dark blue: *Various artists* / Free and easy: *Various artists* / What's it gonna be: *Various artists* / Rockin' the boogie: *Various artists* / Rockabye lullaby blues: *Various artists* / Teenage bop: *Various artists* / Most, The: *Various artists* / Can I steal a little love: *Various artists* / Jukebox rock: *Various artists* / Saints rock 'n' roll: *Various artists* / Picnic by the sea: *Various artists* / Young love: *Various artists* / Happy is a boy named me: *Various artists* / Hot Rod: *Various artists* / Big band rock and roll: *Various artists*.
Album: Released Aug '83, on Jasmine by Hasmick Promotions. Deleted Feb '88. Catalogue no: **JASM 1028**

Rock, Rock, Rock
ROCK ROCK ROCK (Film Soundtrack) (Various artists)
CD: Released Jun '88, on MCA (USA) by MCA Records (USA). Catalogue no: **31270**

Rockers
ROCKERS (Film soundtrack) (Various artists)
Tracks: / We 'a' rockers: *Inner Circle* / Money worries: *Maytones* / Police and thieves: *Murvin, Junior* / Book of rules: *Heptones* / Stepping razor: *Tosh, Peter* / Tenement yard: *Miller, Jacob* / Fade away:

Byles, Junior / Rockers: Wailer, Bunny / Slave master: Isaacs, Gregory / Dread lion: Scratch & Upsetters / Graduation in Zion: Kiddus 1 / Jah no dead: Burning Spear / Satta masagana: Third World / Natty takes over: Hines, Justin & The Dominos.

Cass: Released Sep '79, on Island by Island Records. Deleted Jul '87. Catalogue no: **ZCI 9587**

Album: Released Sep '79, on Island by Island Records. Deleted Jul '87. Catalogue no: **ILPS 9587**

Rockestra

ROCKESTRA (Film Soundtrack) (See under Eddy, Duane)

Rockford Files

ROCKFORD FILES (TV Theme) (See under Post, Mike)

Rock'n'Roll High...

ROCK'N'ROLL HIGH SCHOOL (Various artists)
Tracks: / Rock 'n' roll high school: Ramones / I want you around: Ramones / Come on let's go: Ramones / Blitzkrieg bop: Ramones / Teenage lobotomy: Ramones / She's the one: Ramones / California sun: Ramones / Pinhead: Ramones / So it goes: Lowe, Nick / Energy fools the magician: Eno, Brian / Rock'n'roll high school: Soles, P.J. / Come back Jonee: Devo / Teenage depression: Eddie & The Hot Rods / Smoking in the boys room: Brownsville Station / School days: Berry, Chuck / Dream goes on forever: Rundgren, Todd / School's out: Cooper, Alice.

Album: Released Oct '79, on Sire by Sire Records. Deleted '84. Catalogue no: **SRK 6070**

ROCK 'N' ROLL HIGH SCHOOL (Single) (See under Ramones)

Rock'n'Roll Years

ROCK'N'ROLL YEARS (1956-1959) (Various artists)
Tracks: / Rock around the clock: Haley, Bill & The Comets / Rock Island line: Donegan, Lonnie / Great pretender, The: Platters / Be-bop-a-lula: Vincent, Gene / Ain't that a shame: Domino, Fats / Tutti frutti: Little Richard / 6-5 Special: Lang, Don & His Frantic 5 /

Diana: Anka, Paul / That'll be the day: Holly, Buddy & The Crickets / Singing the blues: Mitchell, Guy / Great balls of fire: Lewis, Jerry Lee / At the hop: Danny & The Juniors / When: Kalin Twins / Summertime blues: Cochran, Eddie / All I have to do is dream: Everly Brothers / Donna: Valens, Ritchie / Lipstick on your collar: Francis, Connie / Here comes summer: Keller, Jerry / Living doll: Richard, Cliff / Teenager in love: Wilde, Marty.

Album: Released 15 Jun '87, on BBC by BBC Records. Catalogue no: **REN 631**

Cass: Released 15 Jun '87, on BBC by BBC Records. Catalogue no: **ZCN 631**

ROCK'N'ROLL YEARS (1960-1963) (Various artists)
Tracks: / What do you want: Faith, Adam / Apache: Shadows / Ain't misbehavin': Bruce, Tommy & The Bruisers / Good timin': Beach Boys / On the rebound: Cramer, Floyd / Runaway: Shannon, Del / Johnny remember me: Leyton, John / Walkin' back to happiness: Shapiro, Helen / Runaround Sue: Dion / Take good care of my baby: Vee, Bobby / Let's dance: Montez, Chris / Nut rocker: Bumble, B & The Stingers / Twistin' the night away: Cooke, Sam / Locomotion, The: Little Eva / How do you do it: Gerry & The Pacemakers / Surf city: Jan & Dean / Do you want to know a secret: Kramer, Billy J. & The Dakotas / Sugar and spice: Searchers / She loves you: Beatles.

Cass: Released 15 Jun '87, on BBC by BBC Records. Catalogue no: **ZCN 632**

Album: Released 15 Jun '87, on BBC by BBC Records. Catalogue no: **REN 632**

ROCK'N'ROLL YEARS (1964-1967) (Various artists)
Tracks: / Tobacco road: Nashville Teens / I'm in to something good: Herman's Hermits / You really got me: Kinks / House of the rising sun: Animals / Anyone who had a heart: Black, Cilla / Leader of the pack: Shangri-Las / Go now: Moody Blues / Here comes the night: Them / Little things: Berry, Dave / My generation: Who / River deep, mountain high: Supremes / Keep on running: Davis, Spencer Group / Sun ain't gonna shine anymore, The: Walker Brothers / Good vibrations: Beach Boys / I can't let go:

Webb, Marti / Dedicated to the one I love: Mamas & Papas / Whiter shade of pale, A: Procul Harum / I'm a believer: Monkees / San Francisco: Flowerpot Men / All you need is love: Beatles.

Album: Released 15 Jun '87, on BBC by BBC Records. Catalogue no: **REN 633**

Cass: Released 15 Jun '87, on BBC by BBC Records. Catalogue no: **ZCN 633**

ROCK'N'ROLL YEARS (1968-1971) (Various artists)
Tracks: / This wheel's on fire: Driscoll, Julie / Fire: Brown, Arthur / Crossroads: Hatch, Tony / Nights in white satin: Moody Blues / Voodoo chile: Hendrix, Jimi / Pinball Wizard: John, Elton / I'm the urban spaceman: Bonzo Dog Band / Going up the country: Canned Heat / I'd rather go blind: Various artists / Games people play: South, Joe / Instant Karma: Lennon, John / Rag mama rag: Band / Black night: Deep Purple / Witches promise: Jethro Tull / All right now: Free / My sweet lord: Harrison, George / Your song: John, Elton / Get it on: T. Rex / Malt and barley blues: McGuinness Flint / Maggie may: Stewart, Rod.

Cass: Released 15 Jun '87, on BBC by BBC Records. Catalogue no: **ZCN 634**

Album: Released 15 Jun '87, on BBC by BBC Records. Catalogue no: **REN 634**

Rocky

ROCKY I (Original Soundtrack) (Various artists)
Tracks: / Gonna fly now: Various artists / Philadelphia morning: Various artists / Going the distance: Various artists / Reflections: Various artists / Marine's hymn/yankie doodle: Various artists / Take you back: Various artists / First date: Various artists / You take my heart away: Various artists / Fanfare for Rocky: Various artists / Butkus: Various artists / Alone in the ring: Various artists / Final bell, The: Various artists / Rocky's reward: Various artists.

Cass: Released Jan '89, on Silva Screen by Silva Screen Records. Catalogue no: **182 707.4**

Cass: Released Apr '77, on United Artists by EMI Records. Catalogue no: **TCK 30039**

CD: Released May '87, on EMI by

EMI Records. Deleted Aug '89. Catalogue no: **CDP 746 081 2**
Album: Released Jan '89, on Silva Screen by Silva Screen Records. Catalogue no: **182 707.1**

ROCKY II (Original Film Soundtrack) (Various artists)
Tracks: / Redemption: *Various artists* / Gonna fly now: *Various artists* / Conquest: *Various artists* / Vigil: *Various artists* / All of my life: *Various artists* / Overture: *Various artists* / Two kinds of love: *Various artists* / All of my life: *Various artists*.
Note: Composed by Bill Conti.
Album: Released Apr '80, on United Artists by EMI Records. Catalogue no: **UAG 30257**
Album: Released Jan '89, on Silva Screen by Silva Screen Records. Catalogue no: **182720-1**
Cass: Released Jan '89, on Silva Screen by Silva Screen Records. Catalogue no: **182720-4**
CD: Released Apr '89, on United Artists by EMI Records. Catalogue no: **CDP 746082-2**

ROCKY III (Original film soundtrack) (Various artists)
Tracks: / Eye of the tiger: *Various artists* / Take you back (Tough Gym): *Various artists* / Pushin': *Various artists* / Reflections: *Various artists* / Mickey: *Various artists* / Take you back: *Various artists* / Decision: *Various artists* / Gonna fly now: *Various artists* / Adrian: *Various artists* / Conquest: *Various artists*.
Cass: Released Aug '82, on Liberty by EMI Records. Catalogue no: **TCLBG 30351**
CD: Released May '87, on Liberty by EMI Records. Catalogue no: **CDP 746 561 2**
Album: Released Aug '82, on Liberty by EMI Records. Catalogue no: **LBG 30351**

ROCKY IV (Love theme) (See under B Project)

ROCKY IV (Original soundtrack) (Various artists)
Tracks: / Burning heart: *Survivor* / Heart's on fire: *Gafferty, John* / Double or nothing: *Loggins, Kenny & Gladys Knight* / Eye of the tiger: *Survivor* / War fanfare from Rocky: *Dicola, Vince* / Living in America: *Brown, James* / No easy way out: *Tepper, Robert* / One way street: *Go West* / Sweetest victory, The /

Training montage: *Dicola, Vince*.
Cass: Released Dec '85, on Scotti Bros (USA) by WEA Records. Catalogue no: **40 70272**
Album: Released Dec '85, on Scotti Bros (USA) by WEA Records. Catalogue no: **SCT 70272**
CD: Released Jul '86, on Scotti Bros (USA) by WEA Records. Catalogue no: **CD 70272**

Rocky Horror Show

ROCKY HORROR BOX SET, THE (Original Soundtrack) (Various artists)
Note: Contains 4 LP's, time warp dance steps info, Fan Club membership form, 16 page full colour booklet of photos and lyrics.
LP Set: Released 21 Nov '87, on Ode Catalogue no: **RHBXLP 1**
CD Set: Released Jan '89, on Pacific by Pacific Records. Catalogue no: **RHBXCD 1**

ROCKY HORROR DISCO SHOW (Various artists)
12" Single: Released Nov '85, on ZYX (Germany) Catalogue no: **ZYX 5299**

ROCKY HORROR PICTURE SHOW (Original Soundtrack) (Various artists)

Tracks: / Science fiction double feature (plus reprise): *Various artists* / Dammit Janet: *Various artists* / Over at the Frankenstein place: *Various artists* / Time warp, The: *Various artists* / Sweet transvestite: *Various artists* / I can make you a man: *Various artists* / Hot patootie: *Various artists* / Bless my soul: *Various artists* / Touch-a, touch-a, touch me: *Various artists* / Eddie: *Various artists* / Rose hit my world: *Various artists* / Floor show: *Various artists* / Don't dream it: *Various artists* / Wild and untamed thing: *Various artists* / I'm going home: *Various artists* / Super heroes: *Various artists*.
Album: Released Jul '86, on Ode Deleted '89. Catalogue no: **OSV 21653**
Cass: Released Jul '86, on Ode Deleted '89. Catalogue no: **OSVC 21653**
CD: Released Jan '86, on Ode Deleted '89. Catalogue no: **OSVCD 21653**
LP Pic: Released '87, on Ode Deleted '88. Catalogue no: **OSVP 21653**

ROCKY HORROR SHOW (Original Roxy Cast) (Various artists)

London Cast Recording of *The Rocky Horror Show* **(Dojo)**

Tracks: / Science fiction double feature: *Various artists* / Dammit Janet: *Various artists* / Over at the Frankenstein place: *Various artists* / Sweet transvestite: *Various artists* / Time warp: *Various artists* / Sword of Damocles, The: *Various artists* / Charles Atlas song (reprise): *Various artists* / What ever happened to Saturday night: *Various artists* / Touch-a touch-a touch me: *Various artists* / Once in a while: *Various artists* / Eddie's teddy: *Various artists* / Planest schmanet Janet: *Various artists* / Rose tint my world: *Various artists*
Album: Released '87, on Ode Deleted '89. Catalogue no: **ODE 9009**
Cass: Released '87, on Ode Deleted '89. Catalogue no: **ODEC 9009**
CD: Released '88, on Ode Catalogue no: **ODECD 9009**

ROCKY HORROR SHOW (Original London cast) (Various artists) (See panel on previous page)
Tracks: / Science fiction double feature: *Various artists* / Dammit Janet: *Various artists* / Over at the Frankenstein place: *Various artists* / Sweet transvestite: *Various artists* / Time warp: *Various artists* / Sword of Damocles: *Various artists* / Hot patootie (bless my soul): *Various artists* / Touch-a touch-a touch-a touch me: *Various artists* / Once in a while: *Various artists* / Rose tint my world: *Various artists* / I'm going home: *Various artists* / Superheroes: *Various artists* / Science fiction double feature (reprise): *Various artists*.
Album: Released May '87, on Dojo by Castle Communications Records. Catalogue no: **DOJOLP 54**
Cass: Released '87, on Dojo by Castle Communications Records. Catalogue no: **DOJOTC 54**
CD: Released '87, on Dojo by Castle Communications Records. Catalogue no: **DOJOCD 54**

ROCKY HORROR.(AUDIENCE PARTICIPATION) (Various artists)
Cass: Released '87, on Ode Catalogue no: **ODEC 1032**
Album: Released '87, on Ode Catalogue no: **ODE 1032**

ROCKY HORROR SHOW (1990 London Cast) (Various

artists)
Note: Features Time warp, Sweet transvestite, Dammit Janet and Science fiction double feature.
Album: Released Sep '90, on Chrysalis by Chrysalis Records. Catalogue no: **CHR 1811**
Cass: Released Sep '90, on Chrysalis by Chrysalis Records. Catalogue no: **ZCHR 1811**
CD: Released Sep '90, on Chrysalis by Chrysalis Records. Catalogue no: **CCD 1811**

Rod, Jane & Freddy
HAPPY CHRISTMAS
Tracks: / Happy Christmas.
7" Single: Released Dec '81, on Video Deleted '82. Catalogue no: **VID 001**

Rodgers & Hart
BOYS FROM SYRACUSE (Various artists)
Tracks: / Ladies of the evening: *Various artists* / Falling in love with love: *Various artists* / Shortest day of the year: *Various artists* / Oh Diogenes: *Various artists* / I had twins: *Various artists* / He and she: *Various artists* / What can you do with a man?: *Various artists* / Dear old Syracuse: *Various artists* / This can't be love: *Various artists* / You have cast your shadow on the sea: *Various artists* / Come with me: *Various artists* / Sing for your supper: *Various artists*.
Album: Released Jul '79, on DRG (USA) by DRG Records (USA). Deleted Jan '89. Catalogue no: **DS 15016**

Rodgers, Richard
RICHARD RODGERS & N.Y. PHILHARMONIC (Rodgers, Richard/N.Y.Philharmonic)
Tracks: / Slaughter on tenth avenue / Victory / Lover / Most beautiful girl in the world / Falling in love with love / Oh, what a beautiful morning / March of Siamese children / Carousel waltz.
Album: Released May '80, on CBS by CBS Records & Distribution. Catalogue no: **CBS 61895**

Rogers, Ginger
MISS GINGER ROGERS
Tracks: / Embraceable you / I used to be colour blind / Isn't this a lovely day / But not for me / I'll string along with you / They can't take that away from me / Night and

day / Did you ever see a dream walking? / They all laughed / We're in the money / Fine romance, A / Let's call the whole thing off / I'm putting all my eggs in one basket.
Album: Released '78, on EMI by EMI Records. Catalogue no: **ODN 1002**

Roland Rat
LIVING LEGEND (TV theme)
Tracks: / Living legend / Living legend.
7" Single: Released Sep '86, on Rodent Deleted Jan '88. Catalogue no: **RAT 5**
12" Single: Released Sep '86, on Rodent Deleted Jan '88. Catalogue no: **12 RAT 5**

LIVING LEGEND - THE ALBUM
Note: This album includes the signature tune "Living Legend" and other music featured in the current series.
Cass: Released Oct '86, on BBC by BBC Records. Deleted Apr '89. Catalogue no: **ZCF 614**
Album: Released Oct '86, on BBC by BBC Records. Deleted Apr '89. Catalogue no: **REB 614**

Roll Over Beethoven
ROLL OVER BEETHOVEN (TV theme) (Various artists)
Cass: Released Apr '85, on Telebell Catalogue no: **ZCTV 2**
Album: Released Apr '85, on Telebell Catalogue no: **TVLP 2**

Rollerball
ROLLERBALL (Original Soundtrack) (Various artists)
Album: Released Feb '90, on Silva Screen by Silva Screen Records. Catalogue no: **1831831**
Cass: Released Feb '90, on Silva Screen by Silva Screen Records. Catalogue no: **1831834**

ROLLERBALL (Film Soundtrack) (London Symphony Orchestra)
Cass: Released Jan '89, on Liberty (import) by EMI Records. Catalogue no: **L4N 10291**
Album: Released Jan '89, on Liberty (import) by EMI Records. Catalogue no: **LN 10291**

Rolling Stones
JUMPIN' JACK FLASH (Original)
7" Single: Released May '68, on

Decca by Decca International. Deleted '88. Catalogue no: **F 12782**

JUMPIN' JACK FLASH
Tracks: / Jumpin' Jack Flash / As tears go by.
7" Single: Released Aug '80, on Decca by Decca International. Deleted '83. Catalogue no: **STONE 7**

JUMPIN' JACK FLASH (1987 release)
Note: Used in the film 'Jumpin Jack Flash' starring Whoopi Goldberg.
7" Single: Released May '87, on Decca by Decca International. Catalogue no: **F 102**
12" Single: Released May '87, on Decca by Decca International. Deleted Feb '89. Catalogue no: **FX 102**

PAINT IT BLACK (Original)
7" Single: Released Jun '90, on London by London Records Ltd. Catalogue no: **LON 264**

PAINT IT BLACK
Tracks: / Paint it black / Honky tonk women / Sympathy for the devil (Not on 7" single.).
Note: Used as the theme to the film and TV series 'Tour of duty'.
7" Single: Released May '66, on Decca by Decca International. Deleted '88. Catalogue no: **F 12395**
12" Single: Released Jun '90, on London by London Records Ltd. Catalogue no: **LONX 264**
Cassingle: Released Jun '90, on London by London Records Ltd. Catalogue no: **LONCS 264**
12" Single: Released Jul '90, on London by London Records Ltd. Catalogue no: **LONXR 264**

SYMPATHY FOR THE DEVIL
Tracks: / Sympathy for the devil / Gimme shelter.
Note: Used throughout the film by The Rolling Stones called 'Sympathy for the devil'
7" Single: Released Aug '80, on Decca by Decca International. Deleted '83. Catalogue no: **STONE 12**

Roman Scandals
ROMAN SCANDALS / KID MILLIONS (Film Soundtracks) (See under Kid Millions)

Romance Of The Movies
ROMANCE OF THE MOVIES

(Various artists)
Tracks: / Last tango in Paris: *Various artists* / Look of love, The: *Various artists* / More: *Various artists* / Cabaret: *Various artists* / Casino Royale: *Various artists* / Last horizon: *Various artists* / Love story (where do I begin): *Various artists* / Bless the beasts and the children: *Various artists* / Getaway love theme: *Various artists* / Windmills of your mind: *Various artists* / Man and a woman, A: *Various artists* / Raindrops keep falling on my mind: *Various artists*.
Album: Released Sep '84, on Spot by Pickwick Records. Catalogue no: **SPR 8546**
Cass: Released Sep '84, on Spot by Pickwick Records. Catalogue no: **SPC 8546**

Romance, Romance
ROMANCE, ROMANCE (Original Broadway Cast) (Various artists)
Tracks: / Little comedy, The: *Various artists* / Goodbye Emily: *Various artists* / I'll always remember the song: *Various artists* / Night it had to end, The: *Various artists* / Think of the odds: *Various artists* / Let's not talk about it: *Various artists* / Through a window: *Various artists* / Small craft warnings: *Various artists* / So glad I married her: *Various artists* / Letters: *Various artists* / It's not too late: *Various artists* / Oh what a performance: *Various artists* / Women on Vienna: *Various artists* / Summer share: *Various artists* / Plans A & B: *Various artists* / Words he doesn't say: *Various artists* / Romantic notions: *Various artists* / Romance romance: *Various artists*.
Album: Released Feb '89, on T. E. R. by That's Entertainment Records. Catalogue no: **TER 1161**
CD: Released Feb '89, on T. E. R. by That's Entertainment Records. Catalogue no: **CDTER 1161**
Cass: Released Feb '89, on T. E. R. by That's Entertainment Records. Catalogue no: **ZTER 1161**

Rondo Veneziano
NOT QUITE JERUSALEM LOVE THEME
Tracks: / Not quite Jerusalem love theme.
Note: Featured in the film 'Not quite Jerusalem'

7" Single: Released Mar '85, on Fanfare by Captain Billy's Music. Catalogue no: **RONS 4**

Ronettes
BE MY BABY
Tracks: / Be my baby.
Note: Featured in the film 'Dirty Dancing'.
7" Single: Released Oct '63, on London-American by Decca Records. Deleted '66. Catalogue no: **HLU 9793**
7" Single: Released '80, on Phil Spector Int. by Chrysalis Records. Catalogue no: **LR 8245**

Ronstadt, Linda
SOMEWHERE OUT THERE (Ronstadt, Linda and Richard Ingram)
Tracks: / Somewhere out there (a) / Somewhere out there (b) / Somewhere out there (fievels version) (On Picture disc only.) / Somewhere out there (instrumental) (On Picture disc only.).
Note: Featured in the film 'An American Tail'.
7" Pic: Released Jun '87, on MCA by MCA Records. Catalogue no: **MCAP 1172**
7" Single: Released Jun '87, on MCA by MCA Records. Catalogue no: **MCA 1172**
12" Single: Released Jun '87, on MCA by MCA Records. Catalogue no: **MCAS 1172**

Room With A View
ROOM WITH A VIEW, A (Film soundtrack) (Various artists) (See panel on next page)
Tracks: / O mio babbino caro: *Various artists* (From Gianni Scicchi by Puccini. Vocal-Kiri Te Kanawa.) / Pensione Bertollini, The: *Various artists* / Lucy, Charlotte and Miss Lavish see the city: *Various artists* / In the piazza signoria: *Various artists* / Embankment, The: *Various artists* / Phaethon: *Various artists* / Hi il bel sogno di doretta: *Various artists* (From La Rondine, Act One by Puccini. Vocal-Kiri Te Kanawa.) / Storm, The: *Various artists* / Home and the betrothal: *Various artists* / Sacred lake: *Various artists* / Allan sisters, The: *Various artists* / In the National Gallery: *Various artists* / Windy corner: *Various artists* / Habanera: *Various artists* / Broken engagement: *Various artists* / Re-

**A scene from the film *A Room with a View*
starring Denholm Elliot**

turn to Florence: *Various artists* /
End title: *Various artists*.
Note: Music composed by Richard
Robbins.
Album: Released Jan '89, on
Silva Screen by Silva Screen Records. Catalogue no: **MOMENT 101**
CD: Released Apr '87, on DRG
(USA) by DRG Records (USA).
Deleted Jan '89. Catalogue no:
CDSBL 12588
CD: Released Jan '89, on Silva
Screen by Silva Screen Records.
Catalogue no: **MOMENTCD 101**
Cass: Released Jan '89, on Silva
Screen by Silva Screen Records.
Catalogue no: **MOMENTC 101**

Rosary Murders

**ROSARY MURDERS, THE
(Original Soundtrack) (Various artists)**
Tracks: / In your eyes: *Various
artists* / Jogging: *Various artists* /
Phone company: *Various artists* /
Marble orchard, The: *Various artists* / Second story priest: *Various
artists* / Pull yourself together: *Various artists* / Scratch father steel:
Various artists / Sister blabbermouth: *Various artists* / Confessional call: *Various artists* / Father
Koesler and Pat take a walk: *Various artists* / Fint the obituary: *Various artists* / Sister Ann's last bath:
Various artists.
Note: New film starring Donald
Sutherland, music by Bobby Laurel, Don Sebesky & The Royal

Philharmonic Orchestra.
Album: Released Jan '89, on
Silva Screen by Silva Screen Records. Catalogue no: **EDL 2505.1**
CD: Released Jul '88, on Silva
Screen by Silva Screen Records.
Deleted Apr '90. Catalogue no:
CDC 1004

Rose

**ROSE (Film Soundtrack) (See
under Midler, Bette)**

Rose Marie

**ROSE MARIE / NEW MOON
(Original cast recordings)
(See under New Moon)**

**ROSE MARIE (Original
Soundtrack) (Various artists)**
Note: Starring Howard Keel.
Album: Released Jan '89, on
MCA by MCA Records. Catalogue no: **MCA 25009**
Cass: Released Jan '89, on MCA
by MCA Records. Deleted Mar
'90. Catalogue no: **MCAC 25009**

ROSE MARIE (VIDEO) (Various artists)
VHS: Released '88, on MGM/UA
(Video) by MGM/UA Video. Catalogue no: **SMV 10374**

Rose Of Romance Orch

**TARA'S THEME (From Gone
With The Wind)**
Tracks: / Tara's theme / Masquerade.
7" Single: Released Dec '81, on

BBC by BBC Records. Deleted
'87. Catalogue no: **RESL 108**

Rose Royce
BEST OF CAR WASH
Tracks: / Car wash / Zig zag /
Water / Doin' what comes naturally
/ I'm going down / Put your money
where your mouth is / I wanna get
next to you / Daddy rich / Yo yo /
Sunrise.
Cass: Released '81, on MCA by
MCA Records. Catalogue no:
MCLC 1609
Album: Released Jul '77, on MCA
by MCA Records. Deleted '81.
Catalogue no: **MCF 2799**
Album: Released '81, on MCA by
MCA Records. Catalogue no:
MCL 1609
CD: Released '88, on MCA by
MCA Records. Deleted Sep '90.
Catalogue no: **DMCF 3424**

CAR WASH
Tracks: / Car wash.
7" Single: Released Dec '76, on
MCA by MCA Records. Deleted
'79. Catalogue no: **MCA 267**
12" Single: Released May '88, on
MCA by MCA Records. Deleted
Dec '89. Catalogue no: **MCAT
1253**
7" Single: Released May '88, on
MCA by MCA Records. Catalogue no: **MCA 1253**

CAR WASH (LP)
Album: Released Nov '82, on
Fame by EMI Records. Catalogue
no: **FA 3043**

CARWASH (OLD GOLD)
Tracks: / Car wash / I wanna get
next to you / Which way is up,
Theme from.
12" Single: Released 30 May '89,
on Old Gold by Old Gold Records.
Catalogue no: **OG 4117**
7" Single: Released Apr '83, on
Old Gold by Old Gold Records.
Catalogue no: **OG 9322**

Rosemary's Baby

ROSEMARY'S BABY (Original Soundtrack) (Various artists)
Note: Christopher Komeda score
for the Polanski film.
Album: Released Jan '89, on
Silva Screen by Silva Screen Records. Catalogue no: **254891.1**

Rosenman, Leonard

**MUSIC FROM THE FILMS OF
JAMES DEAN (Rosenman,**

Leonard & His Orchestra)
Tracks: / Rebel without a cause / East of Eden / Giant (There's never been anyone else but you) / There's never been anyone else but you.
Album: Released Mar '79, on Sunset (Liberty) by EMI Records. Catalogue no: **SLS 50420**

Ross, Diana

'DIANA' TV SOUNDTRACK
Cass: Released '88, on Hallmark by Pickwick Records. Catalogue no: **HSC 3203**
Album: Released '88, on Pickwick by Pickwick Records. Catalogue no: **SHM 3203**

DIANA (TV SPECIAL)
Tracks: / Don't rain on my parade / Long to be (close to you) / Remember me / Ain't no mountain high enough / I love you (call me) / Forever young.
Note: A new album from Diana Ross, the title track is co-written and produced by Daryl Hall. The album includes the duet All Of You with Julio Iglesias. Other songs include cover versions of the hit for Fontella Bass Rescue Me, It's Your Move by America and Bob Dylan's Forever Young. Bernard Edwards of Chichas co- written and produced a song for Diana and Lionel Ritchie has contributed a ballad reputed to be dedicated to Marvin Gaye.
Album: Released Jun '88, on Fame by EMI Records. Deleted Apr '90. Catalogue no: **FA 3200**
Album: Released Oct '86, on Capitol by EMI Records. Deleted '88. Catalogue no: **ROSS 1**
Cass: Released Oct '86, on Capitol by EMI Records. Deleted '88. Catalogue no: **TCROSS 1**
CD: Released Oct '86, on Capitol by EMI Records. Deleted '88. Catalogue no: **CDP 746 053 2**
Cass: Released Jun '88, on Fame by EMI Records. Catalogue no: **TC-FA 3200**

LADY SINGS THE BLUES (Film Soundtrack)
Tracks: / Lady sings the blues: Ross, Diana / Baltimore brothel: Ross, Diana / Billie sneaks into Dean and Dean's: Ross, Diana / Swinging uptown: Ross, Diana / T'aint nobody's business if I do: Ross, Diana / Big Ben: Ross, Diana / C.C. Rider: Ross,

Diana / All of me: Ross, Diana / Man I love, The: Ross, Diana / Them there eyes: Ross, Diana / Gardenias from Louis: Ross, Diana / Cafe Manhattan: Ross, Diana / Had you been around: Ross, Diana / Love theme: Ross, Diana / Country tune: Ross, Diana / I cried for you: Ross, Diana / Billy and Harry: Ross, Diana / Mean to me: Ross, Diana / Fine and mellow: Ross, Diana / What a little moonlight can do: Ross, Diana / Louis visits Billie on tour: Ross, Diana / Persuasion: Ross, Diana / Agent's office: Ross, Diana / Love is here to stay: Ross, Diana / Lover man: Ross, Diana / Oh where can you be: Ross, Diana / You've changed: Ross, Diana / Gimme a pigfoot and a bottle of beer: Ross, Diana / Good morning heartache: Ross, Diana / My man: Ross, Diana / Don't explain: Ross, Diana / Strange fruit: Ross, Diana / God bless the child: Ross, Diana / Closing theme: Ross, Diana .
2 LP Set: Released Oct '81, on Motown by BMG Records (UK). Catalogue no: **TMSP 1131**
Cass Set: Released Oct '81, on Motown by BMG Records (UK). Catalogue no: **CTMSP 1131**
CD: Released Nov '87, on Motown by BMG Records (UK). Catalogue no: **WD 72610**
2 LP Set: Released '88, on Motown by BMG Records (UK). Catalogue no: **ZL 72129**
Cass Set: Released '88, on Motown by BMG Records (UK). Catalogue no: **ZK 72129**
CD: Released '88, on Motown by BMG Records (UK). Catalogue no: **ZD 72129**

T.C.B. - THE ORIGINAL SOUNDTRACK (Ross, Diana & The Supremes with The Temptations)
Tracks: / T.C.B. / Stop, in the name of love / You keep me hangin' on / Get ready / Way you do the things you do, The / Taste of honey, A / Eleanor Rigby / Do you know the way to San Jose? / Mrs. Robinson / Respect / Somewhere / Ain't too proud to beg / Hello, young lovers / For once in my life / I know I'm losing you / With a song in my heart / Without a song / Come see about me / My world is empty without you / Baby love / I hear a symphony /

Impossible dream, The.
Cass: Released Mar '82, on Motown by BMG Records (UK). Deleted '88. Catalogue no: **CSTMS 5048**
Album: Released Feb '70, on Tamla Motown by Motown Records (UK). Deleted Feb '75. Catalogue no: **STML 11110**
Album: Released Mar '82, on Motown by BMG Records (UK). Deleted '88. Catalogue no: **STMS 5048**

Rota, Nino

NINO ROTA MOVIES, THE
Tracks: / Godfather, The / Taming of the shrew, The / La dolce vita / Rocco and his brothers / Napoli milionaria / Romeo and Juliet / War and peace / Il gattopardo / Amarcord / La strada / Le notti di cabiria / Giulietta degli spiriti / I vittelloni / Otto e mezzo.
Note: 14 tracks of some of the most beautiful music ever written for movie soundtracks, including 'The Godfather', 'War And Peace' and 'Romeo And Juliet'. Orchestra conducted by Carlo Savina.
CD: Released May '85, on Polydor (Germany) by Polydor Ltd. Catalogue no: **822 747-2**

Round Midnight

ROUND MIDNIGHT (Film soundtrack) (Various artists)
Tracks: / Round midnight: Various artists / Body and soul: Various artists / Berangere's nightmare: Various artists / Fair weather: Various artists / Una noche con Francis: Various artists / Peacocks, The: Various artists / How long has this been going on?: Various artists / Rhythm-a-ning: Various artists / Still time: Various artists / Minuit aux Champ D'Elysees: Various artists / Chan's song: Various artists / Now's the time: Various artists / Autumn in New York: Various artists / Encore: Various artists / April in Paris: Various artists / Parisienne thorotare: Various artists.
Note: D.Gordon, M.Davis, J.Coltrane, C.Parker, B.Powell, L.Young, B.Holiday, C.Hawkins, T.Monk, B.Rich, R.Garland, R.Brown, C.Rouse, O.Peterson, H.Ellis, K.Drew, L.Vinnegar, H.Edison, A.Haig, P.Heath, M.Roach, A.Blakey, J.Mondragon,

B.Webster, J.Rowles, B.Kessel.
Album: Released Nov '86, on CBS by CBS Records & Distribution. Catalogue no: **450079 1**
Cass: Released Nov '86, on CBS by CBS Records & Distribution. Catalogue no: **450079 4**
Album: Released Nov '88, on CBS by CBS Records & Distribution. Deleted Jan '90. Catalogue no: **CBS 70300**
Cass: Released Nov '88, on CBS by CBS Records & Distribution. Catalogue no: **CBS 4070300**
CD: Released Nov '88, on CBS by CBS Records & Distribution. Catalogue no: **CD 70300**

Round The Horne

BEST OF ROUND THE HORNE (Various artists)
Note: With Kenneth Horne, Kenneth Williams, Hugh Paddick, Betty Marsden, Bill Pertwee,Douglas Smith.
Cass: Released '79, on BBC by BBC Records. Deleted 31 Aug '88. Catalogue no: **RMC 4018**
Album: Released Sep '75, on BBC by BBC Records. Deleted 31 Aug '88. Catalogue no: **REH 193**

MORE OF THE BEST OF ROUND THE HORNE (Various artists)
Note: With Kenneth Horne, Kenneth Williams, Hugh Paddick, Betty Marsden, Bill Pertwee,Douglas Smith.
Album: Released Oct '76, on BBC by BBC Records. Deleted 31 Aug '88. Catalogue no: **REH 240**
Cass: Released Oct '76, on BBC by BBC Records. Deleted 31 Aug '88. Catalogue no: **RMC 4044**

ROUND THE HORNE (Various artists)
Note: Starring Kenneth Horne, Kenneth Williams, Hugh Paddick, Betty Marsden and Bill Pertwee.
Cass: Released Sep '88, on BBC by BBC Records. Catalogue no: **ZBBC 1010**

ROUND THE HORNE 2 (Various artists)
Cass set: Released Nov '89, on BBC by BBC Records. Catalogue no: **ZBBC 1092**

ROUND THE HORNE VOL.3 (Various artists)
Note: With Kenneth Horne, Kenneth Williams, Hugh Paddick,

Betty Marsden, Bill Pertwee,Douglas Smith.
Cass: Released Oct '77, on BBC by BBC Records. Deleted Apr '89. Catalogue no: **ZCF 296**
Album: Released Oct '77, on BBC by BBC Records. Deleted Apr '89. Catalogue no: **REH 296**

ROUND THE HORNE Vol.3 (Re-issue) (Various artists)
Cass set: Released Nov '89, on BBC by BBC Records. Catalogue no: **ZBBC 1093**

Roustabout

ROUSTABOUT (Film Soundtrack) (See under Presley, Elvis)

ROUSTABOUT (VIDEO) (Various artists)
VHS: Released '88, on Channel 5 by Channel 5 Video. Catalogue no: **CFV 01162**

Rover

ROVER, THE (L'AVVENTURIERO) (Original Soundtrack) (Various artists)
Note: Ennio Morricone score for the Anthony Quinn film.
Album: Released Jan '89, on Silva Screen by Silva Screen Records. Catalogue no: **SP 8022**

Roxanne

ROXANNE (Film Soundtrack) (Various artists)
Tracks: / Roxanne: *Various artists* / Starry sky: *Various artists* / Just honest - we did it: *Various artists* / Roxanne's theme: *Various artists* / Game, set match: *Various artists* / Panache, The: *Various artists* / Roxanne's eyes: *Various artists* / Blue Danube waltz, The: *Various artists* / Written in the wind: *Various artists* / Roxanne (end title): *Various artists*.
Note: Music by Bruce Smeaton for the Steve Martin/Daryl Hannah comedy.
Cass: Released Nov '87, on Silva Screen by Silva Screen Records. Catalogue no: **FILMC 023**
CD: Released Jul '88, on Silva Screen by Silva Screen Records. Catalogue no: **CDC 1000**
Album: Released Nov '87, on Silva Screen by Silva Screen Records. Catalogue no: **FILM 023**

Royal Philharmonic...

20 FILMHARMONIC GREATS

(Royal Philharmonic Orchestra)
Tracks: / Hawaii / Walk on the wild side / Man with the golden arm / Tara's theme / Spellbound / To kill a mockingbird / Exodus / Magnificent seven / Charade / Born free / Pink panther / Lara's theme / Barsalino / Love story / Lawrence of Arabia / Baby elephant walk / Raindrops keep falling on my head / Gigi / Shadow of your smile / Alfie.
Cass: Released '79, on Pickwick by Pickwick Records. Deleted '84. Catalogue no: **PLC 7009**
Album: Released '79, on Pickwick by Pickwick Records. Deleted '84. Catalogue no: **PLE 7009**

ACADEMY AWARDS (Royal Philharmonic Orchestra)
Tracks: / Lawrence of Arabia / Chim chim cheree / Raindrops keep falling on my head / Somewhere my love / Let it be / Shaft, Theme from / Lapis lazuli / If ever I would leave you / My love / Here's that rainy day / Charade / Bridge over troubled water / Something's coming / Way we were, The / MacArthur Park.
Note: Conducted by Vic Lewis
CD: Released May '89, on PRT by Castle Communications Records. Catalogue no: **CDSNP 7780**

ANDREW LLOYD WEBBER'S CLASSIC MUSICALS (Royal Philharmonic Pops Orchestra) (See under Lloyd Webber, Andrew)

CLASSIC THEMES (Royal Philharmonic Orchestra & friends)
Album: Released '83, on Nouveau Music Catalogue no: **NML 1001**
Cass: Released '83, on Nouveau Music Catalogue no: **ZCNML 1001**
Album: Released Sep '82, on CBS by CBS Records & Distribution. Deleted Sep '87. Catalogue no: **25083**

MOUNTBATTEN (TV soundtrack) (Royal Philharmonic Orchestra)
Tracks: / Mountbatten / Homeless, The / Mob violence / New viceroy, The / Nehru / Jinnah and the Muslim day of action / Banquet, A / Refugee camp / 10,000 patans / Tryst with destiny, A / Independence day / Teachings of Gandhi / Horror train / Upheaval of

nature / Rape of a village / Column, The / Assassination of Gandhi / Farewell dinner / Goodbye India / Last viceroy (end titles), The.
Cass: Released Apr '86, on T. E. R. by That's Entertainment Records. Catalogue no: **ZCTER 1113**
Album: Released Apr '86, on T. E. R. by That's Entertainment Records. Catalogue no: **TER 1113**

ON SCREEN (Royal Philharmonic Orchestra)
Tracks: / America (jazz singer) / Flashdance / Thornbirds / It might be you (Tootsie) / Woman in you (Staying alive) / All time high (Octopussy) / Terms of Endearment / Champions / Up where we belong (Officer & gentlemen) / Dynasty / Terrahawks / Simon and Simon / Loving Walter / Spy ship (a cold wind).
CD: Released Nov '86, on K-Tel by K-Tel Records. Catalogue no: **ONCD 3331**

QUO VADIS (See under Quo Vadis) (Royal Philharmonic Orchestra)

STAGE AND SCREEN FAVOURITES Conducted by Vic Lewis (Royal Philharmonic Orchestra)
Tracks: / Don't cry for me Argentina / M.A.S.H. (theme from) / Serenade for strings / Coco / Always Mademoiselle / Hannie Caulder / 49th Parallel / So much you loved me / Louise / Escape me never / My ship / Little Prince.
CD: Released Jun '90, on Pickwick by Pickwick Records. Catalogue no: **PWK 126**
Cass: Released Jun '90, on Pickwick by Pickwick Records. Catalogue no: **HSC 3299**

Royal Wedding

ROYAL WEDDING (In The Good Old Summertime) (Various artists)
Tracks: / Too late now / Ev'ry night at seven / Happiest day of my life, The / I left my hat in Haiti / You're all the world to me / How could you believe me when I said I loved you... / I don't care / Meet me tonight in dreamland / Play that barber shop chord / Last night when we were young / Put your arms around me honey / Merry Christmas.
Album: Released Feb '87, on CBS by CBS Records & Distribution. Deleted Jun '88. Catalogue no: **450230 1**

Cass: Released Feb '87, on CBS by CBS Records & Distribution. Deleted Jun '88. Catalogue no: **450230 4**

Rozsa, Miklos

BEN-HUR (Film soundtrack) (Rozsa, Miklos/National Philharmonic Orcheastra.)
Tracks: / Fanfare to prelude / Star of Bethlehem and adoration of the Magi / Friendship / Burning desert, The / Arrius / Rowing of the galley slaves / Parade of the charioteers / Mother's love, The / Return to Judea / Ring for freedom / Lepers search for the Christ / Procession to Calvary / Miracle and finale.
Note: Amongst spectacular feature film scores, few have been more dramatic and evocative than Miklos Rozsa's magnificent Academy Award winning effort for the multi-oscar blessed BEN-HUR(1959). Re-recorded under the composers baton for Decca/London's "Phase 4 " series in 1977, it is now repackaged for mid-price with our information packed booklet relating details about its protagonist and his exertions, along with a potted survey of events relating to the movie. An essential addition to the library of cinemagoers and orchestral music lovers alike, it was originally issued at full-price in 1986.
CD: Released '86, on Decca by Decca International. Catalogue no: **417 849 2**
CD: Released Jul '88, on London Records by London Records Ltd. Deleted Jun '90. Catalogue no: **820 190-2**
Album: Released Jul '77, on Phase 4 Deleted '80. Catalogue no: **PFS 4394**
Cass: Released '86, on Decca by Decca International. Catalogue no: **417 849 4**

EPIC FILM SCORES (Various artists)
Tracks: / King of kings main theme / Nativity / Miracles of Christ / Salome's dance / Way of the cross / Resurrection and finale / Ben Hur love theme / Victory parade / Miracle and finale / El Cid overture / Palace music / Legend and epilogue.
Album: on Varese Sarabande Records(USA) by Varese Sarabande Records (USA). Catalogue no: **VC 81104**

CD: on Varese Sarabande Records(USA) by Varese Sarabande Records (USA). Catalogue no: **VCD 47268**

EPIC FILM SCORES (Various artists)
Tracks: / Ben Hur prelude / Ben Hur love theme / Parade of the charioteers / Mother's love, The / El Cid overture / El Cid love theme / El Cid march / King of kings nativity / Way of the cross, The / Pieta / King of kings theme / Quo Vadis triumphal march / Quo Vadis love theme / Domine
Album: Released Dec '86, on Cloud Nine by Cloud Nine Records. Catalogue no: **CN 7013**

IMMORTAL FILM MUSIC OF MIKLOS ROZSA (Royal Philharmonic Orchestra)
Tracks: / Young Bess / Lust of life / Lady Hamilton / Asphalt jungle, The / Thief of Baghdad, The / Lydia / Killers, The / Time to love and a time to die, The / Lost weekend.
Note: Including tracks from Lust For Life, Young Bess, The Thief Of Baghdad.
Cass: Released Nov '84, on Memoir by Memoir Records. Catalogue no: **CMOIR 101**
Album: Released Nov '84, on Memoir by Memoir Records. Deleted Mar '90. Catalogue no: **MOIR 101**

SPELLBOUND (Film Soundtrack) (See under Rozsa, Miklos)

RTE Radio Orchestra

GREATEST THEMES
Album: Released '88, on K-Tel by K-Tel Records. Deleted '89. Catalogue no: **RTE 109C**

Ruffelle, Frances

STRANGER TO THE RAIN (From the musical 'Children of Eden')
Tracks: / Stranger to the rain.
12" Single: Released Sep '90, on London by London Records Ltd. Catalogue no: **LONX 278**
Cassingle: Released Sep '90, on London by London Records Ltd. Catalogue no: **LONCS 278**
7" Single: Released Sep '90, on London by London Records Ltd. Catalogue no: **LON 278**
CD Single: Released Sep '90, on London by London Records Ltd.

Catalogue no: **LONCD 278**

Rumble Fish

RUMBLE FISH (Film Sound-track) (See under Copeland, Stewart)

Run D.M.C.

GHOSTBUSTERS
Tracks: / Ghostbusters / Ghostbusters (Inst.).
Note: Taken from the film *Ghostbusters 2*
Cassingle: Released Aug '89, on MCA by MCA Records. Catalogue no: **MCAC 1360**
7" Single: Released Aug '89, on MCA by MCA Records. Deleted Jul '90. Catalogue no: **MCA 1360**

GHOSTBUSTERS (Import)
12" Single: Released Aug '89, on Profile (USA) by Profile Records (USA). Catalogue no: **PROFT 262**
CD Single: Released Aug '89, on Profile (USA) by Profile Records (USA). Catalogue no: **PROCD 262**

MARY MARY
Tracks: / Mary Mary / Razing hell.
Note: Featured in the film 'Tougher Than Leather'.
7" Single: Released Aug '88, on London Records by London Records Ltd. Deleted Feb '89. Catalogue no: **LON 191**
Special: Released Aug '88, on London Records by London Records Ltd. Deleted Feb '89. Catalogue no: **LONS 191**
12" Single: Released Aug '88, on London Records by London Records Ltd. Deleted Feb '89. Catalogue no: **LONX 191**

RUN'S HOUSE
Tracks: / Run's house / Beat to the rhyme / Run's house (instr) (Only available on 12" version) / Beats to the rhyme (instr) (Only available on 12" version).
Note: Featured in the film 'Tougher than leather'.
7" Single: Released '88, on London Records by London Records Ltd. Deleted Feb '89. Catalogue no: **LONP 177**
7" Single: Released Apr '88, on London Records by London Records Ltd. Deleted Oct '88. Catalogue no: **LON 177**
CD Single: Released '88, on London Records by London Records Ltd. Deleted Jul '89. Catalogue no: **LONCD 177**

12" Single: Released Apr '88, on London Records by London Records Ltd. Deleted Oct '88. Catalogue no: **LONX 177**

TOUGHER THAN LEATHER (Film soundtrack)
Tracks: / Run's house / Mary, Mary / They call us Run D.M.C. / Beats to the rhyme / Radio station / Papa crazy / Tougher than leather / I'm not going out like that / How'd ya do it, Dee? / Miss Elaine / Soul to rock 'n' roll / Ragtime.
Cass: Released May '88, on London Records by London Records Ltd. Catalogue no: **LONC 38**
CD: Released May '88, on London Records by London Records Ltd. Catalogue no: **828 070-2**
Album: Released May '88, on London Records by London Records Ltd. Catalogue no: **LONLP 38**

Run Of The Arrow

RUN OF THE ARROW (Original Soundtrack) (Various artists)
Note: Composed by Victor Young. (western score).
Album: Released Jan '89, on Silva Screen by Silva Screen Records. Catalogue no: **AEI 3102**

Runaway

RUNAWAY (Original Soundtrack) (Various artists)
Note: Jerry Goldsmith score for the Tom Selleck thriller.
Cass: Released Jan '89, on Silva Screen by Silva Screen Records. Catalogue no: **CTV 81234**
CD: Released Jan '89, on Silva Screen by Silva Screen Records. Catalogue no: **VCD 47221**
Album: Released Jan '89, on Silva Screen by Silva Screen Records. Catalogue no: **STV 81234**

Runaway Train

RUNAWAY TRAIN (Original Soundtrack) (Various artists)
Tracks: / Jailbreak: *Various artists* / Moving on: *Various artists* / Destination unknown: *Various artists* / Clear the tracks: *Various artists* / Reflections: *Various artists* / Runaway train: *Various artists* / Prison memories: *Various artists* / Yellow rose of Texas: *Various artists* / Collision course: *Various artists* / Past, present and future: *Various artists* / Red for danger: *Various artists* / Gloria: *Various artists* / End of the line: *Various artists*.
Note: The track on side two "Glo-

ria" is Vivaldi's "Gloria" in "D" (second movement) arranged by Alfredo Casella and performed by the USSR Academic Russian Choir and the Moscow Conservatorie Students Orchestra, conducted by Alexander Aveshnikov. Subtly augmented and mixed with electronics, this section of the soundtrack is causing a great deal of interest resulting in a number of requests for information on the piece and its' availability on record.
Album: Released '86, on IMS by Polydor Ltd. Catalogue no: **A 267**
CD: Released '86, on SPI Milan (France) Catalogue no: **CDCH 267**
Cass: Released '86, on IMS by Polydor Ltd. Catalogue no: **C 267**

Running Loose

RUNNING LOOSE (TV soundtrack) (Various artists)
Album: Released '88, on Westside by Westside Records. Catalogue no: **RUNLP 1**
CD: Released '88, on Westside by Westside Records. Catalogue no: **CDRUN 1**
Cass: Released '88, on Westside by Westside Records. Catalogue no: **ZCRUN 1**

Running Man

RUNNING MAN, THE (Original Soundtrack) (Various artists)
Note: Music by Harold Faltermeyer for the Arnold Schwarzenegger film.
CD: Released Mar '89, on T. E. R. by That's Entertainment Records. Catalogue no: **CDTER 1158**
Cass: Released Jan '89, on Silva Screen by Silva Screen Records. Catalogue no: **ZCTER 1158**
CD: Released Jan '89, on Silva Screen by Silva Screen Records. Catalogue no: **VCD 47356**
Album: Released Jan '89, on T. E. R. by That's Entertainment Records. Catalogue no: **TER 1158**

Running Scared

RUNNING SCARED (Original soundtrack) (Various artists)
Tracks: / Sweet freedom: *McDonald, Michael* / Man size love: *Klymaxx* / I just wanna be loved: *Ready For The World* / Running scared: *Waybill, Fee* / Once in a lifetime: *New Edition* / I know what I want: *Labelle, Patti* / Say you really want me: *Wilde, Kim* / El Chase: *Temperton, Rod* / Never

too late to start: *Temperton, Rod*.
Note: Great new soundtrack
album from the movie starring
Gregory Hines and Bill Crystal.
Also features two excellent tracks
by Rod Temperton,who has writ-
ten and co-produced most fea-
tures of the album.
Album: Released '86, on MCA by
MCA Records. Catalogue no:
MCG 6012
Cass: Released '86, on MCA by
MCA Records. Deleted Jan '88.
Catalogue no: **MCGC 6012**
CD: Released '86, on MCA by
MCA Records. Catalogue no:
DMCG 6012

Runswick, Daryl

**MY FAMILY & OTHER ANI-
MALS**
Tracks: / My family and other ani-
mals / Caterpillars and spiders.
12" Single: Released Oct '87, on
BBC by BBC Records. Deleted
Apr '89. Catalogue no: **12RSL 220**
7" Single: Released Oct '87, on
BBC by BBC Records. Deleted
Apr '89. Catalogue no: **RESL 220**

Rupert & The Frog Song

**RUPERT AND THE FROG
SONG (See under McCart-
ney, Paul)**

Russians Are Coming

**RUSSIANS ARE COMING,
THE (Original Soundtrack)
(Various artists)**
Note: Johnny Mandel score for the
Norman Jewison comedy.
Cass: Released Jan '89, on MCA
by MCA Records. Catalogue no:
MCAC 1428
Album: Released Jan '89, on
MCA by MCA Records. Cata-
logue no: **MCA 1428**

Russkies

**RUSSKIES (Original Sound-
track) (Various artists)**
Note: Composed by James Newton Howard.
Album: Released Jan '89, on

Silva Screen by Silva Screen Records. Catalogue no: **STV 81335**

Ruthless People

**RUTHLESS PEOPLE (Original
soundtrack) (Various artists)**
Tracks: / Ruthless people: *Jagger, Mick* / Give me the reason:
Vandross, Luther / Modern
woman: *Joel, Billy* / Wherever I lay
my hat: *Young, Paul* / No say in it:
Machinations / Waiting to see you:
Hartman, Dan / Dance champion:
Kool & The Gang / Neighbourhood
watch: *Colombier, Michael* / Stand
on it: *Springsteen, Bruce* / Don't
you want my love: *Nicole*.
Album: Released Nov '86, on Epic
by CBS Records & Distribution.
Catalogue no: **EPC 70299**
Cass: Released Nov '86, on Epic
by CBS Records & Distribution.
Catalogue no: **40 70299**
CD: Released Nov '86, on Epic by
CBS Records & Distribution.
Deleted Jan '89. Catalogue no:
CDEPC 70299

Rutles

I MUST BE IN LOVE
Tracks: / I must be in love /
Cheese & onions.
7" Single: Released Apr '78, on
Warner Bros. by WEA Records.
Deleted '81. Catalogue no: **K
17125**

LET'S BE NATURAL
Tracks: / Let's be natural / Piggy
in the middle.
7" Single: Released Jun '78, on
Warner Bros. by WEA Records.
Deleted '81. Catalogue no: **K
17180**

**RUTLES - ALL YOU NEED IS
CASH (Various artists)**
Note: Cert: 15.
VHS: Released '88, on Palace
Video by Virgin Records. Cata-
logue no: **PVC 2065 A**

RUTLES, THE
Tracks: / Hold my hand / Number
one / With a girl like you / I must be

in love / Ouch! / Living in hope /
Love life / Nevertheless / Good
times roll / Doubleback alley /
Cheese & onion / Another day /
Piggy in the middle / Let's be natural.
Note: The songs from the TV programme 'The Rutles' a spoof documentary on the rise of
the'Pre-Fab Four' told by Eric Idle
of Monty Python fame. All the
songs seem strangely familiar to
another 'Fab Four".
Album: Released Mar '78, on
Warner Bros. by WEA Records.
Catalogue no: **K 56459**
Cass: Released Mar '78, on Warner Bros. by WEA Records. Catalogue no: **K4 56459**

RUTLES (VIDEO)
VHS: Released Jul '90, on Telstar
by Telstar Records (UK). Catalogue no: **TVE 6003**

Ryan's Daughter

**RYAN'S DAUGHTER (Film
Soundtrack) (Various artists)**
Tracks: / Main title: *Various artists*
/ Where was I when the parade
went by: *Various artists* / You don't
want me then: *Various artists* / Michael's theme: *Various artists* /
Ride through the woods: *Various
artists* / Obsession: *Various artists*
/ Overture: *Various artists* / Shakes
based on Michael's theme: *Various artists* / Rosy and the schoolmaster: *Various artists* / Michael
shows Randolph his strange treasure: *Various artists* / It was a good
time (Rosy's theme): *Various artists*.
Album: Released '73, on Polydor
by Polydor Ltd. Deleted '78. Catalogue no: **2315 028**
Cass: Released Jan '89, on MCA
by MCA Records. Deleted Feb
'90. Catalogue no: **MCAC 25142**
Album: Released Jan '89, on
MCA by MCA Records. Cata-
logue no: **MCA 25142**

S

The following information was taken from the Music Master database on September 25th, 1990.

Sacco & Vanzetti

SACCO AND VANZETTI (Film Soundtrack) (Various artists)
Note: Composed by Ennio Morricone & Joan Baez.
Album: Released Jan '89, on Silva Screen by Silva Screen Records. Catalogue no: **NL 70231**

Safan, Craig

STAND AND DELIVER (See under Stand & Deliver)

Sahara (film)

SAHARA (Film Soundtrack) (Various artists)
Note: Composed by Ennio Morricone.
Album: Released Jan '89, on Silva Screen by Silva Screen Records. Catalogue no: **STV 81211**

Sailor 2

SAILOR 2 (TV Soundtrack) (Various artists)
Tracks: / To the limit and beyond: *Various artists* / Why all the nice girls: *Various artists* / Mission Wolf rock: *Various artists* / Man o' war: *Various artists* / Tribute: *Various artists* / Immortal memory: *Various artists.*
Cass: Released Jul '81, on BBC by BBC Records. Deleted '86. Catalogue no: **ZCR 411**
Album: Released Jul '81, on BBC by BBC Records. Deleted '86. Catalogue no: **REH 411**

Sakamoto, Ryuichi

LAST EMPEROR, THE (SINGLE) (See also under Last Emperor)
Tracks: / Last Emperor, The (end title theme) / Last Emperor, The (opening title theme).
12" Single: Released Jan '88, on Virgin by Virgin Records. Catalogue no: **VST 1038**
7" Single: Released Jan '88, on Virgin by Virgin Records. Catalogue no: **VS 1038**

MERRY CHRISTMAS MR. LAWRENCE (SINGLE) (See also under Merry Christmas Mr...)
Tracks: / Merry Christmas Mr. Lawrence / Sowing the seed.
7" Single: Released Sep '83, on Virgin by Virgin Records. Deleted May '90. Catalogue no: **VS 627**

Sal, Chris 'N' Trev

DYING FLY (From Tiswas)
Tracks: / Dying fly / Grab a granny.
7" Single: Released Apr '78, on Decca by Decca International. Deleted '80. Catalogue no: **F 13771**

Salad Days

SALAD DAYS (Revival London cast) (Various artists)
Tracks: / Things that are done by a Don, The: *Various artists* / We said we wouldn't look back: *Various artists* / Find yourself something to do: *Various artists* / I sit in the sun: *Various artists* / Oh, look at me: *Various artists* / Hush-hush: *Various artists* / Out of breath: *Various artists* / Cleopatra: *Various artists* / Sand in my eyes: *Various artists* / It's easy to sing: *Various artists* / We're looking for a piano: *Various artists* / Time of my life, The: *Various artists* / Saucer song, The: *Various artists* / We don't understand our children: *Various artists.*
Cass: Released Jul '82, on T. E. R. by That's Entertainment Records. Catalogue no: **ZCTER 1018**
Album: Released Jul '82, on T. E. R. by That's Entertainment Records. Catalogue no: **TER 1018**

Salsa (film)

SALSA (Original Soundtrack) (Various artists)
Album: Released Aug '88, on MCA by MCA Records. Catalogue no: **IMCA 6232**
Cass: Released Aug '88, on MCA by MCA Records. Catalogue no: **IMCAC 6232**
CD: Released Aug '88, on MCA by MCA Records. Deleted Sep '90. Catalogue no: **MCAD 6232**

SALSA (VIDEO) (Various artists)
VHS: Released '88, on Warner Home Video by WEA Records. Catalogue no: **GGV 50121**

Salvation (film)

SALVATION (Original soundtrack) (Various artists)
Tracks: / Salvation: *New Order* / Twanky party: *Cabaret Voltaire* / Play the beat: *Dominique* / Let's go: *New Order* / Salvation have you said: *Hood* / Jesus saves: *Cabaret Voltaire* / Destroy all evil: *Dominique* / Touched by the hand of God: *New Order* / You can blackmail Jesus: *Jumpin' Jesus* / Nightmare: *Hood* / Come on: *Baker, Arthur* / Sputnik: *New Order* / Skullcrusher: *Various artists.*
CD: Released 30 Jan '88, on For A Song Catalogue no: **TWICD 774**
Album: Released Feb '88, on For A Song Catalogue no: **TWI 774**
Cass: Released Feb '88, on For A Song Catalogue no: **TWIC 774**
CD: Released 11 Feb '88, on Crepescule (Les Disques du Crepescule) by Les Disques Du Crepuscule(Belgium). Catalogue no: **IPCD 2022.36**

Sandpebbles

SANDPEBBLES (Film soundtrack) (Various artists)
Album: Released Sep '90, on Silva Screen by Silva Screen Records. Catalogue no: **FILM 048**
Cass: Released Sep '90, on Silva Screen by Silva Screen Records. Catalogue no: **FILMC 048**

Santa Claus: The Movie

SANTA CLAUS: THE MOVIE (Film Soundtrack) (Various artists)
Tracks: / Main title: *Jones, Aled* / Arrival of the elves: *Various artists* / Making toys: *Ambrosian Children's Choir* / Christmas rhapsody: *Various artists* / It's Christmas again: *Ambrosian Children's Choir*

/ March of the elves: *Various artists* / Patch,natch!: *Ambrosian Children's Choir* / It's Christmas all over the world: *Easton, Sheena* / Shouldn't do that: *Kajagoogoo* / Sleigh ride over Manhattan: *Various artists* / Sad Patch: *Various artists* / Patch versus Santa: *Various artists* / Thank you Santa: *Ambrosian Children's Choir*.

Album: Released Nov '85, on EMI-America by EMI Records. Deleted Jul '87. Catalogue no: **AML 3101**

Cass: Released Nov '85, on EMI-America by EMI Records. Deleted Jul '87. Catalogue no: **TCAML 3101**

Santa Sangre

SANTA SANGRE (Film soundtrack) (Various artists)
Tracks: / Fin del mundo: *Boswell, Simon* / Alma: *Boswell, Simon* / Alejandra: *Circus Orgo* / Triste: *Boswell, Simon* / Besame mucho: *Silver Hombre* / Acid revenge: *Boswell, Simon* / Herbage: *Boswell, Simon* / Truck: *Boswell, Simon* / Dejame llorar: *Concha Y Fenix* / Holy guitar: *Boswell, Simon* / Grave business: *Boswell, Simon* / Heart: *Boswell, Simon* / Kids' theme: *Boswell, Simon* / Wingbeat: *Boswell, Simon* / Church tattoo: *Boswell, Simon* / Sweet dreams: *Boswell, Simon* / Karnival: *Boswell, Simon*.

Cass: Released Apr '90, on President by President Records. Catalogue no: **PTLC 1104**

Album: Released Apr '90, on President by President Records. Catalogue no: **PTLS 1104**

CD: Released Apr '90, on President by President Records. Catalogue no: **PCOM 1104**

Sarde, Philipe

ENNEMIS INTIMES (See under Ennemis Intimes)

PIRATES (See under Pirates)

QUI C'EST CE GARCON (See under Qui C'est Ce Garcon)

Saturday Night Fever

SATURDAY NIGHT FEVER (Film Soundtrack) (Various artists)
Tracks: / Stayin' alive: *Bee Gees* / How deep is your love: *Bee Gees* / Night fever: *Bee Gees* / More than a woman: *Bee Gees* / Jive talkin':

Bee Gees / You should be dancing: *Bee Gees* / More than a woman: *Tavares* / Calypso breakdown: *Donaldson, Ralph* / If I can't have you: *Elliman, Yvonne* / Fifth of Beethoven, A: *Murphy, Walter* / Open sesame: *Kool & The Gang* / Boogie shoes: *K.C. & The Sunshine Band* / M.F.S.B.: *K.C. & The Sunshine Band* / K. Jee: *K.C. & The Sunshine Band* / Disco inferno: *Tramps* / Manhattan skyline: *Tramps* / Night on disco mountain: *Tramps* / Salsation: *Tramps*.

2 LP Set: Released Mar '78, on RSO by Polydor Ltd. Deleted '84. Catalogue no: **2658 123**

CD Set: Released '83, on RSO by Polydor Ltd. Catalogue no: **800 068-2**

Cass set: Released Jan '84, on RSO by Polydor Ltd. Catalogue no: **351 701-4**

2 LP Set: Released Jan '84, on RSO by Polydor Ltd. Catalogue no: **SPDLP 5**

SATURDAY NIGHT FEVER (18 VERSION VIDEO) (Various artists)
VHS: Released Mar '90, on CIC Video Catalogue no: **VHR 2362**

SATURDAY NIGHT FEVER (VIDEO) (Various artists)
Note: Cert: PG.
VHS: Released '87, on CIC Video Catalogue no: **VHR 2001**

Satyricon

SATYRICON (Original Film Score) (Various artists)
Tracks: / Teatrino di vernacchio: *Various artists* / Il giardino delle delizie: *Various artists* / Notturni nella suburra: *Various artists* / La schiavetta imnamorata: *Various artists* / La cena de trimalcione: *Various artists* / Madeja - perimadeja: *Various artists* / Mio amato gitone: *Various artists* / Il cena de trimalcione: *Various artists* / Tema di gitone: *Various artists* / Il trionfo del nuovo Cesare: *Various artists* / Encolpio e ascito prigionier: *Various artists* / Sulla nave di lica: *Various artists* / Le nozze sul mare: *Various artists* / Il fuoco delle vestali: *Various artists* / L'oracolo salmodiante: *Various artists* / Mi ascolti gitone: *Various artists* / Storia della matrona de efeso: *Various artists* / Encolpio ha perduto la sua spada: *Various artists* / Il minotauro: *Various artists* / La danse des

singes: *Various artists* / La nuova isola: *Various artists*.
Album: Released '73, on United Artists by EMI Records. Deleted '78. Catalogue no: **UAS 29118**

Say Amen Somebody

SAY AMEN, SOMEBODY (Film Soundtrack) (Various artists)
Tracks: / Highway to heaven: *Various artists* / Singing in my soul: *Various artists* / What manner of man is this: *Various artists* / When I've done my best: *Various artists* / Take my hand, precious Lord: *Various artists* / I'm his child: *Various artists* / He chose me: *Various artists* / No ways tired: *Various artists* / Jesus dropped the charges: *Various artists* / I'll never turn back: *Various artists* / Storm is passing over, The: *Various artists* / It's gonna rain: *Various artists* / He brought us: *Various artists* / Canaan: *Various artists*.

2 LP Set: Released May '84, on DRG (USA) by DRG Records (USA). Deleted Jan '89. Catalogue no: **SB 2 L 12584**

CD: Released Mar '87, on DRG (USA) by DRG Records (USA). Deleted Jan '89. Catalogue no: **CDXP 12584**

Cass set: Released May '84, on DRG (USA) by DRG Records (USA). Deleted Jan '89. Catalogue no: **SB 2 LC 12584**

Sayle, Alexei

FISH PEOPLE TAPES, THE
Tracks: / Metro at the disco / It ain't hard to be an animal / Twenty Tom Waits and a box of swans / That's a Milton Springsteen / Song of the revolutionary stool pigeon / Ullo John got a new motor.
Cass: Released Mar '84, on Springtime by Springtime Records. Catalogue no: **IMC 9**

Scala

BROND, THEME FROM (Featuring Bill Nelson & Daryl Runswick)
Tracks: / Brond, Theme from.
CD Single: Released Jun '88, on Cocteau by Cocteau Records. Catalogue no: **COQ CD 21**

Scales, Prunella

AFTER HENRY (See under After Henry)

Scalphunters

SCALPHUNTERS, THE (Film Soundtrack) (Various artists)
Note: Elmer Bernstein western score for the Burt Lancaster film.
Cass: Released Jan '89, on MCA by MCA Records. Catalogue no: **MCAC 25042**
Album: Released Jan '89, on MCA by MCA Records. Catalogue no: **MCA 25042**

SCALPHUNTERS/HANG 'EM HIGH/THE WAY WEST (Various artists) (See also under Hang Em High)
Tracks: / Scalphunters - prologue: Various artists / Square dance for loco horses: Various artists / Scalphunters theme: Various artists / Forced march: Various artists / Moving on: Various artists / Hang 'em high: Various artists / Rachel (love theme): Various artists / Tumbleweed wagon: Various artists / I'll get 'em myself: Various artists / Rachel (love theme): Various artists / It's no deal: Various artists / Hang 'em high: Various artists / Way west, The: Serendipity Singers / Way west, The - overture (main title): Various artists / Lige celebrates: Various artists / We're crossing first: Various artists / Flowers for Mr. Mack: Various artists / Water and Billy's death: Various artists / Mercy McBee: Serendipity Singers / Buffaloes and indians: Various artists / Becky's theme: Various artists / One to Crystal city - Tadlock's end: Various artists / Reluctant mercy: Various artists / Way west, The - finale: Various artists.
Cass: Released Aug '90, on MGM (EMI) Catalogue no: **794 946 4**
CD: Released Aug '90, on MGM (EMI) Catalogue no: **CDMGM 27**
Cass: Released Aug '90, on MGM (EMI) Catalogue no: **TCMGM 27**
CD: Released Aug '90, on MGM (EMI) Catalogue no: **CDP 794 946 2**
Album: Released Aug '90, on MGM (EMI) Catalogue no: **794 946 1**
Album: Released Aug '90, on MGM (EMI) Catalogue no: **LPMGM 27**

Scandal (film)

SCANDAL (Film Soundtrack) (Various artists)
Tracks: / Nothing has been proved: Springfield, Dusty / Apache: Shadows / What do you want: Faith, Adam / Dreamin': Burnette, Johnny / Jambalaya: Domi-

no, Fats / Those lazy hazy crazy days of summer: Cole, Nat "King" / Come softly to me: Fleetwoods / Only sixteen: Douglas, Craig / You make me feel so young: Riddle, Nelson / Una furtiva lagrima: L'Elixir D'Amour-Donizetti / Twist, The: Checker, Chubby / Three steps to heaven: Cochran, Eddie / My kind of girl: Monro, Matt / Miss Jamaica: Cliff, Jimmy / African waltz: Dankworth, John & His Orchestra / Goodness gracious me: Sellers, Peter/Sophia Loren / I remember you: Ifield, Frank / Do you want to know a secret: Kramer, Billy J. / Johnny remember me: Leyton, Johnny / Scandal (Love theme): Davis, Carl.
CD: Released Mar '89, on Parlophone by EMI Records. Catalogue no: **CDP 791 916 2**
Cass: Released Mar '89, on Parlophone by EMI Records. Deleted Aug '90. Catalogue no: **TCPCS 7331**
Album: Released Mar '89, on Parlophone by EMI Records. Deleted May '90. Catalogue no: **PCS 7331**
CD: Released Mar '89, on Parlophone by EMI Records. Catalogue no: **CDPCS 7331**

Scandalous John

SCANDALOUS JOHN (Film Soundtrack) (Various artists)
Tracks: / Pastures green: Various artists / Iris and Fido: Various artists / Pastures green: Various artists / Desert lullaby: Various artists / Train to Quivira: Various artists / Touch and go: Various artists / Scandalous John: Various artists / Warbag: Various artists / McCanless country: Various artists / Paco the brave: Various artists / Amanda: Various artists / Maripsas D'Amora: Various artists / Tribes: Various artists / Conquistador: Various artists / Quivira: Various artists / City of gold: Various artists / Paco the great engineer: Various artists / Pastures green: Various artists.
Album: Released '73, on Buena Vista by Walt Disney Productions. Deleted '78. Catalogue no: **BVS 5004**

Scarface

SCARFACE (Film Soundtrack) (Various artists)
Note: Music and songs from the

Brian de Palma film.
Album: Released Jan '89, on Silva Screen by Silva Screen Records. Catalogue no: **MCF 3198**

Scarlet & The Black

SCARLET AND THE BLACK, THE (Film Soundtrack) (Various artists)
Note: Gregory Peck TV film with music by Ennio Morricone.
Album: Released Jan '89, on Cerebus (USA) Catalogue no: **C'BUS 120**

Schifrin, Lalo

ANNO DOMINI (Film soundtrack)
Tracks: / Golgotha / Valerius and Sarah / King Herod's march / Eternal land,The / Fisherman, The / Peter and Thomas trek / Roman celebration / Road to Damascus,The / New love / Gladiator school / Majesty of Rome,The / Corina and Caleb / Roman legion / Wedding procession / Nero the lover / Martyrdom / Exalted love.
Album: Released Mar '86, on BBC by BBC Records. Catalogue no: **REB 561**
Cass: Released Mar '86, on BBC by BBC Records. Catalogue no: **ZCF 561**

Schikele, Peter

SILENT RUNNING (See under Silent Running)

School Daze

SCHOOL DAZE (Soundtrack) (Various artists)
Cass: Released '88, on EMI by EMI Records. Deleted Aug '90. Catalogue no: **TCMTL 1031**
CD: on EMI by EMI Records. Deleted Jun '89. Catalogue no: **CDP 748 680 2**
Album: Released '88, on EMI by EMI Records. Deleted Aug '90. Catalogue no: **MTL 1031**

Schulze, Klaus

ANGST (Film soundtrack)
Tracks: / Freeze / Pain / Memory / Surrender / Beyond.
Note: Soundtrack album by the top German electronic musician/composer. High rated original work. (Magnum Music May, 1988).
CD: Released '87, on Thunderbolt by Magnum Music Group. Catalogue no: **CDTB 2.027**
Cass: Released Feb '86, on

Al Pacino (centre) stars in *Sea of Love*

Thunderbolt by Thunderbolt Records. Catalogue no: **THBC 2.027**
Album: Released Feb '86, on Thunderbolt by Magnum Music Group. Catalogue no: **THBL 2.027**

Scott, John

PRAYER FOR THE DYING (See under Prayer For The...)

Scream For Help

SCREAM FOR HELP (See under Jones, John Paul)

Screen Music...

SCREEN MUSIC FOR LOVERS (Various artists)
Album: Released Mar '82, on Denon Deleted '88. Catalogue no: **SX 007**

Screen Themes

SCREEN THEMES 1985/6 (Various artists)
Tracks: / Back to the future: *Various artists* / Goonies: *Various artists* / Santa Claus: *Various artists*.
CD: Released May '86, on Denon Deleted '88. Catalogue no: **37-7815**

Scrooged

SCROOGED (Original Soundtrack) (Various artists)
Tracks: / Put a little love in your heart: *Lennox, Annie & Al Green* / Wonderful life: *Lennon, Julian* / Sweetest thing: *New Voices Of Freedom* / Love you take, The: *Hartman, Dan/Denise Lopez* / Get up'n'dance: *Kool Moe Dee* / We three kings of Orient are: *Davis,*

Miles/Larry Carlton / Christmas must be tonight: *Robertson, Robbie* / Brown eyed girl: *Poindexter, Buster* / Christmas song, The: *Cole, Natalie*.
CD: Released 21 Nov '88, on A&M by A&M Records. Catalogue no: **CDA 3921**
Cass: Released 21 Nov '88, on A&M by A&M Records. Catalogue no: **AMC 3921**
Album: Released 21 Nov '88, on A&M by A&M Records. Catalogue no: **AMA 3921**

Sea Hawk

SEA HAWK (Film soundtrack) (Various artists)
Note: New digital recording of the classic film score by Erich Wolfgang Korngold for the Errol Flynn Swashbuckler.
CD: Released Jan '89, on Silva Screen by Silva Screen Records. Catalogue no: **VCD 47304**

Sea Of Love

SEA OF LOVE (Original Film soundtrack) (Various artists) (See picture above)
Tracks: / Sea of love: *Various artists* / Poetic killing: *Various artists* / Cocktails and fingerprints: *Various artists* / Fear and passion: *Various artists* / Helen's 45: *Various artists* / Is she or isn't she: *Various artists* / Sea of love Reprise: *Various artists*.
Cass: Released Mar '90, on Phonogram by Phonogram Ltd. Catalogue no: **842 170 4**

CD: Released Mar '90, on Phonogram by Phonogram Ltd. Catalogue no: **842 170 2**
Album: Released Mar '90, on Phonogram by Phonogram Ltd. Catalogue no: **842 170 1**

Sea Wolves

SEA WOLVES (Film soundtrack) (National Philharmonic Orchestra))
Album: Released '80, on EMI by EMI Records. Deleted '85. Catalogue no: **EMC 3340**
Cass: Released '80, on EMI by EMI Records. Deleted '85. Catalogue no: **TCEMC 3340**

Search For Paradise

SEARCH FOR PARADISE (Film Soundtrack) (Various artists)
Note: Score by Dimitri Tiomkin.
Album: Released Jan '89, on Silva Screen by Silva Screen Records. Catalogue no: **LOC 1034**

Secombe, Harry

IF I RULED THE WORLD (SINGLE)
Tracks: / If I ruled the world.
Note: From the stage show '*Pickwick*'.
12" Single: Released '88, on Ditto by Pickwick Records. Catalogue no: **DTOL 10212**

Second Chorus

SECOND CHORUS (Film Soundtrack) (Various artists)
Note: Starring Fred Astaire.
Album: Released Jan '89, on Silva Screen by Silva Screen Records. Catalogue no: **HS 404**

SECOND CHORUS (VIDEO) (Various artists)
VHS: Released '88, on Global video Catalogue no: **VEP 0015**

Secret Diary Of Adrian...

SECRET DIARY OF ADRIAN MOLE (See under Dury, Ian)

Secret Of My Success

SECRET OF MY SUCCESS, THE (Original Soundtrack) (Various artists)
Tracks: / Secret of my success, The: *Night Ranger* / Sometimes the good guys finish first: *Benatar, Pat* / I burn for you: *Peck, Danny and Nancy Shanks* / Riskin' a romance: *Bananarama* / Gazebo:

Foster, David / Price of love, The: Daltrey, Roger / Water fountain: Foster, David / Don't ask the reason why: Restless Heart (Co-produced by Tim DeBois and Scott Hendricks) / Themes: Foster, David / Heaven and the heartaches: Taxxi.
Note: Music score by David Foster. Music supervision: Tommy Mottola and Jeb Brian.
CD: Released Jan '89, on MCA by MCA Records. Catalogue no: **MCAD 6205**
Album: Released Apr '87, on MCA by MCA Records. Catalogue no: **MCF 3380**
Cass: Released Apr '87, on MCA by MCA Records. Catalogue no: **MCFC 3380**

Secret Of Nimh

SECRET OF NIMH (Original Soundtrack) (Goldsmith, Jerry)
Album: Released Sep '82, on T. E. R. by That's Entertainment Records. Catalogue no: **TER 1026**
CD: Released Jan '89, on T. E. R. by That's Entertainment Records. Catalogue no: **VCD 47231**

Secret Of Santa Vittoria

SECRET OF SANTA VITTORIA (Film Score) (Various artists)
Tracks: / Song of Secret of Santa Vittoria (stay): Various artists / Big fool Bombolini: Various artists / Swastika: Various artists / Hiding the wine: Various artists / Love and tears: Various artists / Con lo zigo zigo zza: Various artists / Viva Bombolini: Various artists / Streets of Santa Vittoria: Various artists / Search: Various artists / Bei Kerzenlicht: Various artists / Celebration: Various artists.
Album: Released '73, on United Artists by EMI Records. Deleted '78. Catalogue no: **UAS 29053**
Cass: Released Jan '89, on Silva Screen by Silva Screen Records. Deleted Mar '90. Catalogue no: **MCAC 25034**
Album: Released Jan '89, on Silva Screen by Silva Screen Records. Catalogue no: **MCA 25034**

Secret Of The Sahara

SECRET OF THE SAHARA (Original Soundtrack) (Various artists)
Note: TV Mini-series starring Michael York. Ennio Morricone

score.
Album: Released Jan '89, on Silva Screen by Silva Screen Records. Catalogue no: **BL 71559**
CD: Released Jan '89, on Silva Screen by Silva Screen Records. Catalogue no: **BD 71559**
Cass: Released Jan '89, on Silva Screen by Silva Screen Records. Catalogue no: **BK 71559**

Secret Places

SECRET PLACES (Original Soundtrack) (Various artists)
Album: Released Sep '84, on Virgin by Virgin Records. Deleted '88. Catalogue no: **V 2312**

Secret Policeman's Ball

SECRET POLICEMAN'S BALL (Original Soundtrack) (Various artists)
Tracks: / Interesting facts: Various artists / Country and western supersong: Various artists / How do you do it?: Various artists / School master: Various artists / Pregnancy test: Various artists / Name's the game: Various artists / Stake your claim: Various artists / Entirely a matter for you: Various artists / Cheese shop: Various artists / Please: Various artists / Four Yorkshiremen: Various artists / Two little boys in blue: Various artists / End of the world: Various artists.
Cass: Released Dec '79, on Island by Island Records. Deleted Jun '88. Catalogue no: **ICT 9601**
Album: Released Dec '79, on Island by Island Records. Deleted Jun '88. Catalogue no: **ILPS 9601**

SECRET POLICEMAN'S OTHER BALL (Various artists)
Album: Released '81, on Springtime by Springtime Records. Deleted '84. Catalogue no: **HAHA 6003**

SECRET POLICEMAN'S OTHER BALL - THE MUSIC (Various artists)
Album: Released Mar '82, on Springtime by Springtime Records. Catalogue no: **HAHA 6004**

SECRET POLICEMAN'S THIRD BALL (The Comedy) (Various artists)
Note: Intro: Mike Hurley as Bill Bore & Chris Langham/Phil Cool/Emo Phillips / Spitting Image / Hale & Pace as The Two Rons/Mel Smith

& Griff Rhys-Jones (inc. Walk on the wild Side) / Lenny Henry / French & Saunders / Andrew Sachs as Manuel / Warren Mitchell as Alf Garnett / Rory Bremner / Ben Elton / Outro: Mike Hurley as Bill Bore
Album: Released Sep '87, on Virgin by Virgin Records. Deleted Feb '89. Catalogue no: **V 2459**
Cass: Released Sep '87, on Virgin by Virgin Records. Deleted Feb '89. Catalogue no: **TCV 2459**
CD: Released '87, on Virgin by Virgin Records. Delete Feb '89. Catalogue no: **CDV 2459**

SECRET POLICEMAN'S THIRD BALL (The Music) (Various artists)
Tracks: / Running up that hill: Bush, Kate / Save a prayer: Duran Duran / Voices of freedom: Reed, Lou / This is the world calling: Geldof, Bob / For everyman: Browne, Jackson / Victim of love: Erasure / Wouldn't it be good: Kershaw, Nik / Call me names: Armatrading, Joan / Imagine: Knopfler, Mark/Chet Atkins / Biko: Gabriel, Peter / Ship of fools: World Party.
CD: Released '87, on Virgin by Virgin Records. Catalogue no: **CDV 2458**
Cass: Released '89, on Virgin by Virgin Records. Catalogue no: **OVEDC 271**
Album: Released '89, on Virgin by Virgin Records. Catalogue no: **OVED 271**
Album: Released Sep '87, on Virgin by Virgin Records. Deleted Feb '89. Catalogue no: **V 2458**
Cass: Released Sep '87, on Virgin by Virgin Records. Deleted Feb '89. Catalogue no: **TCV 2458**

SECRET POLICEMAN'S THIRD BALL (VIDEO) (Various artists)
VHS: on Virgin Vision by Virgin Records. Catalogue no: **VVD 270**

Seesaw

SEESAW (Original Broadway Cast) (Various artists)
Tracks: / Nobody does it like me: Various artists / Welcome to Holiday Inn: Various artists / It's not where you start it's where you finish: Various artists.
Note: Cy Coleman, Dorothy Fields show.
Album: Released Jan '89, on Silva Screen by Silva Screen Rec-

ords. Catalogue no: **X 15563**
CD: Released Jan '89, on DRG
(USA) by DRG Records (USA).
Catalogue no: **CDRG 6108**
Cass: Released Jan '89, on Silva
Screen by Silva Screen Records.
Deleted Mar '90. Catalogue no: **XT 15563**

Sellers, Peter
PARKINSON INTERVIEW, THE
Album: Released Nov '80, on
BBC by BBC Records. Deleted
31 Aug '88. Catalogue no: **REH 402**
Cass: Released Nov '80, on BBC
by BBC Records. Deleted 31 Aug
'88. Catalogue no: **ZCR 402**

Sembello, Michael
MANIAC
Tracks: / Maniac.
Note: Featured in the film 'Flash-dance'.
7" Single: Released Aug '85, on
Casablanca by PolyGram UK Ltd.
Deleted '87. Catalogue no: **CAN 1017**
12" Single: Released Aug '85, on
Casablanca by PolyGram UK Ltd.
Deleted '87. Catalogue no: **CANX 1017**

Semprini
EXODUS (THEME FROM)
Tracks: / Exodus.
7" Single: Released Mar '61, on
H.M.V. by EMI Records. Deleted
Mar '64. Catalogue no: **POP 842**

Serious Charge
SERIOUS CHARGE (See under Richard, Cliff)

Serpent & The Rainbow
**SERPENT & THE RAINBOW
(Film Soundtrack) (Various artists)**
Note: Horror film from Wes Craven
with Brad Fiedel score.
CD: Released Jan '89, on Silva
Screen by Silva Screen Records.
Catalogue no: **VCD 47362**
Cass: Released Jan '89, on Silva
Screen by Silva Screen Records.
Catalogue no: **CTV 81362**
Album: Released Jan '89, on
Silva Screen by Silva Screen Rec-
ords. Catalogue no: **STV 81362**

Seven Brides For Seven
**SEVEN BRIDES FOR SEVEN
BROTHERS (Film Sound-**

track) (Various artists)
Note: Starring Howard Keel and
Jane Powell.
Album: Released Jan '89, on
MCA by MCA Records. Cata-
logue no: **MCA 25021**
Cass: Released Jan '89, on MCA
by MCA Records. Deleted Mar
'90. Catalogue no: **MCAC 25021**
CD: Released Jan '89, on MCA by
MCA Records. Deleted Mar '90.
Catalogue no: **MCAD 6176**

**SEVEN BRIDES FOR SEVEN
BROTHERS (Original London
Cast) (Various artists)**
Tracks: / June bride: *Various artists* / When you're in love: *Various
artists* / Overture: *Various artists* /
Bless your beautiful hide: *Various
artists* / Wonderful wonderful day:
Various artists / One man: *Various
artists* / Goin' courtin': *Various ar-
tists* / Love never goes away: *Vari-
ous artists* / Sobbin' woman:
Various artists / Townsfolk lament,
The: *Various artists* / Woman
ought to know her place, A: *Vari-
ous artists* / We gotta make it
through the winter: *Various artists*
/ Lonesome polecat: *Various ar-
tists* / Spring spring spring: *Various
artists* / Glad that you were born:
Various artists / Wedding dance:
Various artists.
Album: Released Jun '86, on First
Night by First Night Records.
Catalogue no: **CAST 2**
Cass: Released Feb '87, on CBS
by CBS Records & Distribution.
Deleted Jan '89. Catalogue no:
450232 4
Cass: Released Jun '86, on First
Night by First Night Records.
Catalogue no: **CASTC 2**
Album: Released Feb '87, on
CBS by CBS Records & Distribu-
tion. Deleted Jan '89. Catalogue
no: **450232 1**

**SEVEN BRIDES FOR SEVEN
BROTHERS (ORIGINAL
ISSUE) (Film soundtrack)
(Various artists)**
Album: Released Apr '61, on
MGM (EMI) Deleted '66. Cata-
logue no: **MGM C 853**

**SEVEN BRIDES FOR SEVEN
BROTHERS (VIDEO)**
VHS: Released '88, on MGM/UA
(Video) by MGM/UA Video. Cata-
logue no: **SMV 10091**

**SEVEN BRIDES FOR SEVEN
BROTHERS / ANNIE GET**

**YOUR GUN (Film sound-
tracks) (Various artists)**
Tracks: / Bless your beautiful hide:
Various artists / Wonderful, wonderful day: *Various artists* / Lonesome polecat: *Various artists* /
Goin' co'tin: *Various artists* / Sobbin' women: *Various artists* / June
bride: *Various artists* / Spring
Spring Spring: *Various artists* /
When your in love: *Various artists*
/ I got the sun in the morning: *Various artists* / They say it's wonderful: *Various artists* / You can't get
a man with a gun: *Various artists* /
My defences are down: *Various
artists* / Doin' what comes natur'lly:
Various artists / Girl that I marry:
Various artists / Anything you can
do: *Various artists* / There's no
business like show business: *Various artists*.
Cass: Released '73, on MGM
(Polydor) by Polydor Ltd. Deleted
'78. Catalogue no: **3110 038**
Album: Released '73, on MGM
(Polydor) by Polydor Ltd. Deleted
'78. Catalogue no: **2353 032**

**SEVEN BRIDES FOR SEVEN
BROTHERS/LILI (Film sound-
track) (Various artists)**
Tracks: / Bless your beautiful hide:
Keel, Howard / Wonderful, won-
derful day: *Powell, Jane* / Lone-
some polecat: *Lee, Bill & Brothers*
/ Goin' co'tin': *Powell, Jane & Bro-
thers* / Sobbin' women: *Keel, Ho-
ward & Brothers* / June bride:
Gibson, Virginia & Girls / Spring,
spring, spring: *Various artists* /
When you're in love: *Keel, Howard,
Jane Powell* / Adoration: *Various
artists* / Hi Lili, hi lo: *Caron, Leslie &
Mel Ferrer* / Lili & the puppets, Part
I: *Various artists* / Lili & the puppets,
Part II: *Various artists*.
Cass: Released Jan '90, on MGM
(EMI) Catalogue no: **TCMGM 9**
CD: Released Jan '90, on MGM
(EMI) Catalogue no: **CDP 793 305
2**
Album: Released Jan '90, on MGM
(EMI) Catalogue no: **LPMGM 9**
Album: Released Jan '90, on MGM
(EMI) Catalogue no: **793 305 1**
CD: Released Jan '90, on MGM
(EMI) Catalogue no: **CDMGM 9**
Cass: Released Jan '90, on MGM
(EMI) Catalogue no: **793 305 4**

Seven Deadly Sins
**SEVEN DEADLY SINS (Orig-
inal Broadway Cast) (Various
artists)**

Album: Released Jan '89, on Silva Screen by Silva Screen Records. Catalogue no: **AKL 5175**

Seventeen Seventy Six

1776 (Original Broadway Cast) (Various artists)
Album: Released Jan '89, on Silva Screen by Silva Screen Records. Catalogue no: **JS 3310**

Seventh Sign

SEVENTH SIGN (Original Soundtrack) (Various artists)
Tracks: / Opening, fish, desert, wrath, 1st seal: *Various artists* / Nightmare, The: *Various artists* / David's apartment: *Various artists* / Abby follows David to the synagogue: *Various artists* / World in trouble: *Various artists* / Parchment 2.29: *Various artists* / Stabbing, The: *Various artists* / Attempted suicide: *Various artists* / Lucci revealed: *Various artists* / Last martyr, The: *Various artists* / Walk to the gas chamber: *Various artists* / Birth: *Various artists* / Abby's death: *Various artists* / End credits: *Various artists*.
CD: Released Jan '89, on Silva Screen by Silva Screen Records. Catalogue no: **EDL 2506.2**
Album: Released Jan '89, on Silva Screen by Silva Screen Records. Catalogue no: **EDL 2506.1**

Seventh Voyage Of...

SEVENTH VOYAGE OF SINBAD (Original Soundtrack) (Various artists)
Album: Released Jan '89, on Silva Screen by Silva Screen Records. Catalogue no: **STV 81135**
CD: Released Jan '89, on Silva Screen by Silva Screen Records. Catalogue no: **VCD 47256**

Sex, Lies & Videotape

SEX, LIES AND VIDEOTAPE (Film Soundtrack) (Martinez, Cliff)
Tracks: / Garbage / Looks like a tablecloth / Take my shirt off / Are you comfortable / Here we go / What other men / Sniff the jacket / You've got a problem / I'm gonna drawl.
Cass: Released Oct '89, on Virgin by Virgin Records. Catalogue no: **TCV 2604**
CD: Released Oct '89, on Virgin by Virgin Records. Catalogue no: **CDV 2604**

Album: Released Oct '89, on Virgin by Virgin Records. Catalogue no: **V 2604**

Sex Pistols

C'MON EVERYBODY
Tracks: / C'mon everybody / God save the Queen (symphony) / Watcha gonna do about it.
Note: Featured in the film 'Great Rock'n'Roll Swindle'.
7" Single: Released '79, on Virgin by Virgin Records. Catalogue no: **VS 272**

GREAT ROCK'N'ROLL SWINDLE, THE (Film Soundtrack - Single Album)
Tracks: / God save the Queen (Symphony) / Great rock'n'roll swindle, The / You need hands / Silly thing / Lonely boy / Something else / Rock around the clock / C'mon everybody / Who killed Bambi / No one is innocent / L'anarchie pour le UK / My way.
Album: Released '88, on Virgin by Virgin Records. Deleted Feb '89. Catalogue no: **V 2168**
Cass: Released '88, on Virgin by Virgin Records. Deleted Feb '89. Catalogue no: **TCV 2168**
Album: Released '89, on Virgin by Virgin Records. Catalogue no: **OVED 234**
Cass: Released '89, on Virgin by Virgin Records. Catalogue no: **OVEDC 234**

GREAT ROCK'N'ROLL SWINDLE, THE (Film Soundtrack - Double album)
Tracks: / God save the Queen (Symphony) / Johnny B. Goode / Road runner / Anarchy in the UK / Don't give me no lip, child / I'm not your stepping stone / L'anarchie pour le UK / Silly thing / My way / I wanna be me / Something else / Rock around the clock / Lonely boy / EMI (orch).
Cass: Released '79, on Virgin by Virgin Records. Catalogue no: **TCVD 2510**
2 LP Set: Released '79, on Virgin by Virgin Records. Catalogue no: **VD 2510**
CD: Released Jul '86, on Virgin by Virgin Records. Catalogue no: **CDVD 2510**

GREAT ROCK'N'ROLL SWINDLE, THE (SINGLE)
Tracks: / Great rock'n'roll swindle, The / Rock around the clock.
Note: Taken from the film of the

same name.
7" Single: Released '80, on Virgin by Virgin Records. Catalogue no: **VS 290**

GREAT ROCK'N'ROLL SWINDLE (VIDEO)
Note: Running time for this film is 111 minutes. Cert: 18.
VHS: on Virgin Vision by Virgin Records. Deleted '88. Catalogue no: **VIRV 0101 A**
Beta: Released '88, on Virgin Vision by Virgin Records. Catalogue no: **VVB 010 B**
VHS: Released '88, on Virgin Vision by Virgin Records. Catalogue no: **VVB 010**

I'M NOT YOUR STEPPING STONE
Tracks: / I'm not your stepping stone / Pistols propaganda.
Note: Featured in the film 'Great rock'n'roll swindle.'
7" Single: Released Jun '80, on Virgin by Virgin Records. Catalogue no: **VS 339**

NO ONE IS INNOCENT (A punk prayer by Ronald Biggs)
Tracks: / My way / No one is innocent (7" only) / Biggest blow, The (12" only).
Note: Featured in the film 'Great rock'n'roll swindle'.
7" Single: Released Jun '78, on Virgin by Virgin Records. Catalogue no: **VS 220**
12" Single: Released Apr '83, on Virgin by Virgin Records. Deleted Mar '90. Catalogue no: **VS 220-12**

SILLY THING
Tracks: / Silly thing / Who killed Bambi.
Note: Featured in the 'Great rock'n'roll swindle.'
7" Single: Released Mar '79, on Virgin by Virgin Records. Catalogue no: **VS 256**

SOMETHING ELSE
Tracks: / Something else / Friggin' in the riggin'.
Note: Featured in the film the 'Great rock'n'roll swindle.'
7" Single: Released Feb '79, on Virgin by Virgin Records. Catalogue no: **VS 240**

WHO KILLED BAMBI (Sex Pistols & Tenpole Tudor)
Tracks: / Who killed Bambi.
Note: Featured in the 'Great rock'n'roll swindle.'
7" Single: Released Sep '81, on Virgin by Virgin Records. Deleted

'89. Catalogue no: **VS 443**

Seymour Orchestra

18 FAVOURITE FILM THEMES (Seymour Studio Orchestra)
Tracks: / Star trek / Star wars / 2001 / Superman / Rocky, theme from / Chariots of fire / Cavatina / Diamonds are forever / E.T., Theme from / Close encounters / Good, the bad and the ugly, The / Bright eyes / Do you know where you're going to (Theme from Mahogany) / Godfather, The (theme) / I just called to say I love you / Axel F / Evergreen / Pink panther.
Cass: Released Sep '86, on Castle Showcase by Castle Communications Records. Catalogue no: **SHTC 154**
Album: Released Sep '86, on Castle Showcase by Castle Communications Records. Catalogue no: **SHLP 154**

Shades

RUNNING WILD
Tracks: / Running wild / Running wild (vocal version).
Note: From the TV series of the same name.
7" Single: Released Mar '87, on Sierra by Sierra Records. Catalogue no: **FED 34**

Shadows

DEER HUNTER, THEME FROM
Tracks: / Deer hunter, Theme from / Bermuda triangle.
7" Single: Released Apr '79, on EMI by EMI Records. Catalogue no: **EMI 2939**

DON'T CRY FOR ME ARGENTINA (SINGLE)
Tracks: / Don't cry for me Argentina / Montezuma's revenge.
Note: From the stage show 'Evita'.
7" Single: Released Nov '78, on EMI by EMI Records. Deleted '81. Catalogue no: **EMI 2890**

DON'T CRY FOR ME ARGENTINA (SINGLE)
Tracks: / Don't cry for me Argentina.
Note: From the stage show 'Evita'.
7" Single: Released '80, on EMI by EMI Records. Catalogue no: **LR 4978**

EASTENDERS, THEME FROM
Tracks: / No dancing / Eastenders (theme from) / Howards Way (theme from).

7" Single: Released Nov '86, on Polydor by Polydor Ltd. Deleted Jan '88. Catalogue no: **POSP 847**

RHYTHM AND GREENS
Tracks: / Rhythm & greens.
Note: Taken from the film of the same name.
12" Single: Released '82, on EMI (Europe) by EMI Records. Catalogue no: **K 062Z 07527**
7" Single: Released Sep '64, on Columbia by EMI Records. Deleted Sep '67. Catalogue no: **DB 7342**

SNOWMAN, THE (THEME FROM)
Tracks: / Snowman, The (theme from) / Outigo.
7" Single: Released Jul '87, on Polydor by Polydor Ltd. Catalogue no: **POSP 898**

STINGRAY
Tracks: / Stingray.
7" Single: Released Jun '65, on Columbia by EMI Records. Deleted Jun '68. Catalogue no: **DB 7588**

Shaft

SHAFT (Film Soundtrack) (Various artists)
Note: Composed by Isaac Hayes.
Cass: Released Jan '89, on Silva Screen by Silva Screen Records. Catalogue no: **78.701**
2 LP Set: Released Jan '89, on Silva Screen by Silva Screen Records. Catalogue no: **68.701**

SHAFT, THEME FROM (See under Hayes, Isaac)

Shaft's Big Score

SHAFT'S BIG SCORE (Various artists)
Tracks: / Blowin' your mind: *Various artists* / Other side: *Various artists* / Smart money: *Various artists* / First meeting: *Various artists* / Ashby - Kelly man: *Various artists* / Don't misunderstand: *Various artists* / Move on in: *Various artists* / Symphony for shafted souls (big chase): *Various artists* / Take off: *Various artists* / Dance of the cars water ballet (part 1): *Various artists* / Dance of the cars water ballet (part 2): *Various artists* / Call and response: *Various artists*.
Cass: Released '73, on Polydor by Polydor Ltd. Deleted '78. Catalogue no: **3110 073**
Album: Released '73, on Polydor

by Polydor Ltd. Deleted '78. Catalogue no: **2315 115**

Shane, Paul

HI DE HI (HOLIDAY ROCK) (Shane, Paul & The Yellowcoats)
Tracks: / Hi de hi (holiday rock) / Juke box Saturday night.
7" Single: Released May '81, on Parlophone by EMI Records. Deleted May '84. Catalogue no: **F 3436**
7" Single: Released May '81, on EMI by EMI Records. Deleted May '84. Catalogue no: **EMI 5180**

Sharkeys Machine

SHARKEYS MACHINE (Original Soundtrack) (Various artists)
Note: Music from the Burt Reynolds film.
Album: Released Jan '89, on Silva Screen by Silva Screen Records. Catalogue no: **BSK 3653**

Shaw, Francis

MARY'S THEME (FROM JAMAICA INN) (Shaw, Francis & The L.S.O.)
Tracks: / Mary's theme (from Jamaica Inn).
7" Single: Released Apr '83, on Peach River Deleted '84. Catalogue no: **BBPR 4**

Shaw, Roland

JAMES BOND 007 (Shaw, Roland Orchestra)
Tracks: / You only live twice / Goldfinger / From Russia with love / On Her Majesty's Secret Service / Diamonds are forever / Thunderball / Underneath the mango tree / Pussy Galore's flying circus / Look of love, The / Dawn raid on Fort Knox / Bond below disco volante / 007 theme.
CD: Released Jun '88, on Decca by Decca International. Catalogue no: **CD 417 854 2**
Cass: Released Jun '88, on Decca by Decca International. Catalogue no: **417 854 4**

Shaw, Sandie

ALWAYS SOMETHING THERE TO REMIND ME
Tracks: / Always something there to remind me.
Note: Featured in the film 'Letter To Brezhnev'.
12" Single: Released Apr '89, on

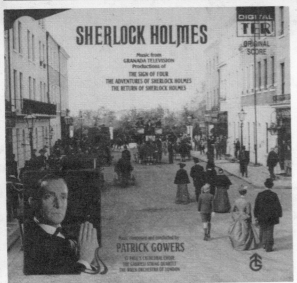

Sherlock Holmes - **music from the Granada TV series (TER)**

PRT by Castle Communications Records. Catalogue no: **PYT 25**
7" Single: Released Oct '64, on Pye Deleted Oct '67. Catalogue no: **7N 15704**
7" Single: Released Apr '89, on PRT by Castle Communications Records. Catalogue no: **PYS 25**

ALWAYS SOMETHING THERE TO REMIND ME (OLD GOLD)
7" Single: Released Jul '82, on Old Gold by Old Gold Records. Catalogue no: **OG 9144**

She Devil

SHE DEVIL (film soundtrack) (Various artists)
Tracks: / I will survive: *Sa-Fire* / You can have him: *Carmel* / C'mon and get my love: *D Mob* / Always: *Kimmel, Tom* / You're the devil in disguise: *Presley, Elvis* / Party up: *Checker, Chubby* / Tren d'amour: *Stewart, Jermaine* / That's what I call love: *Ceberano, Kate* / Tied up: *Yello* / It's getting hot: *Fat Boys*.
Cass: Released May '90, on Polydor by Polydor Ltd. Catalogue no: **841 583 4**
CD: Released May '90, on Polydor by Polydor Ltd. Catalogue no: **841**

583 2
Album: Released May '90, on Polydor by Polydor Ltd. Catalogue no: **841 583 1**

She Loves Me...

SHE LOVES ME (Original Broadway cast) (Various artists)
Album: Released '88, on DRG (USA) by DRG Records (USA). Catalogue no: **DS 2 15008**
Cass: Released '88, on DRG (USA) by DRG Records (USA). Catalogue no: **DS2C 15008**
CD: Released Jan '89, on DRG (USA) by DRG Records (USA). Catalogue no: **831 968-2**

Sheena...

SHEENA: QUEEN OF THE JUNGLE (Film Soundtrack) (Various artists)
Note: Composed by Richard Hartley.
Album: Released May '85, on SPI Milan (France) Catalogue no: **ACH 017**
Album: Released Jan '89, on Silva Screen by Silva Screen Records. Catalogue no: **STV 81225**
Cass: Released Jan '89, on Silva Screen by Silva Screen Records.

Catalogue no: **CTV 81225**

Shenandoah

SHENANDOAH (Film Soundtrack) (Various artists)
Note: Frank Skinner score for the James Stewart western.
Album: Released Jan '89, on Silva Screen by Silva Screen Records. Catalogue no: **254884.1**

SHENANDOAH (Original Broadway cast) (Various artists)
Album: Released Jan '89, on Silva Screen by Silva Screen Records. Catalogue no: **AGL 1 3763**
Cass: Released Jan '89, on Silva Screen by Silva Screen Records. Catalogue no: **AGK 1 3763**
CD: Released Jan '89, on Silva Screen by Silva Screen Records. Catalogue no: **3763.2**

Shepherd, Cybill

BLUE MOON
Tracks: / Blue moon / I told you I loved you so get out.
Note: From the TV series "*Moonlighting*"
7" Single: Released Oct '87, on MCA by MCA Records. Catalogue no: **MCA 1218**
12" Single: Released Nov '87, on MCA by MCA Records. Catalogue no: **MCAS 1218**

Sherlock Holmes...

SHERLOCK HOLMES (Original London cast) (Various artists)
Tracks: / Sherlock Holmes: *Various artists* / Without him, there can be no me: *Various artists* / London is London: *Various artists* / Vendetta: *Various artists* / Anything you want to know: *Various artists* / Her face: *Various artists* / Men like you: *Various artists* / Lousy life, A: *Various artists* / I shall find her: *Various artists* / No reason: *Various artists* / Halcyon days: *Various artists* / Without him, there can be no me (reprise): *Various artists* / Down the apples 'n' pears: *Various artists* / He's back: *Various artists* / Million years ago or was it yesterday, A: *Various artists* / Best of you, the best of me, The: *Various artists* / Sherlock Holmes (reprise): *Various artists*.
Album: Released Jun '89, on RCA by BMG Records (UK). Catalogue no: **BL 74145**
Cass: Released Jun '89, on RCA

Soundtrack to *Shirley Valentine* (Silva Screen)

by BMG Records (UK). Catalogue no: **BK 74145**
CD: Released Jun '89, on RCA by BMG Records (UK). Catalogue no: **BD 74145**

SHERLOCK HOLMES (TV Soundtrack) (Various artists) (See picture on previous page)
Cass: Released Mar '90, on Silva Screen by Silva Screen Records. Catalogue no: **ZCTER1136**
Album: Released Mar '90, on T. E. R. by That's Entertainment Records. Catalogue no: **TER 1136**
CD: Released Jan '89, on T. E. R. by That's Entertainment Records. Catalogue no: **CDTER 1136**

She's Gotta Have It

SHE'S GOTTA HAVE IT (Film Soundtrack) (Various artists)
Tracks: / Opening credits: *Various artists* / Brooklyn bridge: *Various artists* / He's on it: *Vari-*
ous artists / Thought: *Various artists* / Nola: *Various artists* / Ferrybank restaurant: *Various artists* / Work montage: *Various artists* / Who will be the one: *Various artists* / Nola (instrumental): *Various artists* / Thought, A (reprise): *Various artists* / Nola cleans up: *Various artists* / Opal: *Various artists* / Final confession: *Various artists* / She's walkin': *Various artists* / Opal (reprise): *Various artists* / Hawk, The: *Various artists* / Nola - piano: *Various artists* / End credits: *Various artists*.
Note: Featuring Bill Lee, Ronnie Dyson, Harold Vick, Stanley Conell, Kenny Washington, Virgil Jones, Cedar Walton, Joe Chambers. Produced and arranged by Bill Lee.
Cass: Released Mar '87, on Antilles / New Directions by Island Records. Deleted Jun '88. Catalogue no: **ANC 8713**
Album: Released Mar '87, on Antilles / New Directions by Island Records. Deleted Jun '88. Catalogue no: **AN 8713**

She's Out Of Control

SHE'S OUT OF CONTROL (Film Soundtrack) (Various artists)
Tracks: / Where's the fire: *Hinton, Troy* / You should be loving me: *Starr, Brenda.K.* / Concentration: *Thornally, Phil* / Loneliest heart, The: *Boy's Club* / Hunger of love: *Faltermeyer, Harold* / Khey Fm radio sweeper: *Ladd, Jim* / Winning side: *Oingo Boingo* / Daddy's little girl: *Wilson, Brian* / Venus: *Avalon, Frankie* / You really got me: *Kinks* / Feel the shake: *Jet Boy*.
Cass: Released Aug '90, on MCA by MCA Records. Catalogue no: **MCAC 6281**
CD: Released Aug '90, on MCA by MCA Records. Catalogue no: **MCAD 6281**
Album: Released Aug '90, on MCA by MCA Records. Catalogue no: **MCA 6281**

Shining (Film)

SHINING, THE (Original Soundtrack) (Various artists)
Tracks: / Shining, The: *Various artists* / Rocky mountains: *Various artists* / Lontano: *Various artists* / Music for strings, percussion and celesta: *Various artists* / Utrenja: *Various artists* / Awakening of Jacob: *Various artists* / De natura sonoris No.2: *Various artists* / Home: *Various artists*.
Album: Released '80, on Warner Bros. by WEA Records. Catalogue no: **K 56827**

Ship Ahoy / Las Vegas...

SHIP AHOY / LAS VEGAS NIGHTS (Original Soundtracks) (Various artists)
Album: Released Jan '89, on Silva Screen by Silva Screen Records. Catalogue no: **HS 5011**

Shire, David

RETURN TO OZ (See under Return To Oz)

Shirelles

SOLDIER BOY (SINGLE)
Tracks: / Soldier boy.
Note: Featured in the film 'Wan-

derers'.

7" Single: Released May '62, on H.M.V. by EMI Records. Deleted May '65. Catalogue no: **POP 1019**

WILL YOU LOVE ME TOMOR-ROW (CD SINGLE)
Tracks: / Will you love me tomorrow / Boys / Mama said.
CD Single: Released Jun '90, on Charly by Charly Records. Catalogue no: **CDS 12**

WILL YOU LOVE ME TOMOR-ROW (OLD GOLD)
Tracks: / Will you love me tomorrow / Soldier boy / Mama said (CD single only.).
Note: Featured in the film 'Police Academy'.
CD Single: Released Nov '88, on Old Gold by Old Gold Records. Catalogue no: **OG 6105**
7" Single: Released Apr '83, on Old Gold by Old Gold Records. Catalogue no: **OG 9286**

Shirley Valentine

SHIRLEY VALENTINE (Film soundtrack) (Various artists) (See picture on previous page)
Tracks: / Girl who used to be me, The: *Austin, Patti* / Shirley Valentine, Theme from: *Various artists* / Affection: *Various artists* / Crumbling resolve: *Various artists* / Dreams: *Various artists* / Costas: *Various artists* / Coming to Greece: *Various artists* / Nocturne: *Various artists* / Arrival in Mykonos: *Various artists*.
CD: Released Nov '89, on Silva Screen by Silva Screen Records. Catalogue no: **FILMCD 062**
Album: Released Nov '89, on Silva Screen by Silva Screen Records. Catalogue no: **FILM 062**
Cass: Released Nov '89, on Silva Screen by Silva Screen Records. Catalogue no: **FILMC 062**

Shock Treatment

SHOCK TREATMENT (Original Soundtrack) (Various artists)
Album: Released Nov '81, on Warner Bros. by WEA Records. Catalogue no: **K 56957**

Shocker

NO MORE MR NICE GUY (See under Megadeth)

SHOCKER (Film soundtrack) (Various artists)

Tracks: / Shocker: *Dudes Of Wrath* / Love transfusion: *Pop, Iggy* / No more Mr. Nice Guy: *Megadeth* / Sword and stone: *Bonfire* / Timeless love: *Saraya* / Shockdance: *Dudes Of Wrath* / Demon bell (The ballad of Horace Pinker): *Dangerous Toys* / Awakening, The: *Voodoo X* / Different breed: *Dead On* / Shocker (reprise): *Dudes Of Wrath*.
CD: Released Dec '89, on SBK by SBK Records. Catalogue no: **SBKCD 3**
Cass: Released Dec '89, on SBK by SBK Records. Catalogue no: **SBKTC 3**
Cass: Released Dec '89, on SBK by SBK Records. Catalogue no: **793 233 4**
CD: Released Dec '89, on SBK by SBK Records. Catalogue no: **CDP 793 233 2**
Album: Released Dec '89, on SBK by SBK Records. Catalogue no: **793 233 1**
Album: Released Dec '89, on SBK by SBK Records. Catalogue no: **SBKLP 3**

SHOCKER (FILM BACK-GROUND MUSIC) (Goldstein, William)
Album: Released Mar '90, on Silva Screen by Silva Screen Records. Catalogue no: **VS5247**
Cass: Released Mar '90, on Silva Screen by Silva Screen Records. Catalogue no: **VSC5247**
CD: Released Feb '90, on Silva Screen by Silva Screen Records. Catalogue no: **VSD5247**

Shoes Of The Fisherman

SHOES OF THE FISHERMAN, THE (Original Soundtrack) (Various artists)
Note: Alex North score for the 1968 film starring Anthony Quinn.
Cass: Released Jan '89, on MCA by Silva Screen Records. Catalogue no: **MCAC 25130**
Album: Released Jan '89, on MCA by Silva Screen Records. Catalogue no: **MCA 25130**

Shogun (Film)

SHOGUN (Original Soundtrack) (Various artists)
Tracks: / Shogun / Japans, The / Tea and jealousy / Nocturne / Toranga / To the galley / Miriko / Ceremonial / Despair and madness / Anjiro / Blackthorne / Es-

cape from Osaka / Finale / Cloak and dagger / Shock to the heart / Voices from the heart / You are what you are / Love is a game / Cold truth / If tomorrow comes / Can't live without your love / First time / Out of love again.
Note: Music composed and conducted by Maurice Jarre.
Album: Released Mar '88, on Jet by Jet Records. Deleted 10 Jul '89. Catalogue no: **JETLP 248**
Cass: Released Nov '82, on RSO by Polydor Ltd. Catalogue no: **3216 283**
Album: Released Oct '86, on Attack Catalogue no: **ATA 006**
Cass: Released Mar '88, on Jet by Jet Records. Deleted 10 Jul '89. Catalogue no: **JETCA 248**
Album: Released Nov '82, on RSO by Polydor Ltd. Catalogue no: **2394 283**

Shooting Party (film)

SHOOTING PARTY, THE (Original soundtrack) (Royal Philharmonic Orchestra)
Note: Composed by John Scott.
Album: Released Jan '89, on Silva Screen by Silva Screen Records. Catalogue no: **STV 81235**

Show Boat

MAKING OF SHOW BOAT, THE (VIDEO) (Various artists)
Note: Cast includes: Magnolia Hawks-Frederica Von Stade; Gaylord Ravenal-Jerry Hadley; Julie LaVerne-Teresa Stratas; Joe-Bruce Hubbard; Queenie-Karla Burns; Frank Schultz-David Garrison; Ellie May Chipley-Paige O'Hara; Captain Andy Hawks-Robert Nichols; Lady on the Lake-Lillian Gish. Ambrosian Chorus. London Sonfonietta conducted by John McGlinn. The making of 'Show Boat' - the first ever complete recording in it's original version with music by Jerome Kern and lyrics by Oscar Hammerstein 2nd. Running time: 60 mins.
VHS: Released Oct '89, on PMI by EMI Records. Catalogue no: **MVP 99 1194 3**

SHOW BOAT (London Cast Recording) (Various artists)
Note: First complete recording of the Jerome Kern/Oscar Hammerstein II musical with a first rate studio cast featuring the London Sinfonietta.
Cass: Released Jul '86, on CBS

Cass: Released Jul '86, on CBS by CBS Records & Distribution. Deleted Jan '89. Catalogue no: **40 70281**

Album: Released Jul '86, on CBS by CBS Records & Distribution. Deleted Jan '89. Catalogue no: **CBS 70281**

CD: Released Jul '86, on CBS by CBS Records & Distribution. Deleted '89. Catalogue no: **CD 70281**

SHOW BOAT (HMV) (Various artists)

Note: The first ever complete recording of Jerome Kern & Oscar Hammerstein II's great musical, with Frederica von Stade, Jerry Hadley, Teresa Stratas, London Sinfonietta. Conducted by John McGlinn.

2 LP Set: Released 26 Sep '88, on H.M.V. by EMI Records. Catalogue no: **EX 7491081**

CD Set: Released 26 Sep '88, on H.M.V. by EMI Records. Catalogue no: **CD RIVER 1**

Cass set: Released 26 Sep '88, on H.M.V. by EMI Records. Catalogue no: **TC RIVER 1**

LP Set: Released 26 Sep '88, on H.M.V. by EMI Records. Catalogue no: **RIVER 1**

Cass set: Released 26 Sep '88, on H.M.V. by EMI Records. Catalogue no: **EX 7491084**

CD Set: Released 26 Sep '88, on H.M.V. by EMI Records. Catalogue no: **CDS 749 108 2**

SHOW BOAT (ORIGINAL ISSUE) (Studio cast recording) (Various artists)

Album: Released Jun '60, on H.M.V. by EMI Records. Deleted '65. Catalogue no: **CLP 1310**

SHOW BOAT - THE BROADWAY ALBUM (Highlights) (Various artists)

Tracks: / Show boat overture: *Various artists* / Cotton blossom: *Various artists* / Where's the mate for me: *Various artists* / Make believe: *Various artists* / Ol' man river: *Various artists* / Can't help lovin' dat man: *Various artists* / Life on the wicked stage: *Various artists* / Till good luck comes my way: *Various artists* / I might fall back on you: *Various artists* / Queenie's ballyhoo: *Various artists* / You are love: *Various artists* / Show boat Finale Act 1: *Various artists* / At the

fair: *Various artists* / Why do I love you: *Various artists* / Bill: *Various artists* / Goodbye my Lady love: *Various artists* / After the ball: *Various artists* / Hey, feller: *Various artists* / Finale ultimo: *Various artists*.
Note: Highlights album from the complete Show boat released 9/88.(RIVER 1). Frederica Von Stade (Magnolia Hawks); Jerry Hadley (Gaylord Ravenal); Teresa Stratas (Julie LaVerne); Bruce Hubbard (Joe); Karla Burns (Queenie); David Garrison (Frank Schultz); Paige O'Hara (Ellie May Chipley); Robert Nichols (Captain Andy Hawks). London Sinfonietta conducted by John McGlinn.

Album: Released Oct '89, on EMI by EMI Records. Catalogue no: **EL 7498471**

Cass: Released Oct '89, on EMI by EMI Records. Catalogue no: **EL 7498474**

CD: Released Oct '89, on EMI by EMI Records. Catalogue no: **CDC 749 847 2**

SHOWBOAT (Original Broadway Cast) (Various artists)

Album: Released Jan '89, on Silva Screen by Silva Screen Records. Catalogue no: **AC 55**

Cass: Released Jan '89, on Silva Screen by Silva Screen Records. Catalogue no: **BT 55**

SHOWBOAT (Original 1971 London Cast) (Various artists)

Tracks: / Cotton blossom: *Various artists* / Where's the mate for me: *Various artists* / Make believe: *Various artists* / Can't help lovin' dat man: *Various artists* / I might fall back on you: *Various artists* / Ol' man river: *Various artists* / How'd you like to spoon with me: *Various artists* / You are love: *Various artists* / Queenie's ballyhoo: *Various artists* / Nobody else but me: *Various artists* / At the fair: *Various artists* / Bill: *Various artists* / Dance away the night: *Various artists* / Why do I love you?: *Various artists* / Finale: *Various artists*.

Album: Released Apr '83, on T. E. R. by That's Entertainment Records. Catalogue no: **TER 1057**

Cass: Released Apr '83, on T. E. R. by That's Entertainment Records. Catalogue no: **ZCTER 1057**

CD: Released Feb '90, on Silva Screen by Silva Screen Records. Catalogue no: **DUNCD 107**

SHOWBOAT (Original Lon-

don Cast) (Various artists)

Album: Released Jun '88, on First Night by First Night Records. Catalogue no: **OCR 1**

Cass: Released Jun '88, on First Night by First Night Records. Catalogue no: **OCRC 1**

SHOWBOAT (1962 Revival Cast) (Various artists)

Album: Released Jan '89, on Silva Screen by Silva Screen Records. Deleted Mar '90. Catalogue no: **PS 02220**

Cass: Released Jan '89, on Silva Screen by Silva Screen Records. Catalogue no: **PST 02220**

CD: Released Jan '89, on CBS (import) by CBS Records & Distribution. Catalogue no: **CK 02220**

SHOWBOAT/THE BAND WAGON (1953 Film soundtrack) (Various artists)

Tracks: / Ol' man river: *Warfield, William* / Make believe: *Keel, Howard/Kathryn Grayson* / I might fall back on you: *Champion, Gower & Marge* / Can't help lovin' dat man: *Gardner, Ava* / Why do I love you: *Keel, Howard/Kathryn Grayson* / Bill: *Gardner, Ava* / Life upon the wicked stage: *Champion, Gower & Marge* / You are love: *Keel, Howard/Kathryn Grayson* / Ol' man river (reprise): *Warfield, William* / Shine on your shoes, A: *Astaire, Fred* / By myself: *Astaire, Fred* / Dancing in the dark: *Various artists* / Triplets: *Astaire, Fred/Nanette Fabray/Jack Buchanan* / New sun in the sky: *Various artists* / I guess I'll have to change my plans: *Various artists* / Louisiana hayride: *Fabray, Nanette* / I love Louisa: *Astaire, Fred* / That's entertainment: *Astaire, Fred/Nanette Fabray/Jack Buchanan*.

Cass: Released Jan '90, on MGM (EMI) Catalogue no: **793 306 4**

CD: Released Jan '90, on MGM (EMI) Catalogue no: **CDMGM 10**

CD: Released Jan '90, on MGM (EMI) Catalogue no: **CDP 793 306 2**

Album: Released Jan '90, on MGM (EMI) Catalogue no: **LPMGM 10**

Cass: Released Jan '90, on MGM (EMI) Catalogue no: **TCMGM 10**

Album: Released Jan '90, on MGM (EMI) Catalogue no: **793 306 1**

Show Classics

SHOW CLASSICS (Various artists)

Cass set: Released Nov '84, on Telstar by Telstar Records (UK). Catalogue no: **STAC 2010**

LP Set: Released Nov '84, on Telstar by Telstar Records (UK). Catalogue no: **STAR 2010**

Show Hits

SHOW HITS (Orchestra & Singers) (Various artists)
CD: Released Dec '88, on Laser Catalogue no: **CD 86019**

Shy People

SHY PEOPLE (Film Soundtrack) (Tangerine Dream)
Tracks: / Shy people / Joe's place / Harbor, The / Nightfall / Dancing on a white moon / Civilized illusions / Swamp voices / Transparent days / Shy people (reprise).
Note: Score by Tangerine Dream for the Award winning film starring Barbara Hershey and Jill Clayburgh.
Cass: Released Jun '90, on Silva Screen by Silva Screen Records. Catalogue no: **FILMC 027**
CD: Released Jun '90, on Silva Screen by Silva Screen Records. Catalogue no: **FILMCD 027**
Album: Released Jun '90, on Silva Screen by Silva Screen Records. Catalogue no: **FILM 027**

Sicilian

SICILIAN, THE (Film Soundtrack) (Hungarian State Symphony Orchestra)
Tracks: / Sicilian, The / Camilla returns from riding / Stealing grain / Camilla's horses / On the stairs / Monastery ride / I'm not leaving...yet / Off to Palermo / Giuliano recovered / Monastery, The / Fire from heaven / Terranova / They join him / Little Guiliano / Don Massino in Rome / Jewel robbery, The / With this ring / Silvio's blessing / To Frisella's / Confession, The / That's life, gentlemen / Meeting ends, The / Ginestra massacre / Giuliano's funeral / End title.
Note: David Mansfield/Hungarian State Symphony Orch.
CD: Released Jan '89, on Silva Screen by Silva Screen Records. Catalogue no: **90682.2**
Album: Released Feb '88, on Virgin by Virgin Records. Deleted May '90. Catalogue no: **V 2487**
CD: Released 20 Feb '88, on Virgin by Virgin Records. Catalogue no: **CDV 2487**

Cass: Released Feb '88, on Virgin by Virgin Records. Deleted Jun '90. Catalogue no: **TCV 2487**

Sid & Nancy - Love Kills

SID & NANCY - LOVE KILLS (Film Soundtrack) (Various artists)
Tracks: / Love kills: Strummer, Joe / Haunted: Pogues / Pleasure and pain: Jones, Steve / Chinese choppers: Pray For Rain / She never took no for an answer: Cale, John / Love kills: Circle Jerks / Off the boat: Pray For Rain / Dum dum club: Strummer, Joe / Burning room: Pray For Rain / Junk theme: Pogues / I wanna be your dog: Oldman, Gary / Taxi to heaven: Pray For Rain.
Note: Original Soundtrack album to the new Alex Cox movie about the story of Sid Vicious and Nancy Spungen.
CD: Released Aug '86, on MCA by MCA Records. Deleted Apr '88. Catalogue no: **DMCG 6011**
Cass: Released Aug '86, on MCA by MCA Records. Deleted Apr '88. Catalogue no: **MCGC 6011**
Album: Released Aug '86, on MCA by MCA Records. Deleted Apr '88. Catalogue no: **MCG 6011**

SID & NANCY (VIDEO) (Various artists)
Note: A savagely brilliant account of the last days of Sid Vicious. Features music by the Pogues and Joe Strummer. Directed by Alex Cox (Repoman and Straight to hell). Released on the 10th anniversary of Sid's death.
VHS: Released Feb '89, on Channel 5 by Channel 5 Video. Catalogue no: **CFV 04022**

Side By Side By...

SIDE BY SIDE BY SONDHEIM (Original London Cast) (Various artists)
Tracks: / Comedy tonight: Various artists / Love is in the air: Various artists / Little things you do together, The: Various artists / You must meet my wife: Various artists / Getting married today: Various artists / I remember: Various artists / Can that boy foxtrot: Various artists / Too many mornings: Various artists / Company: Various artists / Another hundred people: Various artists / Barcelona: Various artists / Being alive: Various artists / I never do anything twice (Madam's song): Various artists / Bring on the girls: Various artists / Ah, Paree: Various artists / Buddy's blues: Various artists / Broadway baby: Various artists / You could drive a person crazy: Various artists / Everybody says don't: Various artists / There won't be trumpets: Various artists / Anyone can whistle: Various artists / Send in the clowns: Various artists / Pretty lady: Various artists / We're gonna be alright: Various artists / Boy like that, A: Various artists / Boy from ..., The: Various artists / If momma was married: Various artists / Losing my mind: Various artists / Could I leave you: Various artists / I'm still here: Various artists / Side by side by side: Various artists.
2 LP Set: Released '79, on RCA by BMG Records (UK). Deleted '84. Catalogue no: **CBL2 1851**
Cass: Released Apr '90, on RCA by BMG Records (UK). Catalogue no: **GK 81851**
2 LP Set: Released Aug '89, on RCA by BMG Records (UK). Catalogue no: **BL 81851**
CD: Released Apr '90, on RCA by BMG Records (UK). Catalogue no: **GD 81851**
Cass: Released '79, on RCA by BMG Records (UK). Deleted '84. Catalogue no: **DPMK 1037**

Siesta

SIESTA (See under Davis, Miles)

Sign Of Four

SIGN OF FOUR, THE (Original Score) (Gowers, Patrick)
Cass: Released May '89, on T. E. R. by That's Entertainment Records. Catalogue no: **ZCTER 1136**
Album: Released May '89, on T. E. R. by That's Entertainment Records. Catalogue no: **TER 1136**

Sigue Sigue Sputnik

LOVE MISSILE F1-11
Tracks: / Love missile F1-11 / Hack attack / Love missile (dance mix) (Extra track on 12" only).
Note: Featured in the film "Ferris Bueller's Day Off".
12" Single: Released Feb '86, on Parlophone by EMI Records. Catalogue no: **12R 5551**
7" Single: Released Feb '86, on Parlophone by EMI Records. Catalogue no: **R 5551**

Silent Running (film)

SILENT RUNNING (Film soundtrack) (Various artists)
Note: Composed by Peter Schikele and Joan Baez.
Album: Released Mar '79, Catalogue no: **VC 81072**
Album: Released Jan '89, on Silva Screen by Silva Screen Records. Catalogue no: **STV 81072**

Silent Witness

SILENT WITNESS, THE (Film soundtrack) (Various artists)
Cass: Released '80, on Gull by Gull Records. Catalogue no: **ZCGUL 1030**
Album: Released '80, on Gull by Gull Records. Catalogue no: **GULP 1030**

Silk Stockings

SILK STOCKINGS (Film soundtrack) (Various artists)
Tracks: / Too bad: *Various artists* / Paris loves lovers: *Various artists* / Stereophonic sound: *Various artists* / It's a chemical reaction: *Various artists* / That's all of you: *Various artists* / Satin and silk: *Various artists* / Silk stockings: *Various artists* / Without love: *Various artists* / Fated to be mated: *Various artists* / Josephine: *Various artists* / Siberia: *Various artists* / Red blues..: *Various artists* / Ritz roll and rock: *Various artists*.
Album: Released Feb '87, on CBS by CBS Records & Distribution. Deleted Jun '88. Catalogue no: **CBS 70290**
Cass: Released Feb '87, on CBS by CBS Records & Distribution. Deleted Jun '88. Catalogue no: **40 70290**
Album: Released Jan '89, on MCA by MCA Records. Catalogue no: **MCA 39074**
CD: Released Feb '87, on CBS by CBS Records & Distribution. Deleted Jan '89. Catalogue no: **CD 70290**
Cass: Released Jan '89, on MCA by MCA Records. Catalogue no: **MCAC 39074**

SILK STOCKINGS (VIDEO) (Various artists)
Note: Fred Astaire in his last great musical role with Cyd Charisse. Running time: 114 minutes. Cert: U.
VHS: Released '88, on MGM/UA (Video) by MGM/UA Video. Cata-

logue no: **SMV 10051**

SILK STOCKINGS/LES GIRLS (Various artists)
Tracks: / Too bad's: *Astaire, Fred / Peter Lorre / Joseph Buloff / Jules Munshin* / Paris loves lovers: *Astaire, Fred / Cyd Charisse / Janis Paige* / It's a chemical reaction, that's all / All of you: *Astaire, Fred / Cyd Charisse / Carol Richards* / Satin and silk: *Paige, Janis* / Without love: *Astaire, Fred / Cyd Charisse / Carol Richards* / Fated to be mated: *Astaire, Fred / Cyd Charisse / Carol Richards* / Josephine: *Paige, Janis* / Siberia: *Lorre, Peter /Joseph Buloof / Jules Munshin* / Red blues: *Russians* / Ritz roll and rock, The: *Astaire, Fred* / Too bad: *Charisse, Cyd / Peter Lorre/Joseph Buloff / Jules Munshin* / Les girls: *Kelly, Gene / Kendall, Kay / Mitzi Gaynor / Tania Elg* / You're just too too: *Kelly, Gene/Kay Kendall* / Ca, c'est l'amour: *Elg, Tania* / Ladies in waiting: *Gaynor, Mitzi/ Kay Kendall / Taina Elg* / Why am I so gone (about that gal): *Kelly, Gene*.
CD: Released Apr '90, on MGM (EMI) Catalogue no: **CDMGM 16**
Album: Released Apr '90, on MGM (EMI) Catalogue no: **794 251 1**
Cass: Released Apr '90, on MGM (EMI) Catalogue no: **794 251 4**
Album: Released Apr '90, on MGM (EMI) Catalogue no: **LPMGM 16**
CD: Released Apr '90, on MGM (EMI) Catalogue no: **CDP 794 251 2**
Cass: Released Apr '90, on MGM (EMI) Catalogue no: **TCMGM 16**

Silkwood

SILKWOOD (Film soundtrack) (Various artists)
Note: Composed by Georges Delerue.
Album: Released Apr '84, on DRG (USA) by DRG Records (USA). Deleted Jan '89. Catalogue no: **DRG 6107**
Album: Released Apr '84, on PRT by Castle Communications Records. Deleted Jan '89. Catalogue no: **NFP 5501**
Cass: Released Apr '84, on DRG (USA) by DRG Records (USA). Deleted Jan '89. Catalogue no: **DRGC 6107**

Silly Wizzard

TAKE THE HIGH ROAD (TV theme)
Tracks: / Take the high road.
7" Single: Released Oct '80, on Highway by Highway Records. Catalogue no: **SHY 100**

Silsoe

AZTEC GOLD (The Official ITV World Cup Theme)
Tracks: / Aztec gold / On wings of the wind.
7" Single: Released May '86, on CBS by CBS Records & Distribution. Catalogue no: **A 7231**

Silver Bullet (Film)

SILVER BULLET (Film soundtrack) (Various artists)
Note: Based on the Stephen King story. Composed by Jay Chatt away.
Album: Released Jan '89, on Silva Screen by Silva Screen Records. Catalogue no: **STV 81264**

Silverado

SILVERADO (Film soundtrack) (Various artists)
Album: Released '85, on Geffen by Geffen Records (USA). Catalogue no: **GEF 70268**
Cass: Released '85, on Geffen by Geffen Records (USA). Catalogue no: **40 70268**

Simon, Carly

NOBODY DOES IT BETTER
Tracks: / Nobody does it better / After the storm.
Note: From the James Bond film "*The spy who loved me*".
7" Single: Released Mar '82, on Elektra by Elektra Records (UK). Catalogue no: **K 12261**

WHY? (See panel on next page)
Tracks: / Why? / Why? (Instrumental).
12" Single: Released Jun '89, on WEA by WEA Records. Catalogue no: **U 7501T**
7" Single: Released Jul '82, on Elektra by Elektra Records (UK). Catalogue no: **K 79300**
12" Single: Released Jul '82, on Elektra by Elektra Records (UK). Catalogue no: **K 79300T**
7" Single: Released Jun '89, on WEA by WEA Records. Catalogue no: **U 7501**

Carly Simon - "Why?" from the film *Soup for One* (Mirage)

Simon & Garfunkel

GRADUATE, THE (Film soundtrack)
Tracks: / Sound of silence, The / Jungleman party foxtrot / Mrs. Robinson / Sunporch cha-cha / Scarborough Fair / On the strip / April come she will / Great effect / Big bright green pleasure machine.
Album: Released Oct '68, on CBS by CBS Records & Distribution. Deleted Oct '73. Catalogue no: **CBS 70042**
CD: Released Dec '85, on CBS by CBS Records & Distribution. Catalogue no: **CD 70042**

MRS ROBINSON
Tracks: / Mrs. Robinson / Bridge over troubled water.
7" Single: Released Jul '82, on Geffen by Geffen Records (USA). Catalogue no: **GEFA 2221**
7" Single: Released Jul '68, on CBS by CBS Records & Distribution. Deleted Jul '71. Catalogue no: **CBS 3443**

Simon, Paul

ONE-TRICK PONY (Film soundtrack)
Tracks: / Late in the evening / That's why God made the movies / One-trick pony / How the heart approaches what it yearns / Oh Marion / Ace in the hole / Nobody / Jonah / God bless the absentee / Long long day.
CD: Released '87, on Warner Bros. by WEA Records. Catalogue no: **K2 56846**
Cass: Released Aug '80, on Warner Bros. by WEA Records. Catalogue no: **K4 56846**
Album: Released Aug '80, on Warner Bros. by WEA Records. Deleted Jul '90. Catalogue no: **K 56846**

ONE-TRICK PONY (SINGLE)
Tracks: / One-trick pony / Long long day.
7" Single: Released Nov '80, on Warner Bros. by WEA Records. Deleted Nov '83. Catalogue no: **K 17715**

Simple Man

SIMPLE MAN, A (Various artists)
Tracks: / White on white: *Various artists* / Characters appear, The: *Various artists* / Organ grinder, An: *Various artists* / Sitting: *Various artists* / Death of mother: *Various artists* / Going to work: *Various*

artists / Coming from the hill: *Various artists* / Waiting: *Various artists* / Golden room, The: *Various artists* / Three Anns: *Various artists* / Sea scape: *Various artists* / Man with red eyes: *Various artists* / Clogs: *Various artists* / Homage: *Various artists*.
CD: Released Jun '90, on First Night by First Night Records. Catalogue no: **SCENECD 16**
Cass: Released Jun '90, on First Night by First Night Records. Catalogue no: **SCENEC 16**

Simple Minds

DON'T YOU (FORGET ABOUT ME)
Tracks: / Don't you (forget about me) / Brass band in African chimes, A.
Note: Featured in the film 'The Breakfast Club'.
12" Single: Released Apr '85, on Virgin by Virgin Records. Catalogue no: **VS 749-12**
7" Single: Released Apr '85, on Virgin by Virgin Records. Catalogue no: **VS 749**
CD 3": Released '88, on Virgin by Virgin Records. Catalogue no: **CDT 2**

Sinatra, Frank

BROADWAY KICK/ADVENTURES OF THE HEART
Tracks: / There's no business like show business / They say it's wonderful / Some enchanted evening / You're my girl / Lost in the stars / Why can't you behave? / I whistle a happy tune / Girl that I marry, The / Can't you just see yourself? / There but for you go I / Bali ha'i / Where is my Bess? / I guess I'll have to dream the rest / If only she looked my way / Love me / Nevertheless (I'm in love with you) / We kiss in a shadow / I am loved / Take my love / I could write a book / Mad about you / Sorry / On the island of Stromboli / It's only a paper moon.
Cass: Released Jun '85, on CBS (Blue Diamond) by CBS Records & Distribution. Deleted Aug '87. Catalogue no: **40 22182**
Album: Released Jun '85, on CBS (Blue Diamond) by CBS Records & Distribution. Deleted Aug '87. Catalogue no: **CBS 22182**

CHICAGO
Tracks: / Chicago.
Note: From the film "*With a song in my heart*".

7" Single: Released Nov '57, on Capitol by EMI Records. Deleted Nov '60. Catalogue no: **CL 14800**

COFFEE SONG, THE
Tracks: / Coffee song, The.
Note: From the stage show "*Piccadilly hayride*".
7" Single: Released Nov '61, on Reprise by WEA Records. Deleted Nov '64. Catalogue no: **R 20035**

GRANADA
Tracks: / Granada.
Note: From the film "Gay Ranhero".
7" Single: Released Sep '61, on Reprise by WEA Records. Deleted Sep '64. Catalogue no: **R 20010**

GREAT FILMS AND SHOWS
Tracks: / Night and day / I wish I were in love again / I got plenty o' nuttin' / I guess I'll have to change my plan / Nice work if you can get it / I won't dance / You'd be so nice to come home to / I got it bad and that ain't good (CD only.) / From this moment on / Blue moon / September in the rain / It's only a paper moon / You do something to me / Taking a chance on love / Get happy / Just one of those things / I love Paris / Chicago / High hopes / I believe / Lady is a tramp, The / Let's do it (With Shirley MacLaine.) / C'est magnifique / Tender trap, The / Three coins in the fountain / Young at heart / Girl next door, The / They can't take that away from me / Someone to watch over me / Little girl blue / Like someone in love / Foggy day, A / I get a kick out of you / My funny valentine / Embraceable you / That old feeling / I've got a crush on you / Dream / September song / I'll see you again / As time goes by / There will never be another you / I'll remember April / Stormy weather / I can't get started / Around the world / Something's gotta give / Just in time / Dancing in the dark / Too close for comfort / I could have danced all night / Cheek to cheek / Song is you, The / Baubles, bangles and beads / Almost like being in love / Lover / On the sunny side of the street / That old black magic / I've heard that song before / You make me feel so young / Too marvellous for words / It happened in Monterey / I've got you under my skin / How about you / Pennies from Heaven / You're getting to be a habit with me / You brought a new

kind of love to me / Love is here to stay / Old devil moon / Makin' whoopee / Anything goes / What is this thing called love / Glad to be unhappy / I get along without you very well / Dancing on the ceiling / Can't we be friends / All the way / To love and be loved / All my tomorrows / I couldn't sleep a wink last night / Spring is here / One for my baby / Time after time / It's all right with me / It's the same old dream / Wait for me (Johnny Conco theme) / Wait till you see her / Where are you / Lonely town / Where or when / I concentrate on you / Love and marriage.
LP Set: Released Apr '89, on Capitol by EMI Records. Catalogue no: **FS 1**
CD Set: Released Apr '89, on Capitol by EMI Records. Catalogue no: **CDS 792 224 2**
CD Set: Released Apr '89, on Capitol by EMI Records. Catalogue no: **CDFS 1**

HELLO DOLLY (Sinatra, Frank/Count Basie)
Tracks: / Hello Dolly.
Note: From the show "*Hello Dolly*".
7" Single: Released Sep '64, on Reprise by WEA Records. Deleted Sep '67. Catalogue no: **R 20351**

HIGH HOPES
Tracks: / High hopes.
7" Single: Released Aug '59, on Capitol by EMI Records. Deleted Aug '62. Catalogue no: **CL 15052**

LOVE AND MARRIAGE
Tracks: / Love and marriage.
7" Single: Released Jan '56, on Capitol by EMI Records. Deleted Jan '59. Catalogue no: **CL 14503**
7" Single: Released Mar '84, on EMI Golden 45's by EMI Records. Catalogue no: **G45 9**

ME AND MY SHADOW (Sinatra, Frank & Sammy Davis Jr.)
Tracks: / Me and my shadow.
Note: From the film "*Hold that ghost*".
7" Single: Released Dec '62, on Reprise (USA). Deleted Dec '66. Catalogue no: **R 20128**

NEW YORK, NEW YORK (SINGLE)
Tracks: / New York, New York / My kind of town (Track on 12" version only) / LA is my lady (Track on 12" version only).
12" Single: Released Feb '86, on Warner Bros. by WEA Records.

Deleted Jan '88. Catalogue no: **K 14502T**
7" Single: Released Feb '86, on Warner Bros. by WEA Records. Catalogue no: **K 14502**

RADIO DAYS
Cass set: Released '89, on Ditto by Pickwick Records. Catalogue no: **DTO 10304**
CD: Released Dec '87, on Pickwick by Pickwick Records. Catalogue no: **PWK 046**

RADIO YEARS, THE
CD: Released '89, on K-Tel by K-Tel Records. Catalogue no: **NCD 5152**
CD: Released Dec '87, on Tamy. Deleted Jan '89. Catalogue no: **20107**

RARE RECORDINGS 1935-1970
Cass: Released Jan '89, on Silva Screen by Silva Screen Records. Catalogue no: **SH 2040**

REHEARSALS AND BROADCASTS (1942-46)
CD: Released Aug '90, on Victorious Discs. Catalogue no: **VJC 1004-2**

SCREEN SINATRA
Tracks: / From here to eternity / Three coins in the fountain / Young at heart / Just one of those things / Someone to watch over me / Not as a stranger / Tender trap, The / Wait for me (Johnny Conco theme) / All the way / Chicago / Monique - Song from Kings Go Forth / They came to Cordura / To love and be loved / High hopes / All my tomorrows / It's alright with me / C'est magnifique / Dream.
CD: Released Mar '89, on MFP by EMI Records. Catalogue no: **CDMFP 6052**
Album: Released Sep '80, on Capitol by EMI Records. Deleted '88. Catalogue no: **CAPS 1038**
CD: Released Mar '89, on MFP by EMI Records. Catalogue no: **CDB 791 875 2**
Cass: Released Sep '80, on Capitol by EMI Records. Deleted Jul '88. Catalogue no: **TCCAPS 1038**
Cass: Released Sep '88, on MFP by EMI Records. Catalogue no: **TCMFP 5835**
Album: Released Sep '88, on MFP by EMI Records. Catalogue no: **MFP 5835**

SINATRA SCREEN

Tracks: / Continental, The / It's the same old dream / Laura / Stormy weather / I've got a crush on you / House I live in, The / All through the day / I couldn't sleep a wink last night / Time after time / But beautiful / I fall in love too easily / Brooklyn bridge.

Cass: Released Jul '87, on CBS by CBS Records & Distribution. Catalogue no: **460015 4**

Album: Released Jul '87, on CBS by CBS Records & Distribution. Catalogue no: **460015 1**

SINATRA: THE RADIO YEARS 1939-55

Tracks: / All or nothing at all / After all / I've got my eyes on you / Polka dots and moonbeams / Deep night / Whispering / Sky fell down, The / On the Isle of May / It's a blue world / Fable of the rose / Marie / A lover in blue / Careless / I'll never smile again / Our love affair / East of the sun / One I love, The / Shadows on the sand / That's how it goes / I got a kick out of you / Let's get lost / Embraceable you / Night and day / Close to you / I couldn't sleep a wink last night / Falling in love with you / Music stopped, The / My ideal / Speak low / People will say we're in love / Long ago and far away / I'll get by / Sweet Lorraine / Swinging on a star / These foolish things / Very thought of you, The / All the things you are / My melancholy baby / Homesick that's all / Till the end of time / What makes the sunset? / I fall in love too easily / I begged her / Don't forget tonight tomorrow / That's for me / I found a new baby / I'm always chasing rainbows / Aren't you glad you're you / It might as well be spring / Lilly belle / If I loved you / Slowly / Great day / I only have eyes for you / Oh, what it seemed to be / Full moon and empty arms / Exactly like you / I fall in love with you every day / It's a good day / My sugar is so refined / Ole buttermilk sky / Lullaby of broadway / I won't dance / Touch of your hand, The / Why was I born? / All through the day / Make believe / Song is you, The / All the things you are / You can't see the sun when you're crying / Anniversary song / You do / Let it snow, let it snow, let it snow / I wish I didn't love you so / Wrap your troubles in dreams / Nature boy / My haunted heart / Little white lies / Tree in the meadow, A / It only

happens when I dance with you / My happiness / O sole mio / I found a new baby / It isn't fair / Body and soul / When you're smiling / I've got a crush on you / My foolish heart / Best things in life are free, The / I love you / Why remind me? / Just you, just me / Somebody loves me / Polka dots and moonbeams / Sorry / Young at heart / Among my souvenirs / September song / As time goes by / Take a chance / Till we meet again / Meet me in dreamland / There's a long long trail / Don't blame me / 'S wonderful / Night and day / Somebody loves you? / Nevertheless / On the sunny side of the street / Love me or leave me / Try a little tenderness / Out of nowhere / I've got my love to keep me warm / What can I say? / Between the devil and the deep blue sea / One hundred years from today / I'm in the mood for love / Tenderly / Hello young lovers / She's funny that way / I don't know why / Come rain or shine.

Note: Includes a medley of Summertime / It ain't necessarily so / Bess, oh where's my Bess.

LP Set: Released Oct '87, on Meteor by Magnum Music Group. Catalogue no: **MTBS 001**

CD Set: Released Mar '89, on Meteor by Magnum Music Group. Catalogue no: **CDMTBS 001**

SINATRA: THE RADIO YEARS (IMPORT)

Tracks: / Night and day / Laura / Somebody loves me / Tenderly / You make me feel so young / Nevertheless / On the sunny side of the street / Love me or leave me / You are love / They didn't believe me / You are love / They didn't believe me / Out of nowhere / I've got my love to keep me warm / For you / Ol' man river / Music stopped, The / I don't stand a ghost of a chance / You do something to me / Begin the beguine.

CD: Released '89, on Tamy. Catalogue no: **TAMY 20.107**

SONGS BY SINATRA

Note: Complete radio performances, featuring Jimmy Durante.

Album: Released Jan '89, on Silva Screen by Silva Screen Records. Catalogue no: **PJ 003**

Album: Released Nov '88, on Apex. Catalogue no: **AX 7**

TENDER TRAP, THE

Tracks: / Tender trap, The.

Note: From the film "*The tender trap*".

7" Single: Released Jan '56, on Capitol by EMI Records. Deleted Jan '59. Catalogue no: **CL 14511**

THREE COINS IN THE FOUNTAIN

Tracks: / Three coins in the fountain

Note: From the film "*Three coins in the fountain*".

7" Single: Released Jul '54, on Capitol by EMI Records. Deleted Jul '57. Catalogue no: **CL 14120**

Sing

SING (Film soundtrack) (Various artists)

Tracks: / Sing: *Thomas, Mickey* / Birthday suit: *Kemp, Johnny* / Romance (love theme): *Carrack, Paul & Terri Nunn* / You don't have to ask me twice: *Peeples, Nia* / One more time: *Bolton, Michael* / Somethin' to believe in: *Champlin, Bill* / Total concentration: *Labelle, Patti* / (Everybody's gotta) face the music: *Cronin, Kevin* / What's the matter with love: *Wilkerson, Laurnea* / We'll never say goodbye: *Garfunkel, Art.*

CD: Released 5 Jun '89, on CBS by CBS Records & Distribution. Catalogue no: **463455 2**

Cass: Released 5 Jun '89, on CBS by CBS Records & Distribution. Catalogue no: **463455 4**

Album: Released 5 Jun '89, on CBS by CBS Records & Distribution. Catalogue no: **463455 1**

Sing A Song Of...

SING A SONG OF PLAYSCHOOL (Various artists)

Tracks: / Sing a song of play school: *Various artists* / Standing on one leg: *Various artists* / Seagull: *Various artists* / Train song: *Various artists* / Ground: *Various artists* / Underneath the spreading chestnut tree: *Various artists* / Flying: *Various artists* / Elephant wobbles: *Various artists* / Wiper flop: *Various artists* / Simple song: *Various artists* / Whether the weather: *Various artists* / Seeds: *Various artists* / Heads and shoulders, knees and toes: *Various artists* / Time for a bath: *Various artists* / Little ticks of time: *Various artists* / Spiders: *Various artists* / Wouldn't it be funny?: *Various artists.*

Album: Released Oct '76, on BBC

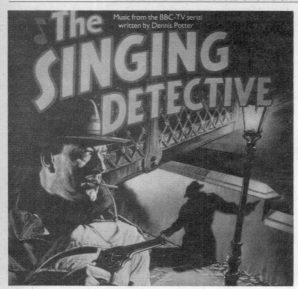

Various Artists - *Singing Detective* (BBC)

by BBC Records. Deleted 31 Aug '88. Catalogue no: **REC 212**
Cass: Released Oct '76, on BBC by BBC Records. Deleted 31 Aug '88. Catalogue no: **MRMC 031**

Sing Out

SING OUT (TV theme) (Various artists)
CD: Released Aug '87, on IMS by Polydor Ltd. Catalogue no: **TMBCD 115**
Album: Released Sep '87, on Tembo by Tembo Records. Catalogue no: **TMB 115**
Cass: Released Sep '87, on Tembo by Tembo Records. Catalogue no: **TMBC 115**

Singin' In The Rain

SINGIN' IN THE RAIN (Original London cast) (Various artists)
Tracks: / Singin' in the rain: *Various artists* / Temptation: *Various artists* / I can't give you anything but love: *Various artists* / Be a clown: *Various artists* / Too marvellous for words: *Various artists* / You are my lucky star: *Various artists* / Moses: *Various artists* / Good morning: *Various artists* / Fit as a fiddle: *Various artists* / Fascinating rhythm: *Various artists* /

Would you: *Various artists* / All I do is dream of you: *Various artists* / Make 'em laugh: *Various artists* / You were meant for me: *Various artists* / Broadway ballet: *Various artists* / Finale: *Various artists*.
Note: Artists include Tommy Steele, Roy Castle, Danielle Carson.
Album: Released Mar '84, on First Night by First Night Records. Catalogue no: **RAIN 1**
Cass: Released Mar '84, on First Night by First Night Records. Catalogue no: **RAINC 1**

SINGIN' IN THE RAIN (Film soundtrack) (Various artists)
Album: Released Jul '86, on CBS by CBS Records & Distribution. Deleted Jan '89. Catalogue no: **CBS 70282**
Cass: Released Jul '86, on CBS by CBS Records & Distribution. Deleted Jan '89. Catalogue no: **40 70282**
CD: Released Apr '87, on CBS by CBS Records & Distribution. Deleted Jan '89. Catalogue no: **CD 70282**

SINGIN' IN THE RAIN (Songs from the film) (Various artists)
Album: Released Dec '82, on

EEC Imports Catalogue no: **6878 134**
Cass: Released Jan '83, on MGM (Polydor) by Polydor Ltd. Catalogue no: **7413134**

SINGIN' IN THE RAIN (VIDEO) (Various artists)
Note: Running time: 99 mins.
VHS: Released '88, on MGM/UA (Video) by MGM/UA Video. Catalogue no: **SMV 10185**

SINGIN' IN THE RAIN/EASTER PARADE (Various artists)
Tracks **(Singin' In The Rain):** / Singin' in the rain: *Kelly, Gene* / Fit as a fiddle: *Kelly, Gene/Donald O'Connor* / All I do is dream of you: *Reynolds, Debbie/Girly Chorus* / Make 'em laugh: *O'Connor, Donald* / You were meant for me: *Kelly, Gene* / Good morning: *Reynolds, Debbie with Gene Kelly & Donald O'Connor* / All I do is dream of you: *Kelly, Gene* / Moses: *Kelly, Gene/Donald O'Connor* / Broadway ballet: *Kelly, Gene* / You are my lucky star: *Kelly, Gene/Debbie Reynolds* / **(Easter Parade):** Steppin' out with my baby: *Astaire, Fred* / Fella with an umbrella, A: *Garland, Judy/Peter Lawford* / Shaking the blues away: *Miller, Ann* / I love a piano: *Various artists* / Snooky Ookums: *Various artists* / When the midnight choo choo leaves for Alabam': *Various artists* / Couple of swells, A: *Garland, Judy & Fred Astaire* / It only happens when I dance with you: *Astaire, Fred* / Better luck next time: *Garland, Judy* / Easter parade: *Garland, Judy & Fred Astaire*.
Album: Released Jan '90, on MGM (EMI) Catalogue no: **LPMGM 4**
Album: Released Jan '90, on MGM (EMI) Catalogue no: **793 300 1**
Cass: Released Jan '90, on MGM (EMI) Catalogue no: **TCMGM 4**
CD: Released Jan '90, on MGM (EMI) Catalogue no: **CDP 793 300 2**
Cass: Released Jan '90, on MGM (EMI) Catalogue no: **793 300 4**
CD: Released Jan '90, on MGM (EMI) Catalogue no: **CDMGM 4**

Singing...

SINGING IN THE BAND (Songs From Play School & Play Away) (Various artists)

Tracks: / When you're in my band: *Various artists* / Reggae Rita: *Various artists* / Fish disco: *Various artists* / On the ning nang nong: *Various artists* / Magnificent sanctuary band, The: *Various artists* / Do your ears hang low?: *Various artists* / Simple Simon says: *Various artists* / Clapping song, The: *Various artists* / All-delicious: *Various artists* / Stop start medley: *Various artists* / Three little fishes: *Various artists* / My hat it has three corners: *Various artists* / Blue blues: *Various artists* / Ugly duckling market day, The: *Various artists* / If you're happy and you know it: *Various artists*.

Note: Jump up time with Floella's Caribbean medley (a) Play mas (b) Brown girl in the ring (c) Yellow bird (d) Dis long time gal (e) Hooray, hooray, it's a holi-holiday (f) Play Mas. Sing along medley (a) Zip-a-dee-doo-dah (b) It's a grand and healthy life (c) Moonstruck (d) Sparrow, The (e) When the red red robin comes bob bob-bobbing along (f) The Tennessee wig walk (g) What I want is a proper cup of coffee

Album: Released Feb '84, on BBC by BBC Records. Deleted 31 Aug '88. Catalogue no: **REC 495**

Cass: Released Apr '84, on BBC by BBC Records. Deleted 31 Aug '88. Catalogue no: **ZCM 495**

Singing Detective

OTHER SIDE OF THE SINGING DETECTIVE (Various artists)
Tracks: / Umbrella man: *Kaye, Sammy Orchestra* / Copenhagen / I'll just close my eyes: *Shelton, Anne* / Old Moses put Pharoah in his place: *Waring, Fred & His Pennsylvanians* / Stop crying: *King Oliver & Orchestra* / Three caballeros: *Crosby, Bing & Andrews Sisters* / That's for me: *Haymes, Dick* / I'll be around: *Mills Brothers* / Sing nightingale sing: *Anderson, Lale* / There's something wrong with the weather: *Stone, Lew & His Band* / Java jive: *Ink Spots* / There's a fellow waiting in Poughkeepsie: *Crosby, Bing & Andrews Sisters* / Till then: *Mills Brothers* / Chinatown, my Chinatown: *Jolson, Al* / Let the people sing: *Payne, Jack Orchestra* / I'm making believe: *Inkspots with Ella Fitz-*

gerald / Little Dutch mill: *Noble, Ray & His Orchestra & Al Bowlly* / Hush, hush, hush, here comes the bogeyman: *Hall, Henry Orchestra* / Later on: *Lynn, Vera* / Bird songs at eventide: *Ronalde, Ronnie with Robert Farnon & Orchestra*.

CD: Released Sep '88, on BBC by BBC Records. Catalogue no: **BBC CD 708**

Cass: Released Oct '88, on BBC by BBC Records. Catalogue no: **ZCN 708**

Album: Released Sep '88, on BBC by BBC Records. Catalogue no: **REN 708**

SINGING DETECTIVE, THE (Various artists) (See picture on previous page)
CD: Released May '87, on BBC by BBC Records. Catalogue no: **BBC CD 608**

Album: Released Oct '86, on BBC by BBC Records. Catalogue no: **REN 608**

Cass: Released Oct '86, on BBC by BBC Records. Catalogue no: **ZCN 608**

CD: Released Oct '86, on BBC by BBC Records. Catalogue no: **CD 608**

Sins

SINS (TV Soundtrack) (Various artists)
Tracks: / It's hard to be tender: *Simon, Carly* / Love and passion: *Various artists* / Oath, The: *Various artists* / Arrival in Paris: *Various artists* / Venezia anziana: *Various artists* / Face to face with the mirror: *Various artists* / At Susumos: *Various artists* / Concerto for Helen: *Various artists* / Hubert: *Various artists* / Despair: *Various artists* / Happy moments: *Various artists* / Golden ball: *Various artists* / Jeanne death: *Various artists* / Remembering: *Various artists* / Holland concertino: *Various artists* / Roofs of Paris: *Various artists*.
Note: The music is by Francis Lai with additional music by Roland Romanelli and Michael Legrand.
Album: Released Jun '86, on Philips (Holland) by PolyGram UK Ltd. Catalogue no: **826 720 1**
Cass: Released Jun '86, on Philips (Holland) by PolyGram UK Ltd. Catalogue no: **826 720 4**

Slaves of New York

SLAVES OF NEW YORK (Film

Soundtrack) (Various artists)
Tracks: / Good life: *Inner City* / Tumblin' down: *Marley, Ziggy & The Melody Makers* / Buffalo stance: *Cherry, Neneh* / Some guys have all the luck: *Priest, Maxi* / Girlfriend: *Boy George* / Warrior: *P.I.L.* / Admit it: *Ambitious Lovers* / Fall in love with me: *Pop, Iggy* / Love overlap: *Ambitious Lovers* / Tongue dance: *Les Rita Mitsouko*.
CD: Released Jul '89, on Virgin by Virgin Records. Catalogue no: **CDV 2597**
Cass: Released Jul '89, on Virgin by Virgin Records. Catalogue no: **TCV 2597**
Album: Released Jul '89, on Virgin by Virgin Records. Catalogue no: **V 2597**

Slipper & The Rose

SLIPPER & THE ROSE, THE (Film Soundtrack) (Various artists)
Note: Starring Richard Chamberlain and Gemma Craven.
Cass: Released Jan '89, on MCA by MCA Records. Catalogue no: **MCAC 1540**
Album: Released Jan '89, on MCA by MCA Records. Catalogue no: **MCA 1540**

Smike

SMIKE (Original Cast Recording)
Tracks: / Doing things by numbers / Here I am / We'll find our day / In the warm light of a brand new day / Brimstone and treacle.
2 LP Set: Released Sep '83, on Smike Catalogue no: **SMIKE 1**
Cass set: Released Sep '83, on Smike Catalogue no: **SMIKE C1**

SMIKE (Original London Cast) (Various artists)
Tracks: / Overture - daily test: *Various artists* / Here I am (looking for my name): *Various artists* / Stop and just think who you could be: *Various artists* / Transition music: *Various artists* / Dotheboys hall: *Various artists* / We've got the youngsters' interest at heart: *Various artists* / Don't let life get you down: *Various artists* / In the warm light of a brand new day: *Various artists* / Brimstone and treacle: *Various artists* / We'll find our day: *Various artists* / Reprise: *Various artists* / Dotheboys rock: *Various*

artists / Dotheboys rock: *Various artists.*
Album: Released Nov '85, on Flashback by Mainline Records. Catalogue no: **FBLP 8085**
Cass: Released Nov '85, on Flashback by Mainline Records. Catalogue no: **ZCFBL 8085**

Smiley's People

SMILEY'S PEOPLE (Music from the television soundtrack) (Various artists)
Album: Released Sep '82, on BBC by BBC Records. Deleted '88. Catalogue no: **REP 439**
Cass: Released Sep '82, on BBC by BBC Records. Deleted '88. Catalogue no: **ZCH 439**

Smith & Jones

BITTER AND TWISTED (Smith, Mel & Griff Rhys-Jones)
Tracks: / Bits we managed to get on side 1 / Rest, The.
Note: In response to the massive success of Smith and Jones Head to Head conversations on ITV, an entire album has now been produced for the lovers of Mel & Griffs humour (there can't be many that are not). WARNING. This record contains material that may shock and may offend. It is also totally unsuitable for children and for broadcast. Sticker will be on all LP's, cassettes and CD's.
CD: Released Nov '88, on 10 Records by Virgin Records. Catalogue no: **DIXCD 79**
Cass: Released Nov '88, on 10 Records by Virgin Records. Catalogue no: **CDIX 79**
Album: Released Nov '88, on 10 Records by Virgin Records. Catalogue no: **DIX 79**

Smith, Mel

ALAS SMITH AND JONES (See under Alas Smith And Jones)

Smokey & The Bandit

SMOKEY & THE BANDIT (Original Soundtrack) (Various artists)
Note: Music from the Burt Reynolds film.
Album: Released Jan '89, on Silva Screen by Silva Screen Records. Catalogue no: **MCA 1673**
Cass: Released Jan '89, on Silva Screen by Silva Screen Records.

Catalogue no: **MCAC 1673**
SMOKEY & THE BANDIT 2 (Original Soundtrack) (Various artists)
Album: Released Jan '89, on Silva Screen by Silva Screen Records. Catalogue no: **MCA 37161**

Snoopy

SNOOPY (Original London cast) (Various artists)
Tracks: / Overture: *Various artists* / World according to Snoopy, The: *Various artists* / Snoopy's song: *Various artists* / Woodstock's theme: *Various artists* / Hurry up face: *Various artists* / Edgar Allan Poe: *Various artists* / Mothers day: *Various artists* / I know now: *Various artists* / Vigil, The: *Various artists* / Clouds: *Various artists* / Where did that little dog go?: *Various artists* / Dime a dozen: *Various artists* / Daisy hill: *Various artists* / When do the good things happen: *Various artists* / Great writer, The: *Various artists* / Poor sweet baby: *Various artists* / Don't be anything less than everything you can: *Various artists* / Big bow-wow, The: *Various artists* / Just one person: *Various artists* / Finale: *Various artists.*
Cass: Released Oct '83, on T. E. R. by That's Entertainment Records. Catalogue no: **ZCTER 1073**
Album: Released Jul '79, on DRG (USA) by DRG Records (USA). Deleted Jan '89. Catalogue no: **DRG 6103**
Album: Released Oct '83, on T. E. R. by That's Entertainment Records. Catalogue no: **TER 1073**

Snow Queen

SNOW QUEEN (Film Soundtrack) (Various artists)
CD: Released '88, on Finesse Catalogue no: **FACD 920**
Album: Released '88, on Finesse Catalogue no: **FA 920**

Snowman

(See also under Auty, Pete)
SNOWMAN, THE (Film Soundtrack & Story) (Cribbins, Bernard)
Album: Released Dec '83, on CBS by CBS Records & Distribution. Catalogue no: **CBS 71116**
CD: Released Nov '87, on CBS (Masterworks) by CBS Records &

Distribution. Catalogue no: **CD 71116**
Cass: Released Dec '83, on CBS by CBS Records & Distribution. Catalogue no: **40 71116**

Snub TV

SNUB TV VOL.1 (VIDEO) (Various artists)
Tracks: / Mercy seat, The: *Ultra Vivid Scene* / Deadbeat descendents: *Fall* / Man to child: *House Of Love* / Only losers take the bus: *Coughlin, Cathal & The Fatima Mansions* / Vamos: *Pixies* / Power: *Sherman, Bim* / Do it better: *Happy Mondays* / Kidney bingos: *Wire* / Eardrum buzz: *Wire* / Downtown: *Throwing Muses* / Hairstyle of the devil: *Momus* / What the moon saw: *Band Of Holy Joy* / Moss side story: *Adamson, Barry.*
Note: Running time: 50 minutes approx.
VHS: Released Mar '90, on PMI by EMI Records. Catalogue no: **MVP 99 1213 3**

Soap Opera...

SOAP OPERA THEMES (Various artists)
Cass: Released '88, on GNP Crescendo (USA) by GNP Crescendo Records (USA). Catalogue no: **GNP5 2200**
Album: Released '88, on GNP Crescendo (USA) by GNP Crescendo Records (USA). Catalogue no: **GNPS 2200**

Sodom & Gomorrah

SODOM AND GOMORRAH (Film soundtrack) (Various artists)
Note: Digital remastered release of the complete Epic score by Miklos Rozsa.
Album: Released Jan '89, on Silva Screen by Silva Screen Records. Catalogue no: **NL 42755**

Solo (Series)

SOLO (Various artists)
Note: This CD and cassette features the six young British virtuoso musicians as seen on the Thames television series.
CD: Released Jul '89, on Chandos by Chandos Records. Catalogue no: **CHAN 8769**
Cass: Released Jul '89, on Chandos by Chandos Records. Catalogue no: **HBTD 1406**

Solomon & Sheba

SOLOMON & SHEBA (Film soundtrack) (Various artists)
Note: Epic starring Yul Brynner. Music by Mario Nascimbene.
Cass: Released Jan '89, on MCA by Silva Screen Records. Catalogue no: **MCAC 1425**
Album: Released Jan '89, on MCA by Silva Screen Records. Catalogue no: **MCA 1425**

Some Kind Of Wonderful

SOME KIND OF WONDERFUL (Film soundtrack) (Various artists)
Tracks: / Do anything: Shelley, Peter / Brilliant mind: Furniture / Cry like this: Blue Room / I go crazy: Flesh For Lulu / She loves me: Duffy, Stephen "Tin Tin" / Hardest walk: Jesus & Mary Chain / Shyest time, The: Apartments / Miss Amanda Jones: March Violets / Cant help falling in love: Lick The Tins / Turn to the sky: March Violets / Dr.Mabuse: Propaganda.
Cass: Released Apr '87, on MCA by MCA Records. Deleted Jan '88. Catalogue no: **MCFC 3365**
CD: Released Feb '90, on Silva Screen by Silva Screen Records. Catalogue no: **MCAD6200**
Album: Released Apr '87, on MCA by MCA Records. Deleted Jan '88. Catalogue no: **MCF 3365**

Some Like It Hot

SOME LIKE IT HOT (Film soundtrack) (Various artists)
Tracks: / Runnin' wild: Monroe, Marilyn / Sugar blues: Deutsch, Adolph & His Orchestra / Down among the sheltering palms: Society Syncopators / Randolph Street rag: Deutsch, Adolph & His Orchestra / I wanna be loved by you: Monroe, Marilyn / Park Avenue fantasy: Deutsch, Adolph & His Orchestra / Down among the sheltering palms: Monroe, Marilyn / La Cumparsita: Various artists / I'm through with love: Monroe, Marilyn / Sugar blues: Deutsch, Adolph & His Orchestra / Tell the whole darn world: Deutsch, Adolph & His Orchestra / Play it again Charlie: Deutsch, Adolph & His Orchestra / Sweet Georgia Brown: Malneck, Matty & His Orchestra / By the beautiful sea: Society Syncopators / Some like it hot: Malneck, Matty & His Orchestra.

LP Pic: Released Nov '83, on Liberty by EMI Records. Deleted '87. Catalogue no: **UASP 30226**
Album: Released Mar '79, on United Artists by EMI Records. Catalogue no: **UAS 30226**
Album: Released '85, on Conifer Catalogue no: **1C 064 82894**

Something For The ...

SOMETHING FOR THE BOYS (Original Broadway Cast) (Various artists)
Album: Released Jan '89, on Silva Screen by Silva Screen Records. Catalogue no: **AEI 1157**

Something Wild

SOMETHING WILD (Film Soundtrack) (Various artists)
Tracks: / Loco de amor: David Y Celia / Ever fallen in love: Fine Young Cannibals / Zero zero seven charlie: UB40 / Not my slave: Oingo Boingo / You don't have to cry: Cliff, Jimmy / With or without you: Jones, Steve / High life: Okossun, Sonny / Man with a gun: Harrison, Jerry / Temptation: New Order / Wild thing: Sister Carol.
CD: Released Jan '89, on MCA by MCA Records. Catalogue no: **MCAD 6194**
Cass: Released Apr '87, on MCA by MCA Records. Deleted Sep '90. Catalogue no: **MCFC 3355**
Album: Released Apr '87, on MCA by MCA Records. Deleted Jul '90. Catalogue no: **MCF 3355**

Somewhere In Time

SOMEWHERE IN TIME (Film soundtrack) (Various artists)
Tracks: / Somewhere in time: Various artists / Old man, The: Various artists / Journey back in time, The: Various artists / Day together, A: Various artists / Rhapsody on a theme of Paganini: Various artists / Is he the one?: Various artists / Man of my dreams, The: Various artists / Return to the present: Various artists / Somewhere in time: Various artists.
Note: Composed by John Barry.
CD: Released Jun '88, on MCA (USA) by MCA Records (USA). Catalogue no: **MCAD 31164**
Cass: Released '86, on MCA by MCA Records. Catalogue no: **MCFC 3333**
Album: Released '86, on MCA by MCA Records. Catalogue no: **MCF 3333**

Song & Dance

SONG AND DANCE (VIDEO) (Various artists)
Tracks: / Let me finish: Various artists / It's not the end of the world: Various artists / Letter home: Various artists / Sheldon bloom: Various artists / Capped teeth and Caesar salad: Various artists / You made me think you were in love: Various artists / Last man in my life, The: Various artists / Come back with the same look in your eyes: Various artists / Take that look off your face: Various artists / Tell me on a Sunday: Various artists / I love New York: Various artists / Married man: Various artists / I'm very you you're very me: Various artists / Let's talk about you: Various artists / Nothing like you've ever known: Various artists.
Note: An Andrew Lloyd Webber Spectacular featuring songs from Sarah Brightman in 'Tell me on a Sunday and dance from Wayne Sleep and company to the 'Variations' music.
VHS: Released Oct '84, on RCA by BMG Records (UK). Catalogue no: **CVT 10336**

SONG AND DANCE/TELL ME ON A SUNDAY (1984 London cast) (Various artists)
Tracks: / Song and dance (overture): Various artists / Take that look off your face: Various artists / Let me finish: Various artists / It's not the end of the world: Various artists / Letter home: Various artists / Sheldon bloom: Various artists / Capped teeth and Caesar salad: Various artists / Exit: Various artists / Second letter home: Various artists / Unexpected song: Various artists / Come back with the same look in your eyes: Various artists / Let's talk about you: Various artists / Tell me on a Sunday: Various artists / Married man: Various artists / Third letter home: Various artists / Nothing like you've ever known: Various artists / Song and dance (finale): Various artists / When you want to fall in love: Various artists / Dance: Various artists.
CD: Released Jun '90, on Polydor by Polydor Ltd. Catalogue no: **8436192**
Cass set: Released '86, on RCA by BMG Records (UK). Deleted Jul '89. Catalogue no: **BK 70480**

CD: Released Feb '90, on Silva Screen by Silva Screen Records. Catalogue no: **RCD37162**

2 LP Set: Released '86, on RCA by BMG Records (UK). Deleted Jul '89. Catalogue no: **BL 70480**

SONG AND DANCE (Original Broadway Cast) (Various artists)
Album: Released Jan '89, on Silva Screen by Silva Screen Records. Catalogue no: **CBL1 7162**
Cass: Released Jan '89, on Silva Screen by Silva Screen Records. Catalogue no: **CBK1 7162**
CD: Released Jan '89, on Silva Screen by Silva Screen Records. Catalogue no: **RCD 1 7162**

SONG AND DANCE (Original London Cast) (Various artists)
Tracks: / Song and dance (overture): *Various artists* / Let me finish: *Various artists* / It's not the end of the world: *Various artists* / You made me think you were in love: *Various artists* / Letter home: *Various artists* / Sheldon Bloom: *Various artists* / Capped teeth and Caesar salad: *Various artists* / Second letter home: *Various artists* / Last man in my life, The: *Various artists* / Come back with the same look in your eyes: *Various artists* / Take that look off your face: *Various artists* / Tell me on a Sunday: *Various artists* / I love New York: *Various artists* / Married man: *Various artists* / I'm very you, you're very me: *Various artists* / Let's talk about you: *Various artists* / Nothing like you've ever known: *Various artists* / Song and dance (finale): *Various artists* / When you want to fall in love: *Various artists*.
2 LP Set: Released Jun '82, on Polydor by Polydor Ltd. Catalogue no: **PODV 4**
Cass set: Released Jun '82, on Polydor by Polydor Ltd. Catalogue no: **PODVC 4**

Song Of Bernadette

SONG OF BERNADETTE, THE/ISLAND IN THE SKY (Original Soundtrack) (Various artists)
Note: Scores by Alfred Newman and Hugo Friedhofer.
Album: Released Jan '89, on Silva Screen by Silva Screen Records. Catalogue no: **STV 81116**

Song Of Norway

SONG OF NORWAY, THE (Original Broadway Cast) (Various artists)
Album: Released Jan '89, on MCA by MCA Records. Catalogue no: **MCA 1524**
Cass: Released Jan '89, on MCA by MCA Records. Deleted Mar '90. Catalogue no: **MCAC 1524**

SONG OF NORWAY (VIDEO) (Various artists)
VHS: Released '88, on Video Gems Catalogue no: **R 1019**

Song Without End

SONG WITHOUT END (Film soundtrack) (Various artists)
Album: Released Feb '61, on Golden Guinea Deleted '64. Catalogue no: **GGL 30169**

Songbook

SONGBOOK (Original London cast) (Various artists)
Tracks: / Songbook: *Various artists* / East river rhapsody: *Various artists* / Talking picture show: *Various artists* / Mr. Destiny: *Various artists* / Your time is different to mine: *Various artists* / Pretty face: *Various artists* / Je vous aime milady: *Various artists* / Les hailes: *Various artists* / Olympics song 1936: *Various artists* / Nazi party pooper: *Various artists* / I'm gonna take him home to momma: *Various artists* / Bumpity bump: *Various artists* / Girl in the window: *Various artists* / Victory V: *Various artists* / April in Wisconsin: *Various artists* / Happy hickory: *Various artists* / Lovely Sunday morning: *Various artists* / Rusty's dream ballet: *Various artists* / Torn on my heart: *Various artists* / Pokenhatchit: *Various artists* / Public protest committee: *Various artists* / I accuse: *Various artists* / Messages: *Various artists* / I found love: *Various artists* / Don't play the love song any more: *Various artists* / Golden oldie: *Various artists* / Climbin': *Various artists* / Nostalgia: *Various artists*.
Album: Released Sep '79, on PRT by Castle Communications Records. Catalogue no: **NSPL 18609**

Sons Of Katie Elder

SONS OF KATIE ELDER, THE (Original Soundtrack) (Various artists)
Note: Elmer Bernstein western

score.
Album: Released Jan '89, on Silva Screen by Silva Screen Records. Catalogue no: **LAALP 001**

Sorcerer

SORCERER (See under Tangerine Dream)

Soul Man

SOUL MAN (Film soundtrack) (Various artists)
Tracks: / Soul man: *Various artists* / Evolution: *Various artists* / Outside: *Various artists* / Love and affection: *Various artists* / Eek-ah-bo-static automatic: *Various artists* / Bang bang bang (who's on the phone?): *Various artists* / Totally academic: *Various artists* / Suddenly it's magic: *Various artists* / Black girls: *Various artists* / Sweet Sarah: *Various artists*.
Note: 17 original soul tracks by Sam & Dave, Eddy Floyd, Martha Reeves, Fontella Bass, Rufus Thomas, Percy Sledge.
Album: Released Jan '87, on A&M by A&M Records. Catalogue no: **AMA 3903**
Cass: Released Jan '87, on A&M by A&M Records. Catalogue no: **AMC 3903**

Sound Barrier (film)

SOUND BARRIER, THE Soundtrack (Royal Philharmonic Orchestra)
Note: CD release of this new digital recording of the classic score by Malcolm Arnold for the David Lean film. The Sound Barrier music consists of a suite of 18 minutes coupled with 3 pieces from Malta G.C. by Sir Arnold Bax. All the music is performed by The Royal Philharmonic Orchestra, conducted by Kenneth Alwyn.
CD: Released Jan '89, on Silva Screen by Silva Screen Records. Catalogue no: **CNS 5446**

Sound Of Music

SOUND OF MUSIC (Original Broadway cast) (Various artists)
Cass: Released Mar '90, on CBS (import) by CBS Records & Distribution. Catalogue no: **PST 32601**
CD: Released Jan '89, on CBS (import) by CBS Records & Distribution. Catalogue no: **CK 32601**

SOUND OF MUSIC (1981 Lon-

Various Artists - *Sound of Music* (RCA)

don Revival Cast) (Various artists)

Tracks: / Sound of music, The: *Various artists* / Overture and preludium: *Various artists* / Morning hymn and allelulia: *Various artists* / I have confidence in me: *Various artists* / Sixteen going on seventeen: *Various artists* / My favourite things: *Various artists* / Climb every mountain: *Various artists* / Lonely goatherd, The: *Various artists* / Sound of music, The: *Various artists* / Do-re-mi: *Various artists* / Something good: *Various artists* / Processional and Maria: *Various artists* / Edelweiss: *Various artists* / Climb every mountain: *Various artists*.

Album: Released Oct '81, on Epic by CBS Records & Distribution. Deleted Oct '86. Catalogue no: **EPC 70212**

Album: Released '79, on RCA by BMG Records (UK). Deleted '84. Catalogue no: **SB 6616**

Cass: Released '79, on RCA by BMG Records (UK). Deleted '84. Catalogue no: **VCS 67257**

CD: Released May '87, on Epic by CBS Records & Distribution.

Deleted Jan '90. Catalogue no: **CD 70212**

SOUND OF MUSIC (Film Soundtrack) (Various artists) (See picture above)

Tracks: / Prelude: *Various artists* / Overture and preludium: *Various artists* / Morning hymn and Alleluia: *Various artists* / Maria: *Various artists* / I have confidence in me: *Various artists* / Sixteen going on seventeen: *Various artists* / My favourite things: *Various artists* / Climb every mountain: *Various artists* / Lonely goatherd, The: *Various artists* / Do-re-mi: *Various artists* / Something good: *Various artists* / Processional and Maria: *Various artists* / Climb every mountain: *Various artists* / Edelweiss: *Various artists*.

Album: Released Sep '81, on RCA by BMG Records (UK). Catalogue no: **PL 82005**

Album: Released Sep '89, on RCA by BMG Records (UK). Catalogue no: **NL 90368**

Album: Released Apr '65, on RCA by BMG Records (UK). Catalogue no: **RB 6616**

Cass: Released Sep '81, on RCA

by BMG Records (UK). Catalogue no: **PK 82005**

Cass: Released Sep '89, on RCA by BMG Records (UK). Catalogue no: **NK 90368**

CD: Released Oct '84, on RCA by BMG Records (UK). Catalogue no: **PD 82005**

CD: Released Sep '89, on RCA by BMG Records (UK). Catalogue no: **ND 90368**

SOUND OF MUSIC (Original London Cast) (Various artists)

Tracks: / Preludium: *Various artists* / Sound of music, The: *Various artists* / Maria: *Various artists* / Bell is no bell, A: *Various artists* / I have confidence in me: *Various artists* / Do-re-mi: *Various artists* / Sixteen going on seventeen: *Various artists* / My favourite things: *Various artists* / Lonely goatherd, The: *Various artists* / How can love survive?: *Various artists* / So long, farewell: *Various artists* / Climb every mountain: *Various artists* / Something good: *Various artists* / Wedding sequence: *Various artists* / Maria (reprise): *Various artists* / Concert do-re-mi (reprise): *Various artists* / Edelweiss: *Various artists* / So long, farewell (reprise): *Various artists* / Climb every mountain (reprise): *Various artists*.

Album: Released Aug '85, on CBS Cameo by CBS Records & Distribution. Catalogue no: **CBS 32670**

Album: Released Jun '88, on First Night by First Night Records. Catalogue no: **OCR 2**

Cass: Released Jun '88, on First Night by First Night Records. Catalogue no: **OCRC 2**

Cass: Released '81, on Epic by CBS Records & Distribution. Deleted '86. Catalogue no: **40 32670**

SOUND OF MUSIC (ORIGINAL ISSUE) (Broadway cast) (Various artists)

Album: Released Jun '61, on Philips by Phonogram Ltd. Deleted '66. Catalogue no: **ABL 3370**

Album: Released Jul '61, on H.M.V. by EMI Records. Deleted '66. Catalogue no: **CLP 1453**

SOUND OF MUSIC (RE-ISSUE) (Film Soundtrack) (Various artists)

SOUTH PACIFIC Soundtrack

Original soundtrack to *South Pacific* (RCA)

Album: Released '90, on RCA International by BMG Records (UK). Catalogue no: **INTS 5134**

SOUND OF MUSIC (VIDEO) (Various artists)
Note: Running time: 160 mins.
VHS: Released Aug '88, on CBS-Fox by CBS-Fox Video. Catalogue no: **1051 50**

Sounds Of The Screen
TV GIANTS
Tracks: / Taxi / M.A.S.H. / Minder (I could be so good for you) / Star trek / Rockford files, The / Dynasty / Jewel in the crown, The / Emmerdale Farm / A-Team, The / Knight rider / Hill Street Blues / Dallas / Fame / Thorn Birds, The.
Album: Released Mar '85, on Elecstar by Elecstar Records. Deleted '88. Catalogue no: **VCLP 8**
Cass: Released Mar '85, on Elecstar by Elecstar Records. Deleted '88. Catalogue no: **ZCVCL 8**

Sounds Supernatural
SOUNDS SUPERNATURAL (Various artists)
Tracks: / Satan speaks: *Various artists* / Dr Jekyll and Mr Hyde: *Various artists* / Rosemary's baby: *Various artists* / King of kings: *Various artists* / Seventh victim: *Various artists* / Exorcist 2: *Various artists* / Heretic, The: *Various artists* / Omen: *Various artists*.
Cass: Released '88, on Decca by Decca International. Catalogue no: **421 267 4**

Sounds Visual
SOUNDS VISUAL (Original TV themes) (Various artists)
Tracks: / Television march, The (BBC TV theme): *London Symphony Orchestra* / ITN news (non-stop): *Malcolm, John Orchestra* / Mainly for women (jockey on the carousel): *Melodi Light Orchestra* / Potter's wheel, The (from the BBC interlude): *Melodi Light Orchestra* / Saturday night out: *Melodi Light Orchestra* / Picture parade: *Queen's Hall Light Orchestra* / Farming (a quiet stroll): *Queen's Hall Light Orchestra* / Big night out (all sports march): *Melodi Light Orchestra* / ITV soccer theme (fanfare in beat): *Hawksworth, Johnny Orchestra* / Compact (city movement): *Roger, Roger & His Orchestra* / Animal magic (Las Vegas): *Johnson, Laurie Orchestra* / BBC-2 service information

theme (walk and talk): *Dale, Syd Orchestra* / Owen M.D. (Sleepy Shores): *Pearson, Johnny & His Orchestra* / News at ten (The awakening): *Group 50 Orchestra* / Mastermind (Approaching menace): *Richardson, Neil Orchestra* / This is your life: *Johnson, Laurie Orchestra*.
Cass: Released May '84, on Radio Six Deleted '86. Catalogue no: **YRS 603**

Soup For One
WHY? (Theme From Soup For One)(See under Simon, Carly)

Soursweet
SOURSWEET (Film soundtrack) (Hartley, Richard)
Cass: Released '89, on Trax by Filmtrax Records. Catalogue no: **MOMENTC 119**
Album: Released '89, on Trax by Filmtrax Records. Catalogue no: **MOMENT 119**

South Bank Orchestra
DEMPSEY & MAKEPEACE
Tracks: / Dempsey & Makepeace / Makepeace not war.
7" Single: Released Jan '85, on Sierra by Sierra Records. Catalogue no: **FED 9**

South Pacific
SOUTH PACIFIC (1986 studio recording) (Various artists)
Tracks: / South Pacific overture: *Various artists* / Dites moi: *Various artists* / Cockeyed optimist, A: *Various artists* / Twin soliloquies: *Various artists* / Some enchanted evening: *Various artists* / Bloody Mary: *Various artists* / Three is nothin' like a dame: *Various artists* / Bali ha'l: *Various artists* / I'm gonna wash that man right outa my hair: *Various artists* / Wonderful guy, A: *Various artists* / Younger than Springtime: *Various artists* / This is how it feels: *Various artists* / Entr'acte: *Various artists* / Happy talk: *Various artists* / Honey bun: *Various artists* / You've got to be carefully taught: *Various artists* / This nearly was mine: *Various artists* / March, The: *Various artists* / Take off, The: *Various artists* / Communications established: *Various artists* / Finale ultimo: *Various artists*.
Album: Released '86, on CBS by CBS Records & Distribution. Catalogue no: **SM 42205**

Cass: Released '86, on CBS by CBS Records & Distribution. Catalogue no: **SMT 42205**

CD: Released '86, on CBS by CBS Records & Distribution. Catalogue no: **MK 42205**

SOUTH PACIFIC (Various artists)

Tracks: / Overture: *Various artists* / Dites-moi: *Various artists* / Cock-eyed optimist: *Various artists* / Twin soliloquies: *Various artists* / Some enchanted evening: *Various artists* / Bloody Mary: *Various artists* / There is nothin' like a dame: *Various artists* / Bali ha'i: *Various artists* / I'm gonna wash that man right outa my hair: *Various artists* / I'm in love with a wonderful guy: *Various artists* / Younger than Springtime: *Various artists*.

Album: Released '79, on RCA by BMG Records (UK). Deleted '84. Catalogue no: **SB 2011**

Cass: Released '79, on RCA by BMG Records (UK). Deleted '84. Catalogue no: **VCS 67259**

SOUTH PACIFIC (Film soundtrack) (Various artists) (See picture on previous page)

Tracks: / South Pacific overture: *Various artists* / Dites-moi: *Various artists* / Cock-eyed optimist: *Various artists* / Twin soliloquies: *Various artists* / Some enchanted evening: *Various artists* / Bloody Mary: *Various artists* / My girl back home: *Various artists* / There is nothin' like a dame: *Various artists* / Bali ha'i: *Various artists* / I'm gonna wash that man right outa my hair: *Various artists* / I'm in love with a wonderful guy: *Various artists* / Younger than Springtime: *Various artists* / Happy talk: *Various artists*.

Album: Released '84, on RCA by BMG Records (UK). Catalogue no: **NL 83681**

Cass: Released '84, on RCA by BMG Records (UK). Catalogue no: **NK 83681**

CD: Released Feb '89, on RCA by BMG Records (UK). Catalogue no: **ND 83681**

SOUTH PACIFIC (1988 London Cast) (Various artists)

Album: Released Jan '88, on First Night by First Night Records. Catalogue no: **CAST 11**

Cass: Released Jan '88, on First Night by First Night Records. Catalogue no: **CASTC 11**

CD: Released 16 Jan '88, on First Night by First Night Records. Catalogue no: **CASTCD 11**

SOUTH PACIFIC (Original Broadway cast) (Various artists)

Album: Released Apr '83, on CBS by CBS Records & Distribution. Deleted Jan '88. Catalogue no: **CBS 32264**

Cass: Released Mar '90, on Silva Screen. Catalogue no: **PST 32604**

CD: Released Jan '89, on CBS (import) by CBS Records & Distribution. Catalogue no: **CK 32604**

SOUTH PACIFIC (Original soundtrack) (Various artists)

Album: Released Jan '89, on Silva Screen by Silva Screen Records. Catalogue no: **3681.2**

SOUTH PACIFIC (ORIGINAL ISSUE) (Various artists)

Album: Released Nov '58, on RCA by BMG Records (UK). Deleted '66. Catalogue no: **RB 16065**

SOUTH PACIFIC (VIDEO) (Various artists)

Note: Running time: 145 mins.

VHS: Released May '88, on CBS-Fox by CBS-Fox Video. Catalogue no: **7045 50**

SPACEBALLS - THE MOVIE (Film soundtrack) (Various artists)

Tracks: / Spaceballs: *Various artists* / My heart has a mind of its own: *Various artists* / Heartstrings: *Various artists* / Spaceballs love theme instrumental: *Various artists* / Winnebago crashes, The (Spaceballs build mega-maid): *Various artists* / Spaceballs: *Various artists* / Hot together: *Various artists* / Good enough: *Various artists* / Wanna be loved by you: *Various artists*.

Album: Released Dec '87, on WEA by WEA Records. Catalogue no: **K 255193 1**

Cass: Released Dec '87, on WEA by WEA Records. Catalogue no: **K 255193 4**

SPARKY'S MAGIC PIANO (Film soundtrack) (Various artists)

Tracks: / Sparky's magic piano: *Various artists* / Sparky and the talking train: *Various artists*.

Note: Henry Blair featuring Ray Turner at the piano. Narration by Verne Smith/music by Billy May/talking piano Sonovox.

Album: Released Nov '86, on Capitol by EMI Records. Catalogue no: **EMS 1188**

Cass: Released Nov '86, on Capitol by EMI Records. Catalogue no: **TCEMS 1188**

SPARTACUS (Film soundtrack) (Various artists)

Note: Composed by Alex North.

Album: Released Aug '88, on Trax by Filmtrax Records. Deleted Jan '90. Catalogue no: **MODEM 1012**

CD: Released Aug '88, on Trax by Filmtrax Records. Deleted Jan '90. Catalogue no: **MODEMCD 1012**

Cass: Released Aug '88, on Trax by Filmtrax Records. Deleted Jan '90. Catalogue no: **MODEMC 1012**

Album: Released Jan '89, on MCA by MCA Records. Catalogue no: **MCA 1534**

Cass: Released Jan '89, on MCA by MCA Records. Catalogue no: **MCAC 1534**

SPEEDWAY (See under Presley, Elvis)

SPELLBOUND/UTAH SYMPHONY (Film soundtracks) (Various artists)

Note: The complete Miklos Rozsa score, recording in Stereo. Also including music from Because of Him, The World The Flesh & The Devil.

CD: Released Jan '89, on Silva Screen by Silva Screen Records. Catalogue no: **DUNCD 116**

Album: Released Jan '89, on Silva Screen by Silva Screen Records. Catalogue no: **DUN 116**

SPELLEOGES (Original Soundtrack) (Various artists)

Album: Released Jun '84, on No-music Catalogue no: **NOMLP 001**

THEME FROM DR KILDARE

Tracks: / Dr Kildare, Theme from.

7" Single: Released Mar '62, on Parlophone by EMI Records. Deleted Mar '65. Catalogue no: R 4872

Spencer, Don

FIREBALL XL-5
Tracks: / Fireball.
Note: From the TV program *Fireball XL-5*
7" Single: Released Mar '63, on H.M.V. by EMI Records. Deleted Mar '66. Catalogue no: POP 1087

SINGS THE SONGS OF PLAY SCHOOL
Album: Released Jan '79, on Nevis Catalogue no: NEVLP 127

Spies Like Us

SPIES LIKE US (Film soundtrack) (Various artists)
Tracks: / Ace tomato company, The: *Various artists* / Off to spy: *Various artists* / Russians in the desert: *Various artists* / Pass in the tent: *Various artists* / Escape: *Various artists* / To the bus: *Various artists* / Road to Russia, The: *Various artists* / Rally 'round: *Various artists* / W.A.M.P.: *Various artists* / Martian act: *Various artists* / Arrest: *Various artists* / Recall: *Various artists* / Winners: *Various artists*.
Note: 'Spies like us' is the latest comedy adventure from director John Landis. It stars Chevy Chase and Dan Aykroyd. The Album features all the orchestral music by Elmer Bernstein, who also did 'Ghostbusters' and 'The Black Cauldron', and is an action score in the style of 'The Magnificent Seven' and 'The Great Escape'. The Film is from the director of 'Into The Night' and the story is by the same writer of 'Ghost Busters'.
CD: Released Jan '89, on Silva Screen by Silva Screen Records. Catalogue no: VCD 47246
Cass: Released Jan '89, on Silva Screen by Silva Screen Records. Catalogue no: CTV 81270
Album: Released Feb '86, on T. E. R. by That's Entertainment Records. Catalogue no: TER 1110

SPIES LIKE US (SINGLE) (See under McCartney, Paul)

Spinal Tap

THIS IS SPINAL TAP (Tour soundtrack)
Tracks: / Hell hole / Tonight I'm gonna rock you / Heavy duty /

Rock'n'roll creation / America / Cups and cakes / Big bottom / Sex farm / Stonehenge / Gimme some money / Flower people.
Album: Released Mar '89, on Priority by Priority Records. Deleted May '90. Catalogue no: LUSLP 2
CD: Released Aug '90, on Polydor by Polydor Ltd. Catalogue no: 817 846-2
Album: Released Aug '90, on Polydor by Polydor Ltd. Catalogue no: 817 846-1
Cass: Released Aug '90, on Polydor by Polydor Ltd. Catalogue no: 817 846-4
Cass: Released Mar '89, on Priority by Priority Records. Deleted May '90. Catalogue no: LUSMC 2

Spinetti, Victor

VERY PRIVATE DIARY, A
Cass: Released May '89, on First Night by First Night Records. Catalogue no: SCENEC 14

Spirit Of St Louis

SPIRIT OF ST LOUIS (Film soundtrack) (Various artists)
Note: James Stewart film with a score by Franz Waxman.
Album: Released Jan '89, on Silva Screen by Silva Screen Records. Catalogue no: ERS 6507
CD: Released Feb '90, on Silva Screen by Silva Screen Records. Catalogue no: VSD5212

Spitfire Band

SPITFIRE BAND SWINGS DOWN BROADWAY, THE
Album: Released '88, on Attic Records by Road Runner Records. Catalogue no: LAT 1230

SPITFIRE BAND SWINGS FROM STAGE TO SCREEN
CD: Released '88, on Attic Records by Road Runner Records. Catalogue no: ACD 2500

SPITFIRE BAND SWINGS THE MOVIES, THE
Album: Released '88, on Attic Records by Road Runner Records. Catalogue no: LAT 1234

Spitting Image

CHICKEN SONG, THE
Tracks: / Chicken song, The / I've never met a nice South African / Hello, you must be going (12" only) / We're scared of Bob (12"only).

12" Single: Released May '86, on Virgin by Virgin Records. Deleted '89. Catalogue no: SPIT 12
7" Single: Released Apr '86, on Virgin by Virgin Records. Catalogue no: SPIT 1

DA DO RUN RON
Tracks: / Da do run Ron / Just a prince who can't say no.
7" Single: Released Jun '84, on Elektra by Elektra Records (UK). Catalogue no: E 9713

SANTA CLAUS IS ON THE DOLE
Tracks: / First athiest / Tabernacle choir / Santa Claus is on the dole.
7" Single: Released Nov '86, on Virgin by Virgin Records. Deleted May '88. Catalogue no: VS 921
12" Single: Released Nov '86, on Virgin by Virgin Records. Deleted May '88. Catalogue no: VS 921-12

SPIT IN YOUR EAR (TV soundtrack)
Tracks: / Spitting Image signature tune / Ronnie and Maggie goodbye / Royal singalong / Weather forecast / Coleman peaks / We've got beards (ZZ Top) / Second coming / Someone famous has died / Tea at Johnnies / Trendy Kinnock / Do do run Ron / Ronnie's birthday / One man and his bitch / Special relationship / Clean rugby songs / O'Toole's night out / Spock the actor / Line of celebrities / Price is right, The / Botha tells the truth / I've never met a nice South African / End announcement / Andy and Fergie / Pete Townsend appeals / Our generation (The Who) / Three Davids, The / Party system, The / Hello you must be going / Naming the Royal baby / Bruno and Ruthless / South Bank show on Ronnie Hazelhurst / Bernard Manning newsflash / Juan Carlos meets the Queen / Chicken song, The (Celebrity Megamix) / Lawson goes bonkers / Talk bollocks / Snooker games / Good old British bloke / Black moustache (Prince.) / Uranus / Dennis Thatcher's pacemaker / John And Tatum - the young marrieds / We're scared of Bob / Trooping the colour / Night thoughts.
Album: Released Oct '86, on Virgin by Virgin Records. Deleted May '90. Catalogue no: OVED 227
Cass: Released Oct '86, on Virgin by Virgin Records. Catalogue no: TCV 2403

Album: Released Oct '86, on Virgin by Virgin Records. Catalogue no: **V 2403**

Cass: Released Oct '86, on Virgin by Virgin Records. Catalogue no: **OVEDC 227**

Splash (film)

SPLASH (Film soundtrack) (Various artists)

Cass: Released Jun '84, on Cherry Lane by Cherry Lane Productions. Catalogue no: **ZCPIP '10**

Album: Released Jun '84, on Cherry Lane by Cherry Lane Productions. Catalogue no: **PIPLP '10**

Spollansky, Mischa

ST JOAN (See under St Joan)

Springfield, Rick

HARD TO HOLD (Film Soundtrack)

Tracks: / Love somebody / Don't walk away / Bop 'till you drop / Taxi dancings / S.F.O. / Stand up / When the lights go down / Great lost art of conversation, The / Go swimming.

Album: Released Aug '84, on RCA by BMG Records (UK). Deleted Nov '88. Catalogue no: **BL 84935**

Cass: Released Aug '84, on RCA by BMG Records (UK). Deleted Nov '88. Catalogue no: **BK 84935**

CD: Released Sep '84, on RCA by BMG Records (UK). Deleted May '89. Catalogue no: **BD 84935**

Springtime In The ...

SPRINGTIME IN THE ROCKIES/SWEET ROSIE O'GRADY (Original Soundtracks) (Various artists)

Album: Released Jan '89, on Silva Screen by Silva Screen Records. Catalogue no: **SH 2090**

Spy Who Loved Me

SPY WHO LOVED ME (Film soundtrack) (Various artists)

Tracks: / Nobody does it better: *Simon, Carly* / Bond '77: *Various artists* / Ride to Atlantis: *Various artists* / Mojave club: *Various artists* / Nobody does it better: *Various artists* / Anya: *Various artists* / Tanker, The: *Various artists* / Pyramids, The: *Various artists* / Eastern lights: *Various artists* / Conclusion: *Various artists* / Spy

who loved me, The (end titles): *Various artists*.

Album: Released Sep '77, on United Artists by EMI Records. Deleted '89. Catalogue no: **UAG 30098**

Album: Released Mar '84, on EMI (Holland) by EMI Records. Deleted '89. Catalogue no: **5C 062 99370**

Cass: Released Sep '77, on United Artists by EMI Records. Deleted '81. Catalogue no: **TCK 30098**

Spy With The Platinum...

SPY WITH THE PLATINUM HEART, THE (Original soundtrack) (Various artists)

Tracks: / Opening titles-masquerade: *Various artists* / Fly by night: *Various artists* / Chinatown: *Various artists* / Passion's killer: *Various artists* / Body in the bay: *Various artists* / Wheelspin: *Various artists* / Adams takes a trip: *Various artists* / S.P.Y.D.A.'s web: *Various artists* / Night with Nuki, A: *Various artists* / Frisco disco: *Various artists* / Tuxedo tussle: *Various artists* / Operation 'H': *Various artists* / End title: *Various artists*.

Album: Released Sep '87, on Disques Noir Catalogue no: **DN 2001**

St. Elmo's Fire

ST. ELMO'S FIRE (Film soundtrack) (Various artists)

Tracks: / St Elmo's fire (man in motion): *Parr, John* / Shake down: *Squier, Billy* / Young and innocent: *Elefante* / This time it was really right: *Anderson, Jon* / Saved my life: *Waybill, Fee* / Love theme: *Foster, David* / Georgetown: *Foster, David* / If I turn you away: *Moss, Vikki* / Stressed out (Close to the edge): *Airplay*.

Cass: Released Oct '85, on Atlantic by WEA Records. Catalogue no: **781 261-4**

Album: Released Oct '85, on Atlantic by WEA Records. Deleted Jan '90. Catalogue no: **781 261-1**

ST ELMOS FIRE (SINGLE) (See under Parr, John)

St. Joan

ST. JOAN (Film Soundtrack) (Various artists)

Note: Mischa Spoliansky score for the Otto Preminger film.

Album: Released Jan '89, on Silva Screen by Silva Screen Rec-

ords. Catalogue no: **LCT 6134**

St. Louis Symphony...

GERSHWIN IN THE MOVIES 1/2 (St. Louis Symphony Orchestra)

Note: With Wilhelmina Fernandez . Orchestra led by Leonard Slatkin.

Cass set: Released May '87, on SPI Milan (France) Catalogue no: **C 249/250**

2 LP Set: Released May '87, on SPI Milan (France) Catalogue no: **A 249/250**

CD Set: Released May '87, on SPI Milan (France) Catalogue no: **CDCH 249/250**

GERSHWIN IN THE MOVIES VOL.1 1931-1945 (St. Louis Symphony Orchestra)

Tracks: / Embraceable you / They all laughed / Love is here to stay / Strike up the band / Fascinating rhythm / But not for me / Rhapsody in blue / Man I love, The / Seconde rhapsodie.

Note: With Wilhelmina Fernandez. Orchestra led by Leonard Slatkin.

Cass: Released Mar '87, on SPI Milan (France) Catalogue no: **C 249**

CD: Released Jan '89, on SPI Milan (France) Deleted Jan '89. Catalogue no: **CD 249**

Album: Released Mar '87, on SPI Milan (France) Catalogue no: **A 249**

GERSHWIN IN THE MOVIES VOL.2 1951-1959 (St. Louis Symphony Orchestra)

Tracks: / I'll build a stairway to paradise / Somebody loves me / American in Paris, An / Someone to watch over me / 'S wonderful / Introduction / Porgy sings / Fugue / Ouragan / Bonjour free.

Note: With Wilhelmina Fernandez. Orchestra directed by Leonard Slatkin.

Album: Released Mar '87, on SPI Milan (France) Catalogue no: **A 250**

Cass: Released Mar '87, on SPI Milan (France) Catalogue no: **C 250**

Staccato

STACCATO (TV Soundtrack) (Bernstein, Elmer)

Album: Released Apr '83, on T. E. R. by That's Entertainment Records. Deleted May '89. Catalogue no: **TER 1021**

Stage Door Canteen

STAGE DOOR CANTEEN / HOLLYWOOD CANTEEN (Film Soundtrack) (Various artists)

2 LP Set: Released Jan '89, on Silva Screen by Silva Screen Records. Catalogue no: **CC 100-11/12**

Stairway To The Stars

STAIRWAY TO THE STARS (Original London cast) (Various artists)

Tracks: / That's dancing: *Various artists* / Who's sorry now: *Various artists* / You stepped out of a dream: *Various artists* / Fine romance, A: *Various artists* / Three little words: *Various artists* / Bye bye baby: *Various artists* / Chatanooga choo choo: *Various artists* / Rose's turn: *Various artists* / Finale, hooray for Hollywood: *Various artists* / Ma belle marguerite: *Various artists* / S'wonderful: *Various artists* / Not even nominated: *Various artists* / Life upon the wicked stage: *Various artists* / Buttons and bows: *Various artists* / I got a girl in Kalamazoo: *Various artists* / Lucky numbers: *Various artists* / Bosom buddies: *Various artists.*

Cass: Released 5 Mar '90, on First Night by First Night Records. Catalogue no: **CASTC 21**
Album: Released 5 Mar '90, on First Night by First Night Records. Catalogue no: **CAST 21**
CD: Released 5 Mar '90, on First Night by First Night Records. Catalogue no: **CASTCD 21**

Stallone, Frank

FAR FROM OVER

Tracks: / Far from over / Waking up.
Note: Featured in the film 'Staying Alive'.
12" Single: Released Oct '83, on RSO by Polydor Ltd. Deleted Oct '86. Catalogue no: **RSOX 95**
7" Single: Released Oct '83, on RSO by Polydor Ltd. Deleted Oct '86. Catalogue no: **RSO 95**

Stand By Me

STAND BY ME (Film Soundtrack) (Various artists)

Tracks: / Everyday: *Holly, Buddy* / Let the good times roll: *Shirley & Lee* / Come go with me: *Del-Vikings* / Whispering bells: *Del-Vikings* / Get a job: *Silhouettes* /

Lollipop: *Chordettes* / Yakety yak: *Coasters* / Great balls of fire: *Lewis, Jerry Lee* / Mr. Lee: *Bobbettes* / Stand by me: *King, Ben E..*
Album: Released Mar '87, on Atlantic by WEA Records. Catalogue no: **781 677-1**
Cass: Released Feb '87, on Atlantic by WEA Records. Catalogue no: **WX 92 C**
Cass: Released Mar '87, on Atlantic by WEA Records. Catalogue no: **781 677 4**
Album: Released Feb '87, on Atlantic by WEA Records. Catalogue no: **WX 92**

STAND BY ME (VIDEO) (Various artists)

Note: Running time: 61 mins.
VHS: Released Sep '89, on Channel 5 by Channel 5 Video. Catalogue no: **CFV 05452**

Stand & Deliver

STAND & DELIVER (Film Soundtrack) (Various artists)

Note: Film score by Craig Safan (The last starfighter)
Album: Released Jan '89, on Silva Screen by Silva Screen Records. Catalogue no: **704.590**
Cass: Released Jan '89, on Silva Screen by Silva Screen Records. Deleted Mar '90. Catalogue no: **C 704.590**
CD: Released Jan '89, on Silva Screen by Silva Screen Records. Catalogue no: **VCD 70459**

Stanley & Iris

STANLEY & IRIS (Film Soundtrack) (Various artists)

Tracks: / Stanley and Irish: *Various artists* / Bicycle, The: *Various artists* / Finding a family: *Various artists* / Putting it all together: *Various artists* / Letters: *Various artists* / Reading lessons: *Various artists* / Factory work: *Various artists* / Stanley at work: *Various artists* / End credits: *Various artists* / Stanley's invention: *Various artists.*
CD: Released May '90, on Varese Sarabande Records(USA) by Varese Sarabande Records (USA). Catalogue no: **VSD 5255**
Album: Released May '90, on Varese Sarabande Records(USA) by Varese Sarabande Records (USA). Catalogue no: **VS 5255**
Cass: Released May '90, on Varese Sarabande Records(USA) by Varese Sarabande Records

(USA). Catalogue no: **VSC 5255**

Star

STAR (Film soundtrack) (Various artists)

Album: Released Sep '68, on Stateside by EMI Records. Deleted '70. Catalogue no: **SSL 10233**

STAR (VIDEO) (Various artists)

VHS: Released '88, on CBS-Fox by CBS-Fox Video. Catalogue no: **118050**

Star Is Born

STAR IS BORN, A (Remastered Soundtrack) (Various artists)

Note: Newly remastered from the original soundtrack of the Judy Garland version. Includes the previously unreleased 'Overture'.
Cass: Released Jan '89, on Silva Screen by Silva Screen Records. Catalogue no: **JST 44389**
CD: Released Jan '89, on CBS (import) by CBS Records & Distribution. Catalogue no: **CK 44389**

STAR IS BORN, A (Film soundtrack) (Various artists)

Album: Released Jan '89, on Silva Screen by Silva Screen Records. Catalogue no: **ACS 8740**
Cass: Released Jan '89, on Silva Screen by Silva Screen Records. Catalogue no: **BT 8740**
Album: Released Feb '77, on CBS by CBS Records & Distribution. Catalogue no: **CBS 86021**
Cass: Released Feb '77, on CBS by CBS Records & Distribution. Catalogue no: **40 86021**

STAR IS BORN (VIDEO) (Barbra Streisand) (Various artists)

VHS: Released Mar '88, on Warner Home Video by WEA Records. Catalogue no: **PES 11047**

Star Spangled Rhythm

STAR SPANGLED RHYTHM (Various artists)

Album: Released '88, on Curtain Calls (USA) by Music & Arts Programs of America(USA). Catalogue no: **CC 100/20**

STAR SPANGLED RHYTHM (Original soundtrack) (Various artists)

Album: Released Jan '89, on Silva Screen by Silva Screen Records. Catalogue no: **SH 2045**

Star Trek

INSIDE STAR TREK (Various artists)
Tracks: / Asimov's world of science fiction: *Various artists* / William Shatner meets Captain Kirk: *Various artists* / Origin of Spock: *Various artists* / Letter from a network censor: *Various artists* / Star Trek philosophy: *Various artists*.
Album: Released Feb '80, on CBS by CBS Records & Distribution. Deleted '85. Catalogue no: **CBS 31765**
Cass: Released Feb '80, on CBS by CBS Records & Distribution. Deleted '85. Catalogue no: **CBS 40 31765**

STAR TREK (TV Soundtrack) (Various artists)
Cass: on GNP Crescendo (USA) by GNP Crescendo Records (USA). Catalogue no: **ZCNCP 706**
Cass: Released '87, on PRT by Castle Communications Records. Catalogue no: **PYM 6041**
Album: on GNP Crescendo (USA) by GNP Crescendo Records (USA). Catalogue no: **NCP 706**
Album: Released Dec '89, on PRT by Castle Communications Records. Deleted Jul '90. Catalogue no: **PYL 6041**

STAR TREK II - THE WRATH OF KHAN (Various artists)
Tracks: / Star Trek (main theme): *Various artists* / Star Trek (closing theme): *Various artists* / Black ship tension: *Various artists* / By any other name: *Various artists* / Vian lab: *Various artists* / Time grows short: *Various artists* / Mirror, mirror: *Various artists* / Trouble with Tribbles, The: *Various artists* / Empath, The: *Various artists* / Help him: *Various artists* / Vian's farewell: *Various artists*.
Album: Released Oct '82, on Atlantic by WEA Records. Deleted Oct '87. Catalogue no: **K 50905**

STAR TREK III - THE SEARCH FOR SPOCK (Film soundtrack) (Various artists)
Tracks: / Prologue and main title: *Various artists* / Klingons: *Various artists* / Stealing the Enterprise: *Various artists* / Mind meld, The: *Various artists* / Bird of prey decloaks: *Various artists* / Returning to Vulcan: *Various artists* / Katra ritual, The: *Various artists* / Star

Trek III (end titles): *Various artists*.
Note: Composed by James Horner.
Cass: Released Aug '84, on Capitol by EMI Records. Deleted Jan '89. Catalogue no: **TCTREK 1**
Album: Released Aug '84, on Capitol by EMI Records. Deleted Jun '89. Catalogue no: **EJ 2401771**
Album: Released Aug '84, on Capitol by EMI Records. Catalogue no: **TREK 1**

STAR TREK III - THE SEARCH FOR SPOCK (2)
Tracks: / Search for Spock.
12" Single: Released Oct '84, on Walt Disney Catalogue no: **RESLD 2**

STAR TREK IV- THE VOYAGE HOME (Film soundtrack) (Various artists)
Tracks: / Main title: *Various artists* / Whaler, The: *Various artists* / Market street: *Various artists* / Crash-whale fugue: *Various artists* / Ballad of the whale: *Various artists* / Gillian seeks Kirk: *Various artists* / Chekhov's run: *Various artists* / Time travel: *Various artists* / Hospital chase: *Various artists* / Probe, The: *Various artists* / Home again: end credits: *Various artists*.
Note: Composed by Leonard Rosenman.
Cass: Released Feb '87, on MCA by MCA Records. Catalogue no: **IMCAC 6195**
CD: Released Jan '89, on MCA by MCA Records. Catalogue no: **MCAD 6195**
Album: Released Feb '87, on MCA by MCA Records. Catalogue no: **IMCA 6195**

STAR TREK (Original TV soundtrack) (Royal Philharmonic Orchestra)
Tracks: / Cage, The / Where no man has gone before.
Note: From the original TV pilot episode.
Cass: Released '88, on GNP Crescendo (USA) by GNP Crescendo Records (USA). Catalogue no: **GNP5 8006**
CD: Released '88, on GNP Crescendo (USA) by GNP Crescendo Records (USA). Catalogue no: **GNPD 8006**
Album: Released '88, on GNP Crescendo (USA) by GNP Crescendo Records (USA). Cata-

logue no: **GNPS 8006**

STAR TREK - SOUND EFFECTS: THE TV SERIES (Various artists)
Note: Sound effects from the original TV series.
Album: Released Jan '89, on GNP Crescendo (USA) by GNP Crescendo Records (USA). Catalogue no: **GNPS 8010**
Cass: Released Jan '89, on GNP Crescendo (USA) by GNP Crescendo Records (USA). Catalogue no: **GNP5 8010**
CD: Released Jan '89, on GNP Crescendo (USA) by GNP Crescendo Records (USA). Catalogue no: **GNPD 8010**

STAR TREK: THE MOTION PICTURE (Film Soundtrack) (Various artists)
Tracks: / Star trek: *Various artists* / Klingon battle: *Various artists* / Leaving drydock: *Various artists* / Cloud, The: *Various artists* / Enterprise, The: *Various artists* / Ilia's theme: *Various artists* / Vefur flyover: *Various artists* / Meld, The: *Various artists* / Spock walk: *Various artists* / End title: *Various artists*.
Note: Composed by Jerry Goldsmith.
Cass: Released Jan '80, on CBS by CBS Records & Distribution. Catalogue no: **40 70174**
Cass: Released Jan '89, on Silva Screen by Silva Screen Records. Catalogue no: **PST 36334**
Album: Released Jan '80, on CBS by CBS Records & Distribution. Catalogue no: **CBS 70174**

STAR TREK: THE NEXT GENERATION (TV soundtrack) (Various artists)
Note: Music from the new TV series by Dennis McCarthy. Theme by Jerry Goldsmith.
CD: Released Jan '89, on GNP Crescendo (USA) by GNP Crescendo Records (USA). Catalogue no: **GNPD 8012**
Album: Released Jan '89, on GNP Crescendo (USA) by GNP Crescendo Records (USA). Catalogue no: **GNPS 8012**
Cass: Released Jan '89, on GNP Crescendo (USA) by GNP Crescendo Records (USA). Catalogue no: **GNP5 8012**

STAR TREK V - THE FINAL FRONTIER (Film soundtrack)

(Various artists)
Tracks: / Mountain, The: *Various artists* / Barrier, The: *Various artists* / Without help: *Various artists* / Busy man, A: *Various artists* / Open the gates: *Various artists* / Moon's a window to heaven, The: *Various artists* / An angry god: *Various artists* / Let's get out of here: *Various artists* / Free minds: *Various artists* / Life is a dream: *Various artists*.
Cass: Released Nov '89, on Epic by CBS Records & Distribution. Catalogue no: **465 925 4**
CD: Released Nov '89, on Epic by CBS Records & Distribution. Catalogue no: **465 925 2**
Album: Released Nov '89, on Epic by CBS Records & Distribution. Catalogue no: **465 925 1**

STAR TREK - THE TV SERIES (TV soundtrack) (Royal Philharmonic Orchestra)
Tracks: / Is there in truth no beauty / Paradise syndrome.
Note: New digital recordings of the music from the original TV series.
CD: Released '86, on Silva Screen by Silva Screen Records. Catalogue no: **LXCD 703**
Cass: Released Jan '89, on Silva Screen by Silva Screen Records. Catalogue no: **LXDC 703**
Album: Released Jan '89, on Silva Screen by Silva Screen Records. Catalogue no: **LXDR 703**

STAR TREK VOL 1 - THE TV SERIES (TV soundtrack) (Royal Philharmonic Orchestra)
CD: Released Jan '89, on Silva Screen by Silva Screen Records. Catalogue no: **VCD 47235**
Album: Released Jan '89, on Silva Screen by Silva Screen Records. Catalogue no: **704.270**
Cass: Released Jan '89, on Silva Screen by Silva Screen Records. Catalogue no: **C 704.270**

STAR TREK VOL.2 - THE TV SERIES (TV soundtrack) (Royal Philharmonic Orchestra)
Tracks: / Conscience of the king / Spectre of the gun / Enemy within', The / I, Mudd.
Cass: Released Jan '89, on Silva Screen by Silva Screen Records. Catalogue no: **LXDC 704**
Album: Released Jan '89, on Silva Screen by Silva Screen Rec-

ords. Catalogue no: **LXDR 704**
CD: Released '86, on Silva Screen by Silva Screen Records. Catalogue no: **LXCD 704**

STAR TREK VOL 2 - THE TV SERIES (Royal Philharmonic Orchestra)
Album: Released Jan '89, on Silva Screen by Silva Screen Records. Catalogue no: **704 300**
CD: Released Jan '89, on Silva Screen by Silva Screen Records. Catalogue no: **VCD 47240**

Star Wars

EMPIRE STRIKES BACK, THE (Star Wars II)
2 LP Set: Released May '80, on RSO by Polydor Ltd. Catalogue no: **RS2 4201**
Cass set: Released May '80, on RSO by Polydor Ltd. Catalogue no: **RSS 23**

STAR WARS (London Philharmonic Orchestra)
Tracks: / Main title / Imperial attack / Princess Leia's theme / Ben's death and the fighter attack / Land of the sand people / Return home, The / End title / 2001, Theme from (Mars) / Mercury / Venus / Space tumble.
Album: Released '77, on Damont by Damont Audio Ltd.. Deleted '82. Catalogue no: **DMT 2001**

STAR WARS (Film soundtrack) (London Symphony Orchestra)
Tracks: / Main title / Imperial attack / Princess Leia's theme / Desert and the robot auction, The / Last battle, The / Ben's death and the fighter attack / Little people work, The / Rescue of the princess / Inner city / Cantina band.
Album: Released Jan '78, on 20th Century by Phonogram Ltd. Deleted Jan '83. Catalogue no: **BTD 541**
Album: Released Sep '82, on RSO by Polydor Ltd. Catalogue no: **2679 092**
Cass: Released Sep '82, on RSO by Polydor Ltd. Catalogue no: **3528 033**
CD: Released '83, on RSO by Polydor Ltd. Deleted Jan '89. Catalogue no: **800 096 2**
Cass set: Released '80, on RSO by Polydor Ltd. Deleted '85. Catalogue no: **C2 2T 541**

2 LP Set: Released '80, on RSO by Polydor Ltd. Deleted '85. Catalogue no: **2T 541**
2 LP Set: Released Sep '82, on RSO by Polydor Ltd. Deleted Jan '89. Catalogue no: **2658 151**

RETURN OF THE JEDI (Star Wars 3)
Album: Released May '83, on Polydor by Polydor Ltd. Catalogue no: **POLD 5105**
Cass: Released May '83, on Polydor by Polydor Ltd. Catalogue no: **POLDC 5105**

STAR WARS THEME (2) (Various artists)
Tracks: / Star wars theme: *Various artists* / Cantina band: *Various artists*.
7" Single: Released Feb '78, on 20th Century by Phonogram Ltd. Deleted '81. Catalogue no: **BTC 2345**

STAR WARS TRILOGY (Film soundtrack) (Various artists)
Tracks: / Main title: *Various artists* / Princess Leia's theme: *Various artists* / Here they come: *Various artists* / Asteroid field, The: *Various artists* / Yoda's theme: *Various artists* / Imperial march: *Various artists* / Parade of the Ewoks: *Various artists* / Luke and Leia: *Various artists* / Fight with tie fighters: *Various artists* / Jabba the Hutt: *Various artists* / Darth Vader's death: *Various artists* / Forest battle, The: *Various artists* / Finale: *Various artists*.
Album: Released Dec '83, on T. E. R. by That's Entertainment Records. Catalogue no: **TER 1067**
Cass: Released Dec '83, on T. E. R. by That's Entertainment Records. Catalogue no: **ZCTER 1067**
CD: Released Dec '83, on T. E. R. by That's Entertainment Records. Catalogue no: **CDTER 1067**
CD: Released Jan '89, on Silva Screen by Silva Screen Records. Catalogue no: **VCD 47201**

Stardust, Alvin

I HOPE AND I PRAY (Stardust, Alvin & Sheila Walsh)
Tracks: / I hope and I pray / Speak of love.
7" Single: Released Mar '86, on Chrysalis by Chrysalis Records. Catalogue no: **ALV 4**
12" Single: Released Mar '86, on Chrysalis by Chrysalis Records. Catalogue no: **ALVX 4**

Stardust (film)

STARDUST (Film soundtrack) (Various artists)
2 LP Set: Released Nov '74, on Ronco Deleted '76. Catalogue no: **RG 2009/10**

Starlight Express

STARLIGHT EXPRESS (Original London cast) (Various artists)
Tracks: / Overture: *Various artists* / Rolling stock: *Various artists* / Call me rusty: *Various artists* / Lotta locomotion, A: *Various artists* / Pumping iron: *Various artists* / Freight: *Various artists* / AC/DC: *Various artists* / Hitching and switching: *Various artists* / He whistled at me: *Various artists* / Race-heat one: *Various artists* / There's me: *Various artists* / Blues, The: *Various artists* / Belle: *Various artists* / Race-heat two: *Various artists* / Race-heat three: *Various artists* / Starlight express: *Various artists* / Rap, The: *Various artists* / Uncoupled: *Various artists* / Rolling stock (reprise): *Various artists* / C.B.: *Various artists* / Race-uphill final: *Various artists* / Right place, right time: *Various artists* / Race-downhill final: *Various artists* / No comeback: *Various artists* / One rock 'n' roll too many: *Various artists* / Only He: *Various artists* / Only you: *Various artists* / Light at the end of the tunnel: *Various artists*.
CD Set: Released Jun '84, on Polydor by Polydor Ltd. Catalogue no: **821 597-2**
Cass set: Released Jun '84, on Polydor by Polydor Ltd. Catalogue no: **LNERC 1**
2 LP Set: Released Jun '84, on Polydor by Polydor Ltd. Catalogue no: **LNER 1**

Starman

STARMAN (Original Soundtrack) (Various artists)
Note: Composed by John Carpenter.
CD: Released Aug '90, on T. E. R. by That's Entertainment Records. Catalogue no: **CDTER 1097**
Album: Released Aug '90, on T. E. R. by That's Entertainment Records. Catalogue no: **TER 1097**
CD: Released Jan '89, on Silva Screen. by Silva Screen Records. Catalogue no: **VCD 47220**
Cass: Released Jan '89, on Silva

Screen by Silva Screen Records. Catalogue no: **CTV 81233**
Cass: Released Aug '90, on T. E. R. by That's Entertainment Records. Catalogue no: **ZCTER 1097**

Starr, Edwin

TWENTY FIVE MILES
Tracks: / Twenty five miles / Never turn my back on you.
Note: Featured in the film '*Twenty Five Miles*' and '*Adventures in baby sitting*'.
12" Single: Released Jan '81, on 20th Century by Phonogram Ltd. Deleted Jan '84. Catalogue no: **TCD 2477**
7" Single: Released Oct '81, on Tamla Motown by Motown Records (UK). Deleted '83. Catalogue no: **TMG 672**

Stars & Garters

STARS FROM STARS & GARTERS (TV soundtrack) (Various artists)
Album: Released Mar '64, on Pye Deleted '69. Catalogue no: **GGL 0252**

Starship

NOTHING'S GONNA STOP US NOW
Tracks: / Nothing's gonna stop us now / Laying it on the line / We built this city (Extra track on 12" only) / Tomorrow doesn't matter tonight (Extra track on 12" only).
Note: Featured in the film 'Mannequin'.
7" Single: Released Mar '87, on RCA by BMG Records (UK). Deleted Sep '90. Catalogue no: **PB 49757**
CD Single: Released Jun '89, on RCA by BMG Records (UK). Deleted Feb '90. Catalogue no: **PD 49451**
12" Single: Released Mar '87, on RCA by BMG Records (UK). Deleted Feb '90. Catalogue no: **FT 49758**

Starting Here...

STARTING HERE STARTING NOW (Broadway Cast) (Various artists)
Note: By David Shire & Richard Maltby.
Cass: Released Aug '90, on Silva Screen by Silva Screen Records. Catalogue no: **GK 82360**
CD: Released Aug '90, on Silva Screen by Silva Screen Records.

Catalogue no: **GD 82360**

State Project

EMPIRE STATE (SINGLE) (Original soundtrack)
Tracks: / Empire State / Money.
12" Single: Released 20 Jun '87, on Priority by Priority Records. Deleted 11 Jan '88. Catalogue no: **12 EMPIRE 1**
7" Single: Released 20 Jun '87, on Priority by Priority Records. Deleted Jan '88. Catalogue no: **EMPIRE 1**

Stay Awake Disney

STAY AWAKE DISNEY (Disney songs) (Various artists)
Tracks: / I'm getting wet and I don't care at all: *Various artists* / Hi diddle de dee: *Nordine, Ken/Bill Frisell/Wayne Horvitz* / Little April showers: *Merchant, Natalie/Michael Stripe/Mark Bingham & The Roches* / I wanna be like you (The monkey song): *Los Lobos* / Baby mine: *Raitt, Bonny/Was (Not Was)* / Heigh ho (The dwarfs marching song): *Waits, Tom* / The darkness sheds its veil: *Various artists* / Stay awake: *Vega, Suzanne* / Little wooden head: *Frisell, Bill/Wayne Horvitz* / Blue shadows on the trail: *Straw, Syd* / Three inches is such a wretched height: *Various artists* / Castle in Spain: *Poindexter, Buster & The Banshees Of Blue* / I wonder: *YMA Sumac* / Mickey mouse march: *Neville, Aaron* / All innocent children had better beware: *Various artists* / Feed the birds: *Hudson, Garth* / Whistle while you work: *NRBQ* / I'm wishing: *Carter, Betty* / Cruella De Ville: *Replacements* / Some day my prince will come: *O'Connor, Sinead* / Technicolour pachyderms: *Various artists* / Pink elephants on parade: *Ra, Sun & His Arkestra* / Zip-a-dee-doo-dah / Second star to the right: *Taylor, James* / Pinocchio medley (do you see the noses growing?): *Various artists* / Desolation theme: *Nordine, Ken/Bill Frisell/Wayne Horvitz* / When you wish upon a star: *Starr, Ringo/Herb Alpert*.
Note: "Stay Awake" - The first album of Disney songs for children and adults. A&M artists Herb Alpert and Suzanne Vega, along with Tom Waits, The Replacements, Los Lobos, Sinead O'Connor and others, are among the performers

Various Artists - *Staying Alive* featuring John Travolta (RSO)

featured on "Stay Awake", a collection of new interpretations of songs from the classic films of Walt Disney. Under the direction of Hal Willner, songs like "Whistle While You Work", "Heigh Ho", "Someday My Prince Will Come" and many others are given collaborations unlike any previously attempted. Willner's previous "Various Artists" concept albums have included tributes to composers Nino Rota, Thelonious Monk and Kurt Weill; the latter two, "That's The Way I Feel Now" and "Lost In The Stars" were compiled for A&M. He will be in the U.K. at the time of these releases for extensive P.R. at radio and with press. "Stay Awake" includes the first single "Baby Mine" beautifully sung by Bonnie Raitt with Was (Not Was).

Cass: Released Oct '88, on A&M by A&M Records. Catalogue no: **AMC 3918**

CD: Released Oct '88, on A&M by A&M Records. Catalogue no: **CDA 3918**

Album: Released Oct '88, on A&M by A&M Records. Catalogue no: **AMA 3918**

Staying Alive

STAYING ALIVE (Film soundtrack) (Various artists) (See picture above)
Tracks: / Woman in you: *Bee Gees* / Love you too much: *Bee Gees* / Breakout: *Bee Gees* / Someone belonging to someone: *Bee Gees* / Life goes on: *Bee Gees* / Stayin' alive: *Bee Gees* / Far from over: *Stallone, Frank* / Look out for number one: *Stallone, Frank* / Finding out the hard way: *Various artists* / Moody girl: *Various artists* / (We dance) so close to the fire: *Various artists* / I'm never gonna give you up: *Various artists*.
Album: Released Jul '83, on RSO by Polydor Ltd. Catalogue no: **RSBG 3**
Cass: Released Jul '83, on RSO by Polydor Ltd. Catalogue no: **TRSBG 3**
CD: Released Jul '83, on RSO by Polydor Ltd. Catalogue no: **813 269-2**

STAYING ALIVE (VIDEO) (Various artists)
Note: Cert: PG.
VHS: Released '89, on CIC Video

Catalogue no: **VHR 2099**
VHS: Released '88, on CIC Video
Catalogue no: **CIC 29924**

Stealing Heaven

STEALING HEAVEN (Film soundtrack) (Various artists)
Album: Released Jul '89, on T. E. R. by That's Entertainment Records. Catalogue no: **TER 1166**
Cass: Released Jul '89, on T. E. R. by That's Entertainment Records. Catalogue no: **ZCTER 1166**
CD: Released Jul '89, on T. E. R. by That's Entertainment Records. Catalogue no: **CDTER 1166**

Steele, Tommy

HANS ANDERSON (See under Hans Anderson)

LITTLE WHITE BULL
Tracks: / Little white bull.
Note: From the film "*Tommy the toreador*".
7"Single: Released '59, on Decca. Deleted '88. Catalogue no: **F 11177**

SINGING IN THE RAIN
Tracks: / Singing in the rain.
7" Single: Released Aug '87, on Safari by Safari Records. Catalogue no: **SAFE 61**

SHIRALEE
Tracks: / Shiralee.
Note: From the film "*Shiralee*".
7" Single: Released Aug '57, on Decca. Deleted '60. Catalogue no: **F 10896**

TOMMY STEELE STORY (Film Soundtrack)
Tracks: / Take me back baby / I like / Butterfingers / Handful of songs / You gotta go / Water water / Cannibal pot / Will it be you / Two eyes / Build up / Time to kill / Elevator rock / Teenage party / Doomsday rock.
Album: Released Aug '81, on Decca. Deleted Aug '86. Catalogue no: **LFT 1288**

Steiner, Max

KING KONG (1933 Film music) (Steiner, Max & the National Philharmonic Orchestra)
CD: Released Feb '90, on Silva Screen by Silva Screen Records. Catalogue no: **SCCD 901**
Album: Released Dec '80, on

Entr'acte by Fith Continent Music Group (USA). Catalogue no: **ERS 6504**

Step Lively

STEP LIVELY (Film soundtrack) (Various artists)
Note: Starring Frank Sinatra.
Album: Released Jan '89, on Silva Screen by Silva Screen Records. Catalogue no: **HS 412**

Steppenwolf

BORN TO BE WILD
Tracks: / Born to be wild / Pusher, The.
Note: Featured in the film 'Easy Rider'.
7" Single: Released Jun '69, on Stateside by EMI Records. Deleted '72. Catalogue no: **SS 8017**

BORN TO BE WILD (OLD GOLD)
Tracks: / Born to be wild / Pusher.
7" Single: Released Apr '83, on Old Gold by Old Gold Records. Catalogue no: **OG 9323**

Steptoe & Son

STEPTOE AND SON (See under Corbett, Harry H)

Stern, Michael

CHRONOS (See under Chronos)

Stevie

STEVIE (Film soundtrack) (Various artists)
Cass: Released Jan '79, on CBS by CBS Records & Distribution. Deleted Jan '84. Catalogue no: **CBS 43 70165**
Album: Released Jan '79, on CBS by CBS Records & Distribution. Deleted Jan '84. Catalogue no: **CBS 70165**

Stewart, David A

LILY WAS HERE (Film soundtrack) (Stewart, David A & Candy Dulfer)
Tracks: / Lily was here / Pink building, The / Lily robs the bank / Toyshop robbery / Toys on the sidewalk / Good hotel, The / Second chance / Here comes the rain again / Alone in the city / Toyshop (part 1) / Coffin, The / Teletype / Inside the pink building / Percussion jam / Peaches / Lily was here (reprise).
Album: Released Apr '90, on

Anxious by Anxious Records. Catalogue no: **ZL 74233**
Cass: Released Apr '90, on Anxious by Anxious Records. Catalogue no: **ZK 74233**
CD: Released Apr '90, on Anxious by Anxious Records. Catalogue no: **ZD 74233**

LILY WAS HERE (SINGLE) (Stewart, David A featuring Candy Dulfer)
Tracks: / Lily was here / Lily robs the bank.
12" Single: Released Feb '90, on Arista by BMG Records (UK). Catalogue no: **ZT 43046**
Cassingle: Released Feb '90, on Arista by BMG Records (UK). Catalogue no: **ZK 43045**
7" Single: Released Feb '90, on Arista by BMG Records (UK). Catalogue no: **ZB 43045**
CD Single: Released Feb '90, on Arista by BMG Records (UK). Catalogue no: **ZD 43046**

Stewart, Rod

INFATUATION
Tracks: / Infatuation / Three time loser / Tonight's the night (on 12" only).
Note: From the film "The sure thing"
7" Single: Released May '84, on Warner Bros. by WEA Records. Deleted '87. Catalogue no: **W 9256**
12" Single: Released May '84, on Warner Bros. by WEA Records. Deleted '87. Catalogue no: **W 9256T**

SAILING
Tracks: / Sailing / Stone cold sober.
7" Single: Released Mar '87, on Warner Bros. by WEA Records. Catalogue no: **K 16600**
7" Single: Released Jun '77, on Riva by Riva Records. Deleted '80. Catalogue no: **RIVA 9**

Stilgoe, Richard

BODYWORK (Musical light opera '88)
Cass: Released Oct '88, on First Night by First Night Records. Catalogue no: **CASTC 15**
Album: Released Oct '88, on First Night by First Night Records. Catalogue no: **CAST 15**
CD: Released Oct '88, on First Night by First Night Records. Catalogue no: **CASTCD 15**

Sting

SPREAD A LITTLE HAPPINESS
Tracks: / Spread a little happiness / Only you.
Note: Featured in the film 'Brimstone & Treacle'.
7" Single: Released Aug '82, on A&M by A&M Records. Deleted '85. Catalogue no: **AMS 8217**

Sting (Film)

STING, THE (Film Soundtrack) (Various artists)
Tracks: / Solace: Various artists / Entertainer, The: Various artists / Easy winners: Various artists / Pineapple rag: Various artists / Gladiolus rag: Various artists / Merry go round music: Various artists / Listen to the mocking bird: Various artists / Darling Nellie Gray: Various artists / Turkey in the straw: Various artists / Ragtime dance: Various artists / Hooker's hooker: Various artists / Glove, The: Various artists / Luther: Various artists / Glove, The: Various artists / Little girl: Various artists.
Cass: Released Sep '86, on MCA by MCA Records. Catalogue no: **MCLC 1735**
Album: Released Mar '74, on MCA by MCA Records. Deleted '79. Catalogue no: **MCF 2537**
CD: Released Feb '87, on MCA by MCA Records. Deleted '88. Catalogue no: **MCAD 1625**
Album: Released Sep '86, on MCA by MCA Records. Catalogue no: **MCL 1735**
CD: Released Sep '87, on MCA by MCA Records. Catalogue no: **MCAD 31034**

STING II (Various artists) (See picture on next page)
Album: Released Jul '83, on RSO by Polydor Ltd. Deleted Jul '88. Catalogue no: **RSBG 3**

Stoloff, Morris

MOONGLOW AND THEME FROM 'PICNIC' (Stoloff, Morris Orchestra)
Tracks: / Moonglow and theme from 'Picnic'.
7" Single: Released Jun '56, on Brunswick by Decca Records. Deleted '59. Catalogue no: **05553**

Stone, Ricky

SOMETHING'S COOKING (Theme from Crazy Kitchen)

Karl Malden as Macalinski in *The Sting II*

Tracks: / Something's cooking / Don't let it happen to me.
7" Single: Released Nov '85, on Magnet by WEA Records. Deleted '87. Catalogue no: **MAG 287**

Stop Making Sense

STOP MAKING SENSE (See under Talking Heads)

Stop The World

(See also under Newley, Anthony)

STOP THE WORLD I WANT TO GET OFF (ORIGINAL ISSUE) (London cast) (Various artists)
Album: Released Sep '61, on Decca by Decca International. Deleted '66. Catalogue no: **LK 4408**

STOP THE WORLD I WANT TO GET OFF (Original London cast) (Various artists)
Tracks: / I wanna be rich: *Various artists* / ABC: *Various artists* / Typically English: *Various artists* / Lumbered: *Various artists* / Gonna build a mountain: *Various artists* / Glorious Russia: *Various artists* / Mellinki Meilchick: *Various artists* /

Typiache Deutsche: *Various artists* / Nag nag nag: *Various artists* / All-American: *Various artists* / Once in a lifetime: *Various artists* / Mumbo jumbo: *Various artists* / Someone nice like you: *Various artists* / What kind of fool am I?: *Various artists*.
CD: Released Jan '89, on T. E. R. by That's Entertainment Records. Catalogue no: **820261.2**
Cass: Released Sep '84, on T. E. R. by That's Entertainment Records. Catalogue no: **ZCTER 1082**
Album: Released Sep '84, on T. E. R. by That's Entertainment Records. Catalogue no: **TER 1082**

Storm, Rebecca

SHOW, THE (Theme from Connie)
Tracks: / Show, The.
Cassingle: Released Jul '85, on Telebell Catalogue no: **ZCTVP 3**
12" Single: Released Jul '85, on Telebell Catalogue no: **TVEP 3**

Stormy Monday

STORMY MONDAY (Film Soundtrack) (King, B.B. & Mike Figgis)

Tracks: / Stormy Monday / Kate and Brendan / Weegee / Thrill is gone, The / On the quay / Dawn and the Tyne / Road to Poland, The / Finney makes a point / Star-spangled banner, The / Carrie / Just a closer walk with thee / Krakow dawn / Niezapomne ciebe (I won't forget you) / Train across the river / Muzac for lovers.
Note: The soundtrack to "*Stormy Monday*" features music by B.B. King and Mike Figgis and includes two of B.B. King's best known tracks "Stormy Monday" and "*The thrill is gone*". (Virgin Records, July 1988).
CD: Released Jul '88, on Virgin by Virgin Records. Catalogue no: **CDV 2537**
Cass: Released Jul '88, on Virgin by Virgin Records. Deleted Jun '90. Catalogue no: **TCV 2537**
Album: Released Jul '88, on Virgin by Virgin Records. Deleted May '90. Catalogue no: **V 2537**

Stormy Weather (film)

STORMY WEATHER (Film Soundtrack) (Various artists)
Note: Starring Lena Horne and Cab Calloway.
Album: Released Jan '89, on Silva Screen by Silva Screen Records. Catalogue no: **SH 2037**
Cass: Released Jan '89, on Silva Screen by Silva Screen Records. Catalogue no: **CSH 2037**

Stowaways On The Ark

STOWAWAYS ON THE ARK (In Der Arche Ist Der Wurm Drin) (Various artists)
Note: Original film soundtrack of the Paramount full length cartoon film featuring songs by Karel Gott & the new age sounds of the ark. Music composed by Frank Player.
CD: Released Dec '88, on JMP (W.Germany) Catalogue no: **JMP 3004018**

Stradivari

STRADIVARI (Film Soundtrack) (Various artists)
Cass: Released Feb '89, on Philips by Phonogram Ltd. Catalogue no: **MC 422 8494 PH**
Album: Released Feb '89, on Philips by Phonogram Ltd. Catalogue no: **LP 422 8491 PH**
CD: Released Feb '89, on Philips by Phonogram Ltd. Catalogue no: **CD 422 8292 PH**

Straight To Hell

STRAIGHT TO HELL (Film Soundtrack) (Various artists)
Tracks: / Good, the bad and the ugly, The: *Pogues* / Rake at the gates of hell, The: *Pogues* / If I should fall from grace with God: *Pogues* / Rabinga: *Pogues* / Danny boy: *Pogues* / Evil darling: *Strummer, Joe* / Ambush or mystery rock: *Strummer, Joe* / Money guns & coffee: *Pray For Rain* / Killers, The: *Pray For Rain* / Salsa y ketchup: *Zander Schloss* / Big nothing: *Macmanus gang, The.*
CD: Released Jul '87, on Hell Catalogue no: **CDIABLO 1**
Cass: Released Jun '87, on Hell Catalogue no: **ZDIABLO 1**
Album: Released Jun '87, on Hell Catalogue no: **DIABLO 1**

Strange, Billy

GREAT WESTERN THEMES
Cass: Released '88, on GNP Crescendo (USA) by GNP Crescendo Records (USA). Catalogue no: **GNP5 2046**
Album: Released '88, on GNP Crescendo (USA) by GNP Crescendo Records (USA). Catalogue no: **GNPS 2046**

Stranger Than Paradise

STRANGER THAN PARADISE (See under Lurie, John)

Streep, Meryl

AMAZING GRACE
Tracks: / Amazing grace.
Note: Featured in the film 'Silkwood'.
7" Single: Released May '84, on PRT by Castle Communications Records. Catalogue no: **7P 309**

Street Fleet

STREET FLEET (Film Soundtrack) (Various artists)
Album: Released Apr '84, on MCA by MCA Records. Catalogue no: **MCF 3204**

Streets Of Fire

STREETS OF FIRE (Film soundtrack) (Various artists)
CD: Released Jun '88, on MCA (USA) by MCA Records (USA). Catalogue no: **MCAD 5492**
Album: Released May '84, on MCA by MCA Records. Catalogue no: **MCF 3221**

Cass: Released May '84, on MCA by MCA Records. Catalogue no: **MCFC 3221**

Streisand, Barbra

BROADWAY ALBUM
Tracks: / Putting it together / If I love you / Something's coming / Not while I'm around / Being alive / I have dreamed / We kiss in a shadow / Something wonderful / Send in the clowns / Pretty women / Ladies who lunch, The / Can't help lovin' dat man / I loves you Porgy / Porgy, I's your woman now / Somewhere.
Album: Released Jan '86, on CBS. Catalogue no: **CBS 86322**
Cass: Released Jan '86, on CBS. Catalogue no: **40 86322**
CD: Released Feb '86, on CBS. Catalogue no: **CD 86322**

EVERGREEN
Tracks: / Evergreen / I believe in love.
Note: From the film "*A star is born*"
7" Single: Released Jul '84, on CBS by CBS Records & Distribution. Deleted '86. Catalogue no: **CBS A4597**
7" Single: Released Apr '77, on CBS by CBS Records & Distribution. Deleted '80. Catalogue no: **CBS 4855**

EYES OF LAURA MARS
Tracks: / Eyes of Laura Mars / Laura and Neville.
Note: From the film of the same name.
7" Single: Released Oct '78, on CBS by CBS Records & Distribution. Deleted '81. Catalogue no: **CBS 6657**

MAIN EVENT
Tracks: / Main event / Fight (instrumental).
Note: From "*Main event*".
7" Single: Released Jul '79, on CBS by CBS Records & Distribution. Deleted '82. Catalogue no: **CBS 7714**

MEMORY
Tracks: / Memory / Evergreen.
7" Single: Released Feb '83, on CBS by CBS Records & Distribution. Catalogue no: **BARB 1**
7" Single: Released Mar '82, on CBS by CBS Records & Distribution. Deleted '85. Catalogue no: **A 1903**

NUTS (Film soundtrack)
Mini-LP: Released Mar '88, on

CBS by CBS Records & Distribution. Deleted 17 Apr '89. Catalogue no: **651379 6**

WAY WE WERE, THE (SINGLE)
Tracks: / Way we were, The.
Note: From the film "*The way we were*".
7" Single: Released Mar '74, on CBS by CBS Records & Distribution. Deleted '77. Catalogue no: **CBS 1915**

YENTL (Original soundtrack)
Tracks: / Where is it written / Papa can you hear me / This is one of those moments / No wonder the way he makes me feel / No matter what happens.
Cass: Released Nov '83, on CBS by CBS Records & Distribution. Catalogue no: **40 86302**
Album: Released Nov '83, on CBS by CBS Records & Distribution. Deleted 10 Jul '89. Catalogue no: **CBS 86302**

Strike Up The Band

STRIKE UP THE BAND (Film soundtrack) (Various artists)
Note: Starring Judy Garland and Mickey Rooney.
Album: Released Jan '89, on Silva Screen by Silva Screen Records. Catalogue no: **HS 5009**

Strummer, Joe

LOVE KILLS
Tracks: / Love kills / Dum dum club.
Note: From the film "*Syd and Nancy*"
7" Single: Released Jul '86, on CBS by CBS Records & Distribution. Catalogue no: **A 7244**
12" Single: Released Jul '86, on CBS by CBS Records & Distribution. Catalogue no: **TA 7244**

Stud

STUD, THE (Film Soundtrack) (Various artists)
Album: Released Mar '78, on Ronco Deleted '82. Catalogue no: **RTD 2029**

Student Prince

STUDENT PRINCE (See under Lanza, Mario)

Stunt Man

STUNT MAN (Film soundtrack) (Various artists)
Album: Released Feb '81, on 20th

Century by Phonogram Ltd. Catalogue no: **T 626**

Style Council

HAVE YOU EVER HAD IT BLUE
Tracks: / Have you ever had it blue.
Note: Featured in the film 'Absolute Beginners'.
12" Single: Released Mar '86, on Polydor by Polydor Ltd. Deleted Aug '87. Catalogue no: **CINEX 112**
Cassingle: on Polydor by Polydor Ltd. Deleted Aug '87. Catalogue no: **CINEC 1**
7" Single: Released Mar '86, on Polydor by Polydor Ltd. Deleted Mar '87. Catalogue no: **CINE 1**

Subway

SUBWAY (Film soundtrack) (Various artists)
Tracks: / Subway: Various artists / Guns and people: Various artists / Burglary: Various artists / Masquerade: Various artists / Childhood drama: Various artists / Man Y: Various artists / Congabass: Various artists / Song to Xavier: Various artists / Speedway: Various artists / It's only mystery: Various artists / Drumskate: Various artists / Dolphin dance: Various artists / Racked animal: Various artists / Pretext: Various artists / Dark passage II: Various artists.
Note: Composed by Eric Serra.
Album: Released Jan '89, on Silva Screen by Silva Screen Records. Catalogue no: **GM 9702**
Album: Released Feb '86, on Virgin by Virgin Records. Catalogue no: **V2371**
Cass: Released Jan '89, on Silva Screen by Silva Screen Records. Catalogue no: **GMK 9702**
CD: Released Jan '89, on Silva Screen by Silva Screen Records. Catalogue no: **GMD 9702**
Album: Released Jun '88, on Virgin by Virgin Records. Catalogue no: **OVED 223**
Cass: Released Jun '88, on Virgin by Virgin Records. Deleted '88. Catalogue no: **OVEDC 223**

Sudden Impact...

SUDDEN IMPACT AND THE BEST OF DIRTY HARRY (Film soundtrack) (Various artists)
Album: Released Mar '84, on Warner Bros. by WEA Records. Catalogue no: **923990 1**
Cass: Released Mar '84, on War-

ner Bros. by WEA Records. Catalogue no: **923990 4**

Sugar Babies

SUGAR BABIES - THE BURLESQUE MUSICAL (Broadway Cast Recording) (Various artists)
Tracks: / Sugar babies overture: Various artists / Good old burlesque show, A: Various artists / Intro: Welcome to the Gaiety: Various artists (Spoken words only.) / Let me be your sugar baby: Various artists / In Louisiana: Various artists / I feel a song coming on: Various artists / Goin' back to New Orleans: Various artists / Broken Arms Hotel, The: Various artists (Cassette & CD only.) / Sally: Various artists / Don't blame me: Various artists / Immigration rose: Various artists / Little red house: Various artists (Cassette & CD only.) / Sugar baby bounce: Various artists (Cassette & CD only.) / Introduction Mme Rentz: Various artists (Spoken words only.) / Down at the Gaiety Burlesque: Various artists / Mr. Banjo man: Various artists / When my sugar walks down the street: Various artists / Candy butcher: Various artists (Spoken words only.) / Entr'Acte: Various artists / I'm keeping myself available for you: Various artists / Exactly like you: Various artists / I'm in the mood for love: Various artists / I'm just a song & dance man: Various artists / Warm and willing: Various artists / Father dear, father dear: Various artists (Cassette & CD only.) / Boss upstairs, The: Various artists (Cassette & CD only.) / Cuban love song: Various artists (Cassette & CD only.) / Every week another town: Various artists (McHugh Medley.) / I can't give you anything but love: Various artists (McHugh Medley.) / I'm shooting high: Various artists / When you and I were young Maggie blues: Various artists / On the sunny side of the street: Various artists / You can't blame your Uncle Sammy: Various artists.
CD: Released Sep '88, on Columbia by EMI Records. Deleted Aug '89. Catalogue no: **CDP 791 144 2**
Album: Released Sep '88, on Columbia by EMI Records. Deleted Aug '89. Catalogue no: **SCX 6714**
Cass: Released Sep '88, on Col-

umbia by EMI Records. Deleted May '90. Catalogue no: **TCSCX 6714**
CD: Released Sep '88, on Columbia by EMI Records. Deleted Aug '89. Catalogue no: **CDSCX 6714**

Suleyman..

SULEYMAN THE MAGNIFICENT (Film Soundtrack) (Various artists)
Note: Original soundtrack of film produced by National Gallery, Washington and Metropolitan Museum, New York, on the occasion of "The Age of Sultan Suleyman The Magnificent", an exhibition of treasures from Turkey's national collection.
CD: Released 30 Jan '88, on Celestial Harmonies(USA) by Celestial Harmonies (USA). Catalogue no: **CDCEL 023**
Cass: Released 1 Feb '88, on Miles Music by Miles Music Records. Catalogue no: **MCCEL 023**
Album: Released 1 Feb '88, on Miles Music by Miles Music Records. Catalogue no: **LPCEL 023**

Summer Holiday

SUMMER HOLIDAY (See under Richard, Cliff)

Summer Of 42

SUMMER OF '42 (Film Soundtrack) (Various artists)
Note: Score by Michel Legrand.
Album: Released Jan '89, Catalogue no: **46098**

Summer Place

SUMMER PLACE, A (See under Faith, Percy)

Summer & Smoke

SUMMER AND SMOKE (Film Soundtrack) (Various artists)
Note: Composed by Elmer Bernstein.
Album: Released Jan '89, on Silva Screen by Silva Screen Records. Catalogue no: **ERS 6519**

Summer Story

SUMMER STORY, A (Film soundtrack) (Delerue, Georges)
Tracks: / Love in the loft / Summer poem / We meet Megan / Sheep shearing / Ashton arrives / Waiting for Megan / Abandoned / Flashback and rescue / Gentle maiden, The (instrumental) / Return to the

hill / At the beach / Megan leaves forever / Missed the train / Megan at work / Night meeting / Megan in the field / Thinking of Ashton / Ashton's son (theme from "A Summer Story") / Falling in love / Coming to town.

Note: This film tells the tragic and bittersweet story of an illicit love affair between a cosmopolitan lawyer and a rural farm girl. The film stars James Wilby ('Maurice') and newcomer Imogen Stubbs. The score is by Georges Delerue, the French composer who is known for his work with such acclaimed directors as Truffaut and Godard and for the scores for such films as 'Julia' and 'A little romance' for which he won an academy award. (Virgin. Oct 1988)

Album: Released 3 Oct '88, on Virgin by Virgin Records. Deleted May '90. Catalogue no: **V 2562**

CD: Released Jan '89, on Silva Screen by Silva Screen Records. Catalogue no: **790961.2**

Cass: Released 3 Oct '88, on Virgin by Virgin Records. Deleted Jun '90. Catalogue no: **TCV 2562**

Album: Released Jan '89, on Silva Screen by Silva Screen Records. Catalogue no: **790961.1**

Cass: Released Jan '89, on Silva Screen by Silva Screen Records. Catalogue no: **790961.4**

CD: Released '88, on Virgin by Virgin Records. Catalogue no: **CDV 2562**

Sun Also Rises

SUN ALSO RISES, THE (Film Soundtrack) (Various artists)
Note: Composed by Hugo Friedhofer.
Album: Released Jan '89, on Silva Screen by Silva Screen Records. Catalogue no: **AEI 3109**

Sunburn (film)

SUNBURN (Film Soundtrack) (Various artists)
Album: Released Feb '80, on Ronco Deleted '82. Catalogue no: **RTL 2044**

Sunday In The Country

SUNDAY IN THE COUNTRY (Film Soundtrack) (Various artists)
Note: Composed by Philippe Sarde.
Album: Released Jan '89, on Silva Screen by Silva Screen

Records. Catalogue no: **STV 81227**

Sunday In The Park...

SUNDAY IN THE PARK WITH GEORGE (Original Broadway cast) (Various artists)
CD: Released Jan '89, on Silva Screen by Silva Screen Records. Catalogue no: **RCD 1 5042**
Album: Released Jan '89, on Silva Screen by Silva Screen Records. Deleted Mar '90. Catalogue no: **HBC1 5042**
Cass: Released Jan '89, on Silva Screen by Silva Screen Records. Catalogue no: **HBE1 5042**

Sundown

SUNDOWN (Film Soundtrack) (Various artists)
Cass: Released Jan '90, on Silva Screen by Silva Screen Records. Catalogue no: **FILMC 044**
Album: Released Jan '90, on Silva Screen by Silva Screen Records. Catalogue no: **FILM 044**
CD: Released Jan '90, on Silva Screen by Silva Screen Records. Catalogue no: **FILMCD 044**

Sunny & Showboat

SUNNY & SHOWBOAT (Original London Casts) (Various artists)
Album: Released Feb '77, on Retrospect by EMI Records. Catalogue no: **SH 240**

Sunshine

SUNSHINE (Film Soundtrack) (Various artists)
Album: Released Oct '74, on MCA by MCA Records. Deleted '78. Catalogue no: **MCF 2566**

Super Gran

SUPER GRAN (See under Connolly, Billy)

Superfly

SUPERFLY (See under Mayfield, Curtis)

Supergirl

SUPERGIRL (Film Soundtrack) (Various artists)
Note: Composed by Jerry Goldsmith.
CD: Released Jul '85, on T. E. R. by That's Entertainment Records. Catalogue no: **CDVCD 47218**
Album: Released Feb '86, on Colosseum (West Germany) Cata-

logue no: **CST 8001**
CD: Released Jan '89, on Silva Screen by Silva Screen Records. Catalogue no: **VCD 47218**
Cass: Released Jan '89, on Silva Screen by Silva Screen Records. Catalogue no: **CTV 81231**
Album: Released Jan '89, on Silva Screen by Silva Screen Records. Catalogue no: **STV 81231**

Supergrass

SUPERGRASS, THE (Film Soundtrack) (Various artists) (See picture on next page)
Tracks: / Slave to the rhythm: *Jones, Grace* / Gotta get you home tonight: *Wilde, Eugene* / Drop the bomb: *Trouble Funk* / Tequila: *No Way Jose* / Two tribes: *Frankie Goes To...* / Arrival at the Royal Hotel: *Tippett, Keith* / No woman no cry / Love theme: *Tippett, Keith* / Move closer: *Nelson, Phyllis* / Harvey's theme: *Tippett, Keith* / Ultimo ballo: *Maimone, Angele* / Supergrass: *Arnold, P.P.*.
Cass: Released Nov '85, on Island Visual Arts by Island Records. Catalogue no: **ICT 11**
Album: Released Nov '85, on Island Visual Arts by Island Records. Catalogue no: **ISTA 11**

SUPERGRASS (SINGLE) (See under Arnold, P.P.)

Superman

SUPERMAN (Studio cast of the 1966 show) (Various artists)
Album: Released Jan '89, on Silva Screen by Silva Screen Records. Catalogue no: **AKOS 2970**

SUPERMAN 2 (Original Soundtrack) (Various artists)
Cass: Released May '81, on Warner Bros. by WEA Records. Deleted '86. Catalogue no: **K4 56892**
Album: Released May '81, on Warner Bros. by WEA Records. Deleted '86. Catalogue no: **K 56892**

SUPERMAN (Film Soundtrack) (Various artists)
Tracks: / Superman (main title): *Various artists* / Planet Krypton, The: *Various artists* / Destruction of Krypton: *Various artists* / Trip to earth, The: *Various artists* / Growing up: *Various artists* / Superman love theme: *Various artists* / Leaving home: *Various artists* / Fortress

Adrian Edmondson, Jennifer Saunders and Peter Richardson in *The Supergrass*

of solitude, The: *Various artists* / Flying sequence (can you read my mind), The: *Various artists* / Super rescues: *Various artists* / Lex Luther's lair: *Various artists* / Superfeats: *Various artists* / March of the villains, The: *Various artists* / Chasing rockets: *Various artists* / Turning back the world: *Various artists* / End title: *Various artists*.
Album: Released '77, on Warner Bros. by WEA Records. Deleted '82. Catalogue no: **K 66084**
Cass: Released '77, on Warner Bros. by WEA Records. Deleted '82. Catalogue no: **K 4 66084**
CD: Released Feb '90, on Silva Screen by Silva Screen Records. Catalogue no: **3257.2**

SUPERMAN III (Film Soundtrack)
Album: Released Jul '83, on Warner Bros. by WEA Records, Catalogue no: **923879 1**

SUPERMAN MARCH
Tracks: / Superman march / Lex escapes.
7" Single: Released Apr '81, on Warner Bros. by WEA Records. Deleted '85. Catalogue no: **K 17778**

Superted

SUPERTED THEME AND OVERTURE
Tracks: / Superted theme / Spotty man song.
7" Single: Released Jan '84, on Rainbow Communication Catalogue no: **TED 1**

Surrender

SURRENDER (Film soundtrack) (Various artists)
Note: Music from the Michael Caine/Sally Fields comedy by Michel Colombier.
CD: Released Jan '89, on Silva Screen by Silva Screen Records. Catalogue no: **VCD 47312**
Album: Released Jan '89, on Silva Screen by Silva Screen Records. Catalogue no: **STV 81348**
Cass: Released Jan '89, on Silva Screen by Silva Screen Records. Deleted Mar '90. Catalogue no: **CTV 81348**

Survivor

BURNING HEART
Tracks: / Feels like love / Burning heart.
Note: From the film "*Rocky IV*"
7" Set: Released Feb '86, on Scotti Bros (USA) by WEA Records. Catalogue no: **DA 6708**
7" Single: Released Feb '86, on Scotti Bros (USA) by WEA Records. Deleted '87. Catalogue no: **A 6708**
7" Pic: Released Feb '86, on Scotti Bros (USA) by WEA Records. Catalogue no: **WA 6708**
12" Single: Released Feb '86, on Scotti Bros (USA) by WEA Records. Deleted '87. Catalogue no: **TX 6708**

EYE OF THE TIGER (SINGLE)
Tracks: / Eye of the tiger / Take you on a Saturday.
Note: From the film "*Rocky III*".

7" Single: Released Jan '84, on Scotti Bros (USA) by WEA Records. Catalogue no: **A 2411**
12" Single: Released Jan '84, on Scotti Bros (USA) by WEA Records. Catalogue no: **TA 2411**
7" Pic: Released Jan '84, on Scotti Bros (USA) by WEA Records. Catalogue no: **SCTA 112411**

Suspect

SUSPECT (Film soundtrack) (Various artists)
Note: Music from the Cher/Dennis Quaid thriller by Michael Kamen.
CD: Released Jan '89, on Silva Screen by Silva Screen Records. Catalogue no: **VCD 47315**
Album: Released Jan '89, on Silva Screen by Silva Screen Records. Catalogue no: **704.390**
Cass: Released Jan '89, on Silva Screen by Silva Screen Records. Deleted Mar '90. Catalogue no: **C 704.390**

Swamp Thing

SWAMP THING (Film Soundtrack) (Various artists)
Note: Composed by Harry Manfredini.
Album: Released Jan '89, on Silva Screen by Silva Screen Records. Catalogue no: **STV 81154**

Swan Down Gloves

SWAN DOWN GLOVES (Original London cast) (Various artists)
Tracks: / Overture: *Various artists* / With the sun arise: *Various artists* / Everything's going to be fine: *Various artists* / Catastrophe: *Various artists* / Let's be friends: *Various artists* / Make your own world: *Various artists* / How's the way: *Various artists* / Going into town: *Various artists* / Stuck in a muddle: *Various artists* / Best foot forward: *Various artists* / Demewer but dangerous: *Various artists* / Muck: *Various artists* / Any old rose: *Various artists* / Firedown: *Various artists* / Finale: *Various artists*.
Cass: Released Apr '83, on T. E. R. by That's Entertainment Records. Catalogue no: **ZCTER 1017**
Album: Released Apr '83, on T. E. R. by That's Entertainment Records. Catalogue no: **TER 1017**

Swan (Film)

SWAN, THE (Film Soundtrack) (Various artists)

Note: 1956 film starring Grace Kelly and Alec Guiness. Music by Bronislau Kaper (composer of Mutiny On The Bounty).n
Cass: Released Jan '89, on MCA by MCA Records. Deleted Mar '90. Catalogue no: **MCAC 25086**
Album: Released Jan '89, on MCA by MCA Records. Catalogue no: **MCA 25086**

Swann In Love

SWANN IN LOVE (Film Soundtrack) (Various artists)
Note: Composed by Hans Werner Henze.
Album: Released Jan '89, on Silva Screen by Silva Screen Records. Catalogue no: **STV 81224**
Album: Released Jun '84, on SPI Milan (France) Catalogue no: **A 240**

Swayze, Patrick

SHE'S LIKE THE WIND (Swayze, Patrick & Wendy Fraser)
Tracks: / She's like the wind / Stay / I had the time of my life (Only available on 12" format.).
Note: Featured in the film 'Dirty Dancing'.
7" Single: Released Mar '88, on RCA by BMG Records (UK). Deleted Sep '90. Catalogue no: **PB 49565**
12" Single: Released Mar '88, on RCA by BMG Records (UK). Deleted Aug '89. Catalogue no: **PT 49566**

Sweeney Todd

HIGHLIGHTS FROM SWEENY TODD (Original Broadway cast) (Various artists)
CD: Released Jan '89, on Silva Screen by Silva Screen Records. Catalogue no: **RCD 1 5033**

SWEENEY TODD (Original Broadway cast) (Various artists)
Tracks: / Ballad of Sweeny Todd: *Various artists* / No place like London: *Various artists* / Barber and his wife: *Various artists* / Worst pies in London: *Various artists* / Poor thing: *Various artists* / My friends: *Various artists* / Attend the tale of Sweeny Todd: *Various artists* / Lift your razor high: *Various artists* / Sweeny Green finch and linnet bird: *Various artists* / Ah Miss Johanna: *Various artists* / Pireli's miracle elixir: *Various artists* / Con-

test: *Various artists* / Wait: *Various artists* / Sweeny pondered and Sweeney planned: *Various artists* / His hands were quick his fingers strong: *Various artists* / Johanna kiss me: *Various artists* / Ladies in their sensitivites: *Various artists* / Pretty women: *Various artists* / God, that's good: *Various artists* / Epiphany: *Various artists* / Little priest: *Various artists* / Johanna: *Various artists* / By the sea: *Various artists* / Wigmaker sequence: *Various artists* / Sweeney'd waited too long before: *Various artists* / Letter: *Various artists* / Not while I'm around: *Various artists* / Parlour song: *Various artists*.
2 LP Set: Released Jul '80, on RCA by BMG Records (UK). Deleted Jul '85. Catalogue no: **CBL2 03379**
CD Set: Released Jan '89, on Silva Screen by Silva Screen Records. Catalogue no: **3379.2**
2 LP Set: Released Jan '89, on Silva Screen by Silva Screen Records. Catalogue no: **CBL 2**
Cass: Released Jan '89, on Silva Screen by Silva Screen Records. Catalogue no: **CBK 2**
Cass set: Released Jul '80, on RCA by BMG Records (UK). Deleted Jul '85. Catalogue no: **CBK2 3379**

Sweet Charity

SWEET CHARITY (1987 Revival of the original Broadway cast) (Various artists)
Album: Released Jan '89, on Silva Screen by Silva Screen Records. Catalogue no: **SV 17179**
Cass: Released Jan '89, on Silva Screen by Silva Screen Records. Catalogue no: **4 XS 17179**

SWEET CHARITY (Film soundtrack) (Various artists)
Tracks: / Overture: *Various artists* / You should see yourself: *Various artists* / Big spender: *Various artists* / Charity's soliloquy: *Various artists* / Rich man's frug: *Various artists* / If my friends could see me now: *Various artists* / Too many tomorrows: *Various artists* / There's got to be something better than this: *Various artists* / Charity's theme: *Various artists* / I'm the bravest individual: *Various artists* / Rhythm of life: *Various artists* / Baby dream your dream: *Various artists* / Sweet charity: *Various artists* / Where am I going?: *Various*

artists* / I love to cry at weddings: *Various artists* / I'm a brass band: *Various artists* / Finale: *Various artists*.
Album: Released Nov '89, on Memoir by Memoir Records. Catalogue no: **MOIR 203**
Cass: Released Nov '89, on Memoir by Memoir Records. Catalogue no: **CMOIR 203**
CD: Released Apr '87, on EMI-America by EMI Records. Catalogue no: **CDP 746 562-2**

SWEET CHARITY (Original Broadway cast) (Various artists)
Album: Released Sep '85, on CBS Cameo by CBS Records & Distribution. Catalogue no: **CBS 32662**
Cass: Released Sep '85, on CBS Cameo by CBS Records & Distribution. Deleted Aug '87. Catalogue no: **40 32662**
CD: Released Feb '90, on CBS (import) by CBS Records & Distribution. Catalogue no: **CK 02900**
Cass: Released Feb '90, on Silva Screen by Silva Screen Records. Catalogue no: **PST02900**

Sweet Dreams (film)

SWEET DREAMS (Life And Times Of Patsy Cline) (Cline, Patsy)
Tracks: / San Antonio rose / Seven lonely days / Your cheatin' heart / Lovesick blues / Walking after midnight / Foolin' around / Half as much / I fall to pieces / Crazy / Blue moon of Kentucky / She's got you / Sweet dreams.
Note: Directed by Harold Reidz (The French Lieutenants' Woman) and produced by Bernard Schwartz (Coal Miner's Daughter), 'Sweet Dreams' starring Jessica Lange as Patsy Cline has opened to excellent reviews in the UK which will certainly lead to demand for this attractive album. In essence a 'Greatest Hits', 'Sweet Dreams' contains twelve of Patsy Cline's most successful recordings including 'She's Got You', 'Heartaches', 'Crazy', 'Leavin' On Your Mind', and the classic 'I Fall To Pieces'. Produced by Owen Bradley the album features Patsy Cline's original vocal tracks complemented by new backing tracks performed by the cream of Nashville session musicians including Hargus Robbins, Floyd Cramer

and The Jordanaires. The end result brings a sparkling new dimension to the sound of Patsy Cline which has resulted in millions of record sales in the past and will continue to do so in the future.

Cass: Released Feb '86, on MCA by MCA Records. Catalogue no: **MCGC 6003**

CD: Released Feb '86, on MCA by MCA Records. Catalogue no: **MCAD 6149**

Album: Released Feb '86, on MCA by MCA Records. Catalogue no: **MCG 6003**

Sweethearts (film)

SWEETHEARTS (Film Soundtrack) (Various artists)

Note: Radio performance by starring Jeanette MacDonald and Nelson Eddy.

Cass: Released Jan '89, on Silva Screen by Silva Screen Records. Catalogue no: **CSH 2025**

Album: Released Jan '89, on Silva Screen by Silva Screen Records. Catalogue no: **SH 2025**

Sword & The Sorcerer

SWORD & THE SORCERER (Film Soundtrack) (Whitaker, David)

Album: Released Apr '83, on T. E. R. by That's Entertainment Records. Catalogue no: **TER 1023**

Sylvian, David

FORBIDDEN COLOURS (Sylvian, David & Ryuichi Sakamoto)

Tracks: / Forbidden colours / Bamboo houses (CD only) / Bamboo music (CD only) / Seed and the sower, The (7 & 12" only).

Note: From the film "*Merry Christmas Mr Lawrence*".

7" Single: Released Jun '83, on Virgin by Virgin Records. Deleted May '90. Catalogue no: **VS 601**

CD 3": Released Jun '88, on Virgin by Virgin Records. Catalogue no: **CDT 18**

12" Single: Released Jun '83, on Virgin by Virgin Records. Catalogue no: **VS 601-12**

Synergy

JUPITER MENACE (Film soundtrack)

Tracks: / Alignment, The / Alien Earth / Rampage of the elements (the Jupiter menace) / Pueblo bonito / Prophecy - the prophecy fullfilled - warriors, The / Earth in space / Ancient gods / Plunge solar observatory, The / Survivalists / Cities on the brink / Mystery of Piri Reis, The / Final alignment, The / Closing theme.

Album: Released Sep '84, on Shanghai by Shanghai Records. Catalogue no: **HAI 105**

Synthetic Orchestra

E.T., THEME FROM

Tracks: / E.T., Theme from.

7" Single: Released Feb '83, on PRT by Castle Communications Records. Catalogue no: **7VJ 102**

The following information was taken from the Music Master database on September 25th, 1990.

Tabor, June

SPY SHIP THEME
Tracks: / Spy ship theme.
7" Single: Released Nov '83, on BBC by BBC Records. Deleted Sep '87. Catalogue no: **RESL 140**

Taffetas

TAFFETAS, THE (Original off-Broadway cast) (Various artists)
Tracks: / Sh'boom: *Various artists* / Mr. Sandman: *Various artists* / Three bells, The: *Various artists* / I'm sorry: *Various artists* / Ricochet: *Various artists* / I cried: *Various artists* / Cry: *Various artists*/ Smile: *Various artists*/ Achoo cha-cha: *Various artists* / Mockin' bird hill: *Various artists* / Tonight you belong to me: *Various artists* / Happy wanderer, The: *Various artists* / Constantinople: *Various artists*/ My little grass shack: *Various artists*/ C'est si bon: *Various artists* / Sweet song of India: *Various artists* / Arrivederci Roma: *Various artists*/ See the USA in your Chevrolet: *Various artists* / Allegheny moon: *Various artists*/ Tennessee waltz: *Various artists* / Old Cape Cod: *Various artists*/ Fly me to the moon: *Various artists* / Nel blue de pinto di blue: *Various artists* / Around the world: *Various artists* / Music! Music! Music!: *Various artists* / You're just in love: *Various artists* / Love letters in the sand: *Various artists* / L-O-V-E: *Various artists* / I-M-4-U: *Various artists* / Rag mop: *Various artists* / You, you, you: *Various artists* / Puppy love: *Various artists* / How much is that doggie in the window: *Various artists*/ Hot canary, The: *Various artists*/ Tweedlee dee: *Various artists*/ Lollipop: *Various artists*/ Sincerely: *Various artists* / Johnny Angel: *Various artists* / Mr. Lee: *Various artists* / Dedicated to the one I love: *Various artists* / Where the boys are: *Various artists* / I'll think of you: *Various artists* / Little darlin': *Various artists* / Spotlight on the music: *Various artists*.

Album: Released Jun '89, on T. E. R. by That's Entertainment Records. Catalogue no: **TER 1167**
CD: Released Jun '89, on T. E. R. by That's Entertainment Records. Catalogue no: **CDTER 1167**
Cass: Released Jun '89, on T. E. R. by That's Entertainment Records. Catalogue no: **ZCTER 1167**

Tai Pan

TAI PAN (Film soundtrack) (Various artists)
Note: Maurice Jarre score for the film based on the James Clavell novel.
Album: Released Jan '89, on Silva Screen by Silva Screen Records. Catalogue no: **STV 81293**
Cass: Released Jan '89, on Silva Screen by Silva Screen Records. Deleted Mar '90. Catalogue no: **CTV 81293**
CD: Released Jan '89, on Silva Screen by Silva Screen Records. Catalogue no: **VCD 47274**

Take Me High

TAKE ME HIGH (Film Soundtrack) (See under Richard, Cliff)

Take Me Out To ...

TAKE ME OUT TO THE BALL PARK (Film soundtrack) (Various artists)
Note: Starring Gene Kelly and Frank Sinatra.
Album: Released Jan '89, on Silva Screen by Silva Screen Records. Catalogue no: **CC 100.18**

TAKE ME OUT TO THE BALL PARK (VIDEO) (Various artists)
VHS: Released Sep '89, on MGM/UA (Video) by MGM/UA Video. Catalogue no: **SMV 10503**

Take My Breath Away

TAKE MY BREATH AWAY (18 Romantic Film Themes) (Various artists)
CD: Released '88, on Laser Catalogue no: **CD 86010**

Take The Floor

EIGHTEEN OF THE BEST (From Radio Scotland's 'Take the floor') (Various artists)
Tracks: / Marches: *Various artists* / Bonnie lass: *Various artists* / Eva three step: *Various artists*/ Modern gaelic waltz: *Various artists* / Reels: *Various artists* / Strip the willow: *Various artists*/ Strathspey: *Various artists* / Red house reel: *Various artists*/ Dashing white sergeant: *Various artists* / Baron's piper, The: *Various artists* / Canadian barn dance: *Various artists* / Speed the plough: *Various artists*/ Old tyme waltz: *Various artists* / Campbell's frolic: *Various artists* / Roxborough castle: *Various artists* / Gay gordons: *Various artists*.
Album: Released Dec '89, on BBC by BBC Records. Catalogue no: **REH 762**
Cass: Released Dec '89, on BBC by BBC Records. Catalogue no: **ZCF 762**
CD: Released Dec '89, on BBC by BBC Records. Catalogue no: **BBCCD 762**

Tale Of A Donkey's....

TALE OF A DONKEY'S TAIL (And other Playschool stories) (Various artists)
Cass: Released Jun '76, on BBC by BBC Records. Deleted '87. Catalogue no: **MRMC 045**
Album: Released Jun '76, on BBC by BBC Records. Deleted '87. Catalogue no: **REC 232**

Tales Of Beatrix

TALES OF BEATRIX POTTER (Film Soundtrack) (Various artists)
Album: Released Mar '71, on H.M.V. by EMI Records. Catalogue no: **CSD 3690**

Talk Radio

TALK RADIO/WALL STREET (Film Soundtrack) (Various artists)
Tracks: / Unpredictable: *Kent*/ We

know where you live: *Tick* / He has a heart: *Trend* / Bud's scam: *Copeland, Stewart* / Trading begins: *Copeland, Stewart* / Break up: *Copeland, Stewart* / End title: *Copeland, Stewart* / Just come right in here please: *Dietz* / We feel too much: *Tick* / Are you with me: *Copeland, Stewart* / Tall weeds, The: *Copeland, Stewart* / Anacott steal: *Copeland, Stewart*.

Album: Released May '89, on Varese Sarabande Records(USA) by Varese Sarabande Records (USA). Catalogue no: **VS 5215**
CD: Released Feb '90, on Varese Sarabande Records(USA) by Varese Sarabande Records (USA). Catalogue no: **VSD 5215**
Cass: Released Mar '90, on Varese Sarabande Records(USA) by Varese Sarabande Records (USA). Catalogue no: **VSC 5215**

Talking Heads

STOP MAKING SENSE (Film soundtrack)

Tracks: / Psycho Killer / Swamp / Slippery people / Burning down the house / Girl friend is better / Once in a lifetime / What a day that was / Life during wartime / Take me to the river.

Note: The band have a huge following in this country, all of their recent albums have gone Top 30. This album includes live versions of classic tracks such as "Psycho Killer", "Once in A Lifetime" and "Burning Down The House". "Once in A Lifetime" was a No.14 hit in 1981. The cassette contains several extended versions of the album tracks.

Album: Released Oct '84, on EMI by EMI Records. Deleted '89. Catalogue no: **TAH 1**
Cass: Released Oct '84, on EMI by EMI Records. Deleted '89. Catalogue no: **TAHTC 1**
Album: Released Oct '84, on EMI by EMI Records. Deleted '89. Catalogue no: **EJ 2402431**
Cass: Released Oct '84, on EMI by EMI Records. Deleted '89. Catalogue no: **EJ 2402434**
Album: Released Mar '90, on EMI by EMI Records. Catalogue no: **ATAK 147**
Cass: Released Mar '90, on EMI by EMI Records. Catalogue no: **TCATAK 147**
CD: Released Mar '90, on EMI by

EMI Records. Catalogue no: **CZ 289**

STOP MAKING SENSE (VIDEO)

Tracks: / Psycho killer / Heaven / Thank you for sending me an angel / Found a job / Slippery people / Cities / Burnin' down the house / Life during wartime / Making flippy floppy / Swamp / What a day that was / Naive melody (this must be the place) / Once in a lifetime / Big business / Genius of love / Girlfriend is better / Take me to the river / Cross eyed and painless.

Note: Produced by Gary Goetzman, directed by Jonathan Demme, Executive producer - Gary Kurfirst, Edited by Lisa Day, Director of photography - Jordan Cronenmeth, Visual consultant - Sandy McLeod. A film by Jonathan Demme and Talking Heads. Running time: 99 mins.

VHS: Released Feb '86, on Palace Video by Virgin Records. Catalogue no: **PVC 3010M**

TRUE STORIES (See panel below)

Tracks: / Love for sale / Puzzlin' evidence / Hey now / Papa Legba / Wild wild life / Radio head / Dream

operator / People like us / City of dreams / Wild wild life (Long E.T. mix) (CD only.).

Note: This is not the actual soundtrack to 'True Stories' but Talking Heads interpretation of songs from the film.

Cass: Released Sep '86, on EMI by EMI Records. Catalogue no: **TCEMC 3511**
Cass: Released Sep '89, on Fame by EMI Records. Catalogue no: **TCFA 3231**
CD: Released Sep '89, on Fame by EMI Records. Catalogue no: **CDFA 3231**
Cass: Released Sep '86, on EMI by EMI Records. Deleted Oct '89. Catalogue no: **TCEU 3511**
CD: Released Oct '86, on EMI by EMI Records. Deleted Aug '89. Catalogue no: **CDP 746 345 2**
Album: Released Sep '86, on EMI by EMI Records. Deleted Aug '89. Catalogue no: **EMC 3511**
Album: Released Sep '86, on EMI by EMI Records. Deleted Oct '89. Catalogue no: **EU 3511**
Album: Released Sep '89, on Fame by EMI Records. Catalogue no: **FA 3231**

True Stories - A film by David Byrne of Talking Heads

Tall Guy

IT MUST BE LOVE (See under Madness) (See panel below)

Tangerine Dream

FLASHPOINT (1985 film soundtrack)
Tracks: / Going west / Afternoon in the desert / Plane ride / Mystery tracks / Lost in the dunes / Highway patrol / Love phantasy / Madcap story / Dirty cross roads / Flashpoint.
CD: Released Apr '87, on Heavy Metal Worldwide by FM-Revolver Records. Catalogue no: **HMI XD 29**
Cass: Released Feb '85, on Heavy Metal Worldwide by FM-Revolver Records. Catalogue no: **HMI MC 29**
Album: Released Feb '85, on Heavy Metal Worldwide by FM-Revolver Records. Catalogue no: **HMI LP 29**

LEGEND (USA Version) (See under Legend)

NEAR DARK (Film soundtrack)
Tracks: / Caleb's blues / Pick up at high noon / Rain in the third house / Bus station / Goodtimes / She's my sister / Mae comes back / Father and son / Severin dies / Flight at dawn / Mae's transformation.
Album: Released Jun '90, on Silva Screen by Silva Screen Records. Catalogue no: **FILM 026**
Cass: Released Jun '90, on Silva Screen by Silva Screen Records. Catalogue no: **FILMC 026**
CD: Released Jun '90, on Silva Screen by Silva Screen Records. Catalogue no: **FILMCD 026**

SHY PEOPLE (Film Soundtrack) (See under Shy People)
SORCERER (Original Soundtrack)
Tracks: / Search / Call, The / Creation / Vengeance / Journey, The / Grind / Rain forest / Abyss / Mountain road, The / Impressions of sorcerer / Betrayal.
Album: Released Jul '77, on MCA by MCA Records. Deleted '80. Catalogue no: **MCF 2806**
Cass: Released Feb '82, on MCA by MCA Records. Catalogue no: **MCLC 1646**
Album: Released Feb '82, on MCA by MCA Records. Deleted

Sep '90. Catalogue no: **MCL 1646**

STREET HAWK (TV theme)
Tracks: / Street hawk / Tear garden.
7" Single: Released Aug '85, on Jive Electro by Zomba Records. Catalogue no: **JIVE 101**
12" Single: Released Aug '85, on Jive Electro by Zomba Records. Catalogue no: **JIVET 101**

THIEF (Film Soundtrack)
Tracks: / Beach theme / Doctor Destructo / Diamond diary / Burning bar / Beach scene / Scrap yard / Trap feeling / Igneous.
Album: Released Aug '88, on Virgin by Virgin Records. Catalogue no: **OVED 72**
Album: Released Apr '81, on Virgin by Virgin Records. Deleted '84. Catalogue no: **V 2198**
Cass: Released '87, on Virgin by Virgin Records. Catalogue no: **OVEDC 72**
CD: Released Jun '88, on Virgin by Virgin Records. Catalogue no: **CDV 2198**

THREE O'CLOCK HIGH (Film Soundtrack) (See under Three O'Clock High)

Tangos

TANGOS - THE EXILE OF GARDEL (Film Soundtrack) (Various artists)
Note: Music by Astor Piazolla for the award winning Argentinian film.
Album: Released Jan '89, on Silva Screen by Silva Screen Rec-

ords. Catalogue no: **A 280**

Tap

TAP (Film soundtrack) (Various artists)
Tracks: / Bad boy: *Various artists* / All I want is forever: *Various artists* / Baby what you want me to do: *Various artists* / Strong as steel: *Various artists* / Forget the girl: *Various artists* / Can't escape the rhythm: *Various artists* / Lover's intuition: *Various artists* / Somebody like you: *Various artists* / Max's theme (instrumental): *Various artists* / Free: *Various artists*.
Cass: Released 5 Jun '89, on Epic by CBS Records & Distribution. Catalogue no: **465081 4**
Album: Released 5 Jun '89, on Epic by CBS Records & Distribution. Catalogue no: **465081 1**
CD: Released 5 Jun '89, on Epic by CBS Records & Distribution. Catalogue no: **465081 2**

TAP (VIDEO) (Various artists)
Note: Running time: 107 mins. Cert: PG. Starring Sammy Davis Jr, Gregory Hines. Directed by Nick Castle.
VHS: Released Dec '89, on RCA/Columbia (video) by BMG Records (UK). Catalogue no: **CVT 11878**

Tap Dance Kid

TAP DANCE KID (Original Broadway Cast) (Various artists)
Tracks: / Overture: *Various artists* / Another day: *Various artists* /

***The Tall Guy* - Starring Jeff Goldblum, Emma Thompson and Rowan Atkinson.**

Four strikes against me: *Various artists* / Class act: *Various artists* / They never hear what I say: *Various artists* / Dancing is everything: *Various artists* / Fabulous feet: *Various artists* / I could get used to him: *Various artists* / Man in the moon: *Various artists* / Like him: *Various artists* / My luck is changing: *Various artists* / Someday: *Various artists* / I remember how it was: *Various artists* / Tap tap: *Various artists* / Dance if it makes you happy: *Various artists* / Williams song: *Various artists* / Finale: *Various artists*.
CD: Released Jan '89, on T. E. R. by That's Entertainment Records. Catalogue no: **820210.2**
Cass: Released Mar '85, on T. E. R. by That's Entertainment Records. Catalogue no: **ZCTER 1096**
Album: Released Mar '85, on T. E. R. by That's Entertainment Records. Catalogue no: **TER 1096**

Tarka The Otter
TARKA THE OTTER (Film Soundtrack) (Various artists)
Album: Released '79, on Argo Deleted '84. Catalogue no: **ZSW 613**
Cass: Released '79, on Argo Deleted '84. Catalogue no: **KZSWC 613**

Tati, Jacques
ORIGINAL SOUNDTRACKS
Album: Released Aug '83, on Phonogram (France) Catalogue no: **8122 311**
Cass: Released Aug '83, on Phonogram (France) Catalogue no: **8122 314**

Taxi
TAXI (Theme from) (See under James, Bob 'Angela')

Taxi Driver
TAXI DRIVER (Film soundtrack) (Various artists)
Tracks: / Taxi driver, theme from: *Various artists* / I work the whole city: *Various artists* / Betsy in a white dress: *Various artists* / Days do not end, The: *Various artists* / All the animals come out at night: *Various artists* / 44 Magnum is a monster, The: *Various artists* / Sport and Iris: *Various artists*.
CD: Released Jun '88, on Arista by BMG Records (UK). Catalogue no: **258 774**

CD: Released Feb '90, on Silva Screen by Silva Screen Records. Catalogue no: **ARCD8179**

Taylor, John
I DO WHAT I DO
Tracks: / I do what I do / Jazz / I do what I do (Film mix) (Track on 12" version only.)
Note: Taken from the film *Nine & a Half Weeks*
7" Single: Released Mar '86, on Parlophone by EMI Records. Catalogue no: **R 6125**
12" Single: Released Mar '86, on Parlophone by EMI Records. Catalogue no: **12R 6125**

T.C.B
T.C.B. (Film Soundtrack) (See under Ross, Diana)

Teachers
TEACHERS (Film soundtrack) (Various artists)
Tracks: / Teacher teacher: *Thirty Eight Special* / One foot back in your door: *Roman Holliday* / Edge of a dream (Theme from "Teacher"): *Cocker, Joe* / Interstate love affair: *Night Ranger* / Fooling around: *Mercury, Freddie* / Cheap sunglasses: *ZZ Top* / Understanding: *Seger, Bob & The Silver Bullet Band* / I can't stop the fire: *Martin, Eric* / In the jungle: *Motels* / I'm the teacher: *Hunter, Ian*.
Note: Teachers, starring Nick Nolte, is a contemporary comic drama about daily life in an urban American high school.
CD: Released Feb '85, on Capitol by EMI Records. Deleted Jan '88. Catalogue no: **CDP 746 062 2**
Album: Released Feb '85, on Capitol by EMI Records. Catalogue no: **EJ 2402471**
Cass: Released Feb '85, on Capitol by EMI Records. Catalogue no: **EJ 2402474**

Teen Wolf
TEEN WOLF (Film soundtrack) (Various artists)
Tracks: / Flesh on fire: *House, James* / Big bad wolf: *Wolf sisters, The* / Win in the end: *Safan, Mark* / Shootin' for the moon: *Holland, Amy* / Silhouette: *Palmer, David* / Way to go: *Viena, Mark* / Good news: *Morgan, David* / Transformation: *Teen Wolf* / Boof: *Teen Wolf*.

CD: Released Jan '89, on Silva Screen by Silva Screen Records. Catalogue no: **829092.2**
Cass: Released Oct '87, on Silva Screen by Silva Screen Records. Catalogue no: **SCRSC 1010**
Album: Released Oct '87, on Silva Screen by Silva Screen Records. Catalogue no: **SCRS 1010**

Teenage Mutant...
TEENAGE MUTANT NINJA TURTLES (Various artists)
Tracks: / This is what we do: *M.C. Hammer* / Spin that wheel: *Hi Tek 3 featuring Ya Kid K* / Family: *Riff* / 9.95: *Spunkadelic* / Turtle power: *Partners In Kryme* / Let the walls come down: *Kemp, Johnny* / Every heart needs a home: *St. Paul* / Shredder's suite: *Various artists* / Splinter's tale I & II: *Various artists* / Turtle rhapsody: *Orchestra On The Half Shell*.
Note: Album box set contains LP picture disc (in PVC bag), Hero turtle postcard, four laminated turtle masks. Cassette box set contains cassette, four laminated turtle masks, giant full colour poster, turtles sticker.
CD: Released Jun '90, on SBK by SBK Records. Catalogue no: **SBKCD 6**
Cass set: Released Nov '90, on SBK by SBK Records. Catalogue no: **SBKTCBOX 6**
CD: Released Jun '90, on SBK by SBK Records. Catalogue no: **CDP 791 066 2**
Cass: Released Jun '90, on SBK by SBK Records. Catalogue no: **791 066 4**
LP Set: Released Nov '90, on SBK by SBK Records. Catalogue no: **795 232 1**
Album: Released Jun '90, on SBK by SBK Records. Catalogue no: **SBKLP 6**
Cass: Released Jun '90, on SBK by SBK Records. Catalogue no: **SBKTC 6**
Cass set: Released Nov '90, on SBK by SBK Records. Catalogue no: **795 232 4**
Album: Released Jun '90, on SBK by SBK Records. Catalogue no: **791 066 1**
LP Set: Released Nov '90, on SBK by SBK Records. Catalogue no: **SBKLPBOX 6**

Television's Greatest

TELEVISIONS GREATEST HITS (TV Toons Compilation) (Various artists)
Album: Released June '87, on TV Toons. Catalogue no: **TVT 1100**
Cassette: Released June '87, on TV Toons. Catalogue no: **TVTC 1100**

TELEVISION'S GREATEST HITS VOL.1 (65 themes from the 50's and 60's) (Various artists)
Tracks: / Flintstones, The: *Various artists* / Popeye: *Various artists* / Yogi bear: *Various artists* / Fireball XL5: *Various artists* / Beverly hillbillies: *Various artists* / Addams family, The: *Various artists* / Star Trek: *Various artists* / Batman: *Various artists* / Flipper: *Various artists* / Mission impossible: *Various artists* / Perry Mason (theme from): *Various artists* / Munsters, The: *Various artists* / Ironside: *Various artists* / Bugs bunny: *Various artists* / Felix the cat: *Various artists* / Top cat: *Various artists* / Jetsons, The: *Various artists* / Mr. Ed: *Various artists* / I love Lucy: *Various artists* / Lost in space: *Various artists* / Twilight zone: *Various artists* / Bonanza: *Various artists* / Man from Uncle, The: *Various artists* / Get smart: *Various artists* / Dragnet: *Various artists* / Secret agent man: *Various artists* / FBI: *Various artists* / Hawaii five-O: *Various artists* / 77 Sunset strip: *Various artists*.
2 LP Set: Released Nov '88, on Silva Screen by Silva Screen Records. Catalogue no: **FILM 024 D**
Cass: Released Nov '88, on Silva Screen by Silva Screen Records. Catalogue no: **FILMC 024**
CD: Released Nov '88, on Silva Screen by Silva Screen Records. Catalogue no: **FILMCD 024**

TELEVISIONS GREATEST HITS VOL 2 (65 favourites from the 50's and 60's) (Various artists)
Tracks: / Looney tunes: *Various artists* / Peanuts: *Various artists* / Odd couple, The: *Various artists* / Bewitched: *Various artists* / Monkees: *Various artists* / Time tunnel, The: *Various artists* / Rawhide:

artists / Daktari: *Various artists* / Virginian, The: *Various artists* / Peter Gunn: *Various artists* / Saint, The: *Various artists* / I spy: *Various artists* / Avengers, The: *Various artists* / Monty Python's flying circus: *Various artists* / Road runner: *Various artists* / Merrie melodies: *Various artists* / Huckleberry hound: *Various artists* / Mighty mouse: *Various artists* / Pink panther: *Various artists* / Spiderman: *Various artists* / Partridge family: *Various artists* / Car 54 where are you?: *Various artists* / Voyage to the bottom of the sea: *Various artists* / Maverick: *Various artists* / Wagon train: *Various artists* / Route 66: *Various artists* / Outer limits: *Various artists*.
2 LP Set: Released Nov '88, on Silva Screen by Silva Screen Records. Catalogue no: **FILM 034 D**
Cass: Released Nov '88, on Silva Screen by Silva Screen Records. Catalogue no: **FILMC 034**
CD: Released Nov '88, on Silva Screen by Silva Screen Records. Catalogue no: **FILMCD 034**

TELEVISION'S GREATEST HITS VOL 3 (65 favourite Themes from the 70's & 80's) (Various artists)
Tracks: / Muppet show, The: *Various artists* / Mr. Magoo: *Various artists* / Dastardly & Muttley: *Various artists* / Scooby Doo: *Various artists* / Cheers: *Various artists* / Taxi: *Various artists* / Happy days: *Various artists* / L.A. law: *Various artists* / St. Elsewhere: *Various artists* / M*A*S*H: *Various artists* / Hart to Hart: *Various artists* / A-Team, The: *Various artists* / Miami vice: *Various artists* / Hill Street blues: *Various artists* / Dallas: *Various artists* / Dynasty: *Various artists* / Love boat: *Various artists* / Sesame Street: *Various artists* / Inspector Gadget: *Various artists* / Archies, The: *Various artists* / Barney Miller: *Various artists* / All in the family: *Various artists* / Knots Landing: *Various artists* / Waltons - theme: *Various artists* / Little House on the Prairie, Theme from: *Various artists* / Wonder woman: *Various artists* / Streets of San Francisco: *Various artists* / Starsky & Hutch: *Various artists* / Kojak: *Various artists* / Magnum: *Various*

artists / Rockford files: *Various artists*.
Cass: Released Nov '88, on Silva Screen by Silva Screen Records. Catalogue no: **FILMC 035**
2 LP Set: Released Nov '88, on Silva Screen by Silva Screen Records. Catalogue no: **FILM 035 D**
CD: Released Nov '88, on Silva Screen by Silva Screen Records. Catalogue no: **FILMCD 035**

Telly Hits

TELLY HITS (Various artists)
Tracks: / Cagney and Lacey: *Various artists* / Howards way: *Various artists* / Eastenders: *Various artists* / Dallas: *Various artists* / Big deal: *Various artists* / Edge of darkness: *Various artists* / Tomorrows world: *Various artists* / Front line, The: *Various artists* / Whickers world: *Various artists* / Tripods, The: *Various artists* / Bergerac: *Various artists* / Miss Marple: *Various artists* / Voyage of the heroes: *Various artists* / Tender is the night: *Various artists* / In search of the Trojan War: *Various artists* / Snooker: *Various artists*.
2 LP Set: Released Nov '85, on Stylus by Stylus Music Records. Deleted '88. Catalogue no: **BBSR 508**
Cass set: Released Nov '85, on Stylus by Stylus Music Records. Deleted '88. Catalogue no: **BBSC 508**

TELLY HITS VOLUME 2 (Various TV themes) (Various artists)
Tracks: / World cup '86: *Various artists* / Bread: *Various artists* / Marriage, The: *Various artists* / Miami vice: *Various artists* / Lovejoy: *Various artists* / Mastermind: *Various artists* / Hideaway: *Various artists* / Film '86: *Various artists* / Dead head: *Various artists* / I, Claudius: *Various artists* / Ski Sunday: *Various artists* / Hold the back page: *Various artists* / A.D. - Anno domini: *Various artists* / Strike it rich: *Various artists*.
Cass: on Stylus by Stylus Music Records. Catalogue no: **BBSC 616**
Album: on Stylus by Stylus Music Records. Catalogue no: **BBSR 616**

Ten...

"10" (Film soundtrack) (Various artists)

Tracks: / Don't call it love: *Various artists* / He pleases me: *Various artists* / Keyboard harmony: *Various artists* / It's easy to say: *Various artists* / Something for Johnny: *Various artists* / Hot sound Mexican Band: *Various artists* / I have an ear for love: *Various artists* / Bolero (Ravel): *Various artists*.

Album: Released '79, on Warner Bros. by WEA Records. Catalogue no: **BS 3399**

Album: Released Apr '80, on Warner Bros. by WEA Records. Deleted '85. Catalogue no: **K 56775**

Ten Commandments

TEN COMMANDMENTS, THE (Film soundtrack) (Various artists)

Tracks: / Prelude: *Various artists* / In the bulrushes: *Various artists* / Bitter life, The: *Various artists* / Love and ambition: *Various artists* / Hard bondage, The: *Various artists* / Egyptian dance: *Various artists* / Crucible of God, The: *Various artists* / And Moses watered Jethro's flock: *Various artists* / Bedouin dance: *Various artists* / I am that I am: *Various artists* / Overture: *Various artists* / Thus says the lord: *Various artists* / Plagues, The: *Various artists* / Exodus: *Various artists* / Pillar of fire, The: *Various artists* / Red sea: *Various artists* / Ten commandments: *Various artists* / Go, proclaim liberty: *Various artists*.

Note: Score by Elmer Bernstein.
Album: Released Aug '88, on Trax by Filmtrax Records. Deleted Jan '90. Catalogue no: **MODEM 1010**
CD: Released Aug '88, on Trax by Filmtrax Records. Deleted Jan '90. Catalogue no: **MODEMCD 1010**
Cass: Released Aug '88, on Trax by Filmtrax Records. Deleted Jan '90. Catalogue no: **MODEMC 1010**

Ten To Midnight

10 TO MIDNIGHT (Film Soundtrack) (Various artists)

Note: Robert Ragland score for the Charles Bronson film.
Album: Released Jan '89, on Silva Screen by Silva Screen Records. Catalogue no: **STV 81172**

Tender Is The Night

TENDER IS THE NIGHT (Various artists)

Tracks: / Tender is the night: *Various artists* / Rosemary's waltz: *Various artists* / I'm forever blowing bubbles: *Various artists* / Nicole and Tommy: *Various artists* / Jovial Joe: *Various artists* / Hindustan: *Various artists* / Poor butterfly: *Various artists* / I ain't gonna give nobody none of this jelly : *Various artists* / Clap hands here comes Charlie: *Various artists* / Tea for two: *Various artists* / Wedding of the painted doll, The: *Various artists* / Let's misbehave: *Various artists* / Fascinating rhythm: *Various artists* / Painting the clouds with sunshine: *Various artists* / Harlems Araby: *Various artists* / Ain't she sweet: *Various artists* / Keep your temper: *Various artists* / Thank your father: *Various artists*.

Album: Released '86, on BBC by BBC Records. Deleted Apr '89. Catalogue no: **REB 582**
Cass: Released '86, on BBC by BBC Records. Deleted Apr '89. Catalogue no: **ZCF 582**

Tender Mercies

TENDER MERCIES (Film Soundtrack) (Various artists)

Album: Released Aug '83, on Liberty by EMI Records. Deleted '88. Catalogue no: **LBG 7511471**

Tenebrae

TENEBRAE (Film soundtrack) (Goblin)

Album: Released Jul '83, on T. E. R. by That's Entertainment Records. Catalogue no: **TER 1064**

Tepepa

TEPEPA (Film Soundtrack) (Various artists)

Note: Ennio Morricone western score.
Album: Released Jan '89, on Cerebus (USA) Catalogue no: **C'BUS 106**

Tequila Sunrise

TEQUILA SUNRISE (Film soundtrack) (Various artists)

Tracks: / Surrender to me: *Wilson, Ann/Robin Zander* / Do you believe in shame?: *Duran Duran* / Recurring dream: *Crowded House* / Give a little love: *Marley, Ziggy & The Melody Makers* / Don't worry baby: *Everly Bros. & Beach Boys* / Dead on the money: *Taylor, Andy* / Unsubstantiated: *Church* / Beyond the sea: *Darin, Bobby* / Tequila dreams: *Gruisin, Dave/Lee Ritenour* / Jo Ann's song: *Gruisin, Dave/David Sanborn* .

Note: Major film starring Mel Gibson, Michelle Pfeiffer and Kurt Russell. Directed by Robert Towne.
Album: Released Mar '89, on Capitol by EMI Records. Catalogue no: **EST 2086**
Cass: Released Mar '89, on Capitol by EMI Records. Catalogue no: **TCEST 2086**
CD: Released Mar '89, on Capitol by EMI Records. Deleted May '90. Catalogue no: **CDEST 2086**
CD: Released Mar '89, on Capitol by EMI Records. Deleted May '90. Catalogue no: **CDP 791 185 2**

TEQUILA SUNRISE (Original Film Score) (Various artists)

Album: Released Jan '89, on Silva Screen by Silva Screen Records. Catalogue no: **C 11 H 91185**
Cass: Released Jan '89, on Silva Screen by Silva Screen Records. Catalogue no: **C 41 H 91185**
CD: Released Jan '89, on Silva Screen by Silva Screen Records. Catalogue no: **C 21 Z 91185**

Terminal City...

TERMINAL CITY RICHOCHET (Original Soundtrack) (Various artists)

Album: Released 1 Nov '89, on Alternative Tentacles by Alternative Tentacles Records. Catalogue no: **VIRUS 075**
CD: Released 1 Nov '89, on Alternative Tentacles by Alternative Tentacles Records. Catalogue no: **VIRUS 075CD**

Terminator

TERMINATOR, THE (Film soundtrack) (Various artists)

Note: Composed by Brad Fiedel.
Cass: Released Jan '89, on Silva Screen by Silva Screen Records. Catalogue no: **ENG 72000.4**

CD: Released Jan '89, on Pacific by Pacific Records. Catalogue no: **CD 72000**

Album: Released Jan '89, on Silva Screen by Silva Screen Records. Catalogue no: **ENG 72000.1**

CD: Released Jan '89, on Silva Screen by Silva Screen Records. Catalogue no: **ENG 72000.2**

Terms Of Endearment

TERMS OF ENDEARMENT (Film soundtrack) (Various artists) (See panel opposite)

CD: Released Feb '90, on Silva Screen by Silva Screen Records. Catalogue no: **CDP 7460762**

Album: Released May '84, on Capitol by EMI Records. Deleted Jan '89. Catalogue no: **EST 2401221**

Terrahawks

TERRAHAWKS THEME (TV theme)

Tracks: / Terrahawks theme.

7" Single: Released Nov '83, on Anderburr by Anderburr Records. Catalogue no: **HX 1010**

12" Single: Released Nov '83, on Anderburr by Anderburr Records. Catalogue no: **HXT 1010**

Terror Vision

TERROR VISION (Film Soundtrack) (Various artists)

Note: Composed by Richard Band.

Album: Released Jan '89, on Silva Screen by Silva Screen Records. Catalogue no: **ENG 2120.1**

Terry & Gerry

BANKING ON SIMON (TV theme)

Tracks: / Banking on Simon / Joey.

Note: Theme for ITV's Poparound

12" Single: Released Jul '85, on In Tape by In Tape Records. Catalogue no: **ITT 019**

7" Single: Released Jul '85, on In Tape by In Tape Records. Catalogue no: **IT 019**

Tess

TESS (Film soundtrack) (Various artists)

Note: Score by Philippe Sarde for the Roman Polanski film.

Cass: Released Jan '89, on MCA by MCA Records. Deleted Mar '90. Catalogue no: **MCAC 1543**

Jack Nicholson and Shirley MacLaine star in *Terms of Endearment*

Album: Released Jan '89, on MCA by MCA Records. Catalogue no: **MCA 1543**

Album: Released Apr '81, on Philips (Import) by PolyGram UK Ltd. Catalogue no: **9101 279**

Testimony

TESTIMONY (Film Soundtrack) (Music of Shostakovich)

Note: Shostakovich Symphonies No's 5 & 7; 2nd Piano Concerto etc.

Cass: Released Jun '88, on Virgin by Virgin Records. Deleted Jun '90. Catalogue no: **TCV 2536**

Album: Released Jun '88, on Virgin by Virgin Records. Deleted May '90. Catalogue no: **V 2536**

CD: Released Jun '88, on Virgin by Virgin Records. Catalogue no: **CDV 2536**

Texas Chainsaw......

TEXAS CHAINSAW MAS-SACRE 2 (Film soundtrack) (Various artists)

Tracks: / Good to be bad: *Lords Of The New Church* / Lords Of The New Church / Goo goo muck: *Cramps* / Haunted head: *Concrete Blonde* / Over your shoulders: *Concrete Blonde* / Life is hard: *Timbuk 3* / Shame on you: *Timbuk 3* / Torch song: *Timbuk 3* / White night: *Timbuk 3* / Strange things happen: *Copeland, Stewart* / No-one lives forever: *Oingo Boingo.*

Cass: Released Nov '86, on I.R.S

(Illegal) by I.R.S. Records. Deleted Jan '88. Catalogue no: **MIRFC 1017**

Album: Released Nov '86, on I.R.S (Illegal) by I.R.S. Records. Deleted Jan '88. Catalogue no: **MIRF 1017**

Thank God It's Friday

THANK GOD IT'S FRIDAY (Film Soundtrack) (Various artists)

Album: Released May '78, on Casablanca by PolyGram UK Ltd. Deleted '80. Catalogue no: **K 66076**

Thanks A Million

THANKS A MILLION/ON THE AVENUE (Film Soundtrack) (Various artists)

Note: Starring Dick Powell and Alice Faye.

Album: Released Jan '89, on Silva Screen by Silva Screen Records. Catalogue no: **SH 2083**

That Summer

THAT SUMMER (Film Soundtrack) (Various artists)

Tracks: / I don't want to go to Chelsea: *Costello, Elvis* / Watching the detectives: *Costello, Elvis* / Sex and drugs and rock and roll: *Dury, Ian & The Blockheads* / What a waste: *Dury, Ian & The Blockheads* / She's so modern: *Boomtown Rats* / Kicks: *Boomtown Rats* / Spanish stroll: *Mink Deville* / Because the night: *Smith, Patti Group* / Rockaway beach: *Ramones* /

Whole wide world: *Wreckless Eric* / I love the sound of breaking glass: *Lowe, Nick* / Another girl, another planet: *Only Ones* / Do anything you wanna do: *Eddie & The Hot Rods* / New life: *Zones* / Teenage kicks: *Undertones* / Blank generation: *Hell, Richard & The Voidoids*.

Cass: Released '79, on Arista by BMG Records (UK). Deleted '84. Catalogue no: **TCART 1088**

Album: Released '79, on Arista by BMG Records (UK). Deleted '84. Catalogue no: **SPART 1088**

That Was The ...

THAT WAS THE WEEK THAT WAS (TV soundtrack) (Various artists)

Album: Released Feb '63, on Parlophone by EMI Records. Deleted '68. Catalogue no: **PMC 1197**

That's Entertainment

THAT'S ENTERTAINMENT (TV Soundtrack) (Various artists)

Album: Released Apr '87, on BBC by BBC Records. Deleted 31 Aug '88. Catalogue no: **REC 638**

Cass: Released Apr '87, on BBC by BBC Records. Deleted 31 Aug '88. Catalogue no: **ZCM 638**

THAT'S ENTERTAINMENT-PART II (TV soundtrack) (Various artists)

Tracks: / Rebound: *Various artists* / Lonely weekends: *Various artists* / Stairway to nowhere: *Barton, Ernie* / She's gone away: *Various artists* / You don't care: *Felts, Narvel* / I wanna rock: *Holcolm, Patsy* / Memories of you: *Priesman, Magel* / Judy: *Grayzell, Rudy* / Overture: *Various artists* / Drive in: *Vickery, Mack* / That's entertainment: *Astaire, Fred, Gene Kelly & Jack Buchanan* / For me and my gal: *Garland, Judy & Fred Astaire* / I've got a feelin' you're foolin': *Taylor, Robert & June Knight* / Hi Lili hi Lo: *Caron, Leslie* / All of you: *Astaire, Fred* / Lady is a tramp, The: *Horne, Lena* / Smoke gets in your eyes: *Grayson, Kathryn* / Rock baby rock it: *Various artists* / Temptation: *Crosby, Bing* / Tennessee zip: *Wheeler, Kenny* / Taking a chance on love: *Waters, Ethel* / Love crazy baby: *Various artists* / Treat me right: *Various artists* / Inka dinka doo: *Durante,*

Jimmy / Get it off your mind: *Various artists* / What's the reason: *Various artists* / Easter parade: *Astaire, Fred & Judy Garland* / You call everybody darlin': *Various artists* / Couple of swells, A: *Astaire, Fred & Judy Garland* / Go ahead baby: *McDaniel, Luke* / Huh babe: *Various artists* / High high high: *Various artists* / Good morning: *Reynolds, Debbie with Gene Kelly & Donald O'Connor* / My baby don't rock: *Various artists* / That's what I tell my heart: *Various artists* / Triplets: *Astaire, Fred , Nanette Fabray & Jack Buchanan* / Last time I saw Paris, The: *Shore, Dinah* / Born to sing the blues: *Jenkins, Harold* / I need your lovin' kiss: *Various artists* / I'll build a stairway to paradise: *Guetary, Georges* / Goin' crazy: *Self, Mack* / There's no business like show business: *Keel, Howard & Betty Hutton* / Mad at you: *Various artists* / Have yourself a merry little Christmas: *Garland, Judy* / Good lookin' woman: *Williams, Jimmy* / Rock-a-bye baby: *Various artists* / I got rhythm: *Kelly, Gene* / Sweet rocking mama: *Various artists* / Sonny boy: *Various artists* / Fire engine red: *Various artists* / Tomorrow: *Various artists* / Please don't cry over me: *Various artists* / That depends on you: *Various artists* / All I want is you: *Various artists* / I remember it well: *Chevalier, Maurice & Hermione Gingold* / My one desire: *Various artists* / Down on the border: *Simmons, Gene* / Don't let me down: *Various artists* / Shake, rattle and roll: *Various artists* / It's me baby: *Yelvington, Malcolm* / Rocking with my baby: *Various artists* / Trumpet: *Various artists* / Ten cats down: *Miller Sisters* / Fools hall of fame: *Richardson, Rudi* / Cheese and crackers: *Gordon, Roscoe* / Sally Jo: *Various artists* / We wanna boogie: *Burgess, Sonny* / Red headed woman: *Various artists* / Ain't got a thing: *Various artists* / Feelin' good: *Various artists* / Truckin' down the avenue: *Various artists* / Restless: *Various artists* / Find my baby for me: *Various artists* / Sadie Brown: *Various artists* / Itch: *Various artists* / Rock 'n' roll Ruby: *Various artists* / Stop the world: *Various artists* / Uranium rock: *Various artists* / Dear John: *Various artists* / Flyin' saucers rock 'n' roll: *Riley, Billy Lee* / I want you

baby: *Various artists* / Red hot: *Various artists* / Blue suede shoes: *Various artists* / My baby done left me: *Various artists*.

CD: Released Mar '87, on CBS by CBS Records & Distribution. Deleted Jan '89. Catalogue no: **CD 70280**

Album: Released Mar '87, on CBS by CBS Records & Distribution. Deleted Jun '88. Catalogue no: **CBS 70280**

Cass: Released Mar '87, on CBS by CBS Records & Distribution. Deleted Jan '89. Catalogue no: **40 70280**

THAT'S ENTERTAINMENT: PART 1 (VIDEO) (Various artists)

VHS: Released '88, on MGM/UA (Video) by MGM/UA Video. Catalogue no: **SMV 10007**

THAT'S ENTERTAINMENT PART 2 (VIDEO) (Various artists)

VHS: Released '88, on MGM/UA (Video) by MGM/UA Video. Catalogue no: **SMV 10075**

That's The Way It Is

THAT'S THE WAY IT IS (Film Soundtrack) (See under Presley, Elvis)

Themes...

THEMES (Various TV and Film themes) (Various artists)

Tracks: / Onedin line theme, The: *Various artists* / Diamonds are forever: *Various artists* / Love story: *Various artists* / Madly: *Various artists* / Summer knows, The: *Various artists* / Time for us, A: *Various artists* / Sleepy shores: *Various artists* / Rosy's theme: *Various artists* / For all we know: *Various artists* / Red tent, The: *Various artists* / Death in Venice theme: *Various artists* / Look around and you'll find me there: *Various artists* / Sunrise, sunset: *Various artists*.

Cass: on Spot by Pickwick Records. Catalogue no: **SPC 8572**

Album: Released Apr '81, on K-Tel by K-Tel Records. Catalogue no: **NE 1122**

Cass: Released May '81, on K-Tel by K-Tel Records. Catalogue no: **CE 2122**

THEMES ALBUM, THE (Various artists)

Tracks: / Bolero: *Hartley, Richard*

/ Thorn birds - love theme: *Martin, Juan & Royal Philharmonic Orchestra* / Educating Rita: *Musicale* / Only he has the power to move me: *Musicale* / Way he makes me feel, The: *Musicale* / Who pays the ferryman: *Musicale* / Bird of paradise: *Musicale* / Reilly, ace of spies - theme: *Olympic Orchestra* / Woman: London Symphony Orchestra / Nights in white satin: London Symphony Orchestra / Take that look off your face: London Symphony Orchestra / She's out of my life: London Symphony Orchestra / Arthur's theme: London Symphony Orchestra / Country diary of an Edwardian woman: *Central Concert Orchestra* / Greatest love of all, The: *Royal Philharmonic Orchestra* / Terms of endearment: *Royal Philharmonic Orchestra* / It might be you: *Royal Philharmonic Orchestra* / Up where we belong: *Royal Philharmonic Orchestra* / All time high: *Royal Philharmonic Orchestra* / Champions: *Royal Philharmonic Orchestra* / Thorn birds: *Royal Philharmonic Orchestra* / Loving Walter: *Royal Philharmonic Orchestra* / Memory: *Royal Philharmonic Orchestra* / Major Yeates' fancy: *De Danann* / Hill street blues: *Hinde, Derek Quartet* / Jewel in the crown, The: *Fenton, George Orchestra* / Derry air, The: *Coulter, Phil Orchestra* / Winds of war, The: *Nuremberg Symphony Orchestra* / Chariots of fire: *Masterworks* / Cacharpaya: *Incantation.*
CD: Released Nov '86, on K-Tel by K-Tel Records. Catalogue no: **ONCD 3323**
Cass: Released May '84, on K-Tel by K-Tel Records. Catalogue no: **OCE 2257**
2 LP Set: Released May '84, on K-Tel by K-Tel Records. Catalogue no: **ONE 1257**

THEMES AND SCREENS (Various artists)
Tracks: / Somewhere my love: *Mathis, Johnny* / Godfather love theme: *Williams, Andy* / What I did for love: *Three Degrees* / Aquarius/Let the sun shine in: *Mathis, Johnny* / Tomorrow: *Rawls, Lou* / How deep is your love: *Mathis, Johnny* / Evergreen: *Lewis, Ramsey* / Maria: *Williams, Andy* / Climb every mountain: *Bennett, Tony* / Wouldn't it be loverly: *Conniff, Ray*

/ Memory: *Mathis, Johnny* / Windmills of your mind: *Paul, Billy* / I don't know how to love him: *Conniff, Ray* / Born free: *Barry, John* / Up where we belong: *Lewis, Ramsey* / Last of the summer wine: *Hazelhurst, Ronnie.*
Album: Released Jun '86, on Warwick Reflections by Warwick Records. Catalogue no: **WW 2009**
Cass: Released Jun '86, on Warwick Reflections by Warwick Records. Catalogue no: **WW 2009 4**

THEMES FROM THE 60'S (Various artists)
Tracks: / Avengers, The: *Various artists* / To sir with love: *Various artists* / On her majesty's secret service: *Various artists* / Man in a suitcase: *Various artists* / Prisoner: *Various artists* / Up the junction: *Various artists* / Captain Zeppos: *Various artists* / Man from UNCLE, The: *Various artists* / Mission impossible: *Various artists* / 4x4: *Various artists* / You only live twice: *Various artists* / Batman: *Various artists.*
Album: on Pinnacle by Pinnacle Records. Catalogue no: **WSR 002**

Themes & Dreams

THEMES & DREAMS (Various artists)
Tracks: / Anna of the five towns: *London Film Orchestra* / Lillie: *South Bank Orchestra* / Thorn birds - love theme: *Martin, Juan & Royal Philharmonic Orchestra* / Mapp and Lucia: *South Bank Orchestra* / Reilly, ace of spies - theme: *Olympic Orchestra* / Bouquet of barbed wire: *South Bank Orchestra* / Waltons - theme: *Giltrap, Gordon* / Sahara: *Morricone, Ennio* / Married man, A: *South Bank Orchestra* / Woman of substance, A: *London Film Orchestra* / Cavatina: *Williams, John* / Onedin line, The: *Keeting, John & London Symphony Orchestra* / Drummonds: *South Bank Orchestra* / Song of freedom: *Mansell Chorale* / Make peace not war: *South Bank Orchestra* / Atlantis: *London Film Orchestra* / Love for Lydia: *South Bank Orchestra* / Upstairs downstairs: *South Bank Orchestra.*
Album: Released Apr '85, on Sierra by Sierra Records. Catalogue no: **FEDL 101**
Cass set: Released Apr '85, on Sierra by Sierra Records. Catalogue no: **CFEDL 101**

There's No Business..

THERE'S NO BUSINESS LIKE SHOW BUSINESS
Album: Released Sep '86, on MCA by MCA Records. Catalogue no: **MCL 1727**
Cass: Released Sep '86, on MCA by MCA Records. Catalogue no: **MCLC 1727**

THERE'S NO BUSINESS LIKE SHOW BUSINESS (VIDEO) (Various artists)
VHS: Released '88, on CBS-Fox by CBS-Fox Video. Catalogue no: **108650**

They Call That...

THEY CALL THAT AN ACCIDENT (Film soundtrack) (Various artists)
Album: Released Mar '83, on Island by Island Records. Catalogue no: **ISTA 2**
Cass: Released Mar '83, on Island by Island Records. Catalogue no: **ICT 2**

They Live

THEY LIVE (Film soundtrack) (Carpenter, John)
CD: Released Feb '90, on Silva Screen by Silva Screen Records. Catalogue no: **73367.2**
Cass: Released Mar '90, on Silva Screen by Silva Screen Records. Catalogue no: **73367.4**
Album: Released Mar '90, on Silva Screen by Silva Screen Records. Catalogue no: **73367.1**

They're Playing ...

THEY'RE PLAYING OUR SONG (Original London Cast) (Various artists)
Tracks: / Overture: *Various artitsts* / Fallin': *Various artitsts* / If he really knew me: *Various artitsts* / Workin' it out: *Various artitsts* / They're playing my song: *Various artitsts* / If she really knew me: *Various artitsts* / Right: *Various artitsts* / Entr'acta: *Various artitsts* / Just for tonight: *Various artitsts* / When you're in my arms: *Various artitsts* / Fill in the words: *Various artitsts* / They're playing our song (Finale): *Various artitsts.*
Cass: Released Apr '83, on T. E. R. by That's Entertainment Records. Catalogue no: **ZCTER 1035**
Album: Released Feb '81, on Chopper Deleted '83. Catalogue no: **CHOPE 6**

Cass: Released Feb '81, on Chopper Deleted '83. Catalogue no: **CHOPK 6**

Album: Released Apr '83, on T. E. R. by That's Entertainment Records. Catalogue no: **TER 1035**

THEY'RE PLAYING OUR SONG (Original Broadway cast) (Various artists)

CD: Released Jan '89, on Silva Screen by Silva Screen Records. Catalogue no: **826240.2**

Thibeaud The Crusader

THIBEAUD THE CRUSADER (Original Soundtrack) (Various artists)

Note: Historical TV series with music by Georges Delerue.

Album: Released Jan '89, on Silva Screen by Silva Screen Records. Catalogue no: **PST 502**

Thief

THIEF (Film Soundtrack) (See under Tangerine Dream)

Thief Of Baghdad

THIEF OF BAGHDAD (Original Soundtrack) (Various artists)

Note: Score for the 1960 Italian film. Music by Carlo Rustichelli.

Album: Released Jan '89, on Silva Screen by Silva Screen Records. Catalogue no: **PHCAM 010**

THIEF OF BAGHDAD / JUNGLE BOOK (Film Soundtracks) (See under Jungle Book)

Thin Blue Line

THIN BLUE LINE, A (Film Soundtrack) (Glass, Philip)

Tracks: / Opening credits / Interrogation (part one) / Turko (part one) / Vidor / Adam's story / Defense attorney's / Judge, The / Trial, The (part two) / Mystery eyewitness (part two), The / Thin blue line, The / Defense attorney's (part two) / Harris' crimes (part two) / Hell on earth / Confession, The / Prologue / Interrogation (part two) / Turko (part two) / Harris' story / Comets and Vegas / Harris' crimes (part one) / Trial, The (part one) / Mystery eyewitness (part one), The / Mystery eyewitness (part three), The / Electric chair, The / Harris' testimony / Mystery eyewitness (part five), The / Harris' childhood / End credits.

Album: Released Apr '89, on Nonesuch Catalogue no: **K979 2091**

CD: Released Apr '89, on Nonesuch Catalogue no: **K979 2092**

Cass: Released Apr '89, on Nonesuch Catalogue no: **K979 2094**

Thing

THING, THE (Film soundtrack) (Various artists)

Album: Released '82, on MCA by MCA Records. Catalogue no: **MCA 6111**

Album: Released Sep '82, on MCA by MCA Records. Catalogue no: **MCF 3148**

Third Man

THIRD MAN, THE (Film Soundtrack) (Various artists)

Tracks: / Third man, Theme from: Various artists / Charade: Various artists / Mondo Cane: Various artists / Good, the bad and the ugly, The: Various artists / Sandpiper: Various artists / Never on Sunday: Various artists / Big country, The: Various artists / Born free: Various artists / Breakfast at Tiffany's: Various artists / Umbrellas of Cherbourg: Various artists / Alfie: Various artists / Summer place, A (theme from): Various artists / Spellbound: Various artists / Zorba the greek: Various artists.

Cass: Released Aug '88, on Decca by Decca International. Catalogue no: **421 264 4**

CD: Released Aug '88, on Decca by Decca International. Catalogue no: **421 264 2**

HARRY LIME (Theme from Third Man) (See under Koras, Anton)

Thirty Six Hours

36 HOURS (Film soundtrack) (Various artists)

Note: Composed by Dimitri Tiomkin.

Album: Released Jan '89, on Varese Sarabande Records(USA) by Varese Sarabande Records (USA). Catalogue no: **STV 81071**

Thirty-Nine Steps

THIRTY-NINE STEPS (Film soundtrack) (Various artists)

Album: Released '79, on United Artists by EMI Records. Deleted '82. Catalogue no: **UAG 30208**

Cass: Released '79, on United Ar-

tists by EMI Records. Deleted '82. Catalogue no: **TCK 30208**

This Earth Is Mine

THIS EARTH IS MINE (Film Soundtrack) (Various artists)

Note: Composed by Hugo Friedhofer.

Album: Released May '79, on Varese Sarabande Records(USA) by Varese Sarabande Records (USA). Catalogue no: **VC 81076**

Album: Released Jan '89, on Silva Screen by Silva Screen Records. Catalogue no: **STV 81076**

This Is Elvis

THIS IS ELVIS (Film Soundtrack) (See under Presley, Elvis)

This Is The Army

THIS IS THE ARMY (Film soundtrack) (Various artists)

Note: Starring Ronald Reagan and Frances Langford.

Album: Released '88, on Hollywood Soundstage (USA) Catalogue no: **HS 408**

Album: Released Jan '89, on Silva Screen by Silva Screen Records. Catalogue no: **SH 2035**

Thomas & The King

THOMAS & THE KING (Original London Cast)

Album: Released May '89, on T. E. R. by That's Entertainment Records. Catalogue no: **TERS 1009**

Thorn Birds...

THORN BIRDS AND OTHER BBC TV THEMES (Various artists)

Tracks: / Thorn birds: Various artists / By the sword divided: Various artists / District nurse: Various artists / Living planet: Various artists / To serve them all my days: Various artists / News week: Various artists / Threshold: Various artists / Cold wind: Various artists / Russell Harty theme: Various artists / Diana: Various artists / Just good friends: Various artists / Mayfair concert: Various artists / History man: Various artists / Dark side of the sun: Various artists / Johnny Jarvis: Various artists / Flight of the Condor: Various artists.

Album: Released Sep '84, on BBC by BBC Records. Deleted

31 Aug '88. Catalogue no: **REH 524**

Cass: Released Sep '84, on BBC by BBC Records. Deleted 31 Aug 88. Catalogue no: **ZCR 524**

THORN BIRDS (Theme from) See under Mancini, Henry)

THORN BIRDS (Love theme) see under Martin, Juan)

Thorne, Ken

LEGION'S LAST PATROL THEME FROM)
Tracks: / Legions last patrol theme from).
7" Single: Released Jul '63, on H.M.V. by EMI Records. Deleted 66. Catalogue no: **POP 1176**

Thoroughly Modern

THOROUGHLY MODERN MILLIE (Film Soundtrack) (Various artists)
Tracks: / Thoroughly modern Millie: *Various artists* / Baby face: *Various artists* / Do it again: *Various artists* / Poor butterfly: *Various artists* / Stumbling: *Various artists* / Japanese sandman: *Various artists* / Tapioca: *Various artists* / Jewish wedding song: *Various artists* / Rose of Washington Square: *Various artists* / Overture: Orchestra: *Various artists* / Jimmy: *Various artists* / Jazz baby: *Various artists* / Intermission: *Various artists* / Thoroughly modern Millie (reprise): *Various artists* / Exit music: *Various artists*.
Cass: Released Oct '82, on MCA by MCA Records. Deleted Jan '88. Catalogue no: **MCLC 1723**
Album: Released Oct '82, on MCA by MCA Records. Deleted Jan '88. Catalogue no: **MCL 1723**

THOROUGHLY MODERN MILLIE (ORIGINAL ISSUE) (Film Soundtrack) (Various artists)
Album: Released Oct '67, on Brunswick by Decca Records. Deleted '70. Catalogue no: **STA 8685**

Those Sensational...

THOSE SENSATIONAL SWINGING SIRENS OF THE SILVER SCREEN (Various artists)
CD: Released Aug '90, on Victorious Discs Catalogue no: **VJC 1002-2**

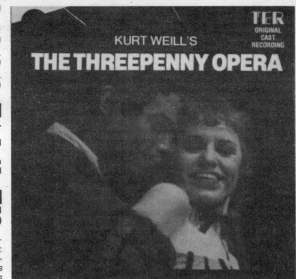

Threepenny Opera - Original Broadway cast recording on T.E.R

Those Wonderful...

THOSE WONDERFUL RADIO YEARS (Various artists)
Tracks: / Itma: *Various artists* / Henry Hall's guest night: *Various artists* / Romance in rhythm: *Various artists* / In town tonight: *Various artists* / Variety bandbox: *Various artists* / Hi gang: *Various artists* / Meet the Huggetts: *Various artists* / Our Gracie: *Various artists* / Piano playtime: *Various artists* / Over to you: *Various artists* / Rocky mountain rhythm: *Various artists* / Stand easy: *Various artists* / Mid day music hall: *Various artists* / Music while you work: *Various artists* / Worker's playtime: *Various artists* / Ray's a laugh: *Various artists* / Take it from here: *Various artists* / Music from the movies: *Various artists* / Goon show, The: *Various artists* / Billy Cotton band show: *Various artists* / 'Appy 'arf 'our: *Various artists* / Jazz club: *Various artists*.
2 LP Set: Released Jan '84, on Recollections (Decca) by Decca Records. Deleted Jan '89. Catalogue no: **RFLD 34**

Thousands Cheer

THOUSANDS CHEER (Film soundtrack) (Various artists)
Note: Starring Judy Garland and Mickey Rooney.
Album: Released Jan '89, on Silva Screen by Silva Screen Records. Catalogue no: **HS 409**

Three Amigos

THREE AMIGOS (Film soundtrack) (Various artists)
Tracks: / Ballad of the 3 Amigos: *Various artists* / Main title: *Various artists* / Big sneak, The: *Various artists* / My little buttercup: *Various artists* / Santa Poco: *Various artists* / Fiesta and flamenco: *Various artists* / El guapo: *Various artists* / Return of the Amigos: *Various artists* / Blue shadows on the trail: *Various artists* / Singing bush, The: *Various artists* / Amigos at the mission: *Various artists* / Capture: *Various artists* / El guapo's birthday: *Various artists* / Chase, The: *Various artists* / Amigo's, amigo's, amigo's: *Various artists* / Farewell: *Various artists* / End credits: *Various artists*.
Album: Released Jul '87, on Warner Bros. by WEA Records. Cata-

logue no: **925558 1**
Cass: Released Jul '87, on Warner Bros by WEA Records. Catalogue no: **925558 4**

Three Bites Of ...

THREE BITES OF THE APPLE (Film Soundtrack) (Various artists)
Note: Score by Robert Armbruster.
Album: Released Jan '89, on Silva Screen by Silva Screen Records. Catalogue no: **MCA 25010**
Cass: Released Jan '89, on Silva Screen by Silva Screen Records. Catalogue no: **MCAC 25010**

Three For The Road

THREE FOR THE ROAD (Film Soundtrack) (Various artists)
Note: Film starring Charlie Sheen. Music by Barry Goldberg.
Album: Released Jan '89, on Silva Screen by Silva Screen Records. Catalogue no: **STV 81319**

Three Fugitives

THREE FUGITIVES (Original Soundtrack) (McHugh, David)
CD: Released Feb '90, on Silva Screen by Silva Screen Records. Catalogue no: **VSD 5219**
Cass: Released Mar '90, on Silva Screen by Silva Screen Records. Catalogue no: **VSC5219**
Album: Released Mar '90, on Silva Screen by Silva Screen Records. Catalogue no: **VS5219**

Three Guys Naked..

THREE GUYS NAKED FROM THE WAIST DOWN (Off Broadway cast) (Various artists)
Tracks: / Overture: *Various artists* / Promise of greatness: *Various artists* / Angry guy/ Lovely day: *Various artists* / Don't wanna be no superstar: *Various artists* / Operator: *Various artists* / Screaming clocks (The dummies song): *Various artists* / History of stand-up comedy, The: *Various artists* / Dreams of heaven: *Various artists* / Kamikaze kaberaet: *Various artists* / American dream, The: *Various artists* / What a ride: *Various artists* / Hello fellas TV special world tour, The: *Various artists* / Father now, A: *Various artists* / Three guys naked from the waist down theme: *Various artists* / I don't believe in heroes anymore: *Various artists* / Finale: *Various artists*.
Cass: Released Apr '85, on T. E. R. by That's Entertainment Rec-

ords. Catalogue no: **ZCTER 1100**
CD: Released '88, on T. E. R. by That's Entertainment Records. Catalogue no: **CDTER 1100**
Album: Released Apr '85, on T. E. R. by That's Entertainment Records. Catalogue no: **TER 1100**

Three Little Girls

THREE LITTLE GIRLS IN BLUE (Film soundtrack) (Various artists)
Note: Starring June Haver and Vivian Blane
Album: Released Jan '89, on Silva Screen by Silva Screen Records. Catalogue no: **HS 410**

Three O'Clock High

THREE O'CLOCK HIGH (Film soundtrack) (Various artists)
Note: Score composed by Tangerine Dream.
Album: Released Jan '89, on Silva Screen by Silva Screen Records. Catalogue no: **STV 81339**
CD: Released Jan '89, on Silva Screen by Silva Screen Records. Catalogue no: **VCD 47307**
Cass: Released Jan '89, on Silva Screen by Silva Screen Records. Catalogue no: **CTV 81339**

Three Of A Kind

THREE OF A KIND (Various artists)
Album: Released Sep '83, on BBC by BBC Records. Deleted 31 Aug '88. Catalogue no: **REB 480**
Cass: Released Sep '83, on BBC by BBC Records. Deleted 31 Aug '88. Catalogue no: **ZCF 480**

Three Wishes...

THREE WISHES FOR JAMIE (Original Broadway cast) (Various artists)
Album: Released '88, on DRG (USA) by DRG Records (USA). Catalogue no: **DS 15012**

Three Worlds...

THREE WORLDS OF GULLIVER (Film soundtrack) (Various artists)
Note: Bernard Herrmann score.
Album: Released Sep '85, on Cloud Nine by Cloud Nine Records. Catalogue no: **CN 4003**

Threepenny Opera

THREEPENNY OPERA (New York Festival production)

(Various artists)
Album: Released Jan '89, on Silva Screen by Silva Screen Records. Catalogue no: **PS 34326**

THREEPENNY OPERA (Original Broadway cast) (Various artists) (See panel on previous page)
Tracks: / Overture: *Various artists* / Ballad of Mack the knife, The: *Various artists* / Morning anthem: *Various artists* / Instead-of-a-song: *Various artists* / Wedding song: *Various artists* / Pirate Jenny: *Various artists* / Army song: *Various artists* / Love song: *Various artists* / Ballad of dependency: *Various artists* / Mellodrama: *Various artists* / Polly's song: *Various artists* / Ballad of the easy life: *Various artists* / World is mean, The: *Various artists* / Barbara song: *Various artists* / Tango ballad: *Various artists* / Jealousy duet: *Various artists* / How to survive: *Various artists* / Useless song: *Various artists* / Solomon song: *Various artists* / Call from the grave: *Various artists* / Death message: *Various artists* / Finale: *Various artists* / Mounted messenger: *Various artists*.
Album: Released Apr '85, on T. E. R. by That's Entertainment Records. Catalogue no: **TER 1101**
CD: Released Jul '89, on T. E. R. by That's Entertainment Records. Catalogue no: **CDTER 1101**
Cass: Released Apr '85, on T. E. R. by That's Entertainment Records. Catalogue no: **ZCTER 1101**

Triangle

TRIANGLE (TV Soundtrack) (See under Perason, Johnny)

Thriller

MAKING OF THRILLER (Video) (See under Jackson, Michael)

Thunderball

THUNDERBALL (James Bond Film Soundtrack) (Various artists)
Tracks: / Thunderball, Theme from: *Jones, Tom* / Chateau fight: *Various artists* / Electrocution - searching Lippe's room: *Various artists* / Switching the body: *Various artists* / Vulcan crash landing - loading bombs into disc: *Various artists* / Cape Martinique - Mr. Kiss Kiss Bang Bang: *Various artists* / Thunderball: *Various artists* /

Death of Fiona: *Various artists* / Bond below Disco Volante: *Various artists* / Search for vulcan: *Various artists* / 007: *Various artists*./ Mr. Kiss Kiss Bang Bang: *Various artists*.

Album: Released Jul '87, on Liberty by EMI Records. Catalogue no: **EMS 1268**
Album: Released Aug '83, on EMI (Germany) by EMI Records. Catalogue no: **IC 054 82923**
Cass: Released Jul '87, on Liberty by EMI Records. Deleted Jun '89. Catalogue no: **TCEMS 1268**

THUNDERBALL (Silva Screen label) (Film Soundtrack) (Various artists)

CD: Released Jan '89, on Silva Screen by Silva Screen Records. Catalogue no: **CD 90628**
Cass: Released Mar '90, on Silva Screen by Silva Screen Records. Catalogue no: **90628.4**

Thunderbirds

THUNDERBIRDS (TV Soundtrack) (See under Gray, Barry)

Thunderbirds Are Go

THUNDERBIRDS ARE GO (Film soundtrack) (Various artists) (See panel opposite)

Tracks: / Thunderbirds theme: *Various artists* / Alan's dream: *Various artists* / Joie De Vivre: *Various artists* / Martian mystery: *Various artists* / Thunderbirds theme (reprise): *Various artists* / Astronauts in trouble: *Various artists* / Zero X theme: *Various artists* / That dangerous game: *Various artists* / Swinging star: *Various artists* / San Marino: *Various artists* / Jeremiah: *Various artists* / Tracy Island: *Various artists*.

Note: In the UK should you mention the name *Thunderbirds* to someone in their late twenties, or early thirties, you're sure to get some sort of recollection and response. For a whole generation of young British viewers very few other TV series in the 1960's made such an impact. Programmes to rival *Thunderbirds* in our affections probably came from the same studios - those of Gerry Anderson. The heroes of *Thunderbirds* were, of course, puppets and Gerry's other production - ranging from a creaky monochrome *Supercar* to a super sophisticated *Captain Scarlet* and *Joe 90* - have passed

into TV legend. What made *Thunderbirds* stand head and shoulders above the rest? Gerry Anderson can't put his finger on it - "If I could all my series would be as big a hit!". Certainly it's hour-long format allowed for greater characterisation - who can forget the wily chauffeur Parker, glamorous Lady Penelope or the eccentric Brains? Maybe the extravagant vehicles left a bigger impression? Special effects in the 32 episodes quite often stand up to the cynical eye of the 1980's youngsters weaned on *Star Wars* and *Star Trek* movies.

However, a major element of all Anderson programmes, particularly *Thunderbirds*, was the magnificent music of the late Barry Gray. In 1966 Lew Grade, for whom Gerry Anderson made the majority of his Supermarionation shows, commissioned a full length feature film: *Thunderbirds Are Go*. Barry Gray was able to let his talents have full reign and the resulting score was probably his finest work. This album includes all the major themes from the feature film, together with other memorable pieces from the TV series - all in stero.(David Nightingale - Editor and publisher of SiG - the official Gerry Anderson fan magazine).

CD: Released Aug '90, on Silva Screen by Silva Screen Records. Catalogue no: **FILMCD 018**
Album: Released Aug '90, on Silva Screen by Silva Screen Records. Catalogue no: **FILM 018**
Cass: Released Aug '90, on Silva Screen by Silva Screen Records. Catalogue no: **FILMC 018**

Tiger Warsaw

TIGER WARSAW (Film soundtrack) (Various artists)

Note: Starring Patrick Swayze (Dirty Dancing). Music by Ernest Troost.

Album: Released Jan '89, on Silva Screen by Silva Screen Records. Catalogue no: **X 1001**

Till The Clouds ...

TILL THE CLOUDS ROLL BY (Film soundtrack) (Various artists)

Note: The story of Jerome Kern starring Judy Garland and Lena Horne.

Cass: Released Jan '89, on MCA by MCA Records. Deleted Mar '90. Catalogue no: **MCAC 25000**

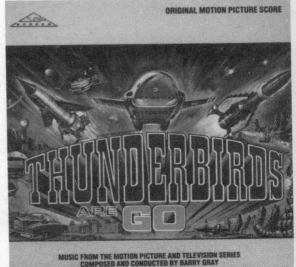

ORIGINAL MOTION PICTURE SCORE

MUSIC FROM THE MOTION PICTURE AND TELEVISION SERIES
COMPOSED AND CONDUCTED BY BARRY GRAY

Thunderbirds Are Go!!! - soundtrack on the Silva Screen label.

Album: Released Jan '89, on MCA by MCA Records. Catalogue no: **MCA 25000**

TILL THE CLOUDS ROLL BY/SUMMER STOCK/LOVELY TO LOOK AT (Various artists)

Tracks: / Till the clouds roll by: *Various artists* / Look for the silver lining: *Garland, Judy* / Can't help lovin' dat man: *Horne, Lena* / Leave it to Jane and Cleopatterer: *Allyson, June* / Life upon the wicked stage: *O'Brien, Virginia* / Who?: *Garland, Judy* / Ol' man river: *Peterson, Caleb* / Get happy: *Garland, Judy* / Howdy neighbour, happy harvest: *Garland, Judy* / You wonderful you: *Kelly, Gene* / Friendly star: *Garland, Judy* / Heavenly music: *Kelly, Gene/Phil Silvers* / If you feel like singing, sing: *Garland, Judy* / Mem'ry island: *De Haven, Gloria/Pete Roberts* / Dig-dig-dig-dig for your dinner: *Kelly, Gene/Phil Silvers* / Lafayette: *Skelton, Red/Howard Keel* / Lovely to look at: *Keel, Howard* / Smoke gets in your eyes: *Grayson, Kathryn* / You're devasting: *Grayson, Kathryn/Howard Keel/Ann Miller/Tommy Rall* / Yesterdays: *Grayson, Kathryn* / I'll be hard to handle: *Miller, Ann* / Touch of your hand/Lovely to look at: *Grayson, Kathryn/Howard Keel/Ann Miller/Tommy Rall*.

Album: Released Aug '90, on MGM (EMI) Catalogue no: **794 873 1**
CD: Released Aug '90, on MGM (EMI) Catalogue no: **CDP 794 873 2**
Cass: Released Aug '90, on MGM (EMI) Catalogue no: **TCMGM 24**
Album: Released Aug '90, on MGM (EMI) Catalogue no: **LPMGM 24**
CD: Released Aug '90, on MGM (EMI) Catalogue no: **CDMGM 24**
Cass: Released Aug '90, on MGM (EMI) Catalogue no: **794 873 4**

Tilt

TILT (Film Soundtrack) (Various artists)
Album: Released '79, on ABC Records by MCA Records. Deleted '84. Catalogue no: **AA 1114**

Time

TIME (Various artists)
Tracks: / Born to rock 'n' roll: *Richard, Cliff* / Time talking: *Ashford & Simpson* / Time: *Mercury, Freddie* / Ascention (The music of the spheres): *Orchestral* / Law of the Universe: *Thompson, Chris / Miriam Stockle* / Time lord theme: *Christie, John* / Charge: *Christie, John* / One human family: *Sayer, Leo* / What on Earth: *Warwick, Dionne* / I know, I know: *Helme, Jimmy* / Case for the prosecution: *Christie, John* / Starmaker: *Ashford & Simpson* / Time will teach us all: *Lennon, Julian* / Object: *Christie, John* / In my defence: *Mercury, Freddie* / Within my world: *Warwick, Dionne* / Because: *Lennon, Julian* / Move the judge: *Helme, Jimmy* / She's so beautiful: *Richard, Cliff* / Beauty, truth, love, freedom, peace: *Olivier, Laurence* / If only you knew: *Lennon, Julian* / We're the UFO: *Head, Murray* / Time, theme from: *Olivier, Laurence* / Harmony: *Christie, John* / Return, The: *Orchestral* / Time (reprise): *Mercury, Freddie* / It's in everyone of us: *Richard, Cliff*

2 LP Set: Released April '86, on EMI by EMI Records. Deleted June '89. Catalogue no: **AMPM 1**
2 LP Set: Released April '86, on EMI by EMI Records. Deleted June '89. Catalogue no: **EQ 5003**
Cass Set: Released April '86, on EMI by EMI Records. Deleted June '89. Catalogue no: **TCAMPM 1**
Cass Set: Released April '86, on EMI by EMI Records. Deleted June '89. Catalogue no: **TCEQ 5003**

TIME (Theme from) (See under Olivier, Laurence)

Time After Time

TIME AFTER TIME (Film Soundtrack) (Various artists)
Tracks: / Fanfare and prelude: *Various artists* / Search for the ripper: *Various artists* / Time machine, The: *Various artists* / Time travel: *Various artists* / Bank montage: *Various artists* / Utopia: *Various artists* / Ripper pursuit, The: *Various artists* / Time machine waltz: *Various artists* / Man before his time: *Various artists* / Redwoods: *Various artists* / Murder: *Various artists* / Fifth victim, The: *Various artists*.
CD: Released May '87, on Silva Screen by Silva Screen Records. Deleted Apr '90. Catalogue no: **SCCD 1014**
Album: Released '80, on Unicorn Deleted '82. Catalogue no: **ERS 6517**

Time Machine

TIME MACHINE, THE (Film Soundtrack) (Various artists)
Tracks: / London 1900: *Various artists* / Time machine model: *Various artists* / Time machine: *Various artists* / Quick trip into the future: *Various artists* / All the time in the world: *Various artists* / Beautiful forest: *Various artists* / Great hall, The: *Various artists* / Fear: *Various artists* / Weena: *Various artists* / Rescue: *Various artists*.
Note: Score by Russell Garcia for the Sci/Fi film starring Rod Taylor.
CD: Released '88, on GNP Crescendo (USA) by GNP Crescendo Records (USA). Catalogue no: **GNPD 8008**
Cass: Released Jan '89, on GNP Crescendo (USA) by GNP Crescendo Records (USA). Catalogue no: **GNP5 8008**
Album: Released Jan '89, on GNP Crescendo (USA) by GNP Crescendo Records (USA). Catalogue no: **GNPS 8008**

Time Of Destiny

TIME OF DESTINY, A (Film soundtrack) (Various artists)
Note: Film starring William Hurt. Music by Ennio Morricone.
Cass: Released Jan '89, on Silva Screen by Silva Screen Records. Catalogue no: **790938.4**
CD: Released '88, on Virgin by Virgin Records. Deleted '89. Catalogue no: **CDV 2539**
CD: Released Jan '89, on Silva Screen by Silva Screen Records. Catalogue no: **790938.2**
Album: Released Jan '89, on Silva Screen by Silva Screen Records. Catalogue no: **790938.1**
Album: Released '88, on Virgin by Virgin Records. Deleted '89. Catalogue no: **V 2539**
Cass: Released '88, on Virgin by Virgin Records. Deleted '89. Catalogue no: **TCV 2539**

Time To Die

TIME TO DIE, A (Film Soundtrack) (Various artists)
Note: Composed by Ennio Morricone.

Album: Released Jan '89, on Cerebus (USA) Catalogue no: **C'BUS 119**

Timerider

COCOON
Note: Used as the theme to ITV's Hitman & Her.
Tracks: / Cocoon / Timerider
7" Single: Released Feb '88, on Lisson by PWL Records, Catalogue no: **DOLE 8**
12" Single: Released Jan '88, on Lisson by PWL Records. Catalogue no: **DOLEQ 8**

Times Square

TIMES SQUARE (Film Soundtrack) (Various artists)
Tracks: / Rock hard: *Quatro, Suzi* / Talk of the town: *Pretenders* / Same old scene: *Roxy Music* / Down in the park: *Numan, Gary* / Help me: *Levy, Marcy & Robin Gibb* / Life during wartime: *Talking Heads* / I wanna be sedated: *Ramones* / Pretty boys: *Jackson, Joe* / Take this town: *XTC* / Damn dog: *Johnson, Robin* / Your daughter is one: *Johnson, Robin* / Babylon's burning: *Ruts* / You can't hurry love: *Byron, David* / Walk on the wild side: *Reed, Lou* / Night was not: *Child, Desmond & Rouge* / Innocent not guilty: *Jeffreys, Garland* / Grinding halt: *Cure* / Pissing in the river: *Smith, Patti Group* / Flowers in the city: *Johansen, David.*
2 LP Set: Released Oct '80, on RCA by BMG Records (UK). Deleted Oct '85. Catalogue no: **265 814 5**
Cass set: Released Oct '80, on RCA by BMG Records (UK). Deleted Oct '85. Catalogue no: **352 422 2**

Tin Drum

TIN DRUM, THE (Film Soundtrack) (Various artists)
Note: Music by Maurice Jarre from the Oscar winning German film.
Album: Released Jan '89, on Silva Screen by Silva Screen Records. Catalogue no: **CL 0006**

Tin Pan Alley

TIN PAN ALLEY (Film Soundtrack) (Various artists)
Note: Starring Betty Grable and Alice Faye.
Album: Released Jan '89, on Silva Screen by Silva Screen Records. Catalogue no: **STK 110**

Tintypes

TINTYPES (Original Broadway cast) (Various artists)
CD: Released '88, on DRG (USA) by DRG Records (USA). Catalogue no: **CDXP 5196**
2 LP Set: Released Jan '89, on DRG (USA) by DRG Records (USA). Catalogue no: **S2L 5196**

Tiomkin, Dimitri

FILM MUSIC OF DIMITRI TIOMKIN
Tracks: / Roman Empire overture / Pax Romana / Guns of Navarone / Wild is the wind / Rhapsody of steel / President's country.
Note: Digitally remastered from the Original film soundtracks the greatest film music by Tiomkin from the 1950's & 60's.
Album: Released Dec '85, on Unicorn-Kanchana by Unicorn - Kanchana Records. Catalogue no: **DKP 9047**
CD: Released Jan '89, on CBS (import) by CBS Records & Distribution. Catalogue no: **CK 44370**
CD: Released '88, on Unicorn Records by Unicorn Records. Catalogue no: **DKPCD 9047**
Cass: Released Jan '89, on Silva Screen by Silva Screen Records. Catalogue no: **JST 44370**

FILM MUSIC VOL 2 (Various artists)
Note: New digital recordings of suites from The Guns Of Navarone, Fall Of The Roman Empire, Rhapsody Of Steel etc.
Album: Released Jan '89, on Silva Screen by Silva Screen Records. Catalogue no: **DKP 9042**

OLD MAN AND THE SEA (Film Soundtrack) (See under Old Man & The Sea)

SEARCH FOR PARADISE (Film Soundtrack) (See under Search For Paradise)

THIRTY SIX HOURS (Film Soundtrack) (See under Thirty Six Hours)

WESTERN FILM WORLD OF DIMITRI TIOMKIN, THE (London Studio Symphony Orch.)
Tracks: / Giant: Prelude / Red River: Prelude / Wagon train / Red River crossing / Challenge and finale, The / Duel in the Sun: Prelude and legend / Buggy ride,The / Trek to the sun/ Love-death and finale / High Noon: main titles /

Clock and the showdown, The / High noon: main titles / Night passage: Follow the river / Rio Bravo: DeGuella / Love theme / Rio Bravo: Main titles.
Note: New digital recording of suites from Red River, Giant, Duel In The Sun, High Noon, Rio Bravo & Night Passage.
CD: Released Jan '89, on Silva Screen by Silva Screen Records. Catalogue no: **UKCD2011**
Album: Released Jan '89, on Silva Screen by Silva Screen Records. Catalogue no: **DKP 9002**

To Be Or Not To Be

TO BE OR NOT TO BE (Film Soundtrack) (Various artists)
Cass: Released Feb '84, on Island by Island Records. Deleted Jul '87. Catalogue no: **ICT 6**
Album: Released Feb '84, on Island by Island Records. Deleted Jul '87. Catalogue no: **ISTA 6**

To Kill A Priest

TO KILL A PRIEST (Film Soundtrack) (Various artists)
Cass: Released Dec '88, on Goldcastle by Virgin Records. Catalogue no: **TCVGC 8**
CD: Released '89, on Goldcastle by Virgin Records. Catalogue no: **CDVGC 8**
Album: Released Dec '88, on Goldcastle by Virgin Records. Catalogue no: **VGC 8**

To Live & Die In L.A.

TO LIVE AND DIE IN L.A. (Original soundtrack) (Wang Chung)
Tracks: / To live and die in L.A. / Lullaby / Wake up, stop dreaming / Wait / City of the angels / Red stare, The / Black-blue-white / Every big city / Dance hall days
Album: Released Jan '86, on Geffen by Geffen Records (USA). Catalogue no: **GEF 70271**
Cass: Released Jan '86, on Geffen Records (USA). Catalogue no: **40 70271**
CD: Released Jan '89, on Silva Screen by Silva Screen Records. Catalogue no: **24081.2**

TO LIVE AND DIE IN L.A. (SINGLE) (Wang Chung)
Tracks: / To live and die in L.A. / Dance hall days / Black-blue-white (Available on 12" only)
7" Single: Released Jun '86, on

Geffen by Geffen Records (USA). Catalogue no: **A 6756**
12" Single: Released Jun '86, on Geffen by Geffen Records (USA). Catalogue no: **TA 6756**

To The Ends Of The

TO THE ENDS OF THE EARTH (Film soundtrack)
Note: John Scott symphonic score to the 1984 documentary about Polar expeditions. First ever release for this major score from one of Britain's best film composers.
CD: Released Jan '89, on Silva Screen by Silva Screen Records. Catalogue no: **PCD 101**

Tom Jones

TOM JONES/IRMA LA DOUCE (Film soundtrack) (Various artists)
Note: 2 scores by John Addison and Andre Previn.
Cass: Released Jan '89, on Silva Screen by Silva Screen Records. Catalogue no: **MCAC 39068**
Album: Released Jan '89, on Silva Screen by Silva Screen Records. Catalogue no: **MCA 39068**

Tom Thumb

TOM THUMB (Film soundtrack) (Various artists)
Note: Starring Russ Tamblyn, Ian Wallace and Stan Freberg.
Cass: Released Jan '89, on MCA by MCA Records. Catalogue no: **MCAC 25006**
Album: Released Jan '89, on MCA by MCA Records. Catalogue no: **MCA 25006**

Tomfoolery

TOMFOOLERY (Original London Cast) (Various artists)
Album: Released Apr '82, on Multi-Media. Deleted '87. Catalogue no: **MMT LP 102**
Cass: Released Apr '82, on Multi-Media. Deleted '87. Catalogue no: **MMT TC 102**
Album: Released May '89, on T.E.R. by That's Entertainment Records. Catalogue no: **TER 113**
Cass: Released May '89, on T.E.R. by That's Entertainment Records. Catalogue no: **ZCTER 11377**
CD: Released May '89, on T.E.R. by That's Entertainment Records. Catalogue no: **CDTER 1137**

Tomita

FIREBIRD (Television Sound-track)
Tracks: / Firebird suite, The / Prelude a l'apres midi d'un faune / Night on the bare mountain.
Note: Originally released February 1976.
Album: Released May '82, on RCA by BMG Records (UK). Catalogue no: **ARLI 1312**
CD: Released May '82, on RCA by BMG Records (UK). Deleted May '89. Catalogue no: **RD 81312**
Album: Released '81, on Leader by Topic Records. Catalogue no: **LER 2075**
Cass: Released May '82, on RCA by BMG Records (UK). Catalogue no: **RK 11718**

Tommy

PINBALL WIZARD (From Tommy) (See under John, Elton)

TOMMY (London Symphony Orchestra)
Cass: Released Aug '90, on Essential by Castle Communications Records. Catalogue no: **ESSMC 029**
CD: Released Aug '90, on Essential by Castle Communications Records. Catalogue no: **ESSCD 029**
2 LP Set: Released Aug '90, on Essential by Castle Communications Records. Catalogue no: **ESSLP 029**

TOMMY (Film Soundtrack) (See under Who)

TOMMY (VIDEO) (Various artists)
Note: Cert: 15.
VHS: Released '88, on Warner Home Video by WEA Records. Catalogue no: **PES 38109**

TOMMY VOL 1 (Various artists)
Album: Released May '84, on Polydor (Italy) by Polydor Ltd. Catalogue no: **2486 161**
Cass: Released May '84, on Polydor (Italy) by Polydor Ltd. Catalogue no: **3186 064**

TOMMY VOL 2 (Various artists)
Cass: Released May '84, on Polydor (Italy) by Polydor Ltd. Catalogue no: **3186 065**
Album: Released May '84, on Polydor (Italy) by Polydor Ltd. Catalogue no: **2486 162**

Tootsie

TOOTSIE (Film soundtrack) (Various artists)
Album: Released '83, on Silva Screen by Silva Screen Records. Catalogue no: **WB 23781**

Top BBC TV Themes

TOP BBC TV THEMES VOL.2 (Various artists)
Tracks: / Onedin line / All creatures great and small/ Empire Road / Great egg race / Blake's 7 / Sexton Blake / Last farewell / Telford's change / Two up, two down / Aphrodite inheritance / My son, my son / Horseman riding by / Mastermind / Don't forget to write
Album: Released Oct '79, on BBC by BBC Records. Deleted '84. Catalogue no: **REH 365**

TOP BBC TV THEMES VOL.3 (Various artists)
Tracks: / Dallas: *Various artists* / Tinker, tailor, soldier, spy: *Various artists* / Tomorrow's world: *Various artists* / Pride and prejudice: *Various artists* / Shoestring: *Various artists* / Body in question: *Various artists* / Man alive: *Various artists* / Holiday 80/81: *Various artists* / Parkinson: *Various artists* / Penmarric: *Various artists* / Knots Landing: *Various artists* / Six wives of Henry VIII: *Various artists* / Breakaway: *Various artists* / Enigma files: *Various artists*.
Album: Released Feb '81, on BBC by BBC Records. Deleted '86. Catalogue no: **REH 391**

TOP BBC TV THEMES-VOL. 4 (Various artists)
Tracks: / Juliet Bravo: *Various artists* / Maybury: *Various artists* / Chinese detective: *Various artists* / Hi de hi: *Various artists* / Not the nine o'clock news: *Various artists* / Speak for yourself: *Various artists* / Cosmos: *Various artists* / Chi mai: *Various artists* / MacKenzie: *Various artists* / Nanny: *Various artists* / We the accused: *Various artists* / Poldark: *Various artists* / I Claudius: *Various artists* / Goodbye darling: *Various artists*.
Album: Released Nov '81, on BBC by BBC Records. Deleted Nov '86. Catalogue no: **REH 424**

Top Gun

TOP GUN (Film soundtrack) (Various artists)
Tracks: / Danger zone: *Loggins,*

Kenny / Mighty wings: *Cheap Trick* / Playing with the boys: *Loggins, Kenny* / Lead me on: *Marie, Teena* / Take my breath away: *Berlin* ('Love theme from 'Top Gun') / Hot summer nights: *Miami Sound Machine* / Heaven in your eyes: *Lover Boy* / Through the fire: *Greene, Larry* / Destination unknown: *Marietta* / Top Gun anthem: *Faltermeyer, Harold & Steve Stevens.*
CD: Released '88, on CBS by CBS Records & Distribution. Catalogue no: **CDCBS 702 96**
Album: Released Sep '86, on CBS by CBS Records & Distribution. Catalogue no: **CBS 70296**
Cass: Released Sep '86, on CBS by CBS Records & Distribution. Catalogue no: **40.70296**

Top Hat
TOP HAT (VIDEO) (Various artists)
VHS: Released '88, on Channel 5 by Channel 5 Video. Catalogue no: **CFV 01072**

Top Hat, White Tie
TOP HAT, WHITE TIE (27 Golden show tunes) (Various artists)
CD: Released '88, on Laser Catalogue no: **CD 86001**

Top Of The Pops
BEST OF TOP OF THE POPS (1975 Edition) (Various artists)
Album: Released Jan '75, on BBC by BBC Records. Deleted '80. Catalogue no: **BELP 001**

BEST OF TOP OF THE POPS (1984 Edition) (Various artists)
Cass: Released Dec '84, on Hallmark by Pickwick Records. Deleted '88. Catalogue no: **HSC 3160**
Album: Released Dec '84, on Hallmark by Pickwick Records. Deleted '88. Catalogue no: **SHM 3160**

TOP OF THE POPS (Various artists)
Album: Released Nov '81, on BBC by BBC Records. Deleted Nov '86. Catalogue no: **REP 018**
Album: Released Feb '81, on BBC by BBC Records. Catalogue no: **BELP 016**

TOP OF THE POPS '89 (Various artists)

THE HERO IS A BERK

TOP SECRET!

MUSIC BY
MAURICE JARRE

From the team that brought you Airplane, Police Squad & Kentucky Fried Movie comes *Top Secret* (Starring Val Kilmer)

Album: Released Nov '89, on Telstar by Telstar Records (UK). Catalogue no: **STAR 2383**
Cass: Released Nov '89, on Telstar by Telstar Records (UK). Catalogue no: **STAC 2383**
CD: Released Nov '89, on Telstar by Telstar Records (UK). Catalogue no: **TCD 2383**

TOP OF THE POPS: THE FIRST 25 YEARS VOL 1 (VIDEO) (Various artists)
VHS: Released Oct '89, on Telstar by Telstar Records (UK). Catalogue no: **TVE 1006**

TOP OF THE POPS: THE FIRST 25 YEARS VOL.2 (VIDEO) (Various artists)
VHS: Released Dec '89, on Telstar by Telstar Records (UK). Catalogue no: **TVE 1009**

TOP OF THE POPS (VIDEO) (Various artists)
Note: Running time: 55 mins.
VHS: Released '88, on BBC Video by BBC Video. Catalogue no: **BBCV/B 3023**

TOP OF THE POPS (Theme from) (See under Hardcastle, Paul 'The Wizard')

TOP OF THE POPS (Theme from) (See under Lynott, Phil 'Yellow pearl')

Top Secret
TOP SECRET (Film Soundtrack) (Various artists) (See panel above)
Note: Composed by Maurice Jarre.
Cass: Released Jan '89, on Silva Screen by Silva Screen Records. Catalogue no: **CTV 81219**
Album: Released Dec '84, on T. E. R. by That's Entertainment Records. Catalogue no: **TER 1090**

Top T.V. Themes
TOP T.V. THEMES (Various artists)
Tracks: / Lillie theme: *Various artists* / Who pays the ferryman?: *Various artists* / Crossroads: *Various artists* / Prince Regent: *Various artists* / Monty Python's flying circus: *Various artists* / Van der Valk theme: *Various artists* / Match of the day: *Various artists* / Horse of the year: *Various artists* / Soap: *Various artists* / Kojak theme: *Various artists* / Sky at night theme: *Various artists* / Nationwide: *Vari-*

Torch Song Trilogy - the true story of Arnold Beckoff (starring Mathew Broderick, Harvey Fierstein & Brian Kerwin)

ous artists / Emmerdale farm: *Various artists* / Hawaii five-o: *Various artists*.
Album: Released Apr '81, on Decca by Decca International. Deleted Apr '86. Catalogue no: **TAB 18**

Topol

IF I WERE A RICH MAN
Tracks: / If I were a rich man / Miracle of miracles.
Note: From the musical 'Fiddler on the roof'
7" Single: Released Jun '83, on CBS by CBS Records & Distribution. Catalogue no: **A 3496**

IF I WERE A RICH MAN (Original)
Tracks: / If I were a rich man
7" Single: Released Apr '67, on CBS by CBS Records & Distribution. Deleted Apr '70. Catalogue no: **202 651**

TOPOL'S ISRAEL (TV soundtrack)
Tracks: / Just one more song: *Topol* / Market song / Promise, The / Remembering / Sea shores / My son are you laughing or crying / Kinneret Kinneret / On and on / Bedouin chant / Jerusalem / Cheribi cheribom / Massada
Cass: Released Oct '84, on BBC by BBC Records. Deleted Apr '89. Catalogue no: **ZCR 529**
Album: Released Oct '84, on BBC by BBC Records. Deleted Apr '89. Catalogue no: **REH 529**

Torch Song Trilogy

TORCH SONG TRILOGY (Film
Soundtrack) (Various artists) (See panel above)
Note: Film version of the highly successful Broadway show.
Album: Released Jan '89, on Silva Screen by Silva Screen Records. Catalogue no: **837 785-1**
CD: Released Jan '89, on Silva Screen by Silva Screen Records. Catalogue no: **837 785-2**
Cass: Released Jan '89, on Silva Screen by Silva Screen Records. Catalogue no: **837 785-4**

Total Recall

TOTAL RECALL (Film soundtrack) (Various artists)
Album: Released Aug '90, on Varese Sarabande Records(USA) by Varese Sarabande Records (USA). Catalogue no: **VS 5267**
CD: Released Aug '90, on Varese Sarabande Records(USA) by Varese Sarabande Records (USA). Catalogue no: **VSD 5267**
Cass: Released Aug '90, on Varese Sarabande Records(USA) by Varese Sarabande Records (USA). Catalogue no: **VSC 5267**

Touch Of Class (Film)

TOUCH OF CLASS, A (Film Soundtrack) (Various artists)
Album: Released Jun '74, on Philips by Phonogram Ltd. Deleted '78. Catalogue no: **6612 040**

Touch Of Evil

TOUCH OF EVIL (Film Soundtrack) (See under Mancini, Henry)

Tough Guys Don't Dance

TOUGH GUYS DON'T DANCE (Film soundtrack) (Various artists)
Note: Music from the Ryan O Neal film. Score by Angelo Badalamenti.
Album: Released Jan '89, on Silva Screen by Silva Screen Records. Catalogue no: **STV 81346**

Tougher Than Leather

TOUGHER THAN LEATHER (Film Soundtrack) (See under Run DMC)

MARY MARY (From Tougher Than Leather) (See under Run DMC)

Tour Of Duty

THEME FROM TOUR OF DUTY (See under Rolling Stones 'Paint it Black')

Town Like Alice

TOWN LIKE ALICE, A (Original TV soundtrack) (Various artists)
CD: Released Jan '89, on Silva Screen by Silva Screen Records. Catalogue no: **SCCD 1013**

Towns, Colin

BLIND JUSTICE (Original Television Theme)
Album: Released Oct '88, on BBC by BBC Records. Catalogue no: **REB 714**
Cass: Released Oct '88, on BBC by BBC Records. Catalogue no: **ZCF 714**
CD: Released Oct '88, on BBC by BBC Records. Catalogue no: **BBC CD 714**

FULL CIRCLE (Film soundtrack)
Album: Released Feb '78, on Virgin by Virgin Records. Deleted '88. Catalogue no: **V 2093**

FULL CIRCLE (THEME FROM)
Tracks: / Full circle (Theme from) / Full circle (Theme from) (Part 2).
7" Single: Released Mar '78, on Virgin by Virgin Records. Deleted '80. Catalogue no: **VS 204**

Trail Of..

TRAIL OF THE PINK PANTHER (Film Soundtrack) (Mancini, Henry & His Orchestra)
Tracks: / Trail of the pink panther

/ Greatest gift, The / Hong Kong fireworks / Shot in the dark / Simone / It had better be tonight / Easy life in Paris / Come to me / Bierfest polka / After the shower / Inspector Clouseau theme / Return of the Pink Panther.

Album: Released Dec '82, on Liberty by EMI Records. Deleted Feb '90. Catalogue no: **LBG 30355**

Cass: Released Dec '82, on Liberty by EMI Records. Catalogue no: **TC LBG 30355**

CD: Released Jan '89, on EMI-America by EMI Records. Catalogue no: **E 21 Y 90627**

Cass: Released Jan '89, on Silva Screen by Silva Screen Records. Catalogue no: **E 41 E 90627**

Transylvania 6-5000

TRANSYLVANIA 6-5000 (Film Soundtrack) (Various artists)
Note: Composed by Lee Holdridge.
Album: Released Jan '89, on Silva Screen by Silva Screen Records. Catalogue no: **STV 81267**

Travolta, John

GREASED LIGHTNIN'
Tracks: / Greased lightning' / Razzamatazz.
Note: From the film 'Grease'.
7" Single: Released Dec '78, on Polydor by Polydor Ltd. Deleted '81. Catalogue no: **POSP 14**

SANDY
Tracks: / Sandy / Rock'n'roll party queen.
Note: From the film "Grease'.
7" Single: Released Oct '78, on Polydor by Polydor Ltd. Deleted '81. Catalogue no: **POSP 6**

SUMMER NIGHTS (Travolta, John & Olivia Newton John)
Tracks: / Summer nights.
7" Single: Released Sep '78, on RSO by Polydor Ltd. Deleted '81. Catalogue no: **RSO 18**

TWO OF A KIND (Film soundtrack)
Cass: Released Nov '83, on EMI by EMI Records. Deleted '87. Catalogue no: **TC-EMC 165461-1**
Album: Released Nov '83, on EMI by EMI Records. Deleted '87. Catalogue no: **EMC 1654611**

YOU'RE THE ONE THAT I WANT (Travolta, John & Olivia Newton John)

Note: From the film 'Grease'
Tracks: / You're the one that I want / Alone at the drive in movie.
7" Single: Released May '78, on RSO by Polydor Ltd. Deleted '81. Catalogue no: **RSO 006**

Treading The Boards

TREADING THE BOARDS Stars of Music Hall & Variety (Various artists)
Tracks: / Photo of the girl I left behind me, The: *Merson, Billy* / Golden dustman, The: *Elen, Gus* / Misery farm: *Handley, Tommy* / Bird in a gilded cage, A: *Forde, Florrie* / It's the first time I've ever done that: *Robey, George* / Little Dollie Daydream: *Elliott, G.H.* / Coster's wedding, The: *Lloyd, Marie Junior* / Call of the Yukon, The: *Bennett, Billy* / She's only been with us a week: *Whelan, Albert* / Whistling: *Jolly Brothers* / What can you give a nudist on her birthday?: *Sarony, Leslie* / Little idea of my own: *Robey, George* / Fill 'em up: *King, Hetty* / 'E dunno where 'e are: *Elen, Gus* / You can't understand the ladies: *Whelan, Albert* / Whistling: *Siziletta* / Spaniard that blighted my life, The: *Merson, Billy* / Lost policeman, The: *Powell, Sandy* / Sunny skies: *Elliott, G.H.* / Goodbye, Dolly Gray: *Forde, Florrie.*
Cass: Released '88, on Conifer Happy Days by Conifer Records. Catalogue no: **MCHD 154**
Album: Released '88, on Conifer Happy Days by Conifer Records. Catalogue no: **CHD 154**

Treasure Girl

TREASURE GIRL / CHEE CHEE (Original show scores) (Lewine, Richard - Betty Comden)
Tracks: / I've got a crush on you / I don't think I'll fall in love today / Where's the boy? here's the girl / I must love you / Better be good to me / Dear oh dear / Moon of my delight / Singing a love song.
Album: Released Apr '83, on T. E. R. by That's Entertainment Records. Catalogue no: **TER 1039**

Treasure Island

TREASURE ISLAND (Film Soundtrack) (See under Oldfield, Terry)

TREASURE ISLAND (Original London cast) (Various artists)

Tracks: / Overture: *Various artists* / Admiral Benbow Inn, The: *Various artists* / 15 men: *Various artists* / Find that boy: *Various artists* / Shipmates: *Various artists* / Partners and pals: *Various artists* / Heave-oh-haul: *Various artists* / Billow the sails: *Various artists* / Land ho: *Various artists* / Deepwater sailors: *Various artists* / Cheese: *Various artists* / Cap'n Silver: *Various artists* / Far away from England: *Various artists* / Never get caught: *Various artists* / Treasure Island: *Various artists* /

Tree Grows In Brooklyn

TREE GROWS IN BROOKLYN (Broadway Cast) (Various artists)
Album: Released Jan '89, on Silva Screen by Silva Screen Records. Catalogue no: **AML 4405**

Trelawny

TRELAWNY (Original London cast) (Various artists)
Tracks: / Pull yourself together: *Various artists* / Walking on: *Various artists* / Ever of thee: *Various artists* / Trelawny of the Wells: *Various artists* / Tom Wrench's letter: *Various artists* / On approval: *Various artists* / Rules: *Various artists* / Back to the Wells: *Various artists* / Old friends: *Various artists* / One who isn't there, The: *Various artists* / We can't keep 'em waiting: *Various artists* / Turn of Avonia Bunn, The: *Various artists* / Arthur's letter: *Various artists* / Two fools: *Various artists* / Life: *Various artists* / Finale: *Various artists.*
Album: Released May '85, on T. E. R. by That's Entertainment Records. Catalogue no: **TER 1081**
Cass: Released May '85, on T. E. R. by That's Entertainment Records. Catalogue no: **ZCTER 1081**

Triangle

TRIANGLE (TV Soundtrack) (See under Pearson, Johnny)

Trick Or Treat

TRICK OR TREAT (Film Score) (Brand, Oscar)
Album: Released May '80 on Caedmon Records (USA). catalogue no: **TC 1624**

TRICK OR TREAT (Film Soundtrack) (Fastway)
Tracks: / Trick or treat / After midnight / Don't stop the fight / Stand

up / Tear down the wall / Get tough / Hold on to the nights / Heft / If you could see.
Album: Released Mar '87, on CBS by CBS Records. Catalogue no: **450 444 1**
Cass: Released Mar '87, on CBS by CBS Records. Catalogue no: **450 444 4**
CD: Released Mar '87, on CBS by CBS Records. Catalogue no: **450 444 2**

Trois Places Pour ...

TROIS PLACES POUR LE 26 (Film soundtrack) (Various artists)
Note: Composed by Michel Legrand. A Jacques Demy film starring Yves Montand and Mathilda May.
Album: Released Feb '89, on Polygram (France) by PolyGram UK Ltd. Catalogue no: **836 733 1**
CD: Released Feb '89, on Polygram (France) by PolyGram UK Ltd. Catalogue no: **836 733 2**
Cass: Released Feb '89, on Polygram (France) by PolyGram UK Ltd. Catalogue no: **836 733 4**

Tron

TRON (Film soundtrack) (Various artists)
Album: Released Nov '82, on CBS by CBS Records & Distribution. Deleted '86. Catalogue no: **CBS 70223**
Cass: Released Nov '82, on CBS by CBS Records & Distribution. Deleted '86. Catalogue no: **40 73665**

Troost, Ernest

TIGER WARSAW (Film Soundtrack) (See under Tiger Warsaw)

Trouble In Mind

TROUBLE IN MIND (Film soundtrack) (Various artists)
Note: Composed by Mark Isham.
CD: Released Feb '90, on Silva Screen by Silva Screen Records. Catalogue no: **90501.2**
Album: Released Jan '89, on Silva Screen by Silva Screen Records. Catalogue no: **90501.1**

Trouble In Tahiti

TROUBLE IN TAHITI (1952 TV Musical) (Various artists)
Album: Released Jan '89, on Silva Screen by Silva Screen Rec-

ords. Catalogue no: **827845.1**
Cass: Released Jan '89, on Silva Screen by Silva Screen Records. Catalogue no: **827845.4**

Troubleman

TROUBLEMAN (Film Soundtrack) (See under Gaye, Marvin)

True Confessions

TRUE CONFESSIONS (Film soundtrack) (Delerue, Georges)
Album: Released Dec '81, on T.E.R. by That's Entertainment Records. Catalogue no: **TER 1013**

True Stories

TRUE STORIES (Film Soundtrack) (Various artists)
Tracks: / Road song: *Byrne, David* / Freeway song: *Byrne, David* / Brownie's theme: *Byrne, David* / Mall musak: *Finch, Carl* / Dinner music: *Kronos Quartet* / Disco hits: *Byrne, David* / City of steel: *Byrne, David* / Love theme from 'True stories': *Byrne, David* / Festa paraum rei negro: *Banda Eclipse* / Buster's theme: *Finch, Carl* / Soy de tejas: *Jordan, Steve* / I love metal buildings: *Byrne, David* / Glass operator: *Byrne, David.*
Album: Released Nov '86, on EMI by EMI Records. Deleted Jul '89. Catalogue no: **EMC 3520**
Cass: Released Nov '86, on EMI by EMI Records. Deleted Jul '89. Catalogue no: **TCEMC 3520**
CD: Released Nov '86, on EMI by EMI Records. Deleted Jul '89. Catalogue no: **7463452**

TRUE STORIES (Byrne, David) (Video)
Note: David Byrne's idiosyncratic and hugely enjoyable documentary on the 100th anniversary celebrations of a fictional Texas town. A cult classic. Running time: 86 mins. Cert: PG.
VHS: Released '88, on Warner Home Video by WEA Records. Catalogue no: **PES 99243**

Tube

TUBE, THE (TV soundtrack) (Various artists)
Album: Released Mar '84, on K-K-Tel by K-Tel Records. Catalogue no: **NE 1261**

Tucker

TUCKER (Film Soundtrack)

(See under Jackson, Joe)

Tuff Turf

TUFF TURF (Film soundtrack) (Various artists)
2 LP Set: Released Jan '86, on Rhino (USA) by Rhino Records (USA). Catalogue no: **RNDF 308**

Turner, Tina

WE DON'T NEED ANOTHER HERO
Tracks: / We don't need another hero / We don't need another hero (instr.).
Note: From the film 'Mad Max III: Beyond The Thunderdome'.
7" Single: Released Jul '85, on Capitol by EMI Records. Deleted Sep '89. Catalogue no: **CL 364**
7" Pic: Released Jul '85, on Capitol by EMI Records. Deleted Nov '88. Catalogue no: **CLP 364**
12" Single: Released Jul '85, on Capitol by EMI Records. Deleted Nov '88. Catalogue no: **12CL 364**

TV & Film Themes

TV & FILM THEMES II (Various artists)
CD: Released Oct '89, on CRC (USA) by Continental Recording Corp.(USA). Catalogue no: **3024 DDD**

T.V. Hits

T.V HITS ALBUM Various artists (Various artists)
Tracks: / Miami vice: *Various artists* / Connie: *Various artists* / Minder: *Various artists* / In sickness and in health: *Various artists* / Auf wiedersehn pet: *Various artists* / Eastenders: *Various artists* / Travelling man: *Various artists* / Roll over Beethoven: *Various artists* / Dempsey and Makepeace: *Various artists* / Lakeland rock: *Various artists* / Shine on Harvey Moon: *Various artists* / Bill: *Various artists* / Smugglers blues: *Various artists* / Nog: *Various artists* / Sons and daughters: *Various artists* / Blott on the landscape: *Various artists.*
Album: Released Sep '85, on Towerbell Catalogue no: **TVLP 3**
Cass: Released Sep '85, on Towerbell Catalogue no: **ZCTV 3**

T.V. HITS VOL.2 (Various artists)
Cass: Released Apr '86, on Towerbell Catalogue no: **ZCTV 10**
Album: Released Apr '86, on

Towerbell Catalogue no: **TVLP 10**

TV Themes

ALL YOUR FAVOURITE TV THEMES (Various artists)
Cass: Released Mar '83, on AIM (Budget Cassettes) Catalogue no: **AIM 39**

BEST AMERICAN TV THEMES, THE (Various artists)
Tracks: / Magnum P.I.: *Various artists* / Airwolf: *Various artists* / Cosby show, The: *Various artists* / Mike Hammer: *Various artists* / Lou Grant: *Various artists* / Cheers: *Various artists* / Hill Street blues: *Various artists* / Hollywood wives: *Various artists* / Cagney and Lacey: *Various artists* / St. Elsewhere: *Various artists* / Touch of scandal: *Various artists* / Taxi: *Various artists* / Simon and Simon: *Various artists* / Rockford files: *Various artists*.
Album: Released Aug '88, on Indiana by Indiana Records. Catalogue no: **USTP 7777**
Cass: Released Aug '88, on Indiana by Indiana Records. Catalogue no: **USTC 7777**

TOP T.V. & MOVIE THEMES (Various artists)
Tracks: / Star trek: *Various artists* / High noon: *Various artists* / 2001: *Various artists* / Shaft, Theme from: *Various artists* / Howards way: *Various artists* / Eastenders: *Various artists*.
CD Set: Released Jan '89, on Sound by Target Records. Catalogue no: **2 - 802**

TV THEME SINGALONG ALBUM (Various artists)
Album: Released Jun '88, on Rhino (USA) by Rhino Records (USA). Catalogue no: **RNIN 703**

T.V. THEMES (Various artists)
CD: Released '86, on Bridge (MCS Bridge) Catalogue no: **100 033**

TV THEMES AMERICA (Various artists)
Tracks: / Dallas: *Various artists* / Perfect strangers: *Various artists* / Knot's Landing: *Various artists* / Midnight caller: *Various artists* / Head of the class: *Various artists* / Mission Impossible: *Various artists* / McGyver: *Various artists* / Cagney and Lacey: *Various artists* / Dynasty: *Various artists* / Odd

couple, The: *Various artists* / High Chaparral, The: *Various artists* / Mash: *Various artists* / Bonanza: *Various artists* / Taxi: *Various artists* / Rockford files, The: *Various artists* / Doctor Kildare: *Various artists*.
Cass: Released Dec '89, on BBC by BBC Records. Catalogue no: **ZCF 763**
CD: Released Dec '89, on BBC by BBC Records. Catalogue no: **BBCCD 763**
Album: Released Dec '89, on BBC by BBC Records. Catalogue no: **REB 763**

WORLD OF BBC TV THEMES, THE (Various artists)
Tracks: / Shadow of the noose: *Various artists* / Eagles eye view: *Various artists* / Supersense: *Various artists* / Franchise affair, The: *Various artists* / Top of the pops: *Various artists* / Atlantic realm: *Various artists* / Christabel: *Various artists* / Doctor Who: *Various artists* / South of the border: *Various artists* / Rockliffe's folly: *Various artists* / Celts, The: *Various artists* / Bread: *Various artists* / Great rift, The: *Various artists* / Rockliffe's babies: *Various artists* / Blind justice: *Various artists* / Victorian kitchen garden: *Various artists* / Pulaski: *Various artists* / Champion: *Various artists* / Chelworth: *Various artists* / Thunder dragons: *Various artists* / First born: *Various artists* / Animal squad: *Various artists*.
Album: Released Jul '89, on BBC by BBC Records. Catalogue no: **REB 705**
CD: Released Jul '89, on BBC by BBC Records. Catalogue no: **BBC CD 705**
Cass: Released Jul '89, on BBC by BBC Records. Catalogue no: **ZCF 705**

WORLD OF TV THEMES (Various artists)
Album: Released '72, on Decca by Decca International. Deleted '88. Catalogue no: **SPA 217**
Cass: Released '72, on Decca by Decca International. Deleted '88. Catalogue no: **KCSP 217**

TV Tunes

TV TUNES (Various artists)
Tracks: / Neighbours: *Various artists* / Prisoner cell block H: *Various artists* / LA Law: *Various artists* /

Hill Street blues: *Various artists* / Dynasty: *Various artists* / Cheers: *Various artists* / Taxi: *Various artists* / St. Elsewhere: *Various artists* / Peter Gunn: *Various artists* / A Team: *Various artists* / Streets of San Francisco: *Various artists* / Hart to Hart: *Various artists* / Sons and daughters: *Various artists* / Young doctors: *Various artists* / WKRP in Cincinnati: *Various artists* / Greatest American hero: *Various artists* / Welcome back Kotter: *Various artists* / Starsky and Hutch: *Various artists* / Mission impossible: *Various artists* / Country practise: *Various artists* / Waltons: *Various artists* / Monkees: *Various artists* / Odd couple: *Various artists* / Addams family: *Various artists* / Monty Python's flying circus: *Various artists* / Happy days: *Various artists* / Laverne and Shirley: *Various artists* / Flintstones: *Various artists* / Yogi bear: *Various artists* / Top cat: *Various artists* / Jetsons: *Various artists* / Woody Woodpecker show: *Various artists* / Sesame Street: *Various artists* / Scooby Doo: *Various artists* / Inspector Gadget: *Various artists* / Mr. Magoo: *Various artists* / Popeye: *Various artists* / Road Runner: *Various artists* / Bugs Bunny: *Various artists* / Dastardly and Mutley: *Various artists* / My three sons: *Various artists* / Mr Ed: *Various artists* / Beverly Hillbillies: *Various artists* / Get smart: *Various artists* / Hogan's heroes: *Various artists* / Car 54: Where are you? *Various artists* / Green acres: *Various artists* / Rawhide: *Various artists* / Dallas: *Various artists* / Batman: *Various artists*.
Album: Released Sep '89, on K-Tel by K-Tel Records. Catalogue no: **NE 3429**
Cass: Released Sep '89, on K-Tel by K-Tel Records. Catalogue no: **CE 3429**
CD: Released '89, on K-Tel by K-Tel Records. Catalogue no: **NCD 3429**

Twang

TWANG! (London Cast) (Various artists)
Tracks: / Welcome to Sherwood: *Various artists* / What makes a star: *Various artists* / Make an honest woman of me: *Various artists* / To the woods: *Various artists* / Roger the ugly: *Various artists* /

Dreamchild: *Various artists* / With bells on: *Various artists* / Twang!: *Various artists* / Unseen hands: *Various artists* / Sighs: *Various artists* / You can't catch me: *Various artists* / Follow your leader: *Various artists* / Wander: *Various artists* / Whose little girl are you: *Various artists* / I'll be hanged: *Various artists*.
Album: Released Apr '83, on T. E. R. by That's Entertainment Records. Catalogue no: **TER 1055**
Cass: Released Apr '83, on T. E. R. by That's Entertainment Records. Catalogue no: **ZCTER 1055**

Twelve Chairs

TWELVE CHAIRS (Original soundtrack) (Various artists)
Album: Released Apr '83, on T. E. R. by That's Entertainment Records. Catalogue no: **TER 1033**

Twenty Great TV Themes

20 GREAT TV THEMES (Various artists)
Tracks: / Vanity fair: *Various artists* / One game, The: *Various artists* / Square deal: *Various artists* / Match eye, The: *Various artists* / Witness: *Various artists* / Doctor Who: *Various artists* / Campion: *Various artists* / Ruth Rendell mysteries: *Various artists* / Agatha Christie's Poirot: *Various artists* / Me and my girl: *Various artists* / World cup: *Various artists* / Wish me luck: *Various artists* / Inspector Morse: *Various artists* / Forever Green: *Various artists* / 7 faces of woman: *Various artists* / Tales of the unexpected: *Various artists* / To have and to hold: *Various artists* / Two of us, The: *Various artists* / Professionals, The: *Various artists* / Upstairs, downstairs: *Various artists*.
CD: Released Apr '89, on Total Record Company Catalogue no: **WEEKCD 2**
Album: Released Apr '89, on Total Record Company Catalogue no: **WEEKLP 2**
Cass: Released Apr '89, on Total Record Company Catalogue no: **WEEKMC 2**

Twilight Zone

TWILIGHT ZONE (1) - MUSIC FROM THE TV SERIES (TV soundtrack) (Various artists)
Tracks: / Invaders, The: *Various artists* / Where is everybody: *Vari-*

ous artists / I sing the body electric: *Various artists* / Jazz themes: *Various artists* / Nervous man in a four dollar room: *Various artists* / Walking distance: *Various artists* / Main title: *Various artists* / End title: *Various artists*.
Album: Released Jan '89, on Silva Screen by Silva Screen Records. Catalogue no: **STV 81171**
CD: Released Jan '89, on Silva Screen by Silva Screen Records. Catalogue no: **VCD 47233**

TWILIGHT ZONE (2) - MUSIC FROM THE TV SERIES (TV soundtrack) (Various artists)
Tracks: / Main theme: *Various artists* / Back there: *Various artists* / And when the sky was opened: *Various artists* / Passerby, The: *Various artists* / Lonely, The: *Various artists* / Two: *Various artists* / End theme: *Various artists*.
CD: Released Jan '89, on Silva Screen by Silva Screen Records. Catalogue no: **VCD 47247**
Album: Released Jan '89, on Silva Screen by Silva Screen Records. Catalogue no: **STV 81178**

TWILIGHT ZONE (3) MUSIC FROM THE TV SERIES (TV soundtrack) (Various artists)
Album: Released Jan '89, on Silva Screen by Silva Screen Records. Catalogue no: **STV 81185**

TWILIGHT ZONE (4) - MUSIC FROM THE TV SERIES (TV soundtrack) (Various artists)
Album: Released Jan '89, on Varese Sarabande Records(USA) by Varese Sarabande Records (USA). Catalogue no: **STV 81192**

TWILIGHT ZONE (5) - MUSIC FROM THE TV SERIES (TV soundtrack) (Various artists)
Cass: Released Jan '89, on Silva Screen by Silva Screen Records. Catalogue no: **STV 81205**

TWILIGHT ZONE - THE MOVIE (Film soundtrack) (Various artists)
Album: on Warner Bros. by WEA Records. Catalogue no: **923887 1**

Twins

TWINS (Film soundtrack) (Various artists)
Tracks: / Twins: *Little Richard & Phil Bailey* / Brother to brother: *Spinners* / It's too late: *Nayobe* / I only have eyes for you: *Scott, Marilyn* / Yakety yak: *Two Live Crew* /

No way of knowin': *Summer, Henry Lee* / Train kept a rollin': *Beck, Jeff* / I'd die for this dance: *Larson, Nicolette* / Going to Santa Fe: *McFerrin, Bobby/Herbie Hancock* / Main title: *Various artists*.
Note: Comedy film starring Arnold Schwarzenegger and Danny De-Vito as identical twin brothers!
CD: Released 6 Mar '89, on Epic by CBS Records & Distribution. Catalogue no: **463266 2**
Album: Released 6 Mar '89, on Epic by CBS Records & Distribution. Deleted Jul '90. Catalogue no: **463266 1**
Cass: Released 6 Mar '89, on Epic by CBS Records & Distribution. Catalogue no: **463266 4**

TWINS (Original score) (Delerue, Georges & Randy Edelman)
Album: Released Jan '89, on Silva Screen by Silva Screen Records. Catalogue no: **SP 45036**
Cass: Released Jan '89, on Silva Screen by Silva Screen Records. Catalogue no: **SPT 45036**
CD: Released Jan '89, on Silva Screen by Silva Screen Records. Catalogue no: **SPK 45036**

Two Of A Kind

TWO OF A KIND (Film Soundtrack) (See under Travolta, John)

Two For The Road

TWO FOR THE ROAD (Film soundtrack) (Various artists)
Note: Composed by Henry Mancini.
Album: Released Jan '89, on Silva Screen by Silva Screen Records. Catalogue no: **NL 45119**

Two For The Seesaw

TWO FOR THE SEESAW (Film Soundtrack) (Various artists)
Note: Composed by Andre Previn.
Cass: Released Jan '89, on MCA by MCA Records. Catalogue no: **MCAC 25016**
Album: Released Jan '89, on MCA by MCA Records. Catalogue no: **MCA 25016**

Two Hundred Motels

TWO HUNDRED MOTELS (Film Soundtrack) (See under Zappa, Frank)

Two Moon Junction

TWO MOON JUNCTION (Film soundtrack) (Various artists)
Note: Thriller with music by Jonathan Elias (Children Of The Corn).
Album: Released Jan '89, on Silva Screen by Silva Screen Records. Catalogue no: **704.520**

Two Ronnies

BEST OF THE TWO RONNIES
Tracks: / Moira McKellar and Kenneth Anderson / Brass band, The / Plumpstead Ladies male voice choir, The / Gilbert and Sullivan / Scouts jamboree show / Russian choir, The / Boys in the ballet / Short and fat minstrels, The.
Album: Released Feb '82, on Spot by Pickwick Records. Catalogue no: **SPR 8518**
Cass: Released Feb '82, on Spot by Pickwick Records. Catalogue no: **SPC 8518**

VERY BEST OF ME AND THE VERY BEST OF HIM, THE
Tracks: / But first the news / Plain speaking / Mark my words / Train of events / British Rail / Night night / Limerick writers / Complete book, The / Restaurant, The / Castaway, The / Language barrier, The / Cheers / Late news, The.
Cass: Released Oct '84, on BBC by BBC Records. Catalogue no: **ZCM 514**
Album: Released Oct '84, on BBC by BBC Records. Catalogue no: **REC 514**

Two Thousand And One

2001: A SPACE ODYSSEY (Film soundtrack) (MCA label)
(Various artists)
Tracks: / Also sprach Zarathustra (thus spake Zarathustra): *Various artists* / Requiem for soprano, mezzo soprano...: *Various artists* (...two mixed choirs and orchestra) / Lux Aeterna: *Various artists* / Blue Danube, The: *Various artists* / Gayane ballet suite: *Various artists* / Atmospheres: *Various artists* / Blue Danube, The: *Various artists* / Also sprach Zarathustra (thus spake Zarathustra): *Various artists*.
Album: Released Jan '89, on MCA by MCA Records. Catalogue no: **MCA 39049**
Cass: Released Jan '89, on MCA by MCA Records. Catalogue no: **MCAC 39049**
CD: Released Jan '89, on MCA by MCA Records. Catalogue no: **MCAD 31195**

2001: A SPACE ODYSSEY (Film Soundtrack) (CBS label) (Various artists)
Album: Released May '81, on CBS by CBS Records & Distribution. Deleted '86. Catalogue no: **CBS 61772**
Album: Released Jul '86, on CBS by CBS Records & Distribution. Catalogue no: **CBS 70275**
CD: Released Nov '86, on CBS by CBS Records & Distribution. Catalogue no: **CDCBS 70275**

2001: A SPACE ODYSSEY (Film Soundtrack) (MGM label) (Various artists)
Album: Released Jan '90, on MGM (EMI) Catalogue no: **LPMGM 6**

Album: Released Jan '90, on MGM (EMI) Catalogue no: **793 302 1**
Cass: Released Jan '90, on MGM (EMI) Catalogue no: **TCMGM 6**
Cass: Released Jan '90, on MGM (EMI) Catalogue no: **793 302 4**
CD: Released Jan '90, on MGM (EMI) Catalogue no: **CDMGM 6**
CD: Released Jan '90, on MGM (EMI) Catalogue no: **CDP 793 302 2**

2001: A SPACE ODYSSEY (Film Soundtrack) (Original MGM Soundtrack)
Album: Released Jun '69, on MGM (EMI) Deleted '74. Catalogue no: **MGM CS 8078**
Album: Released May '72, on MGM (Polydor) by Polydor Ltd. Deleted '77. Catalogue no: **2315 034**

2001: A SPACE ODYSSEY (Film Soundtrack) (A&M label) (Various artists)
Album: Released Mar '85, on A&M by A&M Records. Deleted '88. Catalogue no: **AMA 5038**
Album: Released Mar '85, on A&M by A&M Records. Deleted '88. Catalogue no: **AMA 5038**

Two Thousand And Ten

2010: ODYSSEY TWO (Film Soundtrack) (Various artists)
Album: Released Mar '85, on A&M by A&M Records. Deleted '88. Catalogue no: **AMA 5038**
Cass: Released Mar '85, on A&M by A&M Records. Deleted '88. Catalogue no: **AMC 5038**

The following information was taken from the Music Master database on September 25th, 1990.

U2

ALL I WANT IS YOU
Tracks: / All I want is you / Unchained melody / Everlasting love (12" and CD only) / All I want is you (version) (CD only).
Note: From the film Rattle and Hum.
12" Single: Released May '89, on Island by Island Records. Catalogue no: **12 IS 422**
7" Single: Released May '89, on Island by Island Records. Deleted Feb '90. Catalogue no: **IS 422**
CD Single: Released Jun '89, on Island by Island Records. Catalogue no: **CDCIDP 422**
CD Single: Released May '89, on Island by Island Records. Catalogue no: **CID 422**
7" Single: Released '88, on Island by Island Records. Catalogue no: **ISB 422**
12" Single: Released Jun '89, on Island by Island Records. Catalogue no: **12 ISB 422**
Cassingle: Released May '89, on Island by Island Records. Catalogue no: **CIS 422**

ANGEL OF HARLEM
Tracks: / Angel of Harlem / No room at the heartbreak hotel / Love rescue me (Only on 12" and CD single.).
Note: From the film Rattle and Hum.
7" Single: Released Oct '88, on Island by Island Records. Deleted Apr '89. Catalogue no: **IS 402**
12" Single: Released Oct '88, on Island by Island Records. Deleted Dec '89. Catalogue no: **12ISG 402**
CD Single: Released Oct '88, on Island by Island Records. Catalogue no: **CIDP 402**
12" Single: Released Oct '88, on Island by Island Records. Cata-

logue no: **12IS 402**

DESIRE
Tracks: / Desire / Hallelujah (here she comes).
Note: From the film Rattle and Hum.
7" Single: Released 8 Sep '88, on Island by Island Records. Deleted Apr '89. Catalogue no: **IS 400**
12" Single: Released Sep '88, on Island by Island Records. Deleted Apr '89. Catalogue no: **12 IS 400**
12" Single: Released Sep '88, on Island by Island Records. Deleted Apr '89. Catalogue no: **12 ISG 400**
7" Single: Released Sep '88, on Island by Island Records. Deleted Apr '89. Catalogue no: **ISG 400**

RATTLE AND HUM (Film Soundtrack)
Tracks: / Helter skelter / Hawkmoon 269 / Van Diemen's land / Desire / Angel of Harlem / I still haven't found what I'm looking for / When love comes to town / God part III / Silver and gold / Love and rescue / Love rescue me / Heartland / Star spangled banner, The / All I want is you.
2 LP Set: Released 10 Oct '88, on Island by Island Records. Catalogue no: **U 27**
CD: Released 10 Oct '88, on Island by Island Records. Catalogue no: **CIDU 27**
Cass: Released 10 Oct '88, on Island by Island Records. Catalogue no: **UC 27**

RATTLE AND HUM (VIDEO)
Note: Cert: 15.
VHS: Released Feb '89, on CIC Video Catalogue no: **VHR 2308**

WHEN LOVE COMES TO TOWN
Tracks: / When love comes to town / Dancing barefoot / When

love comes to town (live from the kingdom mix) (12" and CD only) / God part II (hard metal dance mix) (12" and CD only).
Note: From the film Rattle and Hum.
CD Single: Released Mar '89, on Island by Island Records. Catalogue no: **CIDP 411**
CD Single: Released Apr '89, on Island by Island Records. Deleted Jul '90. Catalogue no: **CIDX 411**
12" Single: Released Mar '89, on Island by Island Records. Deleted Dec '89. Catalogue no: **12IS 411**
7" Single: Released Mar '89, on Island by Island Records. Deleted Dec '89. Catalogue no: **IS 411**

ULYSSES (Film Soundtrack) (Various artists)
Note: Italian epic score by Alessandro Cicognini for the film starring Kirk Douglas.
Album: Released Jan '89, on Interior Music by Interior Music Records. Catalogue no: **IM 007**

UMBRELLAS OF CHERBOURG (Original soundtrack) (Various artists) (See also under Legrand, Michael)
2 LP Set: Released Dec '84, on Philips (France) by PolyGram UK Ltd. Catalogue no: **822 457-1**
CD: Released Jan '89, on Silva Screen by Silva Screen Records. Catalogue no: **834 139-2**

NUN OF MONZA (See under Nun Of Monza)

UNBEARABLE LIGHTNESS OF BEING, THE (Film sound-

track) (Various artists)
Tracks: / Fairytale III: *Various artists* / Holy Virgin of Frydek: *Various artists* / In the mist: *Various artists* / Hey Jude: *Various artists* / Joy, joy, joy: *Various artists* / String quartet No. 2 'intimate pages': *Various artists* / Sonata for violin & piano: *Various artists* / Bird of ill omen lingers on: *Various artists* / On the overgrown path, set 2: *Various artists* / String quartet No. 1, III: *Various artists* / Blow-away leaf, A: *Various artists* / Goodnight: *Various artists* / Idyll for string orchestra, II: *Various artists*.
Note: "This selection of mostly Janacek compositions is from the acclaimed Philip Kaufman film starring Daniel Day-Lewis as performed by the various artists on the film soundtrack." (Phonogram Records, June 1988). / Not available on cassette.
CD: Released Jan '89, on Silva Screen by Silva Screen Records. Catalogue no: **FCD 21006**
CD: Released 20 Jun '88, on Metronome by Magnum Music Group. Deleted 17 Apr '89. Catalogue no: **835 918 2**
Album: Released 20 Jun '88, on Metronome by Magnum Music Group. Deleted 17 Apr '89. Catalogue no: **835 918 1**

Uncle Meat

UNCLE MEAT (See under Zappa, Frank)

Under African Skies

UNDER AFRICAN SKIES (TV Soundtrack) (Various artists)
CD Set: Released Oct '89, on BBC by BBC Records. Catalogue no: **BBCCD 2006**
2 LP Set: Released Oct '89, on BBC by BBC Records. Catalogue no: **REQ 745**
Cass set: Released Oct '89, on BBC by BBC Records. Catalogue no: **ZCQ 745**

Under Fire

UNDER FIRE (Film Soundtrack)
Album: Released May '84, on Warner Bros. by WEA Records. Deleted Jan '89. Catalogue no: **923 965-1**

Underneath The Arches

UNDERNEATH THE ARCHES (Original Cast) (Various artists)
Tracks: / Old bull and bush, The: *Various artists* / Just for laughs: *Various artists* / Underneath the arches: *Various artists* / Maybe it's because I'm a Londoner: *Various artists* / Home town: *Various artists* / Umbrella man: *Various artists* / Strollin': *Various artists* / Siegfried line: *Various artists*.
Cass: Released Apr '82, on T. E. R. by That's Entertainment Records. Catalogue no: **ZCTER 1015**
Album: Released Apr '82, on T. E. R. by That's Entertainment Records. Catalogue no: **TER 1015**

Underscore

UNDERSCORE (Original Soundtrack) (Various artists)
Album: Released Jun '87, on Enigma by Enigma Records (USA). Catalogue no: **ENIG 3266 1**

Unmarried Woman

UNMARRIED WOMAN, AN Soundtrack (Various artists)
Album: Released Aug '78, on 20th Century by Phonogram Ltd. Catalogue no: **BT 557**

Unsinkable Molly Brown

UNSINKABLE MOLLY BROWN, THE (Film soundtrack) (Various artists)
Note: Stars Debbie Reynolds.
Album: Released Jan '89, on MCA by MCA Records. Catalogue no: **MCA 25011**
CD: Released Feb '90, on Silva Screen by Silva Screen Records. Catalogue no: **CDP 92054**
Cass: Released Jan '89, on MCA by MCA Records. Catalogue no: **MCAC 25011**

UNSINKABLE MOLLY BROWN, THE (VIDEO) (Various artists)
VHS: Released Sep '89, on MGM/UA (Video) by MGM/UA Video. Catalogue no: **SMV 10578**

Until September

UNTIL SEPTEMBER (Original soundtrack) (Various artists)
Note: Composed by John Barry..
Album: Released Jan '89, on Silva Screen by Silva Screen Records. Catalogue no: **STV 81226**

Untouchables (film)

UNTOUCHABLES (Various

movie hits) (Various artists)
CD: Released Dec '88, on Laser Catalogue no: **CD 86020**

UNTOUCHABLES (See under Morricone, Ennio)

Up In Arms

UP IN ARMS (Film Soundtrack) (Various artists)
Note: Starring Danny Kaye and Dinah Shore.
Album: Released Jan '89, on Silva Screen by Silva Screen Records. Catalogue no: **STK 113**

Urban Cowboy

URBAN COWBOY (Various artists)
Tracks: / Hi lo Texas: *Buffett, Jimmy* / All night long: *Walsh, Joe* / Times like these: *Fogelberg, Dan* / Nine tonight: *Seger, Bob & The Silver Bullet Band* / Stand by me: *Gilley, Mickey* / Here comes the hurt again: *Gilley, Mickey* / Orange blossom special: *Gilley, Mickey* / Hoedown: *Gilley, Mickey* / Could I have this dance: *Murray, Anne* / Cherokee fiddle: *Lee, Johnny* / Lookin' for love: *Lee, Johnny* / Lyin' eyes: *Eagles* / Look what you've done to me: *Scaggs, Boz* / Don't it make you want to dance: *Raitt, Bonnie* / Darlin': *Raitt, Bonnie* / Hearts against the wind: *Ronstadt, Linda* / Devil went down to Georgia: *Daniels, Charlie Band* / Love the world away: *Rogers, Kenny* / Falling in love for the night: *Daniels, Charlie Band*.
Album: Released Jul '80, on Elektra Asylum by Elektra Records (USA). Deleted Jul '85. Catalogue no: **K 99101**
Cass: Released Jul '80, on Elektra Asylum by Elektra Records (USA). Deleted Jul '85. Catalogue no: **K4 99101**

Urgh, A Music War

URGH, A MUSIC WAR (Film soundtrack) (Various artists)
Tracks: / Driven to tears: *Police* / Back in flesh: *Wall Of Voodoo* / Dance: *Toyah* / Enola Gay: *O.M.D.* / Ain't this the life: *Oingo Boingo* / Respectable street: *XTC* / Offshore banking business: *Members* / We got the beat: *Go-Go's* / Total eclipse: *Nomi, Klaus* / Where's Captain Kirk: *Athletico Spizz 80* / Nothing means nothing any more: *Alley Cats* / Foolish I know: *Holland, Jools* / Ku klux klan: *Steel*

Pulse / Uncontrollable urge: *Devo* / Come again: *Au Pairs* / Puppet: *Echo & The Bunnymen* / Tear it up: *Cramps* / Bad reputation: *Jett, Joan & The Blackhearts* / Birdies: *Ubu, Pere* / Down in the park: *Numan, Gary* / Shadow line: *Fleshtones* / He'd send in the army: *Gang Of Four* / Cheryl's going home: *Otway, John* / Homicide: *999* / Beyond and back: *X* / Model worker: *Magazine* / Sign of the cross: *Skafish*.

Cass: Released Sep '81, on A&M by A&M Records. Deleted Sep '86. Catalogue no: **CXM 64692**

Album: Released Sep '81, on A&M by A&M Records. Deleted Sep '86. Catalogue no: **AMLX 64692**

Utu

UTU (Original soundtrack) (Various artists)
Note: New Zealand film with music by John Charles.
Album: Released Jan '89, on Silva Screen by Silva Screen Records. Catalogue no: **SCRS 1008**

The following information was taken from the Music Master database on September 25th, 1990.

Valens, Ritchie

DONNA
Tracks: / Donna / La bamba / Let's dance.
7" Single: Released Mar '59, on London-American by Decca Records. Deleted '62. Catalogue no: **HL 8803**
7" Single: Released Aug '84, on Creole (Replay) by Creole Records. Catalogue no: **CR 215**

DONNA (OLD GOLD)
Tracks: / Donna / La bamba.
7" Single: Released Jun '88, on Old Gold by Old Gold Records. Catalogue no: **OG 9029**

DONNA (OLD GOLD CD SINGLE)
Tracks: / Donna / La bamba / I fought the law.
CD Single: Released Nov '88, on Old Gold by Old Gold Records. Catalogue no: **OG 6106**

LA BAMBA
Tracks: / La bamba.
12" Single: Released Aug '87, on RCA by BMG Records (UK). Deleted '89.Catalogue no:**PT 41436**
7" Single: Released Aug '87, on RCA by BMG Records (UK). Deleted '89.Catalogue no:**PB 41435**

Valli, Frankie

GREASE
Tracks: / Grease.
7" Single: Released Aug '78, on RSO by Polydor Ltd. Catalogue no: **RSO 012**

Valmouth

VALMOUTH (Original London cast) (Various artists)
Album: Released Mar '86, on PRT Flashback Catalogue no: **FBLP 8102**

VALMOUTH (Original Chichester Festival Cast) (Various artists)
Album: Released Jul '82, on T. E. R. by That's Entertainment Records. Catalogue no: **TER 1019**
Cass: Released Jul '82, on T. E.

R. by That's Entertainment Records. Catalogue no: **ZCTER 1019**

Vamp

VAMP (Film soundtrack) (Various artists)
Note: Music from the Grace Jones film by Jonathan Elias.
Album: Released Jan '89, on Silva Screen by Silva Screen Records. Catalogue no: **STV 81288**
Cass: Released Jan '89, on Silva Screen by Silva Screen Records. Catalogue no: **CTV 81288**

Vangelis

ANTARCTICA (Original soundtrack)
Tracks: / Antarctica, Theme from / Antarctica echoes / Kinematic song of white / Life of Antarctica / Memory of Antarctica / Other side of Antarctica / Deliverance.
CD: Released 28 Nov '88, on Polydor by Polydor Ltd. Catalogue no: **815 732-2**
Cass: Released 28 Nov '88, on Polydor by Polydor Ltd. Catalogue no: **815 732-4**
Album: Released 28 Nov '88, on Polydor by Polydor Ltd. Deleted May '90. Catalogue no: **815 732-1**

CHARIOTS OF FIRE (Film Soundtrack)
Tracks: / Titles / Five circles / Abraham's theme / Eric's theme / 100 metres / Jerusalem / Chariots of fire.
Album: Released Mar '81, on Polydor by Polydor Ltd. Catalogue no: **POLS 1026**
CD: Released May '83, on Polydor by Polydor Ltd. Catalogue no: **800 020 2**
Cass: Released Mar '81, on Polydor by Polydor Ltd. Catalogue no: **POLDC 5160**
Album: Released May '84, on Polydor by Polydor Ltd. Catalogue no: **POLD 5160**

CHARIOTS OF FIRE / CHINA / OPERA SAVVAGE (3 LP SET)
Tracks: / Five circles / Abraham's theme / Eric's theme / 100 metres / Jerusalem / Chariots of fire / Chung

kuo (the long march) / Dragon Himalaya / Little fete / Long march / Plum blossom / Summit / Tao of love / Yin and Yang / Chromatique / L'enfant / Flamant roses / Hymne / Irlande / Mouettes / Reve.
LP Set: Released '83, on Polydor by Polydor Ltd. Deleted '88. Catalogue no: **BOX 1**

CHARIOTS OF FIRE (SINGLE)
Tracks: / Chariots of fire / Eric's theme.
7" Single: Released Aug '84, on Polydor by Polydor Ltd. Catalogue no: **POSP 246**

IGNACIO (Original soundtrack)
Note: Music from the film "Entends-Tu - Les Chiens Aboyer ?".
CD: Released Jul '85, on Phonogram (Import) Catalogue no: **813 042 2**

LA FETE SAUVAGE (Film soundtrack)
Tracks: / La fete sauvage (parts 1 & 2).
CD: Released Jul '85, on Phonogram (Import) Catalogue no: **823 756-2**

Vanishing Point

VANISHING POINT (Original Soundtrack) (Various artists)
Album: Released Jun '71, on London Records by London Records Ltd. Catalogue no: **SHU 8420**

Vanishing Prairie

VANISHING PRAIRIE/LIVING DESERT (See under (Living Desert)

Vaughan, Frankie

HELLO DOLLY
Tracks: / Hello Dolly.
Note: From the Stage Show.
7" Single: Released Jun '64, on Philips by Phonogram Ltd. Deleted '67. Catalogue no: **BF 1339**

Vent De Panique

VENT DE PANIQUE (Film Soundtrack) (Various artists)

Note: French film with score by Jean Claude Petit and featuring Philip Catherine on guitar.
Album: Released Jan '89, on Silva Screen by Silva Screen Records. Catalogue no: **A 349**

Verdi (composer)

LA TRAVIATA (Film soundtrack) (Various artists)
Cass set: on WEA by WEA Records. Catalogue no: **250072 4**
CD: Released Jul '89, on Decca by Decca International. Catalogue no: **421 325-2**
2 LP Set: on WEA by WEA Records. Catalogue no: **250072 1**

Vertigo

VERTIGO (Original soundtrack) (Various artists)
CD: Released Aug '82, on Mercury by Phonogram Ltd. Deleted Jan '88. Catalogue no: **422 106-2**
Album: Released Aug '82, on Mercury by Phonogram Ltd. Deleted Jan '88. Catalogue no: **SRI 75117**

Very Good...

VERY GOOD EDDIE (Original Broadway cast) (Various artists)
CD: Released '88, on DRG (USA) by DRG Records (USA). Catalogue no: **CDRG 6100**
Album: Released '88, on DRG (USA) by DRG Records (USA). Catalogue no: **DRG 6100**

Victor

VICTOR, THE (Original cast) (Various artists)
Tracks: / Song of praise: *Various artists* / Everything that love can give: *Various artists* / He is alive: *Various artists* / Easter song: *Various artists* / Can't take my eyes off the clouds: *Various artists* / Victor, The: *Various artists* / Together: *Various artists* / Song of praise (reprise): *Various artists* / Warrior: *Various artists* / Battle belongs to the Lord, The: *Various artists* / He that overcomes: *Various artists* / We shall stand: *Various artists* / Here he comes: *Various artists*.
Cass: Released May '85, on Live Oak by Word Records (UK). Catalogue no: **TCOA 3001**
Album: Released May '85, on Live Oak by Word Records (UK). Catalogue no: **OAK 3001**

Victor Victoria

VICTOR VICTORIA (Film soundtrack) (Various artists)
Tracks: / You and me / Shady dame from Seville, The / Alone in Paris / King's can can / Le jazz hot / Crazy world/ Chicago Illinois / Cat and mouse / Gay Paree / Finale.
Cass: Released Aug '83, on MGM (Polydor) by Polydor Ltd. Catalogue no: **3110 393**
Album: Released Apr '82, on MGM (Polydor) by Polydor Ltd. Catalogue no: **MG 15407**
Album: Released Aug '83, on MGM (Polydor) by Polydor Ltd. Catalogue no: **2315 437**
Cass: Released Apr '82, on MGM (Polydor) by Polydor Ltd. Catalogue no: **CT 15407**

Vidal, Maria

BODY ROCK (Vidal, Maria / Ashford & Simpson)
Tracks: / Body rock / Do you know who I am.
Note: From the film of the same name.
7" Single: Released Aug '85, on EMI-America by EMI Records. Deleted Jan '90. Catalogue no: **EA 189**
12" Single: Released Aug '85, on EMI-America by EMI Records. Deleted Nov '88. Catalogue no: **12EA 189**

Videodrome

VIDEODROME (Film soundtrack) (Various artists)
Note: Howard Shore score for the David Cronenberg film starring Debbie Harry.
Album: Released Jan '89, on Silva Screen by Silva Screen Records. Catalogue no: **STV 81173**

View To A Kill

VIEW TO A KILL, A (Film soundtrack) (Various artists)
Cass: Released Jun '85, on Parlophone by EMI Records. Catalogue no: **TC BOND 1**
CD: Released Jun '85, on Parlophone by EMI Records. Catalogue no: **CDP 746159-2**
Album: Released Jun '85, on Parlophone by EMI Records. Catalogue no: **BOND 1**

VIEW TO A KILL (See under Duran Duran)

Vikings (film)

VIKINGS, THE (Film soundtrack) (Various artists)
Note: Newly re-mastered edition with additional music of the Mario Nascimbene score for the Kirk Douglas/Tony Curtis film.
Album: Released Jan '89, on Silva Screen by Silva Screen Records. Catalogue no: **LD 4**

Villa Rides

VILLA RIDES (Film Soundtrack) (Various artists)
Note: Re-issue of the Maurice Jarre western score for the film starring Yul Brynner, Robert Mitchum and Charles Bronson.
Album: Released Jan '89, on Silva Screen by Silva Screen Records. Catalogue no: **254140.1**

Village People

CAN'T STOP THE MUSIC (See also under Can't stop The Music)
Tracks: / Can't stop the music / I love you to death.
Note: From the film of the same name.
7" Single: Released Aug '80, on Mercury by Phonogram Ltd. Deleted '83. Catalogue no: **MER 16**

Villard, Michel

MUSIC FROM THE CHARLIE CHAPLIN FILMS
Tracks: / Les temps modernes / Une vie de chien / Le dictateur / Le pelerin / Charlot soldat / Les lumieres de la ville / Un roi a New York / Limelight les feux de la rampe / La comtesse de Hong Kong / La ruee vers l'or.
CD: Released Jul '89, on Vogue by Vogue Records. Catalogue no: **670 057**
Cass: Released Jul '89, on Vogue by Vogue Records. Catalogue no: **771 057**

MUSIC FROM THE FILMS OF CHARLIE CHAPLIN
Tracks: / Titina / Le violeter / Green lantern snag / Smile / Mandolin serenade / Marche militaire / Evening star / Hungarian dance no. 5 / Limelight / Pilgrim, The (medley) / This is my song / Shoulder arms (medley) / Spring song / Goldrush (medley).
CD: Released Sep '86, on Vogue by Vogue Records. Catalogue no:

VG 600 009
Cass: Released Jan '89, on GNP Crescendo (USA) by GNP Crescendo Records (USA). Catalogue no: **GNP5 2064**
Album: Released Jan '89, on GNP Crescendo (USA) by GNP Crescendo Records (USA). Catalogue no: **GNPS 2064**

V.I.P.s (Film)

V.I.P.S, THE (Film soundtrack) (Various artists)
Note: Miklos Rozsa score for the Richard Burton and Elizabeth Taylor film.
Album: Released Jan '89, on MCA by MCA Records. Catalogue no: **MCA 25001**
Cass: Released Jan '89, on MCA by MCA Records. Deleted Mar '90. Catalogue no: **MCAC 25001**

Virtue In Danger

VIRTUE IN DANGER (Original London cast) (Various artists)
Cass: Released May '85, on T. E. R. by That's Entertainment Records. Catalogue no: **ZCTER 1079**
Album: Released May '85, on T. E. R. by That's Entertainment Records. Catalogue no: **TER 1079**

Vision Quest

VISION QUEST (Film Soundtrack) (Various artists)
Album: Released Jun '85, on Geffen by Geffen Records (USA). Catalogue no: **GEF70263**

Visions

VISIONS (Various artists)
Tracks: / Flying (theme from ET): *Various artists* / Harry's game (theme from): *Various artists* / M.A.S.H., Theme from: *Various artists* / Hill Street blues: *Various artists* / Chariots of Fire: *Various artists* / Brideshead Revisited, Theme from: *Various artists* / Arthur's theme: *Various artists* / I don't know how to love him: *Various artists* / Don't cry for me Argentina: *Various artists* / Eve of the war, The: *Various artists* / Star wars: *Various artists* / For your eyes only: *Various artists* / Dallas: *Various artists* / Shoestring: *Various artists* / Chain, The: *Various artists* / Angela: *Various artists* / Take that look off your face: *Various artists*.
Album: Released Dec '82, on K-Tel by K-Tel Records. Catalogue no: **NE 1199**

Cass: Released Dec '82, on K-Tel by K-Tel Records. Catalogue no: **CE 2199**
CD: Released Nov '86, on K-Tel by K-Tel Records. Catalogue no: **ONCD 3199**

Voices (Film)

VOICES (Film soundtrack) (Various artists)
Tracks: / I will always wait for you: *Various artists* / Rosemarie's theme: *Various artists* / Disco if you want to: *Various artists* / Children's song, The: *Various artists* / Family theme: *Various artists* / Anything that's rock'n'roll: *Various artists* / I will always wait for you (instrumental): *Various artists* / On a stage: *Various artists* / Across the river: *Various artists* / Bubbles in my beer: *Various artists* / Rosemarie and Drew: *Various artists* / Drunk as a punk: *Various artists* / Children's song (instrumental): *Various artists* / Rosemarie's dance: *Various artists*.
Album: Released '77, on Planet by BMG Records (UK). Deleted '82. Catalogue no: **K 52158**

W

The following information was taken from the Music Master database on September 25th, 1990.

Wake Up & Live

WAKE UP AND LIVE (Film soundtrack) (Various artists)
Note: Starring Alice Faye.
Album: Released Jan '89, on Silva Screen by Silva Screen Records. Catalogue no: **HS 403**

Wakeman, Rick

1984 / THE BURNING (Film Soundtracks)
Tracks: / 1984 Overture part one / 1984 Overture part two / Wargames / Julia / Hymn / Room (brainwash) / Robot man / Sorry / No name / Forgotten memories / Proles, The / 1984 / Burning, The / Chase continues, The / Variations on the fire / Shear terror and more / Burning (end title theme), The / Campfire story / Fire / Doin' it / Devil's creek breakdown / Chase, The.
Cass: Released Mar '83, on Charisma by Virgin Records. Deleted '88. Catalogue no: **CASMC 111**
Cass: Released Jun '81, on Charisma by Virgin Records. Deleted '88. Catalogue no: **7144 136**
Album: Released Jun '81, on Charisma by Virgin Records. Deleted '88. Catalogue no: **CDS 4022**

BURNING, THE (1980 soundtrack music)
Album: Released Jan '82, on Charisma by Virgin Records. Deleted Jan '87. Catalogue no: **CLASS 12**
Album: Released Jan '89, on Silva Screen by Silva Screen Records. Catalogue no: **STV 81162**

CRIMES OF PASSION (1985 film soundtrack)
Album: Released Mar '87, on President by President Records. Catalogue no: **RW 3**

DATABASE (TV theme)
Tracks: / Database / Lytton's diary.
7" Single: Released Jun '85, on TBG by President Records. Catalogue no: **WAKE 2**

12" Single: Released Jun '85, on TBG by President Records. Catalogue no: **12 WAKE 2**

G'OLE (Film soundtrack)

Tracks: / International flag / Dove, The (opening ceremony) / Wayward spirit / Latin reel (theme from G'Ole) / Red island / Spanish holiday / No possibla / Shadows / Black pearls / Frustration / Spanish montage / G'ole.
Album: Released Apr '83, on Charisma by Virgin Records. Deleted May '90. Catalogue no: **CAS 1162**
Cass: Released Apr '83, on Charisma by Virgin Records. Catalogue no: **CASMC 1162**

G'OLE (SINGLE)
Tracks: / G'ole / No possibla.
7" Single: Released Apr '83, on Charisma by Virgin Records. Deleted Apr '86. Catalogue no: **CB 411**

Walker

WALKER (Film soundtrack) (Strummer, Joe)
Tracks: / Filibustero / Omotepe / Sandstorm / Machete / Viperland / Nica Libre / Latin romance / Brooding side of madness, The / Tennessee rain / Smash everything / Tropic of no return / Tropic of no return / Unknown immortal, The / Musket waltz.
Note: Music by Joe Strummer.
Cass: Released '88, on Virgin by Virgin Records. Deleted Jun '90. Catalogue no: **TCV 2497**
Album: Released '88, on Virgin by Virgin Records. Deleted May '90. Catalogue no: **V 2497**
CD: Released 20 Feb '88, on Virgin by Virgin Records. Catalogue no: **CDV 2497**

Walker, Scott

SONGS FROM HIS TV SERIES
Album: Released Jul '69, on Philips by Phonogram Ltd. Deleted '74. Catalogue no: **SBL 7900**

Wall Street

WALL STREET / SALVADOR (Film soundtrack) (Various artists)
Tracks: / Bud's scram: *Copeland, Stewart* / Are you with me: *Copeland, Stewart* / Trading begins: *Copeland, Stewart* / Tall weeds, The: *Copeland, Stewart* / Break up: *Copeland, Stewart* / Anacott steel: *Copeland, Stewart* / End title: *Copeland, Stewart* / Main title: *Vancouver Symphony Orchestra* / El playon: *Vancouver Symphony Orchestra* / Siege at Santa Fe: *Vancouver Symphony Orchestra* / Goodbye Maria: *Vancouver Symphony Orchestra* / At the border: *Vancouver Symphony Orchestra* / Road block: *Vancouver Symphony Orchestra* / Love theme: finale: *Vancouver Symphony Orchestra*.
Cass: Released May '88, on T. E. R. by That's Entertainment Records. Deleted Mar '90. Catalogue no: **ZCTER 1154**
Album: Released May '88, on T. E. R. by That's Entertainment Records. Catalogue no: **TER 1154**
CD: Released May '88, on T. E. R. by That's Entertainment Records. Catalogue no: **CDTER 1154**

Wall

WALL, THE (Various artists)
VHS: Released Jan '84, on Thorn-Emi (Video) by EMI Records. Catalogue no: **1VA 90 1431 2**

Walton, Sir William

FILM MUSIC OF SIR WILLIAM WALTON (London Philharmonic Orchestra)
Tracks: / Henry V (suite) / Battle of Britain (Spitfire music) / Troilus and Cressida / As you like it (suite) / History of English speaking peoples.
Cass: Released '87, on H.M.V. by EMI Records. Catalogue no: **EL 270591-4**
CD: Released '87, on H.M.V. by EMI Records. Catalogue no: **CDC**

747944 2
Album: Released '87, on H.M.V. by EMI Records. Catalogue no: **EL 270591-1**

MUSIC FOR SHAKESPEAREAN FILMS (Royal Liverpool Philharmonic Orchestra)
Tracks: / Richard III / Shakespeare suite / Funeral march (from Hamlet) / Henry V (suite).
Cass: Released '85, on H.M.V. by EMI Records. Catalogue no: **EL 270118-4**
Album: Released '85, on H.M.V. by EMI Records. Catalogue no: **EL 270118-1**

Wanderers (film)
WANDERERS, THE (Film soundtrack) (Various artists)
Tracks: / You really got a hold on me: *Miracles* / Shout: *Isley Brothers* / Big girls don't cry: *Four Seasons* / Ya ya: *Dorsey, Lee* / My boyfriend's back: *Angels* / Soldier boy: *Shirelles* / Pipeline: *Chantays* / Do you love me: *Contours* / Wipe out: *Surfaris* / Wanderer, The: *Dion* / Stand by me: *King, Ben E.* / Tequila: *Champs*.
Album: Released Apr '80, on Gem by RCA Records. Catalogue no: **GEMLP 103**
Album: Released Oct '81, on Pickwick by Pickwick Records. Deleted Oct '86. Catalogue no: **SHM 3069**
Cass: Released Apr '80, on Gem by RCA Records. Deleted '85. Catalogue no: **GEMK 103**
CD: Released '88, on Pickwick by Pickwick Records. Catalogue no: **PWK 058**

WANDERERS, THE (VIDEO) (Various artists)
Note: The time is 1963. The place, New York...but not the City seen by commuters and tourists. This is a world of back alleys and tenements...where the sounds of the Shirelles and the Crystals are never far away...where the gangs challenge each other for supremacy. This is the world of the Wanderers, gangland warfare and teenage conflict - and also one of the funniest and best films of the early 80's. Running time: 112 mins.
VHS: Released Sep '88, on Video Collection by Video Collection. Catalogue no: **VC 3246**
VHS: Released Sep '86, on Picture Time Video Catalogue no: **P 098 D**

Wang Chung
DANCE HALL DAYS
Tracks: / Dance hall days / There is a nation.
Note: From the film 'To Live And Die In L.A.'.
7" Single: Released Jan '84, on Geffen by Geffen Records (USA). Catalogue no: **A 3837**
12" Single: Released Jan '84, on Geffen by Geffen Records (USA). Catalogue no: **TA 3837**
7" Pic: Released Jan '84, on Geffen by Geffen Records (USA). Catalogue no: **WA 3837**

TO LIVE AND DIE IN L.A (Film soundtrack) (See under To Live & Die In LA)

War & Peace
WAR AND PEACE (Film soundtrack) (Ovchinnikov, Vyacheslav)
CD: Released Feb '90, on Silva Screen by Silva Screen Records. Catalogue no: **VSD 5225**
Album: Released Apr '83, on T.E.R. by That's Entertainment Records. Catalogue no: **TER 1020**

War Games
WAR GAMES (Film soundtrack) (Various artists)
Cass: Released Nov '83, on Polydor by Polydor Ltd. Deleted Nov '88. Catalogue no: **815 005-4**
Album: Released Nov '83, on Polydor by Polydor Ltd. Deleted Nov '88. Catalogue no: **815 005-1**
Album: Released Nov '83, on Polydor by Polydor Ltd. Deleted Nov '88. Catalogue no: **POLD 5124**

War In Korea
WAR IN KOREA 1950-1953 (Original TV soundtrack) (Various artists)
Cass: Released Oct '87, on BBC by BBC Records. Deleted Apr '89. Catalogue no: **ZCM 639**
Album: Released Oct '87, on BBC by BBC Records. Deleted Apr '89. Catalogue no: **REC 639**

War Requiem
WAR REQUIEM (Original soundtrack) (Various artists)
CD Set: Released '88, on EMI by EMI Records. Catalogue no: **CDS**

747034-8

Warlock (Film)
WARLOCK (Film soundtrack) (Various artists)
Tracks: / Sentence, The: *Various artists* / Ill wind: *Various artists* / Ring, The: *Various artists* / Trance, The: *Various artists* / Old age: *Various artists* / Growing pains: *Various artists* / Weather vane, The: *Various artists* / Nails: *Various artists* / Uninvited, The: *Various artists* / Salt water attack: *Various artists* / Salt flats: *Various artists*.
Album: Released Jun '89, on Silva Screen by Silva Screen Records. Catalogue no: **FILM 038**
CD: Released Jun '89, on Silva Screen by Silva Screen Records. Catalogue no: **FILMCD 038**

Warner Brothers ....
GREAT WARNER BROTHERS ACTION MOVIES (Warner Brothers Studio Orchestra)
Tracks: / Enter the dragon / Bullitt / John Paul Jones / Adventures of Robin Hood / Wild bunch, The / Bonnie and Clyde.
Cass: Released Jan '80, on Warner Bros. by WEA Records. Deleted Jan '85. Catalogue no: **K4 26120**
Album: Released Jan '80, on Warner Bros. by WEA Records. Deleted Jan '85. Catalogue no: **K 26120**

GREAT WARNER BROTHERS LOVE THEMES (Various artists)
Tracks: / Summer place, A (theme from): *Various artists* / Klute: *Various artists* / Thief who came to dinner: *Various artists* / Lovers must learn: *Various artists* / Love is never out of style: *Various artists* / Parrish: *Various artists* / Hotel: *Various artists* / Summer of '42: *Various artists* / Bullitt: *Various artists* / Enter the dragon: *Various artists* / Petulia: *Various artists* / Madwoman of Chaillot: *Various artists* / Private lives of Elizabeth and Essex: *Various artists*.
Cass: Released Jan '80, on Warner Bros. by WEA Records. Deleted Jan '85. Catalogue no: **K4 26122**
Album: Released Jan '80, on Warner Bros. by WEA Records. Deleted Jan '85. Catalogue no: **K 26122**

GREAT WARNER BRO-THERS SPECTACULARS (Various artists)

Tracks: / Towering inferno: *Various artists* / Battle of the bulge: *Various artists* / Damned, The: *Various artists* / Swarm: *Various artists* / Sea hawk: *Various artists* / Private lives of Elizabeth and Essex: *Various artists*.

Cass: Released Jan '80, on Warner Bros. by WEA Records. Deleted Jan '85. Catalogue no: **K4 26121**

Album: Released Jan '80, on Warner Bros. by WEA Records. Deleted Jan '85. Catalogue no: **K 26121**

Warnes, Jennifer

UP WHERE WE BELONG (Warnes, Jennifer & Joe Cocker)

Tracks: / Up where we belong.

Note: Theme from An Officer And A Gentleman.

7" Single: Released Nov '89, on Island by Island Records. Catalogue no: **WIP 6830**

7" Single: Released Jan '83, on Island by Island Records. Deleted Jan '86. Catalogue no: **WIP 6831**

Warning Sign

WARNING SIGN (Film soundtrack) (Various artists)

Note: Composed by Craig Safan.

CD: Released Jan '89, on Silva Screen by Silva Screen Records. Catalogue no: **SCCD 1012**

Album: Released Jan '89, on Silva Screen by Silva Screen Records. Catalogue no: **SCRS 1012**

Warriors (film)

WARRIORS (Film Soundtrack) (Various artists)

Tracks: / In the city: *Various artists* / Warriors theme: *Various artists* / Baseball furies chase: *Various artists* / Fight: *Various artists* / Echoes in my mind: *Various artists*.

CD: Released Apr '89, on A&M by A&M Records. Catalogue no: **CDA 3151**

Album: Released Jan '89, on Silva Screen by Silva Screen Records. Catalogue no: **SP 3151**

Album: Released Jun '79, on A&M by A&M Records. Deleted '88. Catalogue no: **AMLH 64761**

Cass: Released Jan '89, on Silva Screen by Silva Screen Records. Catalogue no: **CS 3151**

Warwick, Dionne

VALLEY OF THE DOLLS (SINGLE)

Tracks: / Valley of the dolls.

Note: From the film 'Valley of the Dolls'.

7" Single: Released Mar '68, on Pye International Deleted '71. Catalogue no: **7N 25445**

Washington Behind...

WASHINGTON BEHIND CLOSED DOORS (Original TV Soundtrack) (Various artists)

Album: Released Aug '78, on BBC by BBC Records. Deleted '87. Catalogue no: **REB 327**

Cass: Released Aug '78, on BBC by BBC Records. Deleted '85. Catalogue no: **ZCF 327**

W.A.S.P.

SCREAM UNTIL YOU LIKE IT

Tracks: / Scream until you like it / Shoot from the hip / Sleeping in the fire (Extra track available on 12" version only.).

Note: Theme to Ghoulies 2.

7" Single: Released Aug '87, on Capitol by EMI Records. Deleted 31 Jul '88. Catalogue no: **CL 458**

12" Pic: Released Aug '87, on Capitol by EMI Records. Deleted Jan '88. Catalogue no: **12CLP 458**

12" Single: Released Aug '87, on Capitol by EMI Records. Deleted 31 Jul '88. Catalogue no: **12CL 458**

Watch

WATCH (Music & songs from the schools TV series) (Various artists)

Cass: Released Sep '78, on BBC by BBC Records. Deleted '88. Catalogue no: **ZCM 314**

Album: Released Sep '78, on BBC by BBC Records. Deleted '88. Catalogue no: **REC 314**

WATCH AGAIN (Music from the BBC TV schools series) (Various artists)

Cass: Released Jan '80, on BBC by BBC Records. Deleted '88. Catalogue no: **ZCM 375**

Album: Released Jan '80, on BBC

by BBC Records. Deleted '87. Catalogue no: **REC 375**

WATCH - THE THIRD WATCH (Various artists)

Tracks: / Prima ballerina: *Various artists* / Body song, The: *Various artists* / Down the trail: *Various artists* / I am a mole: *Various artists* / Brown girl in the ring: *Various artists* / Hold high the eagles: *Various artists* / This old house: *Various artists* / Indian chants: *Various artists* / Heigh ho: *Various artists* / House is a house: *Various artists* / Parcel song, The: *Various artists* / Catch a germ: *Various artists* / Captain Cook suite: *Various artists*.

Cass: Released Oct '83, on BBC by BBC Records. Deleted '88. Catalogue no: **ZCM 477**

Album: Released Oct '83, on BBC by BBC Records. Deleted '88. Catalogue no: **REC 477**

Water

WATER (Original soundtrack)

Cass: Released Jun '85, on London Records by London Records Ltd. Catalogue no: **YEAMC 2**

Album: Released Jun '85, on London Records by London Records Ltd. Catalogue no: **YEAR 2**

Water Babies

WATER BABIES (Film soundtrack) (Various artists)

Album: Released Aug '79, on Ariola by BMG Records (UK). Catalogue no: **ARLB 5030**

Cass: Released Aug '79, on Ariola by BMG Records (UK). Catalogue no: **ZCARL 5030**

Water Margin

WATER MARGIN (See under Godiego)

Waterman, Dennis

I COULD BE SO GOOD FOR YOU (SINGLE)

Tracks: / I could be so good for you.

Note: Theme from the TV series 'Minder'.

7" Single: Released Sep '80, on EMI by EMI Records. Deleted Jul '87. Catalogue no: **EMI 5009CD 1**

Waters, Roger

BODY, THE (Film soundtrack) (Waters, Roger & Ron Geesin)

Tracks: / Our song / Seashell and soft stone / Red stuff writhe /

Gentle breeze through life / Lick your partners / Bridge passage for three plastic teeth / Chain of life / Womb bit / Embryo thought / March past of the embryos / More than seven dwarfs in Penis-land / Dance of the red corpuscles / Body transport / Hand dance - full evening dress / Breathe / Old folks ascension / Bedtime climb / Piddle in perspex / Embryonic womb walk / Mrs. Throat goes walking / Give birth to a smile.

CD: Released Jun '89, on Harvest by EMI Records. Catalogue no: **CDP 792 548 2**

Album: Released Aug '85, on Harvest by EMI Records. Catalogue no: **ATAK 56**

Album: Released Aug '85, on Harvest by EMI Records. Catalogue no: **SHSP 4008**

Cass: Released Aug '85, on Harvest by EMI Records. Catalogue no: **TCATAK 56**

CD: Released Jun '89, on Harvest by EMI Records. Catalogue no: **CZ 178**

Cass: Released Aug '85, on Harvest by EMI Records. Catalogue no: **TCSHSP 4008**

Watership Down

WATERSHIP DOWN (Original soundtrack) (Various artists)
Cass: Released '78, on CBS by CBS Records & Distribution. Catalogue no: **40-70161**
Album: Released '78, on CBS by CBS Records & Distribution. Catalogue no: **CBS 70161**

Waxman, Franz

FILM MUSIC OF FRANZ WAXMAN, THE (Queensland Symphony Orchestra)
Note: New recordings conducted by Richard Mills, including suites from The Horn Blows At Midnight, Mr Roberts, The Bride Of Frankenstein, Taras Bulba, Botany Bay and The Paradine Case.
Album: Released Jan '89, on Silva Screen by Silva Screen Records. Catalogue no: **704.320**

LEGENDS OF HOLLYWOOD
Album: Released Apr '90, on Colosseum (USA) by Acropole Corp.of America. Catalogue no: **VS 5242**
CD: Released Apr '90, on Colosseum (USA) by Acropole Corp.of America. Catalogue no: **VSD 5242**

Way We Were

WAY WE WERE (Original Soundtrack) (Hamlisch, Marvin)
Cass: Released Mar '90, on Silva Screen by Silva Screen Records. Catalogue no: **JCT 32801**

WAY WE WERE, THE (Film Soundtrack) (Various artists)
Note: Composed by Marvin Hamlisch.
Album: Released Jan '89, on Silva Screen by Silva Screen Records. Catalogue no: **JS 32830**
Cass: Released Jan '89, on Silva Screen by Silva Screen Records. Catalogue no: **JST 32830**

Way West

WAY WEST, THE (Film Soundtrack) (Various artists)
Note: Western score by Bronislau Kaper of the film starring Kirk Douglas and Robert Mitchum, conducted by Andre Previn.
Cass: Released Jan '89, on Silva Screen by Silva Screen Records. Catalogue no: **MCAC 25045**
Album: Released Jan '89, on Silva Screen by Silva Screen Records. Catalogue no: **MCA 25045**

Wayne, John

MUSIC FROM JOHN WAYNE WESTERNS VOL..1 (Various artists)
CD: Released Feb '90, on Coloseum (West Germany). Catalogue no: **VSD 47236**

MUSIC FROM JOHN WAYNE WESTERNS VOL 2 (Various artists)
Tracks: / Shootist, The (main title): Various artists / Ride: Various artists / In the fire: Various artists / Necktie party: Various artists / Nocturne: Various artists / Riders: Various artists / Reunion: Various artists / All Jake: Various artists / Buzzards: Various artists / Going home (finale): Various artists.
Note: New digital recordings of the Elmer Bernstein score for Big Jake, The Shootist and Cahill U.S Marshall.
CD: Released Jan '89, on Coloseum (West Germany). Catalogue no: **VSD 47264**
Album: Released Jan '89, on Silva Screen by Silva Screen Records. Catalogue no: **704.350**
Cass: Released Jan '89, on Silva Screen by Silva Screen Records.

Catalogue no: **C 704.350**

Webb, Marti

ALWAYS THERE (Webb, Marti with the Simon May Orchestra)
Tracks: / Always there / Howard's way (Theme from the BBC-TV series).
12" Single: Released Aug '86, on BBC by BBC Records. Deleted 31 Aug '88. Catalogue no: **12 RSL 190**
7" Single: Released Sep '86, on BBC by BBC Records. Deleted 31 Aug '88. Catalogue no: **RESL 190**

I COULD BE SO GOOD FOR YOU (Theme from Minder) (Webb, Marti with Paul Jones)
Tracks: / I could be so good for you (theme from Minder) / It's still the same dream (Theme from To serve them all my days.).
7" Single: Released Nov '86, on BBC by BBC Records. Deleted Apr '89. Catalogue no: **RESL 209**

STAGES
CD: Released Nov '89, on Telstar by Telstar Records (UK). Catalogue no: **TCD 2391**
Album: Released Nov '89, on Telstar by Telstar Records (UK). Catalogue no: **STAR 2391**
Cass: Released Nov '89, on Telstar by Telstar Records (UK). Catalogue no: **STAC 2391**

TELL ME ON A SUNDAY (TV soundtrack)
Tracks: / Capped teeth and Caesar salad / Come back with the same look in your eyes / I'm very you, you're very me / It's not the end of the world / If he's married -if he's younger - if I lose him / Let me finish / Let's talk about you / Letter home to England / Nothing like you've ever known / Second letter home / Sheldon Bloom / Take that look off your face / Tell me on a Sunday / You made me think you were in love.
CD: Released Jun '90, on Polydor by Polydor Ltd. Catalogue no: **8334472**
Cass: Released Jan '80, on Polydor by Polydor Ltd. Catalogue no: **POLDC 5031**
Album: Released Jan '80, on Polydor by Polydor Ltd. Catalogue no: **POLD 5031**

Webb, Roger

GENTLE TOUCH (SINGLE) (T.V. theme) (Webb, Roger, His Piano & Orchestra)
Tracks: / Gentle touch, The / Best that you can do.
Note: Theme for LWT programme Gentle Touch
7" Single: Released Mar '82, on Chandos by Chandos Records. Catalogue no: **SBR 102**

PARADISE POSTPONED (SINGLE) (Webb, Roger Orchestra) (See also under Paradise Postponed)
Tracks: / Paradise postponed.
Note: From the TV Series Paradise Postponed.
7" Single: Released Sep '86, on Columbia by EMI Records. Catalogue no: **DB 9141**

Weeds (film)

WEEDS (Original soundtrack) (Various artists)
Note: Music by Angelo Badalamenti for the prison drama starring Nick Nolte.
Album: Released Jan '89, on Silva Screen by Silva Screen Records. Catalogue no: **STV 81350**
Cass: Released Jan '89, on Silva Screen by Silva Screen Records. Catalogue no: **CTV 81350**
CD: Released Jan '89, on Silva Screen by Silva Screen Records. Catalogue no: **VCD 47313**

Weekend In Havana

WEEKEND IN HAVANA / THAT NIGHT IN RIO (Original Soundtracks) (Various artists)
Album: Released Jan '89, on Silva Screen by Silva Screen Records. Catalogue no: **CC 100-14**

Weird Science

WEIRD SCIENCE (Film soundtrack) (Various artists)
Album: Released Nov '85, on MCA by MCA Records. Catalogue no: **MCF 3295**
Cass: Released Nov '85, on MCA by MCA Records. Catalogue no: **MCFC 3295**

Weissberg, Eric

DELIVERANCE (1972 Film Soundtrack) (Weissberg, Eric / Steve Mandell)
Tracks: / Duelling banjos / Little Maggie / Shuckin' the corn / Pony Express / Old Joe Clark / Eight more miles to Louisville / Farewell blues / Earl's breakdown / End of a dream / Buffalo gals / Reuben's train / Riding the waves / Fire on the mountain / Eighth of January / Bugle call rag / Hard ain't it hard / Mountain dew / Rawhide.
Note: Eric Weissberg/Steve Mandell/Marshall Brickman.
Cass: on Warner Bros. by WEA Records. Catalogue no: **K 446214**
Album: on Warner Bros. by WEA Records. Catalogue no: **K 46214**
CD: on Warner Bros. by WEA Records. Catalogue no: **K 2446214**

DUELLING BANJOS
Tracks: / Duelling banjos / End of a dream.
Note Theme from the film 'Deliverance'.
7" Single: Released Nov '79, on Automatic by Automatic Records. Deleted Jan '88. Catalogue no: **K 16223**

DUELLING BANJOS (OLD GOLD)
Tracks: / Duelling banjos (Theme from Deliverence) / Reuben's train.
Note: From the film 'Deliverance'
7" Single: Released Mar '86, on Old Gold by Old Gold Records. Catalogue no: **OG 9574**

Welch, Ed

BLOCKBUSTERS (TV theme)
Tracks: / Blockbusters, Theme from / New faces, Theme from.
7" Single: Released 15 Aug '88, on Rainbow by Rainbow Records. Catalogue no: **GRASS 2**

GUS HONEYBUN SONG, THE (T.V. theme)
Tracks: / Gus Honeybun song, The.
7" Single: Released 30 May '87, on TSW Catalogue no: **7 GUS 1**
7" Pic: Released 30 May '87, on TSW Catalogue no: **GUS 1**

SPIKE MILLIGAN & ED WELCH SING SONGS FROM Q8
Tracks: / Q8 theme / Woe is me / Love to make music by / Baboon / I don't have a song about Jesus / Living again / Taken you for granted / One sunny day / Lady / I couldn't wait to tell you / Carpet's always greener / I've got that photograph.
Album: Released Mar '79, on United Artists by EMI Records. Deleted '84. Catalogue no: **UAG 30223**

Welch, Elisabeth

ELISABETH WELCH SINGS IRVING BERLIN SONGBOOK
Note: Through the years one of the great interpreters of Irving Berlin songs has been Elisabeth Welch who has recently recorded 15 of Berlin's choicest numbers that she has sung in nightclubs and on the radio. Miss Welch also has reason to have fond memories of Irving Berlin. In 1930, while she was appearing in a New York nightclub, one of her selection's was Cole Porter's Love For Sale, from a currently running comedy, The New Yorkers. Ray Goetz and Monty Weslley, the show's producer and director, were at the club one night with their friend, Irving Berlin, to audition Miss Welch as replacement for the singer who had introduced the number in the production. The men were enthusiastic about her but Goetz was concerned that she was black. "that's no obstackle," Berlin said. "She's a wonderful singer and if you want her in the show you can always find the right spot for her." And so they did.
The New Yorkers was Miss Welch's last New York appearance in 49 years. For most of that time she was a major attraction in London where she was headlined in some 15 book musicals and revives, the last being Pippin in 1973. She returned to New York in 1980 for a variety program titled Black Broadway, then came back six years later in a revue devoted to Jerome Kern's Hollywood songs and also in a one-woman show.
CD: Released 30 Apr '88, on T. E. R. by That's Entertainment Records. Catalogue no: **CDVIR 8305**
Cass: Released 30 Apr '88, on T. E. R. by That's Entertainment Records. Catalogue no: **ZCVIR 8305**
Album: Released 30 Apr '88, on T. E. R. by That's Entertainment Records. Catalogue no: **VIR 8305**

ELISABETH WELCH SINGS JEROME KERN SONGBOOK
Cass: Released Aug '90, on T.E.R. Catalogue no: **ZCVIR 8310**
Album: Released Aug '90, on T.E.R. Catalogue no: **VIR 8310**

: Released Aug '90, on That's
ertainment(see T.E.R.) Cata-
ue no: **CDVIR 8310**

elcome To L.A.

**ELCOME TO L.A. (Original
undtrack) (Various artists)**
ss: Released Jan '89, on MCA
MCA Records. Catalogue no:
CAC 25040

oum: Released Jan '89, on
CA by MCA Records. Cata-
ue no: **MCA 25040**

e'll Meet Again

**E'LL MEET AGAIN (See
der King, Denis)**

elsh Guards Band

JSIC FROM THE SHOWS
icks: / White Horse Inn (med-
) / Arcadians, The (medley) /
g's rhapsody (medley) / Sound
music (medley) / My fair lady
edley) / West side story (med-
).

oum: Released '79, on RCA by
IG Records (UK). Deleted '84.
italogue no: **LSA 3273**

enders, Wim

**M WENDERS ROADSHOW
OL 1) (Wim Wenders/Jur-
n Knieper)**
oum: Released Mar '90, on
va Screen by Silva Screen Rec-
Is. Catalogue no: **A372**

ss: Released Mar '90, on Silva
reen by Silva Screen Records.
talogue no: **C372**

**M WENDERS ROADSHOW
OL 2) (Wenders, Wim/Jur-
n Knieper)**
ss: Released Mar '90, on Silva
reen by Silva Screen Records.
talogue no: **C519**

oum: Released Mar '90, on
va Screen by Silva Screen Rec-
Is. Catalogue no: **A519**

enzani

**ENZANI (Original Cast)
arious artists)**
ss: Released Dec '84, on
ankton by Plankton Records.
italogue no: **PCN 109**

est Coast All Stars

JAZZ THEMES
oum: Released Feb '88, on
esh Sounds (Spain) by Fresh
unds Records (Spain). Cata-
ue no: **FS 164**

West, Mae

ON THE AIR 1934-1970
Album: Released Jan '89, on
Silva Screen by Silva Screen Rec-
ords. Catalogue no: **SH 2098**

ON THE RADIO
Album: Released Jan '89, on
Silva Screen by Silva Screen Rec-
ords. Catalogue no: **MR 1126**

West Side Story

**WEST SIDE STORY (High-
lights from) (Various artists)**
Tracks: / Jet song: *Various artists*
/ Something's coming: *Various artists* / Maria: *Various artists* / Tonight: *Various artists* / America:
Various artists / Cool: *Various artists* / One hand, one heart: *Various artists* / I feel pretty: *Various
artists* / Somewhere: *Various artists* / Gee Officer Krupke: *Various
artists* / Boy like that, A: *Various
artists* / I have a love: *Various artists* / Taunting scene: *Various artists* / Finale: *Various artists.*
CD: Released '85, on MFP by EMI
Records. Catalogue no: **415 963 2**
Cass: Released '85, on MFP by
EMI Records. Catalogue no: **415
963 4**
Album: Released '85, on MFP by
EMI Records. Catalogue no: **415
963 1**

**WEST SIDE STORY (Studio
cast recording) (Various artists)**
Tracks: / Prologue and jet song:
Various artists / Something's coming: *Various artists* / Dance at the
gym (blues promenade jump):
Various artists / Maria: *Various artists* / Tonight: *Various artists* /
Rumble: *Various artists* / I feel
pretty: *Various artists* / Somewhere: *Various artists* / Gee officer
Krupke: *Various artists* / Boy like
that, A: *Various artists* / I have a
love: *Various artists* / Finale: *Various artists.*
Cass set: Released May '85, on
Deutsche Grammophon by Poly-
Gram Classics. Catalogue no: **415
253 4**
2 LP Set: Released May '85, on
Deutsche Grammophon by Poly-
Gram Classics. Catalogue no: **415
253 1**
CD Set: Released May '85, on
Deutsche Grammophon by Poly-
Gram Classics. Catalogue no: **415
253 2**

**WEST SIDE STORY (Various
artists)**
CD: Released Aug '87, on The
Collection by Object Enterprises.
Catalogue no: **OP 0007**
LP Pic: Released Dec '85, on
Astan (USA) Catalogue no: **AR
30045**

**WEST SIDE STORY (Original
Broadway cast) (Various artists)**
Tracks: / West side story: Prologue: *Various artists* / Jet song:
Various artists / Something's coming: *Various artists* / Dance at the
gym: *Various artists* / Maria: *Various artists* / Tonight: *Various artists* / America: *Various artists* /
Cool: *Various artists* / One hand,
one heart: *Various artists* / Tonight:
Various artists / Rumble, The: *Various artists* / I feel pretty: *Various
artists* / Somewhere: *Various artists.*
Cass: Released Mar '90, on CBS
(import) by CBS Records & Distribution. Catalogue no: **PST
32603**
CD: Released Jan '89, on CBS
(import) by CBS Records & Distribution. Catalogue no: **CK 32603**
Album: Released Sep '82, on
CBS by CBS Records & Distribution. Deleted Jan '90. Catalogue
no: **CBS 32193**
Cass: Released Sep '82, on CBS
by CBS Records & Distribution.
Deleted Aug '90. Catalogue no: **40
32193**

**WEST SIDE STORY (Film
Soundtrack) (Various artists)
(See panel on next page)**
Tracks: / Jet song: *Various artists*
/ Something's coming: *Various ar-
tists* / Dance at the gym (blues
promenade jump): *Various artists* /
America: *Various artists* / Maria:
Various artists / Tonight: *Various
artists* / Gee officer Krupke: *Vari-
ous artists* / I feel pretty: *Various
artists* / One hand one heart: *Vari-
ous artists* / Quintet: *Various artists*
/ Rumble: *Various artists* / Cool:
Various artists / Boy like that, A:
Various artists.
Album: Released '61, on CBS by
CBS Records & Distribution.
Deleted '66. Catalogue no: **BPG
62058**
Album: Released '86, on CBS by
CBS Records & Distribution. Cata-
logue no: **CBS 70006**

Cass: Released '88, on CBS by CBS Records & Distribution. Catalogue no: **407 000 6**

CD: Released '86, on CBS by CBS Records & Distribution. Catalogue no: **CD 70006**

WEST SIDE STORY - HIGHLIGHTS (Studio cast recording) (Various artists)

Album: Released Mar '86, on Deutsche Grammophon by PolyGram Classics. Catalogue no: **45963**

WEST SIDE STORY (ORIGINAL ISSUE) (Broadway cast) (Various artists)

Album: Released Jan '59, on Philips by Phonogram Ltd. Deleted '64. Catalogue no: **BBL 7277**

Album: Released Mar '62, on Philips by Phonogram Ltd. Deleted '67. Catalogue no: **BBL 7530**

Album: Released Jul '60, on Philips by Phonogram Ltd. Deleted '65. Catalogue no: **SBBL 504**

WEST SIDE STORY (VIDEO) (Various artists)

Note: Cert: PG.

VHS: Released '88, on Warner Home Video by WEA Records. Catalogue no: **PES 99244**

WEST SIDE STORY/ON THE WATERFRONT (Film soundtracks) (New York Philharmonic Orchestra)

Cass: on CBS by CBS Records & Distribution. Catalogue no: **40 61096**

Album: on CBS by CBS Records & Distribution. Catalogue no: **CBS 61096**

Western Themes

WESTERN THEMES (Various artists)

CD: Released May '89, on Object Enterprises Catalogue no: **ONN 20**

Weston, Paul

CINEMA CAMEOS (Weston, Paul & His Orchestra)

Tracks: / Gone with the wind / Wuthering heights / Dark victory / Lost horizons / Spellbound / Since you went away / King's Row / Now voyager / Laura / For whom the bell tolls.

Note: Themes from Hollywood's greatest pictures.

Album: Released Mar '79, on Corinthian (USA) by Corinthian Records (USA). Catalogue no: **COR 107**

Westworld (film)

WESTWORLD (Various artists)

Note: Sci/fi thriller starring Yul Brynner. Music by Fred Karlin.

Cass: Released Jan '89, on Silva Screen by Silva Screen Records. Catalogue no: **MCAC 25004**

Album: Released Jan '89, on Silva Screen by Silva Screen Records. Catalogue no: **MCA 25004**

Wetherby

WETHERBY (Original Soundtrack) (Bicat, Nick)

Album: Released Mar '85, on T. E. R. by That's Entertainment Records. Catalogue no: **TER 12 010**

Whale, James

BIMBO (TV theme)

Tracks: / Bimbo / Big big egg, A.

Note: Theme for the James Whale Radio Show

7" Single: Released Jan '89, on Flair by Flair Records. Deleted Sep '89. Catalogue no: **FLA 110**

12" Single: Released Jan '89, on Flair by Flair Records. Deleted Sep '89. Catalogue no: **12FLA 11**

Whales Of August

WHALES OF AUGUST, TH (Film soundtrack) (Various a tists)

Note: Lindsay Anderson film sta ring Bette Davis, Lillian Gish ar Vincent Price. Orchestral score b Alan Price.

Cass: Released Jan '89, on Silv Screen by Silva Screen Records Deleted Mar '90. Catalogue n **CTV 81347**

CD: Released Jan '89, on Silv Screen by Silva Screen Record Catalogue no: **VCD 47311**

Album: Released Jan '89, c Silva Screen by Silva Screen Re ords. Catalogue no: **STV 81347**

What A Crazy World

WHAT A CRAZY WORLD (Fil soundtrack) (Brown, Joe & Th Bruvvers)

Tracks: / What a crazy world we' livin' in / Layabout's lament, A / sure know a lot about love Bruvvers / Oh, what a family / A fred Hichins / Sally Ann / Wasn't a handsome punch-up / Pleas give me a chance / Independenc / I feel the same way too / Just yo

Soundtrack to *West Side Story* on the CBS label

wait and see / Things we never had.
Note: Film version of 60's Cockney musical stars, among others, Marty Wilde and Harry H. Corbett.
Album: Released Jan '84, on President by President Records. Catalogue no: **PLE 512**

When You Wish Upon...

WHEN YOU WISH UPON A STAR (16 Disney Favourites) (Various artists)
Tracks: / When you wish upon a star: *Various artists* / Supercalifragilisticexpialidocious: : *Various artists* / Dream is a wish your heart makes, A: *Various artists* / Mickey Mouse march: *Various artists* / Bella notte: *Various artists* / Give a little whistle: *Various artists* / You can fly, you can fly: *Various artists* / Heigh ho: *Various artists* / Whistle while you work: *Various artists* / Bibbidi bobbidi boo: *Various artists* / Alice in Wonderland: *Various artists* / Cinderella work song, The: *Various artists* / Ballad of Davy Crockett, The: *Various artists* / Some day my prince will come: *Various artists* / Who's afraid of the big bad wolf (medley): *Various artists* / Ferdinand the bull: *Various artists* / Zip a dee doo dah: *Various artists*.
Album: Released Dec '84, on Premier by Premier Records. Catalogue no: **CBR 1011**
Cass: Released Dec '84, on Premier by Premier Records. Catalogue no: **KCBR 1011**

When Father's Away...

WHEN FATHER'S AWAY ON A BUSINESS TRIP (Original soundtrack) (Various artists)
Album: Released Dec '85, on SPI Milan (France) Catalogue no: **A 279**

When Harry Met Sally

WHEN HARRY MET SALLY (See under Connick, Harry Jr.)

When Man Is The Prey

WHEN MAN IS THE PREY (Film Soundtrack) (Various artists)
Note: Rare Ennio Morricone score.
Album: Released Jan '89, on Cerebus (USA) Catalogue no: **C'BUS 0118**

When The Boys Meet ...

WHEN THE BOYS MEET THE GIRLS (Film Soundtrack) (Various artists)
Note: Starring Connie Francis and Herman's Hermits.
Cass: Released Jan '89, on MCA by MCA Records. Catalogue no: **MCAC 25013**
Album: Released Jan '89, on MCA by MCA Records. Catalogue no: **MCA 25013**

When The Whales Came

WHEN THE WHALES CAME (Film soundtrack) (Various artists)
Tracks: / Bryher and the curse of Samson: *Various artists* / Gracie plays truant: *Various artists* / Birdman's gift, The: *Various artists* / Islanders, The: *Various artists* / Tempest, The: *Various artists* / Crown investigators, The: *Various artists* / Daniel's gift for the Birdman: *Various artists* / War and Jack's dilemma: *Various artists* / Birdman's warning: *Various artists* / Lured to Samson: *Various artists* / Clemmie's lament: *Various artists* / Whale beached: *Various artists*.
Album: Released Nov '89, on Silva Screen by Silva Screen Records. Catalogue no: **FILM 049**
Cass: Released Nov '89, on Silva Screen by Silva Screen Records. Catalogue no: **FILMC 049**
CD: Released Nov '89, on Silva Screen by Silva Screen Records. Catalogue no: **FILMCD 049**

When The Wind Blows

WHEN THE WIND BLOWS (Film soundtrack) (Various artists)
Tracks: / When the wind blows: *Bowie, David* / Facts and figures: *Cornwall, Hugh* / Brazilian: *Genesis* / What have they done: *Squeeze* / Shuffle, The: *Hardcastle, Paul* / Towers of faith: *Waters, Roger with the Bleeding Heart Band* / Russian missile, The: *Waters, Roger with the Bleeding Heart Band* / Hilda's dream: *Waters, Roger with the Bleeding Heart Band* / American bomber, The: *Waters, Roger with the Bleeding Heart Band* / Anderson shelter, The: *Waters, Roger with the Bleeding Heart Band* / British submarine, The: *Waters, Roger with the Bleeding Heart Band* / Attack, The: *Waters, Roger with the*

Bleeding Heart Band / Fallout: *Waters, Roger with the Bleeding Heart Band* / Hilda's hair: *Waters, Roger with the Bleeding Heart Band* / Folded flags: *Waters, Roger with the Bleeding Heart Band*.
Album: Released '89, on Virgin by Virgin Records. Catalogue no: **OVED 259**
Album: Released '88, on Virgin by Virgin Records. Deleted 13 Feb '89. Catalogue no: **V 2406**
Cass: Released '89, on Virgin by Virgin Records. Catalogue no: **OVEDC 259**
Cass: Released '88, on Virgin by Virgin Records. Deleted 13 Feb '89. Catalogue no: **TCV 2406**
CD: Released Jan '87, on Virgin by Virgin Records. Deleted 13 Feb '89. Catalogue no: **CDV 2406**

When You're In Love

WHEN YOU'RE IN LOVE (See under Booker, Bob)

Where Eagles Dare

WERE EAGLES DARE (Film soundtrack) (Various artists)
Note: Composed by Ron Goodwin.
Album: Released Jan '89, on Silva Screen by Silva Screen Records. Catalogue no: **MCA 25082**
Cass: Released Jan '89, on Silva Screen by Silva Screen Records. Deleted Mar '90. Catalogue no: **MCAC 25082**

WHERE EAGLES DARE / 633 SQUADRON (Film Soundtracks) (Various artists)
Tracks: / Where eagles dare (main title): *Various artists* (Where Eagles Dare.) / Ascent on the cable car: *Various artists* (Where Eagles Dare.) / Pursued by the enemy: *Various artists* (Where Eagles Dare.) / Booby trap, The: *Various artists* (Where Eagles Dare.) / Encounter in the castle: *Various artists* (Where Eagles Dare.) / On enemy territory: *Various artists* (Where Eagles Dare.) / Descent and fight on the cable car: *Various artists* (Where Eagles Dare.) / Chase to the airfield: *Various artists* (Where Eagles Dare.) / Six three three squadron (main title): *Various artists* (633 Squadron.) / Memories of Norway: *Various artists* (633 Squadron.) / Love theme: *Various artists* (633 Squadron.) / Attack begins, The: *Various artists* (633 Squadron.) /

Murder mission: *Various artists* (633 Squadron.) / Crash flight: *Various artists* (633 Squadron.) / Love theme: *Various artists* (633 Squadron.) / Escape from Norway: *Various artists* (633 Squadron.) / Peace and war: *Various artists* (633 Squadron.) / Apprehension: *Various artists* (633 Squadron.) / Love theme (End title): *Various artists* (633 Squadron.).
CD: Released Apr '90, on MGM (EMI) Catalogue no: **CDMGM 13**
Cass: Released Apr '90, on MGM (EMI) Catalogue no: **TCMGM 13**
Album: Released Apr '90, on MGM (EMI) Catalogue no: **794 094 1**
Cass: Released Apr '90, on MGM (EMI) Catalogue no: **794 094 4**
CD: Released Apr '90, on MGM (EMI) Catalogue no: **CDP 794 094 2**
Album: Released Apr '90, on MGM (EMI) Catalogue no: **LPMGM 13**

Where The River ...
WHERE THE RIVER RUNS BLACK (Film soundtrack) (Various artists)
Note: Composed by James Horner
Album: Released Jan '89, on Silva Screen by Silva Screen Records. Catalogue no: **STV 81290**
Cass: Released Jan '89, on Silva Screen by Silva Screen Records. Catalogue no: **CTV 81290**
CD: Released Jan '89, on Silva Screen by Silva Screen Records. Catalogue no: **VCD 47273**

Where There's Life
OXYGENE PART IV (See under Jarre, Jean Michel)

Whisperers
WHISPERERS, THE (Film Soundtrack) (Various artists)
Note: John Barry score for the Bryan Forbes film starring Edith Evans.
Cass: Released Jan '89, on Silva Screen by Silva Screen Records. Deleted Mar '90. Catalogue no: **MCAC 25041**
Album: Released Jan '89, on Silva Screen by Silva Screen Records. Catalogue no: **MCA 25041**

Whistleblower
WHISTLEBLOWER, THE (Film soundtrack) (Royal Philharmonic Orchestra)

Soundtrack to *White Christmas* on the MCA label

Tracks: / Whistleblower, The / Quiet times with Cynthia / Whistle power, Theme from / Hidden world, The / Frank and Bob (Their secret world) / Back in the cell / Dodgesongs defection / Death of Bob / Tidy room, The / Who is big mole / They have put out the lights / Why was my son killed / Penetrating the hidden world / Meeting big mole / Whistleblowers, The: Epilogue.
Album: Released Aug '87, on T. E. R. by That's Entertainment Records. Catalogue no: **TER 1139**

Whitaker, David
SWORD AND THE SORCERER (See under Sword & The Sorcerer)

White Christmas (film)
WHITE CHRISTMAS (Original soundtrack) (Various artists) (See panel above)
Tracks: / Count your blessings instead of sheep: *Various artists* / Old man, The: *Various artists* / Sisters: *Various artists* / Best things happen while you're dancing: *Various artists* / Snow: *Various artists* / Mandy: *Various artists* / Choreography: *Various artists* / Gee, I

wish I was back in the army: *Various artists* / Love, you didn't do right by me: *Various artists* / What can you do with a general: *Various artists* / White Christmas (finale): *Various artists*.
Album: Released Sep '86, on MCA by MCA Records. Catalogue no: **MCL 1777**
Cass: Released Sep '86, on MCA by MCA Records. Catalogue no: **MCLC 1777**
CD: Released Nov '89, on MCA by MCA Records. Catalogue no: **DMCL 1777**

WHITE CHRISTMAS (VIDEO) (Various artists)
VHS: Released '88, on CIC Video Catalogue no: **VHR 2195**

White Horse Inn
WHITE HORSE INN (Stage play) (Various artists)
Tracks: / White Horse Inn: *Various artists* / Goodbye: *Various artists* / My song of love: *Various artists* / Your eyes: *Various artists* / Sigismund: *Various artists*.
Cass: Released '80, on United Artists by EMI Records. Deleted '85. Catalogue no: **TCSLS 5184**
2 LP Set: Released '80, on United

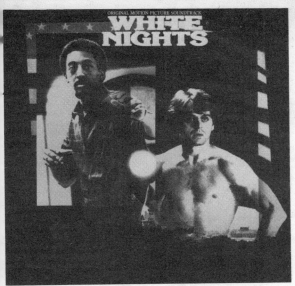

Soundtrack to *White Nights* on the Atlantic label

Artists by EMI Records. Deleted '85. Catalogue no: **SLS 5184**

White Horses

WHITE HORSES (See under Jacky)

White Mischief

WHITE MISCHIEF (Film soundtrack) (Various artists)
CD: Released Feb '90, on T. E. R. by That's Entertainment Records. Catalogue no: **CDTER1153**
Album: Released Feb '90, on T. E. R. by That's Entertainment Records. Catalogue no: **TER 1153**
Cass: Released Feb '90, on T. E. R. by That's Entertainment Records. Catalogue no: **ZCTER 1153**

White Nights

SAY YOU SAY ME (See under Richie, Lionel)

WHITE NIGHTS (Film soundtrack) (Various artists) (See panel above)
Tracks: / Separate lives: *Collins, Phil & Marilyn Martin* / People on a string: *Flack, Roberta* / Snake charmer: *Hiatt, John* / Prove me wrong: *Pack, David* / People have to move: *Burton, Jenny* / Other side of the world, The: *Khan, Chaka* / My love is chemical: *Reed, Lou* / Far post: *Plant, Robert* / Raymond's tune: *Rogers, Nile* / This is your day: *Rogers, Nile & Sandy Stewart.*
Cass: Released Oct '85, on Atlantic by WEA Records. Deleted Jul '90. Catalogue no: **781 273-4**
Album: Released Oct '85, on Atlantic by WEA Records. Catalogue no: **781 273-1**

White Rock

WHITE ROCK (Original Soundtrack) (Various artists)
Cass: Released Jan '77, on A&M by A&M Records. Deleted '88. Catalogue no: **CAM 64614**
Album: Released Jan '77, on A&M by A&M Records. Deleted '88. Catalogue no: **AMLH 64614**

Whitfield, David

DAVID WHITFIELD SINGS STAGE & SCREEN FAVOURITES
Cass set: Released '89, on Ditto by Pickwick Records. Catalogue no: **DTO 10303**
CD: Released '89, on Pickwick by Pickwick Records. Catalogue no: **PWK 096**

Whittaker, Roger

ROGER WHITTAKER IN KENYA (TV soundtrack)
Album: Released Sep '83, on Tembo by Tembo Records. Deleted Jan '89. Catalogue no: **8129491**
Cass: on Tembo by Tembo Records. Catalogue no: **8129494**

Who

BEST OF TOMMY, THE
Tracks: / Overture / It's a boy / Pinball wizard / Tommy can you hear me / I'm free / We're not gonna take it.
Album: Released Sep '88, on Polydor (Holland) by Polydor Ltd. Catalogue no: **2482 588**

KIDS ARE ALRIGHT, THE (Film soundtrack)
Tracks: / My generation / I can't explain / Happy Jack / I can see for miles / Magic bus / Long live rock / Anyway anyhow anywhere / Young man blue / Baba O Riley / My wife / Quick one / Tommy can you hear me / Sparks / Pinball wizard / See me, feel me / Join together / Road runner / My generation blues / Won't get fooled again.
Cass: Released Jun '79, on Polydor by Polydor Ltd. Deleted '84. Catalogue no: **3577 343**
2 LP Set: Released Jun '79, on Polydor by Polydor Ltd. Deleted '84. Catalogue no: **2675 179**

KIDS ARE ALRIGHT, THE (SINGLE)
Tracks: / Kids are alright, The.
7" Single: Released Sep '66, on Brunswick by Decca Records. Deleted '69. Catalogue no: **05965**

KIDS ARE ALRIGHT, THE (VIDEO)
VHS: Released Sep '84, on Polygram by PolyGram UK Ltd. Catalogue no: **791 5142**

QUADROPHENIA
Tracks: / I am the sea / Real me / I'm one / 5.15 / I've had enough / Love reign o'er me / Bell boy / Helpless dancer / Doctor Jimmy / 4 faces / Get out and stay out / Joker James / Punk and the Godfather / Louie Louie: *Kingsmen* / Zoot suit: *High Numbers* / Hi heel sneakers: *Cross Section* / Night train: *Brown, James* / Green onions: *Booker T & The MGs* / He's so fine: *Chiffons* / Rhythm of the

rain: *Cascades* / Be my baby: *Ronettes* / Da doo ron ron: *Crystals*.

2 LP Set: Released Sep '79, on Polydor by Polydor Ltd. Catalogue no: **265 701 3**

Cass set: Released Sep '79, on Polydor by Polydor Ltd. Catalogue no: **352 600 1**

CD Set: Released '88, on Polydor by Polydor Ltd. Catalogue no: **831 074 2**

QUADROPHENIA (Film Soundtrack) (Various artists)
Tracks: / I am the sea: *Who* / Real me: *Who* / I'm one: *Who* / 5.15: *Who*/ I've had enough: *Who*/ Love reign o'er me: *Who*/ Bell boy: *Who* / Helpless dancer: *Who* / Doctor Jimmy: *Who* / 4 faces: *Who* / Get out and stay out: *Who* / Joker James: *Who* / Punk and the Godfather: *Who* / Louie Louie: *Kingsmen* / Zoot suit: *High Numbers* / High heel sneakers: *Cross Section* / Night train: *Brown, James*/ Green onions: *Booker T & The MG's* / He's so fine: *Chiffons* / Rhythm of the rain: *Cascades* / Be my baby: *Ronettes* / Da doo ron ron: *Crystals*.

Cass set: Released Sep '79, on Polydor by Polydor Ltd. Catalogue no: **357 735 2**

2 LP Set: Released Sep '79, on Polydor by Polydor Ltd. Catalogue no: **262 503 7**

QUADROPHENIA (VIDEO)
VHS: Released May '84, on Polygram by PolyGram UK Ltd. Catalogue no: **790 1862**

SEE ME FEEL ME
Tracks: / See me feel me.
Note: From the film 'Tommy'.
7" Single: Released '80, on Mercury by Phonogram Ltd. Catalogue no: **LR 8241**

TOMMY (Film soundtrack)
Album: Released '74, on Track by Polydor Ltd. Catalogue no: **2657 002**

Cass: Released '74, on Track by Polydor Ltd. Catalogue no: **3526 002**

TOMMY (Original Recording) (Various artists)
Tracks: / Overture / It's a boy / 1921 / Amazing journey / Sparks / Eyesight to the blind / Miracle cure / Sally Simpson / I'm free / Welcome / Tommy's holiday camp / We're gonna take it / Christmas / Cousin Kevin.

2 LP Set: Released Jul '84, on Polydor by Polydor Ltd. Deleted Jul '89. Catalogue no: **2486 161/2**
2 LP Set: Released Jun '69, on Track by Polydor Ltd. Deleted '74. Catalogue no: **613 0123/4**
CD Set: Released Apr '89, on Polydor by Polydor Ltd. Catalogue no: **800 077-2**

TOMMY - PART 2
Tracks: / Do you think it's alright / Fiddle about / Pinball wizard / There's a doctor / Go to the mirror / Tommy, can you hear me / Smash the mirror / Sensation / Miracle cure / Sally Simpson / I'm free / Welcome / Tommy's holiday camp / We're not gonna take it.
Album: Released '74, on Track by Polydor Ltd. Catalogue no: **2406 008**
Cass: Released '74, on Track by Polydor Ltd. Catalogue no: **914 625**

Who Framed Roger...

WHO FRAMED ROGER RABBIT (Film Soundtrack) (London Symphony Orchestra)
Tracks: / Maroon logo: *Various artists* / Maroon cartoon: *Various artists* / Valiant and valiant: *Various artists* / Weasels, The: *Various artists* / Hungarian rhapsody: *Various artists* / Judge doom: *Various artists* / Why don't you do right?: *Various artists* / No justice for toons: *Various artists* / Merry go round broke down (Roger's song): *Various artists* / Jessica's theme: *Various artists* / Toontown: *Various artists* / Eddie's theme: *Various artists* / Gag factory, The: *Various artists*.
CD: Released Dec '88, on CBS by CBS Records & Distribution. Catalogue no: **463 059 2**
Cass: Released Dec '88, on CBS by CBS Records & Distribution. Catalogue no: **463 059 4**
CD: Released Jan '89, on Silva Screen by Silva Screen Records. Catalogue no: **CD 013**
Album: Released Dec '88, on CBS by CBS Records & Distribution. Deleted Apr '90. Catalogue no: **463 059 1**

Who Pay's The...

WHO PAY'S THE FERRYMAN (See under Markopoulos, Yannis)

Whoop-Up

WHOOP-UP (Original Broadway Cast) (Various artists)
CD: Released Jul '89, on Silva Screen by Silva Screen Records. Catalogue no: **837196.2**

Who's That Girl

WHO'S THAT GIRL (Film soundtrack) (Various artists) (See also under Madonna)
Tracks: / Who's that girl: *Various artists* / Causing a commotion: *Various artists* / Look of love, The: *Various artists* / 24 hours: *Various artists* / Turn it up: *Various artists* / Best thing ever: *Various artists* / Can't stop: *Various artists* / El loco loco: *Various artists*.
Cass: Released Jul '87, on Sire by Sire Records. Catalogue no: **WX 102 C**
Album: Released Jul '87, on Sire by Sire Records. Deleted Jul '90. Catalogue no: **WX 102**
CD: Released Aug '87, on Sire by Sire Records. Catalogue no: **K 925611 2**

Wild Geese (film)

WILD GEESE, THE (Original Soundtrack) (Various artists)
Album: Released Jul '78, on A&M by A&M Records. Deleted '88. Catalogue no: **AMLH 64730**

Wild Orchid

WILD ORCHID (Original Soundtrack) (Various artists)
CD: Released Aug '90, on Sire by Sire Records. Catalogue no: **7599261272**
Cass: Released Aug '90, on Sire by Sire Records. Catalogue no: **7599261274**
Album: Released Aug '90, on Sire by Sire Records. Catalogue no: **7599261271**

Wild Rovers

WILD ROVERS (Film Soundtrack) (Various artists)
Note: Probably Jerry Goldsmith's finest western score for the Blake Edwards film starring William Holden and Ryan O'Neal.
Cass: Released Jan '89, on Silva Screen by Silva Screen Records. Deleted Mar '90. Catalogue no: **MCAC 25141**

bum: Released Jan '89, on
va Screen by Silva Screen
cords. Catalogue no: **MCA
141**

ild Style

**LD STYLE (Film Sound-
ck)**

acks: / Wild style theme rap 1
MC battle / Basketball throw-
wn / Fantastic freaks at the
xie / Military cut scratch mix /
ld crush brothers at the Dixie /
oop rap / Double trouble at the
pitheatre / Wild style subway
o 2 / Gangbusters scratch mix
ammellzee and shock Dell at
e ampitheatre.

ss: Released Oct '83, on Ani-
l by Chrysalis Records. Cata-
ue no: **ZCHR 1453**

bum: Released Oct '83, on
imal by Chrysalis Records.
talogue no: **CHR 1453**

ildflower

**LDFLOWER (Original Lon-
n Cast)**

bum: Released '79, on Retro-
ect by EMI Records. Cata-
ue no: **SH 279**

ilen, Barney

**OVIE THEMES FROM
RANCE (Wilen, Barney &
al Waldron Trio)**

acks: / Un homme et une
mme / Juliendans l'ascenseur /
rence sur les Champs-Ely-
es / Les parapluies de Cher-
urg / No problem / Manha de
rnaval / Generique / Les feuil-
s mortes / Quiet temple.

te: Personnel - Barney Wilen
nor and soprano saxes), Mal
aldron (piano), Stafford James
ass), Eddie Moore (drums).

D: Released Aug '90, on Time-
ss by Timeless Records. Cata-
ue no: **CDSJP 335**

**N TEMOIN DANS LA VILLE
AZZ SUR SEINE (Original
undtrack)**

acks: / Temoin dans la ville /
pendaison / Melodie pour les
dio-taxis / Poursuite et metro /
nbiance pourpre / Premedita-
n dans l'appartement / La vie
est qu'une lutte / Complainte du
auffeur / Sur l'antenne / S.O.S.
dio-taxis / Final au jardin d'ac-
mata- tion / Swing 39 / Vamp
enilmontant / John's groove / B.
B. (Bag's Barney blues') /

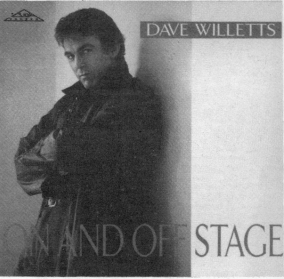

Dave Willetts - *On and Off Stage* (Silva Screen)

Swingin' Parisian rhythm / J'ai ta
main / Nuages / La route enchan-
tee / Que rest et il de nos amours
/ Minor's swing / Epistrophy.
Note: Original jazz soundtrack to
the film Un Temoin Dans La Ville
produced by Edouard Molinaro
plus 1958 recording titles Jazz
Sur Seine featuring Barney Wilen
original compositions as well as
pieces by Django Reinhardt and
Thelonious Monk.
CD: Released Mar '88, on ECM
Catalogue no: **832 658 2**

Wilkinson, Colm

BRING HIM HOME
Tracks: / Bring him home / Who am I?
7" Single: Released Mar '87, on
First Night by First Night Rec-
ords. Catalogue no: **SCORE 7**
STAGE HEROES
Tracks: / Man from La Mancha /
Impossible dream, The / Pity the
child / Anthem (Chess) / Maria /
Somewhere / Phantom of the
opera / Music of the night / Bring
him home / Empty chairs at
empty tables / Some enchanted
evening / This nearly was mine /
How to handle a woman / If ever
I would leave you / Summertime
/ It ain't necessarily so.

CD: Released May '89, on RCA
by BMG Records (UK). Cata-
logue no: **BD 74105**
Cass: Released May '89, on
RCA by BMG Records (UK).
Catalogue no: **BK 74105**
Album: Released May '89, on
RCA by BMG Records (UK).
Catalogue no: **BL 74105**

Willetts, Dave

**ON AND OFF STAGE (See
panel above)**
Tracks: / Phantom of the opera /
Les miserables / La cage aux folles
/ Nine / Guys and dolls / Rose, The
/ Music of the night.
Note: For more than two years
Dave Willetts played *The Phantom*
in the London Production of Andrew Lloyd Webber's *Phantom Of
The Opera* bringing to the role his
own personal and inimitable interpretation, and in the process received great accolades, acclaim
and standing ovations. Prior to his
success in Phantom' Dave played
the leading role of Jean Valjean in
the Royal Shakespeare Company's production of Les Miserables and has since gone on to star
with Petula Clark in the musical
Someone like you. Dave's me-

teoric rise to fame in the Theatre has come within' five years of turning professional and *On and off stage* is his first solo album.

As the title suggests, this album is not merely just another collection of show tunes. Naturally Dave had to record some of the musical numbers which he is famous for. *Music of the night* and *Bring him home* are given memorable and definitive performances by him as well as obvious showstoppers from *Guys And Dolls* and *La Cage Aux Folles*. Less obvious are his selections from *Nine*, which were originally written for the female voice and the ballad *Angel of serenity* form a new musical about the life of the painter Paul Gaugin, called '*Penny Millionaire*'. (On all of the show songs Dave is given sterling support by the Philharmonia Orchestra under the direction of Paul Bateman). The other tracks on this album show Dave's instinctive feel for songs and a more contemporary nature, from dance orientated number like Nights are forever and *Dancing on my own* to the gentler love songs of *One in your life* and *I'll never love anyone anymore' and the power of Umberton Tozzie's international hit Ti amo*. This collection ends with the subtle merging of The Rose and *Hello again to create a poignant epilogue. (Silva Screen)*

CD: Released Jan '90, on Silva Screen by Silva Screen Records. Catalogue no: **SONGCD 902**

Album: Released Jan '90, on Silva Screen by Silva Screen Records. Catalogue no: **SONG 902**

Cass: Released Jan '90, on Silva Screen by Silva Screen Records. Catalogue no: **SONGC 902**

TI AMO
Tracks: / Ti amo.
7" Single: Released Mar '90, on Silver Screen by Creole Records. Catalogue no: **SILVA 103**

William Tell
WILLIAM TELL (TV soundtrack) (Various artists)
Tracks: / Straight through the apple: *Various artists* / Waxing moon, The: *Various artists* / To live and die: *Various artists* / Ballad of William, The: *Various artists* / Ballad: *Various artists* / Shadows: *Various artists* / Fruits of the forest: *Various artists* / Enchantment:

Various artists / Dance, The: *Various artists* / Interlude: *Various artists* / Just pursuits: *Various artists* / Point of no return: *Various artists* / Ride, The: *Various artists* / Song of the crossbow: *Various artists*.

Album: Released Feb '89, on Virgin by Virgin Records. Catalogue no: **V 2585**

CD: Released Feb '89, on Virgin by Virgin Records. Catalogue no: **CDV 2585**

Cass: Released Feb '89, on Virgin by Virgin Records. Catalogue no: **TCV 2585**

Williams, Andy
GREAT SONGS FROM MY FAIR LADY
Album: Released Apr '66, on CBS by CBS Records & Distribution. Deleted '71. Catalogue no: **BPG 62430**

LOVE STORY (SINGLE)
Tracks: / Love story.
Note: From the film *'Love Story'*
7" Single: Released Mar '71, on CBS by CBS Records & Distribution. Deleted '74. Catalogue no: **CBS 7020**

LOVE THEME FROM THE GODFATHER
Album: Released Aug '72, on CBS by CBS Records & Distribution. Deleted '77. Catalogue no: **CBS 64869**

Williams, Danny
MOON RIVER
Tracks: / Moon river.
Note: From the film *Breakfast At Tiffany's.*
7" Single: Released Nov '61, on H.M.V. by EMI Records. Deleted '64. Catalogue no: **POP 932**

MOON RIVER (OLD GOLD)
Tracks: / Moon river.
7" Single: Released Jul '82, on Old Gold by Old Gold Records. Deleted Jul '88. Catalogue no: **OG 9046**

Williams, Deniece
LET'S HEAR IT FOR THE BOY
Tracks: / Let's hear it for the boy.
Note: Featured in the film 'Footloose'.
12" Single: Released May '84, on CBS by CBS Records & Distribution. Deleted '87. Catalogue no: **TA 3419**
7" Single: Released May '84, on CBS by CBS Records & Distribu-

tion. Deleted '87. Catalogue no: **3419**

Williams, Iris
HE WAS BEAUTIFU (SINGLE)
Tracks: / He was beautiful / W don't make each other laugh an' more.
Note: Theme from the 'Dee' hunter'.
7" Single: Released Sep '79, c Columbia by EMI Records. Cat logue no: **DB 9070**

Williams, John (Comp.)
AISLE SEAT (Williams, Joh & Boston Pops)
Tracks: / E.T. / Chariots of fire Raiders of the lost ark / Yes, Gic gio / New York, New York / Gor with the wind / Wizard of Oz, The Singin' in the rain / Friendly pe suasion / Meet me in St. Louis.
CD: Released Jan '83, on Philip by Phonogram Ltd. Catalogue n' **4110372**
Cass: Released Jan '83, on Ph ips by Phonogram Ltd. Catalogu no: **7337 328**
Album: Released Jan '83, on Ph ips by Phonogram Ltd. Catalogu no: **6514 328**

BY REQUEST (Williams, Joh & The Boston Pops Orches tra)
Tracks: / Olympic fanfare an theme / Close encounters of th third kind (excerpts) / March fro Midway / Luke and Leia / Return the Jedi (theme from) / Flying fro E.T. / Liberty fanfare / Superma march / Yoda's / Empire strike back (theme from) / March fro 1941 / Jaws / Imperial march fro the empire strikes back / Missior Star wars (theme from).
Cass: Released '87, on Philips Phonogram Ltd. Catalogue n' **420178-4**
Album: Released '87, on Philip by Phonogram Ltd. Catalogue n' **420178-1**

EMPIRE STRIKES BACK, TH
Album: Released Oct '80, c Chalfont (USA) by Varese S' rabande Records (USA). Cat logue no: **SDG 313**

E.T. - THE EXTRA TERRI STRIAL
Album: Released Dec '82, c MCA by MCA Records. Delete '87. Catalogue no: **MCF 3160**

E.T. THEME (Williams, John Orchestra)
Tracks: / E.T., Theme from / Over the moon.
7" Single: Released Nov '82, on MCA by MCA Records. Catalogue no: **MCA 800**

FIDDLER ON THE ROOF (See under Fiddler On The Roof)

JAWS (See under Jaws)

OUT OF THIS WORLD (Williams, John & Boston Pops)
Tracks: / Return of the Jedi / Battlestar Galactica / Twilight zone / Star trek / E.T. / Alien / 2001.
CD: Released '88, on Polygram by PolyGram UK Ltd. Catalogue no: **411 185 2**
Album: Released Dec '83, on Philips by Phonogram Ltd. Catalogue no: **411 185-1**
Cass: Released Dec '83, on Philips by Phonogram Ltd. Catalogue no: **411 185-4**

THAT'S ENTERTAINMENT (Williams, John & Boston Pops)
Tracks: / That's entertainment / Let me entertain you / Fiddler on the roof / Little night music, A / Pops on Broadway / Gigi / Richard Rodgers waltz.
CD: Released '86, on Philips. Catalogue no: **416 499-2**

WITCHES OF EASTWICK (See under Witches Of Eastwick)

Williams, John (Guitar)
CAVATINA (SINGLE)
Tracks: / Cavatina.
Note: From the film 'Deerhunter'.
7"Single: Released May '77, on Cube. Catalogue no: **BUG 65**
7"Single: Released Oct '82, by CBS. Deleted Oct '85. Catalogue no: **A 2791**

HE WAS BEAUTIFUL (Williams, John & Cleo Laine)
Tracks: / He was beautiful / Charms.
Note: Vocal to the theme from 'The Deerhunter'.
7" Single: Released Dec '77, on RCA by BMG Records (UK). Catalogue no: **PB 9199**

HONORARY CONSUL, THEME FROM
Tracks: / Honorary Consul, Theme from / Clara's theme.
Note: Paul McCartney's theme tune

from the film of the same name.
7" Single: Released Dec '83, on Island by Island Records. Catalogue no: **IS 155**

Williams, Kenneth
MORE WILLO THE WISP STORIES
Album: Released Jul '83, on BBC by BBC Records. Deleted 31 Aug '88. Catalogue no: **REC 473**
Cass: Released Jul '83, on BBC by BBC Records. Deleted 31 Aug '88. Catalogue no: **ZCM 473**

WILLO THE WISP
Tracks: / Bridegroom, The / Food for thought / You know what, The / Chrysalis, The / Flight of Mavis, The / Holidays / Hot hot day, The / Gnome, The / Beauty contents, The / Midas touch, The / Beanstalk, The / Christmas box.
Cass: Released Oct '81, on BBC by BBC Records. Deleted 31 Aug '88. Catalogue no: **ZCM 427**
Album: Released Oct '81, on BBC by BBC Records. Deleted 31 Aug '88. Catalogue no: **REC 427**

Willow
WILLOW (Film Soundtrack) (Horner, James/L.S.O. & King's College Choir)
Tracks: / Elora Danan / Escape from the tavern / Canyon of mazes / Tir asleen / Willow's theme / Willow's journey begins / Bavmorda's spell is cast / Willow the sorcerer.
Note: Fantasy film directed by Ron Howard (Cocoon, Splash) and starring Val Kilmer and Joanne Whalley. Music by James Horner with the London Symphony Orchestra.
Album: Released Jan '89, on Silva Screen by Silva Screen Records. Catalogue no: **790939.1**
Album: Released 14 Nov '88, on Virgin by Virgin Records. Catalogue no: **V 2538**
CD: Released Jan '89, on Silva Screen by Silva Screen Records. Catalogue no: **790939.2**
Cass: Released 14 Nov '88, on Virgin by Virgin Records. Deleted Jun '90. Catalogue no: **TCV 2538**
CD: Released 14 Nov '88, on Virgin by Virgin Records. Catalogue no: **CDV 2538**
Cass: Released Jan '89, on Silva Screen by Silva Screen Records. Catalogue no: **790939.4**

Wind & The Lion
WIND AND THE LION,THE (Film Soundtrack) (Goldsmith, Jerry)
CD: Released Feb '90, on Silva Screen by Silva Screen Records. Catalogue no: **RVF6008D**

Wind In The Willows
WIND IN THE WILLOWS VOL I (TV Soundtrack) (Various artists)
Tracks: / Wind in the willows, The: Various artists / On the river: Various artists / Ducks ditty: Various artists / Open road: Various artists / Mr Toad the motorist: Various artists / Wild wood: Various artists / Mr Badger: Various artists / Dolce Domum: Various artists / Further adventures of Mr Toad, The: Various artists / Hero's song: Various artists / Battle: Various artists / When Toad came home: Various artists.
Cass: Released '83, on Red Bus by Red Bus Records. Catalogue no: **ZCRDB 1150**
Album: Released '83, on Red Bus by Red Bus Records. Catalogue no: **RD BLP 1150**

WIND IN THE WILLOWS VOL II (TV soundtrack) (Various artists)
Cass set: Released Nov '84, on Red Bus by Red Bus Records. Catalogue no: **ZCRDB 1151**
2 LP Set: Released Nov '84, on Red Bus by Red Bus Records. Catalogue no: **RDBLP 1151**

Winds Of War
WINDS OF WAR (Film soundtrack) (Cobert, Robert)
Tracks: / Winds of war, The: Main title / Nazi generals meet with Hitler / Rosenthal / Prelude to Pug's bombing mission / Byron and Natalie / Through Poland to a Jewish village / Refugees on the road / Nazis victorious(Bombing of London) / Rhoda and Kirby / Byron and Natlie's wedding / Pug at the Russian front / Danger! Neutrals at the train station / Pug and Pamela (in love in London) / Pearl harbour/ A day of infamy / Henry family theme / Winds of war,The: End title.
Album: Released Sep '83, on T. E. R. by That's Entertainment Records. Catalogue no: **TER 1070**

Cass: Released Sep '83, on T. E. R. by That's Entertainment Records. Catalogue no: **ZCTER 1070**

Windwalker

WINDWALKER (Film Soundtrack) (Various artists)
Note: Composed by Merril Jenson.
Album: Released Jan '89, on Cerebus (USA) Catalogue no: **C'BUS 0202**

Wings

LIVE AND LET DIE (Film Soundtrack) (See under Live & Live Die)

LIVE AND LET DIE
Tracks: / Live and let die.
7" Single: Released Jun '73, on Parlophone by EMI Records. Catalogue no: **R 5987**

Wings Of Desire

WINGS OF DESIRE (Film soundtrack) (Various artists)
Cass: Released Jul '88, on SPI Milan (France) Catalogue no: **C 316**
CD: Released Jul '88, on SPI Milan (France) Catalogue no: **CD 316**
Album: Released Jul '88, on SPI Milan (France) Catalogue no: **A 316**

WINGS OF DESIRE (Film Soundtrack) (Various artists)
Album: Released Aug '88, on Mute by Mute Records. Catalogue no: **IONIC 2**
CD: Released Aug '88, on Mute by Mute Records. Catalogue no: **CDIONIC 2**

Winnie

WINNIE (Original cast recording) (Various artists)
Tracks: / Army, the Navy and the Air Force: London stage cast / Who's taking you home tonight?: London stage cast / Run rabbit run: London stage cast / Bless 'em all: London stage cast / All over the place: London stage cast / What more can I say?: London stage cast / That lovely weekend: London stage cast / There's something about a soldier: London stage cast / London pride: London stage cast / There'll always be an England: London stage cast / Kiss me goodnight, Sergeant Major: London stage cast / Colonel's complaint, The: London stage cast

/ I would say to the House... (speech): London stage cast / Winnie: London stage cast / Did you call, darling?: London stage cast / Wish me luck as you wave me goodbye: London stage cast / We'll meet again: London stage cast / Yours: London stage cast / Nightingale sang in Berkeley Square, A: London stage cast / Don't cry, darling: London stage cast / You'll never know: London stage cast / I'm going to get lit up when the lights go up in London: London stage cast / Harrow song, The: London stage cast / Song speaks of giants... (speech): London stage cast / VE Day: London stage cast / My dear friends... (speech): London stage cast / Winnie (reprise): London stage cast / In distant tomorrows: London stage cast.
Note: Album produced by Fiachra Trench for Wildwood Music Ltd. Extracts of Sir Winston Churchill's speeches by permission of Her Majesty's Stationery Office.
CD: Released Jul '88, on Columbia by EMI Records. Deleted Nov '88. Catalogue no: **CDSCX 6713**
CD: Released Jul '88, on Columbia by EMI Records. Deleted Nov '88. Catalogue no: **CDP 790 728 2**
Album: Released Jun '88, on Columbia by EMI Records. Deleted Aug '89. Catalogue no: **SCX 6713**
Cass: Released Jun '88, on Columbia by EMI Records. Deleted Aug '89. Catalogue no: **TCSCX 6713**

Wired

WIRED (Film soundtrack) (Various artists)
Tracks: / I'm a king bee: Various artists / Soul man: Various artists / Raven's theme: Various artists / Two thousand pounds: Various artists / Still looking for a way: Various artists / You are so beautiful: Various artists / I can't turn you loose: Various artists / You don't know like I know: Various artists / Choice, The: Various artists / Bee: Various artists / Angel of death: Various artists.
CD: Released Oct '89, on Varese Sarabande Records(USA) by Varese Sarabande Records (USA). Catalogue no: **VSD 5237**
Cass: Released Oct '89, on Varese Sarabande Records(USA) by Varese Sarabande Records

(USA). Catalogue no: **VSC 5237**
Album: Released Oct '89, on Varese Sarabande Records(USA) by Varese Sarabande Records (USA). Catalogue no: **VS 5237**

Wisdom (Film)

WISDOM (Film soundtrack) (Various artists)
Note: Film starring Emilio Estevez with music by Danny Elman (composer of Beetlejuice, Midnight Run & Pee Wee's Big Adventure)
CD: Released Jan '89, on Take 7 Catalogue no: **VSD 5209**
Album: Released Jan '89, on Take 7 Catalogue no: **VS 5209**
Cass: Released Jan '89, on Take 7 Catalogue no: **VSC 5209**

Wish You Were Here

WISH YOU WERE HERE (Original London cast) (Various artists)
Tracks: / Wish you were here: Various artists / Where did the night go?: Various artists / Relax: Various artists / Summer afternoon: Various artists / Mix and mingle: Various artists / Don Jose of far rockaway: Various artists / Camp Karefree song: Various artists / Ballad of a social director: Various artists / Shop around: Various artists.
Cass: Released '88, on DRG (USA) by DRG Records (USA). Catalogue no: **DSC 15015**
Album: Released '88, on DRG (USA) by DRG Records (USA). Catalogue no: **DS 15015**

Witches Of Eastwick

WITCHES OF EASTWICK (Film soundtrack) (Various artists)
Note: Music composed and conducted by John Williams.
Cass: Released Sep '87, on Warner Bros. by WEA Records. Catalogue no: **925607 4**
Album: Released Sep '87, on Warner Bros. by WEA Records. Deleted Jan '90. Catalogue no: **925607 1**
CD: Released Jan '89, on Silva Screen by Silva Screen Records. Catalogue no: **925607.2**

Withnail & I

WITHNAIL AND I (Original soundtrack) (Various artists)
Tracks: / While my guitar gently weeps: Beatles / Voodoo chile:

Hendrix, Jimi Experience / Mar-
wood returns: Various artists /
Whiter shade of pale, A: Curtis,
King / Mother black cap: Various
artists / Crow crag: Various artists
/ All along the watchtower: Various
artists / Chevel blanc: Various ar-
tists / La fite: Various artists / Wolf,
the: Various artists / Margeaux:
Various artists / To the crow: Vari-
ous artists / Monty remembers:
Various artists / Marwood leaves:
Various artists / Withnail's theme:
Various artists.

Album: Released Feb '88, on
Filmtrax by Filmtrax Records.
Deleted Apr '90. Catalogue no:
MOMENT 110

Cass: Released Feb '88, on Filmtrax by Filmtrax Records. Deleted
Apr '90. Catalogue no: **MOMENTC
10**

CD: Released Feb '90, on Silva
Screen by Silva Screen Records.
Catalogue no: **FILMCD 041**

Witness (Film)

**WITNESS (Film soundtrack)
(Jarre, Maurice)**
Album: Released Jun '85, on T. E.
R. by That's Entertainment Rec-
ords. Catalogue no: **TER 1098**
Cass: Released May '89, on T. E.
R. by That's Entertainment Rec-
ords. Catalogue no: **ZCTER 1098**
CD: Released '88, on T. E. R. by
That's Entertainment Records.
Catalogue no: **CDTER 1098**

Witness (Musical)

**WITNESS, THE (Various ar-
tists)**
Tracks: / Witness, The: Various
artists / Nothin' ever happens:
Various artists / When you find the
truth: Various artists / Wedding at
Cana: Various artists / Mary's song
whatever he says): Various artists
Born again: Various artists / Life
giver: Various artists / You are the
Christ: Various artists / My boys:
Various artists / Make me like you:
Various artists / Hosanna (triumphal entry): Various artists / In love
or me: Various artists / Silver and
gold: Various artists / Crucifixion
dirge: Various artists / He came in
love: Various artists / They took
him down: Various artists / Victor,
The: Various artists / I love you,
Lord: Various artists / Lambs
alone: Various artists / Room upstairs, The: Various artists / Get
ready: Various artists / Life giver

(Reprise): Various artists / Born
again (reprise): Various artists /
You are the Christ: Various artists.
Note: A musical by Jimmy & Carol
Owens.
Album: Released May '82, on
Light by Word Records (UK).
Catalogue no: **LSA 7047**
Cass: Released May '82, on Light
by Word Records (UK). Catalogue
no: **LCA 7047**

Wiz

**WIZ, THE (Original sound-
track) (Various artists)**
Tracks: / Wiz, The (main title and
overture): Various artists / Feeling
that we have: Various artists / Can
I go on?: Various artists / Glinda's
theme: Various artists / He's the
wizard: Various artists / Soon as I
get home: Various artists / Home:
Various artists / You can't win:
Various artists / Ease on down the
road: Various artists / What would
I do if I could feel: Various artists /
Slide some oil to me: Various ar-
tists / I'm a mean ole lion: Various
artists / Poppy girls: Various artists
/ Be a lion: Various artists / End of
the yellow brick road: Various ar-
tists / Emerald city: Various artists
/ So you wanted to see the wizard:
Various artists / Is this what the
feeling gets: Various artists / Don't
nobody bring me no bad news:
Various artists / Liberation agitato:
Various artists / Brand new day:
Various artists / Believe in yourself:
Various artists / Liberation ballet:
Various artists / Good witch: Vari-
ous artists / Glinda: Various artists.
2 LP Set: Released '79, on MCA
by MCA Records. Deleted '82.
Catalogue no: **MCSP 287**
Cass set: Released '79, on MCA
by MCA Records. Deleted '82.
Catalogue no: **MCSPC 287**
2 LP Set: Released '79, on MCA
(USA) by MCA Records (USA).
Catalogue no: **MCA2 1430**

**WIZ, THE (VIDEO) (Various ar-
tists)**
Note: The fabulous land of Oz
rocks in the fantastic fun filled
spectacular musical based on the
smash hit Broadway show which,
in turn, was drawn from L Frank
Baum's 'The Wonderful Wizard of
Oz'. Directed by Sidney Lumet, not
content to merely film the stage
production, had the highly imagin-
ative idea of transforming the
physical attributes of New York

City into the fabulous Land Of Oz.
Diana Ross reaches new heights
in her starring role as Dorothy, and
her co stars include Michael Jackson as the Scarecrow, Nipsy Russell as the Tin Man, Ted Ross as
the Cowardly Lion, Lena Horne as
Glinda the good witch and Richard
Pryor as the Oz's great wizard.
With such a cast, exciting musical
numbers and fabulous visual effects, The Wiz will reach every
generation of movie goers. (CIC
Video, October 1989) Running
time: 129 mins.
VHS: Released Nov '89, on CIC
Video Catalogue no: **VHR 1065**

Wizard Of Oz

**WIZARD OF OZ, THE (DIGI-
TAL RECORDING) (Original
cast) (Various artists)**
Note: When Terry Hands Director
of the Royal Shakespeare Company approached Ian Judge with a
view to creating a new Musical for
the Barbican Theatre, there was
no hesitation. It had to be the Wizard of Oz but the starting point for
the adaptation had to be the version created by MGM in 1939.
Apart from a magnificent score by
Harburg and Arlen, the basic novel
by Frank L. Baum was filtered
through the creative sieve of at
least ten top screenwriters before
it reached the screen. The result is
a dramatic structure which could
hardly be bettered.
As a result adapting the film for the
stage was one of the easiest and
happiest jobs I've ever done.
Whenever a scene needed to be
enlarged or elaborated, we returned to the original book and always found material that fitted
perfectly, (which again demon-
strates how true the original
screenwriters had been to the spirit
of Frank L. Baum.
The Wizard opened at the Barbican in December of '87 to critical
reviews which suggested that the
show has managed to improve even
upon the original and great popular
acclaim, a response that was re-
peated when the cast on this album
revived the show in December of the
following year. (John Kane)
CD: Released Mar '89, on T. E. R.
by That's Entertainment Records.
Catalogue no: **CDTER 1165**
Cass: Released Mar '89, on T. E.
R. by That's Entertainment Rec-

ords. Catalogue no: **ZCTER 1165**
Album: Released Mar '89, on T.
E. R. by That's Entertainment
Records. Catalogue no: **TER 1165**

WIZARD OF OZ, THE (Film Soundtrack) (Various artists)
Tracks: / Over the rainbow: *Various artists* / Munchkin land: *Various artists* / If I only had a brain: *Various artists* / If I only had a heart: *Various artists* / If I only had the nerve: *Various artists* / If I were king of the forest: *Various artists* / Courage: *Various artists* / Ding dong the which is dead: *Various artists* / There's no place like home: *Various artists*.
Album: Released Jul '86, on CBS by CBS Records & Distribution. Deleted Jan '89. Catalogue no: **CBS 70289**
Cass: Released Jul '86, on CBS by CBS Records & Distribution. Deleted Jan '89. Catalogue no: **40 70289**
CD: Released Jun '87, on CBS by CBS Records & Distribution. Deleted Jan '89. Catalogue no: **CD 70289**

WIZARD OF OZ, THE (Original Soundtrack) (Various artists)
Tracks: / Wizard of Oz (Main title): *Various artists* / Dialogues: *Various artists* / Over the rainbow: *Various artists* / Munchkin land: *Various artists* / Ding dong the witch is dead: *Various artists* / Follow the yellow brick road: *Various artists* / If I only had a brain: *Various artists* / We're off to see the wizard: *Various artists* / If I only had a heart: *Various artists* / If I only had the nerve: *Various artists* / If I were king of the forest: *Various artists* / Home sweet home: *Various artists*.
CD: Released Jan '90, on MGM (EMI) by EMI Records. Catalogue no: **CDMGM 7**
CD: Released Jan '90, on MGM (EMI) by EMI Records. Catalogue no: **CDP 793 303 2**
Album: Released Jan '90, on MGM (EMI) by EMI Records. Catalogue no: **LPMGM 7**
Cass: Released Jan '90, on MGM (EMI) by EMI Records. Catalogue no: **TCMGM 7**
Album: Released Jan '90, on MGM (EMI) by EMI Records. Catalogue no: **793 303 1**
Cass: Released Jan '90, on MGM

(EMI) by EMI Records. Catalogue no: **793 303 4**

WIZARD OF OZ (VIDEO)
VHS: Released '88, on MGM/UA (Video). Catalogue no: **SMV 10001**

Wolves Of Willoughby

WOLVES OF WILLOUGHBY CHASE, THE (Original soundtrack) (Various artists)
CD: Released Dec '89, on T. E. R. by That's Entertainment Records. Catalogue no: **CDTER 1162**
Cass: Released Dec '89, on T. E. R. by That's Entertainment Records. Catalogue no: **ZCTER 1162**

Woman's Hour

WOMAN'S HOUR (Various artists)
Album: Released Mar '90, on BBC by BBC Records. Catalogue no: **ZBBC 1115**

Woman In Red

WOMAN IN RED (See under Wonder, Stevie)

Wombles

WOMBLING SONG, THE
Tracks: / Wombling song, The.
7" Single: Released Jan '74, on CBS by CBS Records & Distribution. Deleted '77. Catalogue no: **CBS 1794**

Wonder, Stevie

I JUST CALLED TO SAY I LOVE YOU
Tracks: / I just called to say I love you.
Note: From the film 'The Woman In Red'.
12" Single: Released Aug '84, on Motown by BMG Records (UK). Catalogue no: **TMGT 1349**
7" Single: Released Aug '84, on Motown by BMG Records (UK). Catalogue no: **TMG 1349**

WOMAN IN RED (Film soundtrack)
Tracks: / Woman in red / It's you / It's more than you / I just called to say I love you / Love light in flight / Moments aren't moments / Weakness / Don't drive drunk.
Cass: Released Sep '84, on Motown by BMG Records (UK). Catalogue no: **ZK 72285**
Album: Released Sep '84, on Motown by BMG Records (UK). Catalogue no: **ZL 72285**

CD: Released Oct '87, on Motown by BMG Records (UK). Catalogue no: **WD 72609**

Wonder Years

WONDER YEARS (Various artists)
Album: Released Nov '89, on Warner Bros. by WEA Records. Catalogue no: **K 782 032 1**
CD: Released Nov '89, on Warner Bros. by WEA Records. Catalogue no: **K 782 032 2**
Cass: Released Nov '89, on Warner Bros. by WEA Records. Catalogue no: **K 782 032 4**

Wonderful Life

WONDERFUL LIFE (See under Richard, Cliff)

Wonderful Town

WONDERFUL TOWN (Original Broadway Cast) (Various artists)
Album: Released Jan '89, on MCA by MCA Records. Catalogue no: **MCA 1528**
Cass: Released Jan '89, on MCA by MCA Records. Deleted Mar '90. Catalogue no: **MCAC 1528**

WONDERFUL TOWN (Original London Cast) (Various artists)
Tracks: / Wonderful town (overture): *Various artists* / Christopher street: *Various artists* / Ohio: *Various artists* / One hundred ways to lose a man: *Various artists* / What a waste: *Various artists* / Little bit in love, A: *Various artists* / Pass the football: *Various artists* / Conversation piece: *Various artists* / Quiet girl: *Various artists* / Conga: *Various artists* / Darling Eileen: *Various artists* / Swing: *Various artists* / It's love: *Various artists* / Vortex ballet: *Various artists* / Wrong note rag: *Various artists* / Finale: *Various artists*.
Album: Released Nov '86, on First Night by First Night Records. Catalogue no: **CAST 6**
Cass: Released Nov '86, on First Night by First Night Records. Catalogue no: **CASTC 6**

Woo Woo Kid

WOO WOO KID, THE (Original soundtrack) (Various artists)
Album: Released Feb '88, on Atlantic by WEA Records. Catalogue no: **K 781 781 1**

Cass: Released Feb '88, on Atlantic by WEA Records. Catalogue no: **K 781 781 4**

Wood, Victoria

LUCKY BAG (Victoria Wood as seen on TV)
Album: Released Dec '85, on Elecstar by Elecstar Records. Deleted '88. Catalogue no: **VCLP 001**
Cass: Released Jul '85, on Cherry Lane by Cherry Lane Productions. Catalogue no: **2CVCL 1**

Woodhouse, Barbara

TRAINING DOGS THE WOODHOUSE WAY
Album: Released Sep '82, on BBC by BBC Records. Deleted '88. Catalogue no: **REC 455**
Cass: Released Sep '82, on BBC by BBC Records. Deleted '87. Catalogue no: **ZCM 455**

Woodstock

WOODSTOCK (Film soundtrack) (Various artists)
CD: Released '86, on Mobile Fidelity Sound Lab(USA) by Mobile Fidelity Records (USA). Catalogue no: **MFCD 4-861**

WOODSTOCK ONE (Original soundtrack) (Various artists)
Tracks: / I had a dream: *Sebastion, John B/* Going up the country: *Canned Heat* / Freedom: *Havens, Richie* / Rock and soul music: *Country Joe & The Fish* / Coming into Los Angeles: *Guthrie, Arlo* / At the hop: *Sha Na Na* / Fish cheer, The: *McDonald, Country Joe* / I feel like I'm fixin' to die rag: *Various artists* / Drug store truck drivin' man: *Baez, Joan* / Sea of madness: *Crosby, Stills & Nash* / Wooden ships: *Crosby, Stills & Nash* / We're not gonna take it: *Who* / With a little help from my friends: *Cocker, Joe* / Crowd rain chant: *Cocker, Joe* / Soul sacrifice: *Santana* / I'm going home: *Ten Years After* / Volunteers: *Jefferson Airplane* / Rainbows all over your blues: *Sebastian, John* / Love march: *Butterfield Blues Band* / Star spangled banner, The: *Hendrix, Jimi.*
Note: This also includes a Sly and the Family Stone medley which contains "Dance to the music", "Music lover", "I want to take you higher".
LP Set: Released '74, on Atlantic

by WEA Records. Catalogue no: **K 60001**
Cass set: Released '74, on Atlantic by WEA Records. Deleted Aug '87. Catalogue no: **K4 60001**
CD Set: Released Jul '87, on Atlantic by WEA Records. Catalogue no: **260 001**

Woolfe, Rita

BEAUTIFUL LAUNDERETTE
Tracks: / Beautiful launderette / Beautiful launderette (dangerous mix) / Take one look (Track on 12" version only).
Note: From the film *My Beautiful Launderette.*
12" Single: Released May '86, on Stiff by Stiff Records. Catalogue no: **BUYIT 249**
7" Single: Released May '86, on Stiff by Stiff Records. Catalogue no: **BUY 249**

Words & Music

WORDS AND MUSIC/THREE LITTLE WORDS (Various artists)
Tracks: / Manhattan: *Rooney, Mickey* (Words & Music.) / Johnny one note: *Garland, Judy* (Words & Music.) / There's a small hotel: *Garrett, Betty* (Words & Music.) / Lady is a tramp: *Horne, Lena* (Words & Music.) / Where's that rainbow?: *Sothern Ann* (Words & Music.) / I wish I were in love again: *Rooney, Mickey/Judy Garland* (Words & Music.) / Where or when: *Horne, Lena* (Words & Music.) / Thou swell: *Allyson, June* (Words & Music.) / Slaughter on Tenth Avenue (Ballet): *Various artists* (Words & Music.) / All alone Monday: *Robbins, Gale* (Three Little Words.) / Who's sorry now?: *De Haven, Gloria* (Three Little Words.) / I wanna be loved by you: *Kane, Helen* (Three Little Words.) / Nevertheless (I'm in love with you): *Astaire, Fred/Red Skelton/Anita Ellis* (Three Little Words.) / I love you so much: *Dahl, Arlene* (Three Little Words.) / Where did you get that girl: *Astaire, Fred/Anita Ellis* (Three Little Words.) / Thinking of you: *Ellis, Anita* (Three Little Words.) / Three little words: *Astaire, Fred* (Three Little Words.)
Note: Medley My sunny Tennessee/So long! oo-long (how long you gonna be gone) - Fred Astaire/Red Skelton. (Three Little Words).
Album: Released Apr '90, on

MGM (EMI) Catalogue no: **LPMGM 14**
CD: Released Apr '90, on MGM (EMI) Catalogue no: **CDMGM 14**
CD: Released Apr '90, on MGM (EMI) Catalogue no: **CDP 794 159 2**
Album: Released Apr '90, on MGM (EMI) Catalogue no: **794 159 1**
Cass: Released Apr '90, on MGM (EMI) Catalogue no: **TCMGM 14**
Cass: Released Apr '90, on MGM (EMI) Catalogue no: **794 159 4**

Working Girl

WORKING GIRL (Film soundtrack) (Various artists)
Tracks: / Let the river run: *Simon, Carly* / In love (instrumental): *Simon, Carly* / Man that got away, The (instrumental): *Various artists* / Scar, The (instrumental): *Simon, Carly* / Let the river run: *St Thomas Choir Of Men & Boys* / Lady in red: *De Burgh, Chris* / Carlotta's heart: *Simon, Carly* / Looking through Katherine's house: *Simon, Carly* / Poor butterfly: *Rollins, Sonny* / I'm so excited: *Pointer Sisters.*
Note: Main song *Let the river run* released as single by *Carly Simon.* (See under Simon, Carly)
CD: Released '89, on Arista by BMG Records (UK). Catalogue no: **259 767**
Album: Released '89, on Arista by BMG Records (UK). Catalogue no: **209 767**
Cass: Released '89, on Arista by BMG Records (UK). Catalogue no: **409 767**

World Apart

WORLD APART, A (Film Soundtrack) (Zimmer, Hans)
CD: Released Feb '90, on SPI Milan (France) Catalogue no: **CDCH 302**
Cass: Released Jan '89, on Silva Screen by Silva Screen Records. Catalogue no: **C 302**
Album: Released Jan '89, on Silva Screen by Silva Screen Records. Catalogue no: **A 302**
CD: Released Jan '89, on Silva Screen by Silva Screen Records. Catalogue no: **CD 302**

World At War

WORLD AT WAR (TV Soundtrack) (Various artists)
Album: Released Feb '84, on Decca by Decca International. Deleted '88. Catalogue no: **DVL 6**

World Is Full Of..

WORLD IS FULL OF MAR-RIED MEN, THE (Film Sound-track) (Various artists)
2 LP Set: Released Jun '79, on Ronco Deleted '81. Catalogue no: **RTD 2038**

World's Greatest Lover

WORLD'S GREATEST LOVER, THE (Film Sound-track) (Various artists)
Tracks: / Fox trademark: *Various artists* / Adolph Zitz, movie mogul: *Various artists* / Rudy's tango: *Various artists* / Valentino movie: *Various artists* / World's greatest lover tango: *Various artists* / Going crazy in Milwaukee: *Various artists* / Los Angeles train: *Various artists* / You oughta be in pictures: *Various artists* / That's my weakness now: *Various artists* / Hollywood - garden music: *Various artists* / Reaching for someone: *Various artists* / Sex by the numbers: *Various artists* / Enter Uncle Harry: *Various artists* / Red rose Uncle Harry: *Various artists* / I'm bringing a red, red rose: *Various artists* / Love just in your let eye: *Various artists* / Shuffle off to Buffalo: *Various artists* / Rudy meets Valentino: *Various artists* / Gene Valentino montage: *Various artists* / Annie

meets Valentino: *Various artists* / Tent scene: *Various artists* / Fascination: *Various artists* / Ain't it kinda wonderful: *Various artists* / Tent scene (gypsy presto): *Various artists* / Annie and the gangsters: *Various artists* / Getting ready for the finals: *Various artists* / Gangster's walk: *Various artists* / Valentino tango (noche de amor): *Various artists* / Girls kicking: *Various artists* / Final audition, The: *Various artists* / Finale: *Various artists*.
Cass: Released '79, on RCA by BMG Records (UK). Deleted '84. Catalogue no: **BK 12709**
Album: Released '79, on RCA by BMG Records (UK). Deleted '84. Catalogue no: **BL 12709**

Wraith

WRAITH (Film soundtrack) (Various artists)
Tracks: / Where's the fire?: *Feehan, Tim* / Those were the days: *Honeymoon Suite* / Hearts versus heads: *Bush, Stan* / Hold on, blue eyes: *Lamarca* / Young love, hot love: *Michaels, Jill* / Secret loser: *Osbourne, Ozzy* / Never surrender: *Lion* / Bad mistake: *House, James* / Wake up call: *Hunter, Ian* / Matter of the heart: *Tyler, Bonnie*.
Album: Released Jan '86, on Scotti Bros (USA) by WEA Records. Deleted Nov '87. Catalogue no: **450 373-1**

Cass: Released Jan '86, on Scotti Bros (USA) by WEA Records. Deleted Nov '87. Catalogue no: **450 373-4**

Wren, Jenny

EDWARD & MRS. SIMPSON
Tracks: / I've danced with a man / Very thought of you, The / Room with a view / If I had you / Of cabbages and kings / Bring down the curtain / One more dance / Dance little lady / Tango / When love grows cold / Murmurs in the wind.
Album: Released Dec '79, on RK by RK Records. Deleted '82. Catalogue no: **RKLP 5003**

EDWARD & MRS. SIMPSON (SINGLE)
Tracks: / Edward and Mrs. Simpson.
7" Single: Released '79, on RK by RK Records. Deleted '81. Catalogue no: **RK 1017**

Wynette, Tammy

STAND BY YOUR MAN (SINGLE)
Tracks: / Stand by your man.
Note: From the film of the same name.
7" Single: Released Apr '75, on Epic by CBS Records & Distribution. Deleted '78. Catalogue no: **EPC 7137**

The following information was taken from the Music Master database on September 25th, 1990.

Xanadu

XANADU (Film soundtrack) (Various artists)
Tracks: / I'm alive: *E.L.O.* / Fall, The: *E.L.O.* / Don't walk away: *E.L.O.* / All over the world: *E.L.O.* / Xanadu: *Newton-John, Olivia & ELO* / Magic: *Newton-John, Olivia* / Suddenly: *Newton-John, Olivia & Cliff Richard* / Dancin': *Newton-John, Olivia* / Suspended in time: *Newton-John, Olivia* / Whenever you're away from me: *Newton-John, Olivia & Gene Kelly*.
Album: Released Sep '80, on Jet by Jet Records. Deleted Sep '85. Catalogue no: **JETLX 526**
Cass: Released Sep '80, on Jet by Jet Records. Deleted Sep '85.

Catalogue no: **JETCX 526**
XANADU (VIDEO) (Various artists)
VHS: Released '88, on CIC Video Catalogue no: **VHR 1018**

Xarmakos, Stavros

DARK SIDE OF THE SUN, THE (T.V. soundtrack)
Tracks: / Dark side of the sun / Anne's theme / Mendraki harbour / Relentless pursuit / Don's theme / Chasapikol / Road to Lindos, The / Walk on the shore, A / Anne's theme / Carnival / Sadness / Aspri mera / Gathering storm, The / Cafe Niklos / Dark side of the sun: Closing music.
Cass: Released Sep '83, on BBC by BBC Records. Deleted 31 Aug '88. Catalogue no: **ZCF 487**
Album: Released Sep '83, on BBC by BBC Records. Deleted 31 Aug '88. Catalogue no: **REB 487**

DARK SIDE OF THE SUN, THE (SINGLE)
Tracks: / Dark side of the Sun.
7" Single: Released Sep '83, on BBC by BBC Records. Deleted '87. Catalogue no: **RESL 135**

Xtro

XTRO (Film soundtrack) (Various artists)
Album: Released Apr '83, on T. E. R. by That's Entertainment Records. Catalogue no: **TER 1052**

Y

The following information was taken from the Music Master database on September 25th, 1990.

Yaksa

YAKSA (Original soundtrack) (Various artists)
Tracks: / Winter green and Summer blue: *Various artists* / Prologue: *Various artists* / Joy: *Various artists* / Love and solitude: *Various artists* / Uminari: *Various artists* / Gentle snow: *Various artists* / Man once lived in Minami, A: *Various artists* / Dear memories: *Various artists* / Black overcoat: *Various artists* / Tatto yaksa: *Various artists* / Dark wind: *Various artists.*
CD: Released '85, on Denon Catalogue no: **C38 7556**

Yankee Doodle Dandy

YANKEE DOODLE DANDY (Original soundtrack) (Various artists) (See also under Cagney, James)
Note: Starring James Cagney.
Album: Released Jan '89, on Silva Screen by Silva Screen Records. Catalogue no: **CC 100.13**

YANKEE DOODLE DANDY (VIDEO) (Various artists)
VHS: Released '88, on Warner Home Video by WEA Records. Catalogue no: **PES 99312**

Yanks

YANKS (Film soundtrack) (Various artists)
Tracks: / I'll be seeing you: *Various artists* / String of pearls: *Various artists* / Elmer's tune: *Various artists* / Don't sit under the apple tree: *Various artists* / Two o clock jump: *Various artists.*
Album: Released Dec '79, on United Artists by EMI Records. Deleted '84. Catalogue no: **UAG 30282**
Album: Released Jan '89, on MCA by MCA Records. Catalogue no: **MCA 3181**

Yared, Gabriel

CAMILLE CLAUDEL (See under Camille Claudel)

BETTY BLUE (See under Betty Blue)

Year Of Living...

NO WAY OUT / YEAR OF LIVING DANGEROUSLY (Film Soundtracks) (See under No Way Out)

YEAR OF LIVING DANGEROUSLY (Film Soundtrack) (Jarre, Maurice)
Note: Composed by Maurice Jarre.
Cass: Released Jan '89, on Silva Screen by Silva Screen Records. Catalogue no: **CTV 81182**
CD: Released '85, on That's Entertainment(see T.E.R.) Catalogue no: **VCD 47222**
Album: Released Jul '83, on T. E. R. by That's Entertainment Records. Catalogue no: **TER 1065**
CD: Released Feb '90, on SPI Milan (France) Catalogue no: **CDCH 004**

Year Of The Dragon

YEAR OF THE DRAGON (Original soundtrack) (Various artists)
Note: Music from the Michael Cimino film by Dave Mansfield.
Cass: Released Jan '89, on Silva Screen by Silva Screen Records. Catalogue no: **CTV 81266**
Album: Released Jan '89, on Silva Screen by Silva Screen Records. Catalogue no: **STV 81266**

Yello

OH YEAH (REMIX) (IMPORT)
Tracks: / Oh yeah (German remix) / La habanera / Oh yeah (Indian summer version).
Note: Unreleased in UK, this is the German remix version. From the film *Ferris Buler's day off.*
12" Single: Released Oct '88, on Mercury (Germany) Catalogue no: **888 9081**

Yellow Submarine

YELLOW SUBMARINE (See under Beatles)

Yes Giorgio

YES GIORGIO (Original soundtrack) (Various artists)
Tracks: / If we were in love: *Various artists* / Santa Lucia: *Various artists* / Mattinata: *Various artists* / O sole mio: *Various artists* / Ave Maria: *Various artists* / I left my heart in San Francisco: *Various artists* / Cielo e mar: *Various artists.*
Album: Released Sep '82, on Decca by Decca International. Deleted Jan '88. Catalogue no: **SXDL 7589**

YES GIORGIO (VIDEO) (Film Soundtrack) (Various artists)
VHS: Released '88, on MGM/UA (Video) by MGM/UA Video. Catalogue no: **MGM 102089**

Yes Minister

YES MINISTER (TV soundtrack) (Various artists)
Album: Released Nov '81, on BBC by BBC Records. Deleted Apr '89. Catalogue no: **REB 432**
Cass: Released Nov '81, on BBC by BBC Records. Deleted Apr '89. Catalogue no: **ZCF 432**

Yolanda & The Thief

YOLANDA & THE THIEF / YOU'LL NEVER GET RICH (Original soundtrack) (Various artists)
Note: Starring Fred Astaire.
Album: Released Jan '89, on Silva Screen by Silva Screen Records. Catalogue no: **HS 5001**

Yor - Hunter From ...

YOR - HUNTER FROM THE FUTURE (Original soundtrack) (Various artists)
Note: Composed by John Scott and Guido De Angelisa.
Album: Released Jan '89, on

Silva Screen by Silva Screen Records. Catalogue no: **SCRS 1005**

You Only Live Twice

YOU ONLY LIVE TWICE (Film soundtrack) (Various artists)
Tracks: / You only live twice: *Sinatra, Nancy* / Capsule in space: *Various artists* / Fight at Kobe Dock: *Various artists* / Halga: *Various artists* / Tanaka's world: *Various artists* / Drop in the ocean, A: *Various artists* / Death of Aki, The: *Various artists* / Mountains and sunsets: *Various artists* / Wedding, The: *Various artists* / James Bond astronaut: *Various artists* / Countdown for Biofeld: *Various artists* / Bond averts World War III: *Various artists* / Twice is the only way to live: *Various artists*.
Note: John Barry score with Nancy Sinatra.
Cass: Released Jan '89, on Silva Screen by Silva Screen Records. Catalogue no: **E 41 E 90626**
CD: Released Jan '89, on Silva Screen by Silva Screen Records. Catalogue no: **CD 90626**
Album: Released '83, on EMI (Germany) by EMI Records. Catalogue no: **IC 054 82920**

You'll Never Get Rich

YOLANDA & THE THIEF / YOU'LL NEVER GET RICH (Original Soundtrack)(Various artists) (See under Yolanda & The Thief)

Young Blood

YOUNG BLOOD (Original soundtrack) (Various artists)
Tracks: / Opening score: *Orbit, William* / Stand in the fire: *Thomas, Mickey* / Talk me into it: *Jones, Glenn* / Something real: *Mr. Mister* / I'm a real man: *Hiatt, John* / Cut you down to size: *Starship* / Footsteps: *Gilder, Nick* / Soldier of fortune: *Jordan, Marc* / Winning is everything: *Autograph*.
Album: Released Jul '86, on RCA by BMG Records (UK). Deleted May '89. Catalogue no: **BL 87172**
Cass: Released Jul '86, on RCA by BMG Records (UK). Deleted May '89. Catalogue no: **BK 87172**

YOUNGBLOOD (War - Film soundtrack) (Various artists)
Tracks: / Youngblood (livin' in the streets): *Various artists* / Sing a

happy song: *Various artists* / Keep on doin': *Various artists* / Kingsmen sign: *Various artists* / Walking to war: *Various artists* / This funky music makes you feel good: *Various artists* / Junk yard: *Various artists* / Superdude: *Various artists* / Youngblood and Sybil: *Various artists* / Flying machine: *Various artists* / Searching for Youngblood and Rommel: *Various artists*.
Album: Released '79, on MCA by MCA Records. Deleted '84. Catalogue no: **MCF 2864**
Cass: Released '79, on MCA by MCA Records. Deleted '84. Catalogue no: **MCFC 2864**

Young Einstein

YOUNG EINSTEIN (Original soundtrack) (Various artists) (see panel above)
Tracks: / Rock and roll music: *Serious, Yahoo* / Rock and roll music: *Mental As Anything* / Music goes round my head: *Yahoo & Lulu* / Dumb things: *Kelly, Paul & The Messengers* / Hungry town: *Big Pig* / Great southern land: *Icehouse* / Great big brain: *Song Company* / Tasmanian, The: *Serious, Yahoo* / I hear motion: *Models* / Theory of relativity: *Serious, Yahoo* / At first sight: *Stems* / Fist full of scientists: *Lime Spiders* / Weirdo libido: *Lime Spiders* / Young Einstein pacifist: *Serious, Yahoo*.
Cass: Released Oct '89, on A&M by A&M Records. Catalogue no: **AMC 3929**
CD: Released Oct '89, on A&M by A&M Records. Catalogue no: **CDA 3929**
Album: Released Oct '89, on A&M by A&M Records. Catalogue no: **AMA 3929**

Young Girls Of ...

YOUNG GIRLS OF ROCHEFORT (Original soundtrack) (Various artists)
CD: Released Jan '89, on Silva Screen by Silva Screen Records. Catalogue no: **834140.2**

Young Guns

YOUNG GUNS II (See, Bon Jovi, Jon)

Young Lions

YOUNG LIONS, THE (Original

Soundtrack of *Young Einstein* featuring Yahoo Serious on the A & M label

soundtrack) (Various artists)
Note: Hugo Friedhofer score for the Marlon Brando film.
Album: Released Jan '89, on Silva Screen by Silva Screen Records. Catalogue no: **STV 81115**

Young Man With A Horn

YOUNG MAN WITH A HORN (Original soundtrack) (Various artists)
Note: Starring Doris Day and Harry James.
Cass: Released Jan '89, on Silva Screen by Silva Screen Records. Catalogue no: **BT 582**
Album: Released Jan '89, on Silva Screen by Silva Screen Records. Catalogue no: **ACL 582**

Young, Neil

RUST NEVER SLEEPS (Young, Neil & Crazy Horse)
Tracks: / My my, hey hey (out of the blue) / Thrasher / Ride my llama / Pocohontas / Sail away / Powder finger / Welfare mothers / Sedan delivery / Hey hey, my my (into the black).
Album: Released Oct '81, on Reprise (USA) Catalogue no: **K 54105**
Cass: Released Oct '81, on Reprise (USA) Catalogue no: **K4 54105**

RUST NEVER SLEEPS (VIDEO)
VHS: Released '84, on RCA by BMG Records (UK). Catalogue no: **RVT 33006**

Young Ones

YOUNG ONES, THE (VIDEO) (Various artists) (See also under Richard, Cliff)
Note: Cert U. Running time: 108 mins. Teenagers get together to put on a pop show. Lame plot,

great songs including 'Living doll'. Starring Cliff Richard.
VHS: Released Jun '88, on Warner Home Video by WEA Records. Catalogue no: **PES 38075**

Young Savages

YOUNG SAVAGES, THE (Original Soundtrack) (Various artists)
Note: David Amram score.
Album: Released Jan '89, on Silva Screen by Silva Screen Records. Catalogue no: **LAALP 1011**

Young Sherlock Holmes

YOUNG SHERLOCK HOLMES (Original soundtrack) (Sinfonia of London)
Tracks: / Main title / Solving the crime / Library love (Waxflatter's first flight) / Pastries and crypts / Waxing Elizabeth / Holmes and Elizabeth (love theme) / Ehtar's escape / Final duel / Final farewell / Riddles solved - end credits.
Note: Music composed, conducted and produced by Bruce Broughton.
Cass: Released Mar '86, on MCA by MCA Records. Deleted Jan '88. Catalogue no: **MCFC 3311**
Album: Released Mar '86, on MCA by MCA Records. Deleted Jan '88. Catalogue no: **MCF 3311**

Young Warriors

YOUNG WARRIORS, THE (Original soundtrack) (Various artists)
Note: Composed by Rob Walsh.
Album: Released Jan '89, on Silva Screen by Silva Screen Records. Catalogue no: **STV 81186**

Yours, Anne

YOURS, ANNE (Original New York Cast) (Various artists)
Tracks: / Dear Kitty, I'm 13 years

old: *Various artists* / She doesn't understand me: *Various artists* / Schlaf: *Various artists* / In the night: *Various artists* / You don't have to: *Various artists* / Hollywood: *Various artists* / Dear Kitty I have a nicer side: *Various artists* / We live with fear (Parts 1 & 2): *Various artists* / Writer, A: *Various artists* / I am not a Jew: *Various artists* / First chanukah night: *Various artists* / Dear Kitty it's a new year: *Various artists* / We're here: *Various artists* / My life: *Various artists* / Dear Kitty I am longing: *Various artists* / I remember: *Various artists* / I think myself out: *Various artists* / Nightmare: *Various artists* / For the children: *Various artists* / Something to get up for: *Various artists* / When we are free: *Various artists* / Much too young: *Various artists* / I am only 15: *Various artists* / Something is new: *Various artists*.
Note: Musical drama adaptation of 'The Diary of Anne Frank', one of the most famous & moving stories to emerge from the 2nd world war. Recorded from the off Broadway production in 1985, this release ties in with the show's return to NY.
Album: Released Apr '87, on T. E. R. by That's Entertainment Records. Catalogue no: **TER 1118**
Cass: Released Apr '87, on T. E. R. by That's Entertainment Records. Catalogue no: **ZCTER 1118**

Yours Mine & Our

YOURS MINE & OUR (Original Soundtrack) (Various artists)
Note: Composed by Fred Karlin.
Cass: Released Jan '89, on MCA by MCA Records. Catalogue no: **MCAC 1434**
Album: Released Jan '89, on MCA by MCA Records. Catalogue no: **MCAL 1434**

Z

The following information was taken from the Music Master database on September 25th, 1990.

Z (film)

Z (Original soundtrack) (Various artists)
Note: Music from the Costa Gavras political thriller by Mikis Theodorakis.
Album: Released Jan '89, on CBS by CBS Records & Distribution. Catalogue no: **CBS 63639**
Cass: Released Mar '90, on Silva Screen by Silva Screen Records. Catalogue no: **40-63639**

Zabriskie Point

ZABRISKIE POINT (Original soundtrack) (Various artists)
Tracks: / Heat beat, pig meat: *Pink Floyd* / Brother Mary: *Kaleidoscope* / Dark star (excerpt): *Grateful Dead* / Crumbling land: *Pink Floyd* / Tennessee waltz: *Page, Patti* / Sugar babe: *Youngbloods* / Love scene: *Garcia, Jerry* / I wish I were a single girl again: *Holcomb, Roscoe* / Mickey's tune: *Kaleidoscope* / Dance of death: *Fahey, John* / Come in Number 51, your time is up: *Pink Floyd.*
Note: Music from the Antonioni film.
Album: Released Jan '89, on MCA by MCA Records. Catalogue no: **MCA 25032**
Album: Released Apr '90, on MGM (EMI) Catalogue no: **794 217 1**
Cass: Released Apr '90, on MGM (EMI) Catalogue no: **TCGO 2029**
CD: Released Apr '90, on MGM (EMI) Catalogue no: **CZ 285**
Cass: Released Jan '89, on MCA by MCA Records. Catalogue no: **MCAC 25032**
Album: Released Apr '90, on MGM (EMI) Catalogue no: **GO 2029**
CD: Released Apr '90, on MGM (EMI) Catalogue no: **CDP 794 217 2**
Cass: Released Apr '90, on MGM (EMI) Catalogue no: **794 217 4**

Zachariah

ZACHARIAH (Original soundtrack) (Various artists)
Tracks: / Lonely rider: *Various artists* / Camino/used horse salesman: *Various artists* / Zachariah (main title): *Various artists* / Laguna salada: *James Gang* / We're the crackers: *Country Joe & The Fish* / William Tell: *Haskell, Jimmie* / All I need: *Country Joe & The Fish* / Ballad of Job Cain: *Kershaw, Doug* / Country fever: *James Gang* / Camino waltz: *Haskell, Jimmie* / Gravedigger: *New York Rock Ensemble* / Shy Ann: *White Lightning* / Matthew: *Haskell, Jimmie* / Zachariah (end title): *Haskell, Jimmie.*
Album: Released May '87, on See For Miles by See For Miles Records. Catalogue no: **SEE 91**

Zamfir, Gheorghe

THEME LIGHT OF EXPERIENCE
Cass: Released Oct '76, on Epic by CBS Records & Distribution. Catalogue no: **40 81638**

Zappa, Frank

200 MOTELS (Original soundtrack)
Cass: Released Jan '89, on MCA by MCA Records. Catalogue no: **MCAC 2 4183**
2 LP Set: Released Jan '89, on MCA by MCA Records. Catalogue no: **MCA 2 4183**

200 MOTELS 1
Cass: Released Aug '86, on EMI (Italy) by EMI Records. Catalogue no: **3C 254 92854**

200 MOTELS 2
Cass: Released Aug '86, on EMI (Italy) by EMI Records. Catalogue no: **3C 254 92855**

200 MOTELS (VIDEO)
Note: 18 rated. Running time is 96 minutes. Life on the road with a rock band story. In this instance the eccentric Frank Zappa along with Keith Moon and Ringo Starr.
VHS: Released Jun '88, on Warner Home Video by WEA Records. Catalogue no: **PEV 99498**

UNCLE MEAT (Original soundtrack) (Zappa, Frank And The Mothers Of Invention)
CD: Released Oct '87, on Zappa by Music For Nations Records. Catalogue no: **CDDZAP 3**

Z Cars

Z CARS (See under Keating, Johnny)

Zed & Two Noughts

ZED AND TWO NOUGHTS (Original soundtrack) (Nyman, Michael)
Tracks: / Angelfish decay / Car crash / Lapse, The / Prawn watching / Bisocosis populi / Swan rot / Delft waltz / Up for crabs / Vermer's wife / Venus de milo / Lady in the red hat / L'escargot.
Album: Released Feb '90, on Virgin by Virgin Records. Catalogue no: **VE 54**
Cass: Released Feb '90, on Virgin by Virgin Records. Catalogue no: **TCVE 54**
CD: Released Feb '90, on Virgin by Virgin Records. Catalogue no: **CDVE 54**
CD: Released Feb '90, on T. E. R. by That's Entertainment Records. Catalogue no: **CDTER 1106**
Cass: Released Dec '85, on T. E. R. by That's Entertainment Records. Catalogue no: **ZCTER 1106**
Album: Released Dec '85, on T. E. R. by That's Entertainment Records. Catalogue no: **TER 1106**

Zelly & Me

ZELLY & ME (Original soundtrack) (Various artists)
Note: Pino Donaggio score.
CD: Released Jan '89, on Silva Screen by Silva Screen Records. Catalogue no: **VCD 70422**
Cass: Released Jan '89, on Silva Screen by Silva Screen Records. Catalogue no: **C 704.420**
Album: Released Jan '89, on Silva Screen by Silva Screen Records. Catalogue no: **704.420**

Ziegfeld Follies

ZIEGFELD FOLLIES (VIDEO) (Various artists)
VHS: Released Sep '89, on MGM/UA (Video) by MGM/UA Video. Catalogue no: **SMV 10173**

ZIEGFELD FOLLIES OF 1946 (Original soundtrack) (Various artists)
2 LP Set: Released Jan '89, on Silva Screen by Silva Screen Records. Catalogue no: **CC 100-15/16**

Ziegfeld Girl

ZIEGFELD GIRL (Original soundtrack) (Various artists)
Note: Starring Lana Turner and Judy Garland.
Album: Released Jan '89, on CIF Catalogue no: **CIF 3006**

Ziggy Stardust

ZIGGY STARDUST (See under Bowie, David)

Zimmer, Hans

BURNING SECRET (See under Burning Secret)

DRIVING MISS DAISY (See under Driving Miss Dasiy)

Zinja

ZINJA (Original soundtrack) (Various artists)
Cass: Released '85, on Filmtrax by Filmtrax Records. Catalogue no: **MOMENTC 103**
Album: Released '85, on Filmtrax by Filmtrax Records. Catalogue no: **MOMENT 103**

Zorba

ZORBA (Original Broadway cast) (Various artists)
CD: Released Feb '90, on Silva Screen by Silva Screen Records. Catalogue no: **CDP 92053**
Cass: Released Jan '89, on Silva Screen by Silva Screen Records. Catalogue no: **ABK 1 4732**
Album: Released Jan '89, on Silva Screen by Silva Screen Rec-

ords. Catalogue no: **ABL 1 4732**

Zorba The Greek (film)

ZORBA THE GREEK (Original soundtrack) (Various artists)
Tracks: / Zorba the greek: *Various artists* / Full catastrophe, The: *Various artists* / Life goes on: *Various artists* / One unforgiveable sin, The: *Various artists* / Questions without answers: *Various artists* / Zorba's dance: *Various artists* / Fire inside, The: *Various artists* / Clever people and grocers: *Various artists* / Always look for trouble: *Various artists* / Free: *Various artists* / That's me - Zorba: *Various artists*.
Note: Composed by Mikis Theodorakis.
Cass: Released Jan '89, on Silva Screen by Silva Screen Records. Catalogue no: **825245.4**
Album: Released Jan '89, on Silva Screen by Silva Screen Records. Deleted Mar '90. Catalogue no: **826245.1**
Album: Released Feb '80, on 20th Century by Phonogram Ltd. Deleted '85. Catalogue no: **T 903**
Cass: Released Feb '80, on 20th Century by Phonogram Ltd. Deleted '85. Catalogue no: **C 903**
Album: Released Sep '83, on Phonogram by Phonogram Ltd. Catalogue no: **6463 165**
Cass: Released Sep '83, on Phonogram by Phonogram Ltd. Catalogue no: **7145 165**

Zulu (film)

ZULU (Original soundtrack) (Various artists)
Tracks: / Istanchiwania: *Various artists* / News of the massacre: *Various artists* / First zulu: *Various artists* / Wagons over: *Various artists* / Durnford's horses arrive and depart: *Various artists* / Zulus final appearance and salute: *Various artists* / V.C. roll and men of Harlech, The: *Various artists* / Elizabeth theme: *Various artists* / From Russia with love: *Various ar-*

tists / Four in the morning: *Various artists*.
Cass: Released Nov '89, on Silva Screen by Silva Screen Records. Deleted May '90. Catalogue no: **FILMC 022**
CD: Released Nov '89, on Silva Screen by Silva Screen Records. Catalogue no: **FILMCD 022**
Album: Released Nov '89, on Silva Screen by Silva Screen Records. Catalogue no: **FILM 022**

ZULU DAWN (Original soundtrack) (Various artists)
Note: Prequel to Zulu with music by Elmer Bernstein and the Royal Philharmonic Orchestra.
CD: Released Jan '89, on Silva Screen by Silva Screen Records. Catalogue no: **CD 0201**
Album: Released Jan '89, on Cerebus (USA) Catalogue no: **C'BUS 201**

Zygott

TRAP DOOR
Tracks: / Trap door / Ghost chase(The ghost chasers).
Note: Theme from TVS series No.73
7" Single: Released Sep '86, on Columbia by EMI Records. Deleted Oct '87. Catalogue no: **DB 9137**

ZZ Top

DOUBLE BACK
Tracks: / Double back.
Note: Featured in the film 'Back To The Future III'.
7" Single: Released Jul '90, on WEA by WEA Records. Catalogue no: **W 9812**
12" Single: Released Jul '90, on WEA by WEA Records. Catalogue no: **W 9812T**
Cassingle: Released Jul '90, on WEA by WEA Records. Catalogue no: **W 9812C**
CD Single: Released Jul '90, on WEA by WEA Records. Catalogue no: **W 9812CD**